P9-CCF-062

MAN'S PHYSICAL WORLD

McGRAW-HILL SERIES IN GEOGRAPHY

John C. Weaver, Consulting Editor

BENNETT—Soil Conservation
CRESSEY—Asia's Lands and Peoples
CRESSEY—Land of the 500 Million: A Geography of China
FINCH AND TREWARTHA—Elements of Geography: Physical and Cultural
FINCH AND TREWARTHA—Physical Elements of Geography (A republication of Part I of the above)
POUNDS—Europe and the Mediterranean
RAISZ—General Cartography
RAISZ—Principles of Cartography
THOMAN—The Geography of Economic Activity
TREWARTHA—An Introduction to Climate
TREWARTHA, ROBINSON, AND HAMMOND—Fundamentals of Physical Geography
VAN RIPER—Man's Physical World

Vernor C. Finch was Consulting Editor of this series from its inception in 1934 to 1951

U. S. Department of Agriculture

Man's Physical World

JOSEPH E. VAN RIPER

PROFESSOR OF GEOGRAPHY, HARPUR COLLEGE, STATE UNIVERSITY OF NEW YORK

VISITING PROFESSOR OF GEOGRAPHY, AMERICAN UNIVERSITY OF BEIRUT, LEBANON

McGraw-Hill Book Company, Inc. 1962

NEW YORK SAN FRANCISCO TORONTO LONDON

Man's Physical World

Library of Congress Catalog Card Number: 62-10848

III

Cartography by James J. Flannery and P. Yoeli. Cover photograph courtesy of Standard Oil of New Jersey. End paper (rear) climatic map: a modification of the Köppen system by Trewartha; reproduced from "Elements of Geography" by Finch, Trewartha, Robinson, and Hammond.

This book is set in Times Roman, a type face originally designed by Stanley Morison for The Times of London. The chapter titles are Tempo Black Extended. The display heads are Durer Bold.

67153

PREFACE

The objective of this textbook in physical geography is to make meaningful the patterns of physical features on the surface of the earth. Although the central focus is on the description and interpretation of the major global similarities and differences in physical features from place to place, the book also is designed to stimulate the student to an awareness of the fascinating natural world about him. Nature never ceases to astound those who probe into its mysteries. Few readers will have an opportunity to verify the great global patterns presented in this volume, but all will be able to observe, measure, and classify the physical patterns in nature close at hand. For this reason, the text changes back and forth from the global to the local point of view, alternately focusing on the geography of the world and the features of a *landscape,* a section of the earth surface that may be observed by someone standing within it. It is hoped that this book will equip the interested student with sufficient information on the elements of the natural environment to enable him to be an explorer in his own neighborhood. Included at the end of the text material are a list of study questions for each chapter, a carefully prepared glossary of terms, and an annotated list of appropriate reference books for a wide range of interests and backgrounds.

The introductory chapter presents a set of four concepts or principles concerning distributional aspects of natural features. Throughout the text, these principles will be recalled and illustrated. They should not be considered great universal truths that apply without exception and provide an easy means of solving the complexities of physical patterns. On the contrary, they should provide constant warnings against descriptive overgeneralization, one of the greatest tendencies of beginning students in geography—or, for that matter, in most other academic subjects. These principles also should foster a continual awareness of time as a factor in areal distributions. Boundaries of physical conditions on earth are never permanent. Short- and long-term changes are constantly altering man's physical world, and the role of change in the physical geography of the earth is stressed throughout this text.

Another objective of this text is to probe into the meanings of areal physical patterns. The author realizes that, in a volume such as this, the subject of function in areal patterns can be touched only lightly here and there. Since the early part of this century, when many glib overgeneralizations were made concerning environmental determinants in human affairs, scientists have been reluctant even to mention the influence of physical environment on human behavior, for fear of being scornfully labeled "environmentalists." The physical environment, however, always has been, and always will be, among the factors that affect man's day-to-day decisions and activities. The problem lies in the difficulty of isolating such environmental factors from the maze of cultural forces with which they are intertwined. At several places in the text, the intermingling of cultural and natural environmental factors is indicated. Early in the volume, for example, perhaps an undue amount of space is devoted to the meaning of slope. This was done deliberately, to show how subtle and yet how compelling a factor slope can be in human affairs. Similar analyses could be made of many other elements in physical geography. Slope is emphasized, not because it is believed to be of greater ultimate importance than the other factors, but because it appears early in the volume, along with the other elements of surface configuration. Its treatment is intended to be illustrative. In the remainder of the book, the functional significances of the physical geographic elements are mentioned without special emphasis. The dynamic nature of environmental influences is indicated throughout. The meaning of physical patterns changes with the knowledge, techniques, tools, and desires of enlightened peoples.

The world physical patterns can be presented regionally or systematically. In the regional treatment, the world is divided into broad regions, or areas of selected similarities, and the natural elements are discussed region by region. For example, the humid low latitudes could be delimited as a region, and the characteristic features of climate, soils, vegetation, landforms, and other elements described for this area. In the systematic treatment, which is followed in this textbook, the patterns of the natural elements are presented separately. The principal reason for using the systematic approach here is that it makes it far easier to handle the shift in focus from the local or topographic scene to global patterns. Secondly, a certain amount of systematic knowledge is required before a regional presentation can be made. It is not possible, for example, to give the introductory student a meaningful presentation of the soils of the humid tropics unless this description is preceded by appropriate data on soil properties and the variables in soil development.

The careful reader will detect a tendency to group the separate elements of physical geography into features or categories that can be related to climatic patterns. This purely arbitrary organization was considered advisable because the amount of quantitative data available on climatic differences over the earth surface is much greater than the amount available for the other elements. Several other approaches, however, could have been used.

This textbook has been designed primarily for use in an introductory course in physical geography on the college level. The large number of ideas and concepts it contains, however, enable it to be used as a springboard for advanced courses in this subject. Its value can be increased enormously by field and laboratory exercises. There is no substitute for short walks into a countryside, where a capable teacher can soon remove the blindfold of indifference from student eyes and enable them to see nature for the first time in all of its challenging wonderment. Nor is there any substitute for wise training in the use of maps, one of the major contributions that instruction in geography can make to general education. An excellent course in physical geography could be given by a competent teacher using only the maps contained in this volume, without any supplementary text material.

Although the text is designed mainly for courses in physical geography, it could well be used in earth science survey courses. This is another advantage of the systematic treatment of the physical elements in geography. The principal difference between the respective approaches of earth science and physical geography is that the former is concerned mainly with the description and development of individual surface forms and phenomena, whereas the latter emphasizes the distributional aspects of these forms and phenomena. These objectives inevitably overlap broadly. No adequate treatment of volcanoes in an earth science course, for example, could omit the distributional pattern of volcanic and seismic activity, and no good course in physical geography could avoid discussion of the types of volcanic eruptions and their relation to the chemical composition of lavas. Thus, a considerable amount of genetic material is included in this text for the purpose of clarifying the descriptive and interpretive data on distributional patterns.

Two chapters in this text might be considered to lie mainly within the scope of *applied* physical geography, and they differ somewhat, in treatment and objective, from the rest of the book. These are the chapters on mineral resources and water resources. Minerals and fresh water are such vital elements in man's physical world that their significance as resources seemed to merit special treatment. Even here, however, regional differences in the problems of resource availability and utilization are emphasized.

The author humbly acknowledges his presumptuousness in undertaking alone this difficult task of describing and interpreting the physical world of man. No man can profess to be thoroughly competent in as many fields as are represented here. For the inevitable errors, omissions, and overgeneralizations contained within these pages, the author alone is responsible.

It is impossible to acknowledge individually all the help and encouragement graciously given by many individuals during the preparation of this manuscript. The author's special appreciation, however, should go to several of his faculty colleagues: to Lewis Alexander, who spent many hours winnowing the wheat from the chaff, especially in the chapters on climate; to Glenn G. Bartle, college president and competent geologist, who was not too busy with his own important duties to spare time for manuscript reading, suggestions, and personal encouragement; to Clement G. Bowers for his inspiration and invaluable assistance in plant ecology; to Donald Coates, who helped in geomorphology and water resources; and to many others who gladly gave of their professional competence over a cup of coffee or the telephone. Grateful appreciation also is given to the author's wife and son for their patience and understanding during these years of preparation, writing, and polishing.

The author owes most, perhaps, to the many professional critics throughout the country who examined all or portions of the manuscript and who were exceedingly helpful in their constructive criticisms. He is similarly indebted to his cartographers, James J. Flannery and P. Yoeli, for so competently taking over this most important and difficult part of the textbook preparation. Lastly, no teacher-author ever can realize how much he is indebted to his own students for their interest, their achievements, and even their mistakes.

If this volume can impart to some of its readers even a small part of the wonder and curiosity concerning nature that grew and flourished in the author's mind during the preparation of this material, even far more than during his own days as a student, he will feel amply rewarded for the many hours when words squirmed with difficulty from the end of his pencil.

Joseph E. Van Riper

CONTENTS

MAN'S PHYSICAL WORLD

1

The field of physical geography

Geography is the science of areas on the earth surface. It seeks the causes and effects of the association of features and phenomena contained within different parts of the earth surface. The central core of the subject, therefore, is the content of space on earth and the differences and similarities that may be observed from place to place. Astronomy can be termed the "geography of outer space," in that it is a science which aims at explaining the content and arrangement of forms and phenomena in space beyond the earth surface. The features considered by astronomers are limited to those observable from the earth by means of telescopes and other astronomical instruments. The features which characterize areas on earth, on the other hand, and which are considered in geography, include a wide range of things that we can see, smell, feel, or measure in various ways.

The total content of observable features in an area on earth can be infinite if we examine areas closely enough. For this reason, the field of geography is divided into several subdivisions, differing in the type of features treated and also in certain methods of description and interpretation. The broadest subdivisions are *physical geography* and *human geography*. The former deals with those features which are contained within different parts of the earth surface and which would have been present had man never appeared. Human geography considers those features which are the direct result of human activities.

Physical geography and its elements

1.1 THE ELEMENTS OF PHYSICAL GEOGRAPHY. Physical geography attempts to portray and to explain the areal differences and similarities in the so-called "natural" features on or about the surface of the earth. This does not mean, however, that man's actions have no place in physical geography. Rare indeed are the areas on earth where the hand of man has not altered the features of the physical environment in some way. Vegetation, soils, and even climates and surface features have been changed by human beings in many ways in the thousands of years of settling the earth. The aim of physical geography is to include within its framework the elements of the environment that are not *exclusively* man-made, that is, those that would have been present had man never appeared on earth. With this in mind, we may now list the major elements of physical geography as follows: (1) location, (2) scale, (3) landforms and surface configuration, (4) weather and climate, (5) nonhuman life forms, (6) soils, (7) rocks and minerals, (8) continental water bodies, (9) oceans.

The first two elements listed above, *location* and *scale,* differ from the others in being concepts or constructs rather than tangible, observable features. These two are included as essential elements of physical geography, however, because they are involved in all considerations of *area* or *place,* which in turn are distinctive features in any geographic study.

Specializations within the field of physical geography are customarily related to the various elements as shown in Table 1.1.

Like the workers in all the other earth sciences (geology, botany, zoology, etc.), physical geographers are interested in discovering the general laws of nature and in understanding the causes for natural phenomena of all kinds. Unlike the other earth sciences, however, the principal emphasis is on differentiating areas of earth space and on studying carefully the differences and similarities that can be observed from place to place.

TABLE 1.1 Specializations in physical geography

ELEMENT	SPECIALIZED FIELD
Location and scale	Cartography
Landforms and surface configuration	Physiography
Climate	Climatology
Weather	Meteorology
Nonhuman life forms	Plant geography and zoogeography
Soils	Pedology or pedography
Continental water bodies	Hydrography
The oceans	Oceanography

Another distinction that can be made between physical geography and the other earth sciences is that the former tends to focus on *associations of features* rather than on individual forms. This is characteristic of the specialized branches of physical geography as well as of the general field itself. To illustrate, a distinction is made between *plant geography,* a distinct subdivision of geography, and *geographic botany,* which no less clearly belongs in the field of botany. Plant geography deals with the association of plants that exist together and characterize a particular section of the earth surface. Geographic botany, on the other hand, specializes in the distribution of individual plant types—for example, in the distribution of a particular phylum (the *Bryophytes,* or mosses), a genus (*Quercus,* or the oaks), or a species (*Populus tremuloides,* or quaking aspen) of plants. Knowledge of the characteristics of plant growth may be obtained from both directions of study.

Besides attempting to increase the understanding of nature, physical geography has the further task of making meaningful to man the infinite variety of physical differences throughout the earth surface. A single square mile of land surface may present an amazingly complex association of individual features within even a single geographic element. Careful examination of soils, climates, and vegetation, for example, generally shows some differences within a few feet. For some purposes, these minute differences from place to place are significant. Any description of differences or similarities from place to place requires generalizations of the details that can be found. The development of techniques to make such generalizations valid, consistent, and appropriate has been among the principal applied contributions of physical geography.

1.2 THE COVERAGE OF PHYSICAL ELEMENTS IN THIS TEXTBOOK. The physical world of man can be divided into two great realms: the continental realm and the realm of the oceans. Since man is a terrestrial, air-breathing organism, the continental surfaces are his natural habitat. For this reason, all but one of the chapters deal with the various elements observed on the continents. The separate chapter on the oceans, however, indicates that this realm also has complex areal differences and meanings in its physical make-up.

Of the various physical elements that constitute the natural environment of man, two can be considered to be largely independent variables; that is, their major characteristics are the result of factors apart from those belonging to the general environment of the earth surface. One of these is the *lithosphere,* or the solid crust of the earth, the mineralogical nature of which usually is determined by conditions of heat and pressure far below the surface. Crustal movements also may have their origins deep below the surface. The other independent variable is *solar energy,* the prime mover of air, water, and life. Since these two variables, the rock crust and solar energy, greatly influence the other aspects of space on the earth, the chapters dealing with features of the earth crust and climates are presented early in the text material. Preceding them is a chapter dealing with location, scale, and maps. This was thought necessary in order to provide a better understanding of the value and limitations of maps, which are the geographer's main working tool.

The nonhuman life forms are represented in this volume only by the material on plant geography. Zoogeography is not included, partly because of space limitations and partly because it was felt that natural animal life does not have so many intimate connections with man in the areal context as do such elements as landforms, soils, climates, and minerals.

The principles of natural distribution

The task of characterizing the physical differences and similarities from place to place on earth is formidable. Fully as difficult is the task of avoiding misrepresentations in generalizing the content of areas on a global scale. Exceptions can be found for nearly any areal generalization on this scale. The equatorial areas are warm, but snow fields and glaciers crown the summits of Andean mountains in Ecuador. The arctic areas generally are cold, but temperatures of 90°F and over occasionally occur within the Arctic Circle. Soils in the rainy tropics generally are inherently infertile, yet the rich volcanic ash on Java supports some of the densest agricultural populations on earth. The scale limitations of any map mask the details that cannot be presented, yet these omitted details may be exceedingly important in some respects.

In order to indicate the ever-present limitations of areal generalizations, four basic concepts or principles of natural distributions are presented in the paragraphs that follow. They are referred to frequently throughout the remainder of this book, and they should always be kept in mind. They might be considered as a summary of the qualifications that must be made in any characterization of areas and as a frame of reference that, if clearly understood and utilized, can aid greatly in bringing some order out of the chaotic maze of physical differences throughout the earth.

1.3 THE PRINCIPLE OF GRADED LIKENESSES AND INFINITE DIFFERENCES IN NATURAL FORMS AND AREAS.

No two forms in nature, and no two areas on the earth surface, are exactly alike, although similarities appear that permit classification of form or area. The degree of dissimilarity observed varies directly with the closeness of scrutiny. Conversely, similarities become more obvious at broader scales of observation.

The term *cattle* is used to denote a classification of animals that have certain recognizable similarities of form. Different breeds of cattle are also recognized, such as Jersey, Holstein, and Hereford. Jersey cows have definite characteristics that are common to all of their breed, and to most people, all Jersey cows look alike. A farmer with a herd of these animals, however, or a trained judge at a county fair evaluating the qualities of Jerseys, can easily detect significant differences. This general principle of graded likeness amid an infinite variety of differences holds true for clouds as well as cows, trees as well as birds, and soils as well as mountains.

From the street, the front lawns of an urban residential area appear to be similar, yet close examination on one's knees reveals that there are appreciable differences not only between separate lawns but also within any one lawn. Minor differences in available moisture, in soil texture, in exposure to sunlight or shade, or in acidity produce distinguishable differences not only in the types and associations of grasses and weeds but also within accompanying elements of the total environment, including the microclimate and microfauna.

The monkeys, snakes, trees, and landforms of the Amazon Basin in South America show distinct differences from those of the Congo Basin in Africa, and there are easily distinguishable associations within different parts of the Amazon Basin. In contrast to the Mississippi River drainage basin, however, the environmental associations of the Congo and Amazon Basins exhibit many comparable characteristics. They both have monkeys, they both have trees which remain green the year around, their soils have comparable features and properties, and their climates are generally warm and humid throughout the year. The existence of broad similarities within the infinite variety of forms from place to place makes possible the regional approach in geography.

1.4 THE PRINCIPLE OF TRANSITIONAL CHANGE IN AREAL DIFFERENCES.

The change from a region of one generalized association of forms to another always takes place through transitional zones of variable width. The sharpness of transition usually depends on the scale of generalization used in classifying and presenting the regional differences.

To illustrate this principle, suppose we wished to determine the area covered by pine forests in the United States. Whether an area had a pine forest or not would depend in part on how we defined a pine forest. Is it a forest composed entirely of pine trees, or is it one where a certain percentage of the trees are pines? If it is one where 50 per cent or more of the trees are pines, how large an area are the measurements to cover—will they include areas whose size is less than 1 acre, 1 square mile, or 100 square miles? Our "line" separating pine forests from non-pine forests will obviously represent a zone of transition, which will vary in width depending first on the preciseness of definition and second on the detail of observation. Finally, when we present a picture of the distribution of pine forests in the United States, unless we use a map ratio of

1:1,[1] an obvious impossibility, our line on a map will not represent a line at all, but an area, which will become wider as the map's scale of presentation becomes smaller. We cannot assume, furthermore, that the zone of transition is going to be equally wide along all boundaries at the same scale of generalization in definition, observation, and presentation. The zone of transition at the base of a hill separating the hill from the nonhill area is not going to be the same width around the hill if the slopes are uneven. Where the slope increases in steepness, the zone of transition becomes narrower, regardless of how we define the bottom of a hill. An interesting problem in the relation of transitions to definitions involves where to draw a line separating a valley from an adjacent mountain. Does the side of the valley begin at the mountaintop? Does the mountain begin at the bottom of the adjacent valley?

1.5 THE PRINCIPLE OF CONTINUOUS ALTERATION OF AREAL CHARACTERISTICS WITH TIME.

Both long- and short-term changes are taking place continually among the forms and phenomena that make up the environmental complex of an area. Short-term changes usually are best observed in the microfeatures of the complex, whereas the long-term changes are reflected in the larger forms and phenomena. The tempo or rate of change varies.

A perfectly static environment does not exist in nature. Each hour and each second bring changes of some sort to every spot on earth—changes that range from the whisper of air movement around a grass stem and the busy work of soil microorganisms to the thunder of avalanches or the continuous reduction of slopes by the gradational processes of erosion, weathering, and deposition. In presenting and interpreting the patterns of areal differences, distributional patterns should always be placed within an appropriate time continuum or scale. Just as many differences from place to place can be dismissed as unimportant in a portrayal of graded likenesses in geographic description, so also many microchanges that occur in the environmental complex from time to time can be omitted.

In general, the most recognizable short-term changes are those associated with the weather. The changes that have the greatest amplitude and the slowest rate of change generally are those associated with crustal alterations, the great earth movements that raise and lower the continental blocks. The total pattern of change in any environment may be likened to the pattern of waves on the sea. There are small waves and large waves, some of which are fairly regular in their recurrences and others whose periodicity is vague and indefinite. Sometimes the sea of change is calm, with only tiny ripples marking miniature alterations, but at other times it is a confused mass of storm waves, representing periods of turbulent environmental change, with all the dynamic environmental forces passing rapidly from one extreme to another. Some seas are quieter than others. Similarly, some areas on earth tend to be more stable than others in regard to nearly all features of change. The task of presenting geographic patterns in their continuity of change is an essential part of any geographical description and interpretation.

[1] A map ratio represents the ratio of the size of the map projection to the earth area which it represents. A ratio of 1:10,000 signifies, for example, that 1 inch on the projection represents 10,000 inches within the area mapped. It should be remembered, however, that because of the limitations of all map projections in distorting a curved globe surface onto a flat plane, linear scale ratios are never completely correct, although they may be considered thus on large-scale maps of small areas (see Sec. 2.16).

FIG. 1.1 A view of the complexity of wave patterns on a wind-tossed sea. Little regularity of pattern can be seen, yet it is there—amid the larger troughs and crests. [U.S. Navy]

Change is a feature of all natural distributions.

1.6 THE PRINCIPLE OF TRENDS TOWARD RELATIVE EQUILIBRIA IN THE ENVIRONMENTAL ELEMENTS.

Although change continually takes place within the many elements that make up areas or regions, periods of relative stability are marked by mutual adjustments within these elements and a tendency toward relative equilibria. Long- and short-term equilibria may be noted, since the time required for significant changes varies widely with different elements in the environment.

Most elements within a regional environmental complex have some effect on each of the others, although some are more influential than others. Few of them are inert or passive. Climate helps determine whether the vegetation of an area will be a forest or tundra, lays its stamp on landforms and soils, and even affects some of the characteristics of certain mineral resources. Similarly, climate itself is changed to a certain degree by many of the other environmental elements. Mountains divert winds and intercept moisture. Forests and paved city streets differ considerably in their effect as heating surfaces, and farmers long have recognized "cold" soils and "warm" soils in which soil texture and water content influence the soil climate. Even rocks and minerals are not without their influence, and the chemical composition and fertility of soils may be closely related to the composition of the underlying rocks and their included minerals. Prospecting for large low-grade copper and cobalt deposits has been done by flying over an area and noting subtle differences in the color of vegetation.

This interaction between the elements in an environmental complex tends to produce a mutual adjustment, or a tendency to adjust to each other. Absolute equilibrium, or a completely balanced environment, is impossible, because a certain amount of change in one or more of the elements is inevitable. Nevertheless, relatively stable periods can be recognized in which, for all practical purposes, an equilibrium may exist. Some changes are measured in thousands or even millions of years; hence, in the span of human affairs such changes may be relatively unimportant.

To illustrate, imagine an environment which consists of a hillside covered with a fully mature, virgin forest. The kinds of trees and shrubs present, the underlying soil, the animal life, the forest climate, the drainage, and the microlife within the soil have all reached a mutual adjustment which is relatively stable. Geologic processes, however, eventually will alter the slope of the hillside. Long-term climatic changes slowly affect the composition of life forms, including even major species of trees. As the slope gradually recedes, drainage of surface water is not so rapid, and the soil hydrology changes. With increasing age also, the soil becomes deeper. All these changes are noticeable, however, only on a time scale of hundreds or thousands of years. To a human observer, the environment is stable, and on every hand lie the evidences of mutual adjustment between the coexisting elements in the region. To be sure, short-term changes also occur. A tree is blown over during a sudden windstorm; a landslide may produce a sudden gash in the slope; an exceptionally wet year may influence the microlife forms; etc. Although each of these changes sets off a train of minor readjustments, they do not play a significant role in the over-all regional equilibrium.

Now let us alter one of the major elements in the environmental association on our hillside—for example, by having man enter the environment, remove the forest, and cultivate the slope. The resultant changes will be immediate and rapid, and the entire equilibrium will become altered. As long as man continues his cultivation, the environmental factors will tend to operate against the establishment of the old equilibrium, mainly because a new dynamic element has been introduced. Remove man, and a long chain of readjustments will take place, aimed at eventually restoring the former equilibrium.

Just as climates experience short- and long-term periods of stability, environments also develop short- and long-term relative equilibria. The short-term equilibria, however, are developed mainly in the microfeatures of the environment, whereas the larger and more dominant features illustrate the long-term balances. A single unusually cold winter will generally have little effect in altering the species of trees or in decreasing the number and type of larger animals present in a forest, but such a winter may produce a noticeable effect on the general association of small ground plants and animals for several years.

Recognition of the tendency of environments either to move toward relative equilibria under the influence of mutual interaction and adjustment or to move away from such equilibria because of sudden changes in one or more environmental factors is a useful concept in human affairs. Land management programs require such knowledge in order to recognize, develop, or maintain that stability which is the most rewarding to man.

The relativity of similarities and differences in nature

A careful study of the principles of natural distributions given in the preceding sections may well leave the reader with the impression that nature is in a state of total confusion and chaos and that the task of accurately picturing and interpreting areal differences and similarities is a fruitless one. The role of the physical geographer in unraveling the complexities of nature is an important one, and it has a dual aspect.

First, as a scientist, the physical geographer must attempt to be as accurate as possible in his recognition of reality in areal complexes, with all their infinite variety, subtle changes, and complex interrelationships. In seeking an understanding of nature, he cannot dismiss arbitrarily any variable as unimportant, whether the process involved takes one year or several thousand. As his tools of observation improve and the records of environmental changes accumulate, his factual knowledge grows and, with it, his understanding. New explanations are given and old ones discarded.

Second, he has a responsibility to construct appropriate generalizations of the areal differences and similarities throughout the earth surface. In all walks of life there is need for knowledge concerning areas—what they contain, how and why one area is different from another, and where similarities in selected environmental elements occur. Maps are used by nearly everyone, and maps are one of the principal results of applied geographic generalizations.

These two functions of geography offer a continuous challenge, but the results are more rewarding than the complexities of environments would appear to indicate. Order may be perceived in the infinite variety of forms and phenomena contained within earth space, and this order appears at different levels or scales of observation.

Order often becomes apparent only after a great number of different features discovered by small-scale observation have been reexamined in broader terms. If we could shrink ourselves so as to be able to penetrate within the nucleus of a large atom such as uranium, we should find ourselves in a seemingly chaotic world of electrons, protons, neutrons, mesons, and many other minute "forms," some of which appear and disappear constantly. Each of these tiny forms is susceptible to so many interrelationships and outside forces that orderliness appears incomprehensible. If we could observe a molecule of water in a glass among billions of other molecules, however, we should see a certain degree of orderly behavior and arrangement in the constituents of the atom, a consistency that was not apparent at the lower level. Confusion at the molecular level appears to lie mainly in the behavior of the molecules of water themselves. In the glass of water, the molecules are dashing here and there at varying speeds, bumping into one another and showing no more consistency in their movements than do individual bees in a huge swarm. Some molecules in the water break through the surface of the liquid with a burst of speed and fly out into the air; others cling to the sides of the glass, seemingly resting a moment, only to be knocked from their perch under the bombardment of their speeding companions, after which their vacant resting places are seized by still other molecules. Yet, despite all this random behavior of individual water molecules, we have formulated definite laws concerning the behavior of large numbers of water molecules in a liquid state, and these laws have an extraordinarily high degree of statistical reliability.

Each increase in the breadth or scope of observation results in a greater relative orderliness within the multitude of forms and behavior patterns at lower levels. At the level of human observation, water in a drinking glass has properties that appear to be absolutely predictable, and man puts these properties to his own use. The fact that some of the molecules of water are escaping constantly from the surface of the liquid into the air or that others are clinging to the sides of the glass does not concern a person as he tilts the glass to his mouth and drinks. At his scale, the variant behavior of molecules has no significance.

One of the responsibilities of the physical

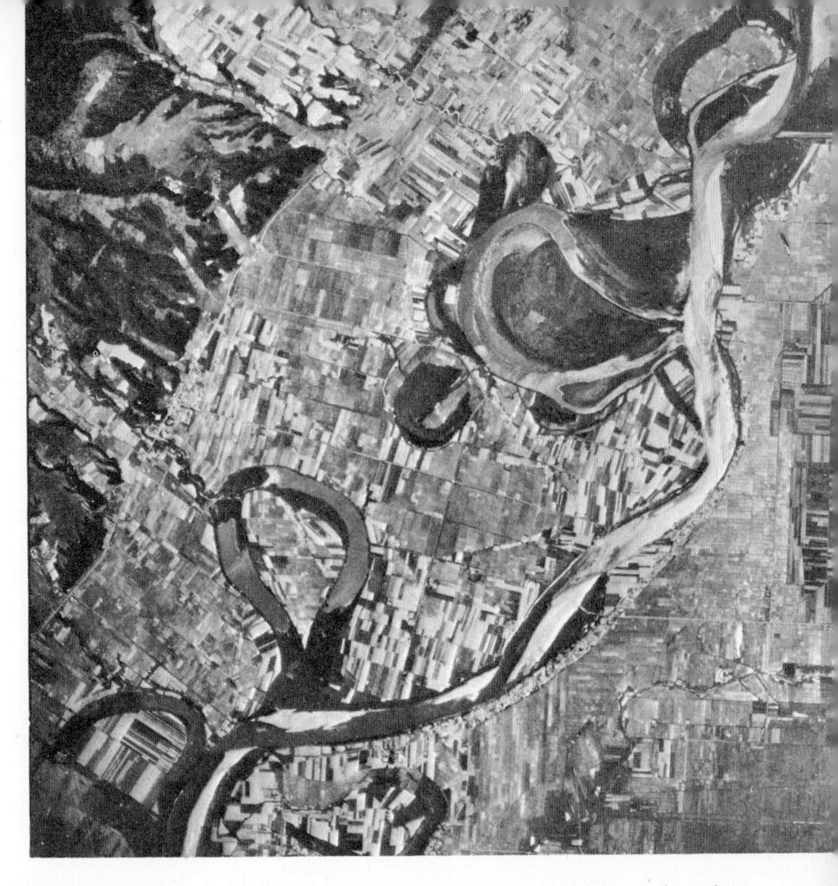

FIG. 1.2 A Hokkaido Island (Japan) landscape—a tiny fraction of the world mosaic to be described and interpreted. [U. S. Air Force (MATS)]

geographer is to perceive the different degrees of order among the composite natural features of areas at different levels of observation and to establish usable generalizations at appropriate levels. Global maps of iron ore deposits may be highly important and reliable in assessing the relative potential industrial strength of nations, but they would be almost useless to a geologist who wishes to prospect for iron ore in Afghanistan. Similarly, the small details of a large-scale hydrographic chart would be of little use to a pilot of an airplane traveling along the coast at 10 miles per minute. Out of the analysis and description of minute areal differences and similarities come the valid generalizations that are useful at broader levels. The geographer's descriptive task is like that of an ant crawling over a large Persian rug. Only by intelligently recording the changes in colors according to distance and position and scaling the changes down to perceptible size could the ant ever comprehend the complete design of the rug. Many of the minute differences in nature about us from place to place are tiny segments of a complex design. These segments begin to have meaning only when seen together and translated into the proper scale or frame of reference.

As we examine the physical make-up of the earth in this volume, the complexity of the natural designs should become readily apparent. The principles of natural distributions discussed in the preceding sections testify to the complexity of areal differences and change, yet at the same time they indicate that concepts of relative reality can be formed and can serve extremely useful ends. While it is true that no two spots on the earth are exactly alike in every detail, it is likewise true that within certain limits, prescribed by the purpose of the study, some spots are alike and may be grouped together to form a *region.*

1.7 GEOGRAPHIC GENERALIZATIONS. When a geographer draws a line on a map representing a boundary between two areas that are unlike *in some selected respects,* he is making three kinds of generalizations: (1) he chooses a classification that recognizes a certain degree of similarity of form or behavior within the area on each side of the line; (2) he generalizes the place of change between one region and another; and (3) he generalizes the changes that continually take place with time, presenting a pattern that is relatively typical only for the period of time appropriate to the purposes of his study.

Generalizations of form, area, and time are standard procedures for geographers. Each generalization is relative to the purpose and scope of the study, and its accuracy must be measured in terms of the scale on which it was made. Of the three kinds of generalizations, geographers specialize in the one dealing with differences from place to place. The physical geographers borrow heavily from the other natural sciences for classifications of form and for knowledge of processes that produce changes in form with time. Other geographers depend greatly on the social sciences for similar kinds of generalizations of form and time. Geography is the correlator of all the sciences with respect to areal content and relationships. It depends on the other sciences for basic data and techniques that must be utilized in any geographic study, but it also has its own tools and techniques, aimed specifically at understanding areal differences and similarities at levels or scales suitable for different human purposes. The other sciences, in turn, borrow the knowledge, tools, and techniques of geography in pursuing their own studies.

2

Location, scale, and maps

Location and scale are essential properties of any geographic presentation. The study of areal arrangements, the core of geography, requires that the areas studied be identified in regard to their position on earth and that they be viewed in their proper size relationship to the earth as a whole. The ability to orient ourselves is something we take for granted in our daily lives, unless, owing to circumstances, we find ourselves without it. Then it becomes the most precious thing in our lives. Anyone who has been lost in a forest while hunting, or who has been separated from familiar landmarks and faces during childhood, or who has experienced a sudden, complete loss of memory, has known utter terror. The requirements of locational measurements depend on the range of a person's mobility and contacts and on his scope of observation, direct or indirect. Such requirements today are far greater than they were in past centuries or decades. The range of man's mobility now is not only the entire surface of the globe but also an area extending several miles above the earth and a mile or so below it. His scope of observation has taken him to distances in space that are measured in millions of light-years, a measurement that is totally without meaning in terms of earthly distances. In recent years, new developments in microscopes have opened new vistas of space relationships in microspace.

Geography does not deal with location or scale in relation to all space—including both outer and inner space. It is the science of *earth* space—the earth surface itself, a few miles above it, and a small fraction of the distance between the surface and the center of the earth.

Determination of the relative location of points on earth

2.1 THE REQUIREMENTS OF POINT LOCATION. In any system of locating points, there must be fixed, recognizable base points, base lines, or base areas from which directions and distances may be plotted. Imagine the problem of establishing one's location on a motionless globe, suspended in space without any outside reference points, and with a perfectly smooth, homogeneous surface. There would be no north or south, and all locations would look alike. Until some identifiable point could be established, there could be no place from which to start. Position in such a situation would be as indefinite as space itself. Once out of sight of a recognizable object, and without the aid of a trail, we should have no means of finding the way back to it. Direction would have meaning only with respect to sight lines leading to distinguishable objects.

Fortunately the earth, though almost a sphere, is not motionless, nor is it simply hung in empty space; moreover, it has a wide variety of features marking different parts of its surface. There also are reference points in the heavens beyond the earth, and even the rhythms of earth movements aid in the construction of an earthly locational system.

The basic principles of any of the various locational systems used on earth are relatively simple. The increasing requirements of accuracy, however, demand constant refinements in the methods and techniques of locational measurements. In closely examining any one system of location, we discover that it is only relatively fixed and true. It represents a series of generalizations, in which the significant factors are taken into consideration and irrelevant minor variations are discarded. In this respect, it is like our continual need for spatial generalizations. The system we happen to be using suits our purposes, but if our purposes change, our precisional requirements may change with them, and, in turn, perhaps the system itself. With our present requirements for accuracy in plotting the courses of speedy, long-range airplanes, we utilize sets of accurate mathematical tables covering data on many subtle variables in determining position—tables that are prepared and brought up to date by governmental agencies at considerable expense. If, on the other hand, only crude, approximate location is desired, simple observational methods may be used. One does not need a sextant to find his way to the corner drugstore.

There are a number of systems for determining position on the surface of the earth. The most primitive of these methods employs prominent landscape features such as hilltops, road junctions, and large trees as reference points. Thus a position may be defined as being 200 yards north of a certain road junction and 500 yards southwest of a large granite boulder. This system is termed *metes and bounds* and was used as the means of determining property boundaries in the United States in those areas settled previous to 1785, after which this system was replaced by the public-land-survey system. In much of the eastern United States, most boundaries on property deeds still are defined in terms of metes and bounds. As a system of location, metes and bounds has only local utility, since its frame of reference is comprised entirely of local features. A further disadvantage is that frequently the reference points are temporary and may be moved or destroyed.

The more useful systems of location consist of orderly arranged sets of lines called *grids,* which have permanently fixed points of origin. The most common of these systems is the one employing lines of latitude and longitude. This grid is structured to the spherical shape of the earth and is based on reference points originated by the rhythms of earth movement. It is usually referred to as the *geographic grid.*

2.2 THE GEOGRAPHIC GRID, OR THE SYSTEM OF LATITUDE AND LONGITUDE.

The two most convenient reference points on earth are the North and South Poles, which represent the two ends of the axis about which the earth turns as it rotates from west to east. The position of the two poles helps to determine a reference line, the *equator,* which is a *great circle*[1] of the earth, midway between the two poles. If we know where the equator is, or the location of the poles, and how far a particular point is from either of them, we have placed our point somewhere along a line which runs east and west around the earth. The shortest angular distance of any point, measured toward the poles from the equator, is termed *latitude.* The imaginary line which connects all points of equal latitude is a *parallel.* Angular or circular measures are used to identify these lines as well as those of longitude, since they are convenient measures of distance on a spherical surface. In expressing angular distance on earth, we continue to use the ancient system that divides the total arc of a circle into 360 parts, each termed a *degree.* These can be divided further into sixtieths, or *minutes,* and these in turn into sixtieths, or *seconds.* Although this method is not conveniently adaptable to our numerical system, which is based on units and multiples of 10, both latitude and longitude are still expressed in degrees, minutes, and seconds. If we examine the parallels of latitude, we discover the following facts:

1. Only one of the parallels, the equator, is a great circle.

2. The parallels gradually diminish in length, becoming smaller circles toward the poles. The smallest parallels are points at the poles. These have a latitude of 90°, because the poles lie at right angles to the equatorial plane.

3. The length of a degree of latitude is approximately the same throughout the earth, and ranges roughly from 69.704 to 69.407 miles. The variation is caused by a slight flattening at the poles and a bulging at the equator.

4. The parallels measure distances north and south.

[1] A *great circle* may be said to represent the outer arch of the earth surface. Any plane that bisects the earth sphere would exhibit a great circle where it intersects the earth surface.

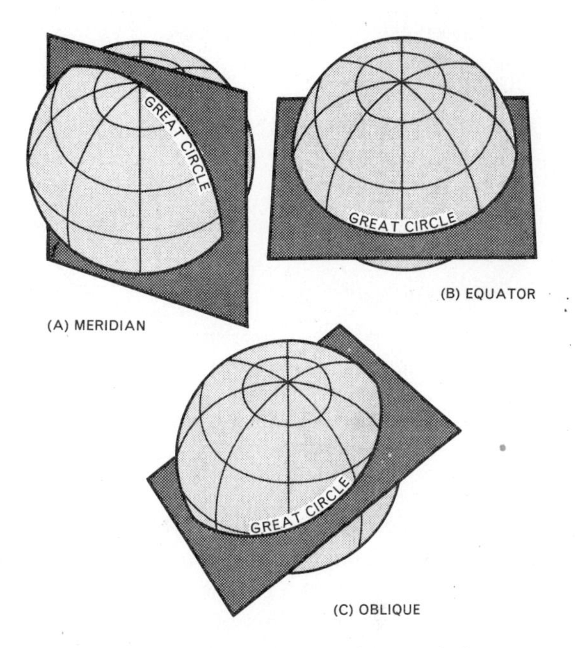

FIG. 2.1 An infinite number of great circles may be located on the earth surface.

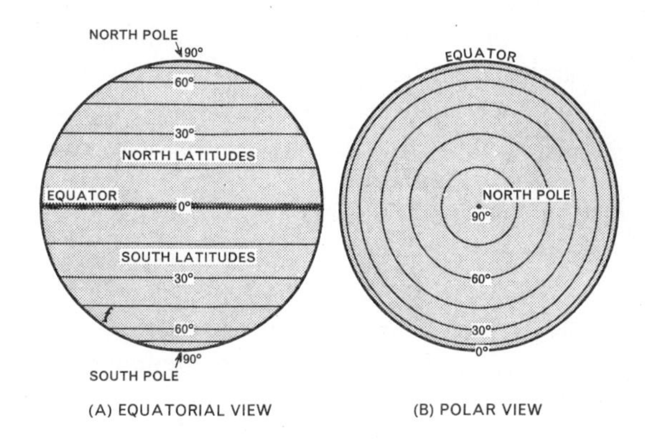

FIG. 2.2 Equatorial and polar view of parallels and latitudes.

Longitude is the angular distance on the earth surface measured 180° east and west of some arbitrary great circle that connects

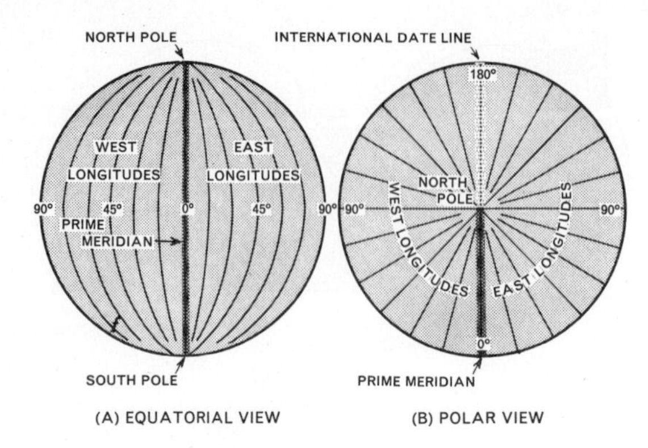

FIG. 2.3 Equatorial and polar view of meridians and longitudes.

the two poles and intersects the equator at right angles. Longitudinal distance, then, is measured along the parallels of latitude. Lines that connect points of equal longitude are termed *meridians*. The arbitrary meridian chosen as the reference line from which to measure longitude is known as the *prime meridian*. A brief examination of the meridians reveals the following:

1. Meridians are halves of great circles.
2. They intersect the equator at right angles.
3. They merge at the poles and are farthest apart at the equator.
4. The value of a degree of longitude, measured in miles along the parallels of latitude, varies from 69.172 (the circumference of the equator divided by 360) to 0 at the poles.
5. Meridians measure distances east and west.

The combination of the angular measurement of both latitude and longitude gives us a system whereby points on the earth can be located with considerable accuracy. For example, the designation lat 35°30′25″ N, long 165°15′35″ E will locate a point within 101 feet of its exact position. For greater accuracy, decimals of seconds can be used.

2.3 DETERMINATION OF LATITUDE.

The geographic grid system of locating points on earth would be impractical if it required direct measurement of distances from the equator or the prime meridian. Such a system must be adaptable to on-the-spot observation. The direct measurement of latitude from observations at a given point is based on the principle of locating oneself with reference to observable points that may be considered to be fixed in space beyond the earth, points that have known positions with reference to the equator.

The basic principle of latitude determination is illustrated in Fig. 2.4. Assume that Polaris (the North Star) is directly overhead above the North Pole. An observer at point *X* observes Polaris to be 40° above the horizon,[2] or at angle *Z*. Plane geometric relationships indicate that this angle is equal to angle *XOE*, assuming that *ON* and *XP* are parallel. This assumption may be made because of the great distance of Polaris from the earth. Since angle *XOE* is the angular distance of point *X* from the equator, it also represents the latitude of *X*. *The angle of elevation of Polaris, then, equals the latitude at the point of observation.* Polaris actually is not directly above the North Pole. It lies slightly to one side; hence it appears to move in a small circle of its own as the earth turns on its axis. Careful observation may fix the exact position of Polaris in its circuit about the true celestial pole (the zenith above the pole) for any particular day of any year. In addition, the earth's axis is not fixed with respect to the heavens; it tends to turn slowly, as does the upper end of a spinning top. This period of turning for the axis,

[2] An artificial horizon may be simply established by the use of a bubble level in a sextant or some other instrument used to determine elevations. Most elevation angles, therefore, are measured from the horizontal plane rather than from the zenith or vertical.

termed *aberration,* is approximately 26,000 years. In A.D. 14,000, the bright star Vega will be our North Star. These and other changing motions of the earth, although slow, require consideration in precise latitudinal measurements and are taken into account in the tables indicating the positions of celestial bodies for any date. Such celestial changes are carefully checked periodically at astronomical observatories, and the navigational tables are revised from time to time.

Polaris cannot be observed in the daytime—nor at night anywhere in the southern hemisphere. In the daytime, the sun is used as a reference point for determining latitude. Several easily identifiable stars are used also at night. These observations are somewhat more complex than those using the elevation of Polaris, but they are based on the same principle—that of knowing where the sun or any star should be at a given time in the vault of the heavens and of measuring the position at which it appears to an observer at some point on earth.

The method of determining latitude customarily used in navigation, where accuracy is extremely important, involves determining the position of at least three easily distinguishable stars at night, or the sun during daylight hours, by means of a sextant. The true position of these heavenly bodies for any given minute on any given date is obtained from the nautical tables.

Determining latitude by means of the sun involves earth-sun relationships that are significant also in explaining variations in the receipt of solar energy at different parts of the earth surface. Since these variations will be important in the later treatment of climatic distributions, the solar method of latitudinal determination is included here. The facts of earth-sun relationships that are pertinent to the determination of latitude are as follows:

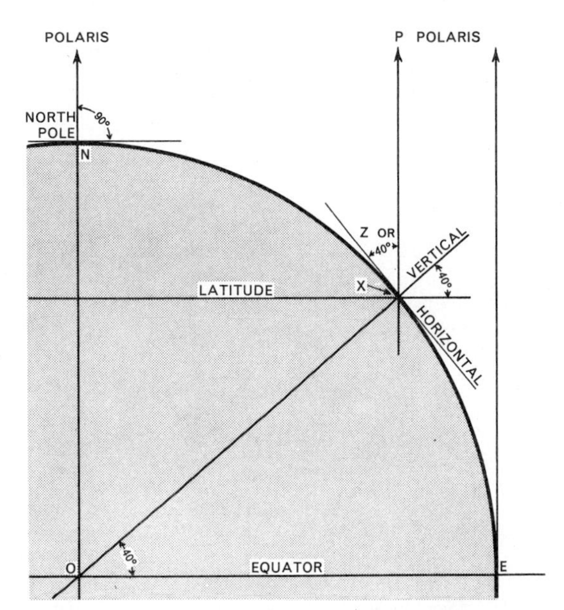

FIG. 2.4 Determination of latitude using Polaris.

1. The earth revolves about the sun in an elliptical path, or orbit, with the sun as one of the elliptical foci (see Fig. 2.5A). The eccentricity, or shape of the ellipse, changes slowly. Since the orbit of the earth is an ellipse, the distance from the earth to the sun varies somewhat. The closer the earth is to the sun, the faster is its speed of revolution.

2. The earth's axis is inclined approximately 23½° from the perpendicular to the *ecliptic* [3] (see Fig. 2.6), and remains approximately parallel to itself at any position in the orbit.

3. The earth rotates on its axis approximately once every 24 hours.

4. The "rays" of the sun may be considered to be parallel at all points of illumination on earth, because of the great distance to the sun (approximately 93 million miles). Figure 2.5 indicates that twice during the year, on dates termed the *equinoxes,* the sun shines directly at the zenith on the equator at

[3] The ecliptic is the imaginary plane surface that connects all points along the orbit of the earth.

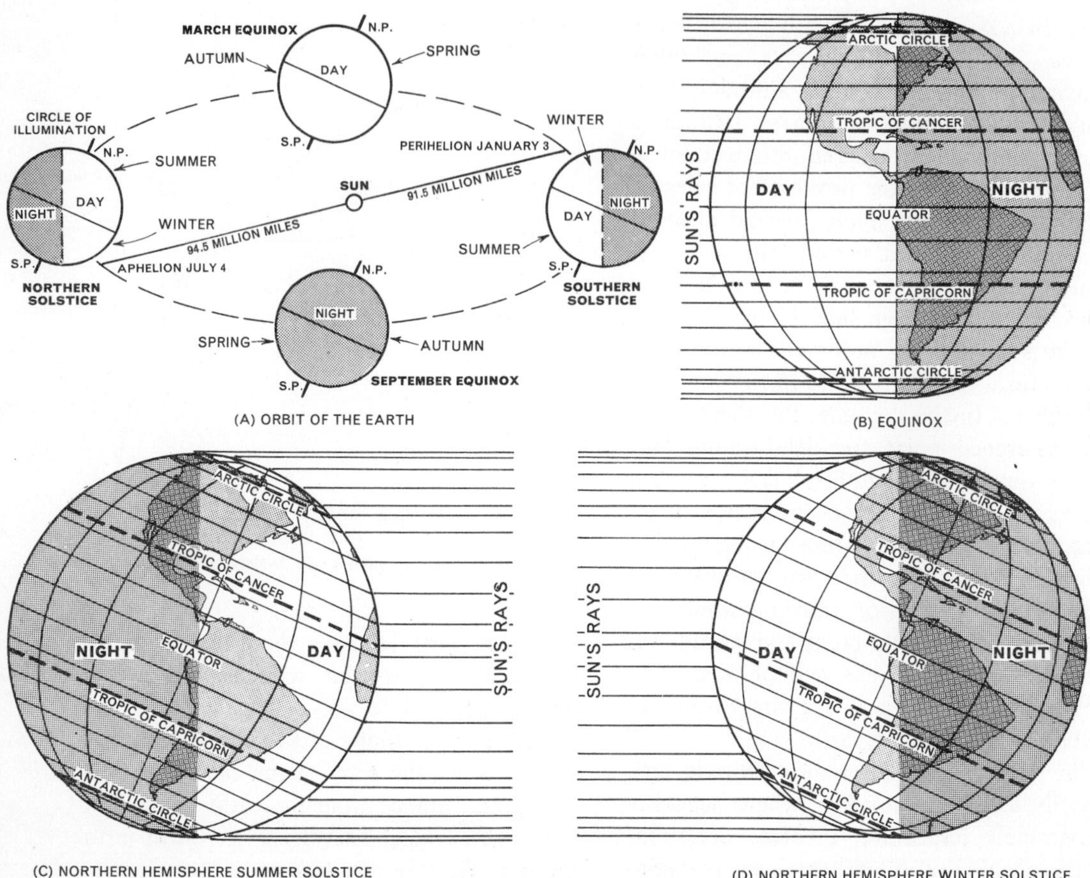

FIG. 2.5 Earth-sun relationships at the solstices and equinoxes.

noon, *sun time*.[4] On these dates, which occur on or about March 22 and September 22, and at noon, sun time, an observer's latitude can be determined by measuring the angle which the sun makes to the zenith or, as is usually done, by taking the angle which the sun makes to the horizontal and subtracting it from 90°.

At all other times of the year, the sun is directly overhead at noon somewhere between the equator and lat 23½° N and S. On or about June 21, the northern hemisphere *summer solstice,* the sun's vertical rays at noon are at their farthest point north of the equator, or at the *Tropic of Cancer* (lat 23½° N). On that date, and at noon, sun time, the angle which the sun makes to the zenith, at any point of observation, represents the number of degrees of latitude north or south that this location is from the Tropic of Cancer, and reference to the equator can then be made. On the northern hemisphere *winter solstice,* which occurs on or about December 21, the observed angle

[4] *Sun time* is the time calculated from the position of the sun in its apparent path across the sky. Noon, sun time, is the highest point along this arcuate path.

of the sun from the zenith indicates the angular distance from the Tropic of Capricorn (lat 23½° S). An observer's location, that is, whether he is north or south of the place where the sun is vertical, is indicated by the half of the sky in which the sun is seen at noon. If the sun is south of the zenith, the observer is north of the latitude where the sun is vertical, and vice versa.

In summary, if an observer knows precisely at what parallel of latitude the sun is directly overhead at the time of observation, the angle of the sun's declination (angle from the zenith) at the point of observation will give him the angular distance from that parallel, and thus fix his own latitudinal position. Observations during the daylight hours other than at noon can be taken by measur-

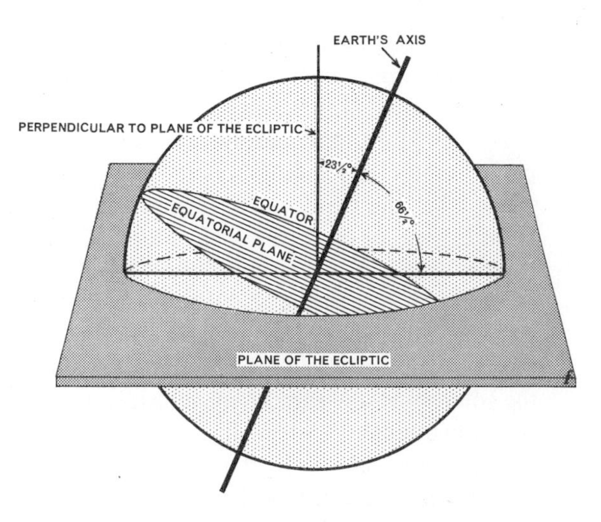

FIG. 2.6 Angular relationship between the earth's axis and the plane of the ecliptic.

FIG. 2.7 Determination of latitude using solar observation. At the equinoxes, the latitude equals the reciprocal angle (angle of solar declination) of the sun's elevation, or 90°—51° = 39° at Washington, D.C. At the solstices, the same reciprocal angle equals the latitudinal distance from the Tropic, where the sun is vertical. On June 21, for example, the reciprocal angle equals 90°—74½° = 15½° north of the Tropic of Cancer, thus yielding a latitude of 15½°+23½° = 39°.

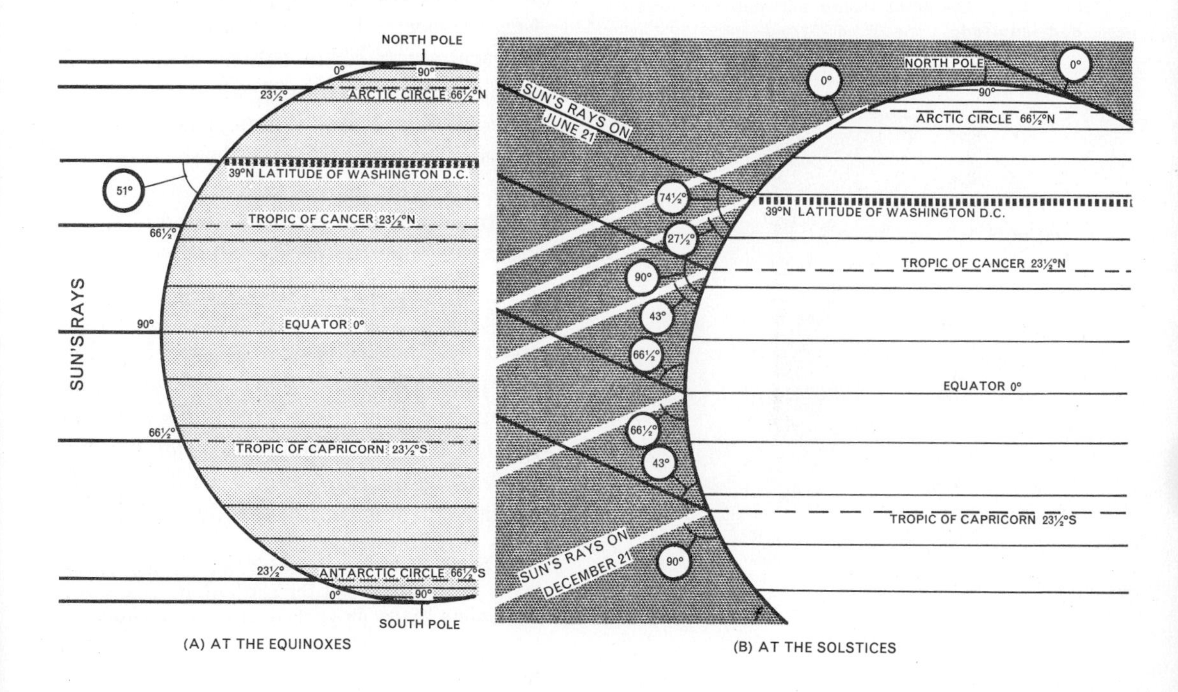

ing the exact position of the sun in its arc across the sky (determining true sun time) and calculating what its elevation would have been at noon, sun time.

As with star observations, carefully prepared tables are necessary to determine where the sun's rays are vertical at any minute, hour, or day of the year. Fluctuations in the speed of revolution, the shape or eccentricity of the orbit, the aberration of the axis, the tilt of the entire ecliptic, and other minor factors influence the exact notations in the solar tables. A careful solar observation, with a high-quality instrument, supplemented with precise tables, will determine the latitude down to the nearest tenth of a second, or within about 10 feet.

2.4 DETERMINATION OF LONGITUDE.

The determination of longitude is based on the relationship between sun time and the period of the earth's rotation. If the earth rotates on its axis one com-

FIG. 2.8 The relationship between sun time and longitude.

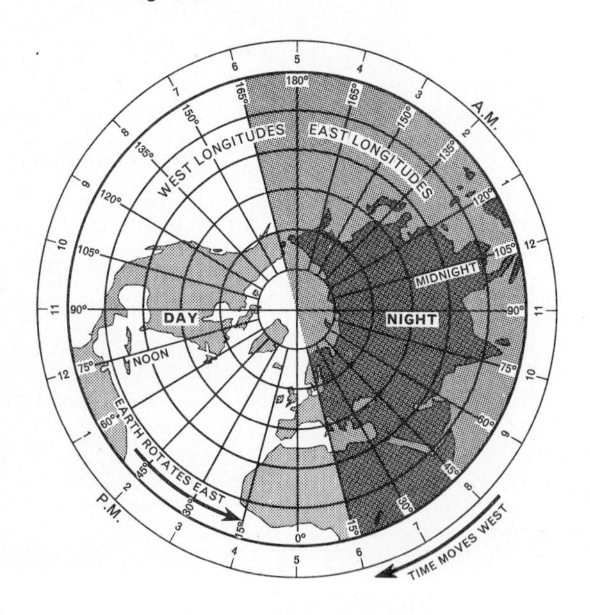

plete turn every 24 hours, it must turn 15° of longitude every hour (see Fig. 2.8). If an observer finds that the sun is at its highest point at a time when his chronometer, which has been set to prime meridian time, reads 1 P.M., then he is 1 hour, or 15°, to the west of the prime meridian, since the earth rotates from west to east. His longitude thus is 15° W. Longitude, then, is based on a comparison of local sun time with sun time at the prime meridian, and it can be obtained by reading an accurate clock or chronometer which records the sun time at the prime meridian. These chronometers may be corrected through the use of radio time signals, originating from an astronomical observatory.

The difference in sun time throughout the world explains the need for time belts, which are approximately 15° in longitude apart and within each of which the local standard time remains constant. The boundaries are adjusted for convenience. The international date line, which roughly follows the 180° meridian, was established to compensate for the gain or loss of a day in traveling east or west, respectively, around the earth.

Local sun time, of course, cannot be determined directly at night, when it is replaced by *sidereal time,* or star time, calculated from the position of certain stars in their apparent path across the heavens. Here a new variable is introduced, since sidereal time differs from mean sun time by one 24-hour interval each year. A sidereal day thus equals 23 hours, 56 minutes, and 4.09 seconds, as compared with the 24-hour solar day (see Fig. 2.9). The reason for this is that, seen from a point beyond the solar system, the earth would appear to make one complete *rotation* [5] with every complete revolution, even if there were no daily turning on its axis; hence a sidereal

[5] The term *rotation,* applied to earth movements, refers to the turning of the earth on its axis; *revolution* refers to its movement around the sun.

year consists of approximately 366¼ days, instead of the 365¼ days observed on earth.

It was noted earlier that the position of the prime meridian is arbitrary. At present, most parts of the world use longitudinal data based on the meridian that passes through Greenwich, England, the former location of the Royal Observatory. Other prime meridians, however, are still in use, such as that based on Jakarta (Batavia), Java, for use in Indonesia, and the Paris meridian, used on some French maps. As communication between people in all parts of the world increases, however, the need for using a universally accepted longitudinal system becomes greater. The Greenwich meridian seems destined to serve this need.

The development of the tools and techniques of astronomical observation has ensured that suitable accuracy in the determination of latitude and longitude can be obtained for nearly all practical purposes, yet refinements are continually being made to keep up with new demands for greater accuracy.

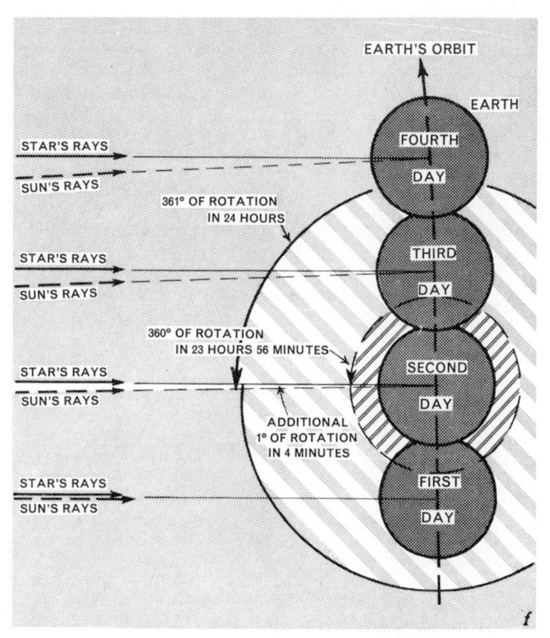

FIG. 2.9 Diagram illustrating the difference between sun time and sidereal time. An observer in outer space (or sighting along the star's rays) would observe that the earth completes its rotation in approximately 4 minutes less time than the 24 hours observed on earth each day. This difference is important in calculating the precise location of stars for navigational purposes.

2.5 THE MILITARY GRID SYSTEM.

Another kind of grid system is that employed by the military. Tactical considerations during a military campaign require a system that will locate points precisely but that can be used more rapidly and accurately than the system based on latitude and longitude. Since most tactical operations are local, military grids are primarily designed for use with large-scale maps representing relatively small areas on the earth surface. The *military grid system* adopted for this purpose consists of using a perfect-square grid, structured to a plane surface, superimposing it on a preliminary map of the area, and locating points by reference to right-angle coordinates.

There are a variety of military grid systems, since most modern nations have, at one time or other, devised systems to meet their specific needs. The present United States military grid was developed in cooperation with several other countries to achieve a uniform and comprehensive coverage of the world. In this system the coordinates are usually spaced at 1,000-meter intervals but sometimes at 10,000- or 100,000-meter intervals. The base of the preliminary map, on which the meter grids are superimposed, is a universal transverse mercator projection; consequently the United States military grid system is commonly referred to as the universal transverse mercator, or UTM, grid. Because the grid disregards the curvature of the earth, position is not indicated in degrees, minutes, and seconds, but by a linear, metric, unit-decimal system, suitable for rapid inter-

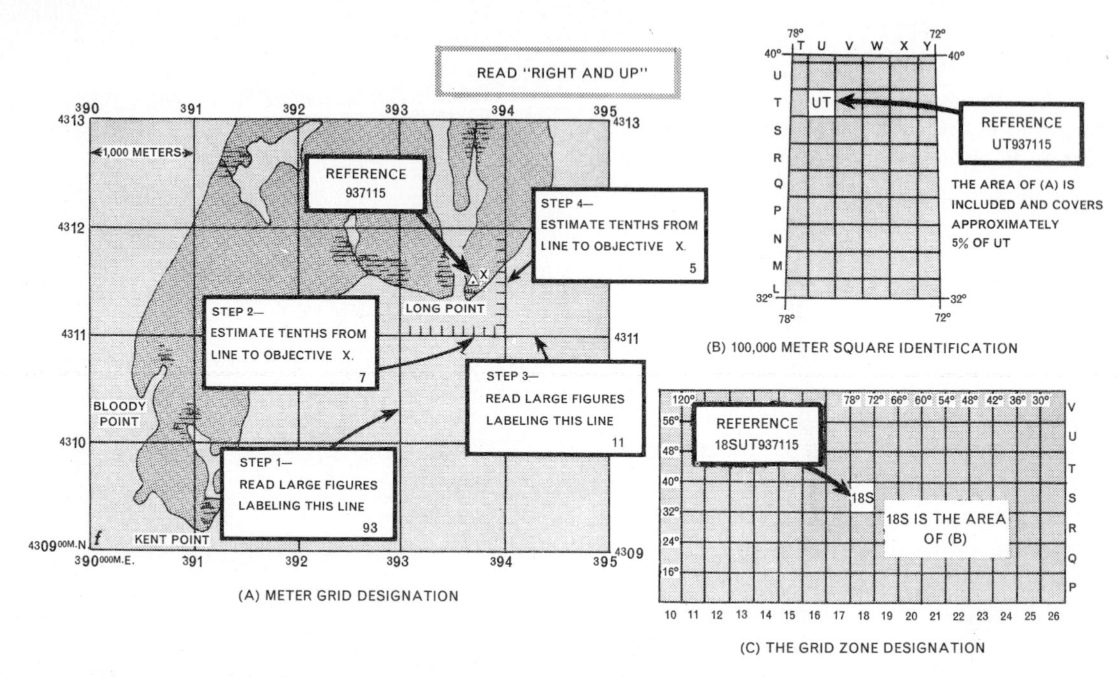

FIG. 2.10 The military grid system. [After AMS Technical Manual 36]

polation. The use and particular advantages of this system are illustrated in Fig. 2.10.

The military grid system of locating points has one obvious limitation. A grid composed of squares can satisfactorily correlate with true directions for only a small part of the surface of the earth. Once a grid is oriented to a point or line on the earth or on a map, its value in indicating directions is limited to the area close to that point or line. As distance from this orientation feature increases, in any direction, military grids progressively lose the property of true direction, even though they accurately express distance. In the United States military grid system, distortion of direction is controlled by extending the grid no more than 3° long on either side of the meridian to which the grid is oriented. Sixty belts of longitude, each 6° wide and each with its own meter grid oriented to a central meridian, are used. Thus the grid selected for a military map of any particular area is determined by the longitude belt in which the map is located.

As long as only short distances are involved, meter grid references are adequate. Since, however, modern warfare possesses great mobility over long distances, a system adaptable to large areas is essential. The system employed by the United States is called the *grid reference system*. It uses belts of longitude 6° wide and belts of latitude 8° wide to form what are termed *grid zones*. These are identified by a number-and-letter combination and are subdivided into 100,000-meter squares which are identified by two-letter combinations. Within the 100,000-meter squares, meter grid designations are used (see Fig. 2.10).

2.6 THE PUBLIC-LAND-SURVEY SYSTEM. Another type of grid system is the United States *public-land-survey system*. This system, devised as a means of subdividing public lands for settlement purposes, was put into effect after 1785 in the central and western states. The basic unit of measurement is an area 6 miles square called a *township*. Each township is subdivided into 36 equal areal units, each containing 1 square mile. These units are called *sections*. These sections in turn can be subdivided into various fractions for greater precision in locating position. The standard homestead unit in the settling of the Middle West was a quarter-section of land, which amounted to 160 acres.

All locations within an area about the size of one or two states are measured, in the public-land-survey system, from two primary lines. One line, running due north and south, is called the *principal meridian*. The other, running due east and west, is called the *base line*. There are about thirty-two principal meridians and twenty-five base lines in the United States. East-west rows of townships extend to the north and south of the base line and are identified as a given number of townships north or south of that line. The north-south rows of townships extending east and west of the principal meridian are similarly identified but are referred to as *ranges*. A specific 6-mile-square township, for example, is located, or identified, as Township 6 North—Range 11 East. Further refinement employs the *sections*, which are numbered 1 through 36. More precise locations can be given by subdividing the sections into quarter-sections, named by compass direction, and even the quarter-sections may be subdivided if necessary (see Fig. 2.11).

FIG. 2.11 The public-land-survey system. Township Y in (A) is designated as Township 2 South, Range 2 East, or more simply, T2S/R2E. Township X would be designated as T7N/R3W. A 40-acre field, as shown in (C), might be designated as the NW¼ of the SE¼ of Section 27, T2S/R2E.

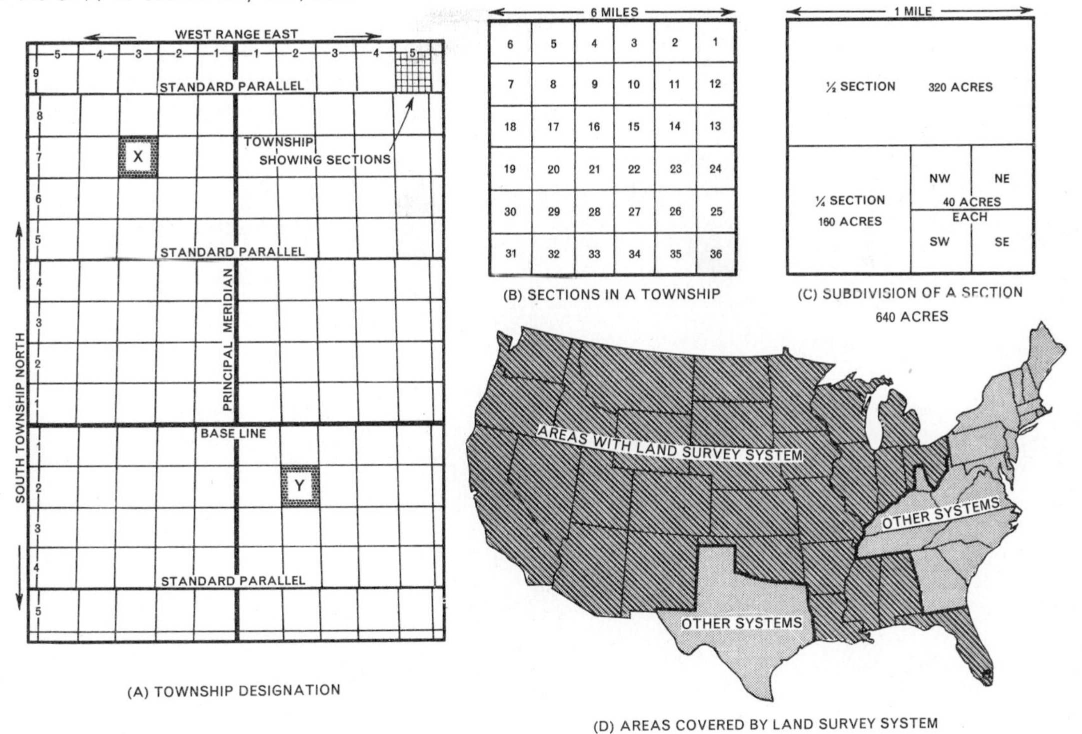

The eastern and western boundaries of townships are meridians that are measured off along the base line in 6-mile units from the principal meridians. Since meridians converge toward the north, the width of townships would diminish northward from the base line if suitable adjustments were not made. Secondary base lines, called *standard parallels,* are therefore established at 24-mile intervals north of the base line, and the widths of townships readjusted to six miles. Consequently, the lines bounding the townships and sections on the east and west are offset along this line. Roads, particularly secondary roads, which follow these lines, as is common in the Central Plains states, have sharp turns or jogs where the standard parallel is crossed (see Fig. 2.12).

Determination of direction

Directions on the surface of the earth are oriented logically to earth features. On a local scale they may be given with reference to local surface features—for example, "in the direction of the church steeple"—but the world-wide system of direction employs, in one way or another, the cardinal points of the compass—north, east, south, and west. Direction usually is expressed in terms of angular measurements from these points. In certain cases, such as in military usage, only one cardinal point may be used. In such cases, the angle measured in determining direction (termed *bearing*) is formed at the intersection of a line drawn to a cardinal point (the *azimuth* line) and the line of direction.

A direction on earth, as properly defined, is the bearing of a great circle, that is, its angular measurement from the azimuth. The reason for this is that directions on a sphere are expressions of the shortest, or "straight-line," distances across the surface of a sphere between two points. This is also the nature of a great circle. Along such a line, angular measurements, or directions, change constantly. In Fig. 2.13, for example, the direction from *A* to *D* is not the same as from *C* to *D,* even though *C* is on the same great circle.

A line on the earth surface which follows a constant compass direction is not a straight line; rather, it is a constantly curving line

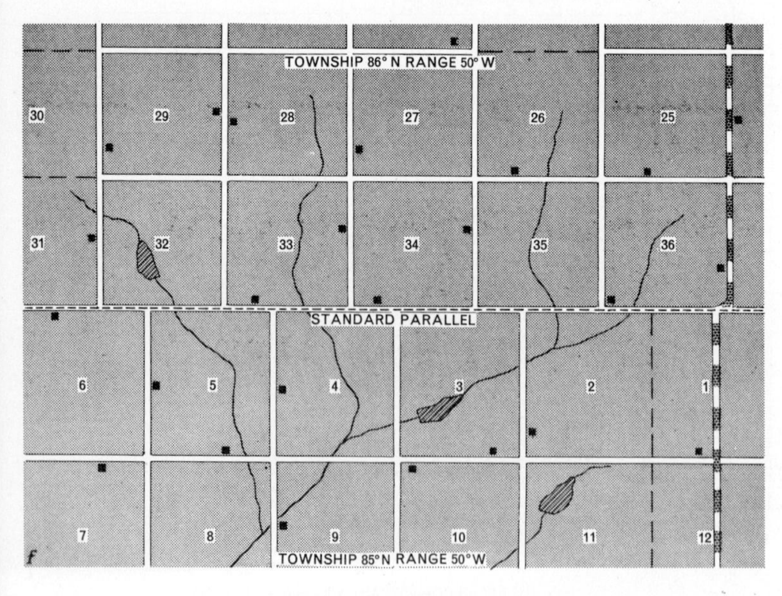

FIG. 2.12 Influence of the public-land-survey system on the location of roads in the Great Plains.

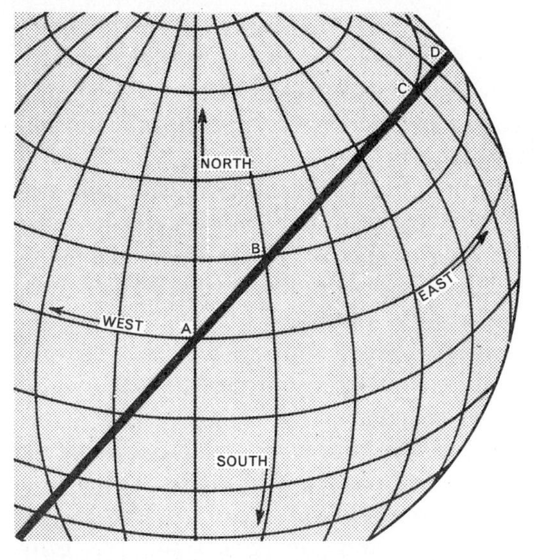

(A) CHANGING DIRECTIONS ALONG A GREAT CIRCLE

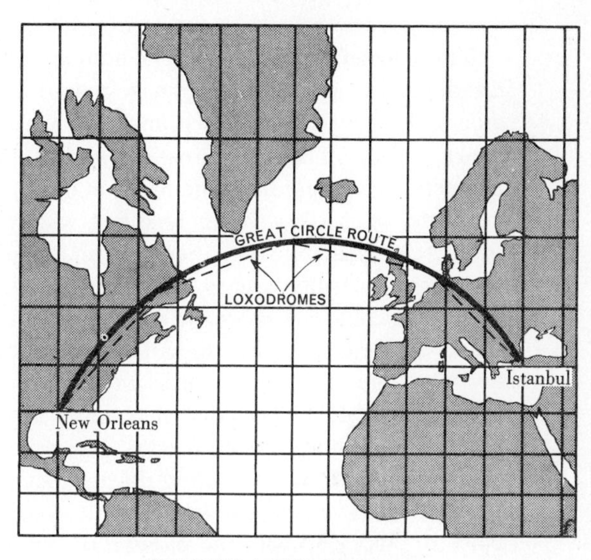

(B) PLOTTING A GREAT CIRCLE ROUTE

FIG. 2.13 Changing direction along great circles. The heavy black lines show the location of a great circle route on two types of map projections. In the left diagram (A), although the great circle is a straight line, the angle at which it crosses the meridians changes. In (B) the great circle is plotted on Mercator's projection. Constant compass directions are shown here by straight lines, while the great circle is an arc. Instead of changing direction constantly to follow the great circle route exactly between New Orleans and Istanbul, the pilot of a plane will fly a series of loxodromes (or rhumb lines). When he reaches the end of one flight leg (rhumb line) he knows how much to alter his compass course to start the new leg.

which spirals in toward the poles, but theoretically never reaches them. Such a line, termed a *loxodrome* or *rhumb line,* is shown on a map as a chord of a great circle. It has little value, directionwise, for the layman but much value for the navigator. In fact, as navigational tools, the great circles and loxodromes are as valuable as the compass.

2.7 THE COMPASS. Crude methods for determining angular direction were known by early man. The direction of prevailing winds, ocean currents, and paths of migratory birds, as well as many other evidences, were used to indicate approximate direction. The Polynesian and early Norse navigators were sufficiently skilled in utilizing the direction of waves and ocean currents and the location of stars to sail confidently for days beyond the sight of land. The magnetic compass originated somewhere in Asia, and the Chinese are usually credited with its discovery. Its principle is simple: a needle of magnetized metal, mounted on a bearing to reduce friction, aligns itself parallel to the lines of force in the magnetic field of the earth.[6]

[6] The earth is a huge magnet, with all the properties of magnets, including two poles, or centers, from which the respective forces of magnetic attraction and repulsion diverge. These magnetic poles, unlike the poles at the ends of the earth axis, are neither directly opposite each other nor fixed in position. The north magnetic pole is presently located on Bathurst Island in the archipelago of islands north of Canada, and the south magnetic pole is located near the margin of Antarctica, south of New Zealand. The pattern of the magnetic force field is neither fixed nor symmetrical. The reasons for its variability are not entirely clear, but one suggested explanation is that it is related to movements of material within the liquid portion of the earth interior.

The magnetic compass has a number of disadvantages as a tool for precise measurements, despite its wide use in making crude measurements of angular direction. First, the magnetic needle parallels the earth magnetic field, the lines of which may differ widely from true north and south. Second, since the magnetic field shifts and is not symmetrical, the rate of change in *magnetic declination,* or the deviation of compass direction from true north or south, is not consistent in any given direction; furthermore, it changes appreciably over the course of years. Near the magnetic poles, the variation in magnetic declination is especially great, both from place to place and with the passage of time. Last, the magnetized needle of a compass is attracted by any nearby magnetic material, such as bodies of magnetic ore or objects of magnetized steel. Many a hunter has wondered at the erratic behavior of his compass, diverted from its true reading by the magnetic zipper of a hunting jacket or a knife sheathed to his belt.

Careful measurements of the earth magnetic force field are continually being made in order to plot the magnetic declination for different parts of the earth surface. Maps showing the distribution of magnetic declination (see Fig. 2.14) are kept up to date in order to serve the numerous users of the magnetic compass.

Other types of compass are replacing the magnetic compass, particularly for airplane and ship navigation. Two of these are the *gyroscopic* and *sun compasses.* The gyroscopic compass utilizes the principle of a gyroscope. When its wheel is rotated with its axis oriented in a known direction, it maintains this direction within narrow limits,

FIG. 2.14 Map of isogonic lines. These lines represent the configuration of the earth magnetic force field, and thus are lines of constant compass declination. The isogonic lines converge at the two magnetic poles. [After a map by U.S. Coast and Geodetic Survey]

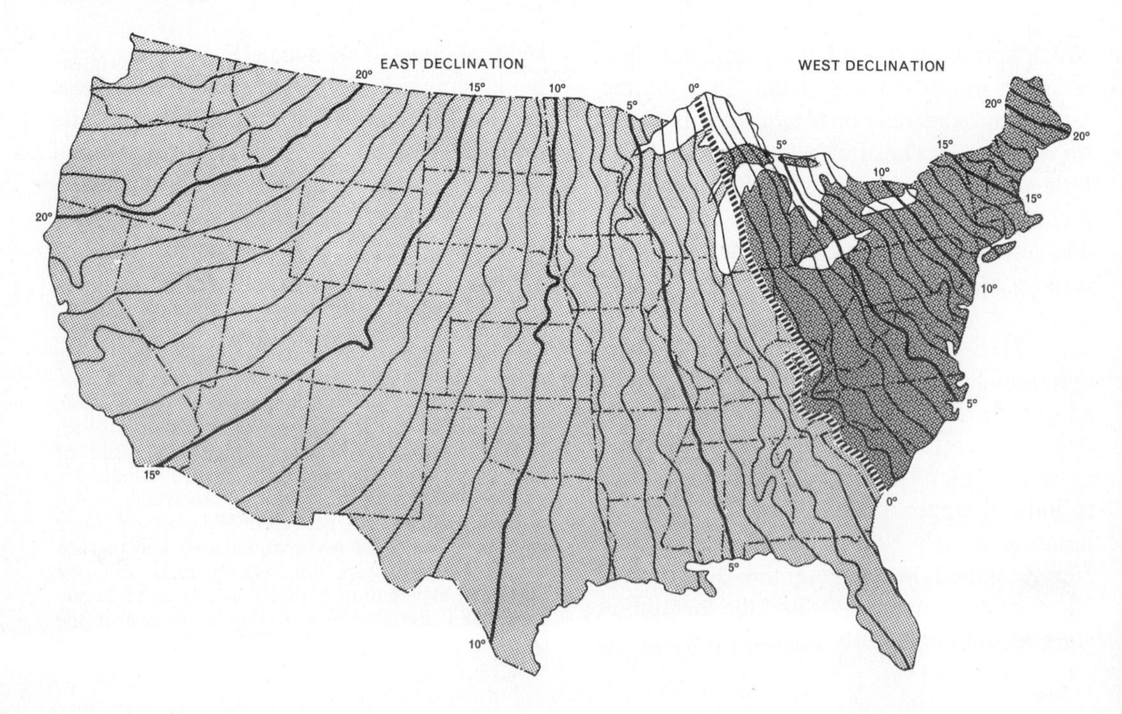

regardless of the motion of the gyroscopic pedestal. The sun compass is perhaps the most accurate compass of all, since it calibrates direction by utilizing the relationship between the sun's elevation, geographic location, and the time of the day or year. It is used primarily for navigation in polar areas, where the errors associated with the use of other compasses are magnified to the extent that these instruments become undependable. The sun compass, however, is not so easy to operate as other compasses, and it cannot be used whenever solar observation is impossible.

The newest direction finders are the *radio compass* and *radar*. The *radio compass* is a radio receiver equipped with a special rotational antenna. Rotating the antenna produces variations in the strength of the signal received from a known transmitter. The direction from which the clearest signal is obtained thus indicates the direction in which the transmitter lies. The intersection of directions from several known radio transmitters can thus establish position.

Radar consists of transmitting short-wave radio waves by means of a special antenna which concentrates the microwaves into a narrow beam. Carefully timed, synchronized radar impulses, when received and interpreted, give not only the direction but the distance from the radar transmitter. Radar beams also are reflected from dense objects, particularly metallic surfaces. By rotating both the transmission beam and a directional receiver antenna, the positions of recognizable echo surfaces are plotted on a radar receiver as small blips of light and calibrated for distance. The course and position of planes and ships can thus be accurately plotted. Determination of position by the intersection of long-range radar beams (*loran*) is used in long-distance plane and ship navigation. Short-range (*shoran*) radar is used for plotting both distances and position within more limited areas. The latter was widely used during World War II for locating approaching planes, ships, and submarines and for spotting bombing targets from above clouds or after dark during air raids. Since then it has had numerous safety applications in peacetime navigation.

2.8 PLOTTING THE DIRECTION OF MOVEMENT. In moving over the earth surface, great circles are followed if possible, since they are the shortest distances between two points. It is difficult, however, for a body in free motion to follow a great circle, or earth arc, because compass directions change continuously along these lines, except on the meridians and the equator, and thus complicate the steering problem. In addition, deflective forces of many kinds, including winds and currents, tend to shift bodies in free motion from their true courses. Consequently, when great-circle routes are plotted on maps for navigation purposes, they are modified by plotting a series of check points along the route. Lines of constant compass directions between these check points are followed to make the task of steering the ship or aircraft easier, and changes in direction are determined at each check point. In addition, accidental deviations from the planned route can be corrected at the check points.

Defining areas

The primary objective of geography is to study areas. The term *area* implies a portion of the earth surface surrounded by a boundary of some kind. Determining the nature of areal boundaries, locating them with reference to the entire earth, and presenting them on an appropriate scale are the principal tasks of the descriptive phase of geographic investigation. The following sections of this chapter are devoted to the methods used in defining, measuring, and presenting areal patterns. Points and lines are relatively easy to define or to locate, although, as indicated earlier, accuracy in location is relative and not absolute. The degree of accuracy in locating points and lines is influenced mainly by the purpose of the determination. The same statement holds true for the definition and location of areas, except that the purposes of areal differentiation and location usually are broader in scope and thus do not demand the precision needed in most determinations of points and lines. (An obvious exception is the problem of defining a piece of real estate in the heart of downtown New York City.) The process of defining areal characteristics on the earth, which constitutes a major part of geographic methodology, necessitates a distinct procedural sequence. No area or region should be shown on a map or described without a clear consideration of these steps.

Before an area or region is described or measured, it first must be defined in terms of its linear boundaries. Second, since most boundaries are arbitrary and conceptual and since they comprise a form of generalization of the earth surface, they should be scaled appropriately; that is, they should bear some stamp indicating the level of generalization made. Last, the scale of generalization, whether it is that of a map or of some other type of description, should be clearly related to the major purpose for which the study was made. The procedure of mapping or describing areas consists of (1) determining the purpose, or selecting the proper frame of reference; (2) selecting the proper scale appropriate to the purpose; and (3) defining boundaries in terms of both purpose and scale. These steps are discussed further in the succeeding paragraphs.

2.9 DEFINITION OF PURPOSE AND SELECTION OF SCALE. Some purpose underlies every map and every other type of areal generalization that was ever made. Explorers entering a new section of the world for the first time always have some frame of reference that enables them to determine what to look for and what to omit from their reports as irrelevant. Sometimes such frames of reference are not conscious, but nevertheless they are always present. The purposive framework should be given especially careful, conscious consideration in anything as precise as mapping an area or selecting a map to illustrate areal differences or similarities.

The maps in this textbook vary in scale, but many of them are world maps shown on a single page. The scale of such maps, the kinds of patterns they present, the breadth of generalization, and even the widths of the lines used—all are related to the objectives of the book. Their principal purpose is to present the *global* patterns of major physical elements. The readers, or those for whom the study was made, presumably are students and others who desire general knowledge concerning physical patterns on the earth. This text, furthermore, is designed for students committed to a semester's or a year's course in geography, not for those who plan to spend years studying world physical patterns. Obviously, too, it was intended neither to give detailed information on areal differences or similarities within a particular part of the United States nor to aid in evolving more effective land-use policies. The scope of the study is thus limited, and its specific purpose is expressed graphically by the type and scale of the maps on which the world physical patterns are shown.

Geographers designate three general levels of scale reduction, applicable not only to maps but also to descriptive generalizations: *global, chorographic,* and *topographic*. Since

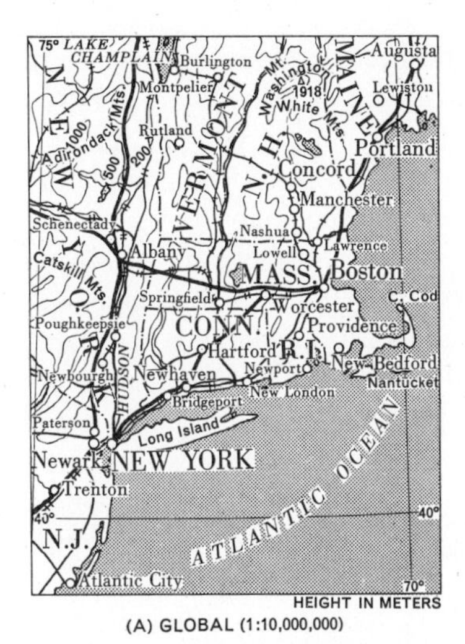

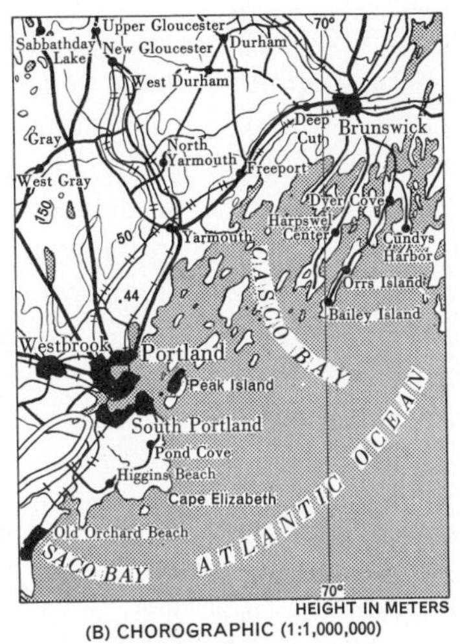

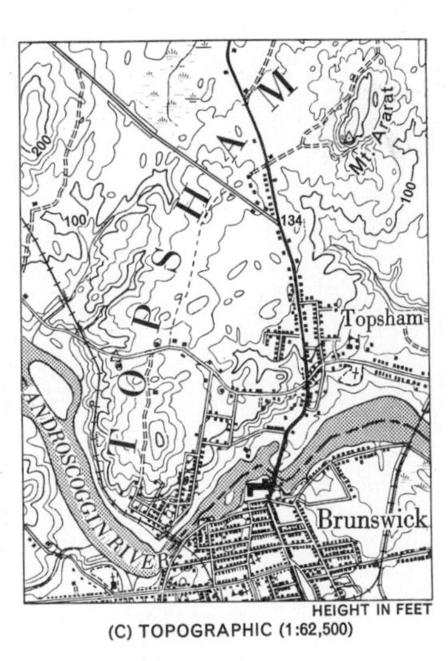

FIG. 2.15 Global, chorographic, and topographic scales. [(A) Bartholomew World Map Series; (B) International Map of the World AMS Sheet NK 19; (C) USGS Bath 15-minute Quadrangle]

these three terms are used repeatedly throughout the text, their meaning should be clarified here.

Global scales are those in which the distributional patterns are presented on maps having a ratio of 1:5,000,000 or more. This ratio signifies that 1 linear unit on the map represents 5,000,000 such units in the area that is mapped. At this scale, recognition is given only to areal differences occupying a space greater than 100 square miles, since areas that occupy less than 1/64 square inch (the equivalent of 100 square miles) are not easily distinguishable on a map.

Chorographic scales are those which portray differences that one can present on maps having ratios roughly between 1:500,000 and 1:5,000,000. With such map scales, areas can be easily distinguished only when they are larger than 1 square mile. Such scales normally are used to present patterns within a single continent or a large political unit, such as a nation, state, or province.

Topographic scales are used wherever areas smaller than 1 square mile are to be distinguished. These map scales, which have ratios under 1:500,000, are generally used to portray differences within areas no larger than an average county in the United States.

2.10 RELATION OF SCALE TO ACCURACY OF AREAL BOUNDARIES.

The scale of the maps used in presenting areal patterns, as determined by the purpose of the study, always creates certain limitations in the accuracy that can be achieved. One of these involves the width of the lines used to indicate boundaries. Obviously, lines having the same width cover a greater area on a map with a scale ratio of 1:1,000,000 than on a map with a scale of 1:1,000. On global maps of textbook size, a line may represent a strip as much as 50 miles wide.

The factor that most limits the degree of generalization in drawing areal boundaries is the amount of detail that can be presented on a map, that is, the degree of irregularity that can be shown for boundaries and the size of the areal units that can be included. To determine this, one must ask, Is the detail readable on the map? And this is dependent on a number of elements in map drafting, such as fineness of lines or selection of colors or shades and the amount of photographic reduction following original drafting. A map may present patterns that technically are readable, but the amount of detail shown may be so great that the generalizations necessary to the purpose of the study are obscured. This consideration represents one of the most difficult problems in presenting patterns of areal differentiation. Geographers are confronted with the problem of devising methods which will indicate accurately the amount of detail that can be effectively included within the generalization.

2.11 DEFINING AREAL BOUNDARIES. Regardless of the scope of the geographic study, or the scale of the map of presentation, boundaries used to separate regions showing areal differences or similarities must be defined. The criteria used for definition must be usable in observational measurements within the limits of accuracy prescribed by the scale of the map and the scope of the study. If a certain part of the United States is represented as having a coniferous forest, there should be no doubt about the common characteristics of this type of forest and about the areas where it is replaced by some other kind of vegetation. There may be patches of forest present within the boundary that clearly do not fit the definition, but these should be too small to be significantly noticed on the map. The validity of a boundary location is tested by observational measurements based on the same degree of accuracy as required by the boundary definition. It would not be quite fair, for example, to deny the worth of a state map of vegetation if one finds a single maple tree in an area marked on the map as a coniferous forest.

In selecting the criteria for defining a boundary between regions, it is not always necessary to proceed inductively, that is, to make generalizations of areal characteristics from more detailed studies. Global generalizations do not have to await the completion of detailed topographic maps covering the entire world. The classification of living organisms, however, requires inductive evidence. Since the parts of animals or plants are functional necessities for the entire organism, animals or plants must be distinguished in terms of differences in these functioning units. A wing feather on a Canada jay serves essentially the same purpose as one on a parrot in Brazil, even though they may look much different. Distinguishing between Canadian and Brazilian birds solely on appearance would be meaningless and illogical. The earth surface, however, is not an organic whole in which each part has a function to perform in relation to the entire earth and where each part is dependent on the whole. Thus the inductive process of classification that is necessary and logical in the biological and geological fields is not obligatory in the geographic process, though it is often useful. Regardless of the process by which the boundary definitions are selected, however, the criteria used must be measurable and must be applicable to the scale of the study.

2.12 TYPES OF AREAL DIFFERENCES. Although there are infinite differences from place to place on the earth, they may be classified into three general categories: (1) differences in morphology or form, (2) differences in quantity, and (3) differences in density. The first is distinguished by either the presence or the absence of particular features or forms, whereas the second and third represent the relative degree in which they are present. The selection of the type of measurement to use in a geographic study depends on the purpose of the study. A mahogany importer might want to know where mahogany trees grow in the world, and a governmental official in Honduras might want to know where mahogany can be found in his country. Such studies would illustrate the need for the first, or morphological, type of geographic study. The same persons, however, might also want to know the quantity of mahogany available in a particular area or the density of a mahogany stand in one area as compared with that of another. Quantity and density are not synonymous. Obviously, the three purposes require different methods of measurement, presentation, and analysis. In each case, however, the findings of the geographic study must be capable of being expressed in terms of location, or of being related to points, lines, or areas on a map.

Map projections and the functions of maps and cartography

Thus far in this chapter we have examined the processes by which points, lines, and areas are identified, generalized, and located geographically. The next step is to present the methods of portraying the patterns thus observed and measured. The two most common means are maps and globes. Both devices are scaled representations of all or parts of the earth. Since globes have the curved surface of the earth spheroid, they are, in this respect, more accurate representations of the earth than are maps. Globes, however, are such bulky and expensive devices that they are limited to small-scale portrayals of only the major earth features. For this reason they are very restricted in their use. Maps, on the other hand, are relatively inexpensive, very easy to handle, and capable of being drawn to almost any scale. These, plus other advantages, adequately compensate for the errors inherent in representing an all-sided curved surface, the earth, on a plane—the map.

The use of maps is almost as old as recorded history, and many early peoples portrayed local surface features in crude representations reduced to an appropriate scale. Among the earliest known maps is a

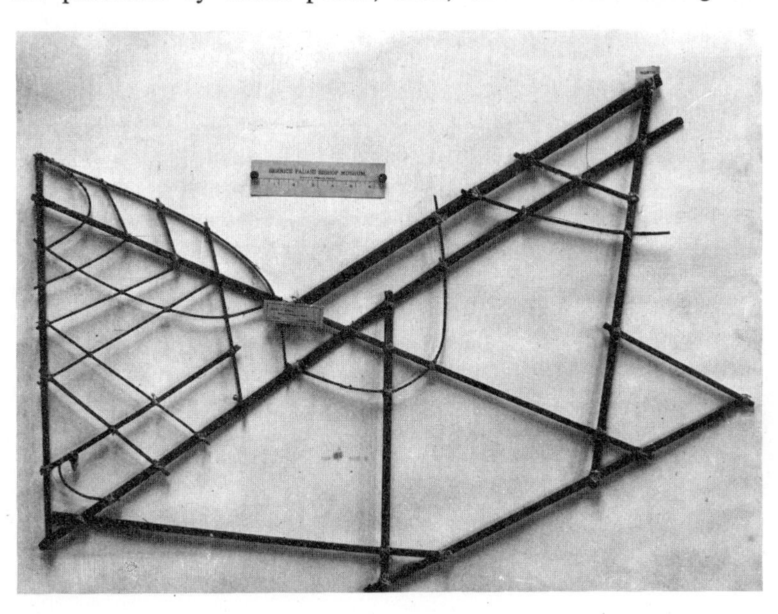

FIG. 2.16 A stick chart used by Marshall Islanders for ocean navigation. The sticks represent prevailing direction of waves and currents. Island positions were marked by placing shells at appropriate places on the frame. [Bernice P. Bishop Museum]

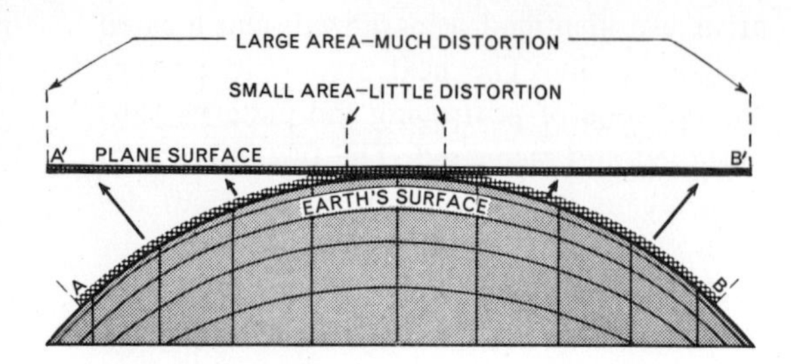

FIG. 2.17 Departure of a spherical surface from a plane surface.

small clay tablet approximately 4,500 years old that was inscribed to show the approximate location of an estate somewhere in northern Iraq. Simple picture maps of coastal outlines have been found on walrus ivory, carved there by early Eskimos. Polynesian navigators, long before they had any contact with white people, used ingenious string or stick maps in which knots or attached shells represented islands, and the strings themselves portrayed the directional patterns of prevailing currents and waves.

As the extent of man's mobility increased, there was need for more accurate maps covering larger areas. When the curvature of the earth became apparent, a new problem in map making appeared, one that has remained with cartographers (map makers) ever since. This unsolvable problem is that the surface of a sphere cannot be converted into that of a plane without some degree of distortion. In order for all or even part of a spherical surface to lie flat contiguously, it must be either compressed or stretched, or both, at various places and in various amounts. Because of this, the space characteristics of distance and direction, and consequently of shape and area, which are true on the earth surface cannot all be transferred onto one map. When such transfers are attempted, distortions of one or more of these characteristics occur. It is possible, however, individually and in certain combinations, to represent selected characteristics truly on a map, but in so doing, distortions will be present for some other properties and, in fact, may be increased as the result of acquiring true representation for a desired characteristic. Everyone who uses maps to any appreciable extent should therefore be trained to recognize the kind, amount, and distribution of the distortion inherent in any particular representation.

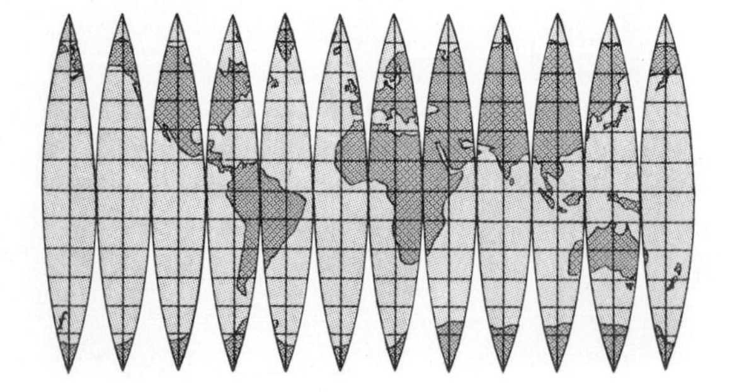

FIG. 2.18 Globe gores.

The departure of the earth spherical surface from a plane is small when only limited areas are represented on a map; therefore, in such cases the amounts of distortion are likewise small (see Fig. 2.17). Thus large-scale maps, except for extremely precise or exact uses, can generally be considered free of all distortion. When areas as large as countries, continents, hemispheres, or the entire world are involved, however, distortion becomes so great that maps of such areas contain significant errors.

To illustrate the problems of distortion, suppose we wished to portray the surface of an orange on a flat plane. If we photographed it, or drew a perspective sketch of it, it might be recognized as an orange, but only one side could be shown. Furthermore, the shape would be distorted, and only our visual habit of perceiving things in perspective would enable us to recognize it as a sphere. We also could spread the entire surface of the orange on a flat plane by peeling it and cutting it into segments termed *gores.* In fact, the surfaces of globes are printed in such segments, or gores, while they are still on a flat plane, and these segments faithfully represent the total area of the globe; but the total surface spread out in no way resembles the shape of the globe (see Fig. 2.18). In a photograph or perspective drawing of an orange, an illusion of correct shape is created at the sacrifice of area. In globe gores, true area is represented at the expense of badly distorted shape and directions.

2.13 MAP PROJECTIONS.

As indicated earlier, the spatial characteristics of the earth surface may be truly represented on a map either individually or in certain combinations. The mechanism which is used to achieve this transfer is called a *map projection.* A map projection may be simply defined as *the orderly or systematic arrangement of the earth grid on a plane surface.* It is possible to devise an infinite number of map projections, and hundreds have been invented. Only a few dozen are commonly used, however, and these are entirely sufficient for the needs of present-day mapping. To acquire a general knowledge of projections does not require that they be studied individually. Despite the relatively large number of projections, several of them have certain characteristics in common and thus can be grouped, or classified, and studied in this way. Projections are usually classified either according to their properties or according to their construction.

2.14 PROPERTIES OF PROJECTIONS.

A map property is a trait possessed by a projection which gives it value for certain purposes. Most such properties are attempts to duplicate on a plane surface the spatial characteristics of the earth surface, such as *distance, direction, shape,* and *area.* Of these, area is the only one which can truly be represented without qualification on an entire map. True distances, true directions, and true shapes, as properties of map projections, have more limited uses. For example, true distances can be shown from only one central point, and there is only one projection which can represent even this limited definition of true distance—the *azimuthal equidistant* projection. Directions, likewise, can be true from only one central point. Even on those projections having the property of true direction from a central point, there will be errors in direction from all other points. Similarly, shapes can be shown as true only for small areas. Over larger areas, the shapes will be distorted because of distortions in both distance and direction.

The four major properties of map projections are as follows:

1. Equivalence (equal-area), in which the ratio between areas on the map is the same as on the earth surface
2. Conformality, in which shapes are true for limited areas
3. Azimuthal, in which directions are true from a central point
4. Compromise, in which distortion is kept to a minimum but no characteristic of the surface is truly represented

In addition to these four major properties, there are minor properties, or attributes, of map projections which have a more specialized utility. These include such traits as true distance, lines of constant compass direction as straight lines, and great circles as straight lines, as well as other characteristics having particular value for certain kinds of mapping.

More than one true property can occur on a single projection. For example, there is an azimuthal projection which is equivalent, and there is also an azimuthal projec-

TABLE 2.1 Summary of map projections

PROJECTION	MAXIMUM FEASIBLE AREA	PROPERTIES	DISTORTION	USES
		Cylindrical		
Mercator's	World	Conformal; lines of constant compass directions shown as straight lines	Increases poleward	Navigation and in transverse form for military mapping
Cylindrical equal-area	World	Equivalent	Increases north and south from equator or standard parallels	Mapping distributions where areal size relationships are important
Miller's	World	Compromise	Increases north and south from two standard parallels	Mapping distributions where areal size relationships are not paramount
Gall's stereographic	World	Compromise	Increases north and south from two standard parallels	Mapping distributions where areal size relationships are not paramount
Plane chart	World	Compromise; easy to construct	Increases north and south from equator or standard parallels	Mapping distributions where areal size relationships are not paramount
		Plane (azimuthal)		
Stereographic	Hemisphere	Conformal; true directions from center point; all circles shown as circles	Distortion increases from center outward	Navigation; mapping distributions where positions are important
Azimuthal equal-area	Hemisphere usually; can show world	Equivalent; true directions from the center point	Distortion increases from center outward	Mapping distributions where areal size relationships are important and for areas less than world size
Azimuthal equidistant	Hemisphere usually; can show world	Distances and directions true from center point	Distortion increases from center outward	Measuring distances from a center point to all other points
Gnomonic	Less than hemisphere	All great circles as straight lines	Distortion increases very rapidly from the center outward	Navigation; to determine great circle routes
Orthographic	Hemisphere	Compromise; gives visual appearance of the earth	Distortion increases from center outward	Pictorial representations of the earth
		Conic		
Simple	Less than hemisphere	Compromise; easy to construct	Increases north and south from a standard parallel	Mapping distributions where relationships of areal size or position are not paramount

TABLE 2.1 Summary of map projections (continued)

PROJECTION	MAXIMUM FEASIBLE AREA	PROPERTIES	DISTORTION	USES
		Conic (continued)		
Alber's equal-area	Less than hemisphere	Equivalent; very little distortion for area, size, and shape of U.S.	Increases north and south from two standard parallels	Mapping distributions where areal size relationships are important at continental or lesser size
Lambert's conformal	Less than hemisphere	Conformal; very little distortion for area size and shape of U.S.	Increases north and south from standard parallels	Mapping distributions where positional relationships are important; weather maps; navigation
Bonne's	Less than hemisphere	Equivalent	Increases away from standard parallel and central meridian	Mapping distributions where areal size relationships are important for "square-shaped" areas the size of Europe or less
Polyconic	Less than hemisphere	Compromise; easy to construct	Increases away from central meridian	Large-scale military mapping
		Miscellaneous		
Mollweide's homolographic	World	Equivalent	Increases away from intersection of lat 40° N & S and central meridian	Mapping distributions where areal size relationships are important
Sinusoidal	World	Equivalent	Increases away from equator and central meridian	Mapping distributions where areal size relationships are important. Good for South America and Africa
Homolosine	World	Equivalent; interrupted; minimizes other distortions; uses best parts of homolographic and sinusoidal	Generally increases away from equator and central meridian	Mapping distributions where areal size relationships are important and where interruptions will not complicate presentation
Eckert series: nos. 2, 4, 6	World	Equivalent	Increases away from equator and central meridian	Mapping distributions where areal size relationships are important
Van der Grinten	World	Compromise; easy to construct	Increases in all directions away from the intersection of central meridian and equator	Mapping distributions where areal size relationships are not paramount

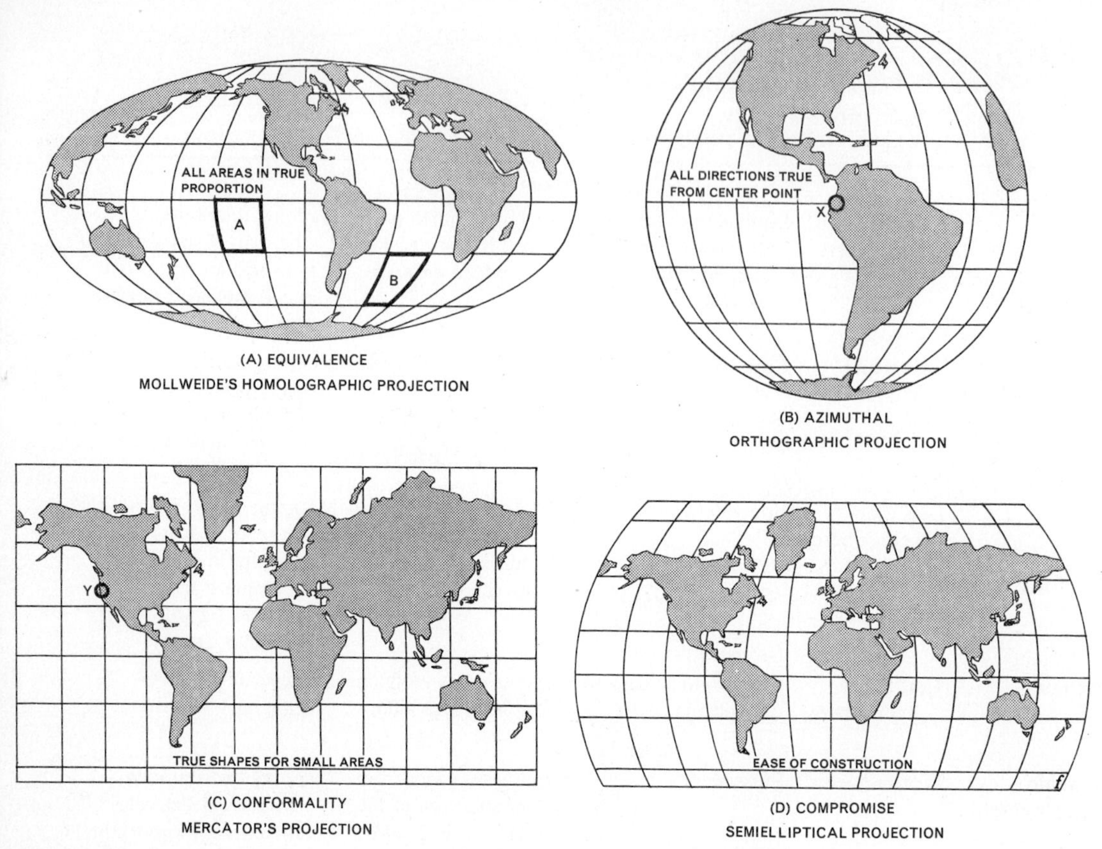

FIG. 2.19 The four major properties of map projections as illustrated by four different projections.

tion which is conformal. Major and minor properties commonly are found on the same projection. It is important to note, however, that no one projection can be both conformal and equivalent. These are mutually exclusive properties. The properties of some of the more common projections are given in Table 2.1.

2.15 THE CONSTRUCTION OF PROJECTIONS. For the purpose of accuracy, all projections employed by professional map makers are constructed by using mathematical formulas to obtain the necessary precise spacing of meridians and parallels. In most cases, these formulas express the geometric transfer of the grid of the spherical earth onto a plane surface or the surface of either a cone or a cylinder. The latter two surfaces can then be flattened into a plane without any subsequent alteration of the arrangement of the meridians or parallels (see Fig. 2.20). The term *map projection* is derived from this process of "projecting" the earth grid onto these surfaces. The methodology can be graphically demonstrated by taking a transparent globe with the grid lines etched on it and, by means of a light, projecting the shadows of the grid onto a plane surface (see Fig. 2.21). Some projections, however, are constructed without employing the principle of geometric projection. The arrangement of meridians and parallels on the plane surface is accomplished in a more arbitrary, but no less precise, manner. In fact, many of the map projections which are derived from theoretical geometric projections *and named after the surfaces involved* are mathematically adjusted or modified in order to achieve some desirable characteristic.

In grouping projections on the basis of their construction, the following four major types occur. The first three obviously are named after the surfaces involved in the geometric projection. The four types are:

1. Plane projections, which are also termed *azimuthal,* because they all have the property of true direction from a central point
2. Conic projections
3. Cylindrical projections, also termed *rectangular,* because of the shape given to world maps on this type of projection
4. Miscellaneous projections, comprising all those projections—such as oval projections—in which no geometric projection is involved

The four major groups of projections are in turn subdivided on the basis of the properties of individual projections. For example, there are equivalent, conformal, and compromise conic projections. Similar variations in properties are, to a greater or less degree, also true of the other groups.

A further difference results from variations in centering, or locating, individual projections. Plane projections may be centered on points, but conic and cylindrical projections are centered on lines, usually parallels. Miscellaneous projections are centered on points or lines, depending on the specific projection. Variations in centering will alter the appearance of the grid but will not alter the basic properties of the map. In this way a plane, equal-area projection, for

FIG. 2.20 Surfaces in map projections and the distribution of distortion. [After Robinson]

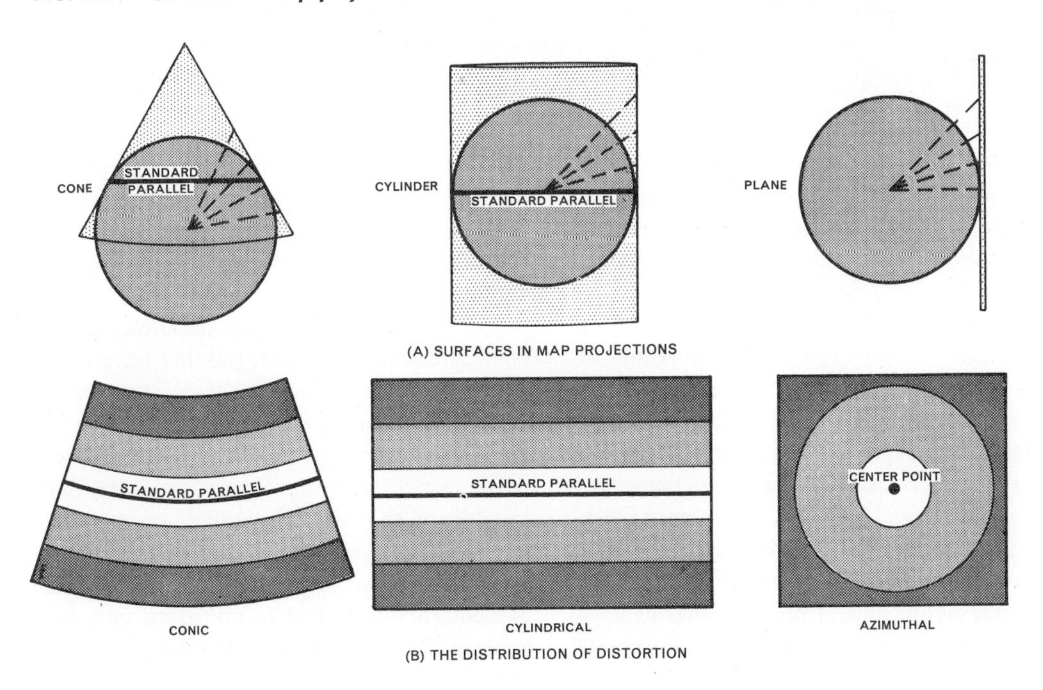

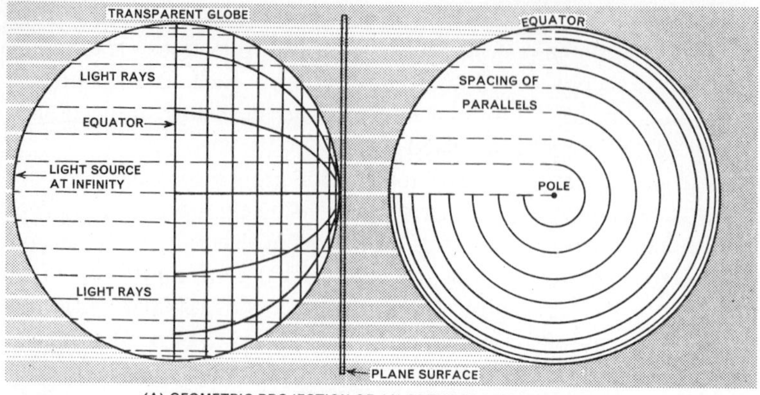

(A) GEOMETRIC PROJECTION OF AN ORTHOGRAPHIC PROJECTION

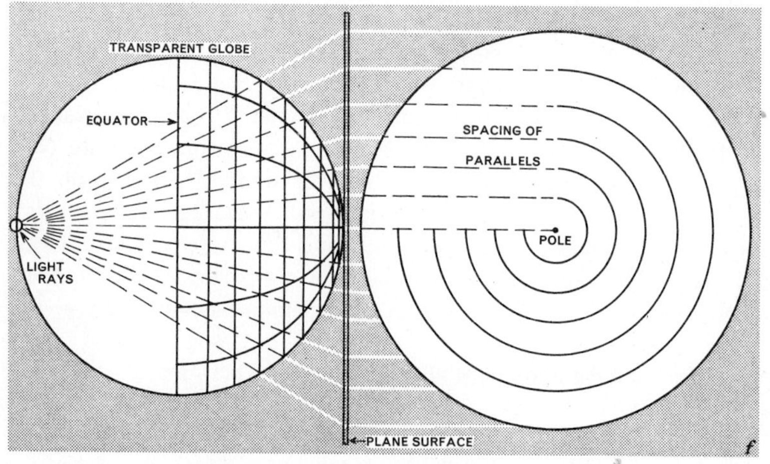

(B) GEOMETRIC PROJECTION OF A STEREOGRAPHIC PROJECTION

FIG. 2.21 Two examples of geometric projections.

example, may be centered on the North Pole, some point on the equator, or any position in between, and it will still retain the property of equivalence (see Fig. 2.22).

In theory, the points and lines on which projections are centered represent points or lines where the surfaces of the projections contact, are tangent to, or sometimes even secant to the earth surface. Such points are termed *center points,* and the lines are termed *standard lines.* If, as is most frequently the case, the line is a parallel, it is termed a *standard parallel* (see Fig. 2.21). Of major significance, from the point of view of distortion, is the fact that, at these points or lines, the projection is true in all respects, and distortion is at a minimum in the immediate vicinity. All places equally distant from the center have equal distortion on point-centered projections, and on most of the projections with standard parallels, places equally distant from that parallel have equal distortion. There are some significant exceptions to the latter generalization, however, particularly among the miscellaneous projections, which may have standard meridians in addition to standard parallels.

Table 2.1 lists some of the more common map projections, grouping them on the basis of construction but also indicating such features as their properties, common usage, and the maximum area possible to map on each. It is again emphasized that all map projections distort the features they represent in a number of ways. However, the smaller the area represented on a map, the smaller the amounts of distortion will be, and very large-scale maps can be considered distortion-free for most purposes.

FIG. 2.22 Examples of some of the more commonly used map projections.

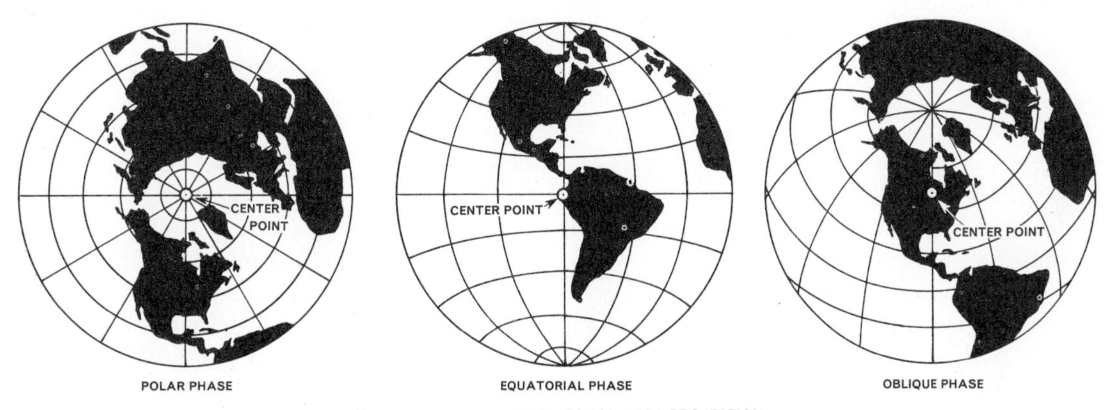

(A) LAMBERT'S AZIMUTHAL EQUAL-AREA PROJECTION

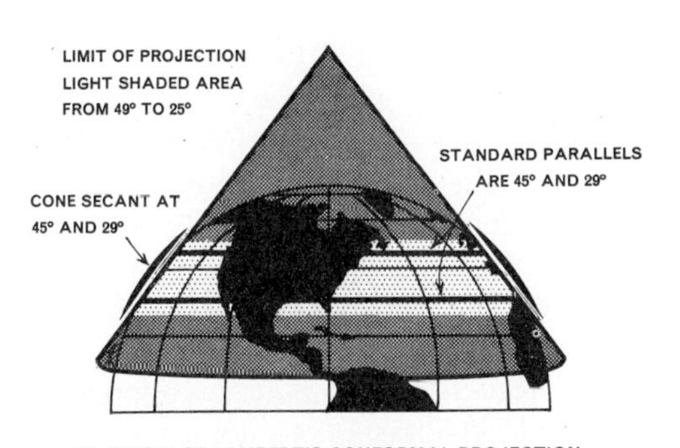

(B) ORIGIN OF LAMBERT'S CONFORMAL PROJECTION

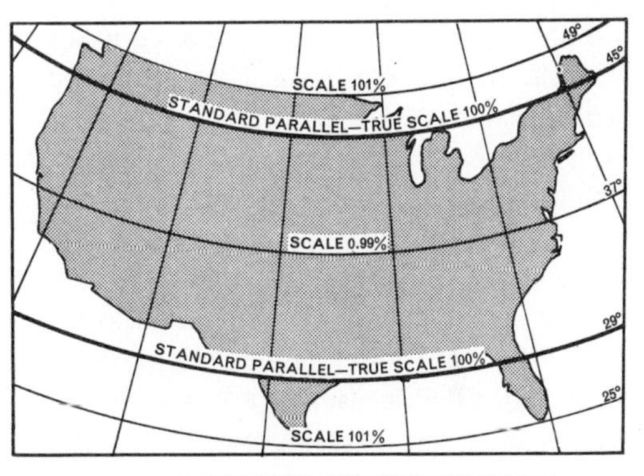

(C) LAMBERT'S CONIC CONFORMAL PROJECTION

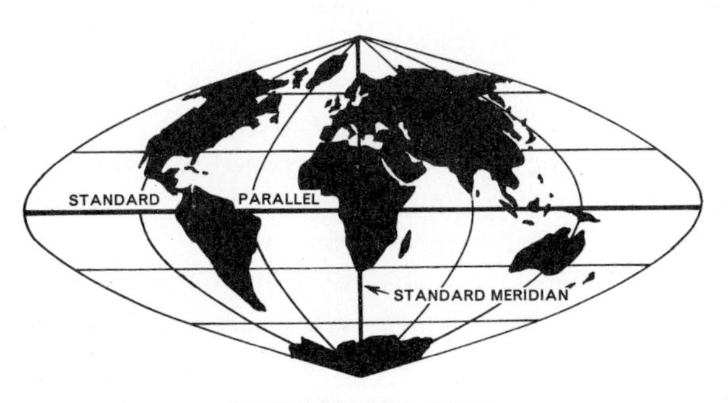

(D) SINUSOIDAL PROJECTION

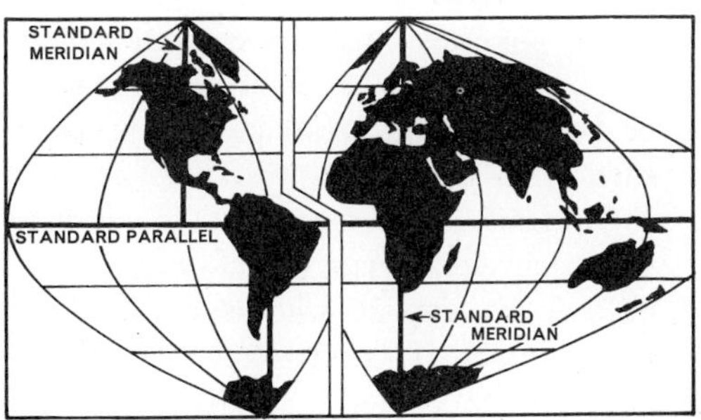

(E) INTERRUPTED AND CONDENSED SINUSOIDAL PROJECTION

2.16 MAP SCALE AND ITS RELATIONSHIPS TO AREAL GENERALIZATIONS.

All maps are reducing instruments, designed to present distributional patterns on the earth scaled down for convenience in perception and use. The ratio between the dimensions of the map and the dimensions of the area on the earth surface which the map represents is termed *map scale*. It usually is expressed in terms of a simple *map ratio,* such as 1:1,000,000, or as a *representative fraction,* such as 1/1,000,000. One linear unit on the map at this scale represents roughly a million such units on the earth surface. Small-scale maps have small representative fractions and represent large earth areas. Large-scale maps, conversely, have relatively large representative fractions, usually above 1/63,360 (1 inch equals 1 mile), and represent small areas. A precautionary note should be introduced at this point. As was mentioned in an earlier section, a flat map can never be scaled so that it is exactly proportional, in all its parts, to the curved surface of the earth, and the amount of distortion increases with the size of the area to be portrayed. The distortion may be distributed unevenly over the map, but it can never be eliminated completely (see Fig. 2.22). A linear scale of miles is thus of little use for accurate measurements on world maps, except in certain directions, such as outward from the center in an azimuthal equidistant projection. Maps of smaller areas may be constructed, however, where the scale error is so small as to be negligible. Linear scales may be used on such maps to measure distances accurately.

Most of the differences and similarities that occur from place to place on earth can be seen by anyone who travels and keeps his eyes open. This often has led to the common misconception that anyone can "do" geography, or at least the descriptive phase of it. If geography consisted entirely of portraying the differences in areas at a map ratio of 1:1, this might be true, provided that the observation was accurate; but since the discipline seeks to reduce this scale of comprehension, in order to "see the forest" and not merely the trees, it requires training, practice, tools, and "know-how." In viewing the differences within a county as compared with a township, or in a state as compared with a county, or in the world as compared with a nation, the geographic questions ultimately arise, How much shall I include? What do I leave out? The answers depend entirely on the purpose of the study and the skilled judgment of the investigator or the cartographer in selecting the areal scale most suited to that purpose.

2.17 MAPS AND MAP SYMBOLS.

Maps are essential tools in the study of areal relationships. They are invaluable not only to the geographer but to those in other disciplines who study phenomena as they are distributed over the earth. Maps function both as means of communicating information about location and as analytical devices for such purposes as discovering relationships between distributions. For example, maps are especially useful in weather forecasting. Meteorological data are plotted on a map, the relationships between these various data are studied, and forecasts are then made for various places within the area covered by the map.

No attempt is made here to classify the infinite variety of maps, except to point out that they are usually grouped according to the kind of information presented and the scale of the representation.

Maps as graphic representations of a part or all of the earth surface are symbolic expressions of this surface. A map may be structured by means of various symbols, and the map itself may be thought of as a symbol. Many map symbols in use today have common meanings which are familiar even to novice map readers. Such symbols typically show kinds of things and, in fact, may even have the appearance of the object as viewed from a considerable altitude. Symbols used to show kinds of things are referred to as *qualitative symbols*. In addition, there are a number of symbols which have no consistent relationship with the kinds of things they represent. Their primary function is to show variations in the amounts of things, and consequently they are called *quantitative map symbols*. Both qualitative and quantitative symbols can have point, line, or areal orientation on a map.

Of the many problems in map symbolization, the one which has concerned cartographers more than any other is the representation of landforms or surface irregularities. This concern has been stimulated in part by the challenge of devising a technique which visually represents the three-dimensional nature and infinite variety of landforms. There has been a demand also from engineers, military men, and others for landform symbols that can be used to make exact measurements of such features of surface configuration as elevation and slope. There are a varicty of methods for showing landforms and surface relief on maps. The more common methods include contour lines, layer tinting, side shading, hachures, and physiographic diagrams. Since each of these has certain advantages and disadvantages as a symbolic representation, there has been a recent tendency to use some of these symbols together on the same map, as a means of improving the landform representation. Note how they give a perspective view of major surface irregularities. Figure 2.23 presents several of the different methods of indicating variations in surface irregularities.

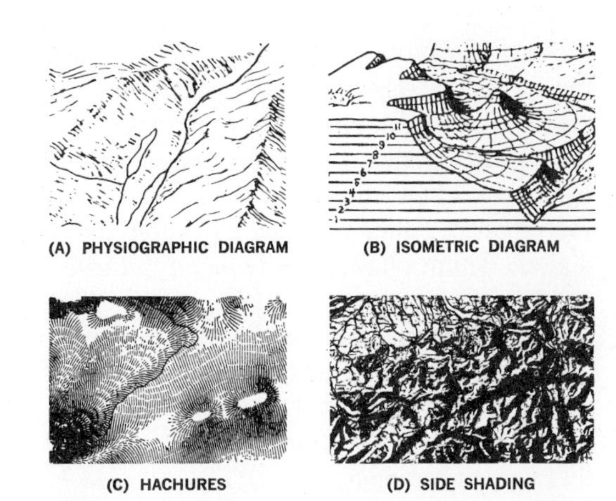

FIG. 2.23 Methods of showing surface irregularities on maps.

The problem of indicating comparative quantitative measurements of areas on maps is also treated in several different ways, but one of the most common methods is the use of a series of lines of equal value, termed *isolines* (Greek, *isos* = equal). Isolines representing specific numerical quantities are termed *isarithms* (Greek, *arithmos* = number). Examples of isarithms include *contour lines,* or lines of equal elevation; *isobars,* or lines of equal barometric pressure; *isotherms,* or lines of equal temperature; and *isobaths,* or lines of equal depth below sea level. The next section of this chapter illustrates the use of isarithms by discussing contour lines. Isolines that indicate simple ratios instead of individual arithmetic quantities are termed *isopleths*. An example of an isopleth would be a map line enclosing an area having a population density of 40 persons per square mile.

2.18 CONTOUR MAPS. Of the many devices mentioned in the preceding section for indicating landforms or surface configurations, the most widely used and perhaps the most adaptable for many different purposes is the contour map. Essentially this type of map indicates comparative elevations by means of *contour lines,* which are lines that connect points of equal elevation above a given datum plane, usually *mean sea level,* or the level about which the ocean tides oscillate. The spacing between the contours varies on different maps, depending on the degree of elevation detail desired; the amount of variability in elevation to be shown, and the scale of the map.

Figure 2.24 represents a contour map of a small island, on which the following features are labeled:

1. A central hill, steeper on one side than on the other
2. A U-shaped valley, with a gently sloping lower portion
3. A steep-sided, narrow, V-shaped stream valley with a steep gradient through its length
4. A ridge which contains a dip or saddle
5. A surface depression surrounded on all sides by higher ground

The coast line of the island at mean sea level constitutes the zero-foot contour line. If the island were submerged through a vertical distance of 20 feet, the new shore line would correspond to the position of the 20-foot contour line prior to submergence. The amount of vertical difference in elevation represented between any two contour lines is known as the *contour interval.* In Fig. 2.24 this interval is given as 20 feet.

An examination of the contour map in Fig. 2.24 reveals a number of characteristics common to all contour maps. These may be listed as follows:

1. Contours are closed, concentric circles.
2. Contours never cross one another.
3. Every contour has an upside and a downside. The latter is on the outside of the closed circles.

FIG. 2.24 A hypothetical contour map of an island, illustrating different topographic forms.

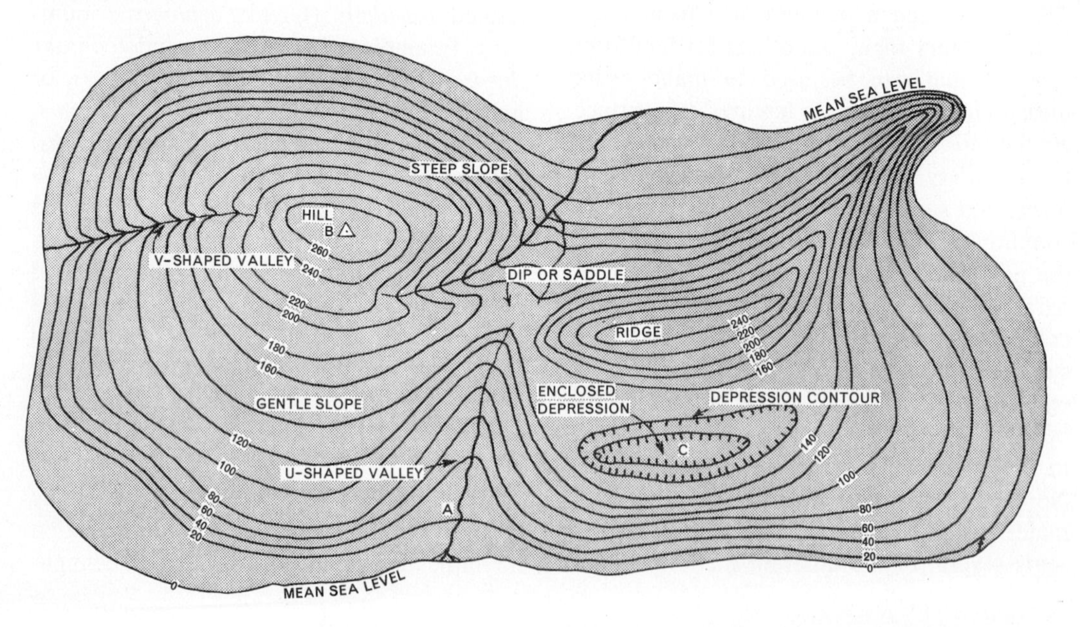

4. The highest elevation lies within the innermost contour.

5. Contours become closer together as the slope of land increases.

6. Contours bend upstream when crossing a flowing stream, and the amount of bend decreases as the gradient of the stream increases.

7. The width of valleys is indicated by the breadth of contour curves in their course across a valley.

8. A dip, or saddle, is indicated by a gap between two adjacent closed contours.

Closed depressions on a land surface, that is, depressions which are surrounded by higher ground on all sides, may be shown by special *depression contours,* which are marked by small lines or hachures on their downsides.

Most contour maps show features other than contours—especially elements of hydrology, such as lakes, rivers, or marshes, and selected cultural features, such as towns, roads, and railroads. Contour maps that contain reasonably accurate portrayals of the major surface features in an area are known as *topographic maps.* Most countries have programs for the governmental preparation of topographic maps, at least for the most important parts of their land areas. The standard topographic maps for the United States are those prepared by the U.S. Geological Survey. They are prepared at various scales, although most of them have a map ratio of 1:62,500, or slightly more than 1 inch to 1 mile in linear scale. The student should familiarize himself with the interpretation and use of such topographic maps.

Perspective

Determining the relative location of points, lines, or areas on a scale appropriate to the purpose of the study is an important objective of the descriptive phase of every geographic investigation. The geographic grid, or the system of latitude and longitude, is an accurate means of fixing the location of any point with reference to the entire earth surface. The military and public-land-survey grids, superimposed on maps, are other systems of location, especially useful for rapid and simple calculations. Locating lines involves establishing not only points but also direction, and numerous types of compass have been developed to determine the latter. The location of areas necessitates a number of steps, including (1) recognition of purpose, (2) selection of the scale of generalization, (3) definition of boundaries, (4) direct and indirect measurement of boundary locations, and (5) graphic presentation of boundaries on a map or globe. Map sizes and details should be adjusted to fit the scope and purpose of the presentation; a map projection should be selected which is suitable to the purpose and which distributes distortions where they interfere least with the map function.

Those who use maps prepared by others should always evaluate the maps critically, and a few simple questions are presented below which may be useful in such evaluations.

1. What type of map projection is used? Does the distortion therein aid or hinder the efficient use of the map for the purpose intended?

2. What is the map scale, and what limitations to areal generalizations does it require?

3. If the map is a large-scale representation of a limited area, what are the cardinal compass directions? Is there a linear scale of miles? Is the location of the area clearly indicated with respect to a suitable grid?

4. Is the detail of generalization roughly

comparable in all portions of the map? Is it suited to the purposes for which the map was intended?

5. Are the major purposive elements on the map clearly readable, understandable, and uncluttered with distractive, irrelevant details?

6. Is the map legend clear and understandable?

7. From what types of data was the map compiled? How reliable are the sources of such data?

3

Topographic landforms

Landforms are forms of the land surface that have characteristic shapes and composition. A volcano is a landform—likewise, a mountain cordillera, a river terrace, and a sand dune. Landforms may be viewed from different perspectives, or scales. A great mountain cordillera, such as the Andes, or a broad coastal plain, such as that along the Gulf of Mexico, is a global landform. This chapter, however, the first of three dealing with landforms and surface configuration, focuses attention on topographic landforms, or those which give distinctiveness to local landscapes. These are the forms that one may see about him and whose characteristic shapes may be recognized on a topographic map, not a world map.

The second chapter of the series shifts to the global scale. At that point we can no longer deal in terms of river terraces or sand dunes; instead, we generalize surface irregularities into five broad landform categories: continents, ocean basins, mountains, hills, and plains. Finally, in the last chapter of the series, we discuss the various attributes of the land surface under the heading of *surface configuration,* including such qualities as slope, drainage, elevation, and surface materials.

The characteristics of topographic landforms on the earth are determined by the kind and arrangement of earth material out of which they are made (*structure*), the active forces that work upon them (*process*), and the degree to which these processes have completed their work (*stage*). Although relatively permanent with respect to the span of human life, landforms are part of the changing scene, part of the eternal struggle between the forces that tend to level off the face of the earth and the internal stresses that buckle and wrinkle the outer surface. A brief examination of structure, process, and stage will indicate a wide range of variables and the roles that they play in developing the variety of topographic landform characteristics.

Structural elements include many types and attitudes of crustal rocks and minerals: hard rocks and soft rocks; rocks with uniform texture and composition, and others having a wide variety of included minerals which change over short distances; crystalline rocks that formed under high heat and

FIG. 3.1 An elongated dome structure, Mackenzie Mountains, Northwest Territories, Canada. This photograph illustrates clearly the role of rock structure in the details of landform development. [Royal Canadian Air Force]

pressure far beneath the earth surface; and the loosely cemented types associated with surface sedimentary deposits. Some rocks are found in extensive flat-lying beds or strata, whereas others are folded or bent upward into huge arches or domes or warped downward into troughs or basins. Some are ruptured and dislocated, and others are within gigantic homogeneous masses that extend to unknown depth and measure thousands of square miles in area.

The geological processes that operate on the various rock structures can be divided into three major groups. The first is *degradation,* which includes the removal of surface irregularities through *weathering,* the breakdown of rocks by atmospheric agents, and *erosion,* the removal of material by transporting agents such as streams, glaciers, wind, or waves. The second group includes the processes of *aggradation,* or the building up of the land surface through the deposition of material. Last are the *tectonic* processes, or those associated with movements of the earth crust. These processes do not act uniformly on the many kinds of rocks and rock structures. Some rocks are extremely resistant to erosion and weathering in one environment but exceedingly vulnerable in another. Some parts of the world experience frequent crustal disturbances, so that the irregularities smoothed by degradation and aggradation are soon replaced, but other areas have remained relatively undisturbed for long periods of geologic time. Geologic processes may vary with climatic regions. For example, the removal of limestone by solution takes place mainly in humid regions, whereas the work of the wind is most efficient in the deserts. The erosive and depositional work of glacial ice is performed only in areas of low temperatures. Thus there arises a regional geography of landforms, related principally to the dominance of certain shaping forces and the type of rock structure that is characteristic of the area.

The *stage* of landform development is not necessarily related to chronological age, or the number of years that a given process has been under way. Instead, it refers to the relative position of the area in the sequence of development. An observer standing at the rim of the Grand Canyon may be awed at the immensity of time required to carve such a gash in the earth surface. If he looks away from the canyon, however, he sees a broad, level, upland plain stretching far into the distance. The Colorado River, despite its chronological age, is only beginning its task of removing this upland surface; hence it is in an early stage of its work.

The concepts of *youth, maturity,* and *old age* frequently are used to represent stages in the operation of erosional processes. Certain landforms are characteristic of each of these stages in the task of dissecting an upland surface by running water. The landforms associated with maturity in this process are far different from those characteristic of maturity in the dissection of a limestone upland by the solvent action of subsurface water and from those representing maturity in the arid-land sequence of erosion.

The stages in landform development do not always follow in logical order until the objective of the process is completed. An upward warping of a section of the earth crust may interrupt the local sequence of erosion, forcing the procedural sequence back into an earlier stage. This process is termed *rejuvenation.*

A summary of global topographic landform differences presented in a single chapter must, of necessity, omit many of the details of structure, process, and stage. Only those surface landforms are included which appear to be unusually representative over relatively large segments of the earth surface. Space limitations also preclude any extended discussion of the evolution of these landforms. We shall be primarily interested in their appearance, meaning, and distribution. Some discussion of the processes that shape these landforms, however, should be both helpful and stimulating in understanding their geography.

Landforms produced by surface streams and underground water in humid regions

3.1 EROSIONAL FEATURES OF STREAM VALLEYS. Stream valleys form the principal surface irregularities in nonglaciated humid regions wherever there is sufficient elevation of land to create slopes. Here we are concerned mainly with the major characteristics and differences in valleys caused by stream erosion. For more complete explanations of the processes involved, the student is referred to the references listed at the end of this book. The major characteristics may be summarized as follows:

1. The longitudinal profile (the shape along the valley length) is concave to the sky. This curved profile normally is steepest near the source and flattest near the mouth. Differences in the rate of stream erosion caused by variations in the durability of material or by differential earth movements along the streams produce irregularities in the smoothness of the longitudinal profile curve.

2. Stream valleys in transverse profile (across the valley) are wider at the top than at the bottom. When downward cutting is rapid, the transverse profile is V-shaped and steep-sided. When downward cutting ceases, valley flats tend to form, roughly increasing in width with the size of the stream, and valley sides gradually decrease in slope. Transverse profiles rarely are symmetrical; usually one valley side exceeds the other in steepness, especially with increasing age of the valley. The steepest side usually alter-

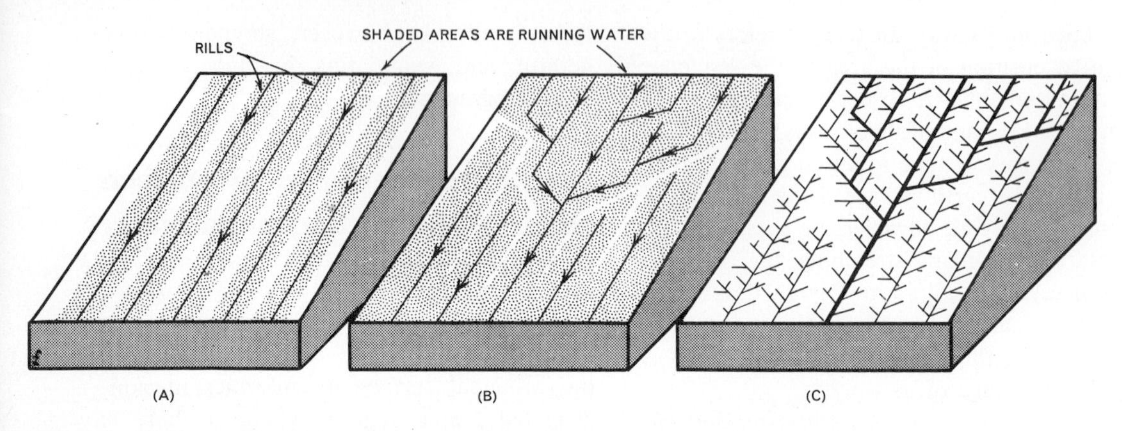

FIG. 3.2 Cross grading. On a uniform slope the initial runoff is in parallel rills (A). Minor irregularities divert some of the water diagonally to adjacent rills, producing the beginning of a dendritic pattern (B). Later there is a development into primary, secondary, and tertiary tributary systems (C). [After Horton]

nates from the right to the left bank along the stream course.

3. As rain water flows down a slope near the headwaters of streams, it tends to concentrate in rivulets, or rills. Competition between rills for the gathering of water usually leads to the development of a treelike, or *dendritic,* pattern. This process (see Fig. 3.2), termed *cross grading,* is responsible for the normal pattern of streams as they dissect an entire drainage basin. It is best developed in areas of homogeneous rock material. Individual drainage basins tend to be pear-shaped where dendritic patterns predominate.

FIG. 3.3 Dendritic and trellis drainage patterns.

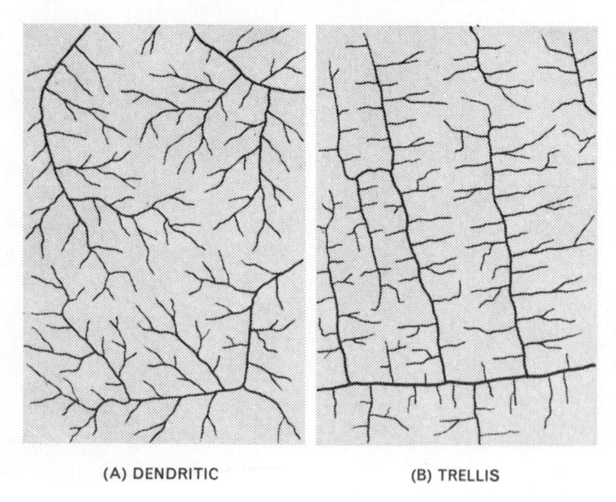

4. Valley bottoms may be widened by the lateral swinging of streams against the side walls of the valleys. This occurs mainly where the gradient of the stream is low and where surplus energy for downward cutting is not present. Valley flats, therefore, may be erosional as well as depositional.

5. When an upland surface is thoroughly drained by the headward extension of tributaries, drainage divides are narrow and vary in height, owing to competition of tributaries from opposite slopes. Crest lines in a thoroughly drained area commonly have a zigzag pattern.

Variations in rock structure and localized uplift or subsidence of land result in exceptions to the above generalizations. A linear pattern of hard and soft rocks, for example, controls the stream pattern through the variations in the resistance of the material to erosion. In the folded Appalachians, for example, the durable sandstones and conglomerates stand out as long, narrow ridges.

Stream valleys that cut across such a structure show marked differences in transverse profiles along their courses. Divides are straight, and the drainage pattern tends to develop a right-angle, or *trellis,* pattern instead of the more common dendritic form. In the weaker rock belts, streams wind back and forth, widening their valleys by lateral erosion, unable to cut deeper, because of the more durable rock formations downstream.

An excellent example of the effect of differential land uplift and structure on stream profiles is presented by many of the great rivers of central Africa, such as the Congo and Zambezi. In their upper middle courses, they flow for hundreds of miles across broad plains. As they near the coast, however, they descend the steep edge of the uplifted continental block and take on valley characteristics usually more common in stream headwaters, with narrow V-shaped canyons, rapids, and waterfalls. In rough outline, their longitudinal profiles are convex to the sky. Eventually, if the continent remains stable long enough, erosion will migrate upstream, and normal profiles will be established.

3.2 THE CYCLE OF EROSION BY STREAMS IN A HUMID REGION.

Near the beginning of the present century, a well-known American physical geographer, William Morris Davis, proposed a concept known as the cycle of erosion, which could be used to identify recognizable forms as typical of various stages in the beveling of land surfaces by stream erosion. Different erosional processes produce different features, but they all aim at the same objective,

FIG. 3.4 Stages in the cycle of erosion by running water in a humid region. [After Strahler]

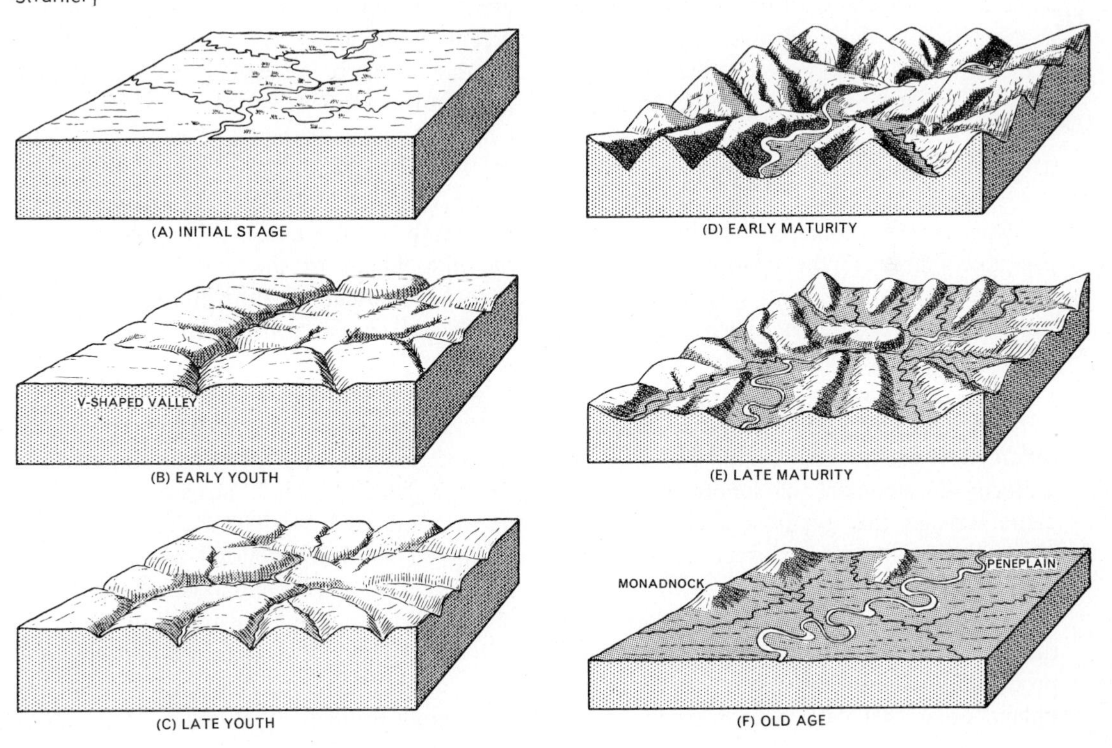

that of reducing elevations on the earth surface. Davis's cycle of erosion first assumes a smooth upland surface created by one of the constructive processes of nature, such as regional uplift, lowering of sea level, or volcanic accumulations. The stages in the work of beveling such an upland are considered as youth, maturity, and old age. Essentially, the goal of erosion is the development of an erosional plain near sea level, the characteristic feature of old age. Davis postulated different cycles to fit different erosional processes—for example, (1) erosion by running water in humid regions, (2) erosion by underground solution in a limestone region, (3) erosion in arid regions, (4) glacial erosion, and (5) erosion by wave and current action. Each of these processes has characteristic landforms associated with youth, maturity, and old age. This conceptual framework has been bitterly condemned by some and grossly abused by overenthusiastic supporters. For our purpose, that of understanding the associations of landforms in the world, the concept has real value, provided that we keep in mind its major limitations. These may be summarized as follows:

1. Forms associated with old age are rarely, if ever, encountered over broad areas, principally because the erosional processes are retarded as the land surface becomes subdued and because the earth crust rarely remains stable long enough to enable such processes to reach their objective.

2. Differences in underlying structure and differential earth movements prevent the uniform development of landforms. Thus, characteristics that typify a single stage of erosion are not present over wide areas; there are always local exceptions.

3. Not all extensive low, flat plains are the products of erosion. Some have been produced by deposition, and others represent upland areas that have been warped downward by subsidence. The lower Mississippi Valley often has been cited incorrectly as an example of old-age topography. Instead, it is an alluvial plain, constructed entirely by stream deposition.

The next three paragraphs describe landforms typical of stream erosion in youth, maturity, and old age within a humid region. The sequence should be thought of as a spectrum of change, in which each stage merges gradually with the next.

A humid region in the *youthful stage* (see Fig. 3.4) is characterized by broad interstream areas and many V-shaped valleys, although narrow stream flats or flood plains may be found in places, separated by steep gorges. The streams often have steep gradients, and stretches of rapids and cascades are frequently encountered. Tributaries are poorly developed. Swamps and marshes sometimes may be found in the upland areas. The interior plains of central Africa include many areas typical of this stage. The interior uplands of British Columbia and parts of the Yunnan Plateau of southwestern China are other examples. The glacial plains of Illinois and Indiana are depositional plains in which dissection by streams is just beginning to take place. Although many of the high plains of the world, such as the Colorado Plateau and the Bolivian Plateau, are in arid or semiarid climates, they exhibit many of the forms characteristic of this stage.

In the *mature stage,* little of the upland surface remains, and the maximum local relief has been attained. Stream divides are narrow and irregular. The major streams are beginning to develop flood plains through lateral cutting, although most of the tributaries still are cutting downward in steep, V-shaped valleys. The drainage pattern has been established, and the entire region is thoroughly drained by streams. Large areas of hilly terrain in the world are typical of this stage, including the Appalachian hill country of the eastern United States, much of China, and parts of the Brazilian and Guiana uplands in South America. Most unglaciated hill lands are in this category.

Erosional plains at low elevations predominate in *old age*. Such old erosional surfaces are termed *peneplains*. On such surfaces, stream valleys no longer are pronounced, because of the low divides and the gentle slopes resulting from the slow mass movement of unconsolidated material downhill (*mass wastage*), surface soil flowage (*sheet erosion*), and other forms of soil erosion. There are fewer streams than in maturity, and a few major streams drain the area, mainly through collection of subsurface water. There is a gradual merging of depositional and erosional surfaces. Occasional low prominences, termed *monadnocks,* may rise above the general level of the surrounding plains. They represent erosional remnants, preserved through the erosional sequence. As was mentioned earlier, there are few large areas representative of this stage anywhere in the world. There are, however, a number of broad erosional surfaces that have been uplifted and that are in the process of being dissected. In the United States, the general upland level of the Appalachian Plateau is an example of an uplifted peneplain that already has been rather thoroughly dissected. Several peneplain surfaces also can be observed at high elevations in the Rocky Mountains (see Fig. 3.5). Other examples include the plains of northern France, parts of southern Russia, central Manchuria, and portions of the unglaciated Mississippi drainage basin. None of them, however, represent the last stages of dissection; rather, they are former erosional plains which are being attacked once more by streams.

FIG. 3.5 Remnants of an ancient peneplain, Beartooth Mountains, Montana. The flat tops of these mountains represent an ancient erosional surface now being dissected by erosion. [U. S. Air Force (MATS)]

The absence of typical examples of broad regions in the last stage of erosion does not necessarily detract from the usefulness of the concept. This is the end toward which the erosional processes of streams are working, and in many of the ancient elevated surfaces, we may see the forms associated with such a stage, preserved as examples of what may develop in the distant future, provided that the earth crust remains sufficiently stable. Furthermore, we live in a geological period of somewhat exceptional crustal instability, and under such conditions, peneplain surfaces near sea level should be unusual.

3.3 SPECIAL EROSIONAL LANDFORMS OF THE HUMID TROPICS.

The hills and mountains of the the rainy tropics are distinctly different in general appearance from those of the midlatitudes. The sides are steeper, and the tops, when below the snow line, are rounder. Sugarloaf Mountain, a huge crystalline rock mass that guards the entrance to the harbor

FIG. 3.6 Steep and narrow ravines, typical of the rainy tropics. These are well illustrated by this scene in New Guinea, near Wau. The native covering of forest has been stripped by fire or cultivation and is replaced by tough, wiry kunai grass. Some of the forest may be seen clinging to the ravine bottoms. [Australian News and Information Bureau]

at Rio de Janeiro, may be considered an example of this general shape. Although such forms develop best on homogeneous rocks, such as granites or massive limestones, steep, rounded hills of this type are conspicuous in many tropical areas. A suggested explanation for them lies in the rapid weathering of rock and soil material on the slopes of hills and mountains and in the retardation of gravity pull on such material because of the covering of dense tropical vegetation; thus steeper slopes are preserved longer. Ravines and valleys generally tend to have steeper sides in the humid tropics (see Fig. 3.6). The scars of landslides often can be observed along such steep slopes, indicating that even the anchorage of forest vegetation cannot continue indefinitely to maintain such steep slopes in the face of gradually deepening soils. Landslides have a tendency to subdue the lower slopes of hills and oversteepen the upper slopes.

The sugarloaf form is particularly, but by no means exclusively, well developed on pure, massive limestones, because of the soluble effect of water equipped with traces of acids. Upland blocks of limestone become rounded and smoothed, in much the same way as a block of salt left in a pasture. In the tropics advanced stages of erosion of limestone by solution may produce a series of rounded knobs, appropriately termed *haystack topography,* since, viewed from the air, they look like a succession of haystacks. Although rarely occupying a large continuous area, they are found in parts of the Visayan Islands in the Philippines, in western New Guinea, in southern Java, in northern Indochina, and in the West Indies. In the Greater Antilles, such limestone knobs are termed *mogotes.*

The sugarloaf form, although prominent in the tropics, is not exclusively a tropical feature. Among the best-known exceptions are the rounded summits of Yosemite Park in California, which are end products of weathering processes that have stimulated some interesting controversies among geomorphologists. Continental glacial erosion in hard-rock uplands also may produce somewhat comparable shapes, as in some parts of the Adirondacks of New York State and along the fjord coasts of the world.

Tablelands, or broad, flat uplands with steep edges, are another type of landform found in some parts of the humid tropics. They are rather similar to the flat-topped *mesas* of dry lands, but they lack the bare slopes of loose rock rubble at the base and are somewhat less angular in profile. Tablelands are mainly the result of the preservation of tabular blocks of resistant rock strata, generally of three types: (1) sandstones that are cemented with iron or silica; (2) quartzites, which are sandstones that have had their constituent grains fused together; and (3) massive beds of impure limestones or dolomites. Good examples of tablelands occur in parts of the Brazilian and Guiana uplands, in the Monts des Cardomoms of southern Cambodia, along the flanks of the Annam Mountains in Indochina, and in parts of central Africa. Huge limestone tablelands mark some of the border between Venezuela and Brazil. Their precipitous edges make their forested summits almost inaccessible (see Fig. 3.7).

3.4 EROSIONAL LANDFORMS PRODUCED BY UNDERGROUND WATER. Limestones that do not contain a high percentage of insoluble impurities are vulnerable to attack by water that contains traces of carbonic or other acids readily obtainable from decaying organic material in humid regions. Haystack topography resulting from solution already has been described as a landform type more or less restricted to the rainy tropics. Other types of features associated with solution, however, abound in humid regions wherever such limestones occur. The characteristic pitted surface—containing many depressions without surface stream outlets, occasional disappearing streams, and openings leading to extensive underground caves and caverns—contrasts so markedly with the erosional surfaces created by surface streams that it early attracted the attention of geomorphologists. Such a land surface is known as *karst topography,* named after the Kras (Karst in German) district of Yugoslavia, where it covers several thousand square miles. As solution by underground water slowly erodes an upland limestone region, characteristic features appear (see Fig. 3.8), marking different stages in the development of this type of topography.

In youth, or the early stage of erosion, the upland surface still predominates. Occasional *sinkholes,* or *dolines,* dot the surface. These funnel-shaped depressions represent widened crevices or collapsed roofs of underground caverns excavated by solution. Surface soil material is sometimes washed into a sinkhole, plugging the bottom, whereupon surface water that drains into the sinkhole forms a small sinkhole pond. Surface streams are rare, most of the surplus water draining downward into subterranean channels. The underground water actively works its way along cracks and crevices, widening them and developing caves and underground passageways. Eventually it finds its way into a distant surface stream at a lower level.

As the erosional process continues, sinkholes may enlarge or coalesce to form larger

FIG. 3.7 Typical tableland in southeastern Venezuela. The high, cliffed edges of these tablelands make them almost inaccessible. Note the sharp boundary between grassland and forest, a good indication of the influence of clearing and the use of fire. [U. S. Air Force (MATS)]

depressions with steep sides, termed *uvalas*. In the mature stage, local relief is at a maximum, and because of the occurrence of limestone cliffs and the lack of continuity in either upland or lowland surfaces, cross-country travel is exceedingly difficult. Surface runoff is restricted mainly to the large, master drainage ways which have reached insoluble rocks such as shales within or below the limestone. Openings to underground caves and caverns are frequently encountered along the flanks and bases of limestone cliffs that mark the sides of the solution depressions. Spectacular displays of *stalactites* (stone icicles) and *stalagmites* (protuberances that extend upward from the floor) are found in the caves that lie above the water table. Subterranean openings are excavated mainly during the earlier stages of erosion and become partially filled with dripstone during later stages. The larger basins and uvalas of the mature erosional stage are preferred places for settlement, because limestone usually weathers into productive soil and the water supply is much more dependable than in the surrounding upland areas. Accessibility, however, may be difficult. Much of the limestone country of western Yugoslavia, southern China, and northern Indochina corresponds to a mature stage of erosion by solution.

In old age, a soluble limestone region is characterized by a predominance of flat-to-undulating surfaces located at the local base of erosion. Erosional remnants, honeycombed and rilled with solution channels, dot the surface of the plain. They vary in height according to the thickness of the limestone strata, and where the limestone beds are unusually thick, they form cliffed *pinnacles,* somewhat reminiscent of the sugarloaf peaks of the humid tropics. The classic area for such pinnacle forms lies in southern China and northeastern Indochina, especially near Kweilin and east of Yungning in China and along the coast northeast of Haiphong in Indochina.

Parts of the limestone regions of Kentucky, Tennessee, southern Illinois, and southern Indiana in the United States have a miniature karst topography in a late youthful stage of erosion. Local relief is only about 20 to 100

FIG. 3.8 Stages in the cycle of erosion by underground solution in a limestone region. [After Lobeck]

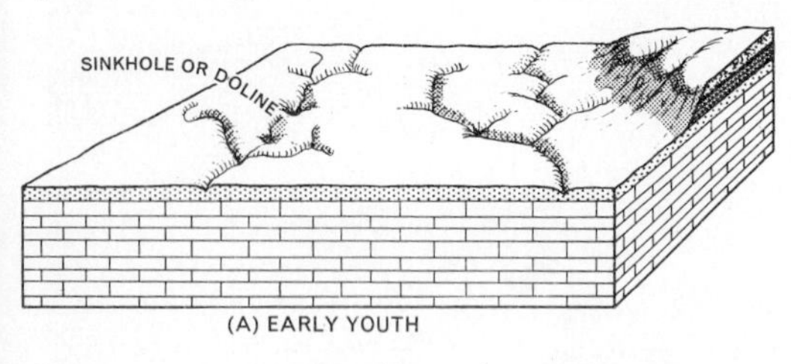

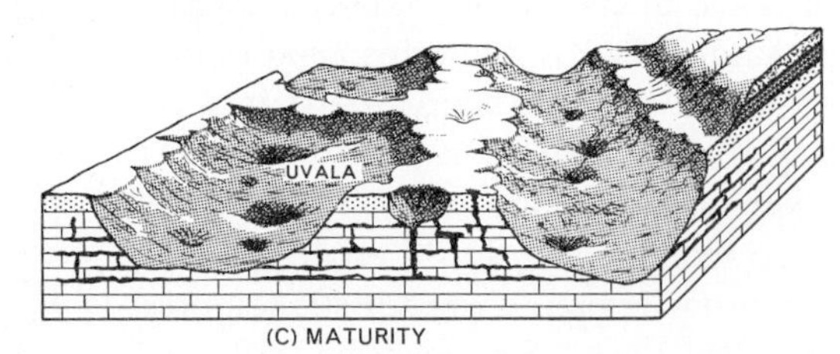

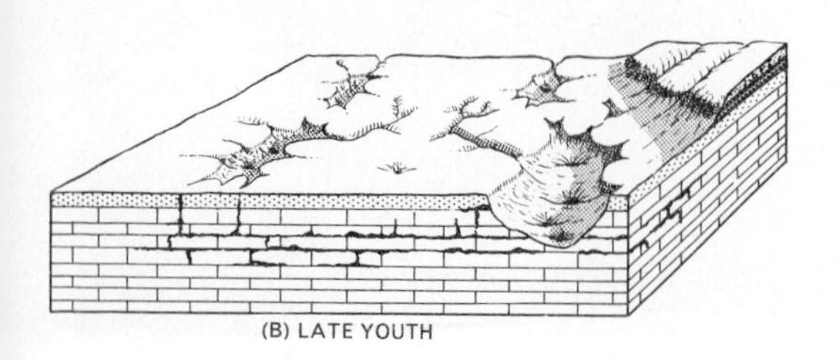

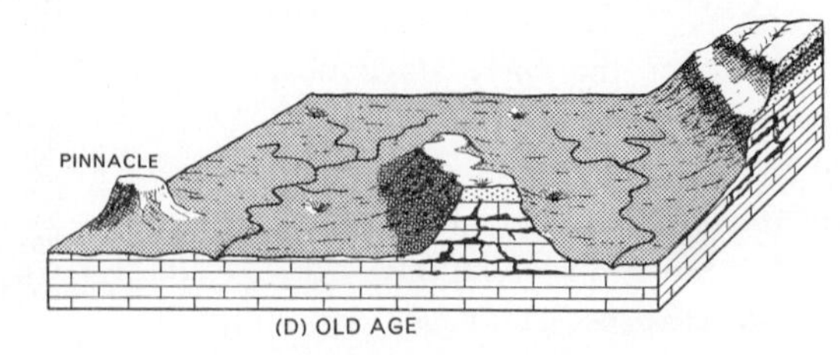

feet, and the irregularities form no serious obstacles to cultivation in this fertile agricultural region. Cavern openings adjacent to the surface are an advantage to landowners. A few caverns have been cleaned, equipped with lights, and developed as tourist attractions. Hundreds of others serve as coolers or natural "root cellars" for perishable farm produce or as refuges from the extreme summer heat in this area, since cave temperatures here usually remain at near 52°F, winter and summer.

Caverns in karst areas throughout the world were favorite sites for early primitive cultures, and cultural relics have been preserved in the dry cave dust for thousands of years. One of the most studied regions of this type in western Europe is found along the western flanks of the Massif Central of southern France, particularly in the basin of the Dordogne River. This region has long been famous for its underground caverns, which contain traces of early human cultures that date back to the ice age.

FIG. 3.9 Limestone cave and underground stream near Baliem in western New Guinea. The steep, rocky cliffs are characteristic of limestone country in a mature stage of erosion. The trees near the cave mouth are 100 to 150 feet high. [U. S. Air Force (MATS)]

Elevated coral reefs form terraces along many tropical coast lines, particularly in southeastern Asia and on many of the Pacific Islands. Composed of calcium carbonate and containing many small openings for water penetration, these reefs are rapidly attacked by ground-water solution, resulting in exceed-

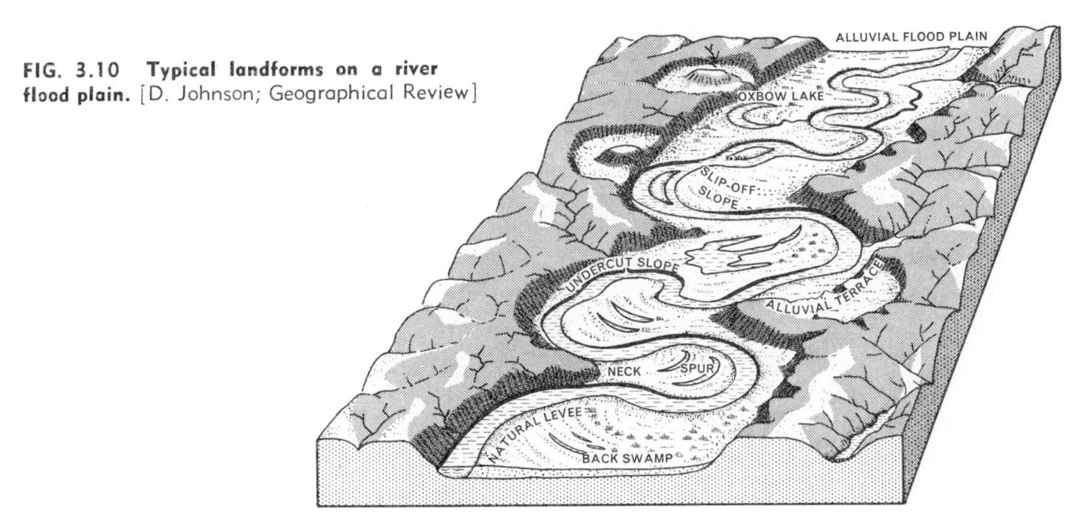

FIG. 3.10 Typical landforms on a river flood plain. [D. Johnson; Geographical Review]

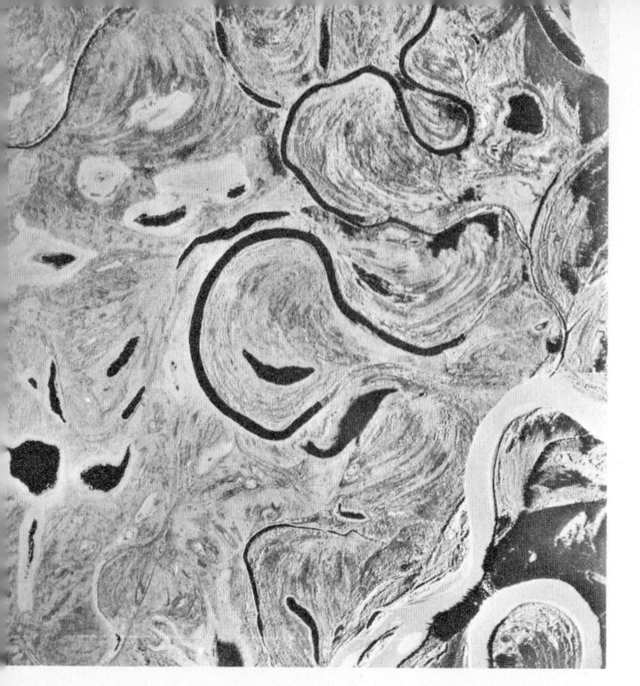

FIG. 3.11 Meanders, oxbow lakes, and crescentic natural levees on the flood plain of the Yukon River near Fort Yukon, Alaska. This air photo illustrates how a river winds back and forth, beveling its flood plain when not confined by dikes and artificial levees. [U. S. Air Force (MATS)]

ingly rough land surfaces. During World War II, the Japanese found that these dissected coral terraces offered excellent defensive positions, and the use of underground defenses in Japanese military tactics persisted to the end of the war. Caves and caverns in karst regions may play a meaningful role as defensive redoubt areas in future wars, because of their underground protection for critical personnel and material during atomic-bomb attacks. The rougher types of terrain in karst areas, furthermore, prevent the effective use of mechanized equipment. The karst region bordering the Red River delta in northern Indochina undoubtedly was a major cause of the inability of French forces to subdue the Communist guerrillas, whose periodic raids in the late 1940s and early 1950s finally forced the military evacuation of the entire area and led to the establishment of the Communist Viet-Minh state. Yugoslavia was another guerrilla haven during World War II, as the Germans learned through bitter experience. Although they controlled all major centers within the country, they could have used elsewhere the divisions tied down by partisan activity in the rugged karst "back country."

3.5 STREAM DEPOSITIONAL LANDFORMS IN HUMID REGIONS. As a stream reaches the lower portion of its course, its slope generally decreases. This reduction in gradient, or slope, produces a decrease in velocity and carrying power. A stream which is able to carry large quantities of rock debris in its upper course usually is forced to drop some of this load along its lower reaches. The sediment dropped is graded according to size, with the coarsest materials near the upstream limit of deposition. Large rivers that have gentle downstream gradients tend to develop broad *alluvial flood plains,* widened by the retreat of the valley slopes and by the lateral swinging of river loops (meanders) and veneered by *alluvium* or river depositional material, deposited during high-water periods. When a river overflows its banks during flood periods, the first sudden decrease in velocity occurs next to the river channel. This results in a low ridge of alluvium, termed a *natural levee,* which slopes gradually away from the river. Since the rivers on flood plains change their courses from time to time, flood plains may contain a series of crescent-shaped natural levees, marking the borders of former river-channel loops. Natural levees are favorite sites for roads and settlements on flood plains, because, lying a few feet above the level of the flood plain, they are less likely to be inundated during flood periods. *Oxbow lakes,* or crescentic ponds representing abandoned meander channels, are occasional features on flood plains. *Alluvial terraces,* which are sometimes found bordering flood plains, mark former levels of deposition below which the streams have since cut. In many parts of the Mississippi drainage basin, such terrace levels are known as *bottoms*. The first, or lower, bottoms are preferred sites for cultivation.

Flood plains generally provide fertile soils for agriculture. The alluvium, commonly silt, is easily worked, is not too heavy or too coarse for cultivation, is young and relatively little leached by rainfall, and represents a mixture of fragmental rock material from the entire upper drainage basin. Drainage is the principal agricultural problem. The difficulty of draining off floodwaters in the lowest portions often may result in swamps or marshes (sometimes termed *back swamps*), especially near the outer margins of the flood plain. Some of the densest rural populations of the world are found on the alluvial flood plains

FIG. 3.12 Types of deltas.

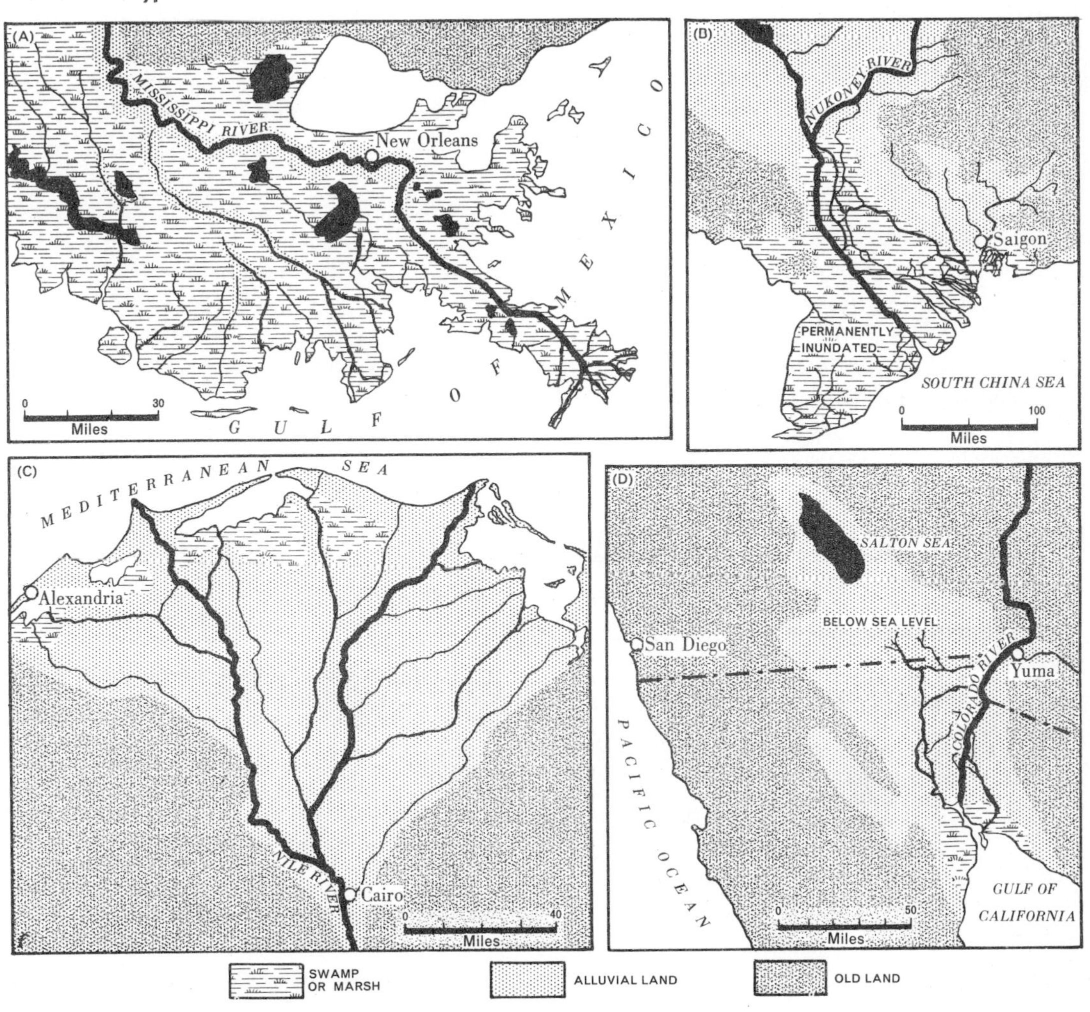

of large rivers, as in Asia, where alluvial plains are favored for the cultivation of paddy (wet-field) rice, the food base for many cultural groups in this part of the world.

Deltas are alluvial plains that streams have built at their mouths and in ponded water. The term is derived from the Greek letter Δ (delta), which represents the general shape of the Nile delta. Not all deltas take this shape, however, as indicated by the representative examples in Fig. 3.12. Being flood plains, they have many of the features associated with the lower valleys of large rivers, including natural levees and marshes. The delta depressions lie so near the base level of the stream that the floodwaters have difficulty in draining away. Shallow lakes frequently are found. Rivers usually divide into branches, or *distributaries,* upon reaching their deltas. The natural levees of distributaries that intersect each other may coalesce and enclose broad, shallow depressions or lakes. Silting at the mouths of delta tributaries makes such waterways relatively unsuited to the passage of deep-water vessels, unless dredging is used to keep the channels clear. Deep water and swift ocean currents may prevent the development of a delta at a river mouth or limit its growth. Neither the Hudson nor the Columbia River has an appreciable delta for this reason. The St. Lawrence River lacks one because the river contains only a trace of suspended material.

Deltas are usually favored sites for agriculture because of their alluvial soils, but flood danger and poor drainage in swales and depressions generally are present as local problems. The densely populated deltas of southeast Asia usually are crisscrossed with a close network of large and small waterways, constructed to provide drainage, silt that may be added to the fields to help maintain soil productivity, and irrigation water for rice cultivation. Other intensively cultivated delta plains include those of the Mississippi, Nile, Po, Rhine, and Colorado Rivers. The extensive delta of the Amazon is interesting in that it is largely wasteland and has only a sparse pastoral population.

The lower valley of the Mississippi is an unusual example of a delta plain. Several million years ago the mouth of the river emptied into a long embayment of the sea near Cairo, Illinois. As the delta progres-

FIG. 3.13 Cross section of the Barton (Gulf Coast) geosyncline. See Fig. 13.26 for typical stratigraphic detail in the vicinity of a salt dome in this area. [After Carsay]

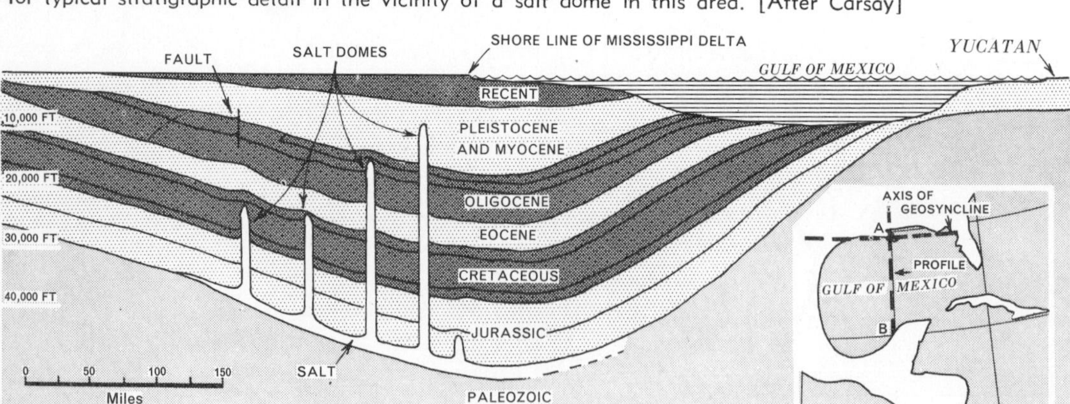

sively extended toward its present position, the alluvial plain rose gradually behind it, built upward partly by deposition and partly by slow regional uplift. Today the rock floor of the lowland lies far below the present flood plain. After the delta reached the vicinity of its present position, local subsidence within a great synclinal trough, the Barton geosyncline (see Fig. 3.13), roughly kept pace with deposition, thus preventing the extension of the delta far into the Gulf of Mexico. Deep oil-well drillings on the delta have revealed the enormous thickness of these sediments that have been warped downward into the earth crust.

Some coastal plains are produced through the joining of adjacent deltas. The plains along the eastern side of Sumatra, the northern part of Java, the coast of the Gulf of Guinea in western Africa, and parts of the Guiana coast of northern South America are of this type. Alluvial plains that border the ocean in tropical areas such as those above are almost always bordered by dense tangles of mangroves that penetrate the deltas along tidal channels and greatly hinder reclamation of the seaward margins.

FIG. 3.14 Talus slopes at the foot of a mountain slope, Holy Cross National Forest, Colorado. [U. S. Department of Agriculture]

The landforms of dry regions

3.6 GENERAL SHAPES AND PROFILES. The smooth, rounded profiles that are identified with most surface irregularities in humid regions are largely absent in dry areas. Sharp, angular profiles are characteristic of hilly to mountainous terrain where there is little rainfall and only sparse vegetation. Cliffs are prominent, and accumulations of loose rock rubble, termed *talus,* collect at their bases. Because of insufficient rainfall and the lack of organic acids to decompose the broken rock fragments, the talus slopes remain essentially as they were formed. Bare, uncovered by vegetation, they comprise conspicuous features of hill and mountain landscapes. Talus slopes are present at the foot of cliffs in humid regions also, but soil soon forms on them, and the covering of vegetation tends to hide their fragmental nature. Regions of flat-lying sedimentary rock strata of varying degrees of resistance to rock weathering exhibit step-like profiles of flat or gently sloping benches and cliffed edges (see Fig. 3.17). Although in humid regions small rock ledges along the sides of hills are often hidden from distant view by forests or brush cover, they stand

FIG. 3.15 An example of wind erosion. This cave has been scoured by sand abrasion near the summit of Ayer's Rock, a tableland that rises several hundred feet above the surrounding plain in central Australia. [Australian News and Information Bureau]

out sharply in desert landscapes, contributing to the general impression of angularity.

Wind is an active erosive agent in arid regions, where there is little forest growth to check ground velocities and where tiny, loose rock fragments lie on the surface ready to be picked up and swept along by the air currents. Sandblasting by desert winds etches out less durable spots on bare rock surfaces, producing a rough, honeycombed surface. As the air currents sweep across a desert plain, equipped with their fine, sandy, abrasive tools, an airfoil surface tends to develop, or one that affords a minimum amount of air resistance. This is an undulating surface, not a flat one, and is developed by the smoothing of rock irregularities and also by the deposition of wind-borne material in depressions.

3.7 EROSIONAL LANDFORMS IN DRY REGIONS. Even though running water is relatively scarce in dry regions, it is still the major erosional force in reducing upland areas. Runoff on desert slopes is rapid, being unchecked by vegetation. Most of the rain falls in sudden, violent cloudbursts. Little of the rainfall sinks into the ground, soil on slopes being thin or absent. Even in humid regions, the major part of stream erosion is carried on during widely spaced periods of high water, since the carrying power and erosive ability of running water increase rapidly with volume. Because of its sudden force, dry-land stream erosion, though infrequent, still can carry on its task of reducing uplands. Occasional flash floods in watercourses are a serious regional hazard. Stream valleys that carry water only during rare desert storms are often flat-bottomed as well as steep-sided. These are called *arroyos* in the southwestern United States, but the term *wadi,* current throughout most of North Africa and the Middle East, is more widely used in the contemporary geographic literature. Sands and gravels are dropped by receding floodwaters and during less violent runoff periods, gradually building up the flat wadi floors (see Fig. 3.16). Since subsurface water often can be found in the sands and gravels of wadi bottoms, they are favorite sites for oasis wells. The agriculture of the Hopi Indians of the southwestern United States and many inhabitants of the western Sahara is based on irrigation from wadi wells.

The elapsed time necessary for degradation usually is greater in desert areas than in humid lands, given comparable rock materials and slopes. The reason for this is that there is much less total stream runoff in dry areas. Stream erosion is rapid, but infrequent. For this reason, landforms characteristic of earlier stages of dissection appear to be more dominant than in humid lands. Highly dissected regions, with completely developed drainage systems, are relatively rare in deserts, although not unknown. *Badland topography,* however, is a noteworthy exception. This is an extremely rough land surface that is highly sculptured by rainwash. It is restricted to unusually fine-textured, unconsolidated silts and clays that have little protective covering of vegetation and are highly susceptible to the rilling and gullying effects of the occasional desert rains.

Perhaps the most characteristic erosional landforms in the dry regions of the United States are the *buttes* and *mesas* that are so frequently encountered in areas of sedimentary rocks (see Fig. 3.17). These are erosional remnants that stand out abruptly from flat plains. Mesas are broad, flat-topped, cliff-edged, tabular upland blocks, usually rimmed with rock-rubble slopes. Buttes are similar, but they are isolated hills, much smaller than mesas and with narrower summits. Many mesas and buttes are capped with a resistant rock layer, such as a sandstone or a lava flow. The recession, or sapping, of the durable cap rock often results in high, needlelike forms, such as those in Monument Valley, Arizona. In the heart of the Ahaggar Mountains of the central Sahara Desert, unusually tall, grotesque spires, like huge

FIG. 3.16 A desert wadi of the Nedj, Saudi Arabia. The bush vegetation indicates somewhat more abundant water in the wadi. Note the pebbly surface of the foreground, typical of reg desert surfaces. Most of the well oases of Saudi Arabia are found in valleys such as this. [Standard Oil Company (N.J.)]

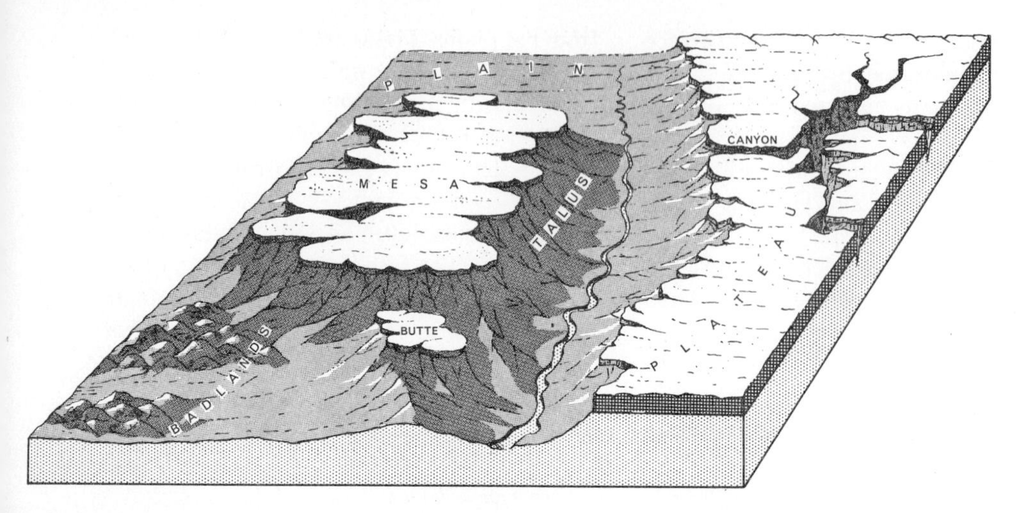

FIG. 3.17 Typical landforms developed on nearly horizontal sedimentary rocks in dry regions. [After Strahler]

FIG. 3.18 An advanced stage in the erosion of an arid region (southern Saudi Arabia). Note the network of wadis and coalesced basins. Both deposition and erosion operate to bevel the land surface. Scattered low bushes mark the site of subsurface moisture in the wadi stream channels. [U. S. Air Force (MATS)]

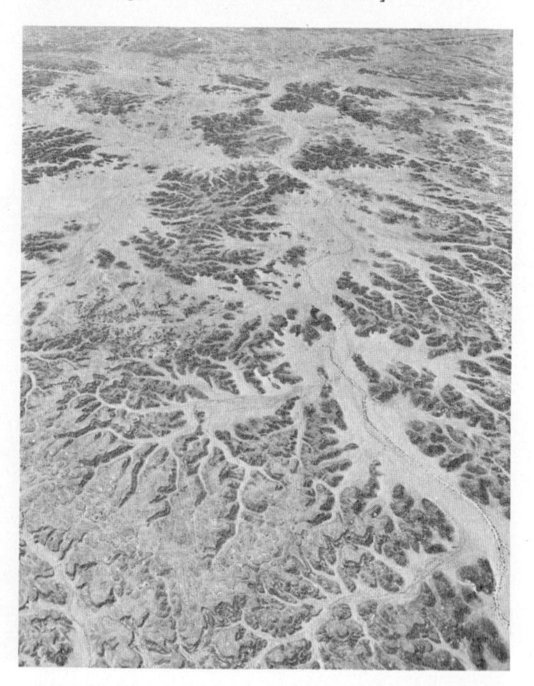

stone monoliths, have been formed by the sapping of volcanic plugs, which represent lava tubes of ancient volcanoes.

Many of the desert surfaces in the world consist of wind-swept rock plains termed *hamadas*. Sometimes these are bare rock surfaces, free of soil material and constituting some of the most lifeless, sterile areas on earth, especially where wadi channels are rare. The Tanezrouft region, west of the Ahaggar Mountains in the Sahara, is illustrative. Usually, however, the hamadas contain some wadis, with their bush-covered stream gravels, and the interstream areas bear a mantle of loose sand, gravel, or rock rubble which is sufficient to support a sparse covering of desert shrubs. Hamada plains form much of the land surface of dry areas in both northern and southern Africa, western Australia, Patagonia, and the Gobi Desert of Mongolia.

The surfaces of many desert plains are covered with a layer of rounded polished pebbles, sometimes referred to as *desert pavement*. It results from the brushing away of finer material by wind action. Broad areas of such pebbly surfaces are termed *reg* and are common on the hamada plains of the Sahara.

3.8 DEPOSITIONAL LANDFORMS IN DRY REGIONS. Sediments carried by wind and water in desert areas accumulate mainly within interior depressions. Permanently flowing streams that link dry areas with the sea are rare; hence, in general, all the eroded material remains within the deserts, principally in the lowest spots. Some deserts are comprised of alternating mountain ranges and nearly flat basins (*bolsons*). The streams that descend into these basins drop their load of sediment when their velocities are suddenly checked, and fan-shaped deposits accumulate along the margins of the mountains. These are *alluvial fans,* which are common landforms in many parts of the world. The alluvial-fan slopes are slightly concave to the sky and are frequently entrenched in their upper portions by steep-sided gullies. The material in fans is roughly graded, with the coarsest material at the steep upper end. Coalescing fans may produce a sloping plain rimming the mountain margins; this is known as a *piedmont alluvial plain.* Long piedmont alluvial plains are located along the margins of the Central Valley of California, the western foot of the Andes in Peru and northern Chile, the southern border of the Atlas Mountains in northern Africa, and the rims of the great interior basins of central Asia, such as those in the Tarim Basin of Sinkiang. Sites near the apexes of alluvial fans are favorite places for desert oases, because there the stream flow from the mountains can easily be tapped, led by gravity, and used to irrigate fan slopes.

Agricultural land use on alluvial fans and piedmont plains frequently is in broad zones corresponding to variations in the texture of the alluvial material. Coarse gravels and cobbles usually lie at the apexes of the fans, and do not retain enough water for cultivation. The gradation from coarse sands to fine silts during the descent down the fan slopes often is accompanied by a gradation in the type of crops grown. Tree crops normally do well on intermediate portions of the fan, since their roots may draw on water from

FIG. 3.19 An interdune depression in an Arabian erg, or sandy desert, in the oil district north of Abqaiq, Al Hasa, Saudi Arabia. Note the pebbly surface, wind ripples, and bush vegetation. [Standard Oil Company (N.J.)]

FIG. 3.20 The Great Western Erg in the Algerian Sahara. This wasteland of billowing sand dunes extends for hundreds of miles. Note the irregularity of dune crests and the occasional flat depressions free of dune sand. [U. S. Air Force; American Geographical Society]

considerable depths. In areas where frost may be a hazard, the intermediate positions also are favored locations for plants susceptible to frost, partly because they are above the cold air that accumulates below on clear nights, and also because the air movement along the slopes retards freezing somewhat.

Many people believe deserts to be only vast expanses of billowing sand dunes, possibly because such settings invariably were chosen for most desert scenes in the earlier motion pictures. The sandy deserts, or *ergs,* are by no means as predominant as often believed. A large supply of sand is required for their formation and is brought into large interior basins by networks of wadis. The dunes of an erg slowly shift position and change in form under the turbulent action of the air stream blowing over them. Desert dunes vary in height, but normally small ones are between 10 and 50 feet high (see Fig. 3.19). Dunes 100 to 300 feet high are fairly common in larger ergs, and some individual dunes 700 feet high and almost a mile long at the base have been observed in southern Iran. There is a tendency in most ergs for single dunes to develop ridges roughly at right angles to the direction of prevailing winds, whereas the ridges formed by the combination of dunes trend with the wind. Occasionally the ergs afford sources of water for oasis settlements, for since they lie in the lower portions of desert basins, ground water may occur not far below the interdune depressions. The date palm oases in the vicinity of Ouargla in eastern Algeria are of this type. Cultivation here consists mainly in preventing the dunes from slowly burying the date orchards. The lower elevations in the Sahara contain some of the largest ergs in the world, particularly those of eastern Libya and Algeria. The Libyan Erg (see Fig. 3.20), largely waterless, is one of the most desolate areas on earth, and has constituted an effective natural barrier protecting Egypt from western desert raiders for centuries. Other great ergs are found in southern Arabia, in the Takla Makan Desert of the central Tarim Basin, in the Thar Desert of northwestern India, and in central Australia. A small but most unique erg is found in the United States in the White Sands National Monument near Alamogordo, New Mexico. It is unusual in that the dunes are composed largely of gypsum flakes (calcium sulfate), a salt that accumulated on the surface of an adjacent dried lake bed.

Temporary salt lakes, or *playas,* are frequently found in interior desert basins that concentrate water runoff from adjacent uplands. Such lakes are mainly found in those parts of the world that have a succession of short mountain ranges and small, irregular basins without outlets, such as those in Nevada, Iran, and parts of central Turkey. The playas are supplied with water largely from flash floods that rush down the stream valleys from the adjoining mountains. Because the water always contains small quantities of salt dissolved from minerals, this salt is concentrated by evaporation in the playa basins, much as a kitchen teakettle in time accumulates a crust of lime and other salts. When a playa lake evaporates repeatedly, it may leave behind a salt-encrusted flat, termed a *salina.* Unusually large playas are found in the basins that adjoin the Atlas Mountains in Algeria and Tunisia, where they are known as *shotts.* Some playas or salinas have been important sources of various salts, such as nitrates, borates, and potash. Probably the best known of these are the nitrate deposits of northern Chile and southern Peru, which are composed largely of sodium nitrate and which have been concentrated into a shallow, hardpan soil layer by evaporation. Sometimes the surface of desert basins is formed of cracked, sunbaked clay without noticeable salt encrustations.

Coastal landforms

Waves and currents along the margins of oceans, seas, and lakes continually assist in the work of shaping the earth surface. Their erosional and depositional processes are different from those of streams and rivers; hence they tend to produce distinctive types of landforms. Differences in the arrangement and composition of shore-line surface materials influence the type of landforms produced and the rate of progress in the eternal attack on shore lines. Fluctuations in sea level result in breaks in the sequential stages of erosion and deposition. Landforms and the natural processes that operate along coasts have meaningful relationships to human needs and desires. Millions of dollars are spent annually in attempting to check shore-line erosion and in maintaining navigational channels in the face of sedimentation by shore currents.

3.9 EROSIONAL SHORE-LINE FEATURES. Erosional features are common along steep shore lines, just as they are in the steeper areas of continental interiors. A steep, rugged coast usually signifies deep water near shore, and since storm waves in deep water do not have to spend their energy through friction on the bottom, the waves are able to attack the shore line directly (see Fig. 3.21). The erosive action of storm waves is many times greater than normal wave action, just as floodwaters are more effective in stream work than normal discharge. Waves pounding against a cliffed shore line will undermine it, producing a *notched cliff.* They also etch rocky shores, concentrating on the weaker spots in the rocks, widening cracks and crevices, and bringing out into bold relief the hitherto hidden rock structure. *Wave-cut terraces* sometimes border sea cliffs, representing the erosional recession surface of the cliffs. They are usually mantled with a thin veneer of rock debris that has broken from the cliffs and that is being rounded and reduced in size by the to-and-fro surges of wave motion. As the wave-cut terrace grows following this recession of cliffs, more of the wave energy is spent in friction on the bottom; hence less energy can be spent by waves on the shore line itself, and the rate of recession is retarded.

Stacks, arches, caves, and other miscellaneous erosional forms can be found along cliffed coasts. Caves are simply weak places in the shore cliffs that have been excavated by wave action. If a cave extends through a narrow point or promontory, an arch is formed. Collapse of the roof of an arch will result in a towerlike mass of rock termed a stack. Such features, when found well above the water level, are evidences of shore-line emergence.

FIG. 3.21 Erosional and depositional landforms along shorelines. [(A) After Stamp; (B) after Strahler]

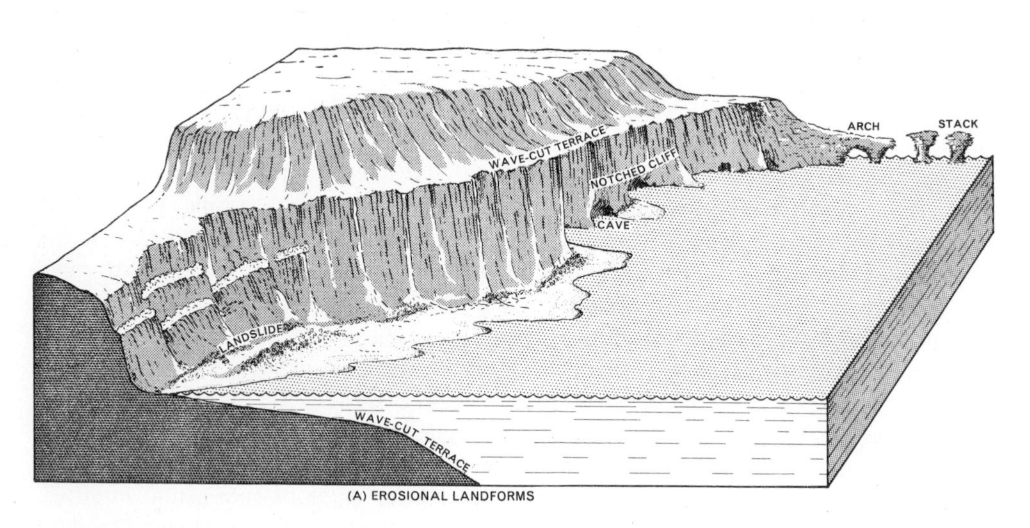

(A) EROSIONAL LANDFORMS

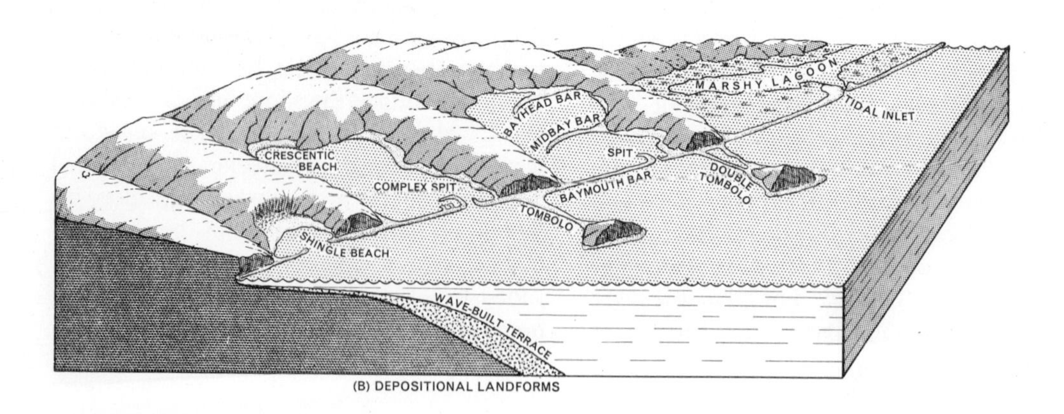

(B) DEPOSITIONAL LANDFORMS

3.10 DEPOSITIONAL LANDFORMS ALONG SHORE LINES.

The material eroded from shore lines by waves is distributed along the coast both by the backwash of waves and by shore currents. Since the movement of water below the surface is not strong, boulders, cobbles, and gravel usually stay near the pounding surf zone where they were formed. As they become reduced in size, they are more easily moved outward into deeper water. Sometimes the coarse, rounded stones form stony *shingle beaches* along the shore, particularly in small coves adjacent to cliffed headlands. The finer material, usually composed of sand, accumulates beyond the wave-cut terrace to form a *wave-built terrace,* thus extending the general gradual slope away from shore. Steep coast lines commonly are irregular, with pronounced headlands and bays. As erosion attacks the headlands, the eroded material may be washed to one side, into the protected waters of the adjacent bays. A protruding tongue of sand extending from the side of a promontory is termed a *spit.* If the tongue moves completely across the bay or joins a spit from the opposite headland, it is known as a *bay-mouth bar.* More frequently, such material is carried along the margins of the adjoining bays, rimming them to form *crescentic beaches.*

FIG. 3.22 Beachy Head, a famous English landmark along the soft, chalk cliffs of Sussex County, England. The lighthouse marks the shoals of the wave-cut terrace at the base of the cliffs. [British Travel Association]

Not all the depositional material along shore lines is derived from wave erosion. Much of it may be carried into the body of water by streams and subsequently distributed along the coast by shore currents. Fine clays and silts are sometimes carried far out to sea, but sands and gravels usually remain relatively close to the shore line. So much sandy material may be deposited along a coast that wave and current energy is expended entirely in distributing the material and in smoothing the shallow bottom.

Low seacoasts with a gradually sloping bottom profile, where sands and gravels are found in abundance, frequently are fronted by a low ridge of sand that parallels the coast and often extends above sea level. These are known as *barrier beaches* or *barrier islands.* Such ridges are constructed by huge storm waves that pound against the gently sloping sandy bottom, excavating it and piling the sandy debris into low ridges. The broad, marshy *lagoons* that lie back of barrier islands are connected to the sea by narrow *tidal inlets,* or passageways that separate the barrier islands. Low sand dunes sometimes surmount the barrier islands. These offshore islands are rare on inland water shore lines, because storm waves do not reach sufficient size to create them. Here they are represented instead by sand bars in shallow water. Barrier islands are prominent features along many low seacoasts in several parts of the world. A succession of them borders much of the Atlantic and Gulf of

FIG. 3.23 Fringing coral reef, Kusiae Island, Caroline Islands. Note how the waves break against the outer margins of the reef, indicated in white. Kusiae is typical of the high volcanic islands that rise abruptly from the floor of the Pacific Ocean. [Geographical Review]

Mexico coast of the United States, extending from near New York City, around the coast of Florida, and into Mexico. The Frisian Islands along the south coast of the North Sea are famous European examples. Attractions of ocean bathing, fishing, and cool ocean air in summer have helped to make them favorite summer resort areas.

Tidal mud flats are found wherever silts or clays accumulate along a seacoast faster than they can be removed by waves and currents. They generally occur along protected coasts where waves and currents are weak and where streams discharge large quantities of alluvial material. Tides subject them to periodic inundation. They are not easy to reclaim for agricultural use, because of their content of ocean salt. Diking to prevent flooding by sea water, draining by excavating ditches and canals, flushing with irrigation water, and treatment using soil-conditioning material or chemicals must be applied to transform tidal flats into productive agricultural areas. Such projects have been carried on for centuries in parts of the world where land is extremely valuable, as in northern China, the Netherlands, the Po delta, and northern Java.

Coral reefs are shore features that are characteristic of many seacoasts in tropical waters. These are massive calcareous (lime) structures built by large numbers of colonial coral animals that secrete calcium carbonate in order to build a protective outer skeleton. Other types of lime-secreting animals and plants often are associated with the corals in reef building. Warm, shallow, clear sea water, free from silts or clays, is required for coral-reef development. Rapid accumulations of sand from shore currents will prevent coral growth. The most active reefs are found in surf zones, where the water is constantly aerated and where tiny microscopic algae and other small food particles are being carried to within reach of the living coral's arms or tentacles. Coral reefs may be of the *fringing* type (see Fig. 3.23), which occur where waves beat directly against the shore, or of the *barrier* type, which are found in the surf zone within shallow water some distance from shore. A gradual subsidence of low tropical islands may be matched by the upward growth of coral reefs, where the coral colonies extend upward in order to reach the light and aerated zone near the surface. In this way, circular reefs termed *atolls* are formed. Low islets built of coral sand often surmount the atoll reefs. Narrow passageways through the reefs are kept open by strong tidal currents. The lagoons—or sheltered water between barrier reefs and the shore, or within atolls—afford protective anchorages for boats. Navigation of the narrow tidal inlets that are rimmed by jagged coral edges, however, may be hazardous. Seen in detail, coral reefs are wonders of complexity and beauty, alive with a profusion of marine life forms, all living together in a symbiotic, or mutually beneficial, environment. The combination of sea food and coconut, breadfruit, and other land plants on the coral islands has nurtured human inhabitants for many thousands of years. The major environmental hazard of such environments to man has been hurricanes, or severe tropical storms. Low coral islands within the path of such storms sometimes have been swept clean by wind and high water.

Landforms associated with glaciation

During a long period, lasting about 1 million years and ending only about 10,000 to 12,000 years ago, large parts of Europe and North America were invaded four separate times by immense *ice sheets* (see Fig. 3.24). The cause of this period of glaciation was a general lowering of mean temperatures, a climatic condition that was world-wide. Possible hypotheses for such long-range temperature variations are discussed in Chapter 6 (see Sec. 6.15). It is now believed that no phenomenal lowering of temperatures is required and that a general lowering of mean annual temperatures of between 7 and 10°F

FIG. 3.24 World distribution of Pleistocene glaciation. [After Dacque]

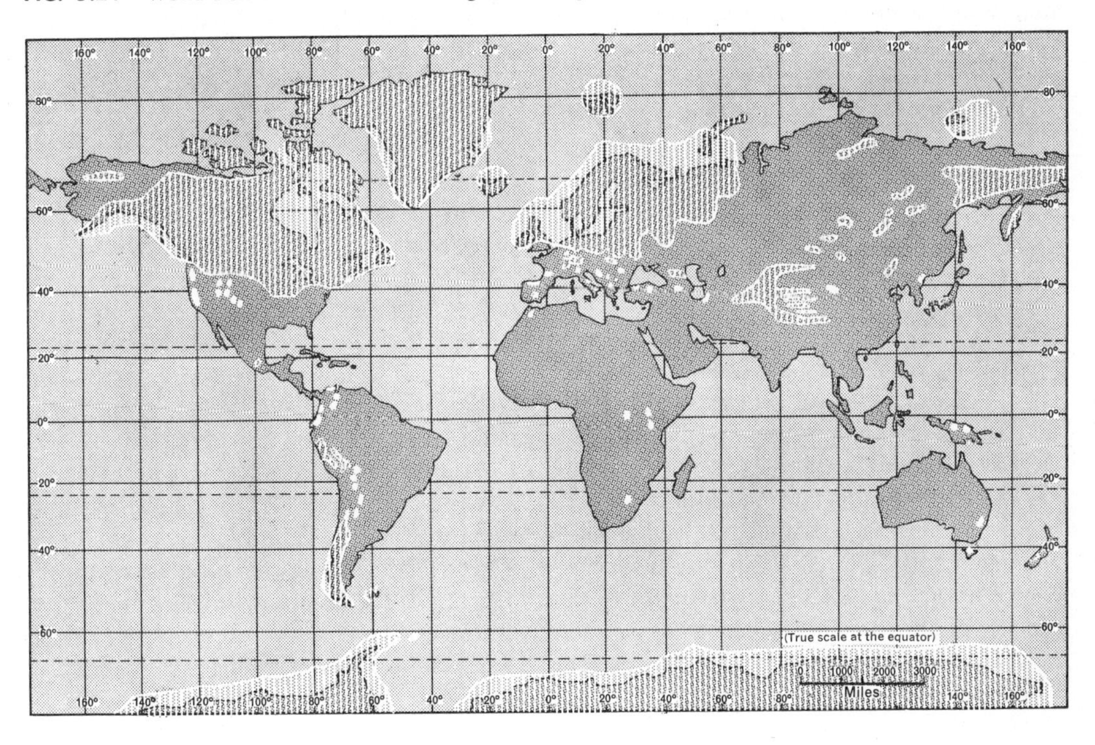

FIG. 3.25 Ice-scoured surface, western Ellesmere Island. Smoothed, rounded surfaces like these are typical of many of the arctic plains. Note how erosion has beveled the rock strata in the foreground; note also the soil polygons (See Sec. 3.15) in the left foreground. [Royal Canadian Air Force]

would be sufficient for continental glaciation. In any event, with the drop in temperatures, more snow gradually accumulated during the winters within the arctic and subarctic regions than melted the following summer; hence the mass of snow became deeper. Alternate freezing and thawing, plus compaction, changed the lower portion of the snow into ice. Once the ice mass became thick enough, it began to flow outward under its own weight.

Several centers of accumulation developed, from which the ice moved outward in all directions. In North America, the three major centers were located in the area to the west of Hudson Bay, in Labrador, and in Greenland. In Europe, the major center of ice movement was the uplands of Scandinavia. Mountain areas over the entire world experienced extensive mountain glaciation, with tongues of ice extending far down the mountain slopes. Much moisture is necessary for continental glaciation, and some regions, such as central Alaska and much of the eastern Soviet Union, were not glaciated because they had insufficient precipitation to nourish ice sheets.

The mass of ice and snow that accumulated in the ice sheets was stupendous, and it is estimated that at least one of the ice sheets reached a maximum thickness of 10,000 feet. Moving slowly forward from their centers, the ice sheets buried hills and valleys alike. During their forward progression, the huge ice sheets greatly modified the underlying land surface. Erosional features associated with ice action now predominate in many areas, as in high mountains and the high-latitude areas of hard, crystalline rocks, whereas glacial deposition has shaped the surface configuration in others. Preexisting drainage patterns were greatly changed, and lakes, swamps, and entirely new drainage systems were instituted.

The boundaries of continental glaciation are shown in Fig. 3.24. Note that the largest areas were located in the northern hemisphere and extended farthest toward the equator in the central United States and the southwestern Soviet Union. The deep waters of the South Pacific and South Atlantic prevented the equatorward penetration of continental glaciation much beyond the present margins of Antarctica. In South America, the only continent that extends into the high latitudes in the southern hemisphere, glaciers extended only for short distances from the Andes into the adjacent lowlands. The distribution of continental ice sheets in the northern hemisphere was influenced by both surface configuration and available moisture supply. Note in Fig. 3.24, for example, the effect of the Appalachians in checking the advance of ice in eastern North America and the absence of ice from plains in central Alaska and Siberia, owing to low precipitation.

Evidence obtained by quantitative analysis of radioactive carbon in organic material indicates that the last ice sheet in North America may have been present over parts of the Great Lakes area as recently as 10,000 years ago. Greenland and Antarctica may well contain the last remnants of these waning ice sheets. Mountain glaciation, with its accompanying erosional and depositional processes, is operative today in all the major mountain cordilleras of the world, and its former greater extent is responsible for the characteristic alpine surface features of high mountain landscapes.

3.11 EROSIONAL LANDFORMS IN AREAS OF CONTINENTAL GLACIATION.

Erosional landforms resulting from continental glaciation are major features of the landscape today in those parts of the glaciated regions that have particularly hard, crystalline rocks, from which a shallow cover of soil and rock rubble was quickly removed to expose bedrock. This condition is best found on the crystalline hard-rock areas of the northern hemisphere, particularly in Canada and in Scandinavia, including Norway, some of Sweden and Finland, the Kola Peninsula of the northwestern Soviet Union, and parts of the arctic rim of Siberia. Frost weathering at high latitudes tends to form a mantle of broken rock rubble relatively rapidly. Prior to glaciation, there must have been a plentiful supply of rock fragments lying on the surface. The fragments were incorporated into the ice as the great ice sheets moved out from their source areas. Thus equipped, they became gigantic rasps which scoured underlying rock surfaces. The hills were rounded and polished by the abrasive action of the glaciers, producing the smooth, polished surfaces known as *glacial pavements*. *Striations*, or scratches on these surfaces, have been used in determining the direction of ice motion. The plucking or quarrying action of ice in areas of highly fractured rock surfaces resulted in steep cliffs, especially on the lee sides of the hills, that is, the sides opposite the direction from which the ice came. These rock cliffs remain today as prominent features of the hilly hard-rock areas and add to the general difficulty of cross-country travel in these regions. Hills that have steep, cliffed lee sides and gentle, scoured slopes facing the direction from which the ice came are termed *roches moutonnées* (sheep rocks), first named in an area of the French Alps where miniature features of this type, produced on a limestone surface, reminded an observer of a flock of sheep lying in a meadow.

Wherever the ice masses were channeled into narrow valleys, oriented in the direction of ice motion, typical *U-shaped valleys* were formed, with steep sides and rounded bottoms. Such forms are commonly encountered in areas of mountain glaciation but were also produced by continental ice sheets. The beautiful, broad, north-south valleys in the northern portion of the Appalachian Plateau, particularly in the Finger Lakes section of New York State, are splendid examples of such valleys. The effectiveness of ice scour in the soft shales of the New York Finger Lakes area is demonstrated by the fact that the bottom of Seneca Lake now lies at a depth that is several hundred feet below sea level.

Patterns of stream drainage were extensively modified by a combination of glacial erosion and deposition. In the northern Appalachians of southern New York State, for example, evidence indicates that the preglacial drainage was mainly toward the southwest. Glacial erosion, by scouring deep trenches in a north-south direction, and deposition of glacial material in the previous northeast-southwest drainage ways altered the entire regional drainage pattern.

Other erosional features resulting from glaciation are *glacial spillways* and *cross channels*. The former are large valleys eroded by melt water from the ice. During the waning stages of continental glaciation, immense quantities of water resulting from glacial melting flowed from the ice margins. Where the terrain was underlain largely by unconsolidated glacial debris, the streams of melt water, which contained many abrasive rock fragments, could carve valleys quickly. Sometimes, also, the glacial waters, ponded behind a terrain obstacle, sought an outlet laterally across the uplands and produced lateral drainage ways across the normal grain of the land surface. Such lateral valleys are termed cross channels. Spillways and cross channels often are encountered throughout glaciated terrain that is rolling to hilly, such as in parts of Wisconsin, southern Michigan, eastern Ohio, and southern New York. The east-west cross channels in northern Germany have provided excellent routes for the canals that connect the north-south rivers, such as the Oder, the Elbe, and the Weser. These landforms may be recognized easily because most of them are large valleys that today carry extremely small streams for their size.

Upon leaving the hard-rock areas of southern Canada and Scandinavia and continuing southward, the ice masses suddenly encountered soft sedimentary rocks, including shales, limestones, and sandstones. With the weight of thousands of feet of ice and with durable boulders of hard rock as abrasive tools, the ice masses gouged deeply at first and were channeled into major lobes, or tongues, by irregularities in the margins of the crystalline-rock uplands. Thus there were excavated the huge basins that later filled with water and became the Great Lakes in North America and the Baltic and North Seas of Europe.

The ice mass in the United States was diverted into the basins of western Lake Superior and Lake Michigan by an upland area of hard rock lying in northern Wisconsin and the Northern Peninsula of Michigan. The lee side of this upland region, located in southwestern Wisconsin and extending into parts of Iowa and Minnesota, never was covered by any of the four ice advances, although it was surrounded by ice on all sides. This unglaciated area is known as the *Driftless Area*.[1] Its landforms, clearly related to stream erosion instead of glaciation, contrast markedly with those of the surrounding glaciated areas. The erosional features of the Wisconsin *Dells*, resulting from erosion by the Wisconsin River in its course through a region of massive sandstones, are illustrative.

Once out of the basins adjoining the crystalline uplands, the ice masses rapidly lost much of their erosive power. The old crystalline tools were increasingly worn away, the newly incorporated rock debris lacked the hardness necessary for good abrasive action, and unconsolidated material began to clog the lower portions of the ice. Ice energy was expended more in carrying material than in performing erosive work. In many parts of the Middle West, unconsolidated glacial deposits have been found buried under later glacial material, indicating that the subsequent ice advances were not able to remove previous loose material. In a few places, interglacial topsoils have been found, complete with surface humus layers. Except for the northern Appalachians and the British Isles, erosional landforms produced by the ice sheets are rarely encountered beyond the margins of the crystalline shields.

[1] The name *Driftless* is derived from *drift,* a term used to designate all unconsolidated material associated with glaciation.

3.12 EROSIONAL LANDFORMS IN AREAS OF MOUNTAIN GLACIATION.

Today glaciation is producing characteristic features of erosion wherever mountains are high enough to have temperatures frequently below freezing and the precipitation is sufficient to nourish snow fields. During the Pleistocene period, or ice age, when temperatures were lower over the entire earth, the snow line, or frost line, descended to lower elevations; thus the distribution of glacial erosional features in mountains is more widespread than the extent of existing glaciation.

The major landforms of mountain glacial erosion (see Fig. 3.26) include the sharp, steep-sided mountain spires called *horns;* the jagged, narrow crests termed *arêtes* or *comb ridges;* the huge amphitheaterlike depressions, or *cirques,* that have been gouged out, seemingly by some gigantic ice-cream scoop; U-shaped passes with knife-edged summits, termed *cols;* U-shaped valleys leading down to adjacent lowlands; and tributary valleys that enter high up on the side slopes, termed *hanging valleys.* Glaciers themselves are striking features to people that view them for the first time, mainly because of their blue-white color that contrasts so sharply with the adjacent dark rock slopes. Where glaciated mountains lie next to oceans, the U-shaped valleys that lead to the sea and that appear to be submerged in their lower portions are known as *fjords.* Fjorded coast lines are found along the entire west coast of North America north of the United States–Canada border, in Labrador, along the Norwegian coast, southern Chile, along parts of the coast of New Zealand, and bordering Greenland and Baffin Island.

Erosion by glacial scour is found mainly in the valleys below the snow line. As in the case of continental glaciers, moving streams of glacial ice, containing stones and boulders, deepened and widened the valleys through which they flowed. Above the snow line, however, where glaciers originate, the dominant erosive work is performed by freezing of water in cracks and crevices and by the plucking action of ice within the cirques. As

FIG. 3.26 Erosional landforms associated with mountain glaciation. [After Lobeck]

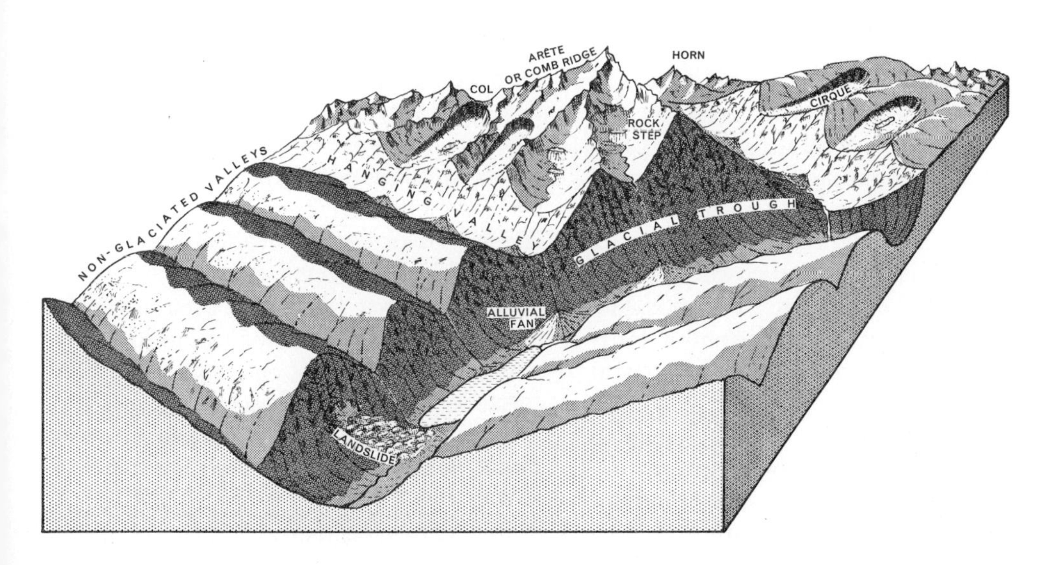

FIG. 3.27 Mount McKinley and Kahiltna Glacier, Alaska. Most of the characteristics of mountain glaciation can be seen in this photo, including cirques, cols, comb ridges (note shadow in right foreground), horns, and crevasses. Note how the lateral moraines of tributary glaciers become medial moraines within the main ice stream. [U. S. Air Force (MATS)]

the ice gradually flows out of the cirques, it removes the rock debris, using it as an abrasive tool on the valleys below.

Cirques formed during the Pleistocene period, and now abandoned by glacial ice, frequently contain shallow lakes, called *tarns* or *cirque lakes*. High, narrow waterfalls are often encountered in glaciated mountain landscapes, marking the entry point of hanging valleys into the main valleys. Bridal Veil Falls, in Yosemite National Park, is a well-known example. Hanging valleys containing lakes with appreciable outflow frequently are choice sites for hydroelectric power developments. The lakes help in regulating the outflow, there is a great fall of water into the valley below, and there is no need for expensive dam structures. Many such power sites have been developed in the Alps and in Norway.

3.13 DEPOSITIONAL LANDFORMS IN AREAS OF CONTINENTAL AND MOUNTAIN GLACIATION. Deposition by the continental ice sheets prevailed over erosion in determining the major features of the present land surface throughout most of the glaciated areas lying south of the Canadian and Fennoscandian (Scandinavia) crystalline-rock uplands. Most of the depositional material was dropped at the margins of the ice sheets. The glacial debris consists of two types of material: (1) *glacial till,* an unassorted mixture of stones and ground-up rock and soil material that was included within the ice mass and deposited as the ice melted; and (2) *fluvioglacial outwash,* composed largely of stratified and sorted sand and gravel that was deposited by glacial melt water as it flowed away from the ice masses. Glacial till and fluvioglacial material collectively are termed *drift.*

Most landforms composed of glacial till (see Fig. 3.28) are collectively known as *moraines.* Where the ice front remained stationary for long periods, as it did, for example, when the forward progression of ice was balanced by melting of the ice margins, large *end moraines* were formed, constituting linear belts of low hills, usually less than a hundred feet in height, although heights of several hundred feet have been observed. Where there is a succession of end moraines, marking several temporary halts in the ice-front retreat, the farthest is known as a *terminal moraine* and the others as *recessional moraines.* The ice margin was typically lobate; that is, it was in great tongues, or lobes; hence the morainic ridges commonly

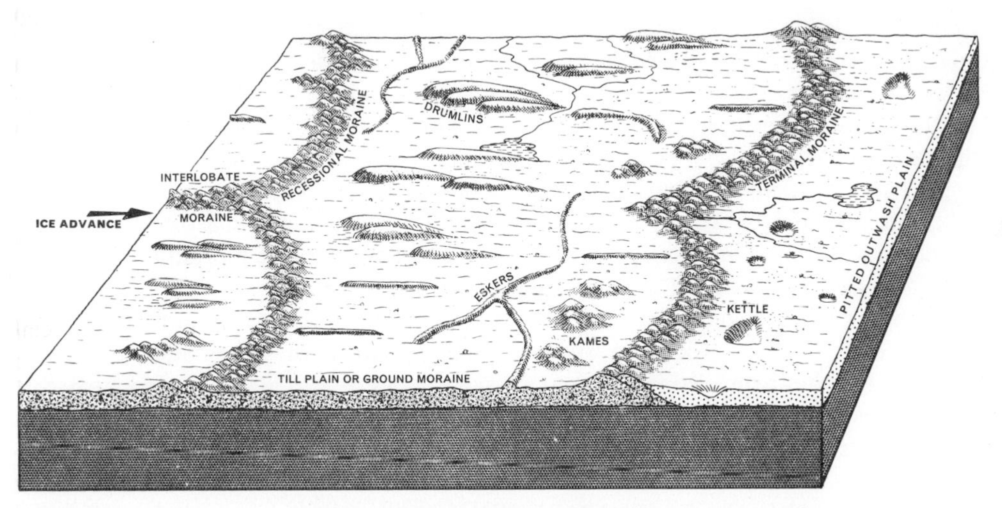

FIG. 3.28 Depositional features of continental glaciation. [After Finch et al.]

are aligned in great loops, or arcs. In the indentations between large, active lobes of ice, moraines are likely to be unusually high and are sometimes designated as *interlobate moraines.* Figure 3.30, which shows the position of morainic belts in the Great Lakes area, clearly illustrates this lobate aspect. Glacial debris also melted out in a broad zone inside the terminal moraines, so that a fairly even veneer of glacial till was deposited, forming what has been termed a *ground moraine.* If the resulting surface was essentially a flat plain, the designating term *till plain* is used. A large part of the flat, glaciated plains of Illinois, Iowa, and Indiana are broad till plains. Others are found in northern Germany and in the area east of the Baltic Sea. Till plains differ in surface relief. In parts of the central United States, such as in southern Illinois, in Iowa, and in Missouri, the till plains associated with the early ice advances underwent considerable dissection by stream erosion. The resulting rolling plains contrast noticeably with the flat-to-undulating till plains of the last, or Wisconsin, glacial advance. Moraines are present within the hard-rock upland regions to the north, but because of the lack of weathered surface material, which was carried far southward in an earlier advance, the glacial deposits are thin and have modified the surface mainly in clogging lowland drainage channels.

Drumlins are unique depositional land-

FIG. 3.29 A close-up of an active moraine along the flanks of a glacier at the head of a Greenland fjord. Note the hummocky surface of the moraine, the mixture of rock debris, and the fluvioglacial sand and silt being spread in front of the moraine. [Louise A. Boyd; American Geographical Society]

forms formed by glacial ice. They are oval-shaped mounds of glacial till, aligned in the direction of ice motion and having steeper slopes on the sides facing the direction from which the ice came. Many glacial experts believe them to be the result of overriding of former clay till moraines by a readvance of the ice, especially in limestone areas, where thick deposits of heavy, plastic till are likely to be found. The classic locality for them is in New York State, between Rochester and Syracuse, although they can also be found in parts of Wisconsin, Michigan, southern Sweden, Ireland, and the area east of the Baltic Sea.

The characteristics of glacial till differ widely from place to place. Although till always contains a mixture of rock debris derived from widely distant sources, its dominant properties as parent material for soils are almost always closely related to the characteristics of the local underlying rock. In the crystalline-rock regions, glacial tills are stony, with a high admixture of sand and a relatively small proportion of clay or silt. Limestone regions usually have till that is extremely heavy, with a high percentage of plastic clay, and that often has a slight pinkish tint. Included stones and boulders of more resistant rock from distant areas frequently are found embedded in these heavy tills. Interbedded sandstones and shales produce a sandy clay till with many small stony fragments. In general, glacial tills form more productive soils for agriculture than those derived from fluvioglacial outwash materials. The quality of soils derived from till, however, may vary widely. The poorest are generally the coarse-sand tills of crystalline-rock areas. The best are those that have a high admixture of limey clays.

Outwash plains are the most common depositional landform type associated with glacial-stream deposition. The melt water from glaciers is heavily charged with rock waste, and much of this debris is dropped as the streams leave the steep front edge of the ice. Cobbles, sand, and gravel are the first to be deposited, and this material accumulates in broad sheets beyond the ice margin. These outwash plains are especially noticeable bordering prominent end moraines. They vary greatly in size—from small, narrow flats in glacial valleys, where they are termed *valley trains,* to extensive plains several hundred square miles in area. The extremely fine material in glacial streams gives the water a milky appearance and is retained in suspension until it is dropped in standing water at the stream mouths.

Blocks of ice, broken from the ice margin and buried in outwash material, later may result in depressions, or *kettles,* in the outwash plains as the ice melts away. The term kettle is often used, however, to designate any depression without an outlet in a glacial depositional surface. A *pitted outwash plain* is one that has a large number of such depressions. Swamps or lakes may occupy the kettles. Outwash plains cover a larger proportion of the glacial depositional surfaces in Europe than in North America, occurring throughout much of the North German Plain and in the northwestern Soviet Union. However, large outwash plains also are found in the northern part of the United States, particularly in Wisconsin, Michigan, and Minnesota. Their sandy soils inherently are rather infertile, often lack plant foods, and are excessively droughty, owing to their low capacity for retaining water in their topsoils. In Europe, the outwash plains produce good yields of rye and root crops, such as potatoes and turnips, mainly because of careful soil management practices. Originally, the sandy outwash plains of the northern United States were covered with valuable stands of white or red pine. Today, owing to many for-

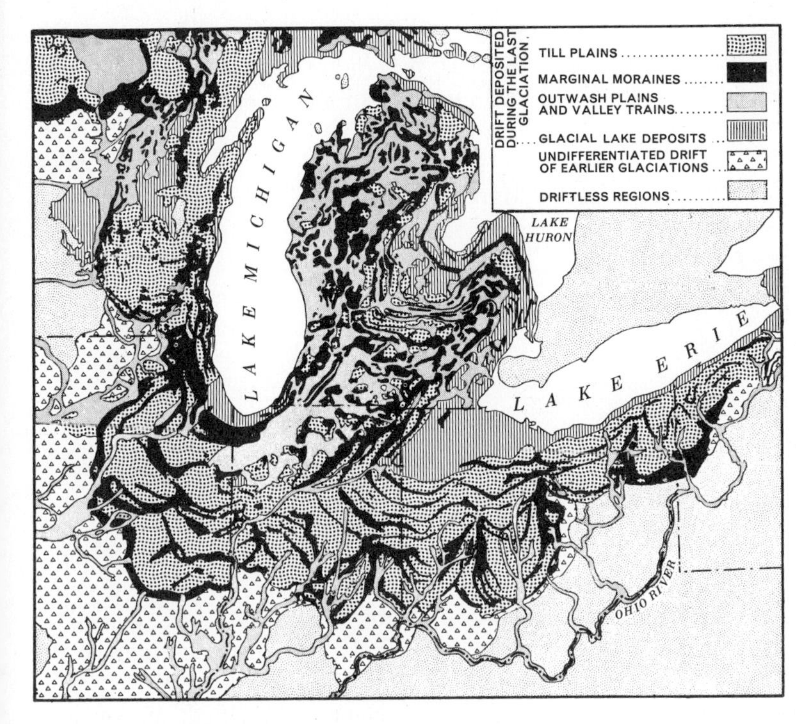

FIG. 3.30 Glacial landforms in the Great Lakes region. [After Graetz and Thwaites]

est fires, most of them are treeless or mantled only with low, scrubby jack pines.

Mounds and ridges of stratified outwash sands and gravels are often encountered in the vicinity of moraines, especially where there is evidence of ice stagnation (little or no ice movement). The mounds are known as *kames,* and the narrow, often sinuous gravel ridges are termed *eskers.* The latter probably were formed by water deposition behind the ice margins in stream channels confined within narrow ice walls. Eskers more than a hundred miles in length have been found in Maine and Sweden, where these forms are especially common features on the ground moraines. Kames probably have a variety of origins, the most frequent being deposition by running water within crevasses, tubes, or wells in the ice mass. Later, as the ice melted, this material was let down as mounds upon the land surface. *Kame terraces* are found bordering the lower slopes of valleys in hilly terrain that underwent continental glaciation, such as in the northern Appalachians, New England, and parts of the northern British Isles. These are irregular benches or terraces that result from fluvioglacial deposition between the ice blocks in the centers of the valleys and the ice-free hill slopes.

Lakes occur throughout glaciated areas. Some of them are tiny, occupying small depressions in moraines or outwash plains. Others, like the Great Lakes, occupy huge basins excavated by ice scour. Many others are the result of clogging of former drainage channels by glacial deposition. Glacial lake plains, rimmed with low, sandy beach ridges, border many of the Great Lakes in the United States (see Fig. 3.30), representing higher lake levels during the waning stages of glaciation. Waters of the Red River, between Minnesota and North Dakota, flowing northward into the Hudson Bay drainage,

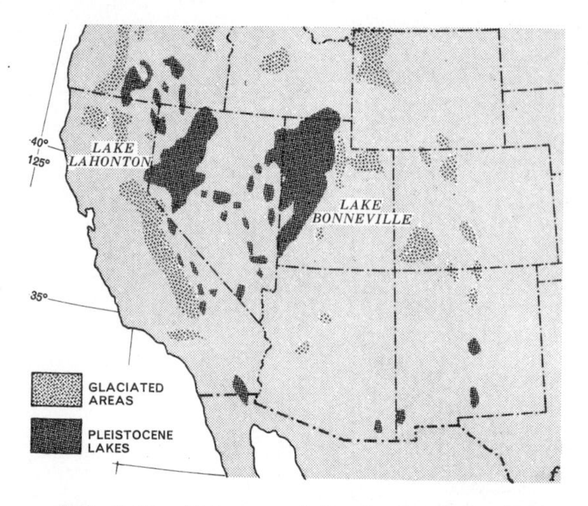

FIG. 3.31 Pleistocene lakes in the Basin Range region of the southwestern United States.

were dammed by the retreating ice, forming a huge lake (Lake Aggasiz). Lake Winnipeg, in southern Manitoba, is a remnant of this huge lake. Increased rainfall associated with the glacial period was responsible for several large lakes in the southwestern United States (see Fig. 3.31).

The glacial period affected climatic patterns well beyond the margins of the ice sheets. One of the effects was a considerably increased precipitation in the semiarid-to-arid parts of the world. The resultant increased runoff in the southwestern part of the United States led to the creation of large lakes in areas that previously had only small lakes or playas. Lake Bonneville, a large lake west of the Wasatch Mountains of Utah, and Lake Lahontan, which covered an immense territory between the mountains of the Basin Range region of Nevada, were examples. Great Salt Lake is a remnant of Lake Bonneville. When the lake level of Bonneville dropped below the level of its outlet, owing to resumed dryness, the basin once more became an interior drainage basin, and the lake decreased its area and increased its salinity to its present high concentration. Lake Lahontan disappeared in a similar manner. A series of beaches and terraces remain to mark former levels of these two huge lakes.

Large parts of eastern Poland (the Pripet Marshes) and the western Soviet Union are the poorly drained beds of former lakes that resulted from the glacial damming of north-flowing rivers. The huge marshy basin of the Ob River east of the Urals in the Soviet Union may well have been formed in the same manner. Glacial-lake plains usually are underlain by extremely heavy, plastic clays, originally the finely ground rock material carried by glacial streams and deposited in the ponded waters of glacial lakes. Some of these clays have a distinct layered, or laminated, appearance, owing to seasonal variations in deposition. Such clays, known as *varve clays,* have been used to compute the length of time the lakes were in existence and, by correlation, the length of the post-glacial period.

Depositional features characteristic of mountain glaciation reproduce in miniature nearly all the forms discussed under continental glaciation. Since ice confined within a valley flows more rapidly in the center than at the sides, there is a tendency for included rock waste to be diverted toward the valley sides. After the melting of valley glaciers, ridges of morainic material are thus left behind along the valley flanks, forming what are termed *lateral moraines.* The joining of ice streams results in the junction of lateral moraines to form *medial moraines* farther to the center of the valleys and downvalley from the junctions.

In summarizing the general arrangement of glacial depositional landforms, it should be stated that the various individual forms are scattered and intermingled into highly complex patterns. To illustrate this, a typical small portion of an interlobate morainic area in east-central Wisconsin, with its associated glacial landforms, is shown in Fig. 3.32. In this region, a farmer may have sand, gravel, clay, muck, or stony spots in many different slope conditions, all within the area of his farm. Changes in soil composition may also be found vertically. Bedrock may lie anywhere from 2 to 200 feet below the surface; sand may underlie clay at variable depths, or vice versa; and a layer of sand or clay 3 feet below the surface may be absent a short distance away. The wide differences locally in landforms and soils are matched by great regional differences over broad areas. The American Corn Belt, centered on the till plains of the Middle West, has undoubtedly some of the finest naturally productive soils in the world; on the other hand, the sterile, treeless, sandy outwash plains of Northern Michigan are almost deserts, shunned as a home for man. Similar broad functional differences can be found regionally, as well as locally, in the glaciated parts of Europe. Examples include the sandy outwash plains of northeastern Germany and the marshy lake plains of eastern Poland, each with its local differences, largely the result of fluctuations in the complex behavior of continental ice sheets operating on local differences in the original land surface.

FIG. 3.32 Landform detail in a section of the interlobate moraine area of Wisconsin. [From USGS Oconomowoc, Wis., 15-minute Quadrangle]

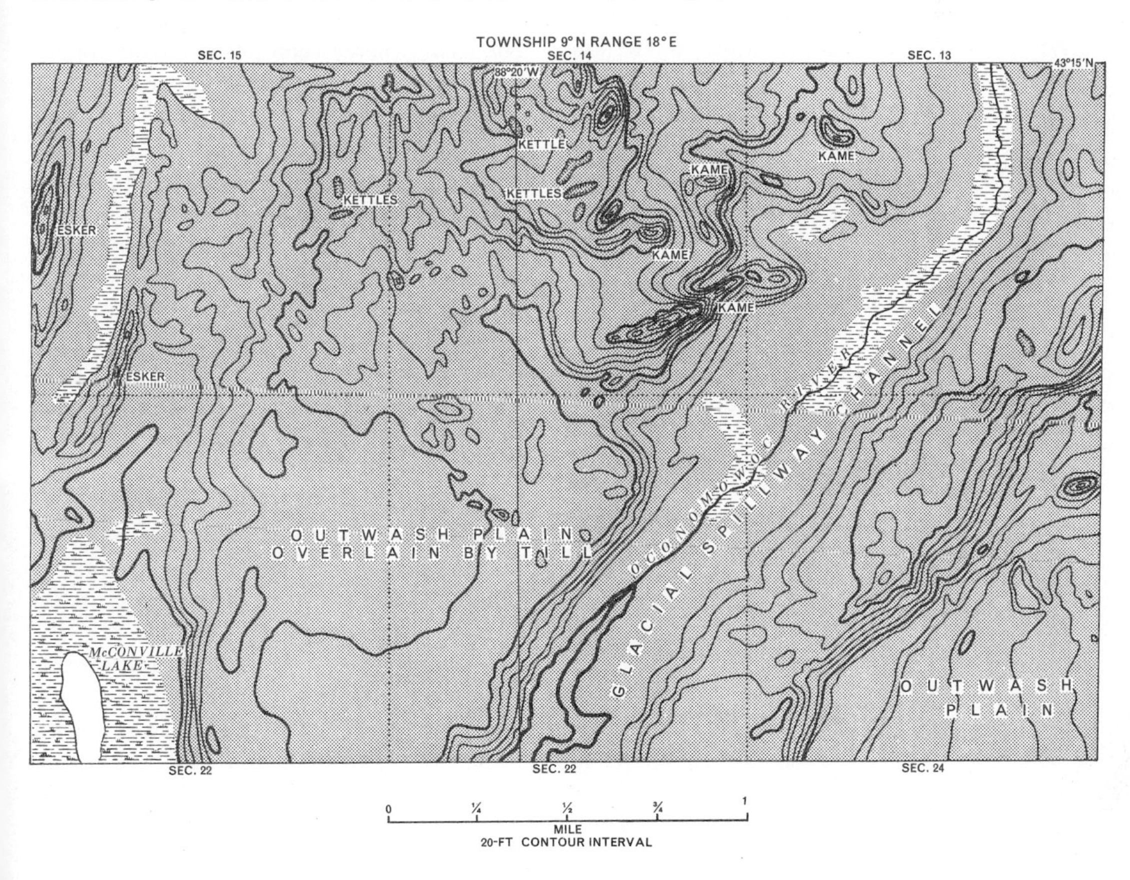

Landforms of polar regions

3.14 GLACIATION AND THE GENERAL LAND-SURFACE FEATURES OF POLAR REGIONS. Stream erosion has played a comparatively minor role in shaping the dominant surface irregularities in high latitudes, not only because the streams are frozen for so much of the year, but also because relatively little time has elapsed since glacial ice overlay the land surfaces. Wherever there is appreciable slope, it has been smoothed and rounded by glacial erosion. Since glaciation, stream action has once more begun to grade the surface irregularities in its own way. Short, steep-sided gorges are slowly working their way into the slopes, and the rubble of glacial debris and weathered rock material is slowly moving into the drainage ways. There are many indications of the relative recentness of continental glaciation. Typical glacial erosional and depositional features abound in every direction. Sharp, jagged profiles are rare in the general landscape, although they are common in the microfeatures, such as in the fragments of rock lying loose on the surface and in the detail of cliffs. There are many evidences of recent irregular uplift of land following the removal of the great weight of glacial ice. Near the coasts, particularly along the borders of many of the islands lying north of the Canadian mainland, abrupt cliffs mark the ascent to broad, ice-scoured plains. Terraces border the flood plains of rivers along their lower courses.

FIG. 3.33 A frost-riven cliff in Greenland. Alternate freezing and thawing shatter the cliff face, and the angular fragments either collect as talus at the base or are incorporated into streams of glacial ice as seen on the right. [Louise A. Boyd; American Geographical Society]

Continental glaciation once covered a large part, but not all, of the polar regions of the northern hemisphere (see Fig. 3.24), and today it covers nearly all of the Antarctic Continent and Greenland. The statement made earlier that glacial erosion produced the major landforms within areas of crystalline rock, whereas deposition largely formed the surface in areas of sedimentary rocks, holds true throughout nearly all of the arctic and subarctic. There are some differences, however, in the glacial landforms here as compared with those in regions farther south. End moraines are relatively rare, and eskers are larger and more common on the broad surfaces of ground moraines. Subjected to the spalling effect of strong frost action, exposed rocks that previously had been burnished by glacial scour have lost most of their polished and smoothed surfaces.

3.15 FROST ACTION IN POLAR REGIONS. The alternate freezing and thawing of water are the principal geological processes modifying the land surface today in polar areas not covered by glaciers. The wedging or prying action of freezing water in cracks and crevices of all sizes breaks rock into a mass of angular fragments ranging from fine sand to immense blocks (see Fig. 3.33). The mechanical rock breakage here is much more rapid than it is in other parts of the world, for the growth of ice crystals exerts enormous force, ranging from 2,000 to 15,000 pounds per square inch. Large areas of the broken rock material have been termed *felsenmeer* (sea of rocks). Unlike the rounded *erratics* (transported glacial boulders) of ground moraines, these stones are sharply angular.

Plains underlain by several feet of fine, loose, unconsolidated material, glacial or fluvial, often are dotted with low mounds, sometimes caused simply by frost heaving, but sometimes also caused by the hydraulic pressure of water compressed between permanently frozen subsoils (*permafrost*) and a freezing surface layer that deepens as winter approaches. (For further details on the effects of permafrost, see Sec. 12.4.) *Polygonal structures* (see Fig. 3.34) are another interesting feature of arctic plains. Some of these are composed of low lines of stones, graded according to size, with the largest lying on the outer rim of the structure. Others are like polygon-shaped saucers, with a low center, rising gradually to a low dirt ridge, only a foot or so high, that has a steep outer slope. The stones commonly are absent in this form. In still others, the polygonal structure is marked only by cracks or lines of vegetation. Polygons vary in diameter from a few feet up to as much as 200 feet. Although their origins are not completely understood, these structures are believed in some way to have been the result of frost action. They also have been observed well above the tree line on mountain slopes in other parts of the world. The large number of perfectly circular ponds which appear so strikingly from the air over arctic plains may be related to these structures.

3.16 LANDFORMS RELATED TO MASS WASTAGE IN THE ARCTIC.

Mass wastage, or the downslope movement

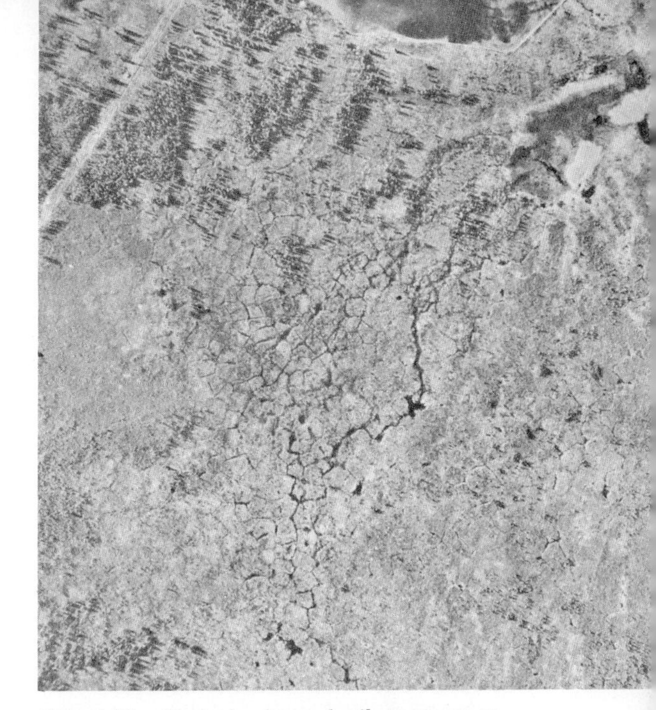

FIG. 3.34 Typical polygonal soil structures at the edge of the tundra north of Fairbanks, Alaska. Note how they have influenced drainage patterns. The polygons here have diameters of 20 to 30 feet. [U. S. Air Force (MATS)]

of soil material under the influence of gravity, occurs at high elevations throughout the world, but it is especially active in polar regions. Contributing to this are the mechanical effects of freezing and thawing, the scarcity of retentive vegetation cover, the abundance of ground water during the short summer season, and the existence of permafrost in the subsoils. Among the resultant surface forms are (1) *stone stripes,* or strips of stones aligned up- and downslope; (2) *stone rivers,* or sinuous lines of boulders following drainage ways; (3) *contour-pressure ridges,* which are low ridges paralleling the contours or at right angles to the slope, resulting from soil slumping; and (4) some curious miniature terraces along the contour that produce an appearance somewhat similar to the "cowpath contours" of a hillside pasture in dairy regions. *Solifluction,* or *soil flowage,* is a major problem in the maintenance of graded highways or railroads in the arctic.

A distinctive landform of arctic coast lines is the *strand flat*. This is a flat, narrow rock bench that borders the sea, just above or just below sea level, along many steep-sided fjords. Its origin still puzzles geomorphologists. It does not appear to have been formed by either wave or glacial erosion. Nansen, the famous arctic explorer, attributed it to a sapping effect caused by freezing along the water line.

3.17 ICE SHEETS AND ICECAPS. Immense sheets of ice cover nearly all of Greenland and Antarctica, and smaller icecaps can be found in the central highlands of Norway and Iceland. Icecaps and ice sheets should perhaps be more appropriately termed *ice domes,* because they usually slope gradually outward from a high center. In Greenland and Antarctica, the ice centers lie at elevations above 9,000 feet. The surface of the central portions usually is relatively smooth, with a fairly uniform covering of snow, hard-packed and smoothed by the high-velocity winds that prevail most of the time. Near the margins of the ice masses, the ice is generally channeled into distinct ice streams by underlying land-surface irregularities, and the ice surface is highly fractured into complex networks of *crevasses.* These deep clefts in the ice, often hidden by snow that has drifted over them, constitute major hazards to explorers seeking to cross these marginal areas.

The Greenland ice sheet is confined within mountain walls near its outer edge, so that, from the sea, this huge island continent appears to be bordered by a chain of mountains whose peaks are separated by ice streams seeking an outlet to the ocean. In Antarctica, on the other hand, the ice sheet overflows the edge of the continent, producing a broad *ice shelf* which in many places has a floating outer margin. Huge blocks of ice, broken from the ice shelf as a result of its buoyancy, form immense *tabular bergs.* These forms, common in waters off Antarctica, differ considerably from the irregular icebergs broken from the highly crevassed surface of the valley ice streams of Greenland.

Rocky peaks that rise above surrounding ice masses and are not covered by glacial ice are known in Greenland as *nunataks.* Riven by frost action, they present sharp, jagged surfaces. They are also found rising above the ice and snow of Antarctica. Such steep, jagged spires are found mainly along the east coast of Greenland but also along parts of the south coast. Elsewhere around the borders of Greenland, rounded, scoured peaks are predominant, indicating that they were once covered by the icecap.

Both major existing ice sheets (on Greenland and Antarctica) show evidence of recent ice recession, although the retreat of the ice margins is irregular and is occasionally interrupted by periods of temporary readvances. Greenland shows the major effects of recession, and appreciable settlement is taking place along some of the exposed marginal plains, especially in the southwest. The recession is caused by a definite rise in average temperatures. A limited amount of agriculture is possible, and this, along with some sheep raising, aids in supplementing the main livelihood, fishing.

Landforms of volcanic areas

Active volcanoes are located principally in two linear belts. One surrounds the Pacific basin, and the other extends in a transverse direction from the Caribbean Sea, via the Azores Islands, to the Mediterranean Sea area, thence eastward through Turkey to the great mountain chains north of India. Their distribution is shown on Fig. 4.5. Exceptions to the two belts just described include the volcanoes in east-central Africa, in Iceland, and on several of the mid-Pacific islands.

The landforms associated with volcanic activity vary with the type of volcanic action. Geologists long have recognized that volcanoes differ widely in the violence of their eruptions, ranging from the slow outpourings of highly fluid lava from cracks or fissures to enormous cataclysmic explosions that may suddenly pulverize several cubic miles of earth material. A wide variety of intervening types has been observed, each associated with distinctive landforms. The causes for this variability are mainly related to the chemical composition of the molten *magma* (lava beneath the surface). Highly fluid lavas include minerals that have a relatively low melting point, especially those having a low content of silica, and a high content of such elements as iron, calcium, magnesium, and phosphorus. The explosive magmas have extremely high melting points, related to high percentages of silica and usually also to a high content of dissolved gases such as chlorine, hydrogen sulfide, water vapor, and sulfur dioxide. Sometimes combinations of high- and low-viscosity magmas are present in the same magma reservoir and result in combinations of explosive and fluid lava eruptions such as characterize Vesuvius and Etna in Italy. Sometimes also, the same vent may, over a long period of time, gradually change from an explosive to a more quiet type. The complex processes of vulcanism causing the eruptions are not pertinent here. The results, however, are important in comprehending the pattern of surface forms on the earth. A convenient approach to the study of volcanic landforms is provided by the three dominant types of volcanic eruptions: *explosive, intermediate,* and *quiet*.

3.18 EXPLOSIVE VOLCANOES. The explosive type is best represented by the high volcanic cones such as Mount Fujiyama in Japan and Mount Mayon in the Philippines (see Fig. 3.35). These are built up, layer on layer, by the intermittent eruption of volcanic ash, cinders, or other fragmental material. Symmetrical cones as large as these, however, are not common. More frequently, such high volcanic peaks are shattered and blown asunder by violent explosions, so that they appear as fragments of cones or as cones within cones.

In areas where explosive eruptions are frequent, many cones of different sizes can be found, ranging from small *cinder cones,* a hundred or so feet high, to towering volcanic peaks, such as Fujiyama or Mayon. The cones may be formed extremely rapidly, as in the case of Parícutin, an ash cone in west-central Mexico, which appeared suddenly, on February 20, 1943, in a farmer's cornfield and grew into a mountain peak within a few weeks. Although its rate of growth is much slower today, Parícutin has reached a height of over 8,000 feet. An explosion pit (*crater*) usually is found at the summit of explosive volcanoes. Unusually wide craters that have a rough amphitheater-like shape are termed *calderas*. Some of them measure several miles in diameter. Crater Lake, located in southern Oregon, is an excellent example of a caldera. This crater may have been formed by a collapse of the volcanic summit instead of by an eruption.

Accompanying the formation of ash cones is the mantling of the adjacent countryside with ejected material. This tends to smooth out surface irregularities, forming *ash plateaus,* or *ash-filled basins*. Such forms are present on northern Kyushu Island in Japan, in the Fort de Kock district of east-central Sumatra, in the Katmai National Monument area on the Alaskan Peninsula, and in the southern part of the central uplands of Mexico and Guatemala.

3.19 INTERMEDIATE TYPES OF VOLCANO. The intermediate types of volcano include those which eject both fragmental and highly viscous fluid material and those which produce only viscous lava flows. The outpourings of lava from the craters or flanks of these volcanoes never move far from their vents, because they quickly solidify upon contact with the air. Thus the volcanoes assume the form of broad lava platforms or domes. Although fragmental explosion cones may be produced by this type of eruption, flows of lava on their sides tend to make them less symmetrical than the purely explosive types. Mounts Vesuvius and Etna in Italy and the high volcanic peaks of the western United States, including Mount Shasta, Mount Rainier, and Mount Hood, are examples.

Shield volcanoes, a subtype in which explosive eruptions do not occur, are characterized by huge, rounded, lava-built domes, frequently with wide craters or calderas at their summits. The volcanoes of the Hawaiian Islands are of this type (see Fig. 3.36). Because they have been built upward from the floor of the ocean, some 20,000 feet below sea level, and rise to 13,000 feet above sea level, the Hawaiian volcanoes rank among the largest individual relief features on earth. Their sides are scarred by the twisted, corded surfaces of numerous lava flows, varying in degree of weathering, depending on their age.

The lavas of the intermediate types of vol-

FIG. 3.35 Mount Hood, a typical explosive volcanic cone, seen from The Dalles, Washington. Note the eroded edges (cuestas) of basaltic lava flows in the foreground. Such flows form a large part of the Cascade Mountains and the Columbia Plateau to the east. [U. S. Air Force (MATS)]

cano generally weather into productive soils, and the flanks of many of the volcanic peaks are intensively cultivated.

3.20 THE QUIET TYPE OF VOLCANO. The *fissure-flow,* or *quiet-type,* volcano results from the rise of highly fluid lavas to the surface. Such volcanoes are not active anywhere in the world today, but during past geologic periods, they produced immense lava plateaus in several parts of the world. In these areas, successive flows of the dark, basaltic lavas spread over thousands of square miles, in some places to depths of several thousand feet. Individual flows rarely are more than about 20 feet in thickness. Unlike the two types of eruptions discussed above, the fissure flows were not located in the areas of major crustal instability, the regions of compressional crustal buckling and earthquakes. According to some geologists, they are related to tensional stresses deep within the crust and were produced as the result of geosynclinal buckling and mountain building in the areas of compressional stresses some distance away. Their general locations are shown in Fig. 5.13 as areas of basaltic lava. The largest areas include the Columbia Plateau of eastern Washington and Oregon, Ethiopia and other parts of Africa, the northwestern Deccan Plateau of India, and the Paraná uplands in southern Brazil. Valleys that cut into these lava uplands generally have unusually steep sides, because of the tendency for the lava sheets to develop either a vertical system of cracks or joints or a fluted structure of hexagonal columns. A most spectacular example of the latter is the Giant's Causeway (see Fig. 3.37) on the north coast of Ireland, where marine erosion has exposed and emphasized the columnar structure.

The highly fluid magmas in some places solidified in their fissures or between layers

FIG. 3.36 Lanai Island, Wahapuu, Hawaii, showing the long, gentle slopes of a typical Hawaiian shield volcano, deeply scored by ravines. [U. S. Air Force (MATS)]

of sedimentary rock below the surface, later to be exposed at the surface by erosion. Vertical or steeply tilted sheets of molten rock that intersect the surrounding rock are known as *dikes.* In areas of less resistant rocks, dikes at the surface may form unusual wall-like landforms. Where the magma penetrated between horizontal or gently sloping rock strata, the resultant sheets of magma are termed *sills.* Dikes and sills vary greatly in size, from an inch or so in thickness to over a hundred feet. The Palisades, along the Hudson River north from New York City, are an example of a sill. Small domelike masses of lava, intruded between sedimentary rock layers, are termed *laccoliths.*

Structural landforms

Several landforms, widely distributed over the earth, have characteristics that are determined mainly by the structure of underlying rocks and not particularly by the type of erosional or depositional processes operating on them.

FIG. 3.37 The Giant's Causeway, County Antrim, northern Ireland. This is a famous tourist attraction. The red and yellow hexagonal and pentagonal stone columns result from contraction following cooling of a basaltic lava sheet [Bord Failte Eireann, Dublin]

3.21 CUESTAS. Durable rock strata underlain by weaker rock layers in many areas of gently dipping sedimentary rocks result in cuestas, which are asymmetrical ridges having a steep slope on one side and a gentle one on the other, with the latter generally conforming to the slope or dip of the underlying rock strata. In areas where the sedimentary rocks are in broad, shallow, structural basins or in large arches or domes, the cuesta escarpments resulting from erosion are aligned into large arcs, the cliffs facing the center of domes, or away from the center of basins or troughs (see Fig. 3.39). In North

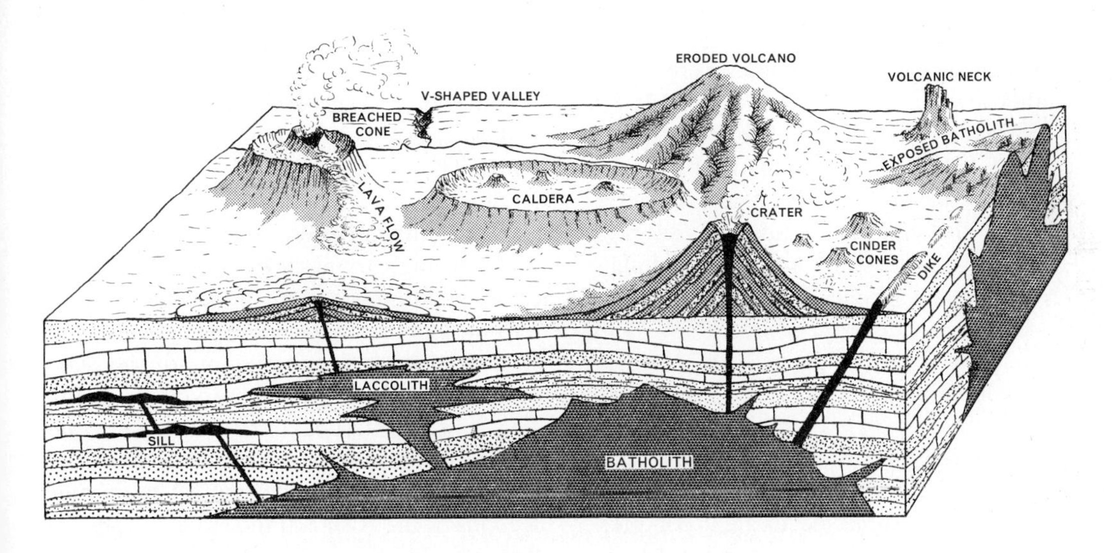

FIG. 3.38 Landforms associated with vulcanism.

America, the cuesta of the Niagara limestone, a particularly massive rock stratum, can be traced as a low ridge from New York State northward across Ontario into Northern Michigan, thence southward through Wisconsin, recurving to the northwest into Minnesota. Another large limestone cuesta forms the steep, curved northeastern edge of the Appalachians in New York State, overlooking the Mohawk Valley. Cuesta escarpments are major landforms in the Colorado Plateau region, the Paris Basin of France, and in many parts of Africa. The famous chalk *Downs* of southern England (see Fig. 12.13) are low cuestas.

In the Paris Basin, the encircling cuesta ridges facing the east and northeast formed the major defensive lines of the Allies protecting Paris during World War I. In World War II, however, they were relatively incon-

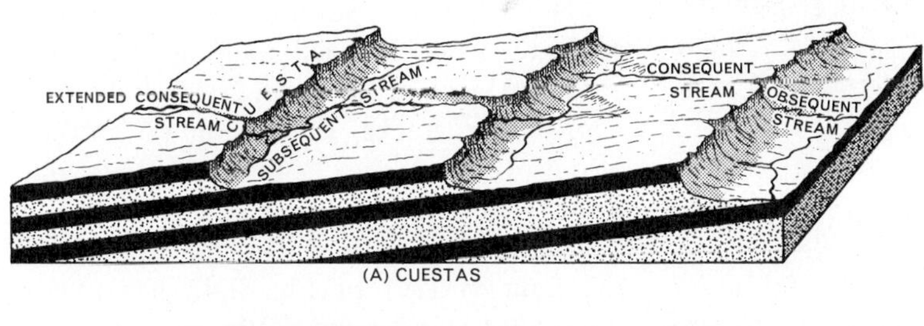

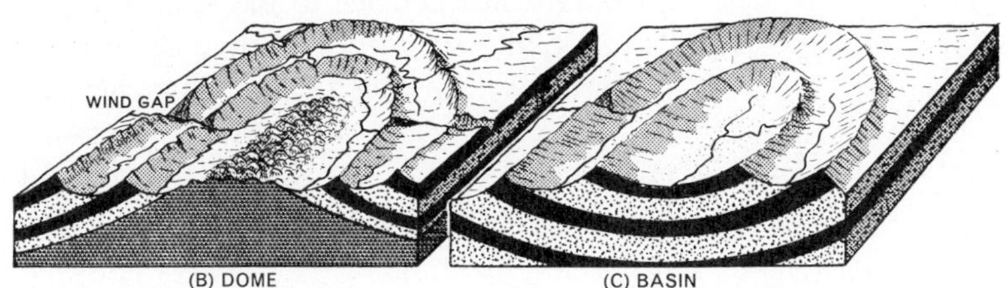

FIG. 3.39 Cuestas, domes, structural basins, and associated landforms. [(B) After Lobeck; (C) after Finch et al.]

sequential, as the decisive battles were fought in other areas. The Atlantic–Gulf of Mexico coastal plain of the United States contains a series of low cuestas that mark the eroded edges of somewhat more resistant sedimentary beds that dip gently seaward (see Fig. 3.40). Most of the strata in this coastal plain are composed of unconsolidated material, and the cuesta ridges are easily eroded. Only fragments of them rise 50 to 100 feet above the adjoining plains.

3.22 LANDFORMS RESULTING FROM ROCK FOLDING (see Fig. 3.41).

When rocks are subjected to great compressional stresses, they may respond either by buckling into folds or by rupturing. The folding evolves over long periods of time, and upfolds (*anticlines*) and downfolds (*synclines*) rarely form prominent landforms by themselves, since erosion usually is active enough to keep pace with the buckling. The erosion of folded rocks, however, produces

FIG. 3.40 Landforms developed on the belted coastal plain of the southern United States.

distinctive landforms, related partly to the attitude, or arrangement, of the rock layers and partly to their varying degrees of durability. The parallel, narrow *ridge-and-valley* landform (see Sec. 4.12) is produced as a result of differential erosion on highly folded rocks having varying degrees of resistance to erosion. Although more noticeable in hilly terrain like the folded Appalachians, this structure also is found in some of the compressional folds of the great mountain chains. The long, continuous ridges of the Atlas Mountains in northern Africa, the Northern Rockies of Canada near Banff, Alberta, and sections of the Alps and the eastern Andes of Peru are examples. The long narrow ridges that result from the differential erosion of highly folded rocks are not always straight. If the longitudinal axes of the folds are not horizontal, the ridges often will develop a curved or zigzag pattern, similar in principle and appearance to the grain pattern in a board that has been sawed on the bias, or diagonally (see the left side of Fig. 3.41). In general, however, parallelism of surface features is characteristic of folded areas.

3.23 FAULTS AND ASSOCIATED LANDFORMS.

Several distinctive landforms are associated with *faulting*, or the slipping of blocks of the earth crust along great ruptures or cracks. Faults can be grouped into two broad classes—*normal faults* and *thrust faults*. In the former, the overhanging side of the fault, shown on the left side of the fault in (A) of Fig. 3.42 has moved downward in reference to the opposite side. Thrust faults are identified by a reverse relationship, one in which the overhanging side has moved upward with reference to the base side. Usually, but not always, normal faults angle much more steeply from the horizontal than do thrust faults. Normal

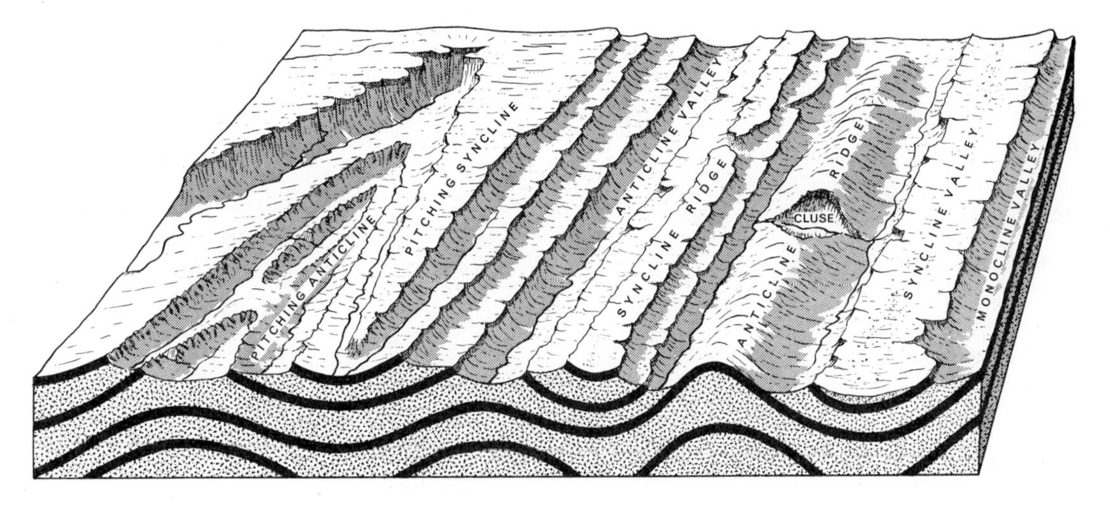

FIG. 3.41 Landforms associated with rock folding. The dark layers represent durable rocks.

faults are caused primarily by tensional stresses, whereas thrust faults result from compressional stresses.

Where rapid and relatively recent faulting has produced a great amount of vertical displacement, the new formation may be a *fault line escarpment,* or an abrupt slope or cliff. Usually, the most prominent fault escarpments have formed along normal faults rather than thrust faults. They often follow broad regional arching and later foundering of the flanks of the resultant arch. A succession of such tensional faults may result in a series of tilted *block mountains,* or large down-dropped troughs or basins termed *rift valleys* or *grabens* (see Fig. 3.43). Some of the great fault basins in the world, however, may possibly have resulted from compressional rather than tensional stresses; the depressed central block of the graben may have been pushed downward, and erosion may have prevented the development of an overhang along the sides.

Many of the great escarpments of the world have resulted from faulting and have formed some of our most effective obstacles

FIG. 3.42 Normal and thrust faults.

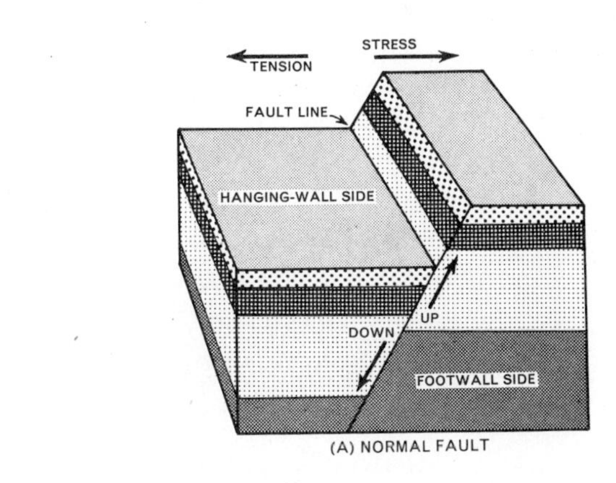

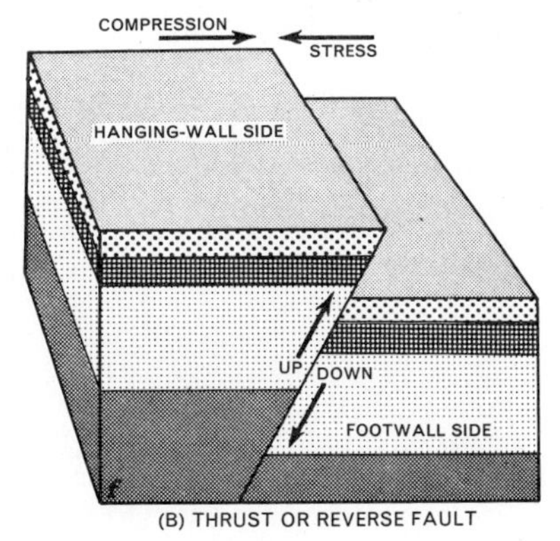

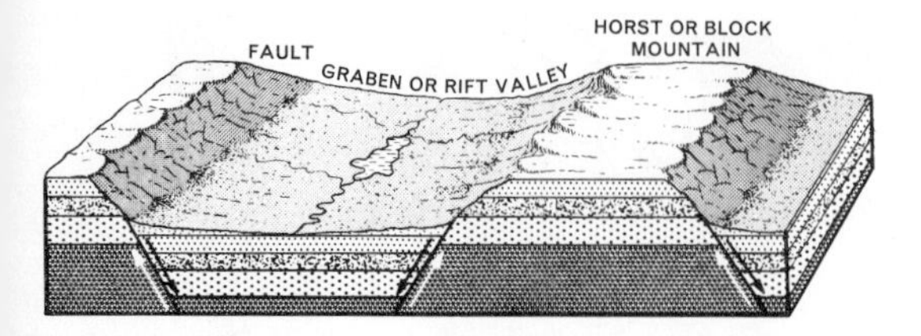

FIG. 3.43 Landforms associated with normal faulting. [After Finch et al.]

to travel. In the United States, excellent examples are the steep eastern wall of the Sierra Nevada, the abrupt western edge of the Colorado Plateau, the western border of the Wasatch Mountains near Salt Lake City, and the eastern face of the Northern Rocky Mountains in Glacier National Park. A long, continuous fault escarpment, termed the Bal-

FIG. 3.44 A thrust fault. The fault may be seen as an almost horizontal line across the photo. Above the fault, the sedimentary beds have moved from right to left and have been folded as a result of frictional drag along the fault. [U.S. Geological Survey; M. R. Mudge]

cones Escarpment, forms an abrupt rise, 1,000 to 2,000 feet high, facing the coastal plain in southwestern Texas. Similar escarpments are found along the flanks of mountain ranges in many other parts of the world. Geologists distinguish between *fault line escarpments,* whose steep slopes are the direct result of crustal movements, and *fault line scarps,* whose abrupt slopes result from differential erosion in rocks of unequal durability on opposite sides of the fault.

Block mountains are exemplified by the short but steep-sided ranges of the Basin Range region of the southwestern United States and northern Mexico. This region comprises about a tenth of the area of the United States. The Blue Mountains of eastern Australia and many of the ranges in Iran and Afghanistan are other examples.

The outstanding example of grabens is the series of great depressions, bounded by high fault escarpments, that extends from the Baka'a Valley east of the Lebanon Mountains, on the north, to Lake Nyasa in East Africa, on the south. The Red Sea basin and the Jordan Valley comprise part of this series, and a succession of grabens with walls several thousand feet high cross the highlands of Ethiopia, Kenya, Uganda, and Tanganyika. Lakes Albert, Rudolf, Tanganyika, and Nyasa occupy parts of these fault trenches. Other examples of grabens include the middle Rhine Valley, between the Vosges Mountains on the west and the Schwarzwald (Black Forest) on the east, and the upper Vardar Valley in Yugoslavia.

Earthquakes are caused by the sudden displacement of rocks along faults. The stresses that cause faulting are gradual and cumulative, and the sudden displacement is only a temporary relief from these stresses. For this reason, active faults are likely to have recurrent displacements with accompanying earthquakes. Individual displacements along a single fault may produce only light tremors, barely detectable on seismographs, whereas others result in violent, destructive shocks. Active faults are dangerous areas for settlement, unless buildings are constructed especially to avoid earthquake damage. Such damage is likely to be greatest in areas overlying unconsolidated material, such as recent stream deposits or coastal sediments.

Perspective

Landforms and geologic processes intermingle in complex patterns throughout the world. Regardless of where one stands and looks out over a section of the land surface, different landforms can be perceived. In some areas the destructional processes of erosion and weathering dominate in shaping the prominent features of the land surface. In others, material is being transported, dropped, or reworked to produce other distinctive landscape patterns. Climatic conditions sometimes play a leading role in determining the features of the landscape. Rock composition and crustal movements are dominant in other areas. Landforms cannot be thought of as exclusively the result of any one environmental factor, and, as we have seen, time changes all. To a suburban dweller along the southwestern shore of Lake Michigan near Evanston, Illinois, shore-line erosion has an immediate, urgent meaning, as storm waves may easily slice into the soft, glacial tills of his back yard. For a resident of the hard-rock coast of Maine, however, erosion has no personal significance; though impressive to contemplate, it is irrelevant to his welfare.

To make some sense and meaning out of the infinite variety of surface characteristics over the earth, we must be flexible in our scale and time perspective. The important thing is to know in general the kinds of features that may be expected in broad areas of the world, the meaning of these features as expressed in terms of relevant cultural frames of reference, and the processes that are shaping these landforms today, in order somehow to predict what will become of them on a useful, relevant time scale. More than anything else, however, it is hoped that this brief excursion into the variety of landforms present on the earth will instill into the reader a curiosity regarding the physical landscape, a habit of observing the world around him, and a desire to penetrate more deeply into the realm of geology. These are prerequisites to understanding the physical world of man.

4

The major lineaments of the earth surface

We have completed a brief review of the landforms that may be observed in landscapes throughout the world. We now shift our perspective and examine the major surface irregularities of the earth as a whole. The first surface features to be distinguished by an observer approaching the earth from outer space would be the outlines of the continents and ocean basins and the snow and ice of the two polar regions. The great mountain cordilleras would appear somewhat later, especially noticeable just after sunrise or before sunset, when objects cast their longest shadows. Hilly areas, finely etched in light and shadow, would appear next, contrasting with the smooth-textured plains of the world. Color would be there too, including the blue oceans, the light greens of the tropical forests, and the dark splotches marking the major areas of coniferous forest. Since this chapter is concerned with surface irregularities, the primary features considered are the continents, ocean basins, mountains, hills, and plains—all of them on a global scale.

As we shall see later, the arrangement of the major lineaments of the earth is not haphazard. There is a design—a pattern that, though neither exhibiting perfect geometric symmetry nor lacking inconsistencies, is still sufficiently clear to be perceived and to stimulate earth scientists to seek logical, consistent explanations. We shall not be concerned here with explanations, however, enticing though they may be. The story is far from complete, and many loose ends remain to be gathered. The interested student may seek his own explanations by consulting the sources given in the suggested reading list at the back of the book or by enrolling in structural and historical geology courses. The task here is the largely descriptive one of generalizing the subtle patterns that appear behind the apparent jumble of surface features on the earth surface.

Continents and ocean basins

The arrangement of continents and ocean basins reveals a number of characteristic features which may be summarized as follows:

1. Antipodal position. The land masses, with few exceptions, are antipodal (directly

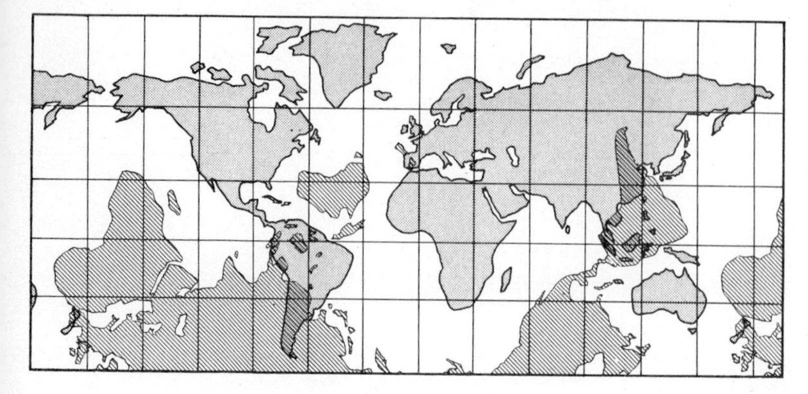

FIG. 4.1 Antipodal arrangement of continents and ocean basins. Note that with few exceptions, continental blocks are faced by ocean basins at opposite points on the globe. Antarctica and its antipode, the Arctic Ocean, cannot be shown on this projection.

opposite on the globe) to ocean areas (see Fig. 4.1).

2. Contrasting size and relationship to sea level. Oceans and water areas occupy almost 70 per cent of the total surface of the globe. Not only are the ocean basins more extensive than the continents, but their average depth below sea level (approximately 12,000 feet) is much greater than the average elevation of the continents above sea level (about 3,000 feet).

3. Tapering of continents. The continental masses, with the exception of Antarctica and Australia, tend to broaden toward the north and taper toward the south. For this reason there is considerably more land in the northern hemisphere than in the southern hemisphere. Also, many more peninsulas extend southward from the continents than in any other direction. Such peninsulas are especially noticeable on the southern sides of North America and Eurasia.

4. Continental "fit." The major outlines of the continents appear to fit together like pieces of a jigsaw puzzle.

5. Continental trend lines. There is an unusually high predominance of continental and oceanic structural lines that are aligned in a northeast-southwest or northwest-southeast direction. This is illustrated in the trend lines or continental coast lines and in the major mountain cordilleras (see Fig. 4.2). The trend of deep trenches or ridges within the ocean basins shows similar alignments. A minor set of trend lines is aligned north-south and east-west.

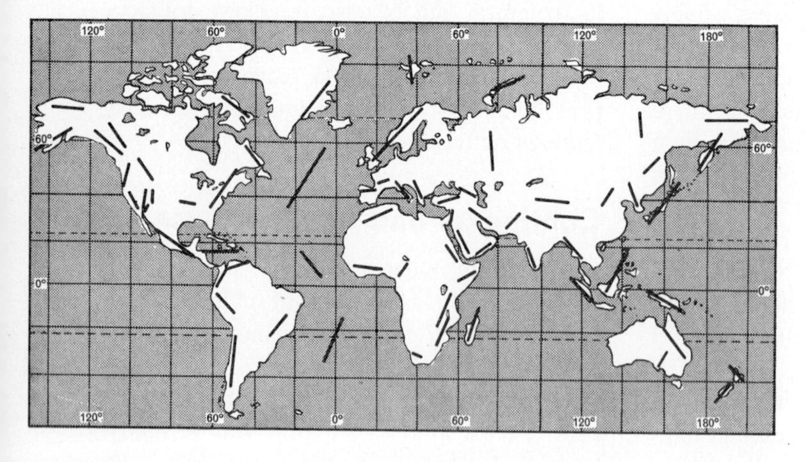

FIG. 4.2 Arrangement of major global structural lines.

6. Exchange of land and sea areas in geologic time. Geologic evidence indicates that shallow seas have invaded the interior of continents several times in the last few hundred million years, but there is no good evidence that the ocean basins were ever continental areas.

It is interesting to note here that Mars and the moon, the only two heavenly bodies whose solid surfaces are visible to us, do not appear to have major upland blocks or depressions comparable to our continents and ocean basins.

The continents and ocean basins are among the oldest and most permanent features of the earth surface. Although recurrently wrinkled, warped, and altered in many ways by geologic processes, these major surface lineaments have remained in essentially the same places throughout period after period of crustal unrest, representing hundreds of millions of years.

The rise and fall of portions of the earth continents appear stupendous to mankind, but in relation to the size of the earth, these recurrent "breathings" are tiny movements indeed. The difference in elevation between the summit of Mount Everest, the highest peak in the world, and the bottom of the deepest gash in the ocean floor, found off the Mariana Islands, is approximately 13 miles. If the world were reduced to the size of a baseball, the proportional representation for such an irregularity would be so small that it would be difficult to feel with one's fingers. The Himalayas would be only about $\frac{1}{500}$ of an inch high, and the Marianas Trench in the Pacific would be only a tiny scratch $\frac{1}{400}$ of a inch deep. Relatively, the earth is nearly as smooth as a billiard ball.

The arrangement of ocean basins and continental masses is a primary fact of global geography, and this arrangement exerts its influence on the distribution of all other geographic patterns, from climate to political power relationships. The mystery of its development is not entirely clear, for the evidence is not yet complete. No one can foresee what new facts will be discovered concerning the processes of earth formation and transformation as new tools and observational techniques are developed.

Mountains

What is a mountain? There is no universally accepted definition, except for the general acknowledgment that the term implies a prominent relief feature. The word *prominent,* however, is a relative descriptive term. No one would deny that the Himalayas, the Alps, and the Rockies are mountains. The difficulty arises in determining the point at which hills become mountains. Since our task is to delimit the mountain areas of the world, some arbitrary limit must be used. The definition selected is that *mountainous areas are those having a local relief greater than 2,000 feet and having narrow summits.* Local relief, as used here, signifies the difference in elevation between the summits of the peaks or ridges and the bottoms of the included or adjacent valleys and basins. The figure 2,000 feet has no special significance, except that this difference in elevation is usually sufficient to produce a distinct vertical zonation of vegetation.

In comparison with the size of the earth, the great mountain ranges of the world are but diminutive wrinkles on the surface, but they exert a major influence on global climatic patterns and on the distribution of life forms on earth, including man.

4.1 THE GLOBAL PATTERN OF MOUNTAINS. The distribution of mountain areas, like the arrangement of conti-

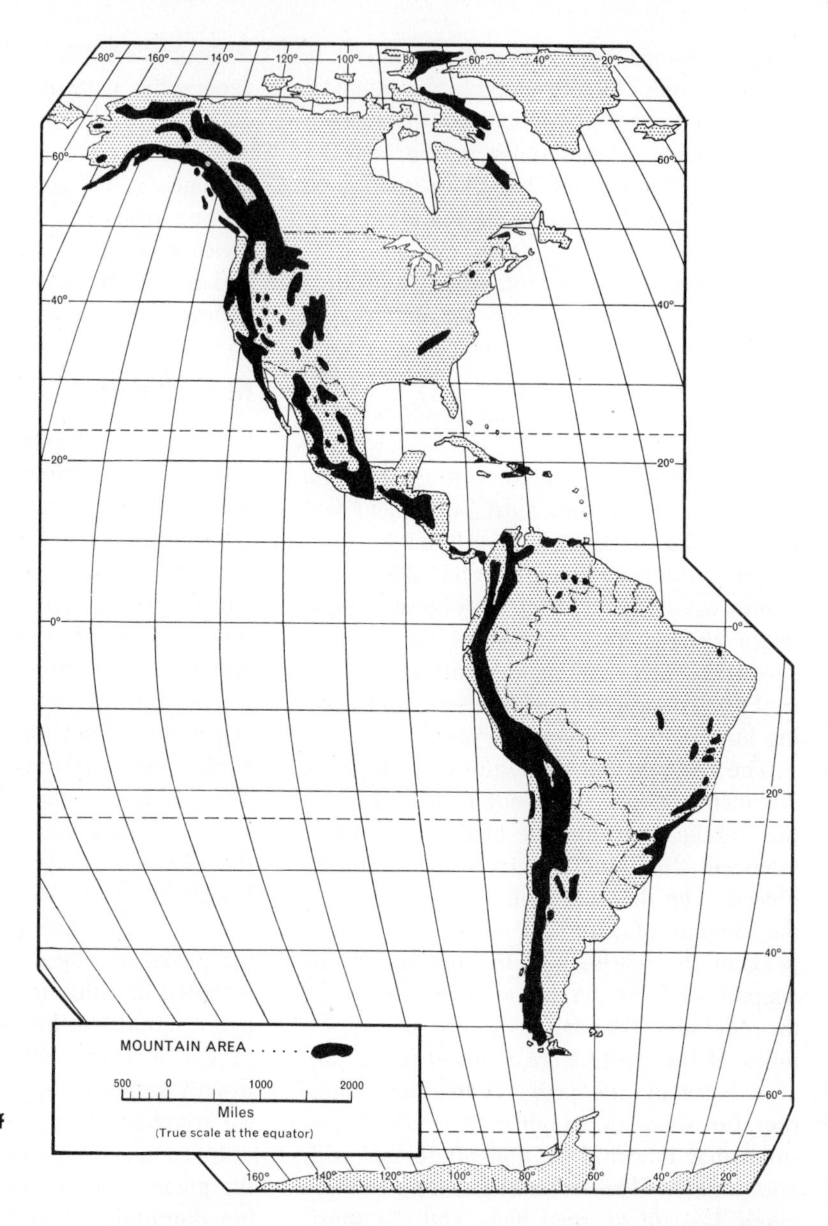

FIG. 4.3 World map of mountain areas.

nents and ocean basins, is remarkably consistent. The gross features of the global distribution of mountains may be summarized as follows:

1. A belt of high mountains surrounds the Pacific Ocean. Among the included ranges are the Alaskan Range, the Canadian Coastal Mountains, the Cascades, Sierra Nevada, the Sierra Madre Occidental of Mexico, the Andes, the New Zealand Alps, and the many ranges of Indonesia, the Philippines, Formosa, Japan, and Kamchatka.

2. A transverse belt of mountains crosses the southern portion of the great Eurasian

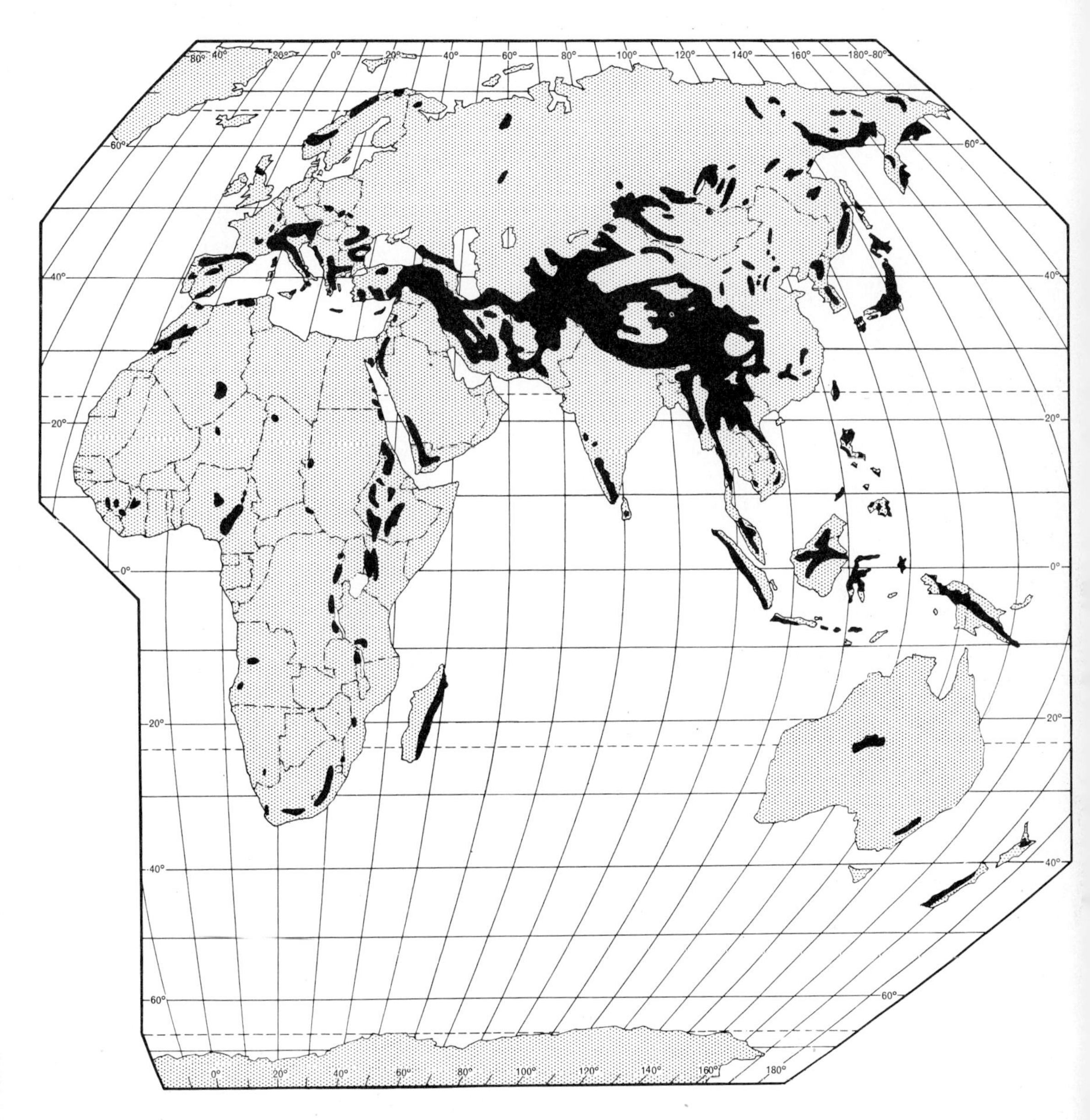

continent north of the three major peninsulas of Iberia (Spain and Portugal), Arabia, and India. Although the general trend roughly is west-east in this transverse belt, few of the included ranges have this direction. Most of them trend roughly toward the east-southeast or the east-northeast. This general belt of cordilleras includes the Pyrenees, the Alps, the Balkan Mountains, the Pontus and Taurus Ranges of Turkey, the Elburz, Hindu Kush, and the Himalayas. Several ranges that are offset from this belt may also be considered part of it. These include the Atlas Mountains of North Africa,

FIG. 4.4 Mount Assiniboine, in the Canadian Rocky Mountains near Banff. The jagged crest lines produced by glacial erosion are typical of high mountains throughout the world. Note the horizontal rock strata indicating that this area once was in a sedimentary basin. [Royal Canadian Air Force]

the Carpathians, the Caucasus, and the huge ranges radiating from the Pamir Knot, that high mountain complex, known as the "roof of the world," which is located in the area where India, Pakistan, Tibet, Afghanistan, and the Soviet Union approach one another.

3. The eroded "stumps" or roots of old mountain ranges can be found in many places bordering the Atlantic and Indian Oceans and the Arctic Sea. Some of them still are high enough and rugged enough to be mountains, such as the Great Smokies–Blue Ridge Mountains and the White Mountains of the eastern United States, the mountains of northeastern Labrador and eastern Baffin Island, parts of the Grampian Mountains of Scotland, the eastern edge of the Brazilian upland, and central Madagascar. High and rugged ranges bordering Greenland and Norway form a rim along the northern part of the North Atlantic basin.

4. High, rugged mountain ranges are now, and generally have been (at least for the last third of earth history), unusual in the interior of continents. Exceptions include the mountains of east-central Eurasia, the Urals, and the Rocky Mountains of Canada and the United States. The latter, however, have sometimes been considered as the eastern margin of a wide section of the circum-Pacific zone of crustal instability.

5. Most mountain cordilleras are arranged in great arcs or festoons. These are particularly well exemplified by the mountain arcs along the western side of the Pacific Ocean. Volcanoes often are found near the intersections of these mountain arcs.

6. Diverging segments of the great global cordilleras usually enclose high plains. Examples include Tibet, Iran, Bolivia, central Mexico, eastern Washington and Oregon, and central British Columbia.

7. The greatest incidence of volcanic activity and earthquakes occurs in the same general areas as the high, rugged mountains of the world (see Fig. 4.5).

8. Geologic evidence of compressional stresses is found in most of the great mountain areas of the world. Strong local differences in the earth gravitational pull also are found in these areas.

No simple hypothesis yet presented explains satisfactorily all the details in the global distribution of mountains. Much of the evidence, however, indicates that the processes responsible for the present distribution of mountains are in some way related to the structure of continents and ocean basins.

Most of the margins of continents and ocean basins are areas of crustal instability that have been unstable for a long period in earth history. Other continental borders are now relatively stable, such as the eastern side of North America, but have been unstable relatively recently in geologic time. Crustal instability is indicated in many ways, including the following:

1. Earthquakes, which are caused by the rupturing of rocks that have reached the breaking point under a gradual accumulation of stresses

2. Volcanic activity, or the appearance of molten rock at the earth surface, having worked its way upward along lines of weakness in the earth crust

3. Rock folds, the anticlines, synclines, domes, and basins that are the visible results of rock bending or buckling under compressional stresses for long periods of time

4. Faults, the rupture lines along which the crustal rocks have slipped in relieving compressional or tensional stresses

5. Mountains and geosynclines, which are the end results of strong uplift and subsidence, respectively

6. Strong variations in the earth gravitational pull within short distances, which indicate sharp contrasts in rock densities and local shifts of rock material within the earth crust

7. Pronounced local variations in the outflow of internal residual earth heat, which constitute evidence of shifts in rock material deep within the earth

All these features are encountered within the mountainous regions of the earth. Figure 4.5 shows the distribution of earthquakes and recent volcanic activity. Note the close correspondence with the general pattern of

FIG. 4.5 World distribution of volcanoes and earthquakes. [After Brockhaus]

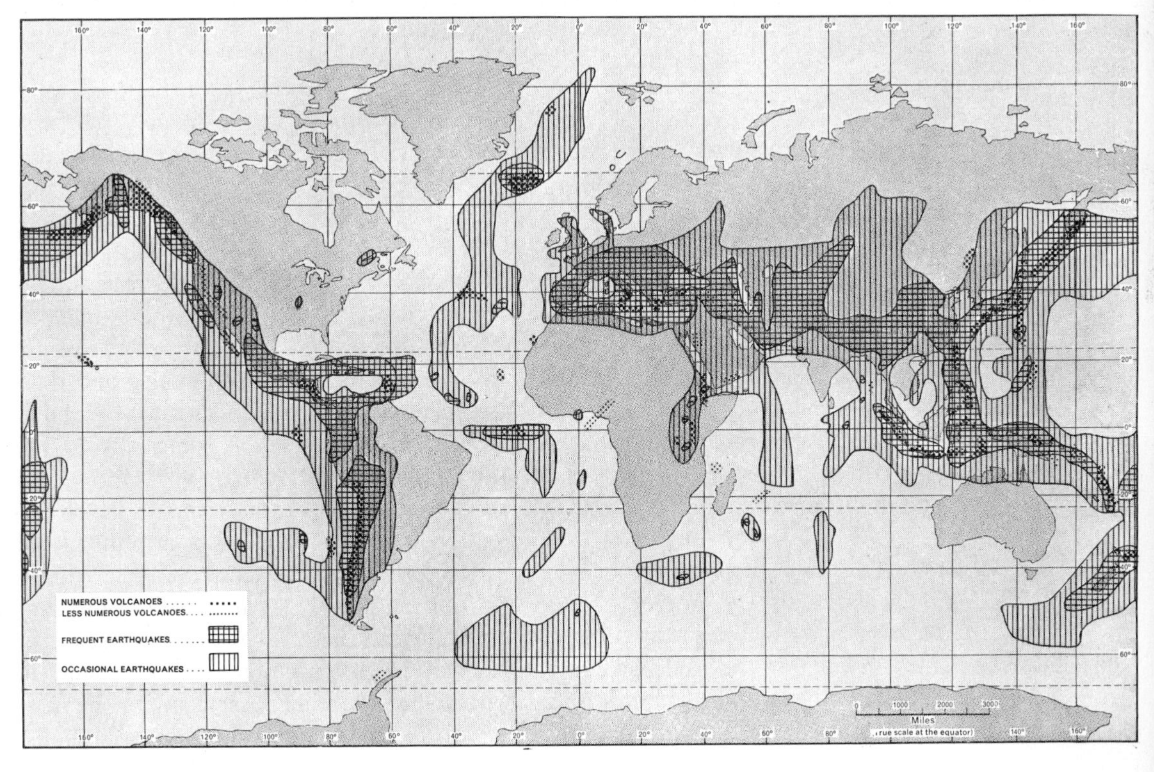

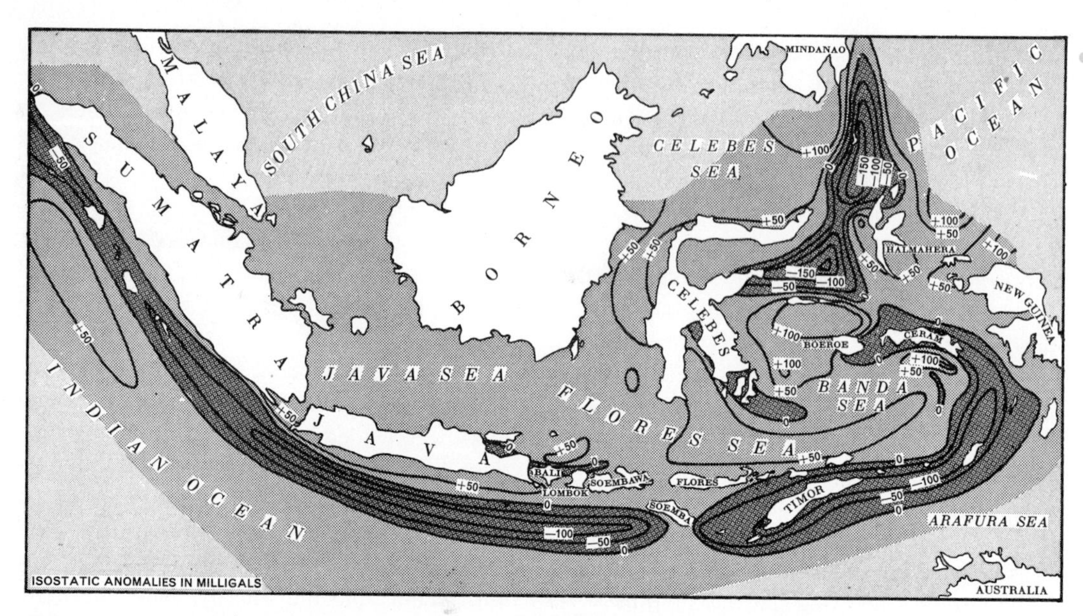

FIG. 4.6 Gravimetric anomalies in southeast Asia and Indonesia. A gravimetric anomaly is a local gravity pull that is greater or less than average for the earth. Note the sudden change from positive to negative anomalies on opposite sides of the Indonesian archipelago, indicative of a sharp change in rock density. Positive anomalies indicate dense, heavy rock near the surface. [After Umbgrove]

mountains (Fig. 4.3). The distribution of gravimetric anomalies (abnormal gravity measurements) for southeast Asia and Indonesia is shown in Fig. 4.6. The sudden changes from strongly positive to strongly negative readings are typical of those found in the vicinity of many continental margins and mountain belts. Pronounced local differences in the gravitational force of the earth generally are indicative of great stresses within the outer portion of the earth interior. Most mountain areas show evidence of having undergone strong compressional stresses, and folds and faults are common.

Although individual mountain ranges do not persist for long in geologic time, being beveled relatively rapidly by erosive processes, the unstable parts of the earth surface have remained in roughly the same general areas. Figure 4.7 shows the location of major crustal disturbances during each of the last three great eras of geologic time, covering a total of approximately 600 million years. Insufficient evidence is available for plotting the location of such disturbances on a global scale for earlier eras. Note again, in comparing Fig. 4.7 with the world map of mountains (Fig. 4.3), that the present areas of instability had their counterparts millions of years ago.

The development of mountains and their accompanying zones of crustal instability appears to be related in some way to the global pattern of continents and ocean basins. Africa, however, seems to be an exceptional continent with respect to the global pattern of mountains. Only the Atlas Mountains of the northwestern margin of the continent fit into the great mountain systems of the world. Other mountains are found in Africa, but they are discontinuous, consisting mostly of isolated volcanic peaks or dissected volcanic uplands. A long row of huge rift valleys or grabens roughly parallels the eastern margin of the continent. These crustal breaks indicate lines of instability on a continental scale, but the great compressional mountain arcs of other continental margins are absent. Nearly all of Africa appears to be a vast block of continental rocks (see Sec. 5.15), which were uplifted relatively recently in geologic time to a fairly uniform elevation of 2,000 to 3,000 feet above sea level. The depressions in the interior, such as the Congo Basin and the rift valleys of eastern Africa, appear to be sections that foundered or sagged downward during or following the continental uplift. The existence of this exceptional continent indicates that the evolution of the present global pattern of mountains cannot be explained solely in terms of consistent continental positions.

4.2 THE HUMAN SIGNIFICANCES OF MOUNTAINS. The human significances of mountains, like the meaning of all the other elements in the physical environment of man, cannot be treated apart from the stage of local cultural or technological development. We usually consider mountains as obstacles to human aspirations; yet for

FIG. 4.7 World map of crustal folding and mountain building during the last three major eras of geologic time. These three eras cover approximately the last 600 million years of earth history. Note that with few exceptions, these zones of crustal instability were located around the borders of the major continental blocks. The present high mountain chains were formed during the Cenozoic folding. [After Umbgrove]

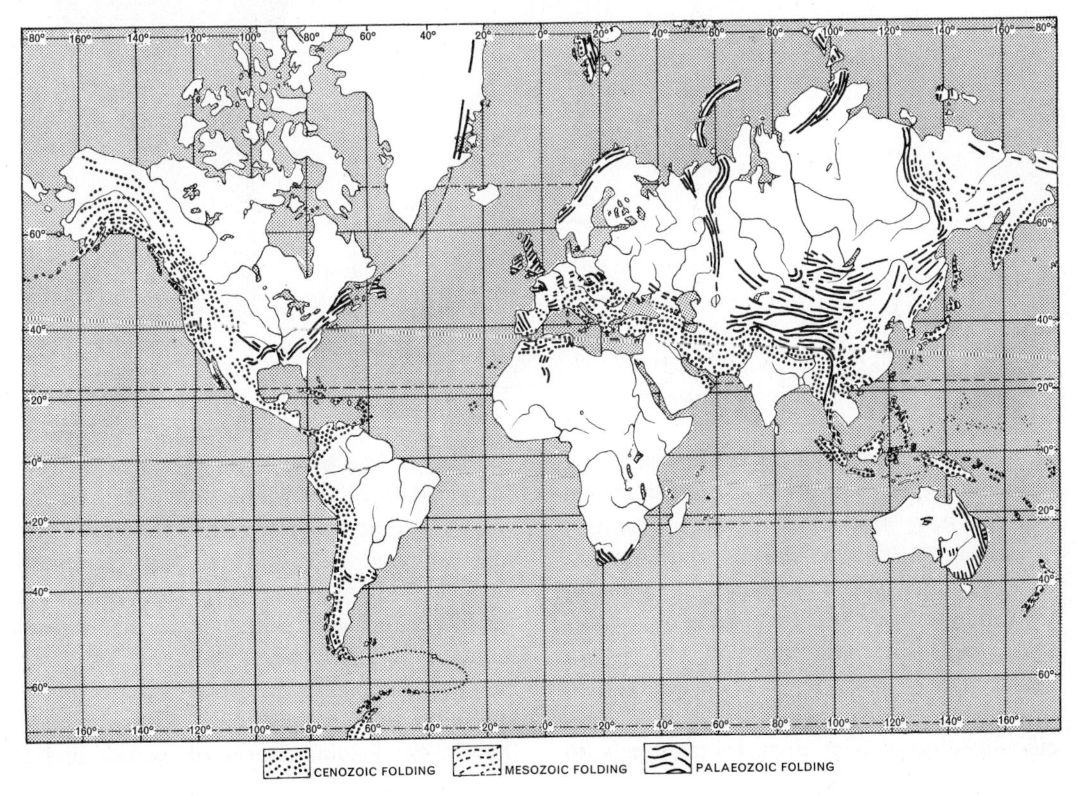

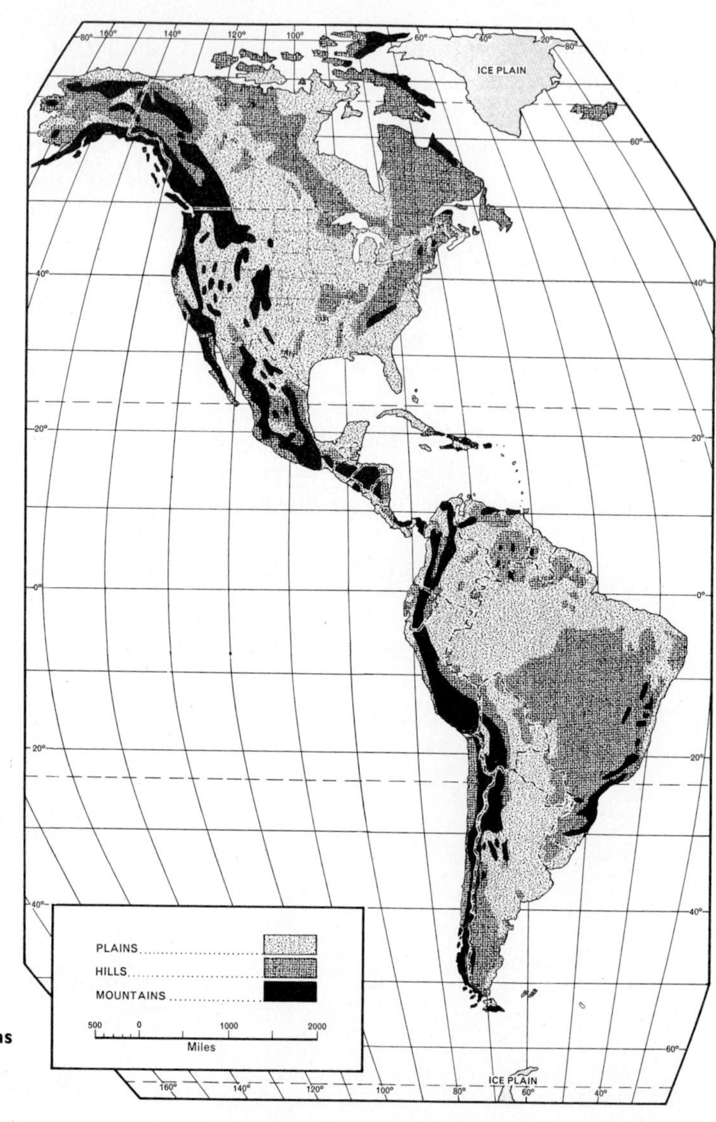

FIG. 4.8 Map of global landforms (mountains, hills, and plains)

some people, mountain lands have provided welcome havens against war-minded neighbors or have furnished valuable resources of minerals, lumber, water, and scenery. Some volcanic mountain slopes, like those of Guatemala, Sicily, or Java, have unusually fertile soils for agriculture. Mountains, of course, can be obstacles, even in the modern world of advanced technology, but the specific meaning of such obstacles changes with the times. The band of hardy pioneers that struggled through Donner Pass high in the Sierra Nevada on their way to the west coast of the United States certainly did not regard these mountains in the same light as does a passenger on a Union Pacific streamliner riding smoothly through the same pass; yet the cost of making the long climb to the summit still must be paid in some way. Today, the leading source of income in the

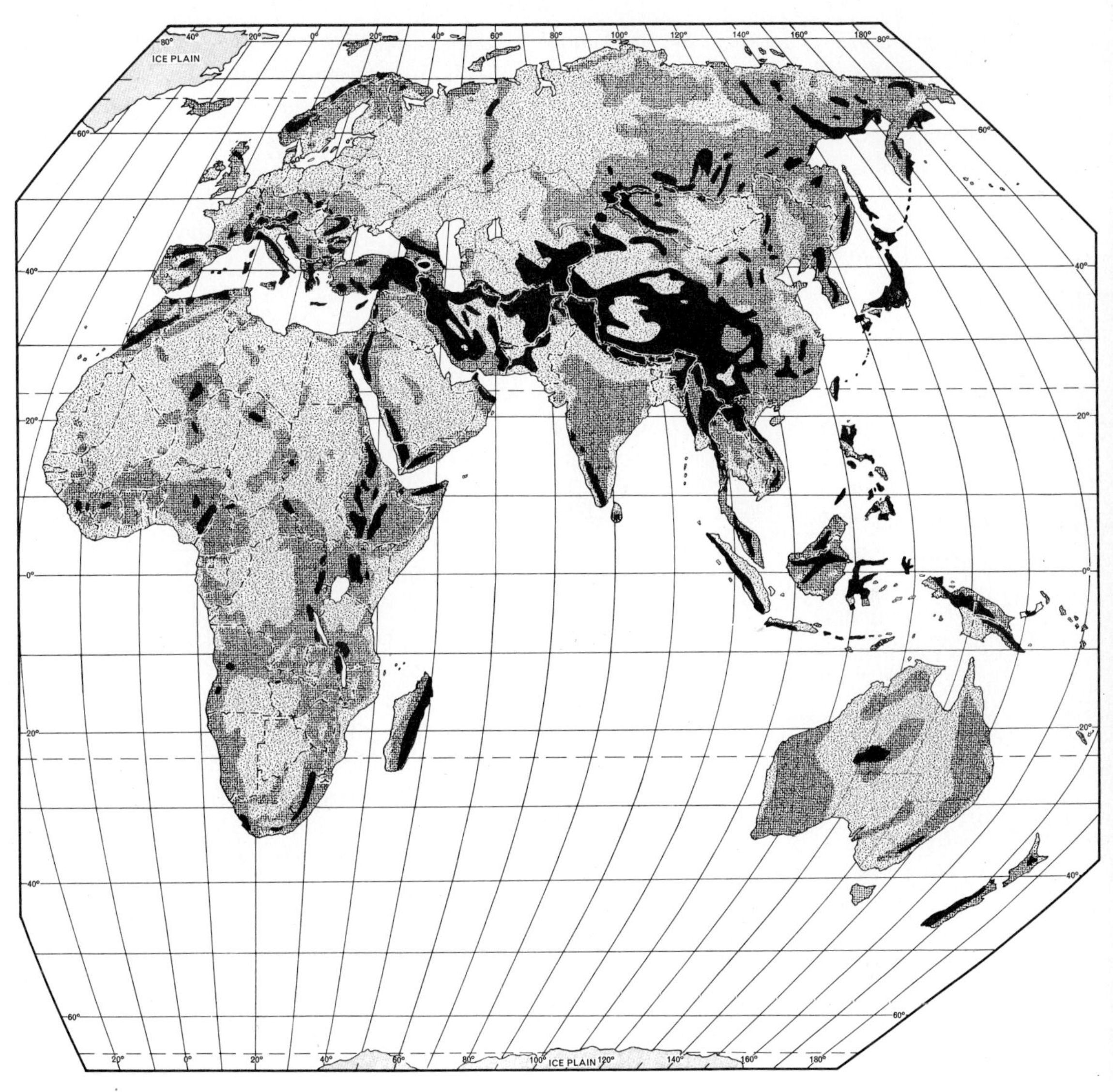

state of Colorado is recreation, which would have been negligible had it not been for the Rocky Mountains, increased leisure time, improved transportation facilities, and the surplus wealth created by modern technologies. Mountainous terrain usually is simultaneously an asset and a hindrance. The Swiss people long have cherished their mountain environment, partly because it has given them a degree of political independence that is unusual in that part of the world, and yet the Swiss have been able to develop a high standard of living only with prodigious effort and ingenuity.

An elaboration of the meaning of mountains on a global scale would be both misleading and unfruitful. The geographer should perform this task on the local topographic level, and probably it would be more appropriate in the systematic fields of economic or cultural geography. We may, however, list some of the more important resource significances and the obstacles that mountain lands have presented to human beings at different times and at different places:

Resource significances of mountain lands

1. Protection
2. Isolation
3. Minerals
4. Timber
5. Water power
   a. regulation
   b. storage
6. Recreational attractions
   a. scenery
   b. camping, fishing, etc.
   c. winter sports
7. Agricultural attractions
   a. volcanic soils
   b. crop variety owing to vertical climatic zones
   c. irrigation

Obstacles of mountain lands

1. Long, steep slopes
2. Avalanches
3. High cost of maintaining transportation lines
   a. landslides
   b. washouts
   c. deep snow
4. Earthquakes and volcanoes
5. Forest fires
6. Erodable, thin, rocky soils
7. Rarefied air at high elevations
8. Wind damage
9. High rainfall
10. High incidence of lightning

Plains

Plains are areas of low local relief. In mapping the distribution of plains in the world, however, a more specific definition than this is needed. As here considered, plains include *areas where the common local relief is less than 200 feet and where slopes of less than 5 per cent predominate.* Isolated hills or even mountains may rise more than 200 feet above the surrounding plain without affecting the estimate of common local relief. Moreover, plains are not restricted necessarily to low elevations; in Bolivia and Tibet, for example, they may occur at elevations well over 12,000 feet.

4.3 THE GLOBAL PATTERN OF PLAINS. The world map of plains (Fig. 4.12) indicates that a much larger percentage of the earth surface is in plains than in mountains. Compared with the distribution of mountains, however, the plains do not have as consistent a pattern of arrangement. There are greater differences in both size and shape, and plains are found in nearly all parts of the world. For our purposes, the global plains may be classified into four main groups as follows:

1. The interior plains
2. The alluvial trough and delta plains
3. The high plains
4. The coastal plains

Each of these major types of plains is discussed in subsequent sections.

4.4 INTERIOR PLAINS. Broad plains extend throughout the interior of the continents, mostly at elevations of less than 600 feet. In North America, the interior plains include nearly all of the Mississippi drainage basin, extending northward into Canada, where they broaden at first, then narrow toward the Arctic Sea. In South America, the interior plains comprise all but the westernmost part of the Amazon Basin and extend southward through the Chaco toward the Argentine *pampas.* As in North America, there is a gradual transition between the interior plains and the depositional trough plains that border the mountains. The interior plains of Eurasia begin in France and southern England, extend eastward across northern Germany and southern Sweden, then broaden into the wide, undulating plains of the Soviet Union. Africa has extensive plains in its interior, but because of their elevation, mostly over 2,000 feet, they are classified as high plains. Australia further illustrates the common tendency of continents to have broad plains in the interior.

With but few local exceptions, the great continental interior plains have been without appreciable relief since early in Paleozoic times (the last 600 million years or so of earth history). Since this time they often have been invaded by shallow seas, as their comparatively thin coverings of sedimentary rock of marine origin testify. The existence of persistent shallow basins, troughs, arches, and domes in the rock structure of the interior plains indicates local areas of uplift or depression. Such movements, however, have been gentle and exceedingly slow, and since deposition and erosion have been able to compensate for them, a subdued relief has been maintained.

The interior plains of the world differ widely in detail of form, depending on the processes that have shaped their low relief. Some of them have resulted from erosion by various processes. Plains resulting from erosion by running water are likely to have an undulating-to-rolling land surface, with occasional local areas of steep slopes. Much of the central Mississippi River drainage basin south of the glaciated area is such an erosion plain, and much of the broad expanse of the central plains of the Soviet Union affords another example. Preferred areas for human settlement include the strips of alluvium that follow the drainage ways through these regions.

Deposition has leveled the surfaces of other sections of the interior plains. The

FIG. 4.9 A cultivated mountain slope in Colombia. Erosion on long cultivated slopes such as these is the scourge of the Andes. [Standard Oil Company (N.J.)]

depositional processes of continental glaciation smoothed the old erosional surfaces of much of the American Middle West, parts of the Great Lakes region of southern Canada, and part of the North European plain. Deposition of alluvium in great shallow basins produced other sections of the interior plains. Parts of the Amazon Basin, the Congo Basin, the Ob River basin just east of the Urals in the Soviet Union, and the Chaco area of Paraguay are examples. Lake plains, ergs, and loessal plains comprise other types of landforms associated with the interior plains formed by deposition.

Regardless of the individual process of gradation or degradation, the interior plains

FIG. 4.10 Pre-Inca agricultural terraces near Machu Picchu, Peru. Laborious work was needed to maintain an agricultural settlement for a long period on these steep slopes. Contrast this with the less enlightened practices shown in Fig. 4.9. [Grace Line]

have a basically low relief because they have been relatively stable portions of the continental masses for long periods of geologic time; their elevation has merely fluctuated occasionally between slightly below sea level and slightly above sea level.

4.5 ALLUVIAL TROUGH AND DELTA PLAINS. The alluvial trough and delta plains are underlain by thick beds of sediments whose deposition has continued for long periods of time. Most of these plains are in geosynclines, or troughs, that are subsiding slowly into the crust of the earth under the weight of accumulated sediments (see Fig. 4.4). Some of them are delta plains which may or may not be located on active geosynclines. The general location of these plains is within the unstable portions of the earth, principally around the continental margins and adjacent to high mountain ranges. Examples are numerous. Within the United States, they include the general area around the delta of the Mississippi, the Imperial Valley at the mouth of the Colorado River, and the Central Valley of California. Examples abroad include the flat sedimentary plains immediately east of the Andes Mountains, from Venezuela to northern Argentina; the Po Valley, the Rhine delta, and the Hungarian and Romanian plains; the Tigris-Euphrates plain of Iraq; the Indus-Ganges plain of northern India; and the east Asiatic delta plains at the mouths of the Irrawaddy, Mekong, Menam, Yangtze, and Hwang Ho (Yellow) Rivers. Some of the present high plains of the world once were geosynclinal or depositional plains that later were elevated high above sea level. The plains immediately east of the Rocky Mountains are of this type.

One of the major features of these plains is their gentle gradients, which are virtually flat on the delta plains and gently sloping in many of the individual depositional basins, such as the Central Valley of California. Another feature is the unconsolidated sedimentary material that underlies the surface everywhere. In humid areas such plains are subject to flood hazards because of their gentle slopes.

4.6 HIGH PLAINS. High plains are those which lie at elevations over 2,000 feet.

FIG. 4.11 The Teton Range, Jackson Hole, Wyoming. The scenic grandeur of this range is a famous tourist attraction a short distance south of Yellowstone Park. Note the small glaciers and landforms associated with mountain glaciation. [U.S. Geological Survey]

Many of them have been called *plateaus,* but this term is avoided as much as possible in this text, mainly because it has been misused so frequently in the past. Presumably the term plateau signifies a fairly level tableland whose upland surface is higher than much of its surroundings. Most of the so-called plateaus of the world do not fit this definition; in fact, true plateaus are relatively rare. The best examples are the plains of interior Africa and the Colorado Plateau of the southwestern United States. For this reason, the term is used here only where it is part of a proper name—for example, the Appalachian Plateau, the Bolivian Plateau, and the Tibetan Plateau.

High plains differ from other plains principally in elevation. Although this feature does not influence the topographic definition of plains, it produces at least two characteristics that are common to most high plains. First, such plains are likely to be drier than other plains, mainly because moisture is removed from air masses as they ascend abruptly to elevations above 2,000 feet or as they pass over the much higher mountains that often adjoin high plains. Second, many (but not all) such plains have steep-sided, deeply entrenched river valleys, representing early stages in the processes of erosion by running water. These deep gorges greatly influence the factor of accessibility and constitute primary terrain obstacles to surface transportation routes. Gorges of more than a few hundred feet or so in depth and width are generally more difficult to cross than mountain ranges.

The general distribution of high plains in the world is principally within the zones of crustal instability. They usually are bordered by great mountain cordilleras. The highest and best-known high plains are located between bifurcating segments of the continental cordilleras, such as those in Tibet, Bolivia, Mexico, Turkey, Iran, Spain, the western United States, and western Canada.

Although the continent of Africa is not located within the major global areas of

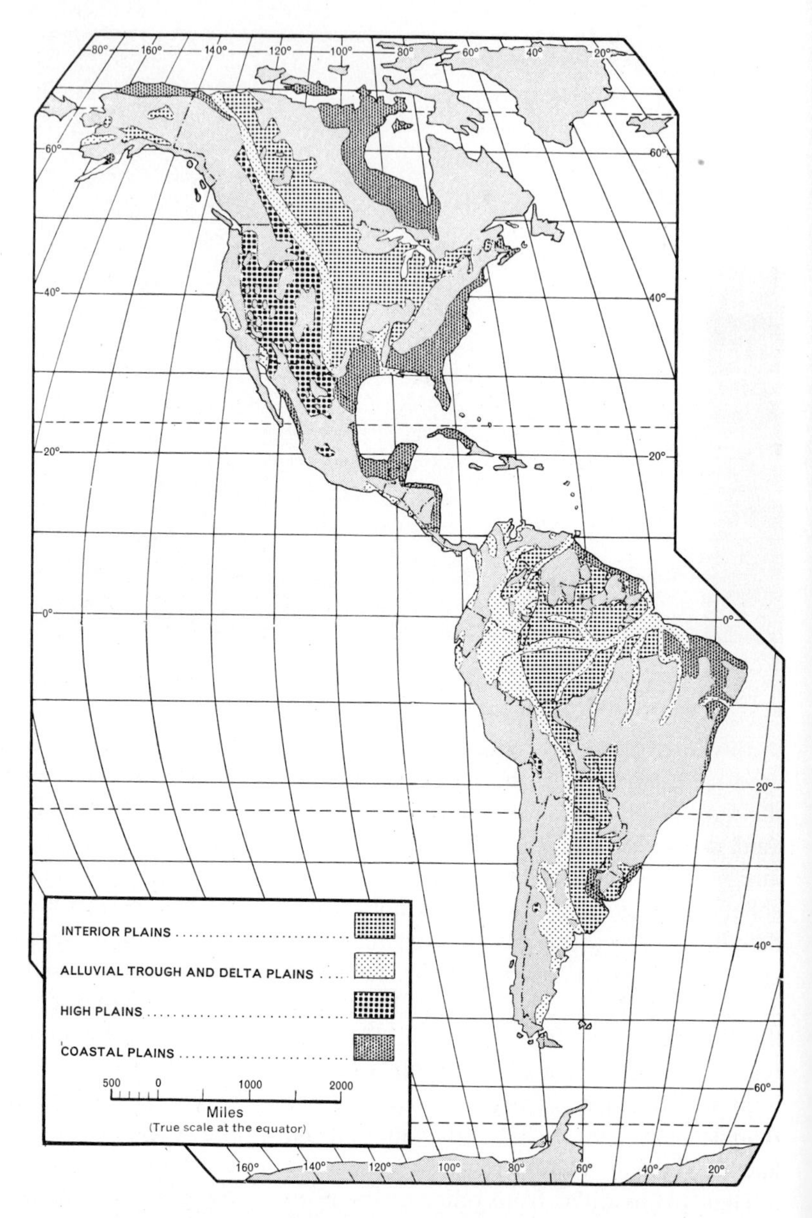

FIG. 4.12 World map of plains.

crustal instability, it contains a large area of high plains. The interior of most of this continent was elevated relatively recently in geologic time, but not to heights comparable with those of the cordillera zones. Most of the African high plains lie at elevations between 2,000 and 3,000 feet above sea level. Exceptions include the volcanic lava surfaces of Ethiopia and Kenya, which rise far higher.

The initial cause for many high plains is broad regional arching, in which the arches may be several hundred miles across. In the United States and Canada, for example,

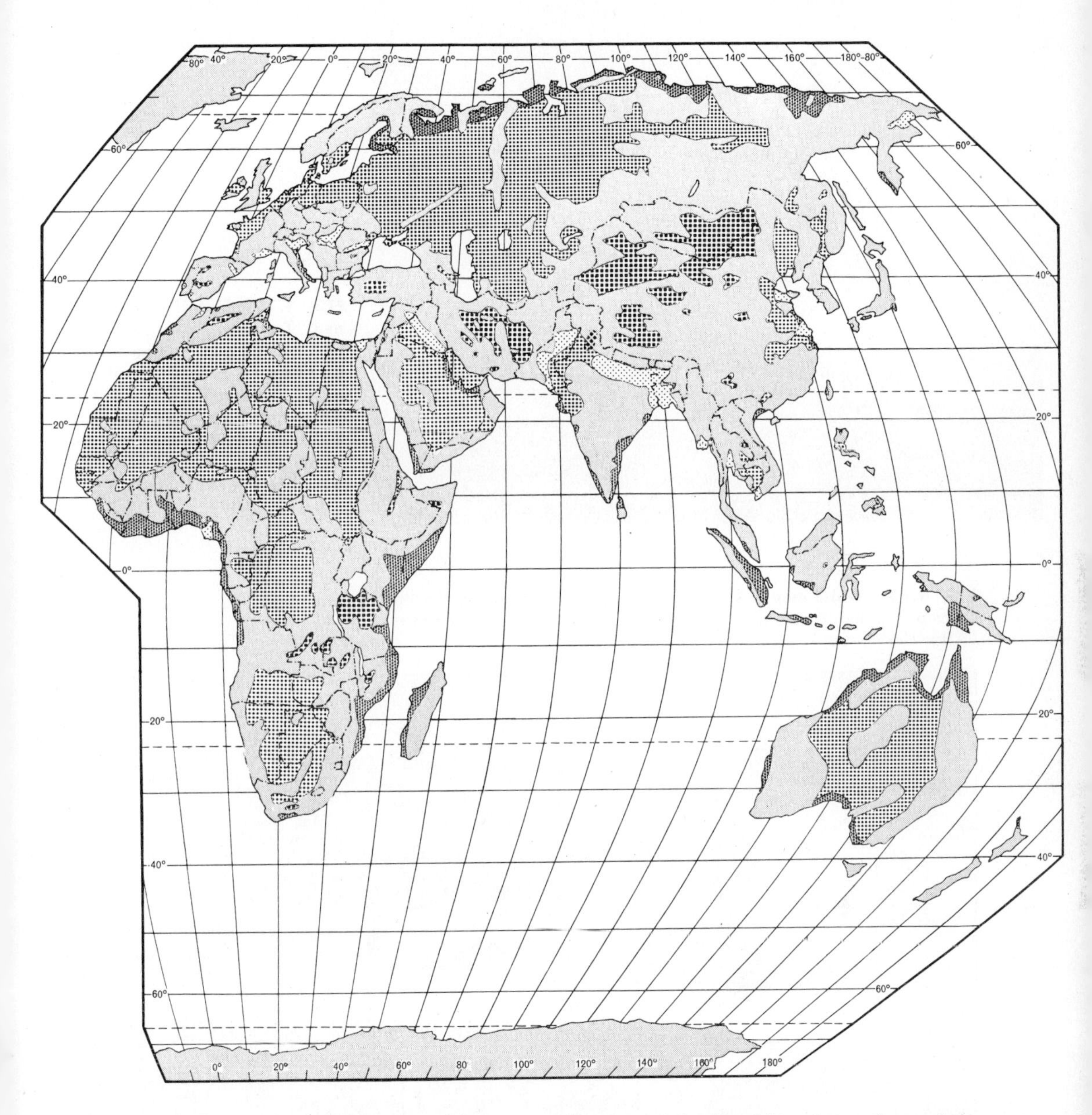

regional arching along a north-south axis elevated much of the western portion of these two countries. The present Middle Rockies of the United States represent durable, resistant rock areas that remained after stripping of the less resistant materials near the higher parts of the regional arch. Slightly to the east of the Rockies, the surface of the Great Plains represents the gentle eastern slope of the regional arch, and there is a gradual transition between the high plains and the interior plains to the east. The amount of dissection of the regional arch, which often determines whether the surface

FIG. 4.13 Flat glacial till plain near Towanda, McLean County, Ill. This is a plain whose levelness is caused by glacial deposition. The combination of level land, black, fertile, and stoneless soils, and skillful farming makes this some of the most productive land in the world. [Standard Oil Company (N.J.)]

FIG. 4.14 World map of synclinal basins. These basins have been rather persistent areas of sagging in the earth crust off and on throughout much of the earth's history. [After Umbgrove]

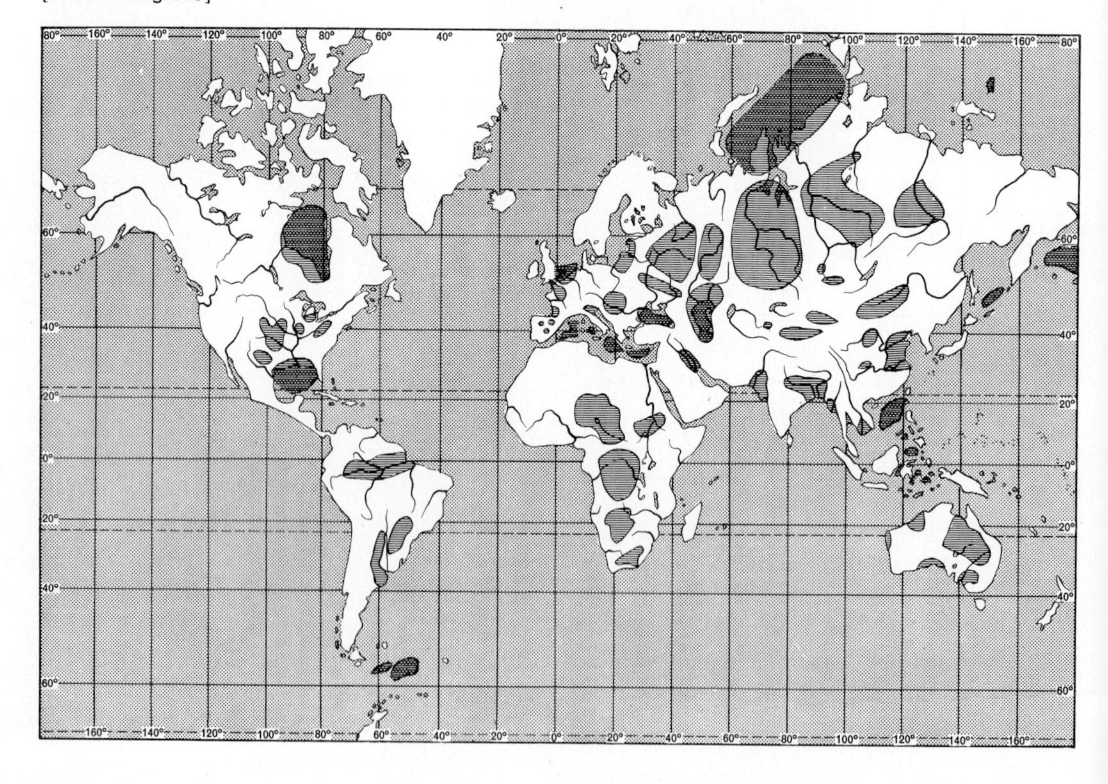

FIG. 4.15 Typical rolling surface of the high plains of central British Columbia. In this area, much farther north than the high plains of the Columbia Plateau in the United States, the low rainfall undergoes much less evaporation and is sufficient to produce a forest cover. This scene is along the Caribou Highway south of Williams Lake, British Columbia. [Government of British Columbia]

becomes mountains, hills, or plains, is related to the amount of runoff of surface water. The drier portions of the regional arches in the world have thus been preserved as high plains. This is perhaps the major reason for the low relief of much of the Colorado Plateau.

The statements made in the previous paragraph on the origin of the high plains should be regarded as broad generalizations. There are several other ways, supplementing broad regional uplift, in which high plains may be formed. Some such plains are of volcanic origin, consisting of thousands of feet of successive lava flows. The Columbia Plateau east of the Cascades and the high plains of Kenya and Ethiopia are examples. Other high plains are produced by deposition of sediments in dry interior basins, supplemented by the development of rock plains in the erosion of adjacent mountain ranges. The original surface may have had a much greater relief. The high plains of much of Iran, Anatolia, the Basin Range region of the southwestern United States, and parts of the Gobi Desert in eastern Asia are examples. In eastern Mongolia and northwestern China, some of the high plains are comprised of basins that have been partially filled by loess.

4.7 COASTAL PLAINS.

Coastal plains are the shelving edges of the continents, plains formed as the result of deposition or erosion below sea level and later raised above sea level. By definition then, coastal plains are of marine origin and do not neces-

FIG. 4.16 The Grand Canyon of the Colorado River. The level skyline represents one of the flat benches that constitute the high plains in the Colorado Plateau region. [U. S. Weather Bureau; Madison Gilbert]

FIG. 4.17 An air view of a portion of the Arctic plain near the mouth of the Mackenzie River, Northwest Territories, Canada. Note the lakes, some of which are being filled with vegetation. [Royal Canadian Air Force; American Geographical Society]

sarily include all plains that lie along the coast. Some are rock plains that represent ancient erosional surfaces, such as those which border the Arctic Sea. Others represent areas of coastal marine sedimentation, such as the Atlantic–Gulf of Mexico coastal plain of the United States and eastern Mexico.

There are only two extensive areas of coastal plains in the world: the Atlantic–Gulf of Mexico plain and the low plains that border parts of the Arctic Sea in Canada and the Soviet Union. Smaller coastal plains, however, may be found bordering most of the continents; these include the narrow plains along parts of eastern Brazil, Mozambique, Nicaragua, and the Guinea coast of Africa.

The characteristics of coastal plains depend partly on the amount of uplift and erosion that has taken place since they emerged from the sea and partly on the composition of the underlying material. In plains that have emerged relatively recently, many of the original depressions have collected water and have become lakes or swamps. The marshes of the Everglades of Florida and the Lake Okechobee region are illustrative. Sometimes the terrain is so flat that it is difficult for water to drain from the surface, and extensive swamps or marshes may result, such as the Dismal Swamp of southeastern Virginia and northeastern North Carolina. Other poorly drained areas are former lagoons back of beach ridges. Some of the coastal swamps of eastern Brazil and the Guianas are of this type.

Not all coastal plains are flat. Sections of the coastal plain in the eastern United States have been uplifted and eroded to form a rolling terrain with a local relief of between 50 and 100 feet. The coastal plain in the vicinity of Chesapeake Bay is far from flat. When depositional coastal plains are uplifted, the soft, unconsolidated material is usually rapidly dissected by streams.

The rock coastal plains of the world show a variety of surface characteristics, and their specific landforms, like those of the depositional plains, are dependent on the degree of uplift, the composition of underlying material, and the erosional processes that now are working on them. The surface features of the Arctic coastal plains (see Fig. 4.17) are related largely to recent glacial erosion and deposition and to the unique features of frost action in high latitudes. Limestone underlies some of the rock coastal plains, such as in the Yucatan Peninsula in Mexico, in parts of Florida, and on some of the narrow tropical coastal plains that represent former coral reefs which have been raised above sea level. Solution by underground water generally has modified such surfaces.

4.8 THE HUMAN SIGNIFICANCES OF PLAINS.

The outstanding significance of plains to human beings everywhere is that surface irregularity generally becomes a relatively minor consideration in the physical environment. Exceptions may be noted, however, in the deep canyons of some of the high plains and in areas where minor topographic irregularities have a special significance because of their drainage or land-use features—for example, natural levees on alluvial plains and deltas, and beach ridges on lake plains. In general, however, slope considerations on plains have mainly local significances. Some of the meanings of slope are treated in detail in Chapter 5; but in connection with the meaning of global plains, it is appropriate to note here that, although slope rarely is an important independent variable in the settlement of plains, dense populations generally do not occur except where many of the environmental factors are favorable, *including low relief*. There are fertile plains and sterile plains and plains whose significances to man have changed with the times. As with the other environmental factors, the significances of plains cannot be treated apart from the associated factors of climate, soil, drainage, vegetation, mineral wealth, and human drives and abilities. Some generalizations on the resources and obstacles of the major types of global plains are presented in the following paragraphs.

The interior continental plains, despite their low relief, have wide areas of low-to-moderate population density. In the rainy tropics, such areas are generally characterized by infertile soils and dense forests; in the central Asiatic plains and in central Australia, the sparsely inhabited sections are dry regions; and in the plains of northern Canada and the Soviet Union, they are the areas of excessive cold. By far the most suitable for agriculture are the humid interior plains of the mid-latitudes, especially where soils are underlain by limestones or material that contains much lime. Examples include the glacial till or loessal plains of the American Middle West, the limestone plains of Kentucky, Tennessee, and southern Indiana, the limestone plains of central France, and the loessal plains of southeastern Germany and the Ukraine.

The alluvial troughs and delta plains,

FIG. 4.18 Cultural patterns developed on a typical flood plain. Note how the buildings and main roads tend to follow the arc of the natural levee next to the river. The radiating lines are drainage ditches that drain into the back marshes away from the river. [From AHS sheet accompanying H. N. Fisk Report on Geological Investigation of the Mississippi River alluvial valley]

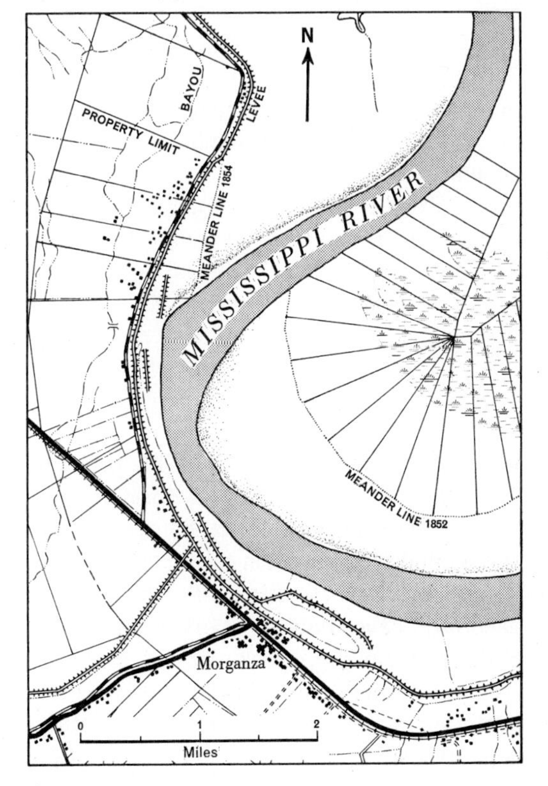

where they are adequately watered and have been occupied for a long time, include some of the most favored agriculture areas on earth. Their soils are mixtures of top soils from extensive areas of the drainage basins and are largely stoneless and easily cultivated. The rice plains of eastern and southern Asia are illustrative. The quality of alluvial soils depends partly on their age, and some of the older alluvial deposits, such as those along the middle course of the Ganges, are relatively poor because of leaching (the washing out of soluble plant foods). In some of the structural troughs and basins adjacent to mountains, the sloping plains are well adapted to the use of irrigation. Floods are a recurrent threat on many of these plains, and as the clearing and cultivation of watershed areas continue, this problem becomes more and more difficult to control. Not all the alluvial troughs and delta plains are favored places for human settlement. The delta of the Amazon has relatively few inhabitants, and agriculture is only beginning in that area. The alluvial basins included within the mountain ramparts of Asia, such as the Tarim Basin, are too dry to support more than a sparse population subsisting by means of irrigation and grazing. The great alluvial trough that lies immediately east of the Andes has been handicapped by inaccessibility, dense tropical forests, and also by alternate floods and droughts.

The high plains in general are inhospitable to man. Wind-swept, usually arid, generally far from the main centers of world population, and usually hindered by terrain obstacles that separate them from more suitable plains at lower elevations, the high plains generally have only a sparse population. Some of them support clusters of oasis settlements where irrigation water from adjacent mountains is available, and others support a sparse pastoral population that depends on grazing for subsistence, as in interior Asia or Africa. Exceptions always should be noted, and in the United States and Canada, the great granaries of the western Great Plains and portions of the Columbia Plateau constitute valuable segments of our productive terrain. Inhabitants of Mexico City, Nairobi, Ankara, and La Paz could also rightfully claim that their environs had opportunities which they would not exchange for the advantages of many lowland plains.

In general, coastal plains are not among the preferred sites for human settlement, although there are also many exceptions to this statement. Marine shallow-water sediments are frequently composed of quartz sands or gravels and are deficient in minerals that release plant nutrients following rock decomposition. Limestones produce the best soils for agriculture, but solution by underground water and rapid removal of water via underground streams frequently result in deficiencies of water in the soils for plant use. The dry soils of Yucatan are illustrative of this. Poor drainage is another major handicap on many coastal plains. Coastal-plain rivers, although relatively far apart, are likely to be broad and deep and to have low banks. Suitable sites for bridges are few.

Hills

Hill lands are areas *where a local relief is between 200 and 2,000 feet and where slopes of over 5 per cent predominate*. Hill lands thus include the continental surfaces that are intermediate in surface irregularity between plains and mountains (see Fig 4.8).

The global distribution of hills is related to the geological processes involved in their formation. Most hilly terrain results from one of two basic causes: (1) regional land uplift to elevations at which subsequent erosion produces a local relief of between 200 and 2,000 feet; or (2) the advanced erosion of former mountainous areas, in which the hills represent the remaining "roots" of the earlier mountains. Most mountainous areas have a transitional belt of hills, termed *foothills,* between the mountains and the adjacent plains. Such intervening hill zones result either from intermediate heights of crustal uplift or from the progression of erosion from the borders of the adjacent plains. Several different types of hilly terrain may be distinguished and are described separately in the following sections. In general, however, the texture, or grain, of hilly terrain is more even than in plains or mountain areas; that is, the areal spacing of valleys and summits is likely to be more uniform regionally. Slope is usually the dominant environmental factor, and sudden areal changes in slope are reflected in complex local patterns of soils, vegetation, and land use. These variations, however, are topographic in scale. At broader scales of observation, hilly areas exhibit a regional uniformity which frequently contrasts with the irregularities that are discernible in adjacent plains and mountains.

4.9 SHIELDS. Perhaps the most extensive hill lands in the world are associated with great blocks of ancient rocks known as shields. These rocks are largely composed of siallic (continental) igneous rocks (see Sec. 5.15), mainly the light-colored acidic varieties, such as granites or syenites. Such crystalline areas are known as shields because their surface usually is broadly convex in general profile. Unlike the continental margins, which are subject to recurrent strong uplift or subsidence, and unlike the interior plains, which show evidences of alternate slight uplift or subsidence in past geologic periods, the igneous intrusive shields evidently have been areas of consistent, but extremely slow, crustal uplift for enormous periods of geologic time. Evidence indicates that most of these shield areas have been above sea level at least throughout most of the last third of earth history. Poleward of about lat 35°, the crystalline rocks of the shields are highly resistant to weathering and erosion, and granite hills here tend to have correspondingly long "lives." In the humid tropics and subtropics, however, crystalline rocks crumble much more readily. Tropical shield areas involved in regional uplifts are soon finely etched with ravines, producing a hilly terrain that is far different in appearance from the knobby terrain found in the shields of higher latitudes. Continental glaciation has been a factor in producing the rounded, knoblike country that characterizes much of the Canadian and Fennoscandian shields.

The major shields of the world are shown on Fig. 4.20. If this map is compared with the map of the distribution of hill lands, the association of hilly terrain with the shields can be seen. Some parts of the shields do not have sufficient relief to be hill lands, and no clear-cut border exists between the shield hills and the interior plains of the continents. Thin sheets of sedimentary rocks, furthermore, mantle portions of some of the ancient shields, indicating short periods of subsidence and deposition of sediments. This is true, for example, of the Ethiopian shield, which covers almost two-thirds of the African continent; the Brazilian uplands; and the Angara shield of central Siberia. Such sedimentary layers comprise broad upland tablelands in places that contrast markedly with the etched crystalline areas which adjoin them.

4.10 ERODED SEDIMENTARY UPLANDS. Extensive hilly areas also are

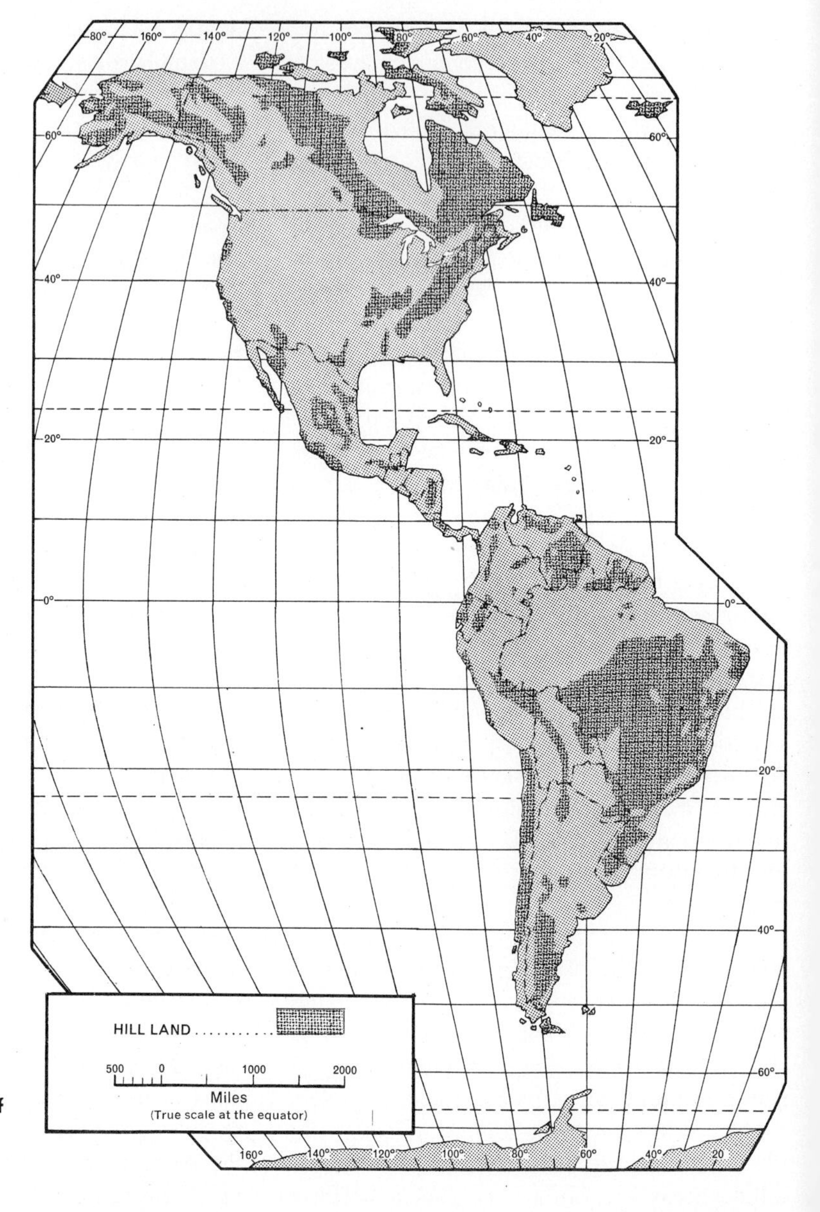

FIG. 4.19 World map of hill land.

located around the borders of some of the interior continental plains and apart from the crystalline shields. Examples include the Appalachian uplands and the hill lands of southern Europe and the southwestern Soviet Union. These are mainly areas of former depositional plains that have been warped upward and are in the process of being eroded. For the most part, the topographic landforms of these hill lands are related to the processes of erosion operating on various types of rock structure and to the stages in the work of degradation. There are various stages of gradation, from flat plains to ex-

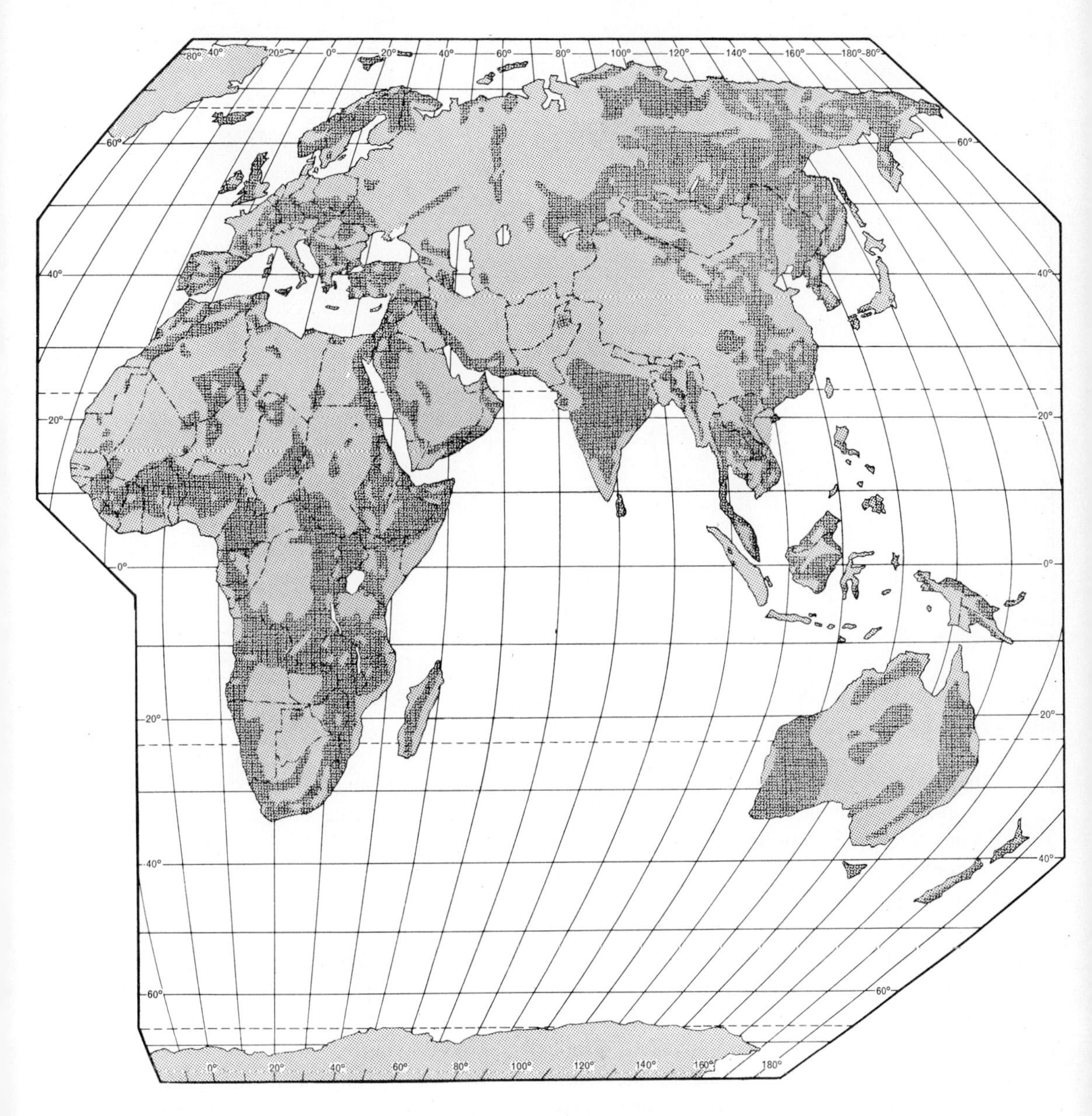

tremely rough hill country, throughout the continental interiors.

4.11 KARST HILL COUNTRY. Karst topography, the irregular terrain produced by underground solution in massive limestone areas, was mentioned in Chapter 3. Although many karst areas do not have sufficient local relief to be termed hill land, some of them do; in fact, karst hill country covers sufficient area to be noteworthy even on a global scale. Two large sections of such land are (1) the type area for karst topography east of the Adriatic Sea, in which some of

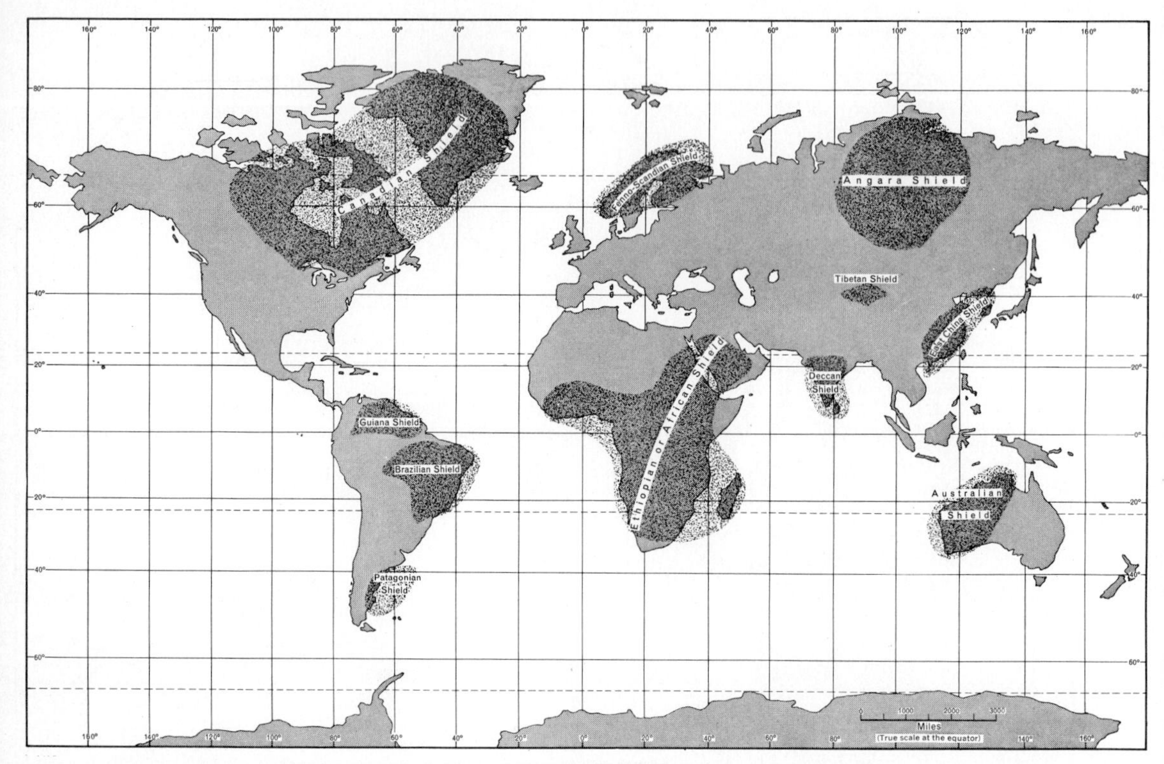

FIG. 4.20 The major crystalline shields of the world. [After Schuchert and Dunbar]

the terrain even attains mountainous relief, as in the Dalmatian Alps, and (2) southeast Asia, including southern China, northern Indochina, and northeastern Thailand. All stages of dissection by solution are found in these regions, including broad, level uplands pitted with occasional sinkholes, hilly-to-mountainous terrain, and plains dotted with high, steep limestone pinnacles. Smaller areas of karst hills are found in southern France (the Causses district), some of the Caribbean islands, western New Guinea, Venezuela, and the Philippines.

4.12 PARALLEL RIDGE-AND-VALLEY HILL LANDS. Parallel ridges and valleys form another distinctive type of hilly terrain. The parallel alignment of the included landforms is caused by the differential erosion of highly folded sedimentary rocks of varying degrees of resistance. The best example in the world is the folded Appalachian area of the eastern United States, a belt 10 to 100 miles wide extending for a distance of about 800 miles from New York State southward into Alabama. Other examples can be found in Arkansas, in western Burma, in Morocco adjoining the Atlas Mountains, along the eastern flanks of the Andes, and near the southern tip of Africa. A few of these areas also attain mountainous relief.

4.13 OTHER TYPES OF HILLY TERRAIN. Several other types of hilly land surfaces are interspersed within the major plains of the world, but they do not have sufficient areal extent to be distinguished on a global scale. Most of them are found in areas of rough terrain, having a high incidence of steep slopes despite a local relief of less than 200 feet. Examples include continental glacial *moraines, badlands* (highly sculptured areas of soft unconsolidated sediments), *sand dunes, wadi* networks in desert hamadas, dissected *lava flows,* and elevated *coral reefs.*

4.14 THE HUMAN SIGNIFICANCES OF HILLS. The major hill lands of the world generally are neither particularly disadvantageous nor especially attractive for human settlement. It is true that some of the hill country of the northern high latitudes is essentially unoccupied and that the narrow stream valleys included within the hilly terrain of India and China contain dense populations; but, on the whole, the above generalization is valid. As noted earlier, hilly terrain is characterized by sharp and frequent areal changes in slope conditions. This variability tends to decrease both the obstacle effects of steep slopes and the advantages of level or gently sloping terrain, for neither of these features has local continuity. Any given gradient in hill lands is likely to be less of a hindrance than the same gradient in mountain lands, because the slopes are not so long. The areas of flat land in hill country are likely to be narrow and discontinuous, despite the fact that there are many of them. Population concentrations everywhere usually tend to be cumulative, since the opportunities for earning a living increase where populations are contiguous. A single block of favorable land 50 square miles in size offers more

FIG. 4.21 Karst hilly terrain, Jamaica. Some idea of the roughness of typical karst terrain may be obtained from this air photo. Such country is difficult to cross despite a fairly low local relief. [U.S. Air Force (MATS)]

advantages to human beings than the same amount of comparable land that is fragmented and scattered over a total area of 5,000 square miles. Thus it is possible that some mountain lands may be more densely populated than hilly areas, since the included plains are likely to be larger in individual size, if not in total area.

Many hill lands throughout the world have been designated as problem areas with respect to increasing or maintaining standards of living. This is closely linked with their susceptibility to deforestation and soil erosion. Hill lands are much more accessible than mountain lands; hence hill forests are likely to be favored areas for forest exploitation. The narrow stream valleys of hill lands are often as favorable for agriculture as the adjacent plains, but the restricted extent of these strips of superior land may force an expanding population to extend lowland cultivation practices to adjacent slopes.

Hill lands, however, are not necessarily submarginal for human occupancy. An understanding of the erosive forces and the limitations of different land practices will indicate the extent to which cultivation or grazing may fit into the natural equilibrium of hillside environments. The barren, eroded slopes of Lebanon, which once supported magnificent stands of timber, the gullied, brush-covered slopes of Korea, and the scarred, grassy hillsides of India testify to a lack of human foresight in the management of hill areas. Even in the United States, where so much has been done to advertise the dangers of soil erosion, where technical assistance is available to every farmer and sheepherder, where so much surplus production can be invested in corrective and preventive measures, and where available machinery can duplicate the work of many hands, harmful crop and grazing practices still are lowering the carrying capacity of many hillside soils. Fortunately, such practices are becoming much less common, and the smooth, rounded patterns of fields under contour cultivation and terracing are becoming a characteristic feature of hill landscapes in many parts of the country.

The hilly shield areas of crystalline rock contain local areas of exceptional importance because of their mineral wealth. The major iron deposits of the world—including the Lake Superior district of the United States, the Swedish and Brazilian deposits, and the newly discovered iron ores of the Knob Lake area of northeastern Canada—are found in hilly shield areas. The multiple-ore mining districts of Rhodesia, the Republic of the Congo, Canada, and the eastern Soviet Union, most of which are included within hilly shield country, contain many valuable metals, including uranium, copper, nickel, precious metals, manganese, chromium, and cobalt.

The hilly shields, apart from their mineral wealth, have decided disadvantages for human settlement. The Canadian shield of North America, the Fennoscandian shield of northern Europe, and part of the Angara shield in Siberia were covered by large sheets of glacial ice about 10,000 or 12,000 years ago. This ice removed the accumulated soil from the hard-rock hills and deposited much of it in the stream valleys. This interrupted the normal drainage patterns and resulted in a succession of rocky knobs, lakes, and swamps. Constructing highways and railroads through such terrain is expensive. Swamps must be dredged of their organic accumulations and filled with rock ballast, lakes must be skirted, and roads must be cut through granite—a difficult, costly, and time-consuming process. Problems in the

FIG. 4.22 Knob Lake, the iron mining district in the heart of the Labrador Peninsula. The large number of lakes seen in the photo is typical of much of the Canadian shield. The railroad leading south to the St. Lawrence River can be seen to the right. The succession of lakes, swamps, and hard-rock knobs made the completion of this railroad a major engineering feat. [Royal Canadian Air Force]

construction of the new Trans-Canada Highway through the hilly terrain north of Lake Superior proved to be as troublesome as those encountered in the Rocky Mountain section. Recently, however, the mineral exploitation of the Canadian shield has been greatly facilitated by the use of airplanes and tractor trains (see Fig. 5.12). The latter are particularly suitable for winter travel, since they need no roads and can utilize the frozen surfaces of lakes. The many lakes, formerly a major obstacle to overland travel, are becoming one of the region's major assets, not only for winter travel by float or ski planes, but for summer recreational purposes as well.

The shield areas of low latitudes are not so difficult for cross-country routes. Crystalline rock in the humid tropics weathers quickly into a deep soil covering, and although gullying by streams tends to create a fine network of ridge-and-valley lines, grading and filling for roads can be done relatively easily. Swamps and lakes are notably absent.

Dissected sedimentary upland hill country, such as the Appalachian region, affords both advantages and disadvantages for human settlement. Except in some of the limestone valleys, or along narrow alluvial flats bordering rivers, soils are likely to be stony and poor. Erosion has deteriorated many of the cleared hillside farms, and standards of living for most farm families are notably poorer than on adjacent plains. The principal assets of the Appalachian hill country lie in (1) its sources of inanimate energy, derived from deposits of mineral fuels (coal, petroleum, and natural gas) and hydroelectric power; (2) its forest wealth, increasing as the competition for manpower withdraws population from submarginal hillside farms; and (3) recreational attractions, including fishing, camping, and touring. This region well illustrates the changes in the significance of landforms that may occur as cultural patterns are altered.

Landforms and the principles of natural distributions

Now that we have examined the major and minor surface irregularities, or landforms, of the earth, let us see whether the principles of natural distributions, which were described in Chapter 1, are valid with respect to this portion of the physical world.

The validity of the first principle, that of the *infinite variety of forms amid graded likeness,* is clearly perceived in the examination of landforms. No two mountains appear exactly alike if we examine them closely enough; yet an explosive volcanic peak has certain characteristics by which it may be recognized in Sicily, Guatemala, Bali, or Kenya. Significant differences may be observed between the deltas of the Mississippi, Nile, and Yangtze Rivers; yet we recognize them as deltas and find that some features of each are analogous. Perhaps this principle is best illustrated by considering the view from the crest of a high dune in the center of one of the vast Saharan ergs. Billowing dunes extend as far as the eye can see, and the observer is struck by the thought that, although no two dunes are exactly alike, it is difficult to find recognizable differences to use as reliable landmarks. Here the problem is one of homogeneity in the midst of infinite differences in detail. Landforms evolve from natural processes; for this reason they must exhibit consistencies of form and be subject to classification.

The second principle, that of the *transitional aspect of areal change,* was illustrated in Chapter 1 by the question, Where does a valley cease to be a valley and become a hillside? Our boundary between mountains and hills, corresponding to a local relief of 2,000 feet, is an arbitrary one, and observable boundaries of such divisions of surface configuration are rarely found in nature. Our use of the term *foothill* implies the recognition of transitional landforms. Sharp boundaries, however, sometimes occur in the world of landforms. On the flanks of many fault-block mountains in the Basin Range region of the southwestern United States, the fault escarpments are so straight and even that they look as if some giant had sliced them with an enormous cleaver. Faulting also has produced linear boundaries dividing distinctly different underlying rocks with correspondingly different regional landforms. As indicated above, however, such sharp boundaries are rare. Even the southern boundary of that relatively recent geologic event, continental glaciation, is not an easily distinguished border line but, rather, a zone of transition that requires some interpretive skill to identify. The rates, or gradients, of change vary areally with respect to landforms. They are greatest in the mountainous regions and are broad and less clear on the old stable portions of the continents.

The *continuous change in areal characteristics with the passage of time,* the third principle of natural distributions, applies to the landforms of the earth as it does to all other features of the physical environment. One of the great scientific debates of all time raged during the eighteenth century, when James

Hutton, a Scottish geologist and philosopher, first propounded his theory that all landforms evolve through continuing, gradual processes that may be observed today, and not through simultaneous creation. The relative permanence of hills, valleys, and mountains, compared with the relatively fleeting span of human life, led to the stubbornness of the simultaneous-creation hypothesis, convenient as it was to religious formalism. Though the processes of change in landforms are infinitely slower than the more perceivable changes in climate or vegetation, we no longer question them; in the subtle processes of stream erosion, the pounding of waves against a coast line, and the slow flexing of portions of the earth crust, we recognize the same forces that produced the present landforms throughout the earth surface and that will continue to alter them for eons to come.

The last principle, that of the *tendency toward the mutual adjustment of environmental factors,* is not so obvious with respect to landforms as it is with respect to features that change more rapidly, but it is no less valid. The ultimate equilibrium of gradational processes produces a plain near sea level. All terrain irregularities, therefore, are in disequilibrium, and various processes operate to remove them. The time required to establish such eventual topographic equilibrium is so vast, however, that the end results are rarely observable over sizable portions of the earth surface. Structural changes in the earth crust, especially in the more unstable portions, tend to oppose the gradational forces, thus providing more work for the latter to accomplish and retarding the progression toward the final equilibrium. Features and factors of *relative equilibrium* are of more concern to us as we make use of the land. The processes of erosion and deposition can be so accelerated through removal of protective vegetation on slopes as to produce harmful effects on land-use patterns. The influence of stream erosion on local levels of subsurface water supply may be overlooked until too late. Even climatic changes may influence land-surface characteristics. Recognizing this, we may, for example, wish to increase our efforts toward relative slope stabilization on farms during exceptionally rainy periods. The relationships between climate and landforms and between type of rock and landforms were treated in several places in Chapter 3.

Perspective

The major patterns of mountains, plains, and hills, with the major exception of those on the continent of Africa, appear to be related to the distribution of ocean basins and the continental shield areas. The mountains generally are aligned around the borders of the ocean basins and away from the continental shields. Plains are largest in the zones between the shields and the mountain belts, but smaller ones are interspersed among, and adjacent to, the mountain regions. Hills are found mainly in the shields and bordering the mountain belts or interior plains. This general pattern is related to variations in the susceptibility of different parts of the earth crust to varying degrees of uplift or subsidence.

Each area of mountains, hills, or plains has its own human significances in terms of its resources or obstacles. The degree to which a particular physical environment affects man is determined partly by the physical characteristics of the area and partly by the social, economic, and political behavior patterns of the inhabitants. In general, plains are the preferred places for human habitation, but slope is only one of many physical factors that influence the habitability of different parts of the earth surface. The appearance and significances of terrain types change with different scales of observation. Any generalization concerning the description, interpretation, and significances of terrain patterns must be viewed in terms of the scale on which it is based. However, the four basic principles of natural distributions apply to landforms on a global scale as well as to those on a local, topographic scale.

5

The elements of surface configuration

Surface configuration refers to various attributes of the land surface. Included within it are such elements as slope, elevation, drainage, and surface materials. Each of these elements has a distinct influence on the shaping of landforms and acts as a separate variable in the physical world of man. We shall examine each of them, noting differences in their expression on the earth surface and in their meanings to man.

Slope

5.1 TERMINOLOGY AND MEASUREMENT OF SLOPE. Slope is one of the principal attributes of surface configuration. Its quantitative measurement is not difficult for a simple inclined plane surface, but measuring it for purposes of areal differentiation introduces challenging problems of generalization. Smooth, inclined planes are extremely rare in nature. The sides of hills and mountains are likely to be irregular, not only along any line drawn directly down the slope, but also along any line extending around the surface feature. No two hills or mountains, furthermore, are shaped exactly alike. The irregularity of slope likewise increases with the scale of observation; for example, a person crawling up the side of a hill on his hands and knees will notice more irregularities than one looking down from the summit. This areal variability of slope is not unique in comparison with the other physical patterns in nature. Vegetation, soil, climate, and human behavior patterns all exhibit this increasing variability of form with areal change and with increasing scales of observation.

The task of describing areal differences in surface configuration requires several different types of slope measurement, each of which has its own purposes. Among these types are *degree slope, per cent slope, slope length,* and *area slope* (see Fig. 5.1). The first three refer to the measurement of slope along a line. Degree slope is the angular measurement of slope from the horizontal and is expressed in degrees, or units of arcs. Per cent slope is the direct ratio between vertical distance and horizontal distance multiplied by 100. A 1-foot rise in elevation over a horizontal distance of 100 feet is equivalent to a 1 per cent slope. Elementary trigonom-

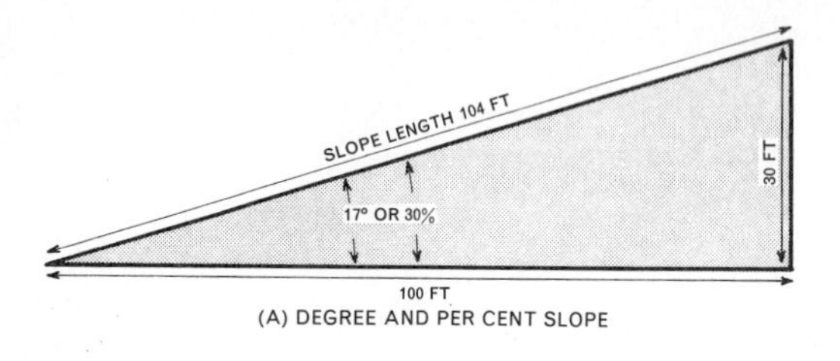

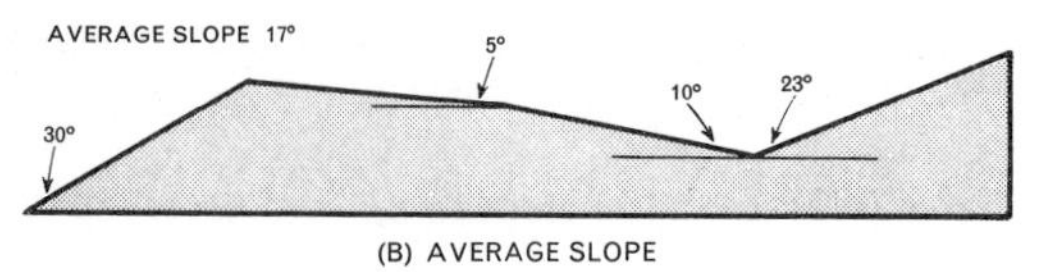

FIG. 5.1 Types of slope measurement.

etry reveals that per cent slope is 100 times the tangential function of degree slope; thus a 45° slope equals a 100 per cent slope.

Slope length refers to the linear measure of a particular slope in the direction of maximum inclination. The factor of momentum, which is highly important in the amount of energy output needed to overcome slope conditions, is dependent on length of slope as well as on the relative steepness. Area slope is the generalization of slope conditions in a particular area. No completely satisfactory method has yet been devised to measure it quantitatively. One method involves averaging the slope conditions along a series of straight lines, or transects, which cross an area in different directions. The degree of accuracy depends on the amount of slope detail considered along the transects, as well as the number and direction of the transects. Maps showing selected categories of area slope may be compiled from contoured topographic maps by observing variations in contour spacing. These maps may have considerable value in generalizing slope details for presentation at reduced scales, but they have two major limitations: (1) the liability of errors during the generalization process and (2) the exclusion of the slope-length factor. The greatest area slope is not always found in mountainous terrain, and the area slope of some hilly regions is surprisingly great. Probably the most irregular land surfaces in the world are found in such areas as the Bad Lands of South Dakota, the surfaces of fresh lava flows, and some of the eroded, elevated coral reefs of the Pacific Islands; yet these are by no means the most difficult areas to cross in terms of energy output.

5.2 THE SIGNIFICANCE OF SLOPE TO TRADE AND TRANSPORTATION.

Perhaps the most important meaning of slope in the modern world involves its relation to the movement of people and materials from place to place. Trade and transportation are the lifeblood of the Occidental industrial culture. The world is made up of an indefinite number of economic areas, each becoming more and more dependent on the others for the welfare of its inhabitants. If each part of the world had developed a complete self-sufficiency, adjustments of transportation to slope conditions would have been relatively simple and direct. Now, however, the desires of widely separated people are involved in the problems of moving both people and things from any one place to another.

The price charged for shipping a crate of oranges from California to New York includes the cost of overcoming the slope factor in the mountain passes of the West. The original decision to expend the effort necessary to project a railroad across the western ranges was a subtle one, determined by the collective and highly variable desires of a large number of people throughout the United States. The meaning of a particular slope is influenced by many things besides its length or steepness.

In order to illustrate more clearly the factors involved in the significance of slope to transportation, let us examine a hypothetical situation. City A and city B are located about 60 miles apart. Midway between them is a rugged mountain range. Obviously, there are a number of ways of overcoming the slope obstacle in order to exchange goods and services between the two cities. There are not only alternative routes, such as over the range, around its ends, or through it by means of tunnels, but also alternative means of travel—for example, on foot, on horseback, by wagon, by automobile via different types of trails or highways, by railroad, or by plane. The choice of the particular route and means of transportation depends in part on the kinds of goods and services to be exchanged, each with its own factor of price or economic pressure. It also may depend on the capabilities of the inhabitants to develop alternative routes, which in turn may involve not only technological arts but a sufficient quantity of capital, labor, and equipment. Political considerations may be another significant factor, involving tariffs, subsidies, or complete or selective prohibitions.

It might be thought that, since man has developed air travel, he has freed himself from the limitations of slope considerations in moving from place to place on the surface of the earth. This is not true, however, since air travel obviously involves cost factors which limit its use. Energy is always required to raise people and goods to high elevations, and this energy, plus the amount needed to increase speed, is reflected in the greater cost of air travel. In some circumstances, the cost of air travel is justifiable; in others it is not. Even in the United States, which has done so much to develop mass transport, the footpath and horse trail have not been entirely neglected, and the elaborate surveys of slope conditions made prior to highway construction or relocation indicate that slope limitations are still important. It is likewise true, however, that if man has incentive enough, expressed in terms of economic, political, or social pressures, he is capable of overcoming any slope limitation in his desire to move from place to place.

FIG. 5.2 Train nearing the crest of the Andes near Ticlio, Peru. The Ticlio copper deposit induced this railroad to reach an elevation of 15,000 feet at the mountain pass. The mine can be seen in the distance. [Standard Oil Company (N.J.)]

The restrictions placed on surface transportation by slope conditions vary with different types of carriers. In general, *the larger the mass to be transported, the greater the limitation of sustained grades and route trajectories in overcoming surface irregularities.* A person on foot is able to negotiate extremely steep slopes even for considerable distances, mainly because he is able to follow sharp bends and turns in order to take advantage of easier grades. A railroad, on the other hand, not only is restricted to relatively easy grades, unless equipped with such special devices as cogs or cable lifts, but also must follow routes with broad, open curves.

5.3 THE SIGNIFICANCE OF SLOPE IN LAND CULTIVATION. The principal food materials for man are derived either directly or indirectly from the cultivation of

FIG. 5.3 Ifugao rice terraces near Bontoc, Luzon, Philippine Islands—a marvelous example of hydraulic engineering and stabilization of steep slopes by an indigenous people. [Philippine Bureau of Science]

surface soils. Slope is one of the factors that determine whether or not an area is suitable for agricultural use. Here also, as in the case of the influence of slope on trade and transportation, human pressures and abilities play a real role in determining the degree to which slope acts as a hindrance to man's occupation of the earth surface. A man using a hoe obviously is less restricted by slope than one driving a tractor that is drawing a large grain combine or gang plow. It is difficult to establish any upper limit of slope beyond which cultivation is impossible. Among the most spectacular examples of cultivation on steep slopes are the rice terraces of the Ifugao, a native tribe in the mountain interior of Luzon, in the Philippine Islands (see Fig. 5.3). Rising tier upon tier, these terraces extend hundreds of feet above the narrow valley bottoms, clinging to the sides of rocky slopes that have grades averaging between 30 and 50°. The stone retaining walls, some of which are 20 to 30 feet high and which have stood for generations, and the remarkable hydraulic system that permits irrigation water to seep slowly from terrace to terrace constitute one of the truly great engineering achievements of mankind. Many other examples of the use of terraces on steep hill and mountain slopes can be cited. Magnificent examples can be found in some of the mountain valleys of Peru, now largely abandoned; rice terraces march up the volcanic slopes of Java; the Far East in general has extensive terracing; and terraced vineyards and orchards are a characteristic of the landscape along the steep hillsides bordering the Mediterranean Sea.

Terracing is an attempt to overcome the disadvantages of slope, particularly soil erosion, which is perhaps the most important limitation of slope upon cultivation. The examples given above represent enormous expenditures of human effort and time, and undoubtedly many pressures were involved in the decisions to terrace steep slopes. To the Ifugaos and the ancient Peruvians, terraces offered a means of increasing their numbers in a natural fortress. Security undoubtedly was a motivating force.

In most parts of the world having sloping terrain, one can find examples of the ill effects resulting from failure to compensate for the disadvantages of slope in cultivating the land. The greatest erosional damage to farmland has occurred in areas of moderate-to-gentle slopes, not steep ones, since the effects of soil erosion in the former are more insidious and more likely to be neglected until corrective measures have become impractical.

Slope may not be entirely a hindrance to agriculture. In fact, on flat, level plains, cultivation may be restricted by the absence of slope and the consequent lack of adequate drainage. Surplus water may create marshes or swamps. Subsoils saturated with water lack proper aeration for plant root growth. Hardpan soils often develop because of water saturation on level plains, and such soils may resist root penetration and thus increase the problem of draining surplus surface water. In dry regions, inadequate drainage on flat plains often results in saline or alkaline soil conditions, preventing effective soil utilization.

In summary, the extent to which slope is an impediment or an asset to cultivation is relative. The environmental factor of slope, like all other such factors, never operates entirely by itself. It must be reckoned with in any attempt to cultivate the land, but only in association with other factors, such as erosion, drainage, the depth and fertility of soils, and human motivations. With sufficient incentive, man is capable of greatly extending the cultivated acres of the world, even in areas of excessive slope. Unfortunately, if he neglects the slope factor, he can also greatly reduce the carrying capacity of the land. The Ifugao rice terraces are an effective reminder of the potentialities of human drives in overcoming environmental obstacles, even on the part of a much less "enlightened" people than those equipped with machinery and inanimate energy sources. The sterile, eroded slopes found in some parts of the United States are likewise a reminder that many shortsighted farmers, even in the most "advanced" countries, have failed to compensate for the slope factor in cultivation.

5.4 OTHER SLOPE INFLUENCES.

Areas of excessive slope have a contemplative value to man, which may in turn have important economic values. The grandeur of the Grand Canyon, the inspiration of Fujiyama's symmetry, the majesty of jagged crest lines in the Alps, the fantastic pinnacles of Bryce Canyon in Utah, and hundreds of other scenic points are enjoyed by millions of visitors at a price which can be translated into a livelihood for thousands of other people. In parts of the world where high productivity suffices to provide surpluses of time and income, recreation is big business, and mountainous areas have an appeal that rivals that of the seashore or climatic retreats.

Also, in many cities that include areas of excessive slope within their borders, or nearby, vantage points commanding urban views usually are developed for upper-class residential purposes. Such land often cannot be subdivided into small plots, and it is generally unsuited for other than residential or recreational purposes because of the difficulty of access. As urban areas grow around or into areas of steep slopes, such steep areas frequently create serious problems in traffic flow. San Francisco, Los Angeles, Pittsburgh, Cincinnati, Nashville, and Hamilton, Ontario, all have critical traffic bottlenecks, since surface transportation lines attempt to carry people and goods around or through such obstacle areas.

The relative inaccessibility of areas of excessive slope frequently has operated to retard the cultural progress of their inhabitants. This need not always be true, as the cultural and technological achievements of the Swiss people indicate, but most countries recognize certain cultural differences between their plains people and their hill and mountain folk. The tempo of cultural change varies directly with population density and the efficiency and ease of transportation and communication. A general discussion of the significance of cultural inertia is not appropriate here, but some of the possible cultural ramifications of inaccessibility resulting from excessive slope should be obvious.

As repeatedly indicated in this volume, the physical characteristics of the environment can be considered from many different points view and scales of observation. Any consideration of slope or surface configuration must be relative to the scale of observation, to the factor of changes with time and area, and to their associations with all other elements in the geographic pattern, physical and human. Since even the description of slopes involves generalizations of an infinite variety of realities in time and space, considerations of slope influences likewise must be generalizations, always subject to qualifications, always having exceptions. The understanding of our physical world involves understanding relative generalities. Reduce the earth to the size of a baseball, and its surface becomes as smooth as that of a baseball; now the factor of slope has all but disappeared. Examine a hillside under a microscope, and both the form and influences of slope become too complex for total comprehension.

Elevation: its measurement and significances

5.5 ELEVATION: DEFINITION AND MEASUREMENT. Figure 5.4 is a world map of comparative elevations above sea level. It is commonly misinterpreted to be a map of surface relief, mainly because high elevations normally are found in mountainous areas, whereas plains usually occur at low elevations. Elevation in itself, however, is an important factor in the physical environment of man and one of the basic attributes of surface configuration. It is defined as the *distance of a point or area measured vertically from a given datum plane.* The most common datum plane for basing comparative elevations is *mean sea level,* or the plane about which the tides oscillate. Mean sea level is determined by careful observations of tidal fluctuations taken hourly over a period of many years, because there is occasional need for extremely precise measurements of elevation.

Elevation can be measured in a number of ways. Approximate measurements are based on comparing the atmospheric pressure of a given point with that at sea level, utilizing the rate of decrease of atmospheric pressure with increasing elevation above sea level. Mercury and aneroid barometers are used for such purposes. Variations in atmospheric pressure caused by the passage of different air masses, however, are a source of error in such determinations. Another approximation may be reached by comparing the temperature of the boiling point of water at different elevations. This temperature decreases with diminishing atmospheric pressure. More precise determinations of elevation are made by geodetic surveying, using careful measurements of vertical angles and horizontal distances from known elevation points. Comparative elevations usually are indicated on topographic maps by spot numbers or contour lines (see Sec. 2.18).

5.6 ELEVATION: ITS HUMAN SIGNIFICANCES. The principal significances of differences in elevation from place to place are associated with conditions of temperature and atmospheric pressure. Both of these tend to decrease with increasing elevation above sea level. Although the rate of decrease in air temperature with elevation is somewhat irregular, varying with moisture content, wind, solar radiation, and other factors, a rough mean figure has been determined: a decrease of 3.56°F for each 1,000-foot increase in elevation. This decrease in temperature as one passes from lower to higher elevations, termed the *lapse rate,* does not operate within the far upper zones of the atmosphere, but it is in effect throughout lower levels. Occasionally, however, chilling of the bottom layer of air next

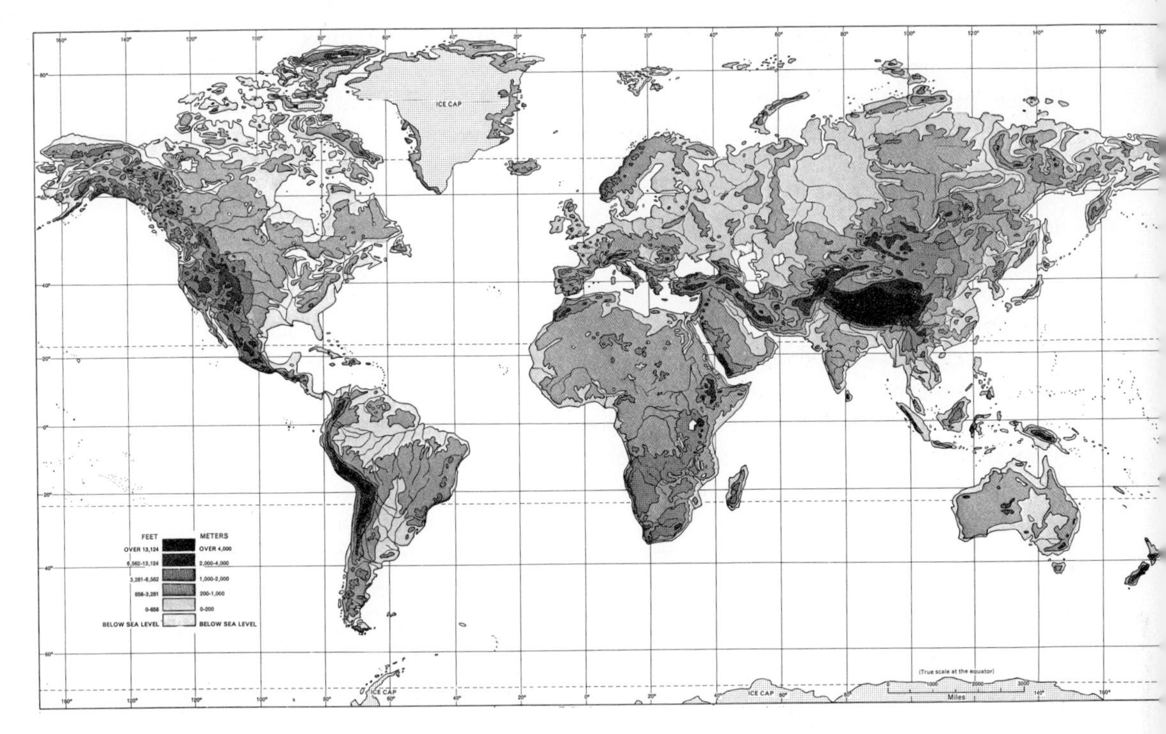

FIG. 5.4 World hypsometric map of comparative elevations. [American Geographical Society]

to a cold ground surface—particularly on calm, clear, and cold nights—may result in a local reversal of the lapse rate, causing a *temperature inversion,* that is, an increase in temperature with altitude. Sometimes also, subsiding air at high elevations may cause an inversion. These inversions are observed only along a narrow horizontal zone, however, and have little influence on the major temperature changes with altitude.

The influence of the lapse rate is most noticeable in mountain areas or on high plains, where elevations are sufficiently above sea level to produce appreciably lower temperatures. One noteworthy result is the tendency for mountain slopes to have a succession of temperature zones. In the high mountain areas of low latitudes, these zones may reproduce the sequence between tropical and polar temperatures, with a corresponding sequence in vegetation, fauna, and human use (see Fig. 5.5). This vertical zonation of mountain areas has certain advantages. It

FIG. 5.5 Diagram of land use and altitudinal zones in the Andes. [After Sapper]

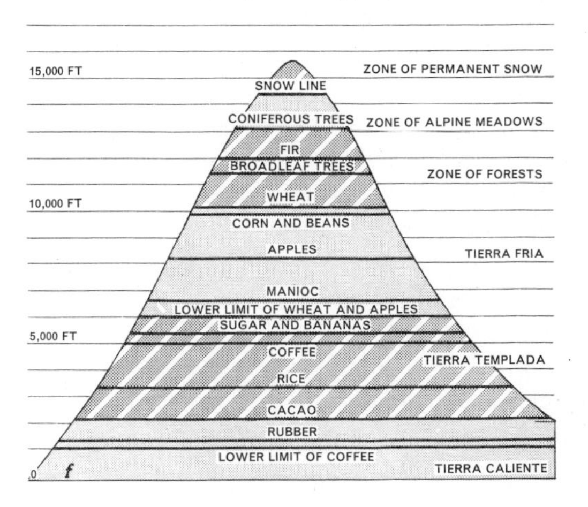

makes possible a wide range of agricultural and forest products within a short distance. In low latitudes, intermediate elevations are important as residential retreats from the oppressive heat of lower elevations. As the standard of living rises in low latitudes, residential *hill stations* will undoubtedly become more common. In areas subject to great seasonal variations in rainfall, mountain summits high enough to have freezing temperatures store precipitation in their snow fields for redistribution during summer seasons. The importance of mountain snow fields is well illustrated in California, where snow conditions in the Sierra Nevada are described periodically in newspapers.

The effects of low atmospheric pressure at high elevations are much better known now than they were a few decades ago. Evidence indicates that people can gradually acclimatize themselves to the lower pressures at elevations of considerably more than 10,000 feet. Sudden shifts, however, from low to high elevations, or vice versa, may produce harmful physiological effects. The temporary visitor to high elevations finds himself short of wind after only mild exertion; the pulse rate increases, and some people suffer from nausea, dizziness, and other symptoms of oxygen deficiency. Reports of greatly reduced human fertility rates appear to be somewhat questionable. Among people who have lived at high elevations for several generations, certain physiological compensations take place, such as a great increase in lung capacity. Both Tibetans and Bolivians have remarkably large chest expansions. People acclimatized to low atmospheric pressure, however, are particularly susceptible to respiratory infections. The ancient Inca rulers found that an effective method of eliminating suspiciously rebellious elements among the military forces was to assign them to low-elevation outposts, where they often contracted tuberculosis, pneumonia, or influenza. Even the common cold can be a dangerous ailment for such people. The psychological effects of high elevations is inadequately understood and demonstrated, although reports of chronic irritability and instability are remarkably persistent and perhaps warrant investigation.

Other problems associated with low air pressure that have hindered human occupation of high elevations include difficulties in cooking and in operating motor vehicles. In such areas, boiling water is not hot enough for cooking food, and water-cooled automobile motors will overheat at normal operating temperatures.

The increase in demand for air travel at high altitudes has led to much research on the physiological effects of low air pressures on the operating efficiency of personnel and equipment. The human body seems to be adaptable to conditions at all but the highest points of the earth surface. The highest human habitation on earth has been reported at an elevation of 17,100 feet in the Andes of southern Peru, just below the snow line. At higher elevations, however, the rarefied air requires the use of oxygen and special pressurized equipment.

Drainage: its forms, patterns, and significances

5.7 THE SURFACE WATERS OF THE CONTINENTS. Bodies of water, such as rivers, streams, lakes, and swamps, are integral elements of surface configuration. Like the other elements of surface configuration, they have their own characteristic forms and patterns of arrangement, and their distributional patterns involve differences in their human significance from place to place. Continental water bodies represent surplus water that accumulates over and above (1) the amount used by plants and animals, (2)

FIG. 5.6 Scene near the upper limits of land settlement in Colombia. Some wheat and potatoes are grown in this bleak meadowland above the timberline and at about 11,000 feet above sea level. A few long-haired cattle find sparse grazing. [Standard Oil Company (N.J.)]

the amount that returns to the air as the result of evaporation, and (3) the amount needed to replenish the empty storage spaces in rocks and soils. The world map of stream frequency [1] (see Fig. 5.7) indicates the uneven distribution of this surplus surface water. The principal categories of stream frequency and their associated physical conditions are described in the four sections that follow.

5.8 AREAS OF HIGH STREAM FREQUENCY. A comparison of the pattern of high stream frequency (Fig. 5.7) with that of the humid climatic regions of the world (Fig. 6.19) reveals a close correspondence. The correlation with humid climates is not surprising, since streams represent surplus water which must flow away. The highest stream frequency is found in areas of sloping terrain where there is high rainfall and where sufficient geologic time has elapsed for streams to develop elaborate tributary systems, such as those found in the mountain cordilleras and in humid hill lands. The hill lands of the eastern United States, eastern China, and southeastern Brazil offer excellent examples of close and intricate stream patterns.

Humid plains with appreciable surface relief, within the limits of their definition as plains, may also have a close network of streams. Much of the Congo Basin in Africa and large areas of the central and lower Amazon Basin in Brazil are dissected by numerous tributaries of the main rivers, entrenched below the general level of the basins.

5.9 AREAS OF MODERATE STREAM FREQUENCY. In some areas, such as portions of the glaciated plains of Illinois and Iowa, insufficient time has elapsed since glaciation for streams to have developed a thor-

[1] Stream *frequency* as here used refers to the areal spacing of streams that normally contain water throughout the year. It should not be confused with the frequency of flow.

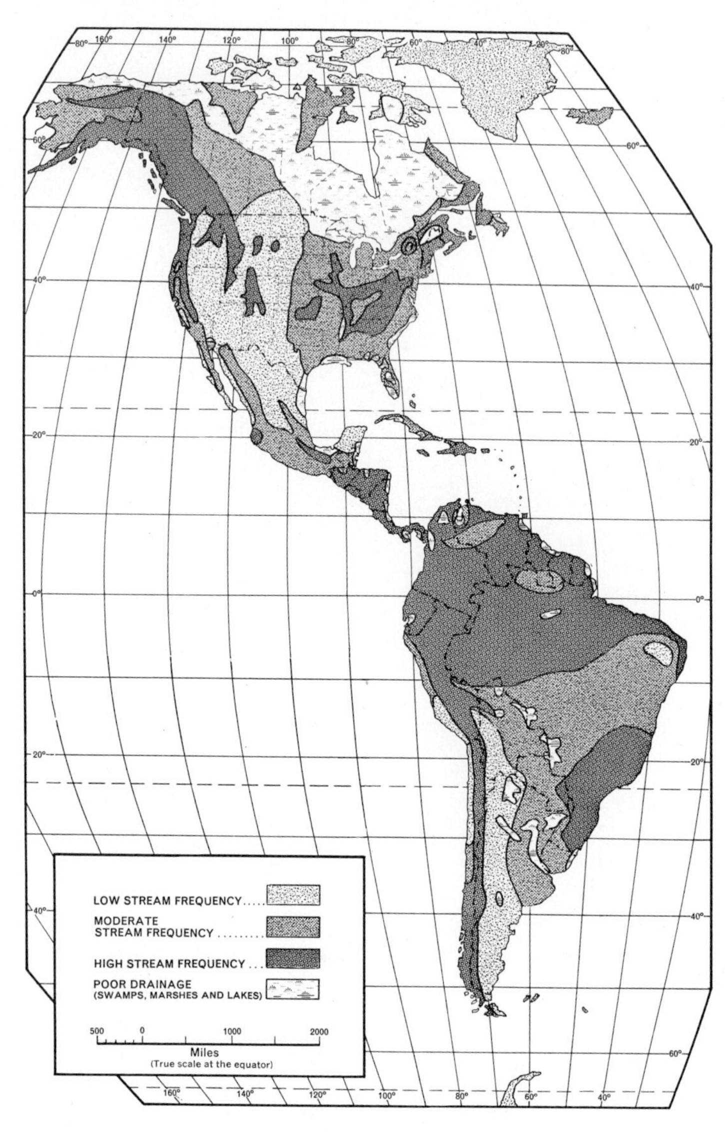

FIG. 5.7 World map of stream frequencies.

ough drainage pattern. In others, subhumid conditions permit runoff only during certain seasons or in regular amounts insufficient to establish a close network of permanent streams. Large areas of the low latitudes that have pronounced dry periods, such as the northeastern Brazilian uplands, the Sudan in Africa, and peninsular India, are examples. The streams in areas of karst topography likewise have poorly developed tributaries, since much of the tributary drainage is underground. The rivers of unglaciated plains situated at latitudes higher than 50° on the equatorial side of the tundras are also likely to have few tributaries. Dissection is slow in such areas, since streams and soil are frozen during the long winter seasons.

Flat plains rarely have many streams, even in humid areas, mainly because there is insufficient slope to channel surplus water into

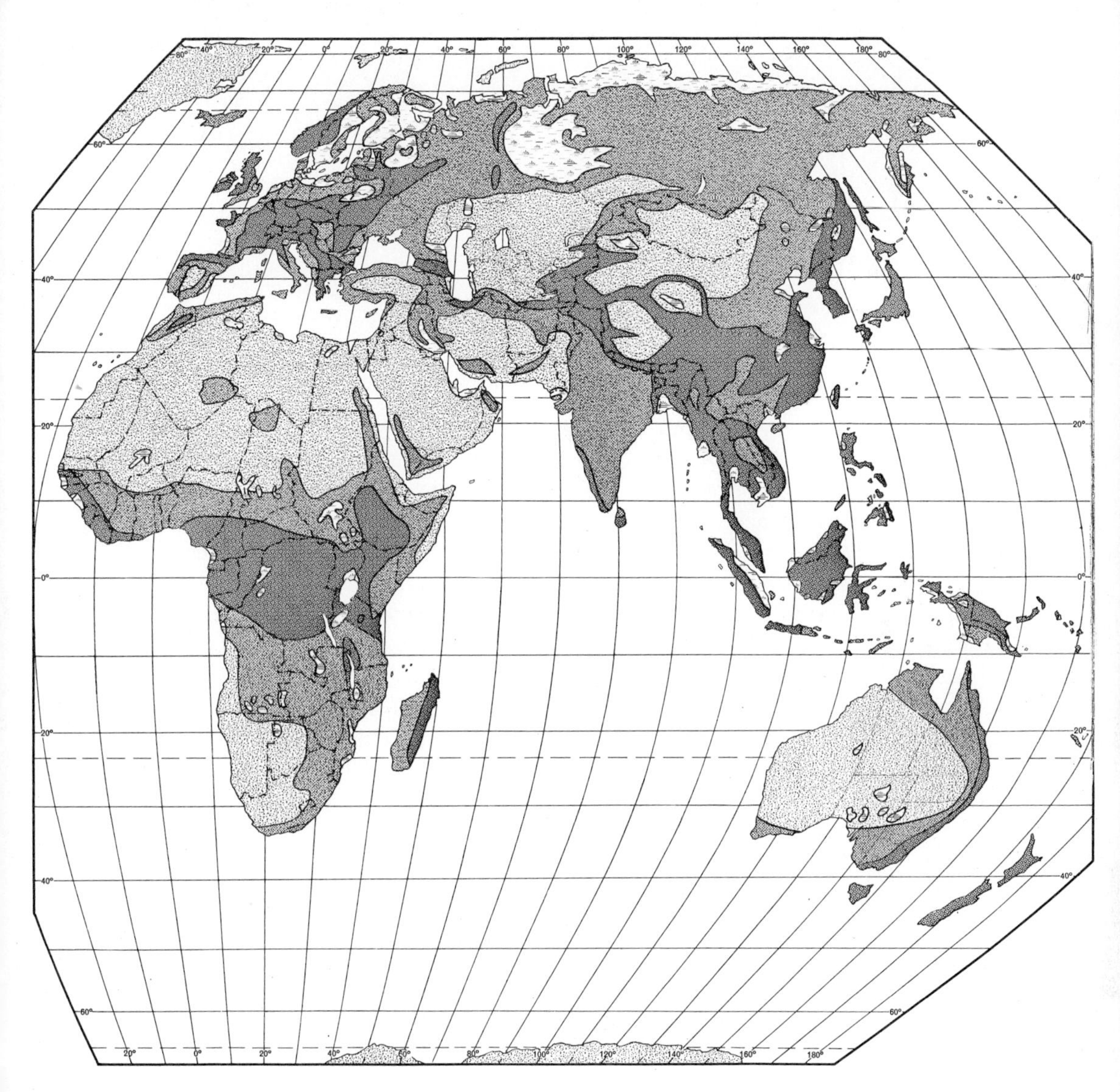

intricate drainage ways. Instead, the surplus water accumulates in marshes and swamps or is drained away by a relatively few large, sluggish streams, fed mainly by subsurface seepage. The coastal margins of the North European Plain; the broad, monotonously flat plains of continental glacial deposition in the central United States and the western Soviet Union; the coastal plain of the southeastern United States; and the pampas of Argentina are all notable examples of plains within humid climates that are sufficiently flat to have a moderate stream-frequency pattern.

5.10 AREAS OF LOW STREAM FREQUENCY. Areas of low stream frequency include the arid and semiarid regions of the world. They have high evaporation rates; the rainfall is slight and irregular; the water reservoirs of soils require constant

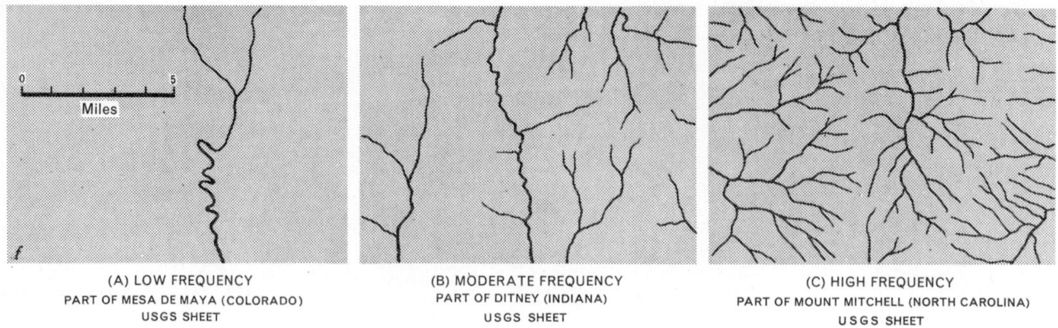

(A) LOW FREQUENCY
PART OF MESA DE MAYA (COLORADO)
USGS SHEET

(B) MODERATE FREQUENCY
PART OF DITNEY (INDIANA)
USGS SHEET

(C) HIGH FREQUENCY
PART OF MOUNT MITCHELL (NORTH CAROLINA)
USGS SHEET

FIG. 5.8 Examples of stream-frequency types.

replenishing. When rain comes, it sinks rapidly into the soil, evaporates quickly, or rushes down the few, normally dry watercourses. The few permanent streams that are located in these areas have sources in more humid sections and are forced to cross the dry regions on their way either to the sea or toward some interior basin where the runoff will collect, finally disappearing through evaporation. In the dry areas of low latitudes, rains are likely to be torrential and of short duration; therefore the time available for replenishing underground water reservoirs is short. It is noteworthy that the low frequency of streams is not necessarily synonymous with the wide spacing of stream valleys. Thoroughly dissected areas are found in some dry regions. Some parts of the Sahara have a dense network of *wadis,* or dry river channels. The Bad Lands of South Dakota are another example. The infrequent runoff is sometimes able to accomplish severe erosion even in dry regions, because of lack of vegetation cover, particularly in easily eroded materials.

In general, stream channels are relatively infrequent in dry regions. The rapid runoff in most of the dry parts of the world results in the paradoxical situation of desert floods. The flat-bottomed stream channels, which are usually dry, are popular routes of travel, and travelers who have camped overnight along such stream beds have been engulfed without warning by flash floods resulting from storms in the headwater areas.

Areas of low stream frequency are not wholly confined to dry regions; small sections of this type may be found in all parts of the world, regardless of climate. Sandy flats near coast lines and extremely porous limestone areas may be devoid of any permanent surface streams, despite a humid climate. The Yucatan Peninsula of Mexico is included in the region of low stream frequency because of its low elevation, pronounced dry period, and porous limestones.

5.11 AREAS OF POOR DRAINAGE. The areas of poor drainage are those where lakes, swamps,[2] or marshes form the major part of the land surface. Fig. 5.7 reveals that the largest areas of this type are found in the northern parts of North America and Eurasia. Poorly drained depressions are characteristic of the tundra plains that border the Arctic Ocean. These plains are part of the continental-shelf zone that has recently risen from beneath the sea. Accumulations of moss not only mark slight surface depressions that are not filled with water but may aid in ex-

[2] A *swamp* is here considered as an area where water stands slightly above or below the ground surface and where there is a tree vegetation. A *marsh* differs only in being essentially treeless.

tending the borders of the poor drainage by holding water during the short summer season (see Sec. 10.11). Permanently frozen subsoils also impede the free circulation of water in the tundra soils, emphasizing the effect of slight surface irregularities on water runoff. The tundra should not be considered a vast marshland, however. Slight rises in the land surface frequently have physiologically dry soils, because of strong drying winds and low precipitation.

Other large poorly drained areas extending equatorward from the Arctic demonstrate the effects of continental glaciation during the Pleistocene period, or ice age. This glaciation resulted in gouged-out depressions of various sizes, which fill with water to become lakes or swamps, or in deposits of irregular masses of glacial rock debris over the land surface, interrupting the preglacial drainage systems. Most of the Canadian shield is an area of poor drainage, despite its predominantly hilly surface (see Fig. 5.9), because swamps and lakes are found in nearly every depression between the low hills. The large poorly drained areas of the western Soviet Union and eastern Poland and those in western Siberia are the result of glaciation damming north-flowing streams, either by the ice itself during its retreat northward or by the deposition of moraines (low, hilly belts of glacial debris) across their courses. The resulting lakes were partially filled with sediment or vegetation during the several thousand years since the ice age or were incompletely drained by erosion of the morainic dams at the marsh or lake outlets.

Swamps and marshes are also common along flat coastal plains, as in the eastern United States, northern China, the larger islands of Indonesia, and the Guianas of South America. Some of these poorly drained coastal areas, such as the Everglades in Florida, represent former sea bottoms uplifted slightly above sea level; others are the result of flooding by rivers. Tidal marshes form narrow strips along most low coast lines. The deltas of large rivers generally are poorly drained, although their fertile soils make them attractive for agricultural use. The deltas of the Yangtze, Si-kiang, Mekong, Salween, and Irrawaddy Rivers of eastern Asia all are poorly drained, but the plentiful water supply and fertile soils provide ideal conditions for the growing of wet-field rice. Swamps are also found along the flood plains of large rivers, such as the Amazon, Mississippi, Congo, Tigris, and Euphrates. Most of the flood-plain swamps, however, are too narrow and discontinuous to be shown on a world map.

Structural depressions, or downwarped blocks of the earth surface, may collect the drainage waters from adjacent uplands. Lacking suitable outlets, these waters may accumulate up to the level of the lowest outlet to form lakes, swamps, or marshes. Some may have no outlets. The lakes of eastern Africa, the Caspian and Aral Seas, the Dead

FIG. 5.9 Typical drainage pattern in the Canadian shield. [Toronto-Ottawa Sheet No. 31 S.W., National Topographic Series, Canada, Department of Mines and Resources]

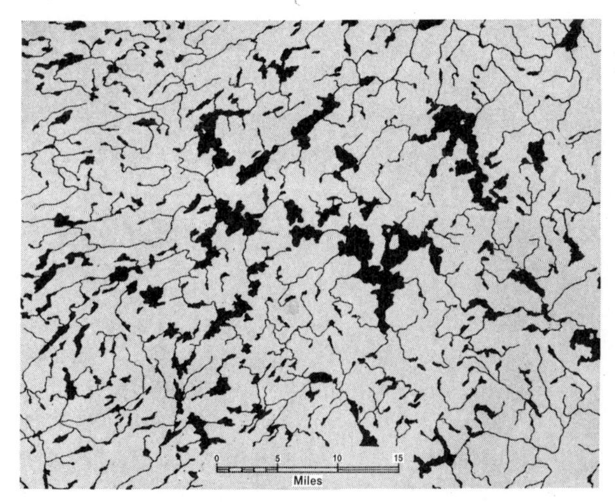

FIG. 5.10 Marshland in eastern Sumatra near Sungei Gerong, where DDT and oil are sprayed to eliminate malarial mosquitoes. [Standard Oil Company (N.J.)]

Sea and the marshes of Israel, parts of the Imperial and San Joaquin Valleys in California, and the Tsaidam and Dzungaria marshlands in central Asia are examples. The large swamps and marshes along the upper Nile and Niger probably were caused by crustal downwarping across their courses.

Large swamps and marshes are located east of the central Andes in South America. They appear to be the result of different causes. Some of them, such as those in the western part of the pampas in northern Argentina, are due to the damming of major drainage ways that parallel the Andean mountain front by fan-shaped deposits of sediments formed by lateral streams from the Andes. The Chaco plains of eastern Bolivia, western Brazil, and northern Paraguay also contain large marshes. These plains have been formed largely by alluvial deposition by streams from both the Andes and the southern Brazilian uplands. The flat terrain, wide fluctuations in stream flow, altered stream courses, and channel filling by sediments result in indefinite drainage patterns and consequent poor and interrupted drainage.

Nearly all flat areas, regardless of their location or origin, are likely to be poorly drained and to have a high *water table* [3] under humid conditions. A large part of the glacial depositional plains of northern Iowa and southern Minnesota was wet prairie or marshland prior to white settlement (see Fig. 5.11). Today, after extensive drainage developments, this area comprises some of the richest agricultural land in the United States. The use of tile drains and the construction of broad drainage ditches were essential preliminaries to successful farming throughout broad areas of the glaciated American Middle West.

Hardpan formation, or the creation of a relatively impermeable layer within soils, is an additional cause for poor drainage on humid, flat, or undulating terrain nearly everywhere. Such hardpans commonly form at or near the top of water tables that lie near the surface. Once formed, these hardpans further impede the downward percolation of rain water and add to the poor drainage of topsoils. They are discussed further in Chapter 12.

5.12 THE HUMAN SIGNIFICANCES OF DRAINAGE PATTERNS. The world map of stream frequency (Fig. 5.7) indicates generally the areas where surpluses and de-

[3] A *water table* is the general upper limit of the water-saturated zone below the surface of the ground.

ficiencies of surface water are to be found.

The areas of high stream frequency are susceptible to soil erosion, particularly to gullying, although local factors of vegetation cover and cultivation practices are important variables. High stream frequencies generally signify a high incidence of local relief and runoff. These are not the best areas for agriculture, at least not on a global scale, because of the relatively small amounts of level–to–gently sloping land. The combination of high runoff and narrow valleys makes these areas important, however, as water-control areas for hydroelectric power and water supply. The control of erosion and floods and the regulation of runoff to increase minimum stream flow for power utilization have led to the promotion of increased forest cover in much of this region. Since runoff is comparatively rapid and abundant, local water supplies are likely to be derived from surface streams rather than from subsurface wells. Contamination of surface streams is thus an important local problem throughout. The high frequency of streams and stream valleys results in problems in the construction and maintenance of surface transportation facilities. Slope is a constant hindrance, and the need for bridges adds to the transportation costs.

The areas of moderate stream frequency are handicapped in many sections by high seasonal fluctuations in the flow of surface waters. Floods tend to recur constantly in the areas of gentle slopes. Local water supplies are likely to be obtained from wells, except in the vicinity of the larger streams. Since it is much more difficult to regulate subsurface

FIG. 5.11 Distribution of drainage projects in the United States. Flat humid plains, such as the coastal plain, Mississippi bottoms, and the glacial till and lake plains of the Great Lakes area, require extensive drainage facilities to make them productive farm land. [U. S. Department of Agriculture]

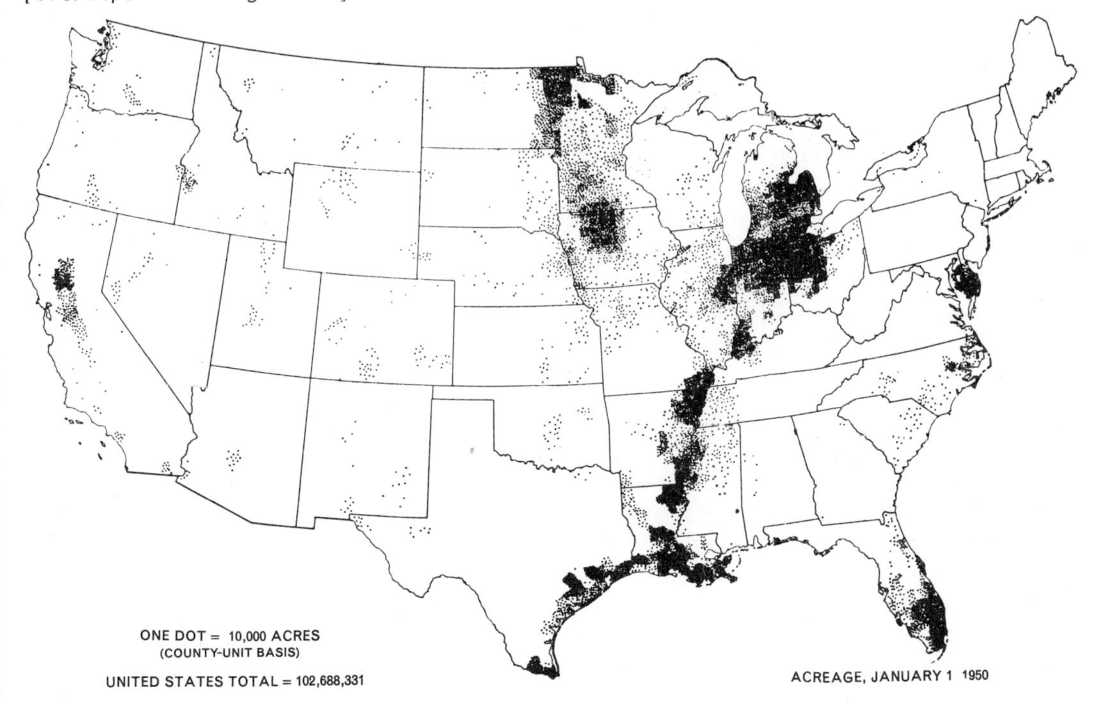

FIG. 5.12 Port Radium, Great Bear Lake, Northwest Territories, Canada. This uranium outpost, close to the Arctic Circle, is supplied entirely by air or by tractor trains during the winter. The use of the frozen lake surfaces for both landing strips and trailer trains is illustrated here. Note the knobby terrain, typical of the Canadian shield, and the sparse spruce vegetation. [Royal Canadian Air Force]

water supply than surface runoff, many of these wells suffer from too rapid withdrawals. The wide interstream areas, not being adequately drained of surplus water, may contain soils that are difficult to cultivate because of poor drainage, even though they may not be swamps or marshes.

In general, however, the areas of moderate stream frequency in the mid-latitudes are hospitable to man. Some of them contain the most fertile agricultural plains in the world. The American Middle West, the Hungarian and Romanian plains of Europe, the Ukraine of the Soviet Union, the plains of northern China and Manchuria, and the fertile grasslands of the Argentine pampas and eastern Australia are included. Slopes are gentle enough for easy cultivation, and the soil cover is usually thick and somewhat less leached than in more humid areas. Low-latitude drainage areas of this type are mostly savanna grasslands or forest lands, in which agriculture is precarious, owing to irregular precipitation combined with high evaporation rates. Many streams normally are without water during the dry season and are subject to floods during the wet season.

The global areas of low stream frequency are universally handicapped by lack of water, owing to inadequate precipitation. Irrigation makes use of the few permanent streams, which have their sources in more humid regions. Flash floods along the normally dry watercourses are a regional hazard. Wells tapping subsurface water supplies supplement the meager surface flows. Hydroelectric developments are possible only along the larger rivers, such as the Nile, Colorado, and Indus. Except for the occasional oases capable of being irrigated and the sections supporting small groups engaged in pastoral occupations, the areas of low stream frequency are essentially unpopulated.

The poorly drained regions of the world impose restrictions on human occupation but also provide some important resources, although their obstacles generally exceed their resource value. They are not suited to agriculture, unless the swamps and marshes are drained, and this is generally a costly procedure. Small areas, such as the marshlands in parts of Florida, the poorly drained deltas of eastern Asia, the Mississippi bottomlands, and the tidal marshes of the Low Countries of western Europe, have been drained and turned into exceedingly productive land. Poor drainage coupled with the handicaps of long winters and short growing seasons has made large areas of northern North America and Eurasia generally unsuitable for human settlement. Poor drainage aids the propagation of certain forms of insect life, such as the mosquito, and the swamps and marshes of the tropics are notorious as breeding places for the carriers of malaria, yellow fever, and other diseases. At higher latitudes, although mosquitoes are rarely carriers of disease, their numbers and voracious blood-thirst are distinct annoyances to people and to domestic animals.

The thousands of small lakes of the Canadian shield, Scandinavia, and some of the Baltic countries have a growing resource value for recreational purposes and, when frozen, for cross-country travel (see Fig. 5.12). Hydroelectric power is an added resource of the northern glaciated shields, since the lake basins and swamps ensure a more constant flow of water in the connecting streams. The hard underlying crystalline rock affords firm foundations for anchoring dam structures. The obstacles of these shields were discussed earlier.

Some swamp and marsh areas are the major or exclusive sources of certain highly prized products. Louisiana ranks first among the states in value of furs produced, largely because of the muskrat, which abounds in the bayous and sloughs of the Mississippi delta. Cranberries are produced only on marshlands. Sago, a swamp palm of southeastern Asia and the Pacific tropical islands, is the source of a starch that is the basic food for many cultural groups in the area. Taro, obtained from the bulb of a marsh plant, is another Pacific island staple. Mangrove, a tree of muddy coasts in the tropics, is an unusually durable and decay-resistant wood, of high value when large enough for timber. Much of the pulpwood of the world is derived from the swamp conifers of Canada and the Soviet Union. Cypress and some cedar lumber, also derived from swamp forests, are prized for their resistance to decay in the presence of water.

Swamps and marshes may also have a recreational value. Some of them, such as those along the Atlantic and Gulf of Mexico coastal plains and in the Mississippi bottoms, are favorite areas for hunting both small and large game. Others offer unusual scenery or wildlife, which draws visitors who are willing to pay for guides and transportation. Fishing also is an attraction in parts of these poorly drained lands.

The relative inaccessibility of swamps and marshes, like mountains, may provide refuge for cultural groups who wish to preserve their way of life with as little interference as possible from others. "Swamp folk" are scattered throughout the world.

Surface materials: types, distribution, and significances

The inorganic rock and mineral material that lies at the surface of the earth is an essential factor in man's physical environment. The rock crust of the earth is far from uniform in its general characteristics. A visitor to the edge of the Grand Canyon sees before him a spectacular example of rock variety, expressed in color and texture and in the differential resistance to weathering and stream erosion. The solid rock that underlies all land surfaces is usually overlain by a mantle of unconsolidated rock debris. The unconsolidated material, of variable depth, may or may not be derived from the underlying rock. Some of the fragmental debris may have been transported long distances by rivers, glaciers, wind, or ocean currents. After exposure at the surface for many years, soils form out of the unconsolidated mantle of the earth. The properties of the soils, in turn, are influenced by many factors other than the mineralogical characteristics of the surface materials. In summary, the infinite variety of surface materials is the result of three

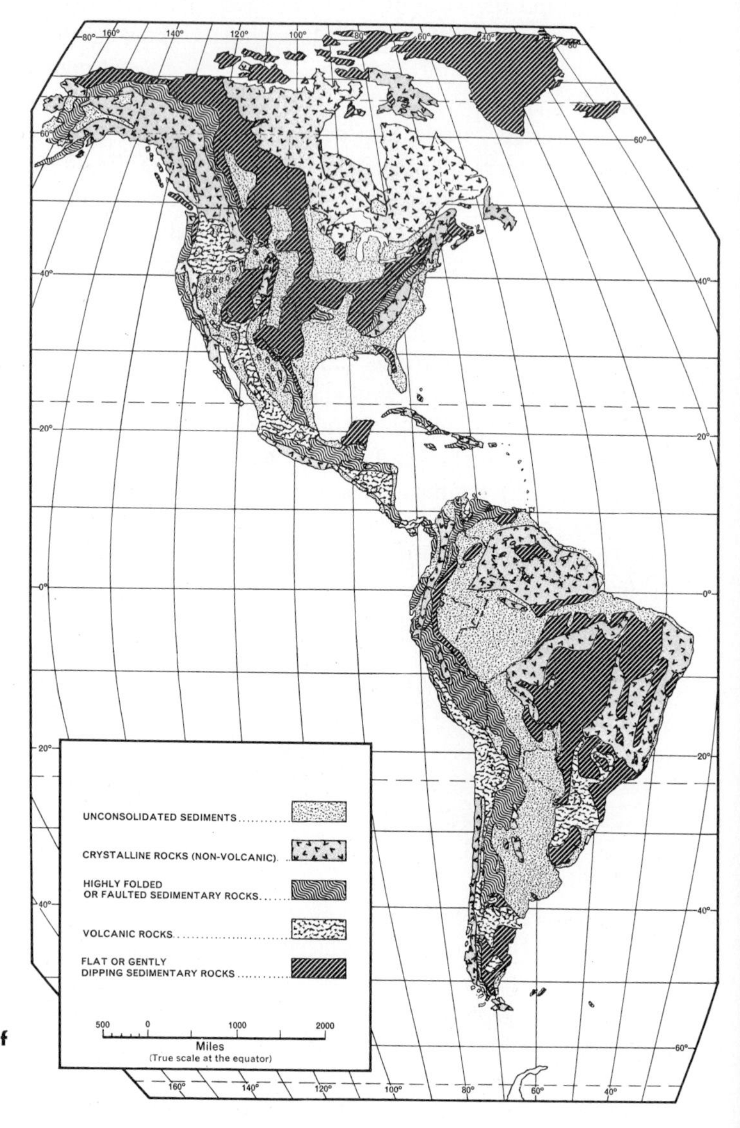

FIG. 5.13 World distribution of surface materials.

main factors: (1) the wide variety of rock types underlying the surface, related in form and composition to the many conditions that affect rock development, both upon and below the earth surface; (2) the existence of fragmental material, carried long distances by many transporting agents and deposited under variable local conditions; and (3) the modification of exposed material by atmospheric agencies and various soil-forming processes.

The significances of surface materials are almost as varied as their general characteristics. Differences in resistance to the general processes of rock breakdown and erosion are important factors in the development of landforms and surface relief. The chemical composition of rock material is one of the

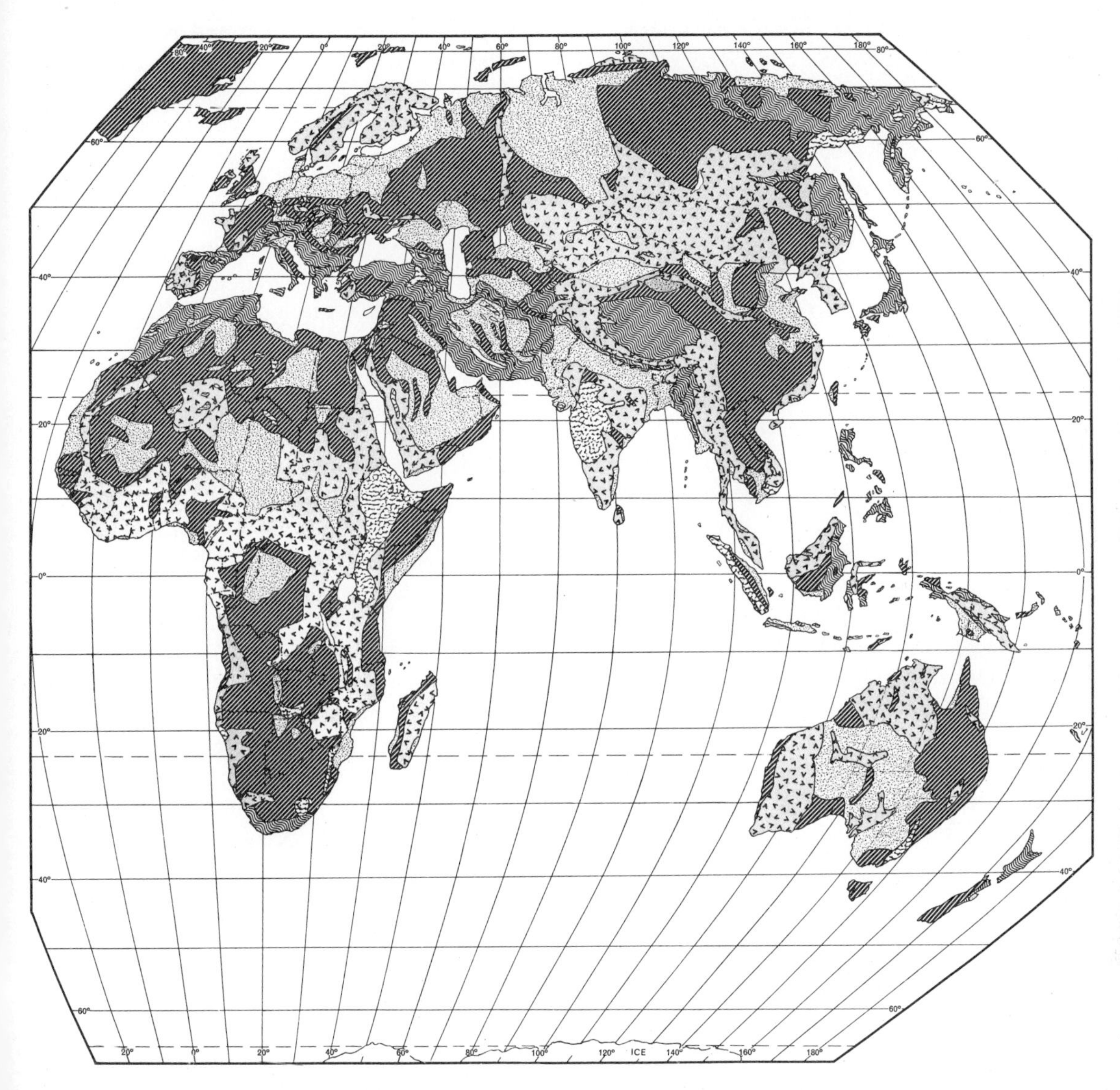

main factors influencing soil properties, including soil fertility and its implications for human welfare. Man utilizes the material beneath his feet in a host of ways, and he has taken advantage of differences in this material wherever he lives.

The scope of this section does not permit a detailed treatment of the enormous variety of surface materials that form the surface of the continents. Some 1,500 well-defined minerals have been identified, and rock types number in the hundreds. A brief outline of common rocks and a broad classification of surface materials are presented below, partly to show that a certain degree of likeness can be found over broad areas and partly to give the reader at least an introduction to this important part of his physical environment.

5.13 IGNEOUS, SEDIMENTARY, AND METAMORPHIC ROCKS.

Rocks are solid, natural aggregates of a mineral or minerals. In classifying the large variety of rocks, geologists have long recognized three major types—*igneous, sedimentary,* and *metamorphic.*

IGNEOUS ROCKS. Igneous rocks are those which have solidified from a molten state. They differ in mineral or chemical composition and in the degree to which crystallization has appeared in the solidification process. According to chemical composition, igneous rocks can be subdivided into two broad groups, which grade into each other: *acidic* and *basic* rocks. The former are those which tend to be high in silica (silicon tends to form silicic acid easily, hence the term acidic) and relatively low in such elements as calcium, magnesium, and iron (common bases). Acidic rocks also tend to be light in color, relatively light in weight, and especially abundant in *quartz* (SiO_2) and *orthoclase* (a variety of potash feldspar). In contrast, the basic igneous rocks are dark in color, low in silica, high in bases, somewhat heavier than acidic rocks, and generally abundant in *hornblende, pyroxene,* and *olivene.*

A second classification of igneous rocks refers to the degree of crystallization during the cooling process. Under some conditions of chemical composition and rapid cooling, the molten rock may solidify into a noncrystalline, glassy solid such as *obsidian,* or volcanic glass. Where the cooling is slower, as it is when it occurs far below the surface, the mineral crystals in rocks grow gradually and may form a coarsely granular or *granitic*[4] texture. An even, fine-textured, crystalline texture is termed *aphanitic.* A mixture of large crystals set in a matrix of finer crystals is termed *porphyritic.*

Igneous rocks of volcanic origin, or those ejected at the surface from a volcanic vent, often are termed *extrusive,* and those which have solidified below the surface are termed *intrusive.* Most extrusive igneous rocks are aphanitic or glassy in texture, whereas the intrusive types are likely to be granitic.

SEDIMENTARY ROCKS. Sedimentary rocks are those which have resulted from the cementation, compaction, or hardening of depositional sediments. They may include fragmental materials, such as sand or gravel; fine-textured materials, such as clay or silt; or even chemical precipitates, such as lime oozes or silica gels. For this reason, sedimentary rocks usually occur in distinct beds or

[4] The term *granitic* is not synonymous with *granite,* but it signifies a *granitelike,* or coarsely crystalline, texture. Granite itself is a distinct type of coarsely textured acidic igneous rock composed largely of quartz and orthoclase feldspar.

TABLE 5.1 Classification of some common igneous rocks

TEXTURE	ACIDIC (LIGHT IN COLOR, HIGH IN SILICA, LOW IN BASES; HIGH MELTING POINT)	INTERMEDIATE	BASIC (DARK IN COLOR, LOW IN SILICA, HIGH IN BASES; LOW MELTING POINT)
Granitic	Granite (+ quartz), syenite (− quartz)	Diorite	Gabbro, augite, pyroxenite
Aphanitic	Felsite	Andesite	Basalt, diabase
Vesicular (full of holes)	Pumice		Scoria

strata. The more usual types of sedimentary rocks are shown in Table 5.2.

METAMORPHIC ROCKS. *Metamorphic* rocks are those that have been altered in form when in a solid state, mainly as the result of pressure, heat, or chemical reactions. Probably the most common causes of rock metamorphism are the compressional stresses associated with mountain building or other warpings of the earth crust. The results of metamorphism vary with the type of rock undergoing change and the intensity of the alteration. Limestone, for example, when subjected to great heat and pressure, has its amorphous calcium carbonate molecules rearranged into a crystalline structure and becomes *marble,* a metamorphic rock. Sandstone may undergo a change in which its individual sand particles fuse together to form *quartzite.* The alteration of shale to *slate,* and bituminous coal to *anthracite,* further illustrates the transformation of sedimentary rocks into metamorphic rocks.

Igneous rocks may also undergo metamorphism, especially deep within the earth crust, where rock pressures and temperatures are extremely high. Such environments may rearrange atomic structures within some of the common rock minerals. The *micas,* which are a family of minerals with a characteristic arrangement of molecules in bundles of flat sheets or flakes, are frequently encountered in rocks that have undergone extreme pressure-metamorphism. Metamorphic rocks that have a laminated or leaf-like structure, owing to the abundance of the platy crystals such as mica, are known as *schists.* Sometimes entirely different mineral crystals begin to grow among the flat schist minerals, finding favorable conditions for crystal growth in the intense heat and pressure. Many of our precious stones, such as garnet or tourmaline, have been formed under such extreme metamorphism.

Under somewhat less pressure and temperature, igneous rocks such as granites and diorites may be altered by rearranging the constituent minerals into rough parallel bands. Such a banded crystalline metamorphic rock is known as a *gneiss.* The gneisses and schists are often found in the great continental shields and in the cores of ancient eroded mountain ranges.

TABLE 5.2 Types of sedimentary rocks

SEDIMENTARY ROCK	CORRESPONDING SEDIMENT
Conglomerate	Gravels, rounded pebbles
Sandstone	Sand
Shale	Muds, clays
Limestone	Lime oozes, marine shells, chalk, marl, etc.
Chert and flint	Precipitated silica gels
Siltstones, graywacke	Silts
Bituminous coal	Peats

5.14 A GENERAL CLASSIFICATION OF SURFACE MATERIALS. The classification of surface materials presented below includes both rocks and fragmental materials. It does not include soils, which are treated as a separate environmental factor in later chapters. The classification utilizes five major groups:

1. Nonvolcanic crystalline rocks: granitic intrusive igneous rocks and some of the crystalline metamorphics, such as gneiss or schist
2. Volcanic (extrusive) or near-volcanic rocks: lavas of various types, including some aphanitic types that may have cooled a short distance below the earth surface
3. Relatively undisturbed sedimentary rocks: rocks in horizontal or gently dipping strata
4. Steeply folded or contorted sedimentary or former sedimentary rocks: rocks in beds or strata that have been folded or buckled into various forms
5. Unconsolidated or fragmental inorganic material: sediments and rock debris, which may later form soils or become sedimentary rock

FIG. 5.14 Gneiss, a banded crystalline rock that is folded and contorted under heat and pressure, in Hampshire County, Mass. [U.S. Geological Survey; W. C. Alden]

Each of these five categories is discussed separately in succeeding sections of the chapter.

5.15 NONVOLCANIC CRYSTALLINE ROCKS. Nonvolcanic crystalline rocks constitute a large part of the outer crust of the earth and form what is known as the *basement complex*. This term is appropriate, because these highly diverse crystalline rocks underlie the entire earth surface, being hidden only by a relatively thin veneer of other rocks and fragmental materials. Nearly all these crystalline rocks once were molten, although under different conditions of heat and pressure. Formed well within the crust, they have reached the surface through crustal deformation and through the removal of overlying material by erosion. They are exposed at the surface principally in two types of areas—in the great continental shields and in the cores of mountain ranges.

Although a large variety of rock types is included, *granite* and its close "cousin," *syenite,* make up an exceedingly large proportion of the total land surface within the continental shields. They are also found in the cores of mountain ranges, but the crystalline metamorphic rocks, such as the schists and gneisses, are frequently encountered here as well. Although we do not know for certain, evidence derived from seismographic records indicates that the "basement" rocks below the ocean basins are predominantly the dark, basic igneous types rather than the light-colored, acidic types which prevail over the continents. Geologists recognize the light, acidic, continental rocks as *sial* (a term derived from the chemical symbols for *si*licon and *al*uminum) and the dark, heavy, basic rocks as *sima* (so-called because of their high proportion of *olivene,* a complex *si*licate of *ma*gnesium). It is believed that the sima also underlies the continents, but at a great depth. The dark sima rocks found on continents usually have worked their way in molten form through the sial toward the surface; hence they are usually of relatively small areal extent.

Solid rock rarely remains solid for long when it is exposed at the surface to *weathering,* that is, to the general attack of atmospheric agents. The crystalline igneous and metamorphic rocks are no exception, despite the general hardness of their included minerals. As a rule, they are fairly resistant to the mechanical forms of weathering (*disintegration*), or the processes of making "little rocks out of big ones," except in areas where such rocks are highly fractured. For this reason, these rocks generally form soil exceedingly slowly in arid or very cold regions. Wherever water is present, however, they break down relatively rapidly under the various chemical processes of rock *decomposition*—rapidly, that is, in terms of geologic processes, if not by our customary measurement in years. Aiding in the chemical decay of the crystalline rocks are a variety of included minerals, some of which (like the feldspars) are particularly vulnerable to attack by weak acids in nature. Since the chemical breakdown of even one important included mineral may be sufficient to crumble such rocks, they rarely form prominent terrain features in warm, humid regions, though they do so in dry or cold areas. The resistance of these crystalline rocks in cool areas is exemplified in the northeastern United States, where the hard crystalline rocks of the Adirondack and White Mountains stand out in bold relief from the sedimentary rocks of the adjacent lowlands. The crystalline uplands of Brazil, on the other hand, have a much more subdued surface than adjacent steep-faced, tabular highland blocks of sandstones and limestones. Many exceptions, however, can be found to such correlations of relief, climate, and rock composition. Differences in crustal deformation and in the length of time that erosion and weathering have been operative are among the factors that may account for such exceptions.

The areas of nonvolcanic crystalline rock are characterized by a general uniformity of slope conditions. The composition of the rocks is likely to be fairly regular over broad areas. Unequal weathering or erosion, therefore, does not provide the sharp local contrasts of relief texture that are so frequently encountered in the areas of other rock groups. The etching of the land surface, whether in mountain chains or in the shields, proceeds fairly uniformly. Ridge lines and valley lines are irregular, and long parallel ridges are rare. The Canadian shield presents a typical pattern of a vast sea of hilly rock knobs rising in a monotonous confusion from irregular land-surface depressions between them.

5.16 VOLCANIC ROCKS. The distribution of volcanoes, mainly in a circum-Pacific belt and a transverse east-west belt, has been noted earlier (see the sections on volcanic landforms in Chapter 3). This distribution conforms closely to that of the principal mountain belts and corresponds to the present lines of weakness in the earth crust.

The map of surface materials (Fig. 5.13) indicates that large areas of volcanic rocks are found apart from the areas of present active volcanoes. The large sheets of basalt (a black, fine-grained lava) located on the Deccan Plateau of India, in southern Brazil, and Ethiopia are examples. The Columbia Plateau of eastern Washington and Oregon contains some 200,000 square miles of lava flows, much of which is composed of basalt. Although thicknesses of 5,000 feet can be found here, the average thickness is about 200 feet. The basaltic lavas comprise the largest areas of volcanic rocks in the world. They resulted from highly fluid lavas welling up to the surface along cracks and fissures and spreading outward in all directions. The lavas of the Hawaiian volcanoes are the only contemporary outpourings that somewhat resemble the great basaltic flows of previous geologic periods. Most of the present active volcanoes are of the explosive type, more spectacular in eruption but much more limited in areal extent.

Volcanic rocks, which commonly contain holes or gas pockets, do not have the durability of the intrusive igneous rocks, hence are seldom quarried except for use as crushed stone. Also, unlike the intrusive rocks, they are not likely to contain valuable metallic mineral veins, although some of our most precious gems, such as diamonds, rubies, and emeralds, are found in old volcanic rocks. The holes in ancient porous lavas have sometimes been filled with molten metals, as exemplified by the copper ores of Northern Michigan and the gold ores of South Africa. Sulfur is extracted from craters of active or recently active explosive volcanoes, since sulfur dioxide is one of the common gases discharged during this type of eruption. Both Italy and Japan are self-sufficient in this important resource because of their volcanic areas. Most of the explosive volcanoes release fragmental material in the form of cinders and ash. These volcanic ejecta are discussed later, in connection with special forms of unconsolidated surface materials.

The basalts, which form so much of the world area of volcanic rocks, are highly important because of the fertility of the soils that usually are derived from them. These rocks are fairly porous, they crumble quickly in tropical environments, and they form thick soils containing high proportions of calcium and magnesium, bases that are essential in good soils. The cotton of India and the coffee of Brazil owe much to the inherent fertility of the soils weathered from these rocks. Some lava flows, however, are composed of light-colored rocks, such as *rhyolites* or *felsites*, that are high in silica and low in bases. Lavas of this type underlie much of the Snake River high plains in southern Idaho. In general, wherever found, the rhyolitic lavas tend to develop soils that are not nearly so fertile as those derived from the basalts.

5.17 LEVEL–TO–GENTLY DIPPING SEDIMENTARY ROCKS. The level or gently sloping rocks include sandstones, limestones, shales, and conglomerates, which result, respectively, from the compaction and cementation of sand, lime oozes or shell debris, clays, and gravels. They are formed by the deposition of material in shallow seas or low continental basins. A comparison of the map of their distribution (Fig. 5.13) with that of the zones of crustal instability (Fig. 4.7) indicates that sandstones, shales, etc., occur most commonly in the central, relatively stable zone of the continents, between

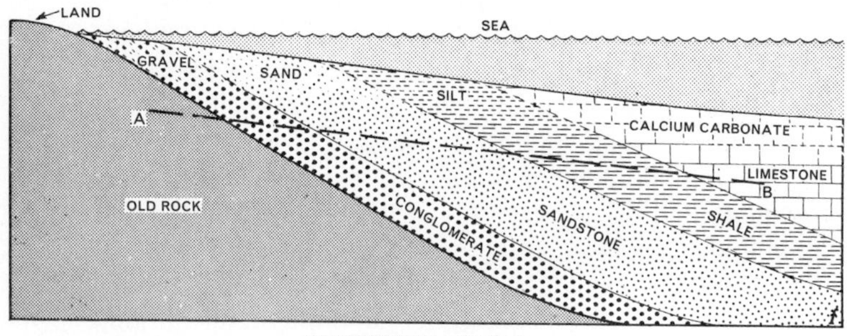

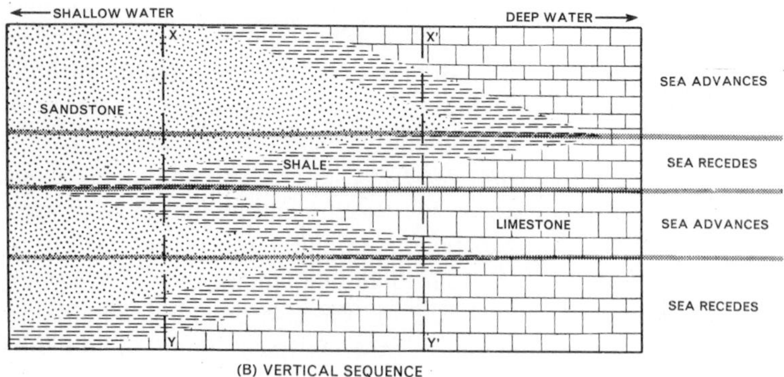

FIG. 5.15 Typical stratigraphic sections in sedimentary rocks. The horizontal sequence (A) from coarse to fine material with increasing depth of water is typical of relatively stable coastlines. Rapid fluctuations in sea level, however, may produce complex vertical rock-strata sequences (B). Two well records of rock sequences (x-y and x'-y'), relatively near each other, may vary widely in rock characteristics.

the shields and the peripheral zone of strong instability and mountain building. These sedimentary rocks usually are in layers, superimposed upon one another. Sheets of limestone may be overlain by shales or sandstones, and such a stratification reflects the differences that occurred from time to time in the local depositional environment. Sandstones may likewise grade laterally into other types of sedimentary rocks, and this indicates transitions from former shallow-water to deep-water conditions. The vertical and horizontal variability in sedimentary rock types results in sharp geographic contrasts from region to region. These rocks vary surprisingly in both physical and chemical properties and hence react quite differently to the various processes of physical and chemical weathering. Some limestones, particularly the purer and highly fractured varieties, weather rapidly under humid conditions, owing to their susceptibility to solution; others, because of their compact, dense nature, form hills and cliffs in both humid tropical areas and dry regions. Sandstones and conglomerates have variable degrees of resistance to erosion and weathering, depending on the durability of the cement that holds the grains together. Shales are soft and erode easily, but they are unusually resistant to further chemical alteration, since they represent chemically decomposed mineral material to begin with. As might be expected, the soils that result from the physical and chemical breakdown of these rocks show strong contrasts, particularly when they are young.

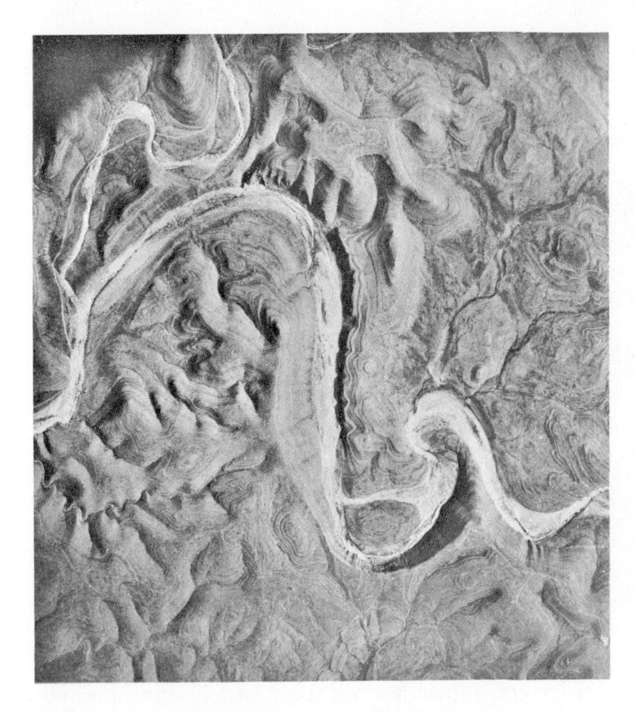

FIG. 5.16 Stream dissection and wind scour in an area of thin, flat-lying sedimentary rock strata, Dark Canyon River, New Mexico. The similarity in pattern between the succession of rock benches and contour lines is striking. [U.S. Air Force (MATS)]

The wide regional differences in surface configuration in sedimentary-rock areas can be illustrated by comparing the karst limestone topography described in Sec. 3.4 with a typical hilly landscape in the Appalachian Plateau. Durable sandstones or conglomerates in the latter form a cap rock which helps to protect weaker underlying shales and limestones. Once streams are able to cut through this cap rock, they rapidly erode the underlying material, forming steep-sided ravines edged by rock ledges, which represent the more durable rock layers. Differential erosion of sedimentary strata in arid regions is even more marked, as can be observed in a view of the Grand Canyon of the Colorado River (see Fig. 4.16). Cliffs mark the change from an area underlain by weak rock layers to one of more durable rocks. Such cliffs are particularly common where the rock layers dip slightly, as is shown in the cuestas of Fig. 3.39.

The economic significance of sedimentary rocks probably is far greater than that of igneous or metamorphic rocks. Sandstone

FIG. 5.17 Steeply dipping sedimentary rock strata in the Andes of Colombia, near Ubate.
Note the serious soil erosion that has followed cultivation and exposed the underlying rock beds. [Standard Oil Company (N.J.)]

and limestone are used widely for building, because they are relatively easily quarried and shaped. Cement is obtained from processing certain kinds of limestones. Shales are used as a source of clay for pottery and tile or as refractory materials. Because many of the sedimentary rocks, especially sandstones, are porous and permeable to water, they form subsurface reservoirs of ground water. Artesian systems (see Sec. 14.3), which supply water in many parts of the world, are found in areas of gently dipping sedimentary rocks. The most important mineral resources supplied by these rocks are the fossil fuels—coal, petroleum, and natural gas. These fuels originated in the processes of sedimentation and are found among sedimentary rock strata throughout many parts of the world. Salt, sulfur, gypsum, and mineral fertilizers also are found in such rocks.

5.18 FOLDED OR CONTORTED SEDIMENTARY ROCKS. The sedimentary rocks that have been subjected to strong regional stresses are folded or faulted into complex structural forms. Instead of lying in horizontal or gently dipping beds, these rocks may assume almost any conceivable angle or direction. When squeezed into tight folds, they may undergo some changes in form and become metamorphic rocks; for example, limestones may be altered to marble, shale to slate, sandstones to quartzite, or soft coal to anthracite. Usually, however, the succession of rock layers is still distinct.

The geographic distribution of the folded rocks is related to the unstable zones of the earth crust. In many parts of the world, the sedimentary debris that was deposited in troughs or basins adjacent to the high mountain regions was squeezed and elevated into uplands (see Fig. 5.18), after which erosion carved it into mountainous or hilly terrain. In some areas, such as in the Alps and in British Columbia (see Fig. 4.4), sediments containing the remains of marine organisms have been raised over 10,000 feet above sea level. In other areas, such as in the Middle Rocky Mountains and the Himalayas, the covering of sedimentary rocks has been removed from enormous arches and folds, so that the crystalline rocks beneath have been exposed. Remnants of the sedimentary folds flank the main ranges on each side. Erosion of folded rocks usually results in a distinct parallel arrangement of relief features. Long, continuous ridges and valleys result from both the initial upfolds (anticlines) and the downfolds (synclines) or from the differential erosion of rocks of different degrees of durability contained within the folds. The long ridge lines of the Northern Rocky Mountains, the eastern Andes, and the Alps are examples. In the folded Appalachian hill country, although previous mountains had been beveled by erosion, a later regional uplift caused erosion to etch out the weaker rocks, leaving the steeply dipping sandstone layers as long, prominent ridges. In a folded series of rocks in which quartzites, marbles, and slates are present, the latter two almost always tend to form lowlands, since they are much more susceptible to weathering and erosion. Quartzites, on the other hand, almost always tend to form ridges.

Settlement patterns and transportation routes in the areas of folded sediments show a close relationship to the parallel arrangements of the rock structures, mainly following the valleys oriented along the major axes of folding. Movement across these ridges and valleys is difficult, owing to the succession of steep grades. The resource significance of the folded rocks is generally not so great as that of the less disturbed sedimentary rocks, despite their similarity in chemical composition. Marble and slate are desired for specific uses, but the local variations in physical structure of the folded rocks are handicaps to large-scale quarrying. Petroleum and natural gas are rare in these rocks, generally having been squeezed out during the deformation processes. Anthracite, particularly desirable for space heating, is a monopoly of these areas, although the amount is small throughout the world. Lack of pore space prevents the folded sedimentary rocks from being significant as *aquifers* (water-bearing strata). The soils produced by these rocks are similar to those derived from the other sedimentary rocks, although local differences are likely to be greater.

5.19 UNCONSOLIDATED SURFACE MATERIALS. A large part of the land surface is underlain by loose, unconsolidated material. This rock debris was deposited after having been carried by natural transporting agents, such as rivers, wind, glacial ice, and ocean and lake currents. Great variety exists in this material, since it was derived from rocks of all types, worked on by various weathering and erosive forces for variable lengths of time, and deposited under different conditions. The map showing the location of unconsolidated materials throughout the world (Fig. 5.13) indicates a widespread pattern of distribution. There is a tendency, however, for such materials to be particularly common in the areas of plains. Exceptions to this on a global scale include only the fragmental ejections of volcanoes in mountain regions, the thick deposits of *loess* (wind-blown dust) that mantle some of the hilly terrain in northwestern China, and glacial rock debris derived from continental ice sheets that deposited material over highlands and lowlands alike. The following paragraphs present a series of broad generalizations concerning the nature and significance of different types of fragmental surface materials, classified according to their transporting agent.

ALLUVIUM. One of the most significant types of fragmental surface material is alluvium, or the rock debris carried and deposited by streams and rivers. It is found principally along the flood plains of rivers and on the gently sloping surfaces which usually mark the junction of mountains and plains. The alluvium of flood plains

FIG. 5.18 Complexly folded sedimentary strata. These flattened rock folds, termed nappes, are common in the zones of high compression found in some of the high mountain systems of the world. The Alps are especially typical. [After von Englen]

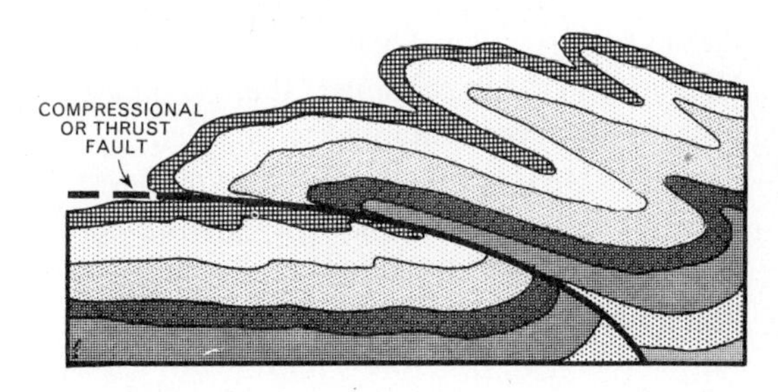

and deltas generally provides unusually fertile soil material. Its texture, usually intermediate between sand and clay, is not too fine, yet is open enough for easy cultivation and drainage. It is composed of a wide variety of small rock fragments recently derived from the entire drainage basin and thoroughly mixed by the turbulent river waters; hence it is not likely to be deficient in any of the essential plant-food minerals. It is generally dark in color, owing to the organic material derived from topsoils upstream or formed in place, and the organic content improves its ability to hold plant foods and moisture.

The principal disadvantage of alluvium lies in its position. Having been formed from river overflow, it is subject to flooding, and its flat, low position is a handicap in draining off surplus water. When adequately ditched and protected, however, alluvial soils are among the most productive in the world. Most of the dense rural populations of the globe are located on alluvial soils.

The material of the alluvial plains bordering mountain regions, especially in dry areas, is likely to be coarser than that of flood plains, since it was deposited by swift mountain streams that suddenly decreased in velocity as they debouched onto adjacent plains. Since swift streams can carry coarser material than large, sluggish rivers, they deposit this coarser material when forced to drop their loads. These *piedmont alluvial plains* are choice areas for agriculture in dry regions, since their surfaces provide ideal conditions for irrigation. Their permeable texture also drains off surplus water, thus helping to prevent the accumulation of toxic salts.

LACUSTRINE AND MARINE SEDIMENTS. Most of the rock debris carried by rivers and streams is finally deposited in the ocean or in lakes. Material deposited in lakes is termed *lacustrine*. Currents driven by winds or tides generally distribute this material into bands or zones, with the coarsest sands and gravels along the shore and the finer clays and silts settling in the quieter, deeper water farther out. The erosion of shore lines by waves and currents also provides fragmental material for redistribution. The banded zones of marine sediments recently raised above sea level are well illustrated by the arrangement of material along the Atlantic and Gulf of Mexico coastal plains. Strong contrasts between heavy clays, lime muds (marls), and coarse sands are characteristic of marine sediments.

Both lake sediments and marine sediments become flat plains after their emergence as land surfaces. Because lake plains are generally smaller than plains of marine deposition, they are likely to have only relatively narrow zones of sandy beach material and broad areas of heavy clays. Tides are not present in lakes, and waves and currents normally do not have sufficient room to develop enough force to distribute coarse material far from shore. Many of the lake plains are in swamps or marshes. When these plains are properly drained and treated so as to loosen the structure of the clays, they can become productive agricultural areas. The sandy beach ridges which border them often are choice sites for fruit orchards, such as those bordering Lakes Michigan, Erie, and Ontario in the United States.

WIND-BLOWN SEDIMENTS. The deposits resulting from material carried by the wind include *sand dunes* and *loess*. The former cover considerable areas in the Sahara, central Arabia, the Thar Desert of northwestern India, the Tarim Basin of Sinkiang in central Asia, and about 20,000 square miles in the Sand Hills region of Nebraska. Narrow dune belts also border the sandy shore lines of oceans and large lakes. Among the best known are those along the eastern side of Lake Michigan and along the southwestern coast of France, the Landes district. Some dune sands, particularly those having an unusually high proportion of quartz grains, are utilized for the preparation of refractory molds, owing to their uniform fine texture and their heat resistance.

Deposits of *loess,* generally believed to be accumulations of wind-blown dust, are found along the leeward margins of some deserts and in areas that once bordered continental glaciers and glacial drainage ways (see Fig. 5.21). Loess is a unique material. Usually yellowish-brown in color, it has a remarkably even, silty texture and is free of stones. A small quantity, if rubbed between the fingers, will disappear in the small pore openings of the skin. One of the distinctive properties of most loess deposits is a vertical, columnar structure, or jointing. This property, which is exhibited by deposits several feet in thickness, is believed to be largely a result of the angularity of the dust fragments, which causes an interlocking of the particles following settling out of the air. This tendency to split into vertical columns makes it possible for loess deposits to retain vertical slopes for long periods without slumping (see Fig. 5.19). Following cultivation, however, which destroys the columnar structure, loess is extremely susceptible to erosion by rainwash or gullying. Where gullying takes place in loess, a distinctive rectangular pattern of steep-sided gullies evolves. Another feature of many loess deposits is the presence of small nodules or masses of calcium carbonate in weathered material.

FIG. 5.19 Exposure of loess along a road cut near Vicksburgh, Miss. Note the columnar structure. Initials carved in the vertical face of the loess columns may remain for years (see lower right), yet where a little water trickles over the side of the cliff, the loess erodes easily. [U.S. Geological Survey; E. W. Shaw]

The largest deposits of loess in the world are found in northwestern China, in the vicinity of the great bend in the Yellow River (Hwang Ho), where it has accumulated up to thicknesses of 300 feet. The loess associated with continental glaciation had its main source in the drainage ways that carried melt water from the ice sheets. These wide drainage channels were choked with the debris derived from the ice masses. During winter seasons in the waning stages of glaciation, these flood plains were dry and barren. Wind swirled great clouds of dust out of the valleys onto the adjacent interstream areas. Even the uplands between the ice margins and the encroaching vegetation must have been dusty places, littered as they were with the material produced from glacial abrasion. Such loess material mantled much of the flat-to-rolling plains of Illinois, Iowa, southern Wisconsin, and other central states; the Palouse country of eastern Washington; parts of Germany; and large areas in the western Ukraine east of the Carpathian Mountains. The North China plain also contains much loess material that has been carried by the Yellow River from its drainage basin and redeposited on its delta and lower flood plain as alluvium. It is believed by some that the stoneless, silty soils of the Argentine pampas may have been loess, redeposited by streams.

Loess forms fertile soils where there is sufficient rainfall for agriculture and where it has not remained in place long enough to have been thoroughly weathered by soil-forming processes. Along the Mississippi River, the loess deposited fairly recently, or shortly after the last advance of the Wisconsin ice sheet, is much more fertile than the older loess, which was laid down during the interglacial periods, hundreds of thousands of years earlier. The steep, vertical loess cliffs along the sides of valleys in the Chinese loess country are honeycombed in many places with cave dwellings, excavated in the compact silt. Excavations made in the loess or loesslike cliffs along the Mississippi River at Vicksburg were a factor in the stubborn defense of this city during the Civil War.

FRAGMENTAL VOLCANIC MATERIAL. Explosive volcanoes eject large quantities of ash and cinders. Although these deposits are seldom extensive enough to appear on a small-scale global map, they are of considerable local importance. Small ash plateaus and ash-filled basins adjoin symmetrical cone-shaped explosive volcanoes in Central America, western South America, Indonesia, Japan, Italy, and Alaska. The chemical composition

FIG. 5.20 Loess country in southern Shensi Province, northwestern China. Despite centuries of care in terracing hillsides, gullies continue to cut into the thick deposits of wind-blown dust. [U.S. Air Force (MATS)]

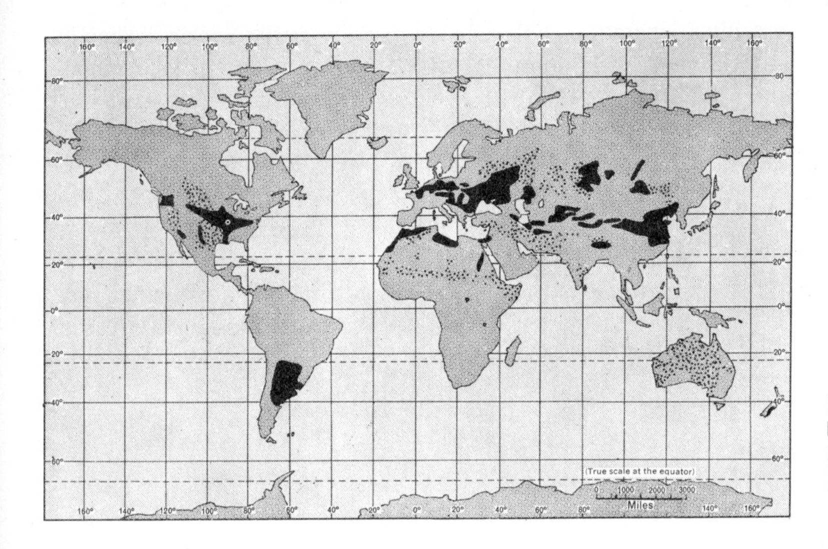

FIG. 5.21 World distribution of loess deposits. The dotted areas indicate scattered occurrences. [After Lobeck]

of the ejected material varies considerably and influences its suitability for agricultural soils. The ash of some volcanoes is unusually rich in plant foods, and since this material is relatively recent, it has not been excessively leached by rainfall. Despite the constant danger of recurrent eruptions, agricultural settlements extend well up the slopes of volcanic cones in many parts of the world. The high agricultural productivity of Java, which supports some 50 million people despite its small size, is largely the result of its soils, most of which are derived from volcanic ash. The ash soils of Central America, the Philippines, and Italy also are prized. Those of Japan, on the other hand, are low in plant foods, high in silica, and consequently much less valuable for agricultural purposes.

FRAGMENTAL GLACIAL MATERIAL. Fragmental glacial material is discussed at length in the section on depositional landforms of continental glaciation (see Sec. 3.13).

Perspective

Slope, elevation, drainage, and surface materials, each in its own way, help to form the physical world of man. Slope operates to assist or hinder man in many different ways, and we have seen how its effects are altered by changes in human cultural patterns. There are several methods of measuring differences in slope conditions, and each serves a useful function. Elevation alone does not appear to hinder man a great deal, except in areas 10,000 feet or more above sea level, but other factors that are frequently associated with it, such as slope and temperature, may be extremely important.

Surface waters and drainage conditions, which are irregularly distributed over the earth, interact with the other elements of physical geography to provide the changing stage settings on which the human drama takes place.

The inorganic rock and mineral material, both solid and fragmental, that underlies the surface of the earth also varies greatly from place to place. Differing in chemical composition as well as in physical properties, the rock and mineral types also vary in their resistance to weathering and in their usefulness to man. Their influence on landforms varies with contrasting climatic conditions.

As a general rule, the crystalline igneous rocks prove quite resistant under dry and cold conditions but decay and crumble under moist tropical conditions. The sedimentary rocks show different degrees of durability, depending on composition, structure, and climate.

The distribution of underlying materials is roughly correlated with the major structural zones of the earth crust. The continental platforms are made up largely of light-colored, low-density siallic rocks, especially granite, which appear at the surface mainly in the great shields and in the cores of high mountain cordilleras. The relatively undisturbed strata of sedimentary rocks cover broad expanses in the continental plains that separate the shields from the unstable mountain and basin zones of the continental borders. The location of fragmental materials corresponds fairly closely to areas of low relief.

6

Temperature, humidity, and precipitation

The ocean of air which flows everywhere about us constitutes the most changeable feature in our physical environment. Day by day, and hour by hour, fluctuations occur in its movement, in its pressure, and in its content of heat and moisture. We speak of the momentary conditions of the atmosphere as *weather,* and in parts of the world that experience great day-by-day fluctuations, weather becomes an important topic of conversation and a significant factor in daily decisions. The broad generalizations of weather conditions are known as *climate.* The pattern of climates in the world plays a major role in the kind of crops we grow, the kinds of trees that make up our forests, the amount of our yearly budgets spent on heating or cooling our homes, and the type of clothing we wear.

The geography of climates exemplifies the basic principles, or concepts, of natural distributions described in Chapter 1. First, climates exhibit infinite variety. They include associations of many different aspects of atmospheric conditions, such as temperature, precipitation, pressure, and winds. Because of this, and also because of the large number of factors influencing each of these variables, no spot on earth is likely to duplicate exactly all the climatic characteristics found in another. There are, however, certain broad similarities between different parts of the earth, and these make regional classifications of climate possible.

Second, climates differ from place to place through various degrees of transition. In some areas the gradients of change are steep, whereas in others change takes place slowly with distance. Differences in weather and climate, furthermore, are found vertically as well as horizontally, from the surface of the earth to heights many miles above it.[1] As with the other environmental elements, the details of areal and vertical differentiation become more noticeable with increased scales of observation.

Third, the atmosphere exhibits the property of alteration with time that characterizes

[1] A large part of the observational data on weather conditions is collected from instruments located at a standardized height of 4½ feet above the ground. Reliable observational data for the upper air have been accumulating for only a few decades and have been recorded at only a relatively few scattered weather stations on earth.

the other elements of the physical environment. The short- and long-term changes that occur continually must be generalized in any portrayal of weather and climate. Man is forced to select certain generalizations, such as averages, as his criteria for describing climates.

Last, climate, like slope, vegetation, and soils, is part of a general environmental association whose constituent elements are interactive, thus tending toward both short- and long-term environmental equilibria. Individual elements in the association may change from time to time, postponing the development of such equilibria, but the tendency or trend is generally present. Surface configuration and climate, for example, exert a definite influence upon each other; similarly, an interaction takes place between vegetation and climate as well as between man and climate.

Although climatology has had only a short history, it already has indicated that there can be no universally applicable system for

TABLE 6.1 Climatic factors in housing design

	HOUSING ELEMENTS *					
CLIMATIC FACTORS	SITE, DIRECTION, PLANNING	INTERIOR LAYOUT	ROOF AND WALLS	OPENINGS	FOUNDATION AND BASEMENT	MECHANICAL EQUIPMENT (FOR HOUSE)
THERMAL HEAT						
Temperature frequencies	X	X	X	X	X	X
Frequency of hot and cold days	X					X
Degree-days		X				X
RADIATION						
Sunshine hours	X			X		X
Clear and cloudy days		X	X		X	X
Solar intensity	X	X	X	X		
Solar height		X	X	X		
WINDS						
Wind direction	X	X	X	X		X
Wind speed	X	X		X		X
Strong winds			X			
ATMOSPHERIC MOISTURE						
Precipitation	X	X	X	X		X
Snowfall	X		X	X		
Excess precipitation	X		X	X	X	X
Rainy days	X	X		X		
Fogs				X		
Thunderstorms						X
Humidity		X	X	X	X	X

SOURCE: Reproduced by permission from H. E. Landsberg and Woodrow C. Jacobs, "Applied Climatology." *Compendium of Meteorology,* American Meteorological Society, Boston, 1951, p. 982. Published through the support and sponsorship extended by the Geophysics Research Directorate, Air Force Cambridge Research Center, Air Research and Development Command.

* Crosses (X) are entered for those elements which are of some importance in the design of the particular feature.

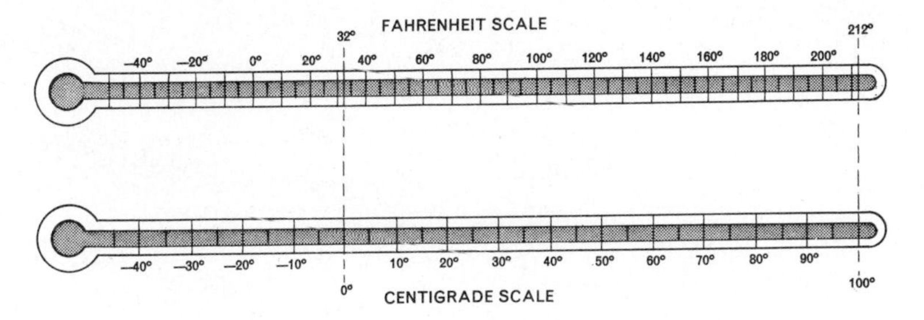

FIG. 6.1 Graphic conversion scale for Centigrade and Fahrenheit temperatures. Note that the two scales meet at −40°.

classifying climatic differences, because the requirements for generalizations change with both the scale of observational measurement and the purposes for which they are made. As indicated in Table 6.1, the problem of designing houses requires knowledge of many different elements of climate. Even more complex are the climatic variables involved in efficient agriculture. Such factors as the probability of late frosts, the reliability of rainfall, and the amount of cloudiness may be of minor significance in designing a house, but they usually are critical in agriculture. A building, furthermore, occupies only a small site, so that areal differences in climate are negligible. Broad, cultivated fields, on the other hand, may well have differences in susceptibility to frost, exposure to wind, and rate of evaporation that may be extremely critical in farming.

Three chapters are devoted to climate in this textbook. The first two deal with the description and analysis of global patterns for each of the major climatic elements individually, including, in order, temperature, humidity, precipitation, pressure, winds, air masses, and storms. The third chapter considers the climatic elements in combination, presenting and interpreting the over-all details of world climatic regions. The reader should keep in mind that progress in climatological research is constantly being made, and as new observational data accumulate, old descriptive generalizations and explanatory hypotheses often must be discarded. Climatological summaries such as those presented in these three chapters generally require revision every few years.

Temperature

Temperature is a measurement of the quantity of heat present in a particular mass. Heat, in turn, is a form of energy. There are several forms of energy in nature besides heat. Among these are chemical energy, electrical energy, and radiant energy. Each may be converted into the others, both by man and by nature. The heat energy contained within that part of the atmosphere that flows about our bodies, however, appears to have a more personal relationship to us than the other types of energy. We sense relatively small variations in it and alter our lives correspondingly almost every day by making adjustments in our food, clothing, and shelter. Variations in the heat content of the atmosphere, moreover, have far greater significances in our study of global physical patterns than the impacts they make on individual human sensibilities.

The Fahrenheit and centigrade scales are the systems usually used for expressing temperature differences. The Fahrenheit scale is not so convenient in many ways as the centigrade scale, which is based on degrees that are one-hundredth the difference in temperature between the freezing point and the boiling point of water at sea level. Tradition, however, is a powerful motivating factor, and

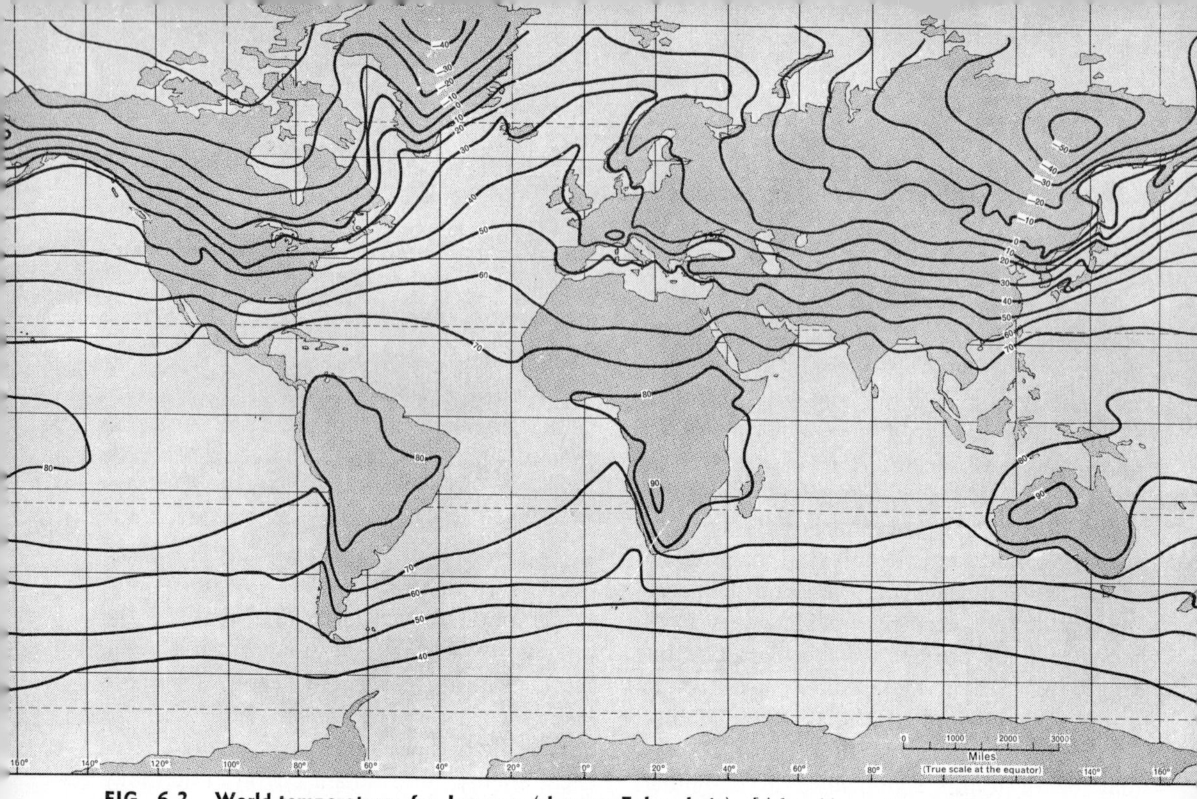

FIG. 6.2 World temperatures for January (degrees Fahrenheit). [After Haurwitz and Austin]

because the Fahrenheit scale is customarily used in the United States, it will be used throughout this text, except where the centigrade scale is specifically designated. The conversion from Fahrenheit to centigrade or vice versa can be done easily through the use of the formulas $C = \frac{5}{9}(F - 32)$ and $F = \frac{9}{5}C + 32$. For convenience, however, a graphic conversion scale is presented in Fig. 6.1.

The range of temperatures at the surface of the earth is extremely small compared with the range that astronomers tell us is encountered in outer space. The absolute range between the highest and lowest temperature ever recorded at standardized weather stations on earth is about 250°F, and it rarely exceeds 100°F over most of the earth. Small as our earthly temperature range may be, it is of prime importance to life on earth. Included within it are all the complexities of the geography of world temperatures, which are of great significance to man and toward which we now turn our attention.

In our study of the global distribution of temperature, we shall first examine areal patterns of temperature and then investigate the major factors responsible for these patterns. Finally, we shall consider a few of the human implications of temperature differences.

6.1 THE GLOBAL GENERALIZATIONS OF TEMPERATURE DIFFERENCES.

Figures 6.2 to 6.4 indicate the generalized patterns of global *isotherms* (lines connecting points of equal temperature), with temperature readings equated to sea level. Sea-level temperatures are calculated by increasing observed temperatures 3.6°F for each 1,000 feet of station elevation. This figure corresponds to the normal average *lapse rate,* or the de-

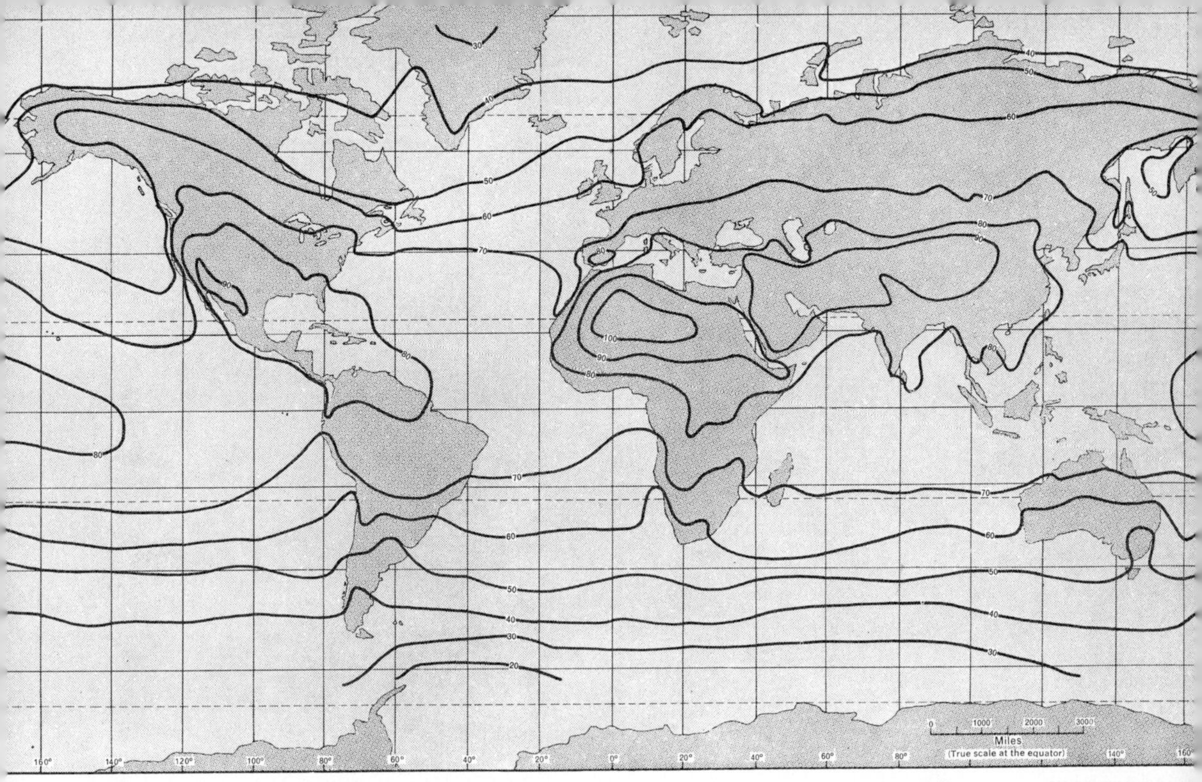

FIG. 6.3 World temperatures for July (degrees Fahrenheit). [After Haurwitz and Austin]

crease in temperature that takes place as one passes from lower to higher elevations. This adjustment is made to compensate for the complexity introduced by differences in elevation. Many of the major generalized patterns of world temperatures can be inferred from the maps showing mean temperatures for January and July and the one giving the mean annual range of temperature. Some of the more important temperature generalizations are presented below, and the reader is asked to examine the evidences on the three maps (Figs. 6.2 to 6.4) in passing from one generalization to another.

1. The general course of mean isotherms is east-west, with the higher temperatures in low latitudes and the lower temperatures in high latitudes.

2. The areas that consistently have the lowest *winter* temperatures are found in the northeastern Soviet Union, northwestern Canada, Greenland, and Antarctica.

3. The areas that consistently show the highest *summer* temperatures, instead of being at the equator, are found in the subtropical desert areas between lat 15 and 30° N.

4. The west coasts of continents in the northern hemisphere from lat 45 to 70° have higher temperatures in both summer and winter than do corresponding positions on the east coasts.

5. The isotherms sweep poleward over the oceans and equatorward over the continents in the mid-latitudes during the winter season, and vice versa during the summer season. The winter northward sweep of isotherms is more pronounced in the North Atlantic than in the North Pacific.

6. The steepest temperature gradients (slopes of temperature change horizontally) in the world are found bordering the Antarctic Continent. Other unusually steep gradients of temperature occur during the winter

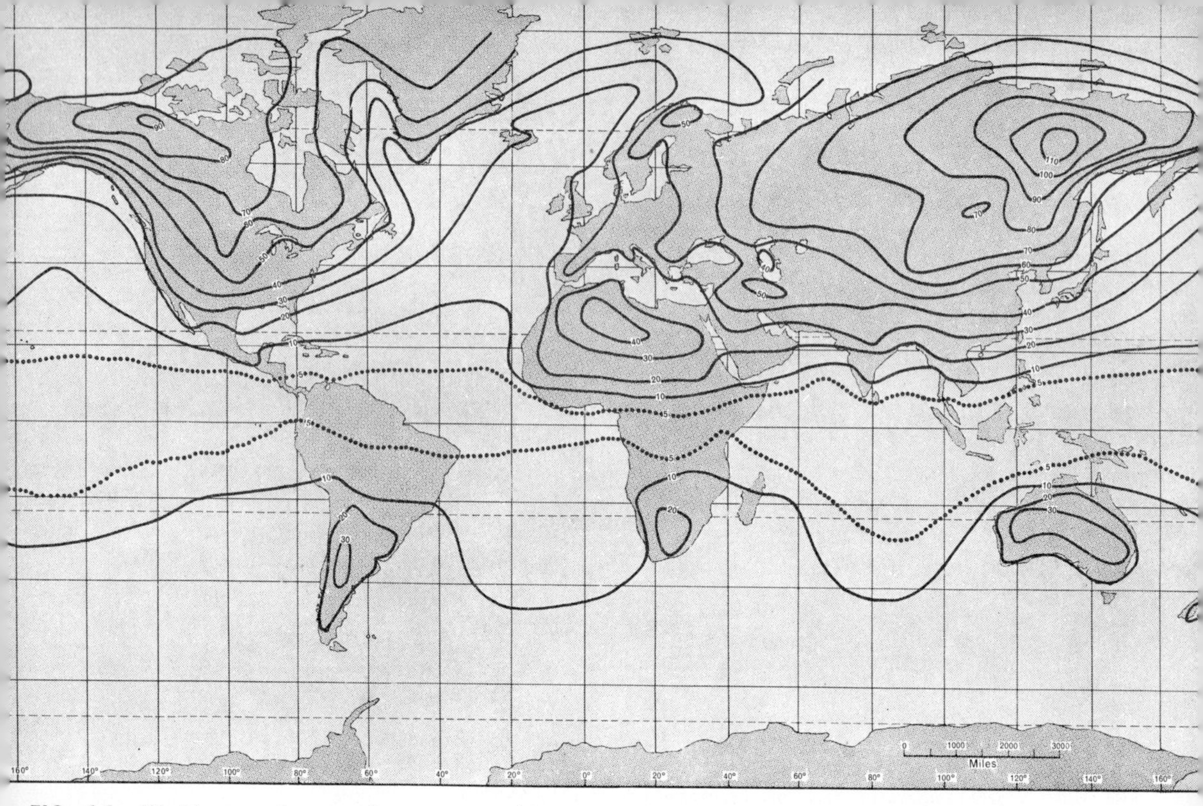

FIG. 6.4 World seasonal range of temperature (degrees Fahrenheit). [After Haurwitz and Austin]

season southeast of Greenland and near the Aleutians.

7. The average temperature gradient between the poles and the equator is steeper at high latitudes than at low latitudes and steeper in winter than in summer in the same latitudinal zone. It also is slightly steeper in the southern hemisphere than in the northern hemisphere, for equivalent positions at equivalent seasons.

8. Continental locations have warmer summers and colder winters than oceanic locations at equivalent latitudes. This is illustrated by the greater latitudinal shifting of the isotherms over continents as compared with those over the oceans. Because of the greater proportion of land in the northern hemisphere, seasonal ranges in general are greater north of the equator than south of it.

9. Seasonal ranges of temperature normally increase with latitude, except for ice-sheet locations (Greenland and Antarctica), given equivalent continental and oceanic positions and comparable percentages of clear skies.

Several generalizations of temperature patterns other than those which can be observed on the seasonal temperature maps are as follows:

1. Mean annual temperatures [2] are slightly

[2] The terms *average* and *mean* may be confusing to the reader. Actually, they signify the same thing, namely, the sum of all the observations divided by the number of observations. The terms *average annual temperature* and *mean annual temperature* are synonymous. One apparent contradiction should be explained. In determining generalizations of daily temperatures, instead of taking a large number of readings and averaging them, an average of the maximum and minimum temperatures is used, the data being obtained from a special type of thermometer capable of recording the maximum and minimum reached during a given period. The *mean*

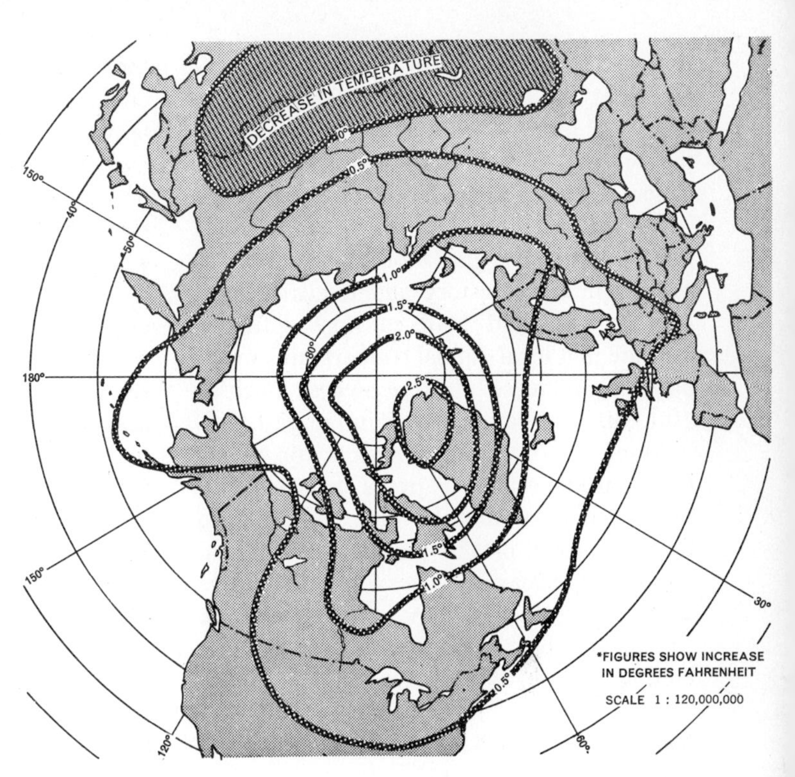

FIG. 6.5 Change in average annual temperatures in the northern hemisphere (1900–1950). [Scientific American, April, 1952]

higher in the northern hemisphere than in the southern hemisphere, for equivalent latitudes.

2. Mean annual temperatures are highest near the equator and decrease toward the poles.

3. Daily ranges of temperature are generally greater in continental than in oceanic locations and tend to increase with the incidence of clear skies.

4. Most locations exhibit some lag, or retardation, of maximum and minimum temperatures beyond the solstices. This retardation is greater in oceanic than in continental locations.

5. Surface temperatures generally decrease with elevation. Although the rate of decrease, termed the *lapse rate,* varies considerably with atmospheric conditions, the *mean* vertical temperature gradient, or *normal lapse rate,* is about 3.56°F per 1,000 feet of elevation.

6. Various fluctuations in temperature continually recur, with periods ranging in length from a few days to millions of years. The amount of variation appears to increase with latitude. As yet the periodicity, if any, is too complex and the data too inadequate to permit accurate predictions.

7. Meteorological observations taken during the past 75 years or so indicate a slow,

daily temperature, therefore, is the highest and lowest temperature for a daily period divided by 2. A mean monthly temperature, however, is the average of all the mean daily temperatures for a given month, over the period of years for which records are available. It is not the highest and lowest for the month divided by 2. Sometimes the term *average mean monthly temperature* is used to emphasize the fact that it is the average over many years, not the mean monthly temperature for a particular year.

irregular trend upward in mean annual temperatures for most of the world (see Fig. 6.5). The increases range from nearly 0 near the equator to 5°F in some high latitudes. A few scattered areas, however, show slight decreases.

8. Continental glaciation during several periods in earth history and fossils of subtropical flora and fauna at high latitudes indicate that local annual temperatures probably have increased or decreased as much as 10 to 40°F at various times in the past.

Many factors are responsible for differences in temperature patterns from place to place and from time to time. In order to interpret most of the patterns generalized above, it is necessary to examine the major contributory factors separately. They are summarized below and are discussed in succeeding sections of this chapter.

Variables in global temperature conditions:

Earth-sun relationships

- Output of solar energy
- Distance of the earth from the sun
- Directness of solar radiation
- Length of day and night

Variables within the earth's atmosphere

- Reflection and scattering of solar and terrestrial radiation
- Absorption of direct and indirect radiation by the atmosphere
- Transportation of heat through horizontal and vertical air movement

Variables on the earth surface

- Continents and oceans
- Variations in land surfaces for reflection or absorption of solar energy
- Human factors

Suggested variables in long-range temperature changes

6.2 OUTPUT OF SOLAR ENERGY.

Nearly all the heat energy contained within the atmosphere is derived from the sun, either directly or indirectly. This solar energy moves through space in the form of *radiant energy*.[3] The solar radiation that is received at the surface of the earth is termed *insolation*. The amount of heat received from the earth interior and from stellar radiation is so slight as to be insignificant in any consideration of atmospheric temperature patterns. Variations in the amount of solar radiation received at the upper level of the atmosphere are not clearly known, mainly because of the difficulty of taking such measurements. Scientists are interested in artificial earth satellites and high-altitude rockets partially because they are possible means of obtaining more accurate information on this variable. Measurements of solar radiation are made in terms of an arbitrary unit termed the *solar constant,* which is the number of *calories*[4] received per square centimeter per minute on a standard flat surface held perpendicularly to the sun when the earth is at its mean distance from the sun (approximately 93 million miles). The solar constant also assumes no loss by atmospheric absorption. Present indications are that the numerical quantity of the solar constant is approximately 1.94 and that it varies only between 1 or 2 per cent of this figure. A few authorities feel that long-term fluctuations in this constant are responsible for major global temperature changes and that observations are not yet sufficiently refined or abundant to permit the discovery of significant trends. Present evidence, admittedly inadequate, ap-

[3] *Radiant energy* is a type of energy that is capable of passing through space in waves. Unlike sound, it requires no mass medium for its transmission. Radio, X-ray, light, infrared, and ultraviolet radiations are varieties of radiant energy that differ only in wavelength.

[4] A *calorie* is the amount of heat energy needed to raise the temperature of one gram of water one degree centigrade at sea level, when the air temperature is fifteen degrees centigrade.

pears to deny fluctuations in solar energy output sufficient to produce significant changes in global temperature patterns.

6.3 DISTANCE OF THE EARTH FROM THE SUN. The intensity of solar energy received at the outer portions of the atmosphere varies slightly at different positions of the earth in its orbit around the sun, owing to differences in distance to the sun. The maximum difference in distance amounts to about 3 million miles. Although measurable in terms of the solar constant, this factor does not appear to be important in present surface atmospheric temperature patterns. The earth is nearest the sun in January and farthest from it in July; hence, if this factor were significant, the northern hemisphere winters should be warmer and the summers cooler than those in the southern hemisphere. Actually the converse is true, owing to the greater proportion of land area as compared with ocean area in the northern hemisphere and the greater heating and cooling of land as compared with water. It is likely, however, that our winters are warmer north of the equator and our summers cooler than they would be if the earth were equidistant from the sun at all seasons.

6.4 DIRECTNESS OF SOLAR RADIATION. The directness of solar radiation comprises one of the most important variables in explaining the occurrence of seasonal temperature changes and the decrease in temperature with increasing latitude. The effect of directness of solar radiation is illustrated in Fig. 6.6. Direct radiation is concentrated over a smaller surface area than oblique radiation and is therefore more intense per unit of area. An accompanying factor is the lesser thickness of atmosphere through which the sun's radiation passes when it is more direct; this makes it possible for a greater amount to be transmitted through to the earth surface.

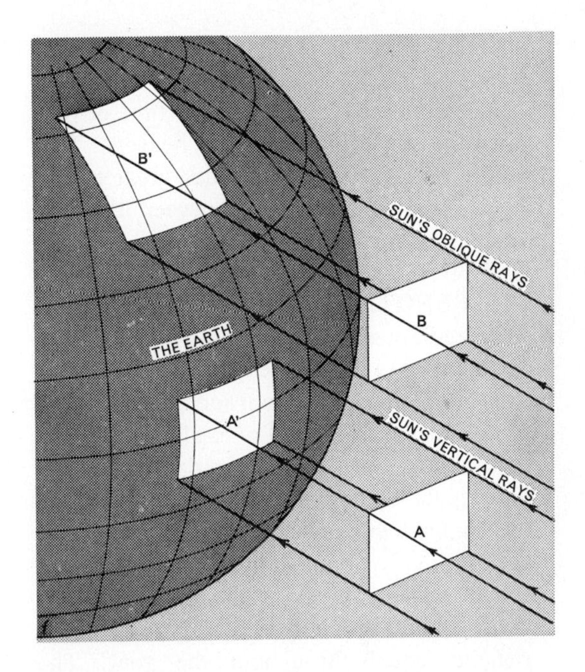

FIG. 6.6 Effect of the angle of insolation on the receipt of solar energy. A given amount of solar energy, represented by the area of A and B, yields different amounts at the surface of the earth. The amount per unit of area at B′ is noticeably less than at A′.

As was indicated in Sec. 2.3 and in Fig. 2.5, the directness of the sun's radiation is related to the tilting of the earth axis and its parallelism within the earth orbit. During the course of a year, beginning at noon on the summer solstice (northern hemisphere), the sun's perpendicular "rays" migrate from the Tropic of Cancer to the Tropic of Capricorn and back again. The receipt of insolation varies in the following ways:

1. Insolation is greatest at noon, local sun time, and decreases toward sunrise and sunset.

2. Insolation is greatest at the particular locality on earth at which the sun is at the

zenith,[5] decreasing gradually away from this point.

3. Insolation is greatest at the time of year when the sun is highest in the heavens. This occurs once a year at latitudes greater than 23½° and twice a year between the two Tropics (Cancer and Capricorn).

6.5 LENGTH OF DAY. The amount of solar radiation received at any locality on earth varies with the length of day. If the axis of the earth were not inclined from the perpendicular to the ecliptic, all parts of the earth would have a 12-hour day and a 12-hour night throughout the year. Owing to this inclination, however, the length of day varies greatly, both latitudinally and seasonally. The equator is the only place on earth where the length of day and night remains equal throughout the year. The poles, on the other hand, experience days and nights that are each theoretically six months long.[6] The latitudinal variation in the length of day, combined with seasonal variations in the directness of solar radiation, explains why the seasons become more pronounced with increasing distance from the equator. One might expect that the long period of continuous daylight near the poles would make the intake of insolation there higher than it is at the equator during the summer and would thus cause higher temperatures. Factors preventing this include (1) the lower angle of the sun in the sky, (2) the greater thickness of atmosphere through which the solar radiation must pass, (3) the high reflection of radiation from snow and ice, and (4) the utilization of absorbed heat to melt or evaporate ice and snow or to evaporate water. All these combine to keep down air temperatures in the polar regions.

Calculations have been made of the average amount of solar radiation that is received at the top of the atmosphere at different latitudes and different times of the year in the northern hemisphere. The two principal variables in this amount are the directness of radiation and the length of day. The results are shown in Table 6.2. Note, for example, that the greatest amount of solar radiation at any one time for any of the latitudes given is received on June 21 within the belt between 60 and 90°. This is a result of the continuous daylight for 24 hours at this solstice within the Arctic Circle. At all other times of the year, the insolation received in the northern hemisphere decreases toward the equator. The length of day and the directness of solar rays are important factors in temperature distributions at the earth surface, but as the lack of correlation between Table 6.2 and the temperature patterns of Figs. 6.2 and 6.3 indicates, other important elements must be considered.

6.6 EVIDENCE OF ATMOSPHERIC INFLUENCES ON THE RECEIPT OF SOLAR RADIATION AT THE EARTH SURFACE. The effects of the atmosphere on the solar radiation that passes through it can be observed directly in many ways. Sunburn, for example, is much more likely on clear days and at high elevations. Clouds, smoke, dust, and fog intercept, reflect, and scatter incoming radiation, reducing the rise in daytime surface temperatures wherever these atmospheric elements occur in abnormal concentrations. Quantitative evidence of the interception of solar radiation by the

[5] Note that there can be only one relatively small area on earth where the sun appears at the zenith. Elsewhere on the same parallel and at the same time, the sun will be moving either toward or away from the zenith.

[6] Owing to the bending (*refraction*) of light as it passes through the atmosphere, the period of sunlight at the poles is longer by about 15 days than the period when the sun is below the horizon.

TABLE 6.2 Average amount of direct solar radiation received at the upper limit of the atmosphere in the northern hemisphere, in calories per square centimeter per minute. (After Baur and Philipps)

DATE	0–10°	10–20°	20–30°	30–40°	40–50°	50–60°	60–90°
Dec. 21	0.549	0.465	0.373	0.274	0.173	0.079	0.006
Mar. 21	0.619	0.601	0.563	0.509	0.441	0.358	0.211
June 21	0.579	0.629	0.664	0.684	0.689	0.683	0.703
Sept. 23	0.610	0.592	0.556	0.503	0.435	0.353	0.208

TABLE. 6.3 Average amount of direct solar radiation received at the earth surface if cloudiness and turbidity (transparency) are considered, in calories per square centimeter per minute. (After Baur and Philipps)

DATE	0–10°	10–20°	20–30°	30–40°	40–50°	50–60°	60–90°
Dec. 21	0.164	0.161	0.134	0.082	0.036	0.013	0.001
Mar. 21	0.191	0.224	0.206	0.161	0.116	0.096	0.055
June 21	0.144	0.170	0.216	0.233	0.183	0.159	0.133
Sept. 23	0.170	0.162	0.201	0.183	0.131	0.079	0.028

SOURCE: By permission from B. Haurwitz and J. M. Austin, *Climatology*, McGraw-Hill Book Company, Inc., New York, 1944.

atmosphere can be obtained by a comparison between Table 6.2 and Table 6.3. Considerably less solar radiation reaches the earth at all latitudes and at all times of the year than is received at the upper limit of the atmosphere. Some other significant conclusions can be drawn from a comparison between these two tables. Note, for example, that the maximum solar radiation observed at the upper limit of the atmosphere, received poleward of 60° on the summer solstice, has decreased to a minimum for the northern hemisphere at the earth's surface on that date. Note also that the pattern of a general increase in direct solar radiation toward the equator in Table 6.2 has changed consider-

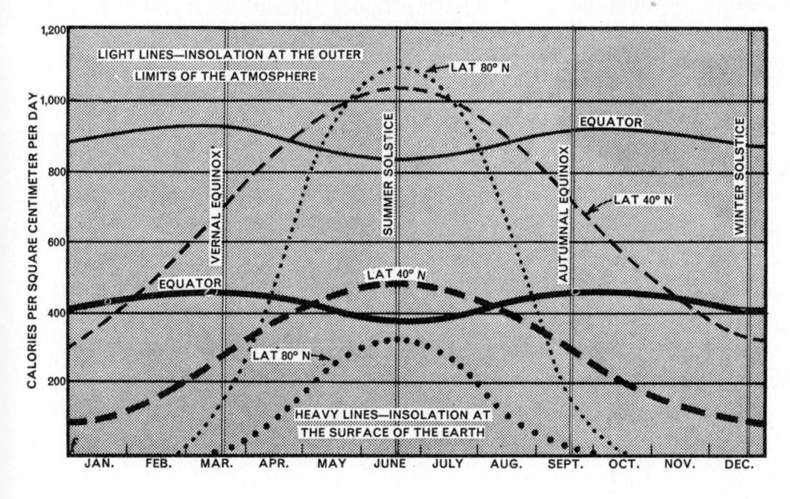

FIG. 6.7 Annual march of insolation. [After Trewartha]

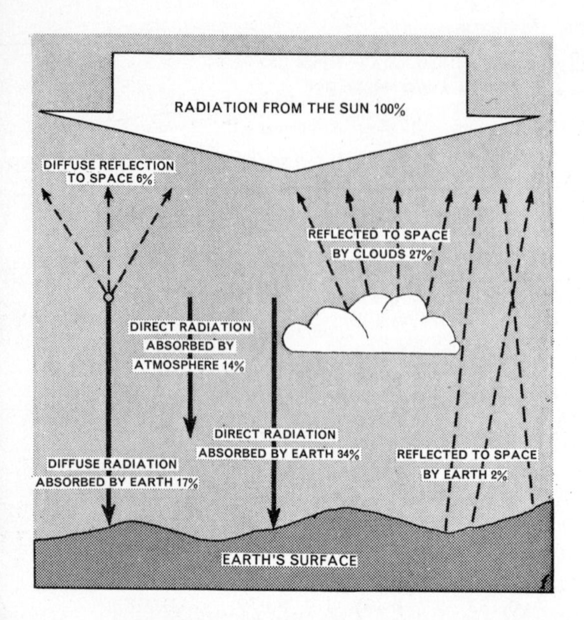

FIG. 6.8 Transmission and scattering of solar radiation in the earth atmosphere. Note that of the incoming solar radiation, only 65% is used to heat the earth and the atmosphere (shown by the solid arrows).

ably at the earth surface. Except for the winter solstice, the maximum solar radiation at the surface is generally highest between lat 10 and 30°, even during the equinoxes, when the sun is at the zenith at the equator and the days and nights are of equal length throughout the world. The high percentage of clear skies in the subtropical deserts is largely responsible for this.

6.7 REFLECTION AND SCATTERING OF INCOMING SOLAR RADIATION BY THE ATMOSPHERE. Incoming solar radiation can be diverted from its path toward the earth surface by particles in the atmosphere in the same way that sunlight is reflected from the mirrorlike surface of a frozen lake in winter. Clouds form by far the best reflector in the atmosphere, as illustrated by the fact that the glare of light from the upper surface of a dense cloud layer often startles the passengers on commercial planes that have suddenly climbed out of murky weather below. Dust, plant pollen, small droplets of oil, and tiny fragments of sea salt suspended in the air also are able to reflect incoming rays whose wavelengths are narrower than their own surfaces. The earth surface also reflects some of the incoming radiation before it has had an opportunity of being absorbed or transformed into heat energy. Nearly all this reflected insolation returns swiftly to outer space and hence plays no part in heating either the atmosphere or the surface.

Molecules of various atmospheric gases, though extremely small, are able to reflect some radiant energy. Because of their small size, however, they can reflect only the shorter wavelengths. The extremely large number of these molecules, especially in the lower portion of the atmosphere, and the various angles of their reflecting surfaces produce a scattering of the short wavelengths of radiation. Their scattering action may be compared with that of the piles of an ocean wharf, which permit large waves to pass by but which intercept and reflect the small ones that lap against their surfaces.[7] Not all of this scattered radiation is lost to space. Some of it, comprising the diffused "skylight," is reflected toward the earth.

The radiation that is lost to outer space by direct reflection or scattering is known as the *albedo* of the earth. Its value varies from about 30 to 40 per cent of the incoming solar radiation, depending on the amount and type of cloud cover and the quantity of

[7] The blue of a clear sky is caused by the *selective scattering* of the radiation near the short end of the visible wavelength spectrum. Balloonists and plane pilots who have risen far into the rarefied upper atmosphere have noted the gradual change in color of the sky from blue through violet to black. This is caused mainly by a decrease in the number of air molecules.

dust and other foreign particles in the air. Again, it should be emphasized that clouds form the main variable. Reflection from clouds in the humid tropics definitely is a factor in keeping surface temperatures there from rising as high as they otherwise would.

6.8 HEATING THE ATMOSPHERE. The two principal ways in which the atmosphere is heated are (1) through the absorption of radiant energy and (2) by *conduction*, or the direct transfer of heat. The main direct source of heat in both of the above processes is the earth, although the ultimate source is, of course, the sun.

ABSORPTION OF RADIATION BY THE ATMOSPHERE. Absorption of radiation implies the transformation of radiant energy into the kinetic energy of molecular motion (heat), or into some other type of energy, on the part of some substance. Different materials have different capacities for performing this alteration. The earth surface is capable of absorbing an exceptionally wide range of radiational wavelengths. The atmosphere, on the other hand, is more selective, absorbing mainly the longer wavelengths. Also, its capacity for absorption of radiation is higher if it contains a large amount of certain materials, particularly water vapor, carbon dioxide, and ozone. Unlike the other two, ozone is concentrated in upper levels within the atmosphere. Incoming solar radiation is made up principally of short-wave radiation. For this reason, the atmosphere absorbs directly only a relatively small amount (about 14 per cent) of incoming radiation. Most of this absorption occurs either near the surface in the lower 1½ miles of the atmosphere, where the air is relatively dense and contains appreciable quantities of water vapor and carbon dioxide, or in the upper atmosphere, where the ozone content is high.

Once the earth is heated by absorption of solar energy, it becomes a radiating body. The outgoing, or terrestrial, radiation differs from insolation in that it is principally made up of longer wavelengths, mainly those above the range of visible light, or within the infrared range. Since the atmosphere is more capable of absorbing longer wavelengths than the shorter ones (it can absorb a maximum of about 90 per cent of the terrestrial radiation), it consequently derives considerably more heat through radiation from the earth than directly from the sun. This has been termed the *greenhouse effect* (see Fig. 6.9), since it may be compared to the influence of glass in a greenhouse, which permits a large part of the incoming radiation to pass through it, while intercepting the longer wavelengths of terrestrial radiation.

One of the principal results of the greenhouse effect is to retard maximum air temperatures beyond the time of maximum insolation, both daily and seasonally. The curve of incoming radiation, shown in Fig. 6.10, begins shortly before sunrise, reaches a maximum at noon (local sun time), and

FIG. 6.9 The greenhouse effect. Incoming solar radiation, having a short wavelength, easily passes through the glass. After absorption, the resulting longer, terrestrial radiation is intercepted by the glass and returned for reabsorption.

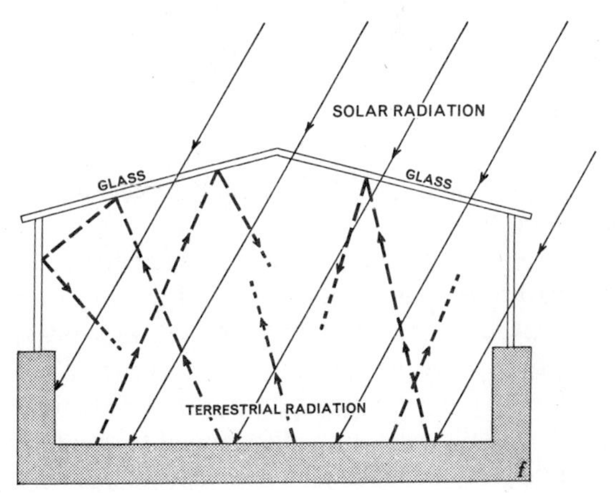

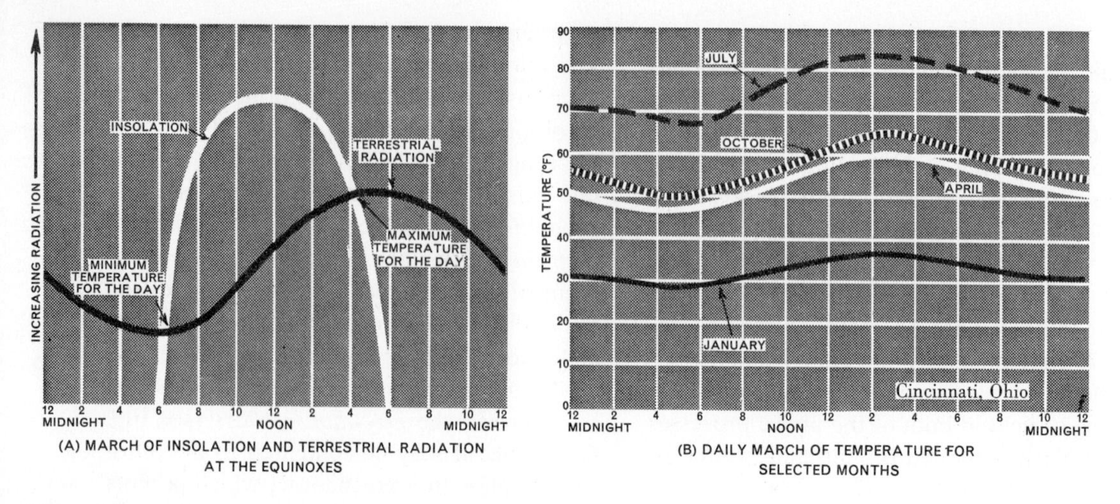

FIG. 6.10 Daily march of insolation and temperature. [After American Atlas of Agriculture; U.S. Department of Agriculture]

diminishes to zero shortly after sunset. The outgoing earth radiation, on the other hand, which follows absorption at the surface, never totally ceases, but falls to a minimum shortly before sunrise, reaches a maximum in mid-afternoon, and slowly diminishes throughout the afternoon and night. The intersection of these two curves, normally occurring in early afternoon, usually takes place shortly before the time of highest temperatures. For a similar reason, the maximum seasonal heating of the atmosphere is retarded well beyond the summer solstice. The amount of seasonal retardation of maximum temperatures, usually between 30 and 40 days on the continents, depends on the capacity of the earth for retaining heat before transforming it and releasing it as radiant energy.

Atmospheric differences play an important part in the absorption of terrestrial radiation as well as solar radiation. Water vapor and clouds have a high absorptive capacity for the long wavelengths of terrestrial radiation. A cloud cover and high humidity tend to reduce differential air temperatures between day and night by diminishing both maximum and minimum temperatures. During the day less solar radiation reaches the surface for heating, and during the night there is a greater interception of terrestrial radiation. The term "blanket of clouds" is more than a figure of speech. The interception of radiation is least where the moisture content of air is lowest and where there are no clouds. Desert areas thus have high surface temperatures at noon and early afternoon, but these temperatures drop rapidly at night. Daily temperature variations of between 80 and 90° have been observed in some of the low-latitude deserts. In areas where frost is a problem, people watch the skies for signs of frost danger. Calm, clear nights are those most likely to result in frosts, because of the rapid loss of heat through radiation. On such critical nights the orange growers of California light oil-burning sheet-metal heaters to maintain air temperatures at slightly above freezing levels.

HEATING BY CONDUCTION. The second means of adding heat to the atmosphere is through the process of *conduction*. Conduction is the transfer of heat by contact. If there is physical contact between two bodies of unequal temperature, heat will move from the warmer to the cooler body until temperatures are equal. Since the surface of the earth can heat to a higher temperature than the atmosphere, air in contact with this surface will be heated by conduction. Air, however, is a poor conductor of heat; thus, if it were not for the fact that air moves, so that heated layers of air are replaced by cooler air, which in turn becomes heated, the influence of conduction would be restricted to a very thin layer of atmosphere next to the surface of the earth. Just as contact with the earth may heat the air above it, conduction of heat from warm air to a cooler surface brings about a drop in air temperature. In general, conduction adds heat to the atmosphere during the daylight hours and summer and subtracts heat from the atmosphere during the night and winter.

6.9 TRANSPORTATION OF HEAT ENERGY BY HORIZONTAL AND VERTICAL AIR MOVEMENT.

An additional factor affecting the distributional pattern of temperatures on or near the earth surface is the movement of air, with its contained heat energy. This movement of air is both horizontal and vertical. Most of us have recognized changes in temperature brought about by changes in horizontal wind directions (*advection*). This is particularly seen in the mid-latitudes, which often experience strong contrasts between cold air masses from high latitudes and warm winds from the humid tropics. The contrasts in winter temperatures between Labrador and the British Isles, both at about the same latitude, are largely due to the difference in the temperatures of their respective prevailing winds. Both locations receive air from westerly directions, but the winter air in Labrador comes from the frozen interior of the North American continent, whereas most of the winter winds of Britain have blown over thousands of miles of relatively warm, open ocean.

Localized upward and downward air movements also help to distribute heat energy throughout the lower part of the atmosphere. Upward currents are of great significance in helping to relieve abnormal concentrations of heat energy at the earth surface. Wherever some part of the surface is highly heated, the air directly above it has its temperature raised by absorption of terrestrial radiation and by conduction. Upon being heated, the air expands, becomes less dense, and is displaced upward by cooler and denser adjacent air. This process of air displacement resulting from unequal heating surfaces is known

FIG. 6.11 Heating the atmosphere by the processes of conduction and convection.

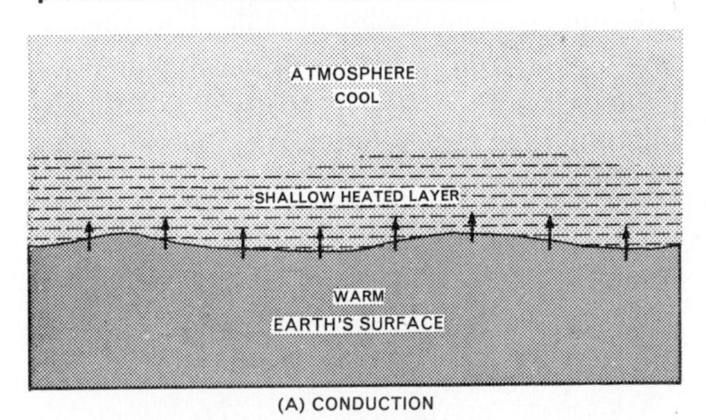

(A) CONDUCTION

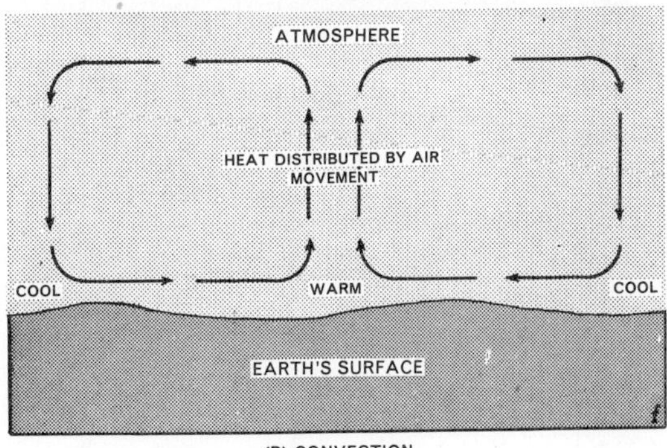

(B) CONVECTION

as *convection.* The bumpy air encountered by airplanes during hot summer days is caused by convectional currents. Such currents are exceptionally strong over hot city pavements or desert surfaces.

6.10 ADIABATIC RATE, LAPSE RATE, AND TEMPERATURE INVERSIONS.

The expansion of air following heating requires energy, which is obtained from the heat energy contained within the air; thus, rising, expanding air undergoes cooling. The rate of cooling caused by the ascent of air is known as the *adiabatic rate.* It is constant for dry air, or air that is less than saturated with water vapor, and this dry adiabatic rate amounts to about 1°F drop per 185 feet of lift, or 5.6° per 1,000 feet. Air subsiding from above undergoes a converse effect; it is warmed at the dry adiabatic rate as the result of *compression.*

As noted earlier, temperature generally declines with increasing altitude. This change, the *lapse rate,* is the change in temperature a person would perceive in moving vertically through the atmosphere. The adiabatic rate, on the other hand, is the change in the temperature of a mass of air resulting from the vertical movement and subsequent expansion or compression of that mass of air. The main factors influencing the lapse rate are (1) the high proportion of atmospheric heat derived from terrestrial radiation and conduction, (2) the decline in atmospheric absorbency of heat with increasing altitude, and (3) the adiabatic factor which lowers the temperature of any warm air mass moving upward.

There are times when an increase in temperature occurs with an increase in altitude; in other words, there is a reversal of the lapse rate. This situation is termed a *temperature inversion.* Inversions occur close to the surface of the earth and also at high elevations. Inversions near the surface occur primarily during the night. During the hours of darkness, the surface cools more rapidly than the air above it, because it radiates heat more rapidly. In turn, the lower layer of the air loses heat by conduction to the earth and consequently becomes cooler than the air above.

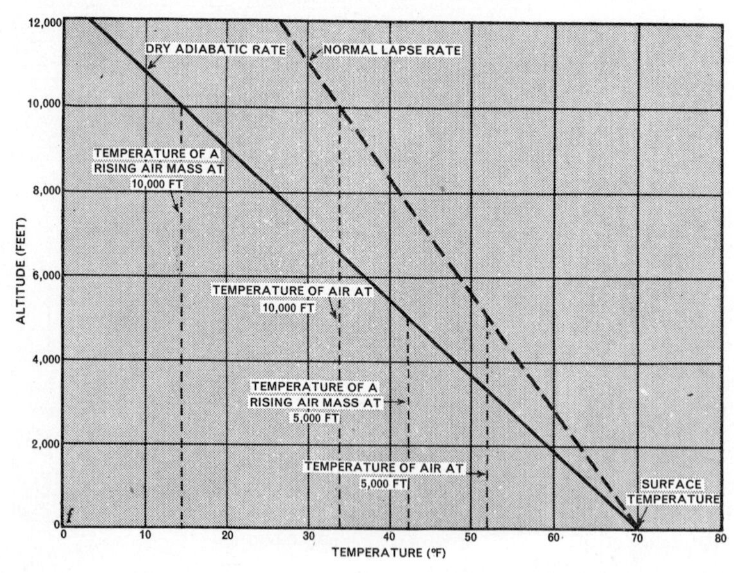

FIG. 6.12 Comparison of normal lapse rate and dry adiabatic rate.

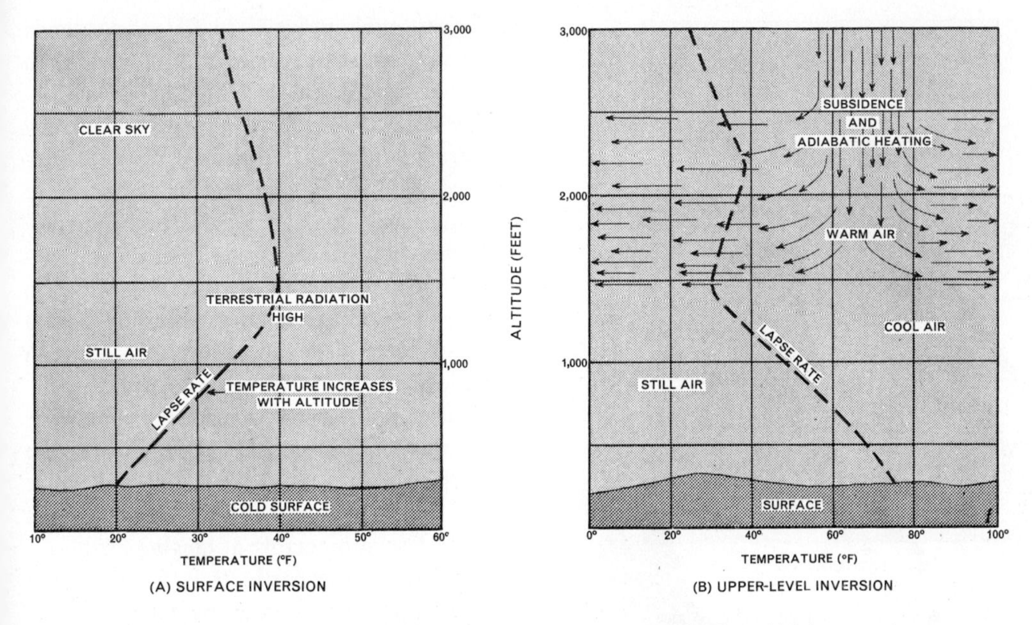

FIG. 6.13 Diagram showing two types of temperature inversion. The first (A) is caused by radiational cooling on calm, clear nights. The second (B) is an upper-air inversion caused by subsidence.

Certain surface and atmospheric conditions favor the formation of inversions. For example, long nights and cloudless, dry air expedite the loss of surface heat by radiation. In addition, a surface cover of snow reflects incoming insolation during the daylight hours and consequently reduces absorption and surface temperatures, as well as prevents the transfer of any heat from below the snow cover, snow being a poor conductor. Motionless air, which prohibits the warming of lower air by preventing it from mixing with air from above, also favors inversion. The tendency for the cooler, and therefore heavier, air to move down slopes into low spots, such as valleys, concentrates inversion conditions in such localities (see Fig. 6.14). This process is called *air drainage*.

Inversions occur at upper elevations when a subsiding and warming air mass reaches a temperature higher than that of the air mass below.

6.11 VERTICAL ZONATION OF THE ATMOSPHERE ACCORDING TO TEMPERATURE. The tendency to encounter lower temperatures in passing from lower to higher altitudes, as experienced when the normal lapse rate prevails, does not hold true for the entire atmosphere; instead,

FIG. 6.14 Air drainage. Air that is chilled by contact with a cold land becomes more dense, flows downhill, and collects in surface depressions, thus forming local temperature inversions.

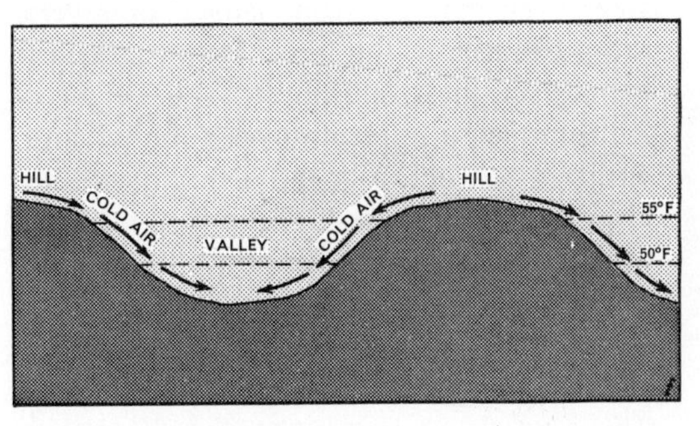

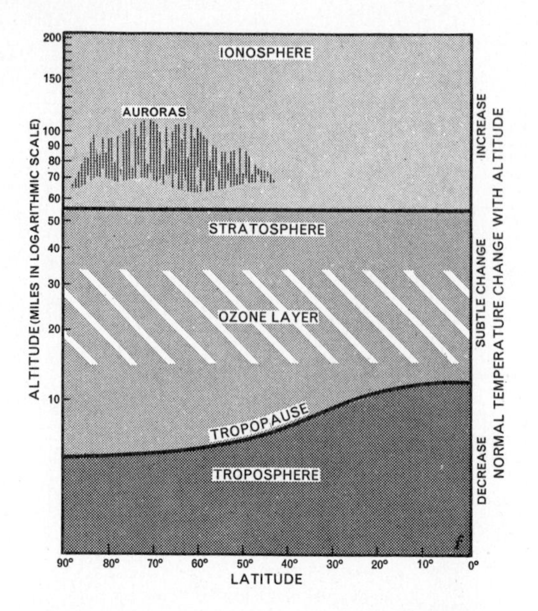

FIG. 6.15 A vertical section through the atmosphere. The boundaries shown fluctuate somewhat from time to time both in sharpness and in altitude.

it is confined to the lower portion. The atmosphere may be divided into broad vertical layers, or zones, distinguished by their temperature conditions.

The lowest zone, termed the *troposphere,* includes the portion of the atmosphere in which the lapse rate is operative, except under localized conditions of temperature inversion. The upper limit of the troposphere, termed the *tropopause,* is sharply defined in some places but uncertain in others. In some areas even multiple tropopauses, or several sharp changes in the lapse rate, occur near the top of the troposphere. The height of the tropopause is greatest near the equator, where it reaches 9 to 10 miles above sea level, and lowest near the poles, where it lies between 4 and 5 miles above the surface. The slope of the tropopause toward the poles is not uniform, and profound undulations and breaks sometimes are found. The descent is steepest at about lat 30 to 40°, and it tends to be somewhat steeper over land areas than over oceans and in winter than in summer.

The zone above the tropopause is termed the *stratosphere*. It contrasts with the troposphere below mainly in that its temperature remains fairly constant or increases slightly with elevation. Recent findings suggest, however, that considerably more variation in temperature occurs in the stratosphere than was formerly believed, especially at high latitudes.

Much less is known concerning the upper atmosphere, that is, the zone above the stratosphere, but evidence collected from rocket flights indicates that air temperatures begin to rise appreciably at heights far above the surface of the earth. It is believed that some of this increase may be related to the presence of ozone, a form of oxygen that has a high absorbency of solar radiation. A band, or zone, of high ozone content, termed the *ozonosphere,* lies between about 15 and 35 miles above the surface of the earth. Further divisions of the atmosphere above the stratosphere are based on varying electric influences of solar radiation on upper-air molecules and the concentration of free electrons. These outer zones, or layers, are known collectively as the *ionosphere*. Space rockets have revealed a double layer (the Van Allen layer) of high-energy radiation surrounding the earth beyond the ionosphere and shaped like a doughnut, being open above both polar regions.

6.12 LAND AND WATER CONTRASTS.

The heating of the atmosphere is influenced not only by different characteristics of the atmosphere but also by different surface conditions on the earth below. Major global differences in surface materials and in their capacity for heating or cooling are well illustrated by the contrast between air temperatures over land and water. Land surfaces experience a greater and more rapid rise in temperature following the receipt of solar energy than do water surfaces; conversely, they tend to lose this heat faster and to a greater degree than water. Four major factors are responsible for this:

1. Transparency. Water, being transparent, permits solar energy to penetrate far below the surface. On land, however, radiation influences only the top inch or so of rock or soil. A given amount of incoming radiation thus will heat a given unit of land surface much more rapidly and to a greater degree than it will the same amount of water surface. For the same reason, the loss of heat through outgoing radiation is also faster and greater over land than over water.

2. Movement. Vertical mixing and horizontal transfer of water latitudinally by waves and currents can distribute heat energy over both wide areas and great depths. This means that the incoming solar energy can influence a much larger mass per unit of area over oceans than over continents, and thus temperature extremes are minimized.

3. Evaporation. A large amount of heat energy is used in the evaporation of water from ocean surfaces, particularly in the tropics. Evaporation increases with temperature; hence this tends to prevent ocean surface temperatures from rising rapidly. This is by far the most important factor in removing surplus energy from warm ocean areas.

4. Specific heat. It takes only about one-third as much energy to raise the temperature of a given volume of land solids (rock, soil, etc.) as it does to heat an equivalent amount of water. Conversely, an equivalent amount of heat loss lowers the temperature of a given volume of land more than it does the same amount of water. This is a relatively minor factor in land and water temperature contrasts, however.

The slower rate of heating and cooling of water as compared with land results in smaller daily and seasonal temperature variations. Sometimes there is also a greater lag in the maximum and minimum temperatures beyond the solstices. Because of the larger proportion of land in the northern hemisphere, temperature ranges north of the equator are greater than those of equivalent latitudes in the southern hemisphere. These tendencies are illustrated by the data in Table 6.4.

The regional contrasts in surface temperatures of oceans, though not so great as those of the continents, are sufficiently large to be significant factors in world temperature patterns. Ocean currents, which carry water over long latitudinal distances, and vertical movements, such as the upwelling of cold water, produce noticeable water *temperature anomalies,*[8] which in turn result in irregularities in the latitudinal course of isotherms as they cross ocean areas.

Figure 15.11 shows the principal negative and positive temperature anomalies for the oceans. Their influence on air temperatures may be seen at several places on the world temperature maps. Note, for example, the sharp bends in the isotherms due to cold water off the west coasts of Peru and southern Africa, those off New England and southeastern Canada during July, and those corresponding to the sharp boundary between cold and warm water along the Japanese archipelago. One of the greatest positive water temperature anomalies in the world is located off the Norwegian coast. Note how far the isotherms bend into the Arctic off this coast. More detailed information on

[8] A *temperature anomaly* is a temperature that is different from the average for the particular latitude. Positive and negative anomalies correspond to higher and lower temperatures, respectively (see Fig. 15.11).

TABLE 6.4 Mean monthly temperatures, in degrees Fahrenheit, of continental and oceanic positions

JAN.	FEB.	MAR.	APR.	MAY	JUNE	JULY	AUG.	SEPT.	OCT.	NOV.	DEC.	RANGE
CONTINENTAL STATIONS												
Pine Bluff, Arkansas (lat 34° N)												
42 *	45	54	64	72	79	82	81	76	63	53	45	40
Srinagar, Kashmir (lat 34° N), elev. 5204 ft.												
31	33	45	56	64	70	73	71	64	53	44	36	41
Rosario, Argentina (lat 33° S)												
77	75	71	65	58	52	52	54	59	63	69	79	25
Semipalatinsk, U.S.S.R. (lat 50° N)												
3	4	14	37	56	67	71	67	56	38	20	9	68
OCEANIC STATIONS												
Mogador, Morocco (lat 32° N)												
57	59	60	63	65	67	68	68	68	67	63	59	11
Evangelist Islands, Chile (lat 51° S)												
47	47	46	45	41	40	37	39	40	42	43	45	10
Scilly Island, Great Britain (lat 50° N)												
46	45	46	49	52	57	60	61	59	54	50	47	15

* Minimum and maximum temperatures are underlined.

the distribution of cold and warm ocean currents can be found in Chapter 15.

6.13 OTHER NATURAL SURFACE CONDITIONS.

A covering of snow and ice exerts a strong cooling influence on the temperature of the air. Ice and snow are cold surfaces, and the air immediately above them loses heat energy by both radiation and conduction. Although conduction does not influence a great thickness of air, owing to the low conductivity of air, horizontal airflow may remove the chilled air (which then influences temperatures elsewhere) and replace it with warmer air, which becomes chilled in turn. Snow, furthermore, is a good reflecting surface, and a fresh fall of snow may reflect as much as 70 to 80 per cent of the radiation received. Moreover, much of the heat resulting from absorption of insolation is not used immediately for raising air temperatures by conduction, convection, or terrestrial radiation, because of the large quantities required for both evaporating and melting ice and snow. This is the major reason why Greenland and Antarctica remain cold even during the long summer period of continuous daylight and why a bright, sunny winter day may produce little rise in air temperatures following a fresh fall of snow in the upper mid-latitudes. If added snowfall did not replenish the supply of melted or evaporated snow or ice and the icecaps wasted away, Greenland and Antarctica would be much warmer in summer than they now are.

Differences in vegetation cover also influence air temperatures, owing to different capacities for reflection or absorption of radiation. On a hot summer day the temperature of a city pavement is raised more than that of an adjacent grassy park surface. The difference in the temperatures of the air above these surfaces is appreciable. The reflection of radiation from the surfaces of broadleaf forests helps to reduce thc absorption of insolation. In forests, insolation also is distributed over a greater surface area than it is in an open field or barren desert, and some heat is converted into chemical energy within the leaves, so that less heat is available for increasing air temperatures. The conical shape of spruce and fir trees in the coniferous forests of high latitudes in the northern hemisphere is a plant adaptation for increasing the absorption surfaces for plant use in these areas of low insolation intensity.

6.14 HUMAN FACTORS IN TEMPERATURE PATTERNS. Man is not a significant variable in global patterns of temperature distribution. Locally, however, some appreciable results of his activities may be noted. Cities exert a noticeable warming effect on the air temperatures within them. Part of this is due to increased radiation from homes and buildings that are heated during the winter months. Part of it also is the result of the large amounts of carbon dioxide released into the air from chimneys and from the exhausts of motor vehicles. These increase the capacity of the air to absorb earth radiation. Bare pavements and roof tops are good heating surfaces during sunny days. The warming effect of cities rapidly decreases near their margins, and sharp temperature drops of between 5 and 10° often can be noticed between downtown locations and the rural environs of a city.

Forest clearing is capable of accelerating the heating and cooling of the atmosphere locally through more rapid absorption or loss of radiation. If, for example, one takes a plane flight on a hot summer day, he may discover that at low altitudes the air over fields is noticeably more turbulent than that over forests. This is the result of local updrafts caused by unequal heating.

6.15 THE GLOBAL HEAT BALANCE. The total intake and outgo of radiation for the earth as a whole are evenly balanced. Of the radiation received at the upper limits of the atmosphere, about 35 per cent is re-

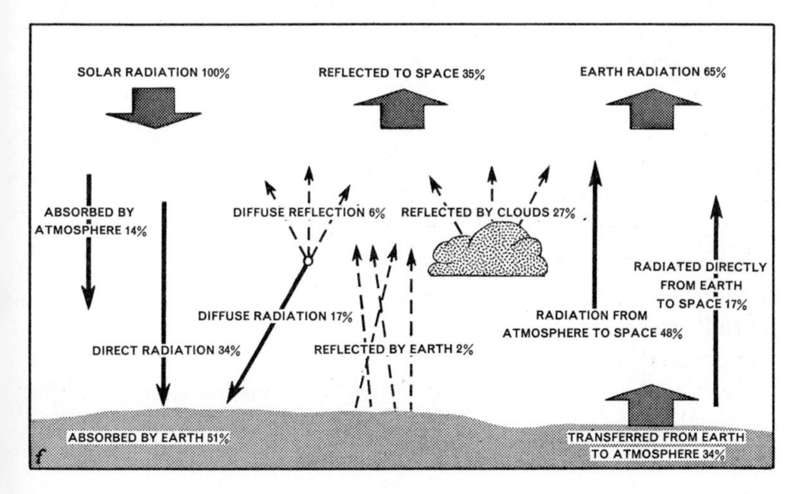

FIG. 6.16 The global heat balance. Despite the different paths taken by radiant energy after it enters the atmosphere, approximately the same amount returns into space, either by reflection (35%) or by radiation from the earth or its atmosphere (65%).

flected (the earth albedo). The remainder (65 per cent) is absorbed either by the atmosphere or by the earth surface. Approximately 17 per cent of the short-wave energy reaching the surface is radiated directly back into space as long-wave energy and does not affect the temperature of the atmosphere. Consequently only about 48 per cent of the solar radiation received at the outer edge of the atmosphere is used to heat the atmosphere. Terrestrial radiation plus radiation from the atmosphere equals the 65 per cent of absorbed solar radiation.

This balance between intake and outgo is particularly remarkable in view of the number of diverse paths that may be taken by solar energy before it finally escapes as terrestrial radiation. It heats the air, indirectly drives ocean currents, evaporates water, provides our food, drives our cars, and performs a host of other tasks. In fact, nearly all movement of any kind on the earth originates as solar energy. We know that the balance exists, because if it were not present, the earth would become either progressively warmer or colder. Except for the relatively minor recurrent rising and lowering of average global temperatures, no such continuous trend has occurred. The chemical energy stores in the fossil fuels and the total mass of plant and animal life on earth represent temporary retentions of solar energy, but, in general, the energy that is received is eventually lost to outer space.

Measurements of incoming and outgoing radiation, however, indicate that, although this balance exists for the earth as a whole, different parts of the earth surface exhibit appreciable differences between incoming and outgoing radiation. In low-latitude areas, for example, the incoming radiation exceeds outgoing radiation, and the converse is true poleward of about lat 37°, where outgoing radiation exceeds insolation. The distribution of energy surpluses and deficiencies, assuming average cloudiness, is given in Table 6.5. In using the table, it should be kept in mind that the areas of these latitudinal belts vary widely. This explains the appreciable drop in net loss near the pole.

Despite the regional net gains and losses in radiant energy, progressive increases or decreases of regional temperature are prevented from occurring by a series of elaborate energy transfer systems. One such transfer system is supplied by the global system of ocean currents, which transport some of the surplus heat from low latitudes into the polar oceans. The amount thus carried, however, is only a small part of the amount to be removed from low latitudes. This flow pattern is discussed in greater detail in Chapter 15. Another energy transfer system, and one which is much more efficient, is formed by the planetary air circulation system, which not only carries warm air upward and poleward but transports immense quantities of water vapor to higher altitudes and higher latitudes, where the *latent heat* (see Sec. 6.18) is released following condensation. Eventually, the energy transported is radiated

TABLE 6.5 Net gains and losses of radiation by latitudinal zones

LATITUDE BELT	10^9 KILOJOULES PER SECOND *
0–10°	+1,109
10–20	+ 941
20–30	+ 544
30–40	+ 167
40–50	− 402
50–60	− 690
60–70	− 833
70–80	− 615
80–90	− 22

SOURCE: Glenn T. Trewartha, *An Introduction to Climate,* McGraw-Hill Book Company, Inc., New York, 1954, p. 25.

* One kilojoule equals 4,157 calories.

into space. It has been estimated that about 80 to 90 per cent of the surplus heat energy over the warm oceans is removed via the evaporation of water. Evaporation and precipitation, then, are powerful means of transferring surplus heat energy.

Energy transfers do not have to be solely in the form of heat. The mechanical energy of winds, waves, and ocean currents; the potential energy of water vapor at high elevations; and even the electrical energy potentials of cloud masses—all are means of shifting energy from one place to another in order to maintain both local and global balances.

6.16 SUGGESTED FACTORS IN LONG-RANGE TEMPERATURE VARIATIONS. As stated earlier, recurrent downward or upward trends in global temperatures have taken place since far back in earth history. Although it is not possible to list definitely, in order of importance, the causal factors for these long-run changes, it is appropriate to present a few of the suggested hypotheses:

1. Variations in solar energy output. Variations in solar energy output were discussed in Sec. 6.2. Future upper-air research may provide more accurate evaluation of this factor. It is now believed that a 10 per cent variation in output, which has been suggested as necessary to produce the requisite temperature changes, is not likely to occur in the atomic energy generation processes within the sun.

2. Variations in ultraviolet radiation from the sun, caused by sunspot activity. It has been suggested that variations in the composition of the upper atmosphere, such as an increase in ozone content, may result from sunspots within the solar atmosphere. Such alterations in the upper atmosphere of the earth might possibly have an influence on the *rates of reflection or absorption* of solar energy.

3. Variations in carbon dioxide content within the atmosphere. Among the atmospheric gases, carbon dioxide is particularly efficient in absorbing earth radiation; therefore, variations in the amount of carbon dioxide within the atmosphere could produce fluctuations in general world temperatures. The possible variables that might influence this content include changes in the amount of vegetation cover, the oxidation of carbohydrates, the rate of limestone formation, and the temperature range of the ocean surface.

4. Variation in atmospheric dust content. An appreciable increase in the dust content of the atmosphere—caused, for example, by unusually large explosive volcanic eruptions—might increase the reflection and scattering of solar radiation, thus reducing the amount that reaches the surface. Also, by acting as nuclei for water-vapor condensation, an increased number of dust particles might cause greater cloudiness, which would similarly increase the earth albedo.

5. Elevation or subsidence of continental masses. Changes in the shape and size of the continents might influence the behavior of the oceanic circulatory system and its heat-exchange properties or might affect the pattern of atmospheric circulation.

No one of these possible explanations for upward or downward trends in world temperatures is currently accepted as thoroughly satisfactory by a majority of climatic experts. Perhaps more than one, or even all of them, have contributed to the puzzling long-range variations in global temperatures.

6.17 RELATIVITY IN THE MEANING OF TEMPERATURE DIFFERENCES. Now that we have described the major differences in temperature patterns on earth, have seen how they vary daily, seasonally, and over the course of years, and have discussed the principal factors responsible for these differences, we shall examine some of the human implications of these patterns. Here again, however, it is important to note, as we did in discussing the meaning of slope differences, that the human impact of any one environmental factor is never an isolated variable that can be measured or interpreted apart from the context of other physical or cultural variables.

Our own sensations of heat or cold, for example, cannot be related directly to a given scale of temperature alone. *Sensible temperature* is a term we use to describe the temperature that our bodies feel. The humidity of the air, as well as the temperature, influences this feeling. High humidity tends to heighten the sensitivity of the human body to changes in temperature by increasing the conduction of heat by clothing and aiding in the transfer of heat between the air and the skin. It also tends to reduce the evaporation of body fluids, thus checking perspiration, an important skin-temperature control. Experiments reveal also that actual cell deterioration at high temperatures is speeded by high atmospheric humidity. Different types and amounts of food intake and general systemic conditioning also can alter the biological adaptation of human beings to temperature conditions. Darwin, in his *The Diary of the Voyage of H.M.S. Beagle,* describes with astonishment the sight of naked Tierra del Fuegan natives going about their daily routines in a sleet storm. The wind also has a considerable effect on sensible temperatures, by influencing evaporation rates and by continually replacing the air next to the skin. A cold, windy day is much more uncomfortable than a calm day with comparable temperatures; on the other hand, a breeze on a hot, humid day relieves the "stickiness" of still air.

Temperature plays an important part in human affairs, not only in affecting the expenditures necessary to maintain body comfort but also in helping to determine suitable patterns of agriculture and other economic activities. The definition of what constitutes a critical temperature boundary, however, like comparable definitions for the other physical elements, depends entirely on the particular functional situation. The temperature considered critical by a banana grower is entirely different from that designated by a corn farmer in Iowa or an asparagus cultivator in New Jersey.

Temperature boundaries may have wide differences in meaning with only slight variations in definition. To illustrate: the isotherm of 32°F, or the freezing point of water, has many human and environmental implications; yet this boundary is as elusive as the weather conditions that produce it. It is far from stationary, since it swings back and forth for hundreds of miles between night and day; it may also outline many islands of higher or lower temperatures. The exact freezing boundary is extremely difficult to trace and, even if it could be located, would represent conditions for only an instant in time. To give some indication of the probability of frost incidence, however, several generalized frost boundaries have been used. These include the following:

1. *Absolute frost limit,* or the boundary of areas where temperatures below freezing have never been recorded

2. *Mean frost limit,* or the boundary of areas having *mean minimum* temperatures above 32°F

3. *Mean length of the growing season,* or the mean number of days per year between the last temperature below 32°F in spring and the first to occur in the fall

4. *Lowest mean monthly isotherm of 32°F,* or the boundary of areas whose *lowest*

mean monthly temperature is above 32°F; frequently used as a climatic boundary in global climatic differentiation

5. *Highest average mean monthly isotherm of 32°F,* or the isotherm bounding areas whose *highest mean monthly* temperature is below 32°F; the boundary usually used in global climatic classifications to designate icecap climates

Dozens of other such generalizations of the frost boundary could be given. Each of them could have a significant meaning for some functional use. A wise application of climatology does not utilize conventional generalizations for their own sake. Instead, the temperature boundaries that have been demonstrated as appropriate for the particular use in question are plotted from statistical data.

Humidity

Humidity is the state of the atmosphere with respect to water vapor. It is a significant element of weather and climate for several reasons. First, water vapor is the source of all precipitation and therefore influences its amount and distribution. Second, since molecules of water vapor absorb solar and terrestrial radiation, such absorption is an important factor in air temperature. Third, through its property of absorbing a large amount of heat in passing from a liquid to a vapor and of releasing this heat energy upon changing back to a liquid, humidity helps to form one of the principal heat-exchange systems in regulating energy balances and temperatures throughout the world. Finally, humidity influences sensible temperatures, or those which the human body feels. Like the other climatic elements (except solar radiation), it is not an independent variable but always acts in conjunction with, and in response to, other climatic elements, such as temperature and pressure.

6.18 ATMOSPHERIC HUMIDITY AND TERMINOLOGY. The water-vapor content of the atmosphere can be described in several ways. *Absolute humidity* is a measurement of water-vapor content that is rarely used by meteorologists, because of its rapid variability. It refers to the weight, or mass, of water vapor contained within a given *volume* of air, as expressed, say, in grains per cubic foot. Its variability results from the fact that air contracts and expands with changes in temperature. A more satisfactory measurement of water-vapor content is *specific humidity,* or the weight of water vapor contained within a given weight of air, expressed, for example, in grams per kilogram. It is used mainly in upper-air observations.

The measure of water-vapor content most widely used by meteorologists is *vapor pressure,* or that part of the general atmospheric pressure that is due to the contained water vapor. Every molecule of water vapor, as well as of the other gases in the atmosphere, has a certain amount of energy which it may direct upon a surface to exert pressure. The total vapor pressure, therefore, is proportional to the number of molecules per unit volume. It is expressed in the same way as atmospheric pressure, that is, in inches of mercury, or *millibars.*[9] Over the surface of a body of water, molecules of water vapor are continually passing from the water to the air, and some are returning. The number returning increases as the water-vapor content (or vapor pressure) in the air increases. Eventually, however, the number of returning molecules equals the number passing into

[9] A *millibar* is a unit of force that exerts a pressure of one-thousandth of a *bar,* which, in turn, is equivalent to a pressure of one million *dynes* per square centimeter. A *dyne* is the amount of force needed to accelerate one gram of mass one centimeter within one second. One inch of mercury is approximately equivalent to thirty-four millibars.

the air. When this happens, the air space is said to be *saturated,* and no further evaporation can take place. This condition is termed *vapor-pressure saturation.* If the temperature of the saturated air is raised, the capacity of the air space to hold vapor increases, evaporation again occurs, and the vapor pressure rises until a new saturation point is reached. The fluctuation of vapor-pressure saturation with changes of temperature is shown in Table 6.6. It will be noted that the change is not in direct arithmetic progression. The higher the temperatures, the more rapid is the change in vapor-pressure saturation. Warm air can hold much more water vapor than cold air, and the rate of increase in capacity increases with rising temperature.

A fourth measurement of humidity is *relative humidity,* or the ratio between the amount of water vapor in the air and the maximum amount that can be held at saturation at a given air temperature and pressure. More simply, it is vapor pressure divided by vapor-pressure saturation, and it is always expressed as a percentage. At saturation, the relative humidity is 100 per cent.

GLOBAL PATTERNS OF ATMOSPHERIC MOISTURE CONTENT. The mean content of water vapor in the air at different sections of the earth surface is indicated by the curves in Fig. 6.17, which show both the vapor pressure and the specific humidity for different latitudinal zones during July and January. A general decrease in water-vapor content with increasing latitude is indicated, corresponding to the influence of temperature on vapor-pressure saturation, or the capacity of air space to hold water vapor (see Table 6.6). For the same reason, winters bring lower values of water-vapor content at all latitudes except near the equator, where seasonal temperature variations are negligible. The wider seasonal range generally found north of the equator is related to correspondingly greater seasonal temperature ranges, which, in turn, occur because of the higher proportion of land as compared with water. It is interesting to note that the desert areas in the subtropics are not indicated latitudinally by a pronounced sag in the curve of vapor pressure. The main reason for this is that the desert areas are not continuous around the globe within their particular latitudinal zones and are exceeded areally within the zones by humid oceanic or continental climates.

Precipitation follows fairly closely the moisture content in the air. In comparing the world map of average precipitation with the charts of vapor pressure (Figs. 6.19 and 6.17), note that the decrease in vapor pressure passing from lower to higher latitudes is roughly matched by a decrease in precipitation. Under comparable conditions of terrain and exposure, the lower the temperature, the less is the precipitation, because of lower moisture content in the air.

Vapor pressure varies appreciably during a 24-hour period, and the characteristic pattern of diurnal (daily) variation over land differs from that over oceans. Over land masses, a double maximum and double minimum occur. The lowest amount corresponds to the lowest temperature, usually encountered

TABLE 6.6 Vapor-pressure saturation, in inches of mercury at various air temperatures. (Assuming constant air pressure)

AIR TEMPERATURE, °F	VAPOR-PRESSURE SATURATION, INCHES OF MERCURY
0	0.038
10	0.063
20	0.103
30	0.164
40	0.247
50	0.360
60	0.517
70	0.732
80	1.022

shortly before sunrise. In the forenoon, under the influence of a rising temperature and increased evaporation, the vapor pressure rises to a first, but slightly lower, maximum. Once the surface is heated, convection and consequent air mixing increase, removing some of the accumulated vapor to higher levels and thus decreasing the amount near the surface. A secondary minimum thus occurs during the early afternoon, when mixing reaches a maximum. Thereafter, toward evening, the vapor content rises slowly with decreasing air turbulence. After sunset, cooling again tends to reduce the intake of water vapor, and the amount contained decreases slowly to the early morning minimum. Over water bodies, the air is more stable and less likely to be influenced by convectional and turbulent mixing; hence a simple relationship between temperature and water-vapor content tends to be found, with a minimum of vapor pressure occurring just before sunrise and a maximum in the early afternoon. Local variations in the intensity of convection and air interchange may produce noticeable variations in both daily and seasonal vapor-pressure readings.

Global variations in the content of water vapor in the air are important primarily because they bring about differences in precipitation and in the mass transfer of heat energy from one place to another. The high relative humidities and high quantities of water vapor in the air within equatorial areas signify that the air is near saturation and that the quantities of water released following condensation are likely to be greater than elsewhere. At high latitudes, although the relative humidity is high and saturation is soon reached, the low water-vapor content permits the release of only small quantities of water or snow following condensation. The heat-exchange effect of water vapor entering and leaving the atmosphere is so vital to the maintenance of

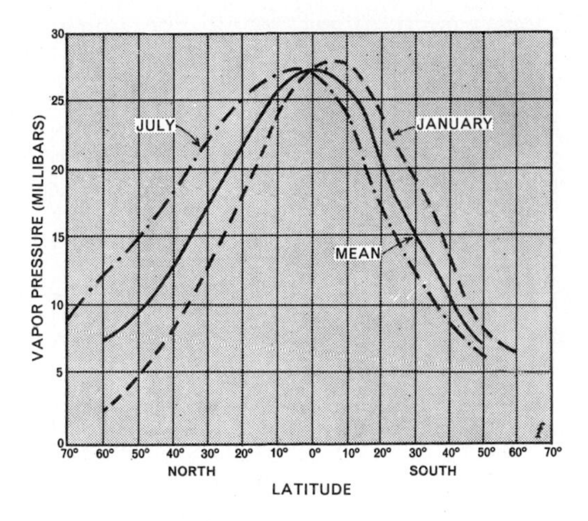

FIG. 6.17 Distribution of vapor pressure by latitude and season. The greater vapor pressure at most latitudes in summer as compared with winter is a reflection of the greater capacity of warm air to hold water vapor. Note the greater seasonal variation in the northern hemisphere, the result of greater land area. [After Haurwitz and Austin]

global energy balances that it is treated separately in a later section.

PATTERNS OF RELATIVE HUMIDITY. As stated earlier, relative humidity is not a measure of the water-vapor content of the air but a ratio between vapor pressure and vapor-pressure saturation at a given air temperature and pressure. It is an important measurement, because it indicates how near the air space is to saturation and hence indicates the general susceptibility of the air space to water evaporation or condensation with changes in temperature or increased vapor intake. Since air can hold much more water vapor as its temperature increases, the relative humidity decreases with an increase in temperature, assuming that the water-vapor content remains the same. Similarly, if the temperature remains constant, an increase in water-vapor content produces an increase in relative humidity.

A highly generalized global pattern of relative humidity is shown in Fig. 6.18. Mean

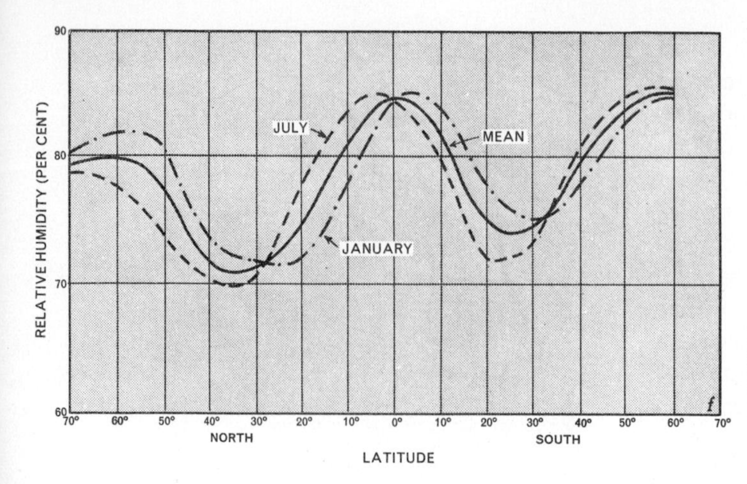

FIG. 6.18 Distribution of relative humidity by latitude and by season. [After Haurwitz and Austin]

figures for latitudinal zones during July and January and also for the year are shown on separate curves. Data for the high latitudes beyond 70° N and 60° S are too incomplete to be reliable. Examination of the curves reveals the following generalizations and explanations:

1. The highest mean maximum relative humidity lies at the equator. This is a reflection of the high evaporation rates in an area plentifully supplied with water. The low-latitude maximum shifts slightly north and south of the equator, corresponding to seasonal shifts in the thermal belts.

2. The minima are located roughly between lat 20 and 40° in each hemisphere. The minimum within the northern hemisphere is lower than that in the southern hemisphere. These minima correspond to areas of subtropical high atmospheric pressure that are characterized by subsiding dry air from above and that are extremely hot during the summer months. Since summer heating over the northern hemisphere continents is greater than that south of the equator, the minimum relative humidity is lower in the northern hemisphere and is located somewhat farther poleward.

3. The rise in relative humidity at latitudes greater than 30 and 40° is mainly the result of decreased temperatures.

4. High latitudes experience a maximum relative humidity in winter and a minimum in summer, owing to seasonal temperature conditions. The converse is true at low latitudes, where there are only slight seasonal temperature variations but where humidity varies under the influence of subsidence of dry air from above. The influence of such subsidence in lowering relative humidity is felt in low latitudes mainly during the winter months.

5. The slight drop in the relative-humidity curves beyond lat 60° N may be due to the deficiency in water-evaporating surfaces and the lesser amount of importation of water vapor by winds. Winter temperatures also are somewhat higher toward the Arctic Ocean. Note that the drop is greatest in winter.

The mean data shown in Fig. 6.18 do not indicate the differences within each latitudinal zone produced by continental and oceanic surfaces. In general, seasonal ranges in relative humidity are appreciably lower over oceanic surfaces than over continental areas, which exhibit wide seasonal ranges. Such ranges correspond to seasonal temperature fluctuations. Daily variations in relative humidity are closely related to temperature, with a maximum usually occurring just before sunrise, when the temperature is lowest, and a minimum occurring during the temperature maximum in the early afternoon.

6.19 WATER PHASES AND THEIR ROLE IN HEAT EXCHANGE.

Water is a unique material, being the only substance on earth that is found in nature as a solid, a liquid, and a gas. These three states, or *phases,* represent different states of molecular equilibrium with respect to the flow of heat energy about them. Each chemical substance has its own range of *phase equilibrium,* or the tendency to maintain the same phase (liquid, gas, or solid) within a given range of temperature (pressure remaining constant), but the molecules of water are the only ones in nature whose range of phase equilibrium lies within the comparatively narrow limits of earth atmosphere temperatures. Let us now examine the three phases of water and see how each is related to energy availability.

Below approximately 32°F, water is in equilibrium as ice, a crystalline solid.[10] In the change of phase from a solid to a liquid, a certain amount of heat energy is required. This quantity, termed the *latent heat of fusion,* amounts to approximately 80 calories per gram in the case of water (the amount varies with different substances). It is termed *latent heat* because it plays no part in raising or lowering the temperature of water. Once in the liquid phase, water will utilize added heat to raise its temperature until it reaches the upper limit of liquid-phase equilibrium. In order to change liquid water into water vapor, heat energy equivalent to about 540 calories per gram must be absorbed. This amount is termed the *latent heat of vaporization.* Every gram of water vapor in the atmosphere, therefore, contains this relatively large reservoir of energy. The absorption of this heat during the process of evaporation lowers the temperature of the medium from which the heat energy was derived. For example, the chilling of one's body when stepping out of a hot shower is caused by the rapid evaporation of the film of warm water left on the skin. The reverse process, or the change from water vapor to the liquid phase (condensation), is accompanied by the release of the latent heat obtained during the vaporization process. Upon release, this energy is known as the *latent heat of condensation.*

Under certain conditions it is possible for water to pass directly from a solid to a gaseous phase, or vice versa, without going through a liquid phase. This process is termed *sublimation,* and the energy involved is equal to a combination of the heat of vaporization plus the heat of fusion. Ice and snow may thus evaporate without melting, but this change requires as much heat energy as it does when melting intervenes.

In summary, evaporation from terrestrial water surfaces removes heat energy from such surfaces and functions as a cooling process, whereas condensation adds heat energy to the air and functions as a heating process. Bearing its load of energy, the evaporated water, in the form of water vapor, either is carried to the upper air, where it releases this latent heat energy following condensation, or is borne horizontally by surface winds toward higher and cooler latitudes, where subsequent condensation aids in raising air temperatures. This atmospheric heat exchange system, and the significance of latent heat in the system, may be likened to the operation of a mechanical kitchen re-

[10] Under certain conditions, *supercooled* water may continue to exist as a liquid. Water in the form of tiny droplets, for example, has been cooled down to −39°F without turning to ice.

frigerator. Inside the refrigerator, the liquid in the coils changes into a gas, absorbing heat energy from the enclosed air and food during the process. The gas is then conducted outside the refrigerator by means of a pump and compressed; this in turn forces the vapor to condense and liberate its heat of condensation into the room, after which it again flows back into the refrigerator. One-way valves maintain a flow of the gas and liquid in the same direction. The functions of evaporation and condensation in the air circulation system are discussed further in Chapter 7, in the section on wind patterns.

Precipitation

A world map of average annual precipitation (Fig. 6.19) reveals a wide range of differences. There are broad areas of both high and low precipitation as well as small, isolated areas of each. Intermediate gradations are both wide and narrow. Exceptions may be found to almost any broad generalization concerning the relationships between precipitation and latitude or longitude.

Comparing the map of rainfall with one of population density indicates that, with few exceptions, the large areas of low precipitation support only a sparse population. Man has learned how to make himself reasonably comfortable within all the temperature ranges on earth, but he cannot live without fresh water. Regardless of developments in techniques for obtaining fresh water from sources other than precipitation, the pattern of precipitation still remains one of the basic factors in outlining the *oekomene,* or habitable world. The major exceptions include the dry regions that are irrigated by water brought from humid regions.

The distribution of precipitation, furthermore, is an integral part of the global system of controls and balances that regulates the accumulation and transfer of heat from place to place at or near the earth surface. As indicated in the earlier sections of this chapter, a a large amount of solar energy is received at the surface, but it is not evenly distributed. Precipitation, among other factors, helps to maintain the relatively low range of temperatures that makes life, as we know it, possible on earth. Principally because of its role in heat transfer and its vital contributions to organic life, to the supply of water for streams, and hence to the processes of sculpturing the face of the earth, precipitation ranks high in importance among the world physical patterns.

6.20 THE GLOBAL WATER SUPPLY SYSTEM. A study of the world system of precipitation reveals that it is similar to the water supply system of municipalities. The major global source areas for water, corresponding to the lakes, reservoirs, wells, or rivers of municipal systems, are the oceans, particularly the warmer portions. Municipal systems normally require pumps to supply the energy necessary to convey water to the consumer, and so too does the global system. The global pump, however, is a far more complicated apparatus than the ones in our water pumping stations. Like the pumps in a kitchen refrigerator, the global pump involves alternate vaporization and condensation. The energy which operates the global pump comes from the sun, and indeed the quantities required are enormous. The heat energy needed to evaporate the water that falls on a single acre during a 1-inch rain, for example, is roughly equivalent to the amount released in burning over 15,000 tons of good-quality coal. This energy of vaporization in the lifting mechanisms might be compared to the energy used in municipal water-pumping stations. Further energy is required to transport this vaporized water

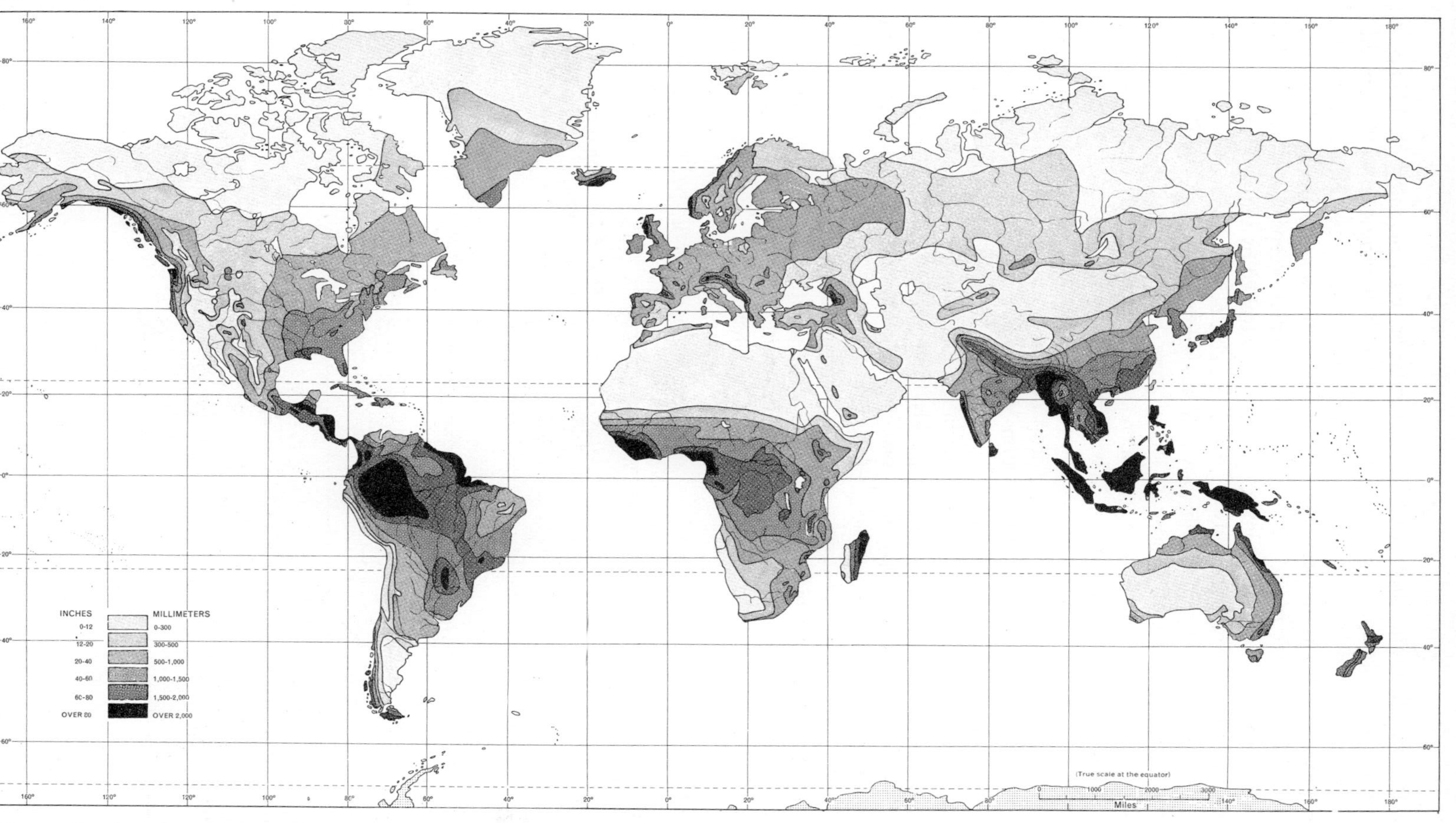

FIG. 6.19 World distribution of average annual precipitation. [After Bartholomew]

from the source to its destination, where it is condensed and dropped as precipitation.

The conduits of our global precipitation system are the general patterns of atmospheric circulation. These "rivers of air" are not perfect closed systems, as are the mains of a city water system, but they frequently are remarkably constant, especially in certain parts of the world. The pattern of atmospheric stream lines is described in the next chapter. The distribution of precipitation in the world is closely related to the characteristics and behavior of air circulation. Where a particular air stream leads directly and strongly from a warm, low-latitude ocean toward a continental land mass, more water is available for precipitation on land than where an air stream moves from a cold, continental source toward warmer areas. The flow of the air streams, with their contained water vapor, is not always horizontal. Areas in which conditions favor the rising of air have greater precipitation than do areas where air subsidence prevails.

The release of water from the planetary air-circulation conduits may be likened to the process of turning the water taps in a home. Turning the taps releases the valves which check the water pressure in the pipes. The valve which keeps water vapor within the air is controlled by temperature. As indicated in Table 6.7, the capacity to hold water vapor at saturation decreases with a drop in temperature. It therefore follows that, if a decrease in temperature is great enough, it will produce saturation, even with a small amount of contained water vapor. A further drop in temperature may lead to condensation. At this point the "valve" is opened.

The mechanics of condensation and precipitation are complex and are still not completely understood. Certain requirements, however, are known, and these include the following:

1. Condensation requires a sufficient decrease in temperature to destroy the phase equilibrium of water vapor.

2. Condensation of any kind, including fog or cloud particles, raindrops, or snow, requires tiny particles of specific kinds of air

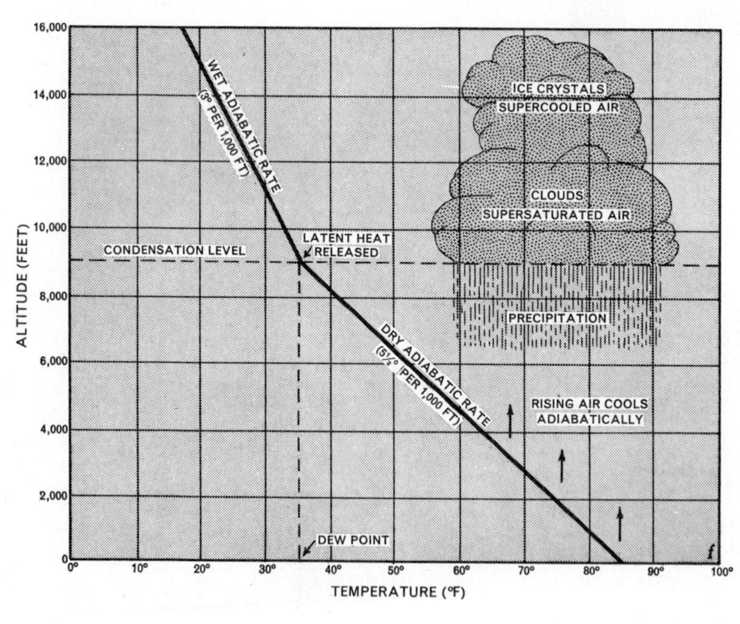

FIG. 6.20 The process of precipitation.

impurities (such as salt, ice, dust, or large ions) and of certain sizes to act as nuclei for the growth of water droplets. Such particles are plentiful in the lower part of the atmosphere, but are much less abundant in the upper reaches, several miles above the earth surface.

3. An undetermined and perhaps variable amount of water-vapor *supersaturation*[11] must be present before water droplets can grow to the size of cloud particles.

4. The size of even the smallest raindrop is many times greater than the maximum droplet size of clouds or fog. The mass of an ordinary cloud droplet, for example, is about one-millionth that of an average-sized raindrop (1 millimeter in diameter). Cooling by conduction and radiation may produce fog or cloud droplets, but *raindrops result from adiabatic cooling.*

5. Raindrop formation requires special conditions in addition to condensation, including *supercooling* of *supersaturated* air to temperatures well below freezing and with the presence of ice crystals or other suitable freezing nuclei as an initial stage. (Unusually high columns of rising air in the tropics may be an exception to this generalization.)

6. Nearly all mid-latitude rain originally forms as snow.

The taps, then, of our global precipitation system are located in places where mechanisms exist for forcing the air streams rapidly to elevations high enough to cause freezing. An air stream may be warm and saturated with water vapor, but *unless it rises, no precipitation can take place.*

Since precipitation normally requires the lifting of air, the mechanisms for this are critical in understanding the world distribution of precipitation.

There are three initial ways in which air is forced to rise from lower to higher elevations: (1) *orographic lifting,* caused by the movement of air up the side of an obstacle; (2) *convectional lifting,* caused by unequal surface heating; and (3) *convergent lifting,* caused by the convergence of air masses. In addition to the initial impetus supplied by the above mechanisms, another critical factor influencing lifting is the *stability* of the air being lifted. Since stability is a factor in all lifting, regardless of the initial cause, it will be discussed first.

6.21 STABILITY AND INSTABILITY AS FACTORS IN PRECIPITATION.

Air masses vary considerably in their tendency to rise. If an air mass resists ascent, it is a *stable* air mass. If it tends to move upward easily, it is *unstable.* The principal factor in stability is the relationship between the adiabatic rate of cooling and the lapse rate (see Fig. 6.21). Since the adiabatic rate of cooling in dry air remains at about 5.6°F per 1,000 feet, the dominant variable in the ascent of dry air is the lapse rate. Although the normal or average lapse rate is 3.56°F per 1,000 feet, lapse rates vary widely from this figure. If the lapse rate is less than the adiabatic rate, the rising air soon will be cooled to the same temperature as the surrounding air, and the rising will be checked. This state is termed *stability.* If the lapse rate is greater than the adiabatic rate, however, the rising air will continue to rise. This condition is known as *instability.* Stability and instability, therefore, are related to the patterns of vertical temperature changes.

A steep lapse rate signifies that the air near the surface is unusually warm as compared with the air above. There are a number of ways in which this condition can occur, but

[11] *Supersaturation* involves the crowding of water-vapor molecules into a given mass of air beyond their normal maximum number. It may occur, for example, where insufficient nuclei are present to accommodate all the demands for condensation.

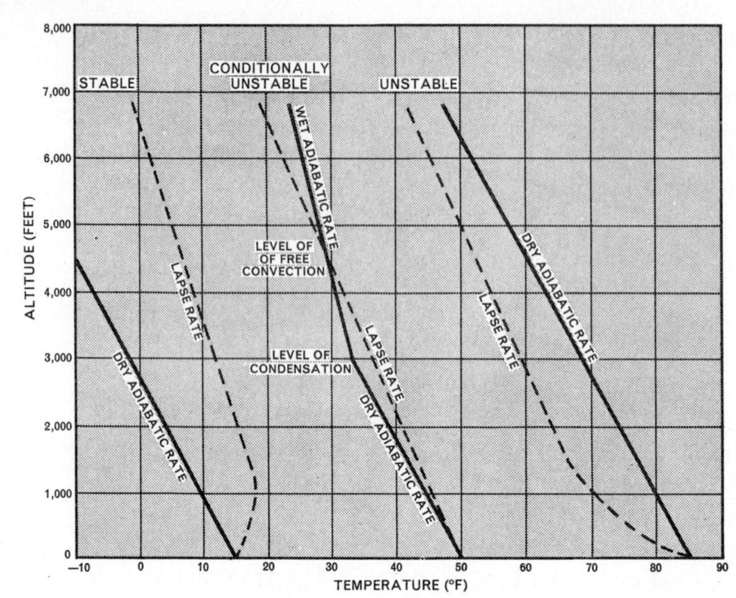

FIG. 6.21 The relationship between adiabatic and lapse rates in stability and instability.

it is most common during the daylight hours, when the surface of the earth and the layers of air immediately above it heat very rapidly. Since the maximum rate of cooling of a rising air mass is 5.6°F per 1,000 feet (*the dry adiabatic rate*), a rising column of air will continue upward if the lapse rate exceeds this figure, because the temperature of the rising air mass will continue to be higher than the surrounding air. Such an air mass would be *absolutely unstable*. If the lapse rate is in excess of about 19°F per 1,000 feet, vertical movement can begin without benefit of any initial lifting mechanism. Such steep lapse rates occur very rarely, but when they do, they are usually the result of cold air overrunning warm air.

When a dry air mass has a lapse rate of less than 5.6°F per 1,000 feet, that is, less than the dry adiabatic rate, it is *stable*. When the lapse rate is less than 2.5°F per 1,000 feet, the air mass is *absolutely stable,* and it makes no difference whether the air is moist or dry, since all adiabatic rates are in excess of 2.5°F per 1,000 feet. An inversion situation, with temperatures increasing with elevation, is an excellent example of a condition that produces absolute stability.

In the case of temperature inversions, the inability of air to rise beyond the inversion boundary is sometimes marked by a layer of smoke or dust, which collects just beneath the warmer upper layer of air. Stability and a reduced lapse rate at upper levels also may be caused by the subsidence of air from above. Fog usually is an indication of stability, since it generally is caused by cooling near the surface. Occasionally the air may become so stabilized that there is insufficient air mixing to remove toxic gases over industrial areas. The accumulation of such gases mixed with fog (known as *smog*) produced the disaster that killed twenty persons in Donora, Pennsylvania, in late October, 1948. It was estimated that over 5,000 persons became ill as a direct result of this unusual atmospheric condition.

The humidity of an air mass may influence its stability through the release of the latent heat of condensation and the effect of this heat on the adiabatic rate. If an air mass is moist and has a lapse rate between 2.5 and 5.6°F per 1,000 feet, it may be unstable, provided that the amount of heat released following condensation as the air mass rises is sufficient to depress the adiabatic rate of cooling below the lapse rate. Since this instability is conditioned by the amount of water vapor in the air, it is termed *conditional instability.*

The following examples of induced stability and instability in North America will illustrate the application of the factors discussed above:

1. The air stream that enters the southern United States from the Gulf of Mexico has been passing over a warm body of water since its descent somewhere in the subtropical North Atlantic. The moisture content of its lower levels thus has been greatly increased, even though the air mass has not gained much temperature since its descent. The high moisture content of the lower air stratum makes it conditionally unstable; thus it is extremely sensitive in summer to (1) lifting by the unequal heating surfaces of the hot, southern United States, (2) orographic lifting along the southwestern slopes of the Appalachians, and (3) lifting by the frontal margins of cooler air masses from Canada.

2. When the type of air mass described above continues northeastward and encounters the cold water of the Labrador Current off the New England and southeastern Canadian coasts, its lower layer becomes chilled and hence becomes more stable. Only a strong, cold air mass is able to force it upward sufficiently to reach a level where the conditional instability can take over the process of precipitation. The cooling below often produces condensation into tiny droplets without causing the air to rise, and the air mass has a low layer of thick fog. A similar condition produces the dense London fogs, where warm, moist Atlantic air passes over the cooler land surfaces of England during the winter season.

3. When cold continental air originating in northern Canada moves into the center of the continent in the summer, it picks up considerable moisture in its lower portion during its passage across the Great Lakes. The lower layer of air, later being heated over the hot plains of Illinois or Indiana, is unstable and produces strong convectional updrafts and summer showers. Orographic lifting is effective in producing precipitation from the same air mass during the winter season, since it has become unstable during its passage over the unfrozen Great Lakes.

6.22 OROGRAPHIC LIFTING. Air that is forced upward by a topographic obstacle such as a hill or mountain will be cooled adiabatically, and condensation or precipitation may result (see Fig. 6.22). The orographic effect on precipitation patterns is most noticeable along the windward slopes of high mountain ranges. There is no minimum height above which condensation or precipitation occurs. If the approaching air stream is nearly saturated with water vapor, only a slight amount of lifting results in condensation. In warm tropical ocean areas, the air

FIG. 6.22 Orographic precipitation.

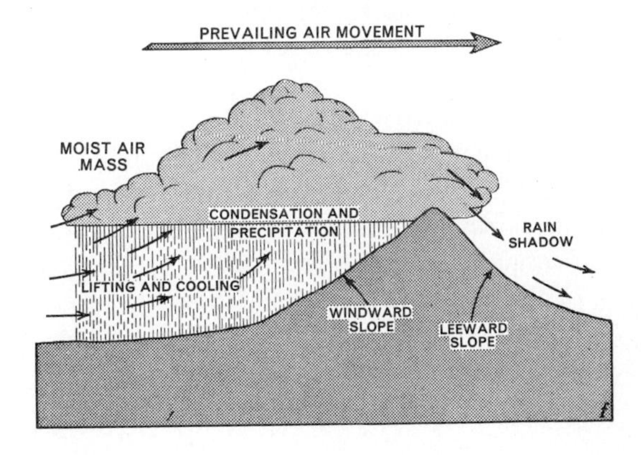

FIG. 6.23 Snow on Mount Mansfield, Vermont. The heavy orographic snowfall of the New England uplands provides ideal conditions for winter skiing. The grotesque forms are spruce trees laden with snow. [Standard Oil Company (N.J.)]

may have such a high relative and specific humidity that even lifting over a low, hilly island results in heavy precipitation. Conditional instability probably is involved in most orographic precipitation, and the warming of air resulting from the release of latent heat takes over the impetus for lifting once the orographic influence has raised the air stream to the condensation level.

Where mountain ranges intercept warm, humid air streams, unusually high precipitation results. The two rainiest weather stations on earth are located on Kauai Island, Hawaii, and at Cherrapunji, on the slopes of the Arakan Hills, which are foothills of the Himalayas. The Kauai station is located on the windward slope of a high volcanic peak. Both of these stations receive well over 400 inches of rain per year.

In most localities where orographic lifting prevails, the precipitation is not confined to the slopes immediately above a critical condensation level but often extends well in front of the terrain obstacle, in a zone that broadens with the increasing height of the obstacle. This is mainly due to the cushioning effect of air immediately next to the terrain obstacle. Here the velocity of the incoming air is checked by increased friction or by the compressive impact of meeting the obstacle, and the air behind this retarded air "cushion" may rise over it, the rising taking place out in front of the obstacle (see Fig. 6.22). A high mountain range may thus cause considerable air convergence and upward flow well in front of its windward side.

Orographic precipitation will be in the form of snow if the air stream rises high enough to reach freezing temperatures. The height of the snow line on mountain slopes generally lowers as latitude increases, although this correlation has many local exceptions, owing to variations in the amount of snowfall, exposure to solar heating, and wind strength and direction.

In the middle latitudes orographic lifting is much more likely to influence the distributional pattern of winter snowfall than that of summer rainfall. The reason for this is that the air in winter does not have to rise to such great heights to produce supercooling and to reach the snow stage. The average relative humidity, furthermore, is likely to be high; thus less lifting is necessary to reach the condensation level. Air that is at or near the freezing point and that contains appreciable quantities of water vapor is susceptible to snowfall with only a slight amount of lifting. Examples of *snow belts* caused by orographic lifting in the nonmountainous parts of the United States include the Keweenaw Peninsula of Northern Michigan, the northern rim of the Appalachian uplands and the western slopes of the Adirondacks in New York State, and the western slopes of the Green and White Mountains in New England. A rise of only a few hundred feet may produce increases in snowfall of 70 to 80 inches per year. Such persistent snow belts may be only a few miles wide and thus may not be indicated in regional weather-station records. Water vapor absorbed during the passage of dry, cold air across the Great Lakes is an important factor in all the above examples. The orographic influence on precipitation in these areas is scarcely distinguishable in the summer months, because the Great Lakes, being cooler than the air passing over them, has a stabilizing effect.

6.23 CONVECTIONAL LIFTING. Convectional lifting is caused by the unequal heating of surfaces. The air above the heated surface is warmed, expands, and rises. Cooling accompanies the raising (see Fig. 6.24). The height reached by the upward convectional current varies with the amount of heating at the surface and the steepness of the lapse rate. Convectional updrafts thus are important in producing precipitation only when they are combined with conditional instability. Conditionally unstable air, however, results in precipitation only when it is lifted to the condensation level and the ascending and condensing air rises sufficiently far to become supercooled. The most favorable conditions for convectional precipitation include (1) warm, moist air; (2) unequal heating surfaces; and (3) a steep lapse rate.

In the humid tropics, where the air is warm and laden with water vapor, convection is an important factor in triggering precipitation. It may also be a factor in many mid-latitude summer rains. Such rain usually is in the form of local but heavy showers. Convectional showers generally are most frequent in the afternoon over land areas, because at this time surface heating and air turbulence are at their maximum and the lapse rate is greatest.

Over warm, humid ocean areas in the tropics, the maximum convectional rainfall tends to occur at night—not during the afternoon and early evening, as on the continents.

FIG. 6.24 Examples of convectional lifting.

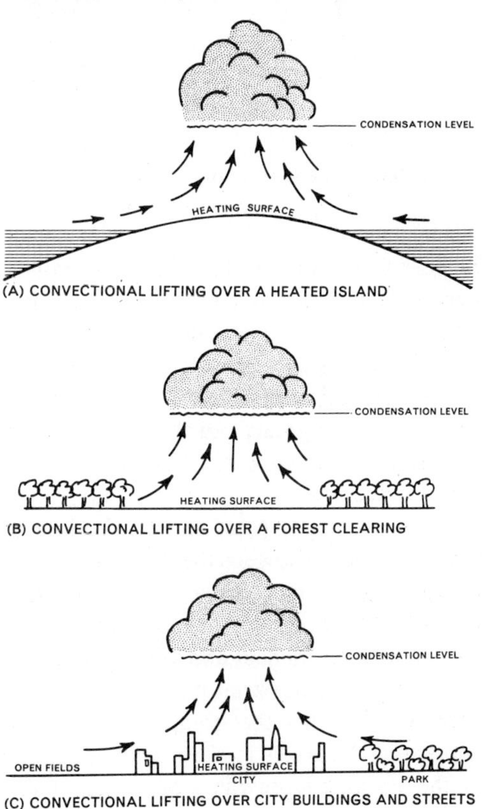

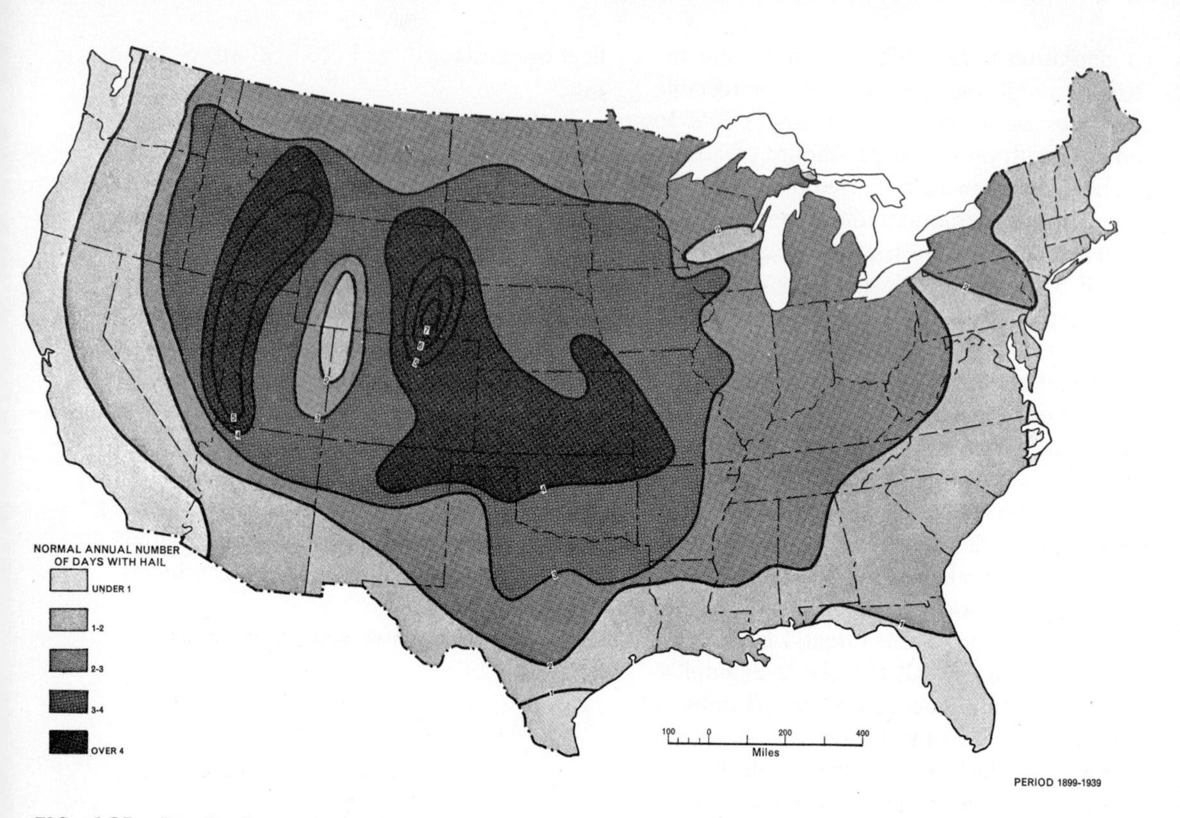

FIG. 6.25 Distribution of hail in the United States. [U.S. Department of Agriculture]

The reason for this is that the lapse rate is steepest during the early morning hours. Because of their uniformity, ocean surfaces do not tend to produce as many unequal heating surfaces as land areas; the intensity of heating is not so great; and there is a greater retardation of maximum diurnal temperatures (appearing usually in late afternoon and early evening). After sunset, the loss of heat by radiation lowers the temperature of the upper air much faster than that near the water surface, which has more water vapor in it to retain heat and which continues to absorb more terrestrial radiation from the warm water. Thus the greatest contrast in temperature between surface and upper air (or the steepest lapse rate) occurs at night.

6.24 CONVERGENT LIFTING. The principle behind convergent lifting is simply that part of the air usually is displaced upward when surface air streams move toward one another. In the case of two converging air masses, one of which is much warmer than the other, the warmer air is forced upward, paralleling the zone of discontinuity (separation) between the two. The line of contact between this separation zone and the earth surface is termed a *front* (see Figs. 7.20 and 7.21). Such lifting is termed *frontal lifting* or *frontal displacement*. The steepness of the rise is related to the steepness of the zone between the air masses. Cold, dense air moving along the ground may have its leading edge slowed by friction, so that a steep frontal surface results. Warmer, lighter air forced against this front will rise steeply. Such a front is known as a *cold front*. If, however, the colder, denser air is without much forward impetus and is shallow, whereas the warm air is steady and strong, the frontal surface may rise at a low angle. This is termed a *warm front*. Warm fronts are most frequently encountered along the trailing edge of a cold air mass. Precipitation will follow frontal lifting if the rise is high enough and the rising air is sufficiently humid. Here again, the release of latent heat and the resultant increase in temperature usually supplement the initial cause of the lifting. Normally precipitation along cold fronts is heavier and more restricted areally than it is along warm fronts. Frontal characteristics are treated in greater detail in Sec. 7.22.

Sharp contrasts in temperature, however, are not a requirement for convergent lifting. In low latitudes, the slow convergence of broad masses of warm, vapor-laden air will result in lifting. As explained in the next chapter, the general zone of convergence between the trade winds of opposite hemispheres that may differ only slightly in temperature promotes lifting and precipitation.

FIG. 6.26 Hail damage to a tobacco field, Virginia. This tobacco field would have averaged 1,500 pounds per acre. It was a total loss. [U.S. Department of Agriculture]

FIG. 6.27 Ice accumulated on a high tension electric power line following a winter glaze storm in New York State. The weight of the ice averaged 7 pounds per foot of wire. Broken lines such as this are only part of the cost of such storms. [U.S. Weather Bureau; New York Power and Light Co.]

6.25 FORMS OF PRECIPITATION.

Precipitation includes snow, hail, and sleet as well as rain. *Snow* occurs when condensation in free air takes place below the freezing point, so that the water vapor crystallizes about a nucleus and passes directly into a solid phase without going through an intermediate liquid phase. Although the moisture content of snow varies widely, 10 inches of snow is taken as the normal precipitation equivalent of 1 inch of rain. Most weather stations today melt the snowfall, recording its water equivalent.

Hail, although not a common form of precipitation, is of extreme significance to man because of its potential damaging effects on crops, greenhouses, and other property. It is always associated with severe thunderstorms

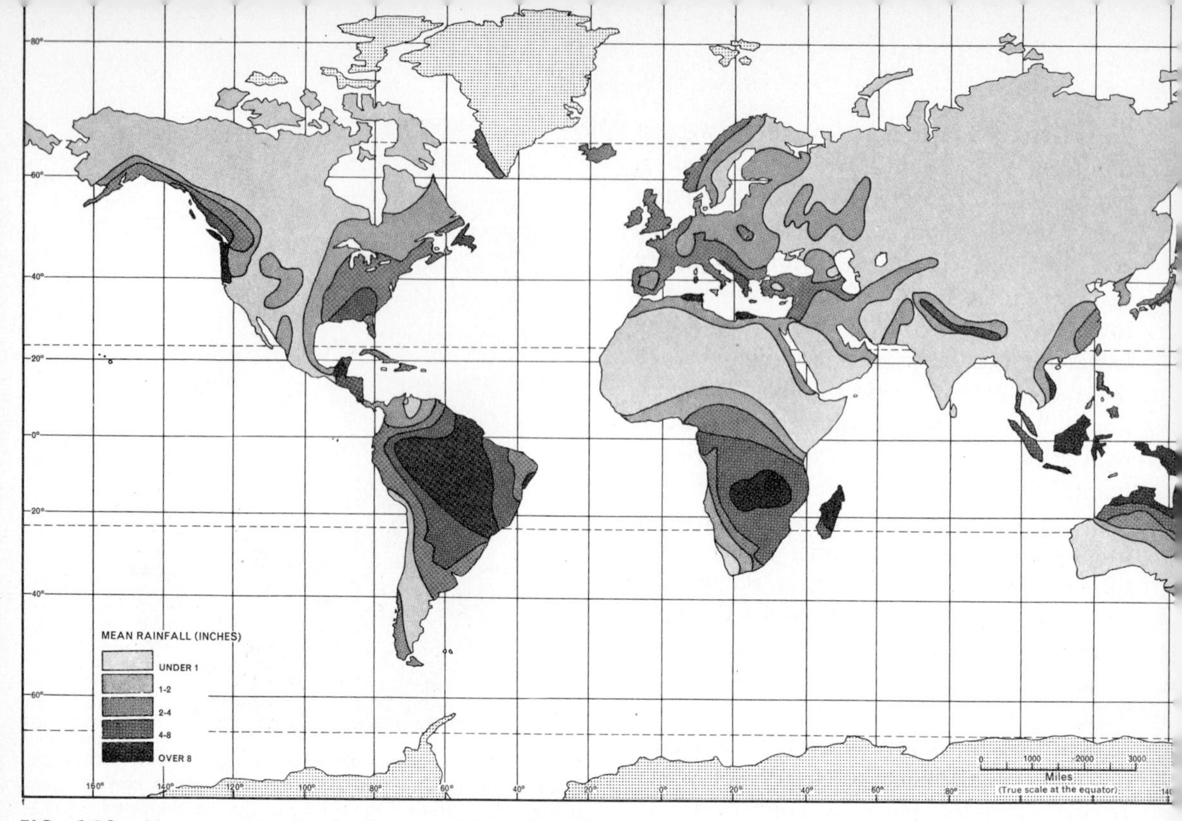

FIG. 6.28 Mean precipitation for January. [After James]

that reach unusually great heights. Hail is comprised of layers of partially melted and refrozen snow and rain. It begins as snow high in the upper cloud zone and gains mass as it falls through a zone of supercooled water droplets. These particles freeze suddenly upon contact with the falling particle. Hailstones are usually small in size, although huge ones, measuring as much as 17 inches in circumference, have been observed.

Sleet, or frozen rain, lacks the layering and rapid growth of hail. It usually results when rain falls through a layer of cold (below-freezing) air near the ground. It is often confused with *glaze,* which results from the sudden freezing of raindrops *after* they strike the ground surface. Both glaze and sleet are frequently encountered along the boundary between freezing and nonfreezing air, particularly along warm fronts.

6.26 THE GLOBAL DISTRIBUTION OF PRECIPITATION. Figures 6.28 and 6.29 illustrate the essential details of precipitation distribution during summer and winter. It will be noted that in some localities there are wide seasonal differences in precipitation, whereas in others there are consistently humid or dry conditions during both seasons. The areas having alternate wet and dry seasons usually are transitional, lying latitudinally between a consistently dry and a consistently wet climate and coming under the influence of each with seasonal shifts in winds, pressures, temperatures, and fronts. All the climatic belts, except perhaps those associated with polar icecaps, shift position according to changes in the directness of solar radiation. Other strong seasonal contrasts in precipitation are caused by seasonal reversals of winds such as monsoons (see

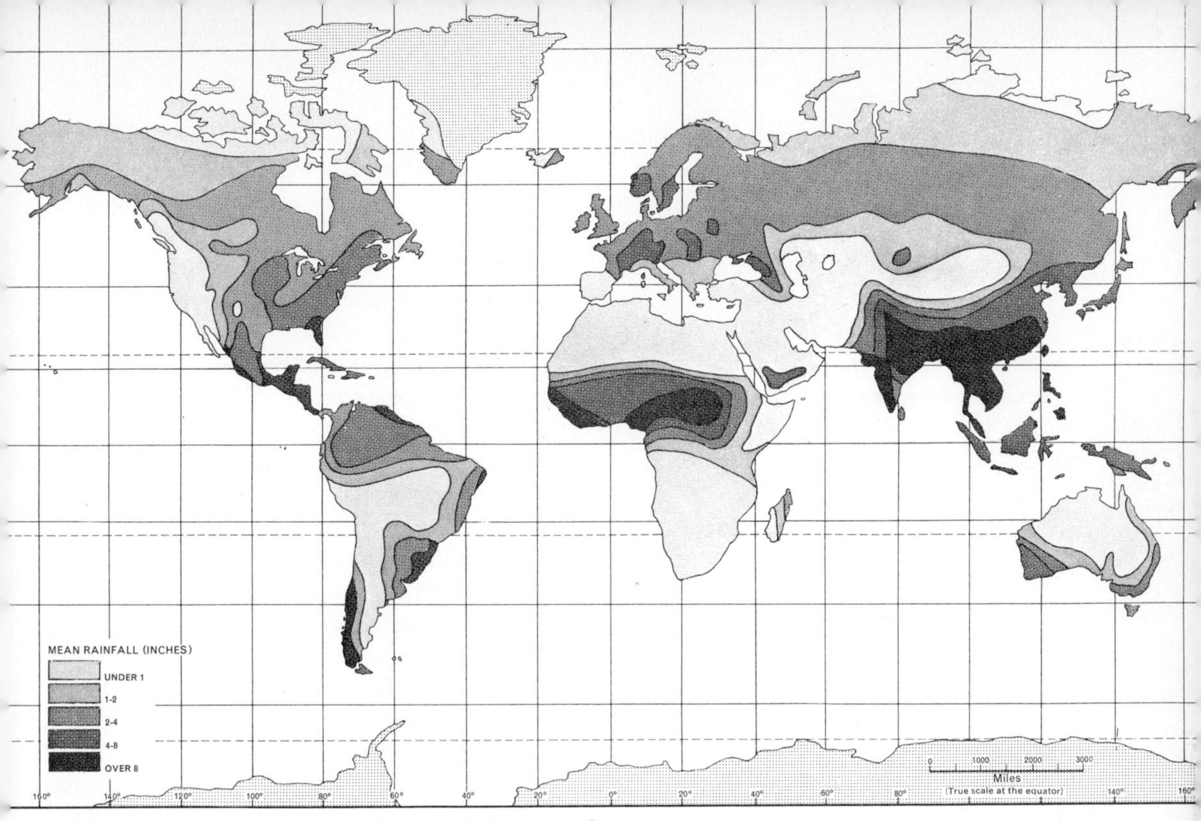

FIG. 6.29 Mean precipitation for July. [After James]

Sec. 7.15). The global distribution of precipitation is outlined below.

Continuously humid

1. Low elevations and windward slopes between lat 5° S and 10° N. *Major exceptions:* Somalia in East Africa and northeastern Brazil.
2. Eastern margins of continents from lat 10 to 60° N and S. *Major exception:* Patagonia in southern Argentina.
3. Western margins of continents between lat 40 to 60° N and S.

Continuously dry

1. The interior of continents between lat 15 and 50° N and S. *Major exception:* North America (Mississippi Valley to Hudson Bay).
2. The western margins of continents between lat 15 and 30° N and S. *Major exception:* The dry west coast of South America, south of lat 5° S.

Dry summers and humid winters

1. West coasts of continents between lat 30 and 40° N and S. *Exceptions:* This regime extends almost to 50° N in North America, and it extends far into the continent in the Mediterranean Sea area. West-facing mountain slopes in Idaho, Utah, and central Asia also have this regime.
2. Coasts and mountain slopes facing onshore winds during the winter (low-sun) season in southeast Asia and Indonesia.

Dry winters and humid summers

1. Transitional positions along the mar-

gins of the humid tropics. *Exception:* The eastern margins of continents.
2. Equator-facing coasts of continents between lat 5 and 25°.
3. Eastern Asia. *Exception:* The immediate coastal area.

Explanations for the generalized patterns of precipitation given above are presented in Chapter 8, which deals with the climatic patterns of the world.

Perspective

The surface of the earth is constantly bathed by radiation from the sun. The total amount received differs widely from place to place, the principal variations resulting from the length of day, the directness of radiant energy, the amount of cloud cover, and the proportion of land and sea. Over long periods, the total intake of radiation is balanced by the total outgoing radiation from the earth. Because the low latitudes receive more energy than they can radiate, the surplus must move to areas where the radiation received is less than the output. Long-range fluctuations in general world surface temperatures indicate that the global heat balance fluctuates within relatively narrow limits. Several hypotheses have been suggested for such long-range fluctuations.

The evaporation and condensation of water—accompanied, respectively, by the absorption and release of latent heat—form perhaps the most efficient way of adjusting regional imbalances of heat energy. The water-vapor content of the air is highly sensitive to temperature changes, and warm air can hold much more water vapor than cold air.

Precipitation always results from the upward movement and consequent cooling of air containing water vapor. Causes for the upward movement include terrain obstacles (orographic), unequal heating surfaces (convection), and the convergence of air masses exhibiting contrasts in temperature. Global patterns of precipitation depend largely on conditions of air instability or stability. Instability tends to increase when air is warmed below or when it greatly increases its water-vapor content. The major source areas for the water that falls throughout the earth surface in the form of rain, snow, sleet, and hail are the warm seas of low latitudes.

7

Atmospheric pressure, winds, air masses, and storms

This chapter deals largely with the movement of air at or above the earth surface. The transportation of energy and water vapor from one place to another utilizes moving air as its major agent. Because horizontal air movement, or wind, is caused primarily by horizontal differences in atmospheric pressure, the latter will be considered first. Despite many short-term fluctuations in pressure and the characteristics of air motion, regional consistencies may be observed about the earth surface and within the atmosphere above. We shall note these patterns and indicate some of the changes that take place within them. It is possible to distinguish several more or less homogeneous air masses whose properties are related largely to the broad source areas from which they originated and to trace certain changes in these air masses as they pass into areas that are warmer, colder, wetter, or drier than the original source regions. Finally we shall consider the sudden paroxysms of the atmosphere—the hurricanes, tornadoes, and thunderstorms that periodically unleash their violence on man and have led him to learn the places where they are most frequent and how to live with them.

Atmospheric pressure

Unlike fluctuations in temperature and precipitation, small differences in atmospheric pressure do not have a direct relationship to human affairs. Their indirect importance, however, is indicated by the presence of barometers in many homes and business establishments today. Man long has realized that pressure differentials are associated with weather changes and that alterations in pressure often precede drastic changes in temperature, precipitation, and winds. Air, a highly compressible and fluid substance, is extremely sensitive to the forces directed against it. Nearly all energy at the earth surface is obtained from solar radiation, and the patterns of atmospheric pressure are related to the balancing mechanisms for maintaining energy equilibria over the entire globe. Pressure patterns have little meaning in them-

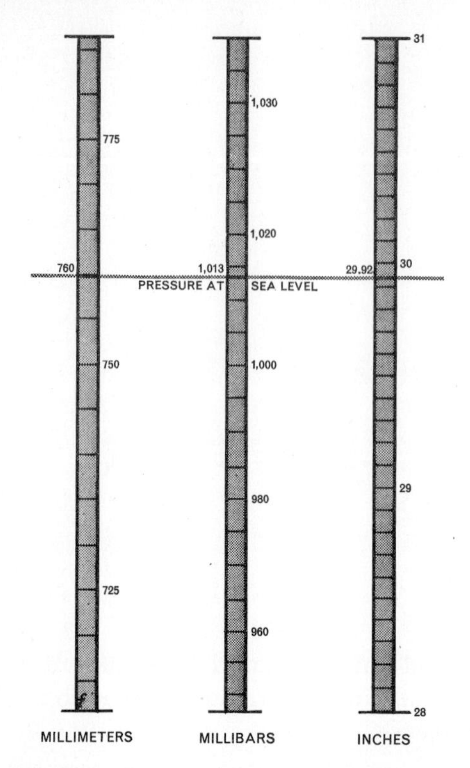

FIG. 7.1 Graphic conversion scale of atmospheric pressure: millibars to inches and millimeters of mercury.

selves. As an integral part of the energy distribution system throughout the world, however, they constitute significant indicators of the various general weather and climatic patterns.

7.1 TERMINOLOGY AND MEASUREMENT.

The atmospheric pressure at any given point on the earth surface and at any given time is a measurement of the total mass weight, or gravitational force, of a column of air extending upward from the surface to the outer limits of the earth's gravitational attraction. At sea level the mean atmospheric pressure is approximately 14.7 pounds per square inch, which means that there are 14.7 pounds of air above a single square inch of sea-level surface. Minute differences in pressure are important in weather and climatic patterns; therefore a finer scale than pounds per square inch is used. For many years pressure was expressed in inches or millimeters of mercury, or the height to which mercury would rise in the tube of a mercurial barometer. Mean sea-level pressure, or the equivalent of 14.7 pounds per square inch, is 29.92 inches, or 760 millimeters of mercury. More recently, in the interest of international standardization, the U.S. Weather Bureau has been using the *millibar* as the basic pressure unit on its weather maps. A millibar is roughly equal to the weight of 1 gram per square centimeter, or 0.014 pound per square inch. For a more precise definition, see footnote 9 in Chapter 6. Mean sea-level pressure expressed in millibars is 1,013.2. Figure 7.1 shows a simple conversion scale which relates millibars to inches and millimeters of mercury. Most home barometers are calibrated in inches.

Pressure patterns on maps usually are shown by means of isobars, which are lines connecting points of equal barometric pressure. Since atmospheric pressure decreases rapidly with elevation, it is customary for pressure maps to have all pressure readings reduced to sea level, in order to eliminate the complexities of differences in elevation. An examination of isobars on a map of atmospheric pressure reveals some similarities to a simplified contour map of comparative elevations. High points and low points are found, having different shapes and separated by different gradations of pressure. The areas of low atmospheric pressure are known as *cyclones*, or simply *lows*, whereas the areas of high pressure are termed *anticyclones*, or *highs*. The direction of pressure change is always at right angles to the isobars, and the pressure gradient, or slope, is determined by the spacing of the isobars. A steep pressure gradient is indicated by isobars that are relatively closely spaced.

7.2 CAUSES FOR CHANGES IN ATMOSPHERIC PRESSURE. Changes in atmospheric pressure result from energy transfers. These can be grouped into two classes: *thermal* and *dynamic*. The thermal causes for pressure changes are related to lateral transfers of air resulting from increases or decreases in heat energy. When air above a given area is heated, it expands, some of the air mass is transferred laterally, and thus the column contains less mass than it did before; thus its weight or pressure drops. Conversely, when air in an area loses heat, it shrinks and subsides, and because air moves into the column, the total mass becomes greater and the pressure rises. Heat energy may be added to air by direct conduction, by the absorption of direct and indirect radiation, and by the release of latent heat following condensation. The first two of these take place mainly near the earth surface. Low-pressure areas at the surface that are thermally controlled include those which receive large quantities of heat energy obtained mainly from the absorption of direct and indirect radiation and from the turbulent mixing of air that has been heated by conduction next to the earth surface. The thermal lows are found in the continental areas of maximum heating in the tropics and subtropics. Heat gains resulting from rapid condensation occur mainly in the cloud zones of rainy areas and thus have only a slight, indirect effect on surface pressure patterns.

The most efficient cooling process within the atmosphere is the loss of heat by radiation. This loss takes place throughout the atmosphere, but it is greatest near the ground, where there is more heat energy to be transformed into outgoing radiation, as well as more radiating surfaces to carry on the process. Areas that lose more heat through radiation than they gain from incoming radiation are sometimes termed *heat sinks*, so called because they drain away heat energy that is brought toward them. Such areas include ice- and snow-covered surfaces under a clear, cloudless sky. Air may lose heat in these regions both by radiation and by conduction. The latter influences only a shallow surface layer, but turbulent mixing increases its effectiveness in depth. The increase in air pressure resulting from excessive loss of heat at the surface may produce a thermally induced area of high pressure. This type of high-pressure area is shallow in comparison with one that is dynamically produced. Another type of heat sink is found in the upper air, where radiation losses, though small compared with those at the surface, still are greater than the absorbed radiation in the thin air. Loss of heat in the upper air may cause horizontal pressure changes, just as it does at the surface.

The dynamic causes for horizontal pressure differences are complex, and we shall not concern ourselves with them here except to note that they involve such factors as the rotation of the earth, friction, and angular momentum. The importance of these dynamic factors is indicated by the number of both high- and low-pressure centers on the earth surface that are not associated with areas of maximum or minimum surface heating. For example, one of the lowest pressure centers on earth is located in winter over the Aleutian Islands in the North Pacific. Temperatures there at this season are far from high.

The pressure patterns at the earth surface are exceedingly complex, and their fluctuations might be compared to the swirling and eddying of a great river as it flows along. The complexities of the local pressure changes that take place from day to day do not particularly concern us in our global survey, although they are of great concern to the forecaster of daily weather changes. Let us now turn our attention to the major pattern of pressure differences during the two seasonal extremes of the year.

7.3 GLOBAL SURFACE PRESSURE PATTERNS FOR JULY.

Figure 7.2 shows the mean pressure conditions for July and indicates the patterns for the northern hemisphere summer season and the southern hemisphere winter. All isobars are related to sea-level pressures. The principal distributional features of this map are discussed in the following paragraphs.

EQUATORIAL LOW-PRESSURE TROUGH. The axis of a low-pressure trough in the low latitudes is shown in Fig. 7.2. It lies entirely north of the equator during July, because this is the summer hemisphere. The trough is by no means uniform in width, depth, or latitudinal position. It is deepest and most pronounced where it lies farthest from the equator, namely, over an area extending from the Red Sea to northwestern India and also over northern Mexico and the southwestern United States. It is least distinct over the western and central Pacific Ocean. Its association with areas of maximum global temperatures is fairly clear. The extreme heating that the dry, subtropical land areas in the northern hemisphere undergo at this time of year is influential in decreasing air pressures at the surface. This trough should not be considered as permanently structured

FIG. 7.2 Distribution of average sea-level pressures for July. [After Haurwitz and Austin]

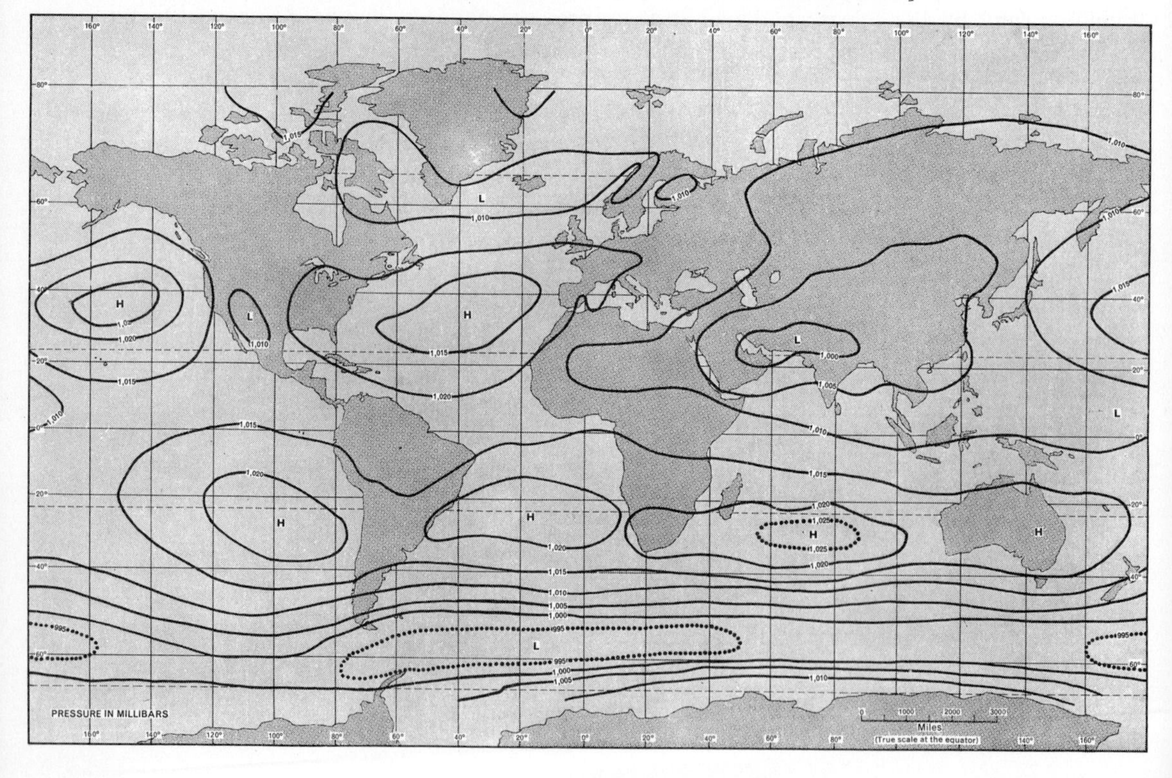

as shown in Fig. 7.2 for this season. Note that the map was made from mean data and that for this part of the world the data are not nearly so complete as for some of the mid-latitudes. Weather stations set up in the low latitudes during World War II revealed that considerable daily pressure changes occur within the trough and that at certain times and places the trough may pinch out entirely, being replaced by separate low-pressure segments or cells, separated by low ridges or waves of higher pressure.

SUBTROPICAL ANTICYCLONES, OR HIGHS. Two large cells of high pressure, elongated somewhat in an east-west direction, are located in the northern hemisphere during July, with their centers in about the eastern third of both the Atlantic and Pacific Oceans, roughly between lat 30 and 40° N. In the southern hemisphere, an elongated ridge of high pressure extends around the world, centered at about lat 25° S. This ridge of high pressure is not of uniform height, and low crests are found on it, most of which are located over the ocean areas. Central Australia and the Kalahari Desert of Africa have secondary centers of high pressure that are somewhat more pronounced than the general belt. The position of the subtropical highs, which at this season is somewhat farther poleward north of the equator than south of it, is related to the seasonal shifting of the pressure belts, these highs being farthest north during the northern hemisphere summer.

The subtropical highs are developed largely by dynamic, rather than thermal, causes, and the mechanics of variations in their behavior are not entirely clear. Variations in their strength and form are one of the most important features of the global energy balance system, since the air that diverges outward from these centers comprises a large part of the entire surface air-circulation pattern. The deepness, size, and number of the passageways between the individual high-pressure cells of the subtropical zone are partly related to the longitudinal temperature contrasts present. The northern hemisphere in July develops deep gaps over the continents between the oceanic high-pressure cells. The southern hemisphere, on the other hand, owing to its smaller land masses, does not have strong mean temperature contrasts within this zone, and the gaps between the individual cells along the subtropical ridge of pressure are less pronounced.

The day-by-day fluctuations for July in the subtropical highs cannot, of course, be shown on a single map. In general, the winter hemisphere experiences the most active daily pressure changes. For the most part, these day-by-day changes are produced by wavelike undulations that ripple along the flanks of the major pressure cells, generally from east to west (easterly waves) on the equatorward sides of the cells and from west to east (westerly waves) on their poleward flanks.

THE ANTARCTIC LOW-PRESSURE TROUGH. One of the deepest and most persistent low-pressure troughs in the world is found bordering the Antarctic Continent and centered roughly at lat 60° S during the July season. It is present at all seasons and continues around the world, shifting slightly with the seasons. This low-pressure trough marks the boundary of air interchange between warm and cold air. It is a strong frontal zone, and the dynamics of air interchange, implemented by the upward displacement of the warmer air, the high condensation, the deflection of the earth's rotation at these high latitudes, and other influences, produce an almost continuous succession of deep, low-pressure centers, or cyclones, that move around the world within the zone of mean low pressure.

THE SUBPOLAR LOWS OF THE NORTHERN HEMISPHERE. One might expect to find a strong frontal zone between lat 60 and 70° N, with accompanying cyclonic lows similar to conditions within the antarctic low-pressure trough. The heating of the continents, even at high latitudes in the northern hemisphere, however, restricts significant chilling to the Arctic Ocean and the Greenland ice sheet. This cooling is not sufficient to generate cold air masses that can move out of the source areas and produce dynamic low-pressure centers following interaction with warmer winds from the south. In summary, since the frontal activity in these latitudes is weak during the summer season, strong subpolar lows do not develop. The weak low-pressure zone bordering southern Greenland and extending across the North Atlantic to Norway is related to the shallow summer cyclonic depressions that pass eastward through this region.

POLAR HIGHS. Until recently, the lack of suitable weather data for most of the polar regions has been a serious handicap in generalizing the pressure conditions at high latitudes. This is why the global maps of air pressure (Figs. 7.2 and 7.3) do not include the Arctic and Antarctic. Data from Antarctica, collected during the International Geophysical Year program, now suggest that, contrary to earlier belief, the continent is not at the heart of a pronounced high-pressure center that is thermally induced and present

FIG. 7.3 Distribution of average sea-level pressures for January [After Haurwitz and Austin]

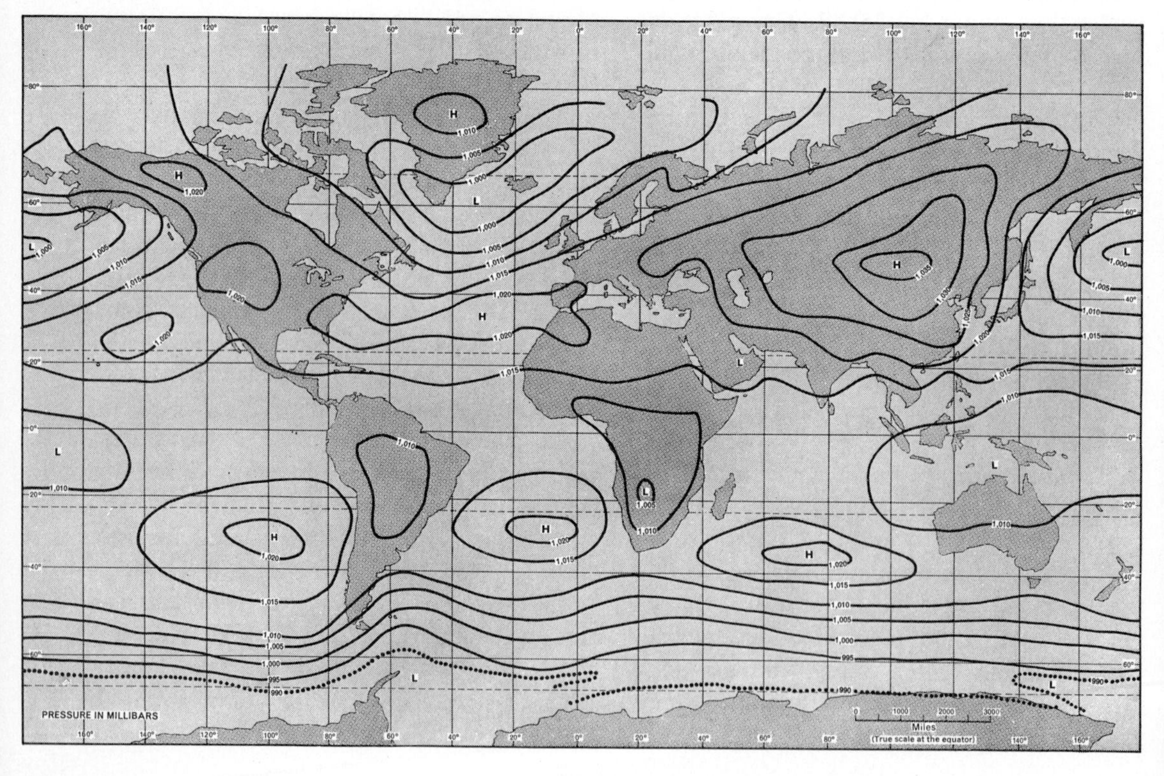

throughout the year. Instead, both high- and low-pressure centers are present, which vary somewhat in intensity and shape seasonally, with the low (located near the continental margin) dominant during most of the year but less strongly developed during the winter season. A high-pressure ridge tends to occupy the highest portion of the continent but is not especially pronounced.

7.4 GLOBAL SURFACE PRESSURE PATTERNS FOR JANUARY.

The pressure patterns for January are shown in Fig. 7.3. The general zones of pressure that tend to develop at this season are the same as those indicated for July, including the equatorial trough, the subtropical highs, the subpolar lows, and the polar highs. Considerable changes take place in these pressure zones, however, during the course of the 6 months between July and January. Noteworthy is the shift southward in the general location of the pressure centers. The equatorial low-pressure trough in January, for example, lies just north of the equator over most of the oceans but bends far southward and deepens in the interior of South America and Africa, that is, following the areas of maximum heating.

The subtropical highs in the southern hemisphere still are observed over the oceanic portions, but low gaps appear between them over the continents. The subtropical high-pressure zone at this season is much less interrupted than that in the northern hemisphere during July. The January subtropical highs north of the equator broaden in an east-west direction to include some of the adjacent continental surfaces. Although not clearly indicated on the map, localized continental high-pressure centers in the subtropics north of the equator tend to develop to a greater degree over plateaus or high plains than over lowlands in the winter season. Examples include the high plains of the southwestern United States, the Sahara in northern Africa, and the Tibetan and Yunnan Plateaus of Asia. Another characteristic of the subtropical high-pressure centers of action, also not clearly indicated on the mean-pressure maps, is that there tend to be more high-pressure cells within this general latitudinal zone in winter than in summer. This can be observed especially in sequences of daily weather maps. The Pacific subtropical cell north of the equator tends to split into two distinct cells, one centered northeast of Hawaii and the other northeast of the Mariana Islands.

The subpolar low-pressure trough bordering Antarctica remains essentially unchanged, except for a slight shift southward. In the northern hemisphere, two strong subpolar low-pressure areas develop in the winter season: one over the North Pacific, termed the *Aleutian low,* and the other over the North Atlantic, termed the *Iceland low*. These are cyclonic areas, with deep, low-pressure centers following each other in rapid succession along the fronts established between warm and cold air masses.

A huge high-pressure area is present over eastern Asia during January, roughly centering in the vicinity of Lake Baikal in the eastern Soviet Union. This is believed to be influenced considerably by surface cooling under the extremely low surface temperatures that this area experiences during the winter season. The winter Asiatic high, although it has unusually high surface pressure, is relatively shallow as compared with the subtropical highs. A somewhat weaker high-pressure center also develops over northwestern Canada during this season. It is believed that a low ridge of moderately high pressure extends over the North Pole, connecting the Asiatic and Canadian highs during the winter.

7.5 PRESSURE CONDITIONS ABOVE THE EARTH SURFACE. Atmospheric pressure everywhere decreases rapidly with increasing altitude. This is due to the compressibility of air and the cumulative effect of the weight of overlying air. This cumulative effect is responsible for the decrease in the *rate* of pressure drop with greater altitude. Despite the enormous thickness of the atmosphere, approximately one-half of its mass, or weight, is contained within 18,000 feet of the surface. Sixty miles above the surface, the air is so rarefied and pressure is so low that its state would be considered nearly a vacuum at sea level. Some of the human implications of decreased pressure with altitude were discussed earlier in Sec. 5.6.

Horizontal pressure differences occur at all levels in the upper air, but they do not show the complexities that are characteristic of the patterns at the earth surface. Except for a fairly narrow zone above the low latitudes, the arrangement of horizontal patterns of pressure differences into distinct cells is unusual at high elevations, and isobars tend to be oriented roughly in an east-west direction. Above 10,000 feet, a low-pressure center, or vortex, develops near each of the two poles (see Fig. 7.4), with a high-pressure belt containing low crests centered somewhat north of lat 10° in the summer hemisphere. The horizontal pressure gradient between the equatorial high-pressure region and the polar lows is not uniform. A steep pressure slope occurs in the lower mid-latitudes, roughly between lat 30 and 40° N and S. The polar low, at an elevation of 10,000 feet in January, bears a definite resemblance in shape and location to the surface high-pressure cells

FIG. 7.4 Elevation (in feet) of the 700 millibar surface in the northern hemisphere during summer and winter. There is a rough correlation in the upper air between pressure and the elevation of the isobaric surface. Note the general tendency toward low pressure over the poles and high pressure over the subtropics, with the difference being greater in winter than in summer. Such maps as these are useful in portraying pressure conditions at various levels above the earth surface. [After Namias and Clapp]

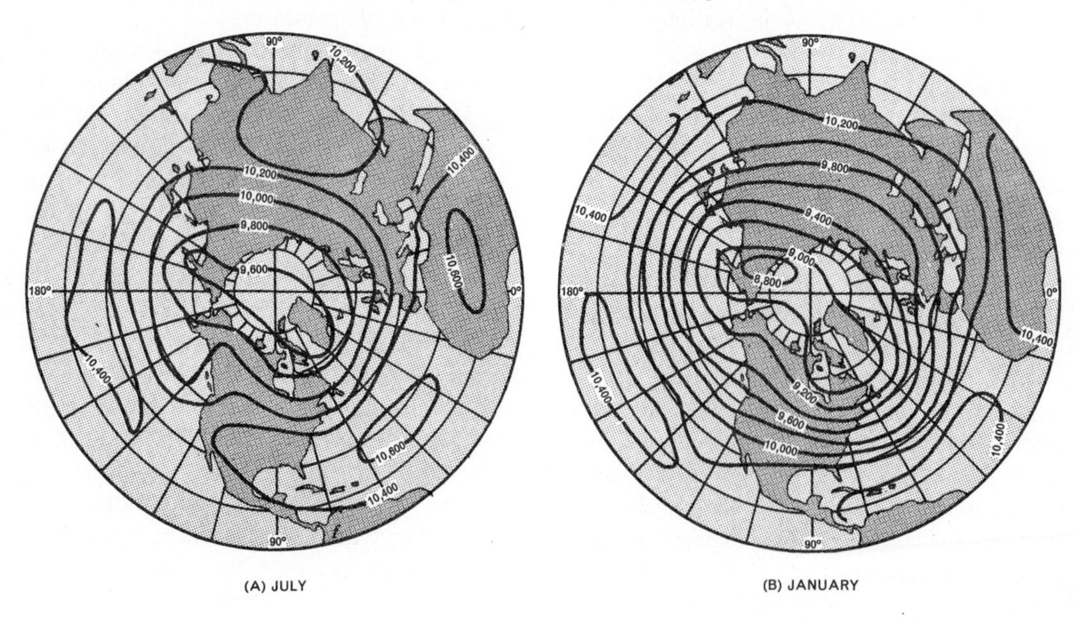

over both Siberia and northern Canada. Wavelike irregularities can be noticed on upper-air-pressure charts as bends in the isobars. They often appear to lie above major migrating highs and lows at the earth surface.

7.6 SUMMARY OF GLOBAL PRESSURE PATTERNS. The generalized mean global pressure pattern consists of a series of latitudinal belts of pressure centers, including (1) an equatorial low-pressure zone of tropical lows, (2) a belt of subtropical highs, (3) a subpolar low-pressure zone, (4) a high-latitude, continental winter high-pressure zone, and (5) a variable pattern of polar lows and highs. The zones are made up of permanent, quasi-permanent, or migrating centers of atmospheric pressure, both highs and lows. Usually either highs or lows predominate within the same latitudinal zone. Seasonal heating and cooling over continents appear to be one of the principal factors in interrupting the mean zonal (east-west) continuity in pressure. Thus the development of distinct pressure cells is greatest in the northern hemisphere. The areas having the most consistent pressure conditions, or those subject to the least seasonal variation in strength, are the subtropical highs over the eastern parts of oceans and the subpolar low-pressure trough off the Antarctic Continent.

Short-term pressure changes occur in all pressure zones and are caused by migrating cyclones, anticyclones, troughs, or ridges, which appear as wavelike irregularities along the flanks of the major high-pressure or low-pressure zones or cells. These are most active during the winter season of each hemisphere and correspond to daily weather changes throughout the world. The direction of their movement generally is that of the dominant zonal wind system in which they are located.

Wind

Wind is air in horizontal motion. The principal cause of wind is the equalization of horizontal differences in air pressure. Gravity seeks to create an equalization of air pressure at a given elevation and will cause lateral air motion toward this end. Since wind occurs to relieve horizontal differences in pressure, the flow is horizontal. It is true, of course, that upward and downward air movements take place, but in comparison to the total amount of horizontal flow, these vertical components are small indeed. There is appreciable upward flow only where quantities of air are mechanically displaced upward, such as in rapid condensation and along the boundaries that separate air masses of contrasting temperatures. Upward or downward air movements approach the strength of horizontal winds only under highly localized conditions, such as in a severe thunderstorm. One of the most common misconceptions about global air circulation is that strong, steady trade winds descend at a rapid rate from the upper air, rush toward the equator, and rise vertically as great upward flows of air in the rainy tropics. The total vertical displacement is not comparable to horizontal flow anywhere on earth. This does not mean that there are no strong winds in the upper air; on the contrary, winds consistently are stronger at the upper levels than they are at the surface. They are, however, horizontal winds, set in motion by horizontal pressure gradients. The term *wind* customarily refers to horizontal air movement, whereas upward or downward movements are called *air currents*.

Since wind is air movement in the process of equalizing horizontal differences in air pressure, it would seem likely that air would move directly down a pressure slope at a speed proportional to the steepness of the pressure gradient, in much the same way as water flows down a slope on the earth surface. Observations indicate, however, that such direct flow is exceedingly rare. Factors other than differences in air pressure influence the speed and direction of winds. Let us now consider the important variables in wind patterns.

7.7 THE APPARENT DEFLECTIVE FORCE OF THE EARTH'S ROTATION.

A French scientist, Foucault, discovered long ago that, if a heavy weight was suspended by a wire to form a long pendulum and was set into motion along a straight line, the arc described by the pendulum would, after a few hours, no longer follow the straight line but instead would veer away from it. The earth, because of its rotation on its axis, turns beneath the swing of the pendulum. This apparent deflective effect later was found to influence all freely moving objects on the earth surface. It is absent at the equator and reaches a maximum at the poles, and the apparent deflection is *toward the right of the direction of motion in the northern hemisphere and toward the left of the direction of motion in the southern hemisphere*. This apparent deflective effect at times has been somewhat inappropriately termed the *Coriolis force*. It is not a true force, since it does not involve any gain or loss of energy (see Fig. 7.5). In fact, if an observer were situated in space beyond the earth, the trajectory of movement would not appear to be a deflection at all, but a continuance in the direction toward which it had originally been set in motion. It is only from

FIG. 7.5 A graphic analogy to the Coriolis effect. Imagine a rotating disk, like a merry-go-round, large enough to carry two persons, one of whom (x) throws a ball to y. Between (A) and (B), x moves to x', and y moves to y'. The ball itself follows a straight line relative to the surface of the disk, leaving it at z by the time the disk has moved to (B). To both x and y, however, the ball has not followed its intended path, and has described an apparent arc in reaching z.

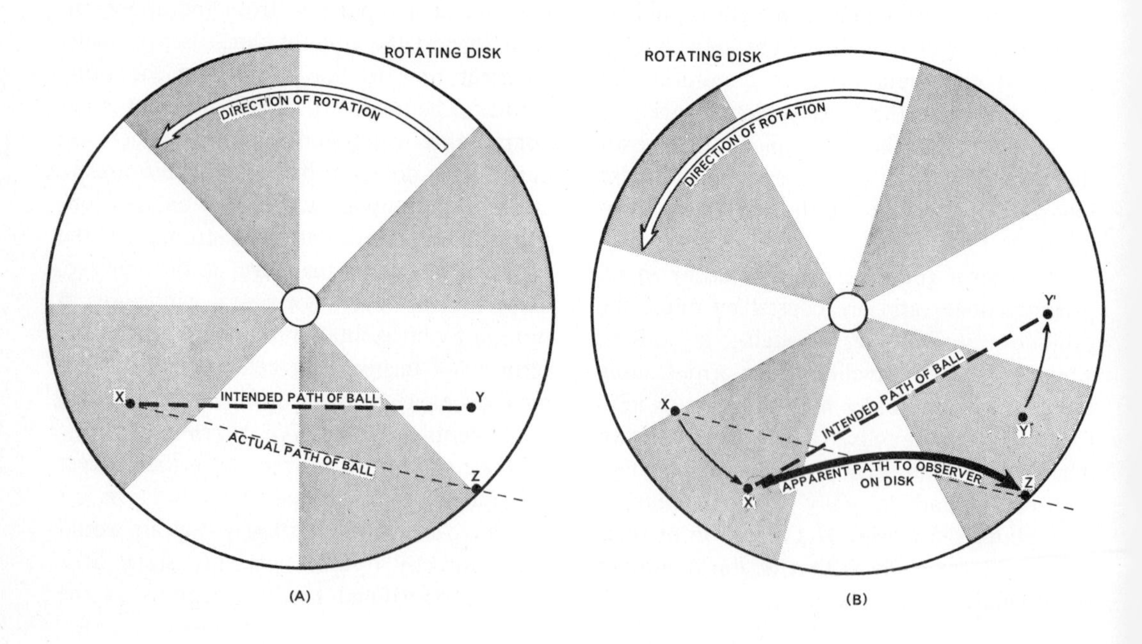

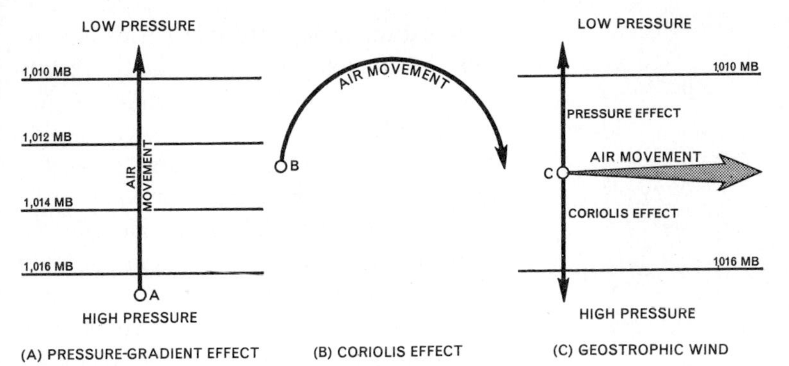

FIG. 7.6 The cause of geostrophic winds. In (A), the pressure factor directs air at right angles to the isobars, or straight down the pressure gradient. The Coriolis effect (B), however, leads to a curvature toward the right (northern hemisphere), which eventually leads back against the pressure gradient. The effect of these two directions of motion, shown in (C), is an air movement paralleling the isobars, termed a geostrophic wind.

a vantage position on the rotating earth that the direction appears to be deflected.

A simple demonstration of the Coriolis effect can be made by placing a paper disk on the turntable of a phonograph. If a pencil line is drawn on the rotating disk by moving one's hand in a straight line, the resulting line will always be a curve. Furthermore, the arc of the curve will have a smaller radius the nearer the line is drawn to the center of rotation; the deflection will be to the left of the direction of hand motion if the table is rotating clockwise and to the right with a counterclockwise rotation. The direction of hand motion makes no difference in the amount or the direction of deflection.

If we consider the hand moving the pencil on the turntable as comparable to the motion of air down a pressure gradient and let the counterclockwise rotation of the turntable represent the rotation of the earth north of the equator (which is counterclockwise), a useful analogy can be presented. All moving air, regardless of direction, is deflected toward the right in the northern hemisphere and toward the left south of the equator. The deflection is zero at the equator and increases with both latitude and velocity.

7.8 GEOSTROPHIC WINDS. Although the Coriolis force may be only an apparent deflection, it produces some significant effects with respect to the observed behavior of wind movement. In terms of observed wind direction, air does *not* flow down a pressure slope but curves away from it. If the deflection were to continue, in time it would appear to circle back toward its origin. Opposing this return motion is, of course, the pressure gradient (see Fig. 7.6). A balance between (1) the deflective component of the earth's rotation, which tends to turn wind back toward its high-pressure source, and (2) the pressure gradient, which tends to move air directly away from the high-pressure source, produces a resultant direction of air movement that *parallels the isobars,* with little exchange of air taking place between the high- and low-pressure areas. Such an airflow, representing a balance between the pressure gradient and the Coriolis effect, is known as a *geostrophic wind.* It is the characteristic wind-flow pattern well above the surface and where frictional influences are negligible. Near the equator, at the surface or above it, geostrophic influences are weak, because of the low Coriolis deflection.

The velocity of geostrophic winds depends on the following three variables:

1. The steepness of the pressure gradient. Other conditions remaining constant, wind velocities increase as the isobars become closer together, or as the steepness of the pressure gradient increases.

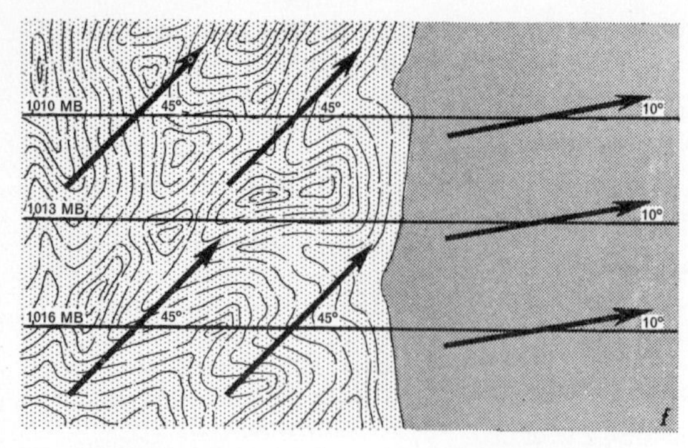

(A) ROUGH LAND SURFACE (B) WATER SURFACE

FIG. 7.7 The effect of friction on wind deflection. Since friction tends to slow down velocity, it decreases the Coriolis effect and favors the influence of the pressure gradient.

2. Latitude. A given pressure gradient produces decreasing wind velocities with increasing latitude. The most rapid change takes place in low latitudes. The Coriolis force increases with latitude; therefore, at higher latitudes, the wind curves back against the pressure gradient in a tighter circle, thus weakening the effect on velocity produced by the pressure gradient. The quantitative expression of this factor decreases somewhat near the earth surface, because of friction.

3. Density. Other conditions remaining constant, the velocity of geostrophic winds decreases with increasing air density. Differences in temperature and atmospheric pressure, which are variables in air density, thus affect the speed of winds. One of the main results of the density factor is an increase in wind velocities at higher elevations and with equivalent horizontal pressure gradients.

It was noted in Sec. 7.5 that above 10,000 feet elevation the horizontal pressure pattern consists of a high-pressure belt at low latitudes and a low-pressure area near the poles. The isobars encircle the globe roughly in an east-west direction. The tendency to develop geostrophic winds in the upper air thus leads to a great dominance of westerly winds except at low latitudes, with a minimum of interchange meridionally (north-south or south-north). This indicates that little transfer of energy takes place latitudinally in the upper air by means of airflow across isobars, despite the high wind velocities present there. Wind as an effective means of transporting energy from the lower to higher latitudes, then, is confined largely to meridional airflow near the earth surface. Exceptions will be noted later, in the section on the behavior of the jet stream (Sec. 7.12). Since there is more meridional exchange of air near the surface than in the upper air, we shall now examine some of the causes for this.

7.9 FRICTION AND ITS EFFECTS ON WIND.

Earlier it was noted that friction tends to decrease air velocities. Air that moves over the earth surface has some of its mechanical energy transformed into other forms of energy because of friction, and thus its velocity decreases. Friction with the surface, since it decreases wind velocity, also tends to decrease the amount of Coriolis deflection, which is proportional to straight-line velocity. This decrease in Coriolis deflection, in turn, tends to alter the resultant wind direction with respect to the pressure gradient. The wind direction no longer parallels the isobars, as in geostrophic flow, but crosses them somewhat in the direction of the pressure gradient. The angle of intersection with the isobars is roughly proportional to the amount of friction encountered at the earth surface.

Surface winds usually cross isobars at about a 10° angle over oceans and may reach angles up to 45° over rough land surfaces. Although the loss of energy by friction takes place only at the surface, the "braking" effect may be transmitted upward into the higher levels of horizontal wind flow.

Usually, however, it is contained within 1,500 to 2,000 feet of the surface.

7.10 MOVEMENT OF WINDS AROUND PRESSURE CENTERS.

The net effect of the pressure gradient, the Coriolis deflection, and friction is to induce a rotational motion in air diverging from a high-pressure center, or anticyclone, and also in air converging toward a low, or cyclone. In the northern hemisphere, the deflection toward the right produces an outward, clockwise rotation for winds around anticyclones and an inward, counterclockwise direction for those circulating around cyclones (see Fig. 7.8). In the southern hemisphere, since the deflection is toward the left, anticyclones rotate in a counterclockwise direction and cyclones clockwise. Each high- and low-pressure area on earth thus can be thought of as generating a spiraling wind pattern about itself. The dominant global highs and lows are not only centers of pressure but also centers of air rotation. The airflow around some of the great permanent anticyclonic high-pressure centers forms some of our major planetary winds.

If the great pressure centers are elongated in an east-west direction, as sometimes happens, a zonal (east-west or west-east) flow tends to predominate. However, when several separate cells of high or low pressure develop, there is greater airflow across the parallels, both east and west of the pressure centers. The traditional concept of fairly uniform latitudinal wind belts encircling the globe is generally not valid at the earth surface, although it appears to be generally true with respect to the airflow at high elevations. As was indicated earlier, contrasts in temperature conditions between oceans and continental areas tend to be influential in the development of the more or less permanent cellular pressure areas. In general, the northern hemisphere, with its greater area of land, has more interrupted latitudinal pressure belts than does the southern hemisphere, and consequently a greater amount of meridional (north-south or south-north) airflow. In relation to the global energy balance, this may indicate that the differential between high and low latitudes with respect to the net accumulation of solar energy is greater in the northern hemisphere than in the southern hemisphere; hence there is a greater need for the transfer of energy across the parallels. Assisting in this is the greater development of cellular pressure centers north of the equator for equivalent seasons. For similar reasons, there are a greater number of cellular pressure areas in winter than in summer in both hemispheres, because latitudinal energy differentials (as indicated by temperature contrasts) are greater during the winter

FIG. 7.8 Circulation of winds around cyclones and anticyclones in the northern and southern hemispheres.

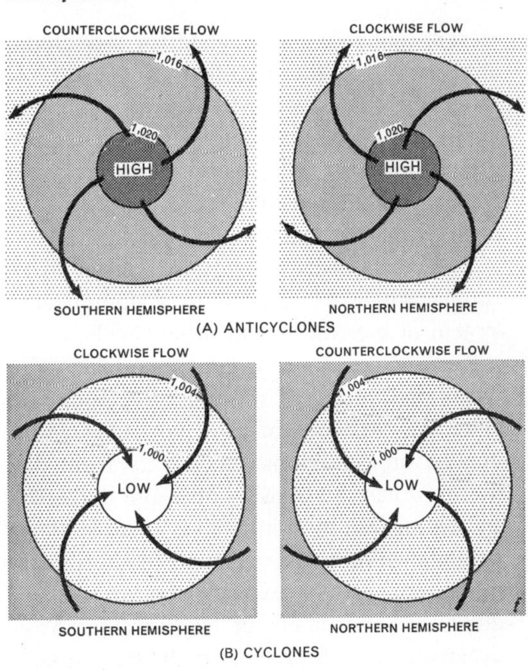

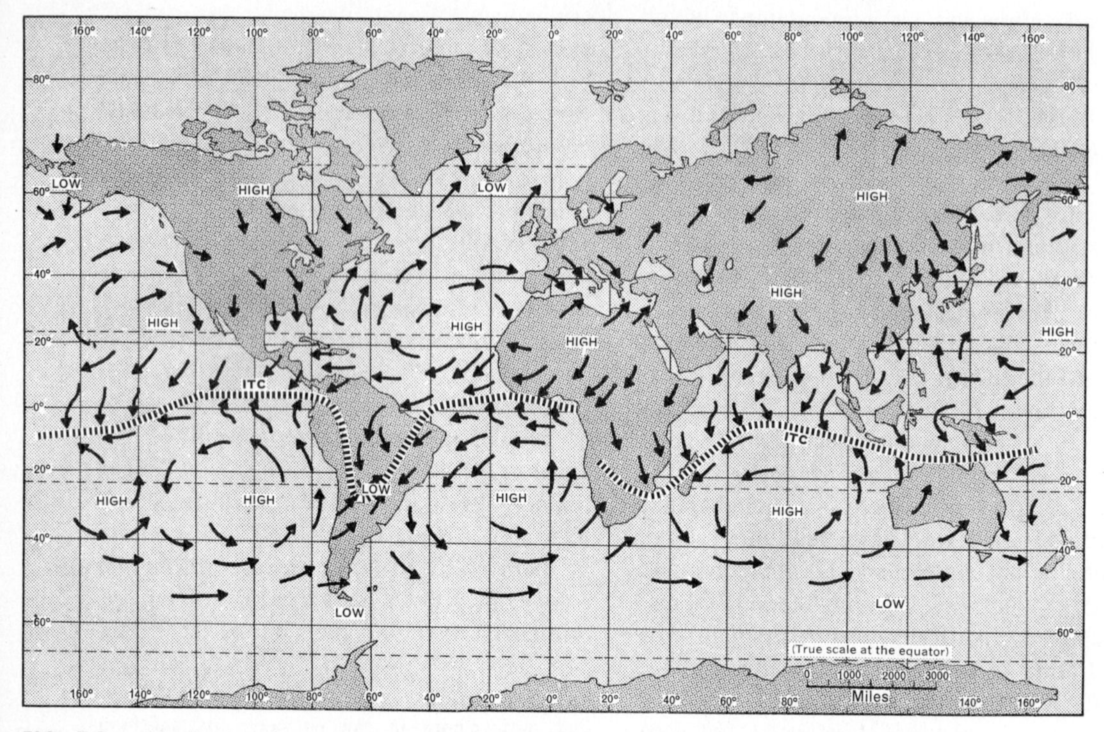

FIG. 7.9a Idealized airflow pattern for January. [After Garbell]

season, and thus the demand for meridional airflow across the parallels is greater. It should be recognized, however, that changes in the amount and intensity of pressure centers take place throughout the year and are largely responsible for the day-to-day fluctuations in weather conditions.

The atmospheric circulation near the earth surface might be likened to a complicated system of big wheels and little wheels, rotating either clockwise or counterclockwise, in which the speed of rotation, the size, and even the existence of any particular wheel depend on conditions which vary from day to day. These "wheels"—or, more correctly, spirals of air motion—have vertical components within them, although the horizontal movement greatly exceeds the upward or downward movement of air currents. Anticyclones, or high-pressure cells, have a subsident flow, whereas cyclones, or low-pressure cells, have an upward, spiraling air motion. With increased elevation, the cellular arrangement of pressure patterns diminishes.

7.11 MOVEMENT IN THE UPPER AIR.

A clear understanding of the patterns of air motion well above the earth surface is not yet possible, because of the scarcity of upper-air observations. Enough of them have been taken, however, to establish at least a few basic generalizations. The upper air is neither a homogeneous medium nor one in which change is related only to decreased air pressure with altitude.

The most outstanding characteristic of the airflow within the troposphere and above the frictional zone is the predominance of zonal flow, or flow from either the west or east

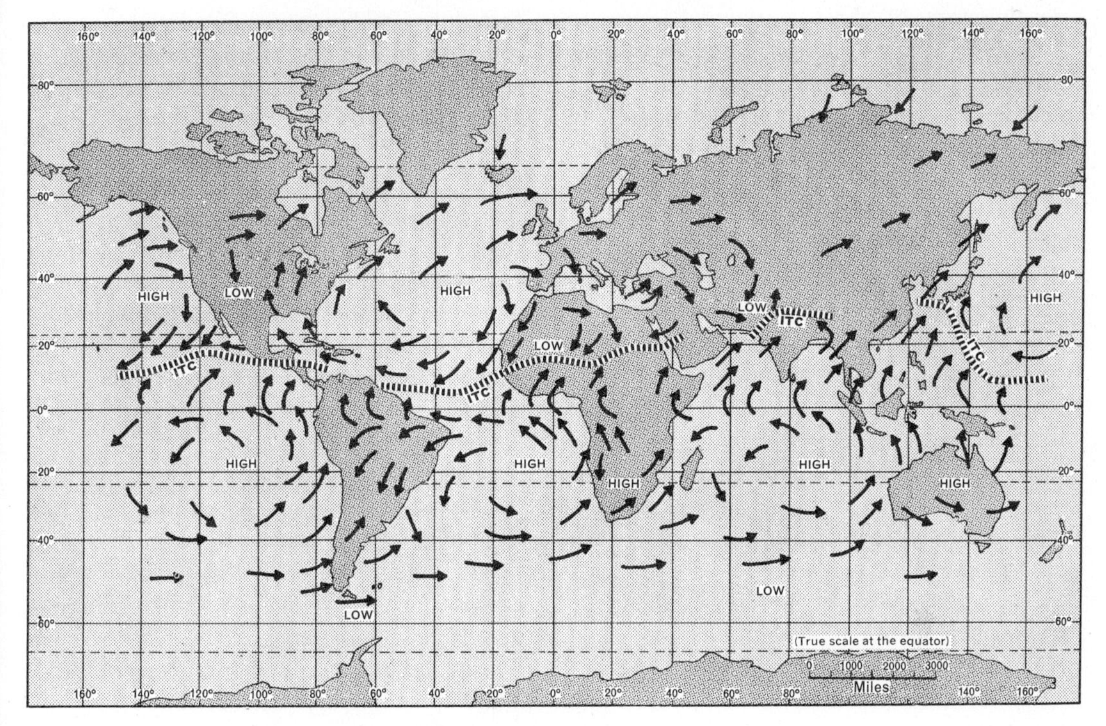

FIG. 7.9b Idealized airflow pattern for July. [After Garbell]

(see Fig. 7.10). The easterly[1] flow is confined to an equatorial zone roughly 40° wide which shifts seasonally between its extreme positions at about lat 30° N and 25° S. This zone of easterlies is somewhat wider at the surface, although the width fluctuates.

The average strength of the easterly zonal winds above the surface is much less than that of the westerly flow. Velocities within this easterly zone generally are greatest within a few thousand feet of the surface. Another feature of the low-latitude easterly wind zone in the upper troposphere is its variable horizontal pressure patterns. Although these pressure patterns are not so localized or so pronounced as they are at the surface, they are far more frequent here than in the rest of the upper-air circulation and give rise to more interruptions in the smooth zonal (east-west) flow. Aiding in the

[1] In describing wind directions, a westerly wind is one that blows from west to east. Wind directions normally are given according to the direction from which they come.

FIG. 7.10 Generalized pattern of high-altitude winds. Zonal, geostrophic winds predominate, with the strongest velocities just poleward of the subtropics. [After Namias]

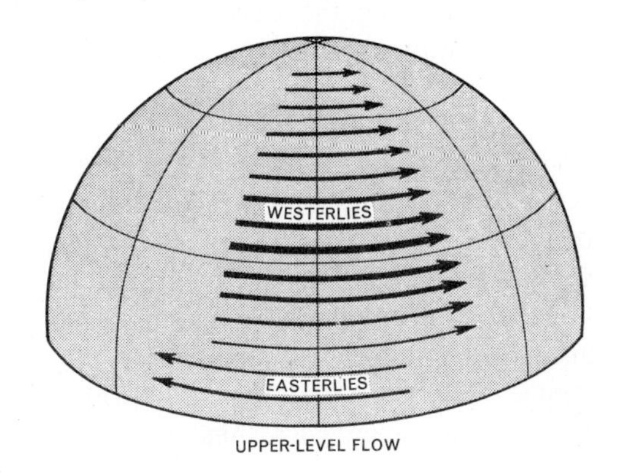

development of these horizontal pressure differences are the increases in temperature produced locally by the release of the latent heat of condensation. Since this is a rainy belt, there is more vertical transfer of heat energy here than elsewhere in the upper air.

The westerly, geostrophic, zonal flow in the upper troposphere extends from the easterly zone to the poles. Unlike the easterlies, it increases in velocity with elevation, reaching a maximum just below the stratosphere. Latitudinally, the mean velocity also is greatest in mid-latitudes, and the highest wind velocities of all are reached just below the foot of the steep slope in the tropopause, where the air movement becomes a distinct, swift, westerly flow known as the *jet stream* (see Sec. 7.12).

The great mass of westerly air in the troposphere is not a straight westerly flow. Huge *longitudinal waves,* or undulations, develop from time to time, superimposed upon the general westerly airflow. These waves influence the zonal airflow throughout a great depth and apparently play a significant role in helping to steer the extrusions of air masses from both the polar highs and the subtropical highs at the surface. A pronounced longitudinal wave usually will favor surface meridional air exchange, with cold polar air penetrating equatorward on the western, or rear, side of the wave and warm, tropical air along the eastern, or forward, side. The waves themselves usually migrate slowly from west to east.

7.12 THE JET STREAM. The jet stream is a narrow, high-velocity, westerly air stream that usually lies near the top of the troposphere encircling the globe in the mid-latitudes. It is a remarkable feature of global air circulation and was first discovered by United States bombers during World War II, when they climbed to high altitudes before their bombing runs over Japan in order to avoid antiaircraft fire or pursuit craft. It shifts latitudinally with the seasons, roughly from 30 to 40°. Occasionally other, weaker jet streams develop at other latitudes and at lower elevations. The latter are more frequent during the winter season, when the main stream lies nearer the equator. A recent discovery is the existence of a low-latitude jet stream that flows from east to west in contrast with the westerly, mid-latitude jets. Although little is known about it yet, apparently it is less strong and less regular in its occurrence than the others.

Much more is known of the northern hemisphere jet stream than of the one that lies south of the equator. On the whole, it behaves much like a rapid and narrow ocean current. Instead of being a single stream of air, it consists of separate filaments of swift air that are separated by air of lesser velocity. Wind speeds vary considerably but may reach 300 miles per hour. In its course around the globe, there are different sectors of maximum and minimum velocity. Usually the most rapid speeds are encountered in the sectors above the eastern parts of the continents and the western parts of oceans (see Fig. 7.11). The lowest velocities are found in the longitudinal sectors nearest the centers of subtropical highs at the surface. The speed of the jet stream also shows a rough periodicity or cyclical trend; it builds up gradually to a maximum, then falls off suddenly to a minimum.

The trajectory of the jet stream at times is almost straight eastward. At other times it begins to twist and meander like a winding stream. Like the twists and loops in the Atlantic Gulf Stream, those in the jet stream may break away from the main current and become incorporated as whirling masses of air at either side (see Fig. 7.12). These intruding masses exhibit strong temperature contrasts with the surrounding air. The amount of lateral swinging in the jet stream generally increases with the velocity; thus there is a periodicity in the irregularity of flow that roughly matches the cycles in jet-stream velocity.

The exact causes and results of jet-stream behavior have not been carefully worked out, but it appears likely that the fluctuations in its flow are part of the dynamic processes for transferring energy latitudinally, or across isobar lines, in the upper troposphere. Some relationship undoubtedly exists between jet-stream fluctuations and the longitudinal waves within the geostrophic westerlies, but the details are not yet clear. It is hoped that further research on the jet stream will yield useful results in long-range weather forecasting.

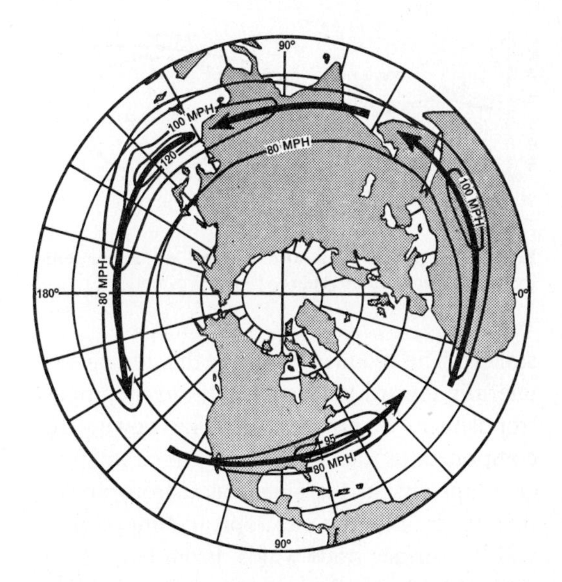

FIG. 7.11 The northern hemisphere jet stream in January. Note the maximum velocities off the continental east coasts and the minimum velocities off the west coasts. These velocities vary considerably cyclically. [After Namias]

7.13 THE TROPICAL AIR CIRCULATION.

It was believed for a long time that a single, hemispheric-cell convectional circulation system prevails at the earth surface, with air rising near the equator, moving poleward at upper levels, then subsiding at high latitudes to become a surface stream of air with a net equatorward component. Now it is certain that a much more complex circulation system exists and that it involves both vertical and horizontal circulation cells.

Between the equator and a mean latitude of about 30°, a general vertical circulation takes place within the troposphere. The first part of this circuit consists of local updrafts of air within the low latitudes, associated with the formation of rain. The total volume of air displaced upward is not large, but this movement can be observed in each of the cumulus cloud masses that tower for many thousands of feet during tropical rain-

FIG. 7.12 Jet-stream oscillations. Increased meanderings of the jet, probably caused by an increase in velocity, may produce a dynamic transfer of air latitudinally and a reestablishment of stable, zonal flow. [After Namias]

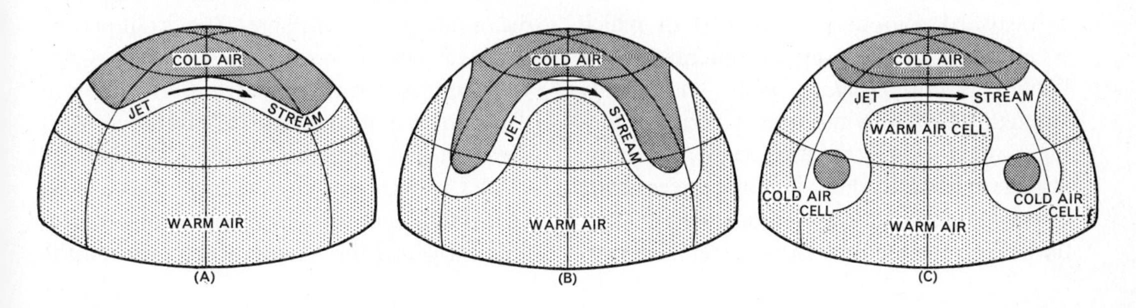

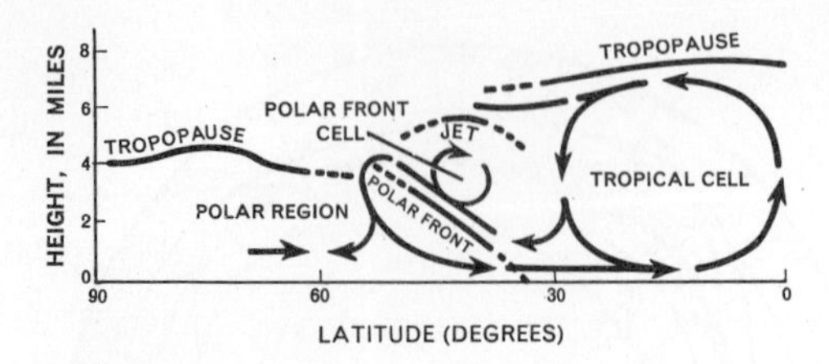

FIG. 7.13 Horizontal and vertical air movement in the northern hemisphere. [After Palmen]

storms. The manner in which this air moves laterally toward higher latitudes in the upper troposphere is not known. The downward component of the tropical vertical circulation cells appears in the subsidence from above that feeds into the subtropical anticyclones and the surface trade winds. From here some of the trade-wind air moves into the low latitudes and is eventually involved in convectional or convergent updrafts, to complete the circuit. This vertical circulation takes place, not within a single cell, but within a series of cells, aligned roughly in the same latitudinal zone and corresponding to the number of major anticyclonic cells. At the surface, the poleward limit of these vertical cells is formed by the centers of the subtropical anticyclones.

There is a strong, steady horizontal flow around the equatorward flanks of the subtropical anticyclones that greatly exceeds the movement of air in the vertical circulation; equatorward winds are dominant near the eastern part of the cells, and a poleward flow prevails near their western boundaries (see Fig. 7.13). The equatorward flow, which has a westward component, and part of which is included in the vertical circulation, is known as the *trade winds.* The steady strength of these winds was a boon to sailing vessels over a century ago. They are strongest and steadiest in the eastern parts of oceans, where pressure gradients are steep and where the high-pressure centers are least variable. North of the equator the trades are predominantly from the northeast, and south of the equator they are principally from the southeast. Subsidence from the upper air is strongest in the eastern portion of the subtropical anticyclones; thus the trades in this sector are unusually stable and dry and frequently have temperature inversions aloft to check the upward passage of air currents.

The poleward flow to the west of the subtropical anticyclones is not nearly so steady or so strong as the trade-wind flow. Pressure gradients are less, and migrating highs and lows occur more frequently and interrupt the basic flow patterns. Wind velocities tend to increase as the flow in this sector reaches higher latitudes, because of the increase in angular momentum.

The centers of the subtropical anticyclones are regions of calms, or light, variable winds. These calm, cloudless regions were dreaded in the days of sailing vessels and were termed *horse latitudes.* An old, but disputed, explanation for this term is that animals often had to be thrown overboard, because of the lack of drinking water on becalmed vessels.

The trade winds within the tropical circulation are not necessarily confined to a single hemisphere but often cross the equator into the opposite hemisphere under the influence of a strong thermal low or some other type of convergence. Once across the equator, the Coriolis deflection in the opposite hemisphere begins to take effect, and the trade winds gradually shift their trajectory somewhat. A northeast trade wind crossing into the southern hemisphere, for example, is changed into a northwesterly wind. Conversely, a southeast trade wind crossing into the northern hemisphere is turned toward the right and becomes a southwest wind.

The tropical circulation cells exhibit both horizontal and vertical components of airflow, in which the former greatly exceed the latter. The mechanism of the cells is designed to remove surplus energy accumulating at the surface in low latitudes. Approximately 50 per cent of this surplus is removed toward higher latitudes, mainly to the west of the subtropical anticyclones, by horizontal airflow with contained water vapor. Some of this surplus may also be in the form of migrating cyclones, which carry warm, humid air into the mid-latitudes, out of the tropics, and around the western ends of the subtropical anticyclones. An unmeasured quantity of the surplus energy is carried into the upper troposphere in the form of latent heat. Here it is released following condensation and later is lost by radiation. A small amount of the energy surplus also is carried poleward by ocean currents.

7.14 THE INTERTROPICAL CONVERGENCE ZONE. Trade-wind air, whose direction represents the equatorward component at the surface within the tropical circulation cells, moves obliquely toward the equatorial low-pressure trough from the subtropical highs of both hemispheres. A zone of air convergence thus is established in the low-pressure trough. The converging air streams do not have strong contrasts in temperature; therefore sharp discontinuity surfaces, or fronts, do not often develop—at least not fronts that are comparable to those along the boundary between tropical air and the air from polar highs. Figure 7.14 shows three types of convergence that are characteristic of the general convergence zone between the two trade winds in the low latitudes.

In the type of convergence shown in *A*, the trades weaken and lose momentum as they approach the equator, eventually developing into a slow westward drift. No real convergence boundary or front develops, and the air movement within this zone is weak, fitful, and variable in direction. The air is highly unstable to great heights, and convectional rain occurs in frequent showers. This zone, often termed the *doldrums,* may be considered a broad, transitional zone between the trade winds of opposite hemispheres. It is not always present, however, because the trade winds from opposite hemispheres may meet more directly along a sharper convergent zone, as shown in *B* and *C* of Fig. 7.14. Some parts of the equatorial zone are more likely to develop a broad, intertrades, or doldrum, zone than others—for example, the area straddling the equator in the Indian Ocean in the summer, the western Pacific, and also for a short distance off the west coasts of Central America and Sierra Leone in western Africa. The doldrums are not usually found over continental areas.

In Fig. 7.14, type *B* indicates a narrow zone of convergence between the trades of opposite hemispheres. Strong fronts such as those in mid-latitudes do not occur in this zone, because the air masses involved do not show marked temperature contrasts. It is believed by some, however, that weak frontal activity can take place in such a zone. In any event, the convergence creates favorable conditions for instability and precipitation. Shallow low-pressure centers (cyclones), with inward- and upward-spiraling air, move slowly from east to west along the narrow convergence zones, bringing extended periods of precipitation and overcast skies (see Sec. 7.23).

The type of convergence shown in *C* of Fig. 7.14 develops more frequently at or following the solstices. Thermal, or "heat," lows developing over a continent in the subtropics tend to result in a steep pressure gradient, which, combined with friction, produces an airflow from the equatorial zone. Note that the Coriolis deflection, which elsewhere works against the pressure gradient, is absent

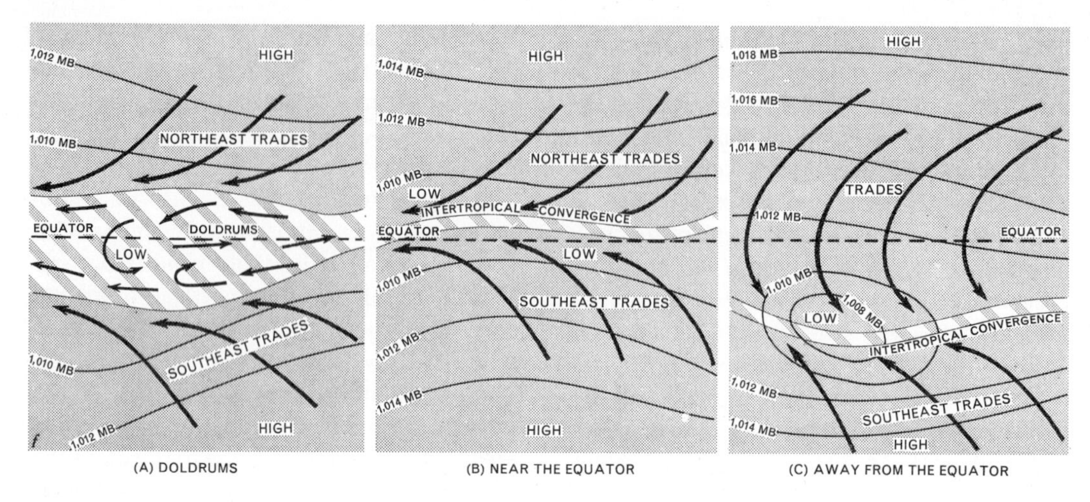

FIG. 7.14 Types of intertropical convergences. [After Trewartha et al.]

at the equator. Air moves across the equator and gradually increases in acceleration toward the east. Such transequatorial trades are exceptions to the more dominant easterly flow in low latitudes. Various interactions between the easterly and westerly winds may produce a series of local convergences, with accompanying precipitation and local wind shifts. This type of convergence is best developed over continental areas.

All types of convergence that take place in the intertropical zone are favorable to the ascent of air, and if the involved air is conditionally unstable, rain usually results. This carries energy to upper levels, where it can be lost through radiation. Weather changes take place from day to day in rapid succession in the convergent zones of low latitudes. Temperature is about the only weather element that remains relatively unchanged. The traditional concept of monotonous weather in the rainy tropics does not conform to the observed facts in the convergent zones.

Before leaving the discussion of wind zones in the tropics, mention should be made of the tropical storms that originate in this region. *Hurricanes,* or *typhoons,* as these tropical cyclonic storms are termed, are discussed more fully in Sec. 7.27. It is appropriate here, however, to indicate that such storms originate along the zone of intertropical convergences as shallow, broad cyclones, not unlike many other such migrating low-pressure centers that pass from east to west along this zone. Occasionally, some of these tropical cyclones develop into hurricanes and move poleward around the western flanks of the subtropical highs into the mid-latitudes. Their enormous energy is self-contained and involves the transformation of latent heat energy into the mechanical energy of air motion. Their evolution is complex, but they represent a concentrated means of removing energy from the tropics toward higher altitudes and higher latitudes by means of both vertical and horizontal air interchange.

7.15 MONSOONS. It has been known for centuries that in some parts of the tropics there is a summer and winter reversal of winds that is accompanied by a distinct seasonal change in rainfall—the wind from one direction being humid, unstable, and conducive to precipitation and the other being dry and stable. The term *monsoon* is a derivation from an Arabic word *mausim,* which signifies "season." India has the classic example of a monsoon, or seasonal wind reversal, and it is notable for the suddenness in which the seasonal reversal takes place. In fact, the dramatic suddenness in which the seasonal reversal takes place in southern Asia marks the monsoon here as unique among many other areas of seasonal wind shift. Usually the shift occurs shortly before the solstice and may be described as follows:

The transition from the winter dry monsoon to the summer monsoon begins first with a gradual weakening of the steady, hot, and dry monsoon. For several weeks prior to this period, daily temperatures rise higher and higher as the noonday sun climbs in the sky toward the zenith. The land lies parched and brown, and a shimmering haze blurs distant views. With the dying away of the wind, the heat becomes almost unbearable, and human tempers are strained. This transitional period of calms varies in length, but usually lasts for about two or three days. Suddenly, in the distance, a line of dark clouds can be seen, much like the squall line of a summer thunderstorm in the mid-latitudes. It approaches rapidly, and wind and rain usually arrive simultaneously. The temperature drops sharply following the rains. People celebrate the arrival of the monsoon by flocking into the open to be soaked by the welcome deluge. Now crops can grow again, flowers bloom, and life in general becomes bustling and exciting.

The appearance of the dry winter monsoon is not so sudden, and it lacks the drama and contrast of the opposite seasonal shift. A temperature change is hardly noticeable, and except for a different "feel," owing to the dry wind, for a gradual widening in the interval between rains, and for the shift in wind direction, this seasonal shift in monsoons is less pronounced.

The term monsoon has been used in various ways, but it typically refers to wind systems that have a pronounced and fairly sudden seasonal reversal of direction, in which one season has a humid, landward wind, the other a dry, seaward wind. Seasonal wind shifts are quite common in low latitudes and occur wherever transequatorial trade winds are found. Such conditions are most usual in areas where subtropical low-pressure centers develop over the interior of continents, some owing to thermal reasons, others perhaps to dynamic causes. Such seasonal reversals merely signify the dominance of different trade winds, and they may or may not be accompanied by pronounced seasonal changes in precipitation. Equatorward-facing coasts between lat 5 and 30° are good places for seasonal reversals of land and ocean winds, and such conditions may be observed not only in India but along the Guinea Coast of Africa and the northern coast of Australia. Monsoon tendencies, although not so pronounced, can be found along the Gulf coast of the United States and the east coast of Asia.

The suddenness of the shift in the monsoons of southern and southeastern Asia has puzzled climatologists for a long time. An explanation that has been proposed recently (and not yet verified) relates the breaking of the monsoon to the shifting of the jet stream. Subsidence of air and anticyclonic conditions normally are found on the earth surface a short distance equatorward of the position immediately below the jet stream. It has been suggested that the jet stream alternately swings around the northern and southern flanks of the high mountain core of central Asia, being north of it in summer and south of it in winter. During the winter season, subsidence along its equatorward side induces a subtropical anticyclonic cell over northern Central India and another over the high plateaus of southwestern China. Also at this season, a strong polar anticyclone develops over Mongolia and eastern Siberia. Divergences from these centers cause the dry, oceanward winter monsoons of India and eastern Asia. It should be noted here, however, that little horizontal airflow passes across the high mountain barriers that border India. The monsoons of India and eastern Asia, although they may be similarly caused, are not directly connected in their airflow. As the winter season recedes, the jet stream slowly moves poleward west of the high Pamir ranges but must continue to skirt the southern ranges until it suddenly "turns the corner" and flows around the northern cordilleras, such as the Tien Shan and Nan Shan. Following this topographic diversion of the jet-stream course, subsidence is reduced in northern India, and the clear skies, the heated surface, and the accompanying convergence result in a humid, unstable airflow from the equatorial areas of the Indian Ocean and the western Pacific. As this summer air stream moves northward away from the equator, it is deflected to the right and becomes the southwest monsoon. The seasonal movement of the southern Asiatic monsoon is illustrated in Fig. 7.15. Climatologists still are not agreed about the causes of monsoons, and the old hypothesis of seasonal continental heating and cooling apparently does not explain some of the observed features of monsoons satisfactorily.

7.16 THE MID-LATITUDE CIRCULATION.

The surface air diverging from the subtropical highs on their poleward flanks forms the great mid-latitude flow of air which has been termed the *westerlies*. One of the most outstanding features of the westerly belt near the surface of the earth is its changeability with respect to direction, strength, and constancy. Although the westerly component in direction greatly predominates statistically, winds may blow from any direction. The variable nature of the winds in this belt is largely the result of migrating highs and lows that enter and move along with the general westerly air streams. Some of these migrating pressure centers and wind spirals are dynamically induced by the interchange between the relatively warm flow from the tropics and the cold polar air masses that penetrate equatorward from the high latitudes. Others are formed as the result of waves that develop within the westerly air streams and that are possibly related to disturbances in the upper troposphere. Unusually strong gale winds are associated with deep cyclones that move along the subpolar low-pressure troughs. The acceleration of airflow poleward toward these deep lows, because of increased angular momentum, influences wind velocities in the westerlies for hundreds of miles from these storm centers. Not without reason do the southern oceans have their "roaring forties," and almost continuous high winds characterize the ocean areas between lat 40 and 70°. Similarly, the Aleutian and Iceland lows, which develop in the winter season in the northern oceans, cause high gale winds and stormy seas.

Two major zones of air convergence are found within the general belt of westerlies and are known as the polar front and arctic front. The former is by far the more important in air and energy interchange. It marks the convergence boundary where relatively warm tropical air injected into the westerly zone meets colder air from higher latitudes. Both warm fronts and cold fronts mark this irregular boundary. Equatorward extensions of cold air and poleward-moving masses of warm air produce the major irregularities in the polar front. Such irregularities often can be correlated roughly with deep, longitudinal waves in the westerly circulation within the troposphere aloft (see

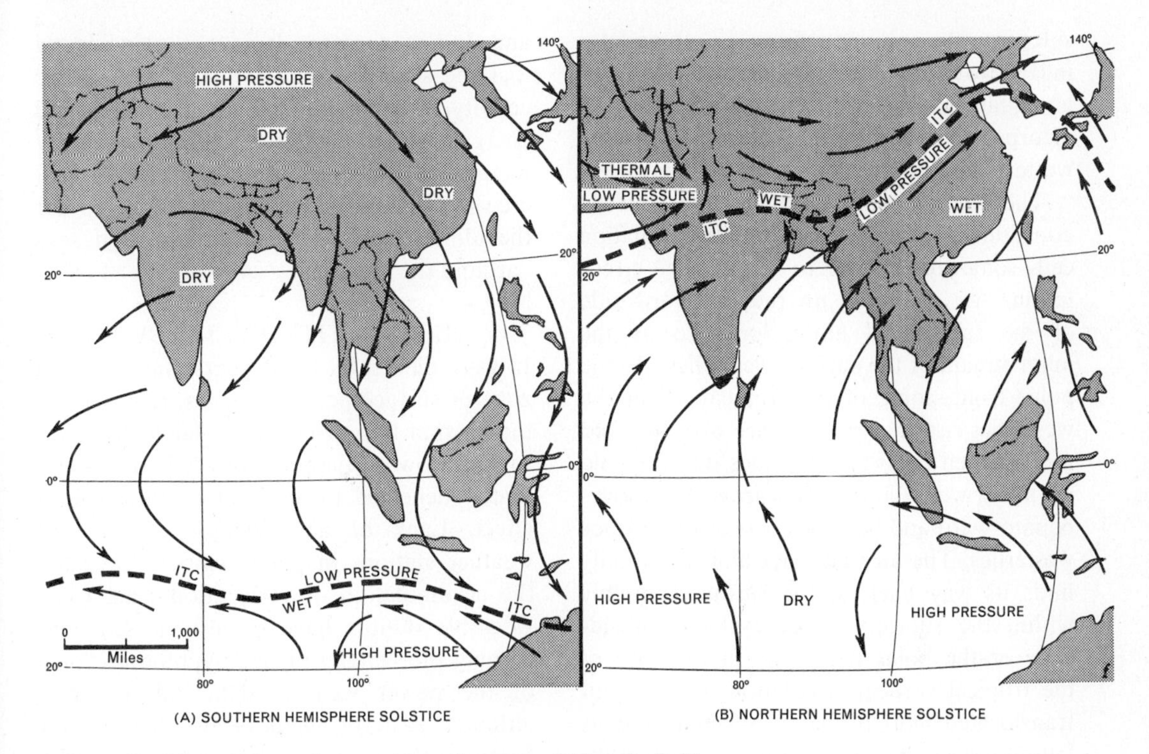

FIG. 7.15 The southeast Asia monsoonal system. [After Garbell]

Sec. 7.11). Under certain conditions, small waves appear along the polar front which develop and widen into pronounced cyclones or lows (see Fig. 7.21). These cyclones move along the frontal zone, intensifying the convergence and producing some of the changing wind directions and velocities within the westerly zone (see Sec. 7.22). Figure 7.18*a* and *b* shows the location of the polar front in the northern hemisphere.

The arctic front develops where unusually cold air from ice- or snow-covered surfaces meets moderately cool air in the poleward reaches of the westerly wind belt. Because of the scarcity of available weather records for high latitudes, we do not have a thorough knowledge of its distributional pattern. Presumably, however, it encircles the globe off the Antarctic Continent and is present there during the entire year. In the northern hemisphere it is likely to be found in summer mainly bordering the Arctic coast of Europe and extending westward to Iceland. It is also believed to adjoin the subpolar low-pressure troughs in the North Pacific and North Atlantic during the winter. The arctic front probably is a significant energy-transfer zone only where the subpolar low-pressure troughs (the Aleutian, Iceland, and Antarctic lows) are strongly developed. Elsewhere the temperature contrasts are not great enough to produce much frontal interchange of air and cyclonic activity.

The cold air masses found on the poleward side of the polar front and the arctic front are relatively shallow, rarely being more than 10,000 to 12,000 feet thick. Much of the warm, westerly air that slides over the shallow cold air masses eventually cools and subsides into the cold air masses, to return later into the westerly zone as a surface flow with an equatorward component. The rest of it is incorporated into the horizontal geostrophic westerly flow aloft.

The westerly winds at or near the surface constitute part of a series of air-circulation cells somewhat similar to the tropical circulation. Air diverging on the poleward side of the subtropical anticyclones forms the main stream of the surface westerlies. At the polar front, some of the tropical air in the westerlies rises a short distance over the cold air and then cools and subsides into the cold air mass, which gradually warms as it moves equatorward and becomes part of the surface westerlies. The air that stays aloft eventually finds its way back to the surface, possibly within the subtropical anticyclonic subsidence or the polar highs. As in the case of the tropical vertical circulation, the amount translocated aloft probably is small, and its lateral movements in the upper air are problematical.

It should be remembered that the meridional components are only a minor part of the total westerly flow at the surface. The amount of this meridional flow depends on the cellular development of pressure centers, or the number and strength of pressure "wheels" that rotate horizontally. When there are few cyclones and anticyclones, when the polar front is without marked irregularities, and when the subtropical highs are elongated, with only low gaps between them, the zonal westerlies prevail throughout the mid-latitudes. This represents a period of energy imbalance, when there is little transfer of energy across the parallels. The strongest meridional energy flow occurs in the areas that have the steepest temperature gradients. As noted in Chapter 6, the steepest latitudinal temperature gradient for mean conditions is found in the southern part of the Atlantic, Pacific, and Indian Oceans. It is not coincidental that the strongest localized area of cyclonic activity, meridional-eddy air exchange, and energy transfer can be found in the stormy sectors of these regions. The officers and crews of sailing vessels had reason to fear the almost continuous gales and high seas "around the Horn."

7.17 HIGH-LATITUDE CIRCULATION. It was believed for many years that there is a zone of surface polar easterlies, representing the air that flows from the polar highs equatorward toward the polar or arctic fronts and that is deflected to the west by the Coriolis effect. Lack of an adequate network of weather stations in polar regions prevented the accumulation of verification data. Considerable doubts have recently arisen concerning the validity of this hypothesis. Some of the newer weather data indicate that, although easterly winds occur, they are far from dominant and are extremely shallow, seldom being found higher than a few hundred feet above the surface. Westerly winds predominate at higher levels and often are found at the surface. Local gravity winds [2] off Greenland and Antarctica have been misinterpreted as polar easterlies and as part of the global circulation system. The most noticeable areas that might be considered to contain polar easterlies include those which lie along the *poleward side* of the deep subpolar low-pressure troughs, such as those off Antarctica and, during the winter months, off Iceland and the Aleutians. In these areas, deep cyclones draw a strong equatorward flow of air toward their centers, and this air-

[2] *Gravity winds* are density currents that flow down a sloping land surface and that are usually generated by excessive radiational and conductive cooling next to the surface. The central ice domes of Greenland and Antarctica, lying over 9,000 feet above sea level, are capable of generating a strong gravity flow of cold air down their sides.

flow has an easterly component because of the Coriolis deflection.

With the possible exception of these cyclonic winds, the easterly winds of high latitudes do not constitute a significant part of the global air circulation system. The quantity of air that the polar highs add to the global circulation is negligible in comparison with the subtropical anticyclones, but the air masses they extrude produce much of the variety in weather conditions within the middle latitudes. Each polar air-mass extrusion that penetrates deeply into the zone of westerlies acts as an independent migrating anticyclone and is supplied with new air from the westerly flow that passes over it and subsides into it after cooling. It is for this reason that the return flow of air from high latitudes toward the equator has been considered part of the horizontal circulation within the westerlies.

7.18 SUMMARY OF GLOBAL AIR CIRCULATION. The most significant focal points in the global air circulation on the earth surface are the centers of high and low atmospheric pressure. The highs, or anticyclones, are areas of diverging winds, and the lows, or cyclones, are regions of converging air streams. Some of these are large, fairly permanent centers, whereas others are temporary and capable of movement within the great global air streams.

The equatorial zone in general is an area of convergence, with air being carried into the upper troposphere, accompanying precipitation. On either side of this zone is a series of great spirals of air—the subtropical anticyclones. Easterly components of flow predominate at the surface along the equatorward side of these huge spirals, whereas westerly flow prevails on their poleward sides. Subsidence and rising of air are prevalent in the southeastern and northwestern quadrants, respectively, of the anticyclonic spirals. Variations in the number and size of these spirals help to influence the amount of air that passes across the parallels of latitude from north to south or south to north. Minor migrating pressure cells provide short-term variations in the meridional flow.

Cooling by both conduction and radiation in high latitudes results in great contrasts in temperature between the surface air masses in these latitudes and the westerly flow which meets them. The polar front forms a zone of convergence which is intensified periodically by the cyclones that develop along this frontal zone. Fluctuations in the outline of this front are responsible for much of the variety of weather conditions in the westerly zone.

The surplus energy accumulating continually at the surface in low latitudes is reduced by flow in two directions toward possible outlets. One of these is a horizontal flow, via both meridional airflow and ocean flow, toward the energy-deficient regions of high latitudes. The other is a vertical movement into the upper troposphere, and perhaps also in places into the stratosphere, where the heat energy can be released through radiation. The vertical movements are upward from the major areas of precipitation and downward toward the eastern parts of the subtropical anticyclones. Although the quantity of air involved in the vertical exchanges is negligible, the energy transported via latent heat is large.

Horizontal air movement apparently is not an efficient method of transferring energy out of the low latitudes, because so much air motion, even at the surface, is involved in zonal flow, which is much greater than meridional flow. Zonal flow is overwhelmingly dominant a short distance above the surface. The surpluses of solar energy that accumulate in some areas and the deficiencies that exist in others are the basic cause for all aspects of the air circulation system, both on the earth surface and far above it.

7.19 LOCAL WINDS. Local conditions provide exceptions to the global patterns of air circulation, as they do with the generalized patterns of all the other elements in the physical environment. Many parts of the world have distinctive winds that result from local terrain conditions and that have been given local names. Many of them have been noted for some unpleasant feature, usually temperature. Among such local winds are the dry *Santa Anas,* gravity winds that descend from the dry high plains of the southwestern United States into the basins and plains of Southern California. Well known also is the *chinook* (snow eater) (see Fig. 7.16), an unusually warm wind that is heated adiabatically by compression as it descends the eastern slopes of the Rocky Mountains. Another reason for the unusually high temperature of the chinook winds is that the air contains the latent heat of condensation which it acquired during its ascent up the windward side of the mountains following precipitation. In the Alps, one sometimes encounters the *foehn,* a gustier variety of the chinook, which is particularly feared because it often causes avalanches. The Mediterranean Riviera of France and Italy is a famed winter resort; yet when the *mistral* blows down the valley of the Rhone or through the Carcassonne Gap, bathing ceases and people use their apartment space heaters. The Mediterranean area also is the home of a hot, searing, dust-laden wind off the Sahara, known in various localities as *sirocco, khamsin, leveche,* or *samiel.* For centuries, Malay or Arab sailors navigating the Strait of Malacca have prayed to their gods to spare them from the *suma-*

FIG. 7.16 Diagram of a typical chinook wind. On the windward side, the temperature of the rising air at 4,000 feet would be 33.5°F. The depressed adiabatic rate above the point, due to the release of latent heat, results in the rising air being cooled to only 15.5° at 10,000 feet. On the leeward side, the air will be warmed at the dry adiabatic rate throughout its descent, and will reach 65° at 1,000 feet, or 15° warmer than the 1,000-foot level at which it began its rise.

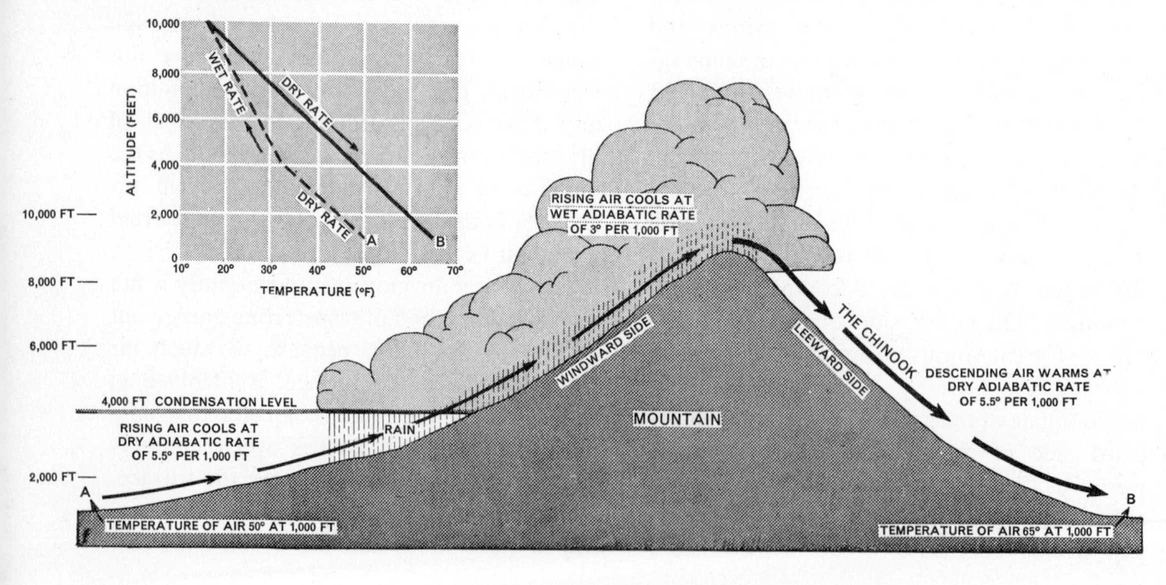

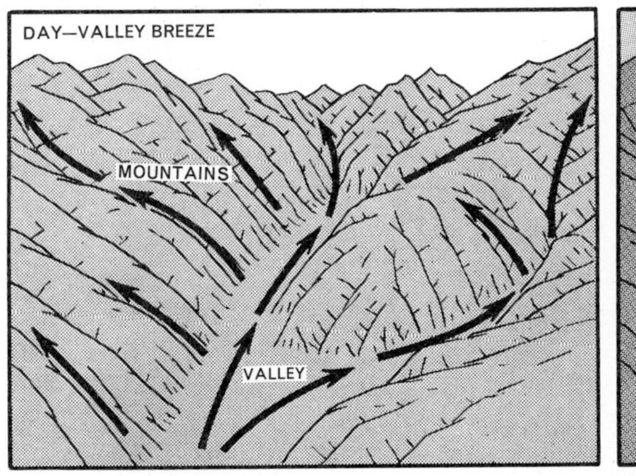

(A) MOUNTAIN AND VALLEY BREEZES

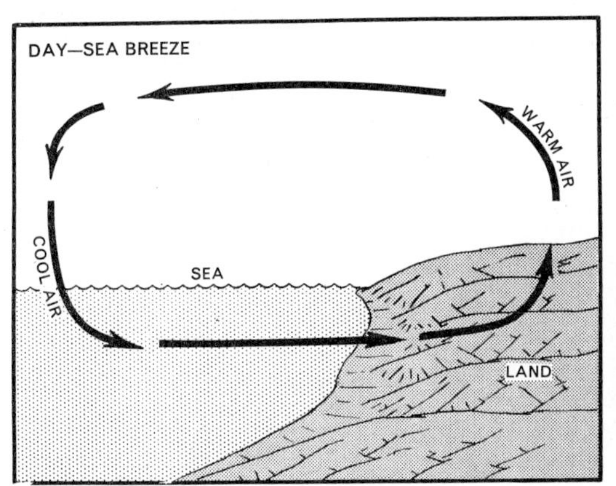

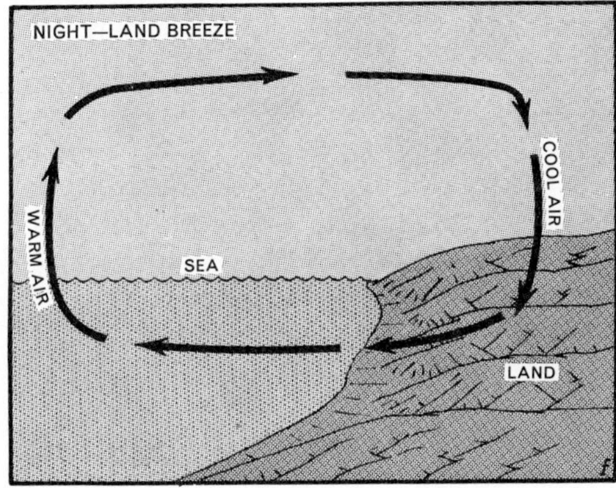

(B) LAND AND SEA BREEZES

FIG. 7.17 Diagram of two types of local winds.

tran, a violent gravity wind that descends without warning from the high volcanic plains of northern Sumatra.

A local wind, common to nearly all coastal areas but best developed along drier coasts, is the *land-and-sea breeze,* which is a landward wind during the daytime and seaward during the night. It is thermally induced, the land being warmer than the sea during the daytime and cooler at night, and it is seldom felt more than 5 to 10 miles from the coast.

Another local wind is the gravity breeze produced by cool air that moves down ravines and long hill slopes in rough terrain and that results from radiational cooling of land surfaces during calm, clear nights. This movement of air often makes slopes preferred sites for fruit orchards in the middle latitudes, because air moving downslope at night is less likely to result in freezing conditions than calm air at lowland sites. Movements of cool air down a mountain valley at night and a reverse, convectional flow of warm air up the valley during the warm daylight hours sometimes produce a daily reversible wind known as a *mountain-and-valley breeze* (see Fig. 7.17). Land-and-sea and mountain-and-valley breezes, because of their short courses, are not appreciably influenced by the Coriolis deflection; hence they move directly down the local pressure gradients.

A close scrutiny of air movement reveals that every building corner or land-surface irregularity produces swirls and eddies in the air currents that stream by. Frontal conditions between conflicting air masses may result in sudden wind shifts through all quarters of the compass. Rare indeed are those areas where the planetary air currents are regular and dependable. The steadiest winds are found mainly over the broad, open expanses of oceans in the trade-wind zone, where no topographic obstacles or unequal heating surfaces occur and where only an occasional convergence or easterly wave creates diversions from the normal airflow. Combine all the regional variations in wind patterns with the changes that occur from day to day, year to year, and century to century, and it becomes apparent that the geographic generalization of wind patterns is subject to the same limitations that are found in the geography of all other natural elements.

Air masses

An air mass is a large quantity of air that has more or less uniform properties. Such uniformity may be considered to be an approach to equilibrium with respect to general environmental factors. Some areas are much more conducive to the formation of homogeneous air masses than others and may be considered as air-mass *source areas*. One type of source area is that in which air stagnates prior to an outward movement. The areas of calms associated with the centers of large, fairly stationary anticyclones are illustrative. A second type of source area includes extensive surface regions of general climatic uniformity, such as the broad expanses of warm oceans in the low latitudes and the extensive snow-covered surfaces of continents in the higher latitudes during the winter season. Such areas are large enough to produce a certain degree of uniformity in depth within the air streams that pass over them.

When air masses leave their source areas and cross surfaces that climatically are distinctly different, they undergo changes in properties. Such modifications may take many forms, but generally they influence first the lower portions of the invading air masses. The great air streams that form the circulation systems at the earth surface thus are continually undergoing some alteration outside their source areas. The extent of modification frequently can be observed by examining the vertical profiles of air masses. Nearly all modified air masses exhibit distinctly different properties in their upper and lower portions, and some remarkably sharp boundaries can be found separating the lower modified portion from the upper. One of the most frequent modifications is formed by changes in temperature. For this reason, a sharp change in the lapse rate of temperature often marks the upper boundary of the modified portion. Temperature inversions in air masses are far more common than was formerly believed, but they were not recognized until measurements of vertical temperature changes could be regularly and easily taken. The principal modifications that take place in surface air masses may be summarized as follows:

Thermodynamic modifications

1. Heating at the earth surface
2. Cooling at the earth surface
3. Addition of water vapor

Mechanical modifications

1. Mixing by passage over rough terrain
2. Orographic, convergent, and convectional lifting
3. Subsidence

7.20 THE BERGERON CLASSIFICATION OF AIR MASSES.

One of the most widely used classifications of world surface air masses is the one created by Bergeron, a Norwegian meteorologist. This classification first recognizes a threefold division into arctic (*A*), polar (*P*), and tropical (*T*) air masses. A fourth primary type, superior air (*S*), is sometimes recognized; this represents mass subsidence from upper-air levels. Arctic and polar air masses both originate in high latitudes, but whereas arctic air masses develop over ice- or snow-covered surfaces, polar air develops over a cold or cool bare ground or open water surface. Arctic air may be modified into polar air. Tropical air is air that originates in the tropics or subtropics.

A secondary classification designates whether a particular primary air mass has a continental (*c*) or a maritime (*m*) source area; the lower-case letter indicating the origin usually precedes the capital letter of the primary classification—for example, *cP* or *mT*. The continental air masses are likely to have a relatively low specific humidity, or water-vapor content, and their lower layers are susceptible to rapid modification by increases and decreases in temperature and by inclusion of water vapor through evaporation. The maritime air masses usually have a high moisture content and are somewhat less sensitive to temperature changes, either by conduction or by radiation. Superior air (*S*) normally is dry and warm for its latitudinal position.

A third phase of the Bergeron classification refers to the temperature modification that the air mass is undergoing in its lower levels. If the air mass is warmer than the surface over which it is passing, and hence is being cooled from below, the letter *w* is added at the end of the symbol—for example, *cPw*. Air that is colder than the surface over which it is passing is designated by the suffix letter *k* (German, *kalt*=cold). A cold air mass that is being warmed below (*k*) is characterized by instability, susceptibility to vertical movements, instability showers, *cumulus* (cauliflower-shaped) cloud forms, and generally good visibility at ground level. A cooling air mass (*w*) is associated with stability, resistance to lifting, *stratus* (layerlike) cloud types, and poor ground visibility. Fog frequently accompanies such stable air masses, and precipitation, when it does occur, is likely to be in the form of a steady drizzle.

The essential characteristics of the major air masses given in Table 7.1 (p. 226). It should be noted, however, that various modifications may greatly alter the basic properties of air masses as they leave their source areas. Only a few of the most important possible modifications could be included in this table.

7.21 AIR-MASS SUMMARY.

Any interpretation of weather and climatic patterns should involve the analysis of air-mass behavior. Predicting the weather at any place on the earth surface necessitates knowing which air masses most often influence the area, to what extent they are likely to have been modified during their passage from the source areas, and whether or not there is likely to be an interplay of air masses, either on the ground or aloft.

The broad global pattern of air masses is relatively simple (see Fig. 7.18*a* and *b*). Superior air (*S*), subsiding from the upper troposphere, predominates in the stagnant centers of the deep anticyclones. The general zone of tropical easterlies, or the circulation of air on the equatorward sides of the subtropical highs, is composed largely of *mT* air masses. If the subtropical highs overlie continental areas, however, such regions consti-

TABLE 7.1 Characteristics of major air masses

NAME OF AIR MASS	SOURCE AREAS	TYPICAL CHARACTERISTICS	MAJOR MODIFICATIONS	ASSOCIATED WEATHER
Arctic (*A*)	Ice- and snow-covered surfaces in Greenland, Antarctica, Hudson Bay, MacKenzie Basin, Mongolia–Lake Baikal region, Scandinavia	Low water-vapor content; temperature inversion above surface cooling zone (2,000–3,000 ft.); subsidence above; generally stable	Rapid rise in humidity in lower levels when passing over water, creating instability; inversion aloft destroyed by passage over rough terrain	Clear skies, except when modified; low temperatures at night; strong winter storms (blizzards) along leading edge (arctic front)
Continental polar (*cP*)	In winter, the cold continental surfaces mostly free of ice and snow; in summer, cool surfaces in Canada and U.S.S.R.; rare in summer south of U.S.S.R.	Found only in northern hemisphere; often modified *cA* air; clear skies at night; scattered cumulus clouds during the day; some subsidence above	Generally becomes highly unstable away from source areas; persistent overcast skies with passage over rough terrain	Clear air; frost hazard in late spring and early fall; summer convectional showers near water bodies; involved in most frontal activity in mid-latitudes
Maritime polar (*mP*)	Ocean areas lat 40–60° N and S	In winter, mainly modified *cA* and *cP* air brought into ocean areas, resulting in instability (*mPk*); surface temperatures rarely subfreezing; summer air generally stable (*mPw*)	*mPk* air on lee side of mountains (as in the Rockies) dry, clear, and warm; passage over cold surfaces produces stability at lower levels	Fog and low overcast skies when passing over a cold surface; cyclonic and orographic conditions produce heavy precipitation; fronts with *mPw* air produce drizzly rain
Maritime tropical (*mT*)	Warm tropical and subtropical ocean areas beneath subtropical anticyclones	Usually subsidence and low lapse rate above; generally fairly stable; some low-level instability; often an inversion aloft	Rising humidity and increasing instability away from source areas; passage over cold land in winter increases stability (*mTw*); in summer, air sometimes unstable over warm land	Hazy air; scattered cumulus clouds; passage over cold land results in broad overcasts; produces most continental snowfall in mid-latitudes; convectional rain with *mTk* in summer
Continental tropical (*cT*)	High plains with subtropical anticyclones (mainly in winter); Sahara, S. Africa, central Australia, S.W. China, N. India, Andean Plains	Extremely low humidity; hot, dusty, turbulent air; subsidence of warm air aloft	Becomes highly unstable in lower levels when passing over water (as over the Mediterranean Sea)	Hot, dry weather; much haze; sometimes associated aloft with tornadoes

tute source areas for *cT* air masses. The great zone of westerlies is made up of a variety of air masses. Feeding into it are air masses originating in both subtropical and polar high-pressure regions, and having source areas over both continents and oceans. The *mT* and *cT* air masses evolve from the subtropical highs, whereas *cP* and *mP* air masses enter the westerlies from poleward sources.

Each air mass has certain identifying characteristics, which are often most clearly revealed in its vertical profile. This is why keen observers, centuries ago, could make some reasonable weather predictions by studying cloud patterns. Clouds often reflect differences or changes in the upper air that are symptomatic of air-mass stratification, modification, or interplay. Two of the most important air-mass properties include the tendencies for stability or instability. These are related mainly to specific humidity and the lapse rate.

The secondary air circulation

Mention has been made, in this and the preceding chapter, of traveling cyclones and anticyclones. These temporary and moving pressure disturbances in the atmosphere are secondary features of the air-circulation pattern. We now turn our attention to these "lesser wheels within the larger wheels" of air circulation. As with all the other weather and climatic phenomena, their behavior is linked with the distribution of energy received from the sun, and the necessity of evening out the local surpluses and deficiencies

FIG. 7.18a Typical world air-mass distribution for July. [After Haurwitz and Austin]

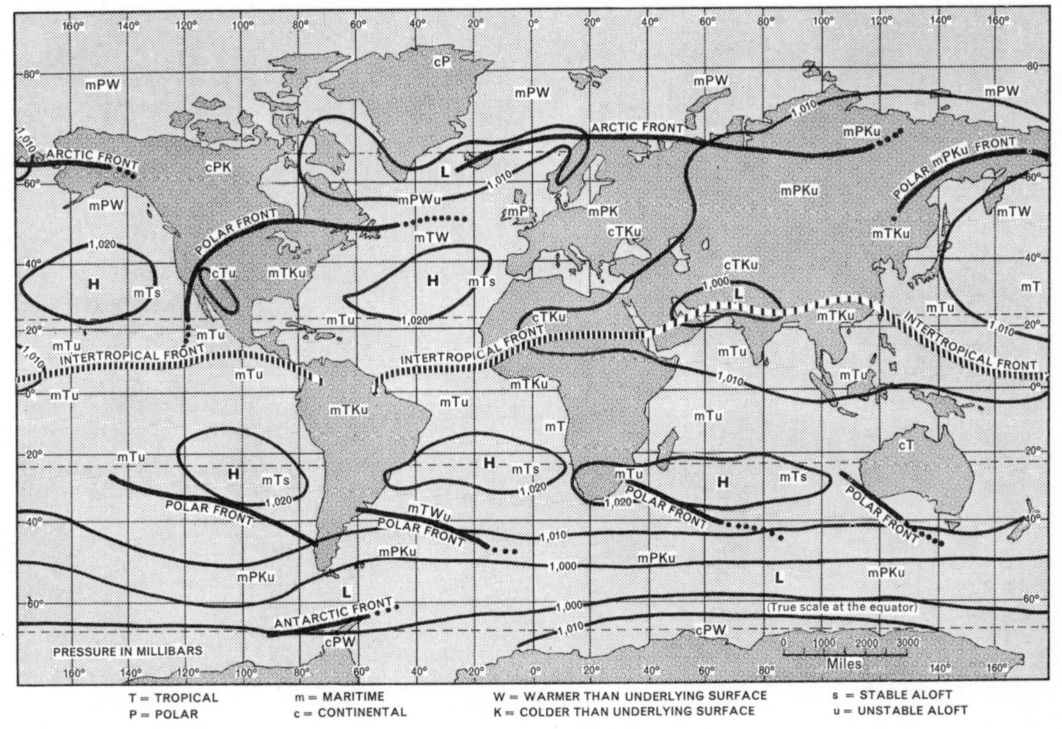

that develop at various places about the earth surface and within the envelope of air that surrounds it. The details of the origin of cyclones and anticyclones will not concern us here, and the interested student is referred to standard textbooks in meteorology for such material. We shall, however, deal with some of the evolutionary features in the behavior of these pressure changes as they develop, grow to a maximum, and finally succumb to disruptive forces. Like the larger permanent or quasi-permanent pressure centers on earth, the traveling highs and lows feature the subsidence of air associated with anticyclones and the rising of air that is typical of cyclones. Disturbances like these involve the atmosphere to great heights, and most well-developed pressure centers are related to waves in the stream lines of airflow throughout the troposphere. The observation of changes in the tropopause and the jet stream has led investigators to debate whether the triggering of the traveling pressure centers is generated by surface energy surpluses and deficiencies or by temperature variations near the upper limit of the troposphere.

7.22 EXTRATROPICAL CYCLONES. The cyclones of the middle and higher latitudes nearly always develop along frontal boundaries of air masses that differ in their basic properties, particularly temperature. These low-pressure centers vary considerably in shape, size, intensity, speed, and duration. A typical mid-latitude cyclone of the northern hemisphere is shown in Fig. 7.20. Note that it has roughly circular isobars that

FIG. 7.18b Typical world air-mass distribution for January. [After Haurwitz and Austin]

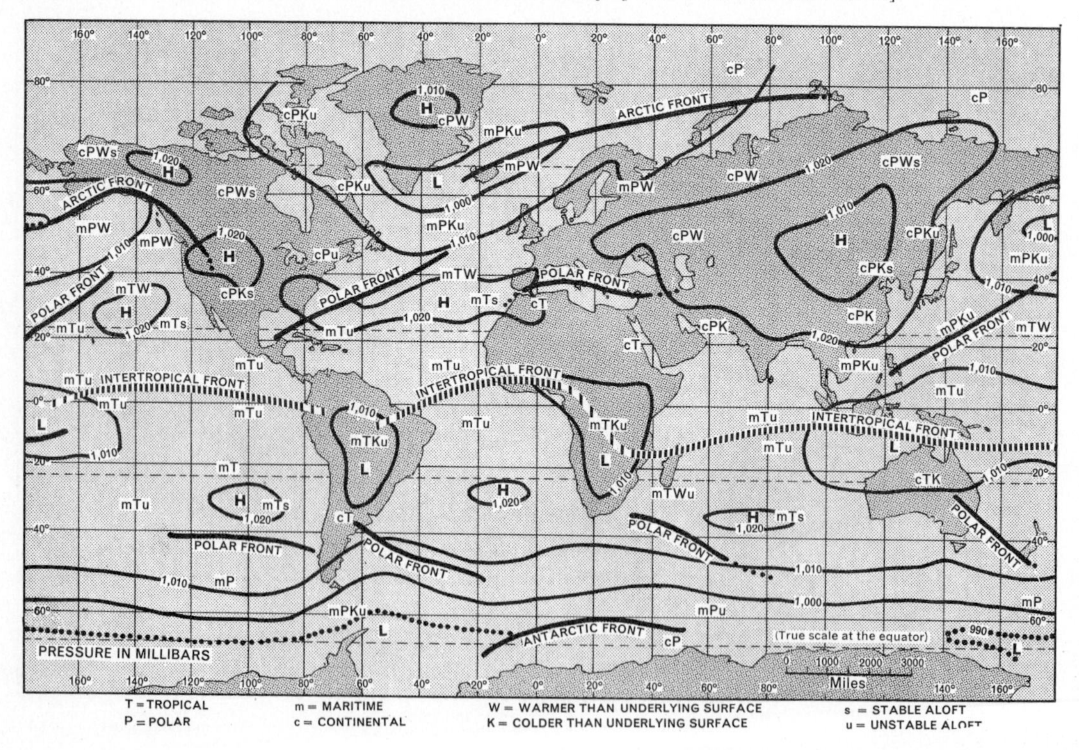

FIG. 7.19 Fractocumulus, or "fair weather," clouds characteristic of cP air masses over the northern U.S. in the summer. [U.S. Weather Bureau; H. T. Floreen]

are slightly kinked at the boundaries of the air masses. Wind directions are angled across the isobars and down the pressure gradient, giving the entire cyclone a convergent, counterclockwise rotation. Wind velocities depend on the steepness of the pressure gradient and on the latitude. Two separate fronts can be identified: a warm front in the southeastern quadrant and a cold front in the southwestern quadrant. Rising air along the frontal surfaces produces cloudiness and precipitation. The size of extratropical cyclones varies, but those which grow and become well-marked pressure centers and which are the most effective in air interchange appear to have a strict size limitation, ranging from 500 to 1,700 miles. Most of them are between 600 and 1,000 miles in diameter. These cyclones normally are oval-shaped, with a longer and shorter diameter. The speed of progression of the entire cyclone is roughly between 20 and 30 miles per hour. Great differences in speed may be noted, however. Winter cyclones travel somewhat faster than summer ones. The pressure differential in cyclones normally is from 10 to 20 millibars, or less than ¾ of an inch of mercury in a barometer. Unusually deep ones, however, may vary as much as a full inch of mercury.

Extratropical cyclones vary in their developmental sequences. Some of them are highly dynamic, with rapid changes in form. Others, once they are formed, remain relatively unchanged for long periods. Mid-latitude cyclones are destroyed mainly by the process of *occlusion,* shown diagrammatically in Fig. 7.21. Note that the cyclone develops first as only a slight wave along a frontal surface. Gradually the wave indentation deepens, and the typical cyclone form appears. The active forward progression of the cold-front sector overtakes the warm front, removes the frontal indentation, and thus produces a new type of front, termed an

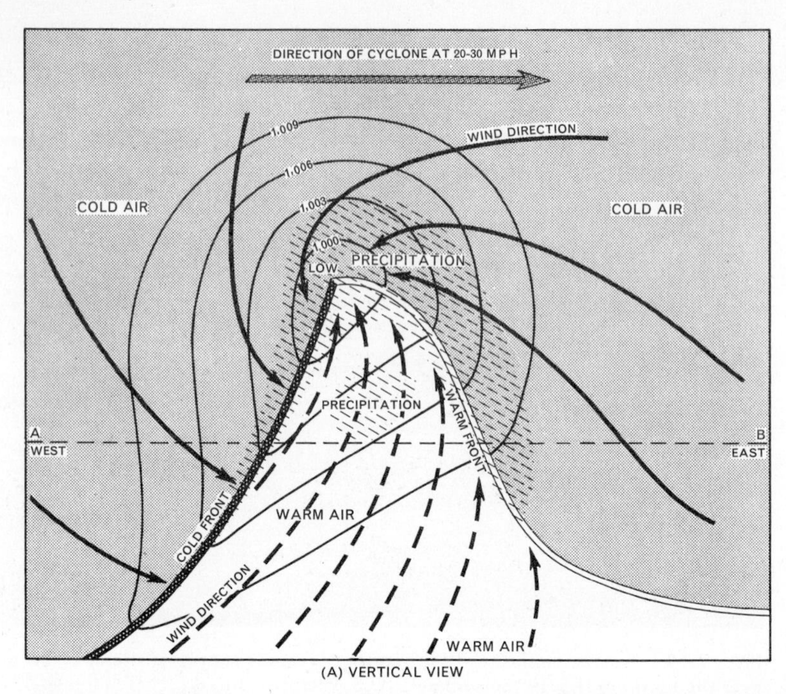

FIG. 7.20 Model of a typical mid-latitude cyclone in the northern hemisphere.
[After Bjerknes]

occluded front, between the newer, deeper, and rapidly moving cold air mass and the older, shallower, and modified cold air that previously adjoined the warm front. If the newer, intruding cold air mass is colder than the older cold air that adjoins the warm front, the older will be displaced in what is termed a *cold-front occlusion* (see Fig. 7.21). If the newer intruding air mass is warmer than the older air mass beneath the former warm front, the new intrusion will be forced to rise in a *warm-front occlusion.* The latter is much less usual and is found mainly in the western parts of continents where incoming *mPk* air meets *cP* air at the occlusion. Each type of occlusion has characteristic associated weather patterns.

Following an occlusion, the cyclonic vortex of warm air, with its convergent air spiraling upward, is present, but it lies above the cold air. Its lower density is effective in maintaining a center of low pressure at the surface. In time, continued filling of the low-pressure center reduces the pressure gradient, and the cyclone disappears. In the meantime, as a result of the cyclonic development, there has been a displacement of energy, with warm air brought poleward as a result of the cyclonic pressure gradient, and cold air brought equatorward for the same reason. The warm air loses heat over a cooler surface, and the cold air warms at lower latitudes. Condensation and precipitation have released large quantities of latent heat energy from the warm air into the cloud zones far above the earth and distributed this heat energy into the upper-air layers. The cyclone in this way accomplishes its mission of providing a means for speeding up energy transfer locally along the frontal boundary.

The extratropical cyclones are located mainly along frontal convergences, particularly along the polar front, which acts as the principal convergence zone between cold *cP* air and warm tropical air masses. Figure 7.18*a* and *b* shows the mean location of the polar front at the solstice seasons. The strength and frequency of cyclonic activity

FIG. 7.21 The development of a cyclone, showing stages in the development and occlusions of an extratropical cyclone. The smaller diagrams (A′, B′, C′, D′, E′, F′) represent vertical cross sections of the air masses along the line x-y. [After Garbell]

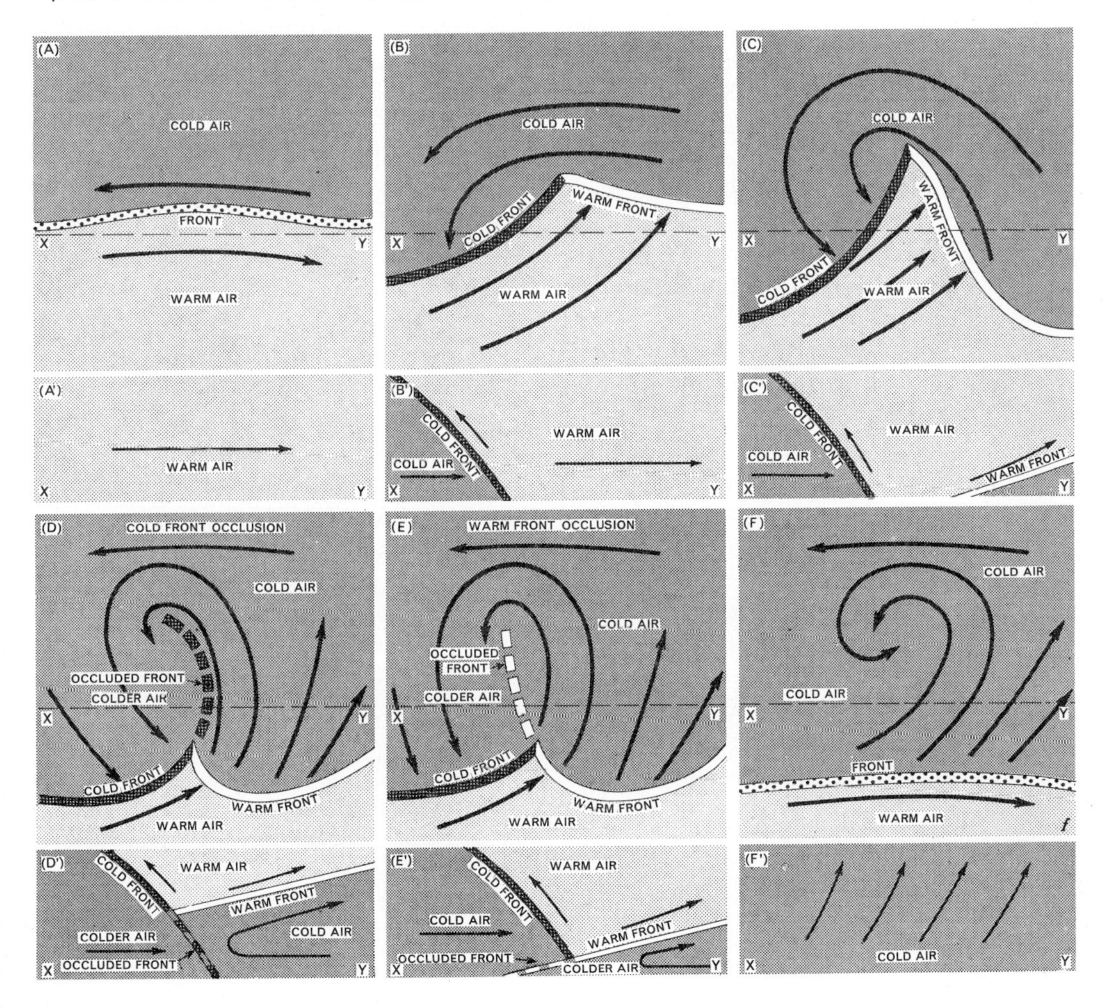

along the polar front are roughly proportional to the temperature contrasts between the converging air masses; thus the winter season marks the period of maximum activity. The cyclones move along the polar front, forming, occluding, and re-forming. Sometimes they follow each other in close succession. As the general trend in the polar front changes, so also does the path of the mid-latitude cyclones. However, they always have an eastward component because of the dominant eastward flow of the westerly wind belt.

Three areas of high, extratropical, cyclonic activity are found over oceans. These include the North Pacific, the North Atlantic during the winter season, and the peripheral ocean area off the coast of Antarctica between lat 50 and 60° S. On the continents, the cyclonic activity is most prevalent in the eastern portions, where the *mT* air masses extend farthest poleward. In Europe, a polar front develops along the length of the Mediterranean Basin during the winter season, and cyclones moving eastward along this frontal zone sometimes are carried far into the Middle East.

A study of the cyclonic model shown in Fig. 7.20 will reveal the weather changes associated with the passage of a cyclone, including cloud types, temperature and pressure changes, wind direction, and precipitation. The sequence of these features varies, depending on whether the cyclonic center passes to the north, to the south, or directly through the point of observation. Not all cyclones conform to the features of the model shown in Fig. 7.20. Some of them, for example, are elongated rather than circular or oval-shaped. Such elongated cyclones, with their long axes usually extending from northeast to southwest in the northern hemisphere, have unusually sharp shifts in wind direction along the cold-front sector.

7.23 TROPICAL CYCLONES. Tropical cyclones typically are broad, shallow, low-pressure centers that are found mainly within the intertropical convergence zone between the trade winds. The absence of strong fronts between air masses in this zone, owing to the small differences in temperature, precludes the development of cyclones similar to those characteristic of higher latitudes. The usual tropical cyclone rarely has a pressure range of more than about 3 to 5 millibars and is much larger in size than the extratropical variety, often reaching 1,500 to 2,500 miles in diameter. They rarely develop occlusions and generally slowly weaken and disappear. Their direction is from east to west within the general easterly flow of low latitudes. Movement is slow, and they frequently remain motionless for several days. Weather changes accompanying them are little more than "spells of weather," with periods of overcast skies and fairly steady rains that may last for several days. They appear to be somewhat more frequent near the equinoctial periods but may occur in any season.

An interesting feature of some tropical cyclones is that they appear within the stream lines of the trade-wind flow and thus do not require an intertropical convergence. Such cyclones are associated with wavelike undulations in the trade-wind flow, termed *easterly waves*. This type of tropical cyclone tends to be located somewhat farther from the equator than the intertropical convergence and is of special interest because it sometimes develops into severe storms, the dreaded tropical hurricanes (see Sec. 7.27). In the easterly waves (see Fig. 7.22), the bending of the airflow at the axis of the wave (roughly from east-northeast in front of the wave to east-southeast in its rear) results in a local convergence in the rear of the axis of the wave. The dynamic lifting here destroys the normal trade-wind inversion in the upper air, thus increasing the lapse rate, making the upper air more unstable, and stimulating condensation and precipitation. Subsidence generally is stronger in front of the easterly waves, resulting in exceptionally clear, dry weather there. The easterly wave cyclones are somewhat smaller than other tropical cyclones. Usually the waves are more pronounced in the upper atmosphere than they are at the surface and may well have been generated as the result of energy patterns in the upper zone of the tropical easterlies. It has been estimated that fewer than 10 per cent of them develop into hurricanes.

7.24 TRAVELING ANTICYCLONES.

Traveling anticyclones are restricted largely to the mid-latitudes and are of two types: the cold, polar anticyclones and the warm, subtropical type. The former are synonymous with the outbreaks of arctic and polar air from their respective source areas. The warm variety represents offshoots from the subtropical, permanent, or quasi-permanent, anticyclonic cells. Both types intrude into the general westerly circulation, but from opposite directions, and trend toward the east.

The polar traveling anticyclones are shallow, rarely over a mile or two in depth. Subsidence within them thus takes place over only a short vertical distance, in contrast with the high columns of rising air typical of cyclonic centers in the subtropics. They are usually slightly larger in diameter than typical extratropical cyclones. Wind patterns are typically divergent, with a deflection that produces a rough, clockwise rotation in the northern hemisphere and a counterclockwise rotation south of the equator. Pressure gradients are likely to be less steep than in most cyclones but are steepest along the southwestern quadrants (north of the equator). Unusually steep gradients behind a cold

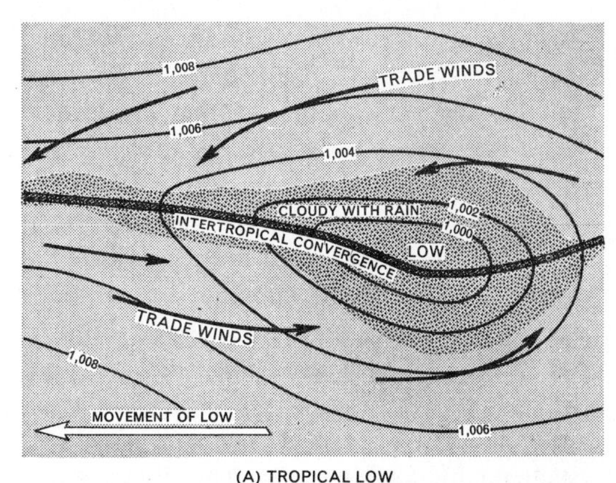

(A) TROPICAL LOW

(B) EASTERLY WAVE

FIG. 7.22 Isobaric patterns associated with weak tropical lows and easterly waves in the northern hemisphere.

front that separates a polar anticyclone from an adjoining cyclonic cell during the winter sometimes generate cold, gale winds. Winds in the center of anticyclones are light and variable with intermittent calms. Cold anticyclones generally do not travel so fast as cyclones and are more likely to remain stationary, especially over rough, hilly terrain. Weather conditions associated with polar anticyclones are characterized by clear, cool weather. Once into the westerly airflow pattern, especially over warm surfaces, the traveling polar anticyclones tend to become shallower and broader and may disappear because of progressive warming from below, since they are maintained thermally by conductive and radiational cooling. A few of them may penetrate into the subtropics and become incorporated into the subtropical anticyclones. Traces of these old polar anticyclones are preserved for long periods in the upper air. The traveling polar anticyclones form equatorward lobes in the polar front.

Traveling subtropical anticyclones are not so well defined as the cold, or polar, type, and they have a much greater tendency to stagnate for long periods. They have much warmer air within them and often are responsible for spells of clear skies and unseasonably warm weather in the mid-latitudes.

Storms

Weather and climate are important variables in human decisions, but in most cases these variables are treated casually. The normal weather changes in all parts of the world are recognized, create their ripples in the everyday affairs of man, but rarely produce much excitement. Occasionally, however, the atmosphere reveals some of the enormous energy potentials that normally are kept under control. Man adjusts his life fairly well to most weather changes, but in the face of severe storms, he is relatively helpless. His best weapon today against storm destruction lies in learning how to follow and predict storm paths; in classifying areas according to their storm probabilities; in using protective devices to reduce property damage, injuries, and loss of life; and in understanding the behavior of storms.

Storms may be defined as any sudden, severe increase in air motion. They result either from the sudden transformation of potential energy into the kinetic energy of air motion (as when cold air subsides and warm air rises) along fronts or from the sudden release of latent heat following condensation in warm, humid air masses and the transformation of this heat energy into the kinetic energy of air motion (as in a thunderstorm). Among the many different types of storms, the most important in terms of potential loss of life and property are thunderstorms, tornadoes, and hurricanes, or typhoons, each of which has a distinctive pattern of occurrence. From an economic standpoint, the geographic patterns of storms are a significant factor in world climates, and they are briefly described and partially explained in the following paragraphs.

7.25 THUNDERSTORMS. Thunderstorms are by far the most frequent convulsions in the atmosphere. Although they are tiny disturbances when viewed on a global scale, they are such frequent and widely distributed phenomena that they warrant an important place in any treatment of atmospheric storms. A thunderstorm is a huge, localized and temporary thermodynamic engine that depends on the release of latent heat of condensation for its energy. An individual thunderstorm seldom lasts for more than an hour or so, because it contains within it the forces of its own destruction. Like a living creature, however, it also brings forth the tiny embryos of new storms during the most active part of its existence.

Thunderstorms develop when warm, conditionally unstable air containing a great deal of water vapor is elevated and cooled to the condensation point. If the lapse rate is steep enough, the air may reach absolute instability and rise of its own accord. As the water vapor in the column of rising air condenses, it forms typical cumulus or cumulo-nimbus clouds, the anvil-shaped cloud forms that are seen so frequently on warm, humid summer afternoons. Thunderstorms develop very rapidly, and involve columns of air that

FIG. 7.23 A thunderstorm cloud (cumulo-nimbus), showing characteristic anvil shape. [From E. Fontsere; Atlas Elémentaire des nuages]

rise to great heights. There is some indication that condensation below the freezing point in the upper cloud zone plays an important role in the violence of these storms, since such condensation releases not only the heat of condensation but also the heat of fusion. The major requirements for thunderstorm development are (1) a high specific humidity associated only with warm air and (2) conditional instability, or the ability of the air mass to maintain adiabatic cooling at a rate below that of the lapse rate.

The rapidity of condensational lifting and rain formation is responsible for the unique features of thunderstorms. The frictional drag of the downward rush of immense quantities of water and ice and the cooling resulting from evaporation of rain during its descent produce downdrafts of cold air. A mature thunderstorm thus contains distinct cells, consisting of warm updrafts and cold downdrafts, the latter found mainly in the bottom half of the storm (see Fig. 7.24). The downdrafts later spread and check the upflow, and the entire storm dissipates. Friction about the edges of both updrafts and downdrafts

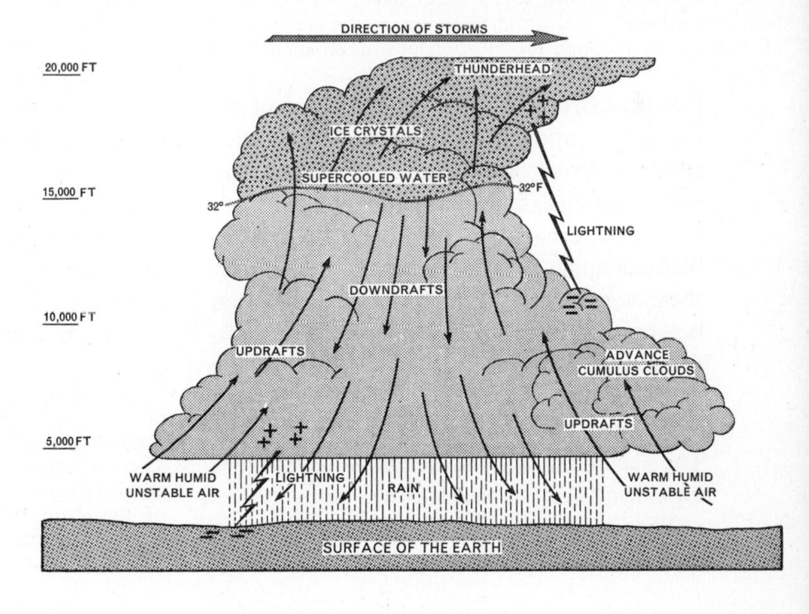

FIG. 7.24 Model of a typical thunderstorm.

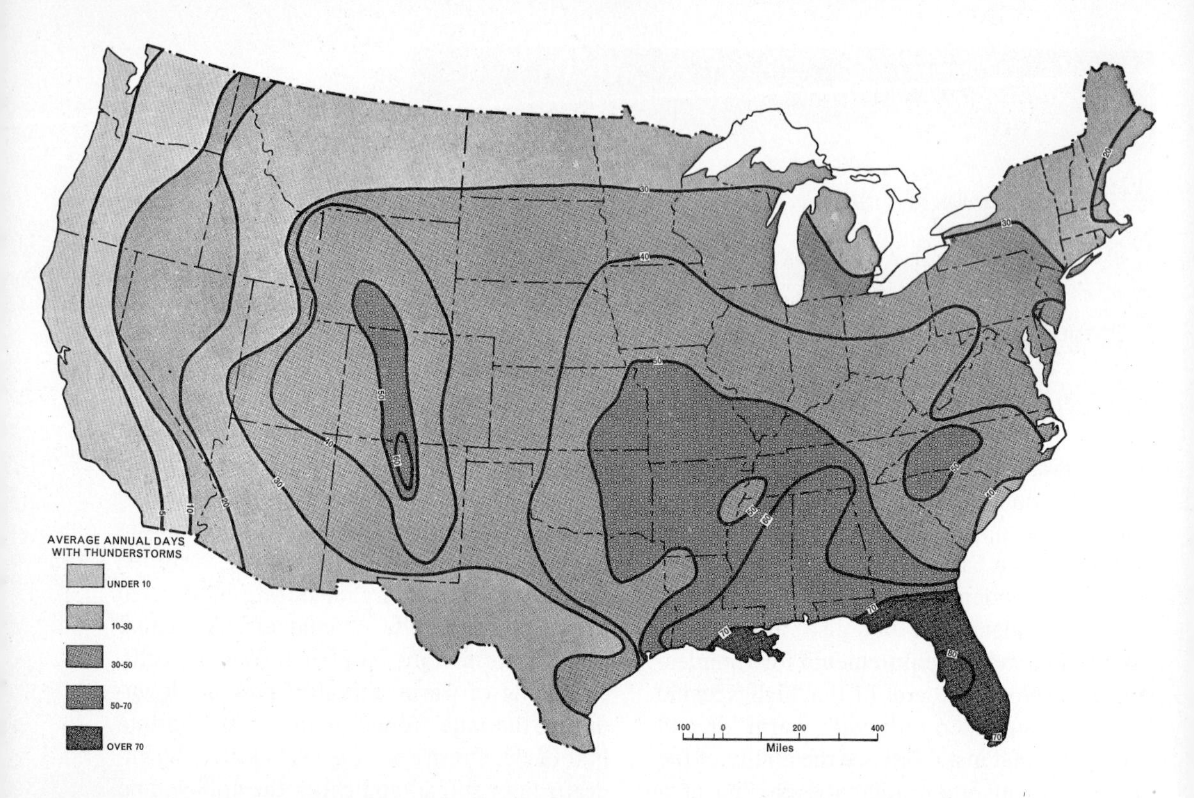

FIG. 7.25 Thunderstorm frequency in the United States. Note the high frequency in the warm subtropical areas bordering the Gulf of Mexico. The orographic influence can be seen in the higher frequencies along the Rocky Mountains and the Southern Appalachians. Note that thunderstorms rarely occur along the Pacific coast, despite a heavy rainfall in the Pacific Northwest. In this region the air is not warm enough to hold the immense quantities of water vapor required for thunderstorm development. [U.S. Department of Agriculture]

produces strong turbulence, and some of the miniature updrafts associated with such eddies may act as the nuclei for new storm cells. Airplane flights in thunderstorms are dangerous because of the sharp boundaries between updrafts and downdrafts, which may shear wings or fuselage surfaces. Hail often is associated with exceptionally violent thunderstorms. This represents a fall of ice particles through an exceptionally deep layer of supercooled water droplets at great heights. The accumulation is sufficient to resist melting during the remainder of the fall.

The exact process of producing lightning discharges during thunderstorms is still not fully understood, but it is believed that the violent opposing air currents and the interaction between falling rain and rising masses of cloud particles are able to rupture drops of water and to produce smaller particles having an electric charge.[3] Through the migration of these charged water droplets, the electric potential builds up at the borders of

[3] Raindrops usually contain varying quantities of positive or negative ions and free electrons, trapped within the drop during its rapid growth. These charged particles may align themselves at opposite sides of the drop, and following rupture of the drop by severe turbulence, the resulting water fragments take on a net positive or negative charge.

clouds, and when it is great enough, a flow of electrons jumps across the gap between one cloud and another or between a cloud and the ground. The sudden flow of electrons in the air generates temperatures momentarily as high as 50,000°F, and the energy flow into the air molecules excites their "bound" electrons, producing a flash of light. The thunder is produced by the shock waves in the air that result from the sudden expansion of air immediately following the lightning flash. It is closely comparable to the waves that are produced by the discharge of a high explosive.

Figure 7.25 shows the distribution of thunderstorm frequencies. It will be seen that thunderstorms occur most frequently in areas that have warm, moist air. Florida has the largest number among the states of the United States, with a definite maximum during the summer. Buitenzorg, a city on the mountain slopes of Java, holds the world's record for thunderstorms, averaging 322 days of such storms per year. They are frequent throughout the humid tropics, and several places in tropical Africa and South America have over 100 per year. During the winter, thunderstorms rarely occur poleward of lat 45°, mainly because the air is too cold to hold sufficient moisture to operate the thermodynamic mechanism of such storms. Thunderstorms are rare at any season along the west coasts of continents poleward of lat 40°, as along the Pacific coast of North America from northern California to Alaska, even though the mean annual precipitation is relatively high. Summer rain generally is drizzly in this region and develops from relatively stable (*mPw*) air that has a fairly low lapse rate. Such rain is likely to be produced from broad stratus clouds or overcasts, resulting either from lifting along fronts or from orographic influences. The *mPk* air of winter in this region is too cool to contain the quantities of water vapor necessary for thunderstorm development.

7.26 TORNADOES. Tornadoes are the smallest, yet the most violent, of the major storm types. They are rotational storms, or miniature cyclonic whirls, often much less than a few hundred yards in diameter. Their funnellike form, hanging downward from a large cumulo-nimbus cloud, usually is visible, owing to the extremely rapid condensation within the upward-spiraling air and the contained dust and debris (see Fig. 7.26). Hail often precedes or follows tornadoes, indicating the strength and height of the updrafts. The atmospheric pressure in the center of

FIG. 7.26 A tornado at Manhattan, Kansas, May 31, 1949. [U.S. Weather Bureau; H. E. Dale]

tornadoes is extremely low; so low, in fact, that buildings in their path may explode outward because of the sudden drop in air pressure.[4] No accurate measurements of wind velocities ever have been made in a tornado, instruments having been destroyed before they could record maximum strengths. Estimates place these velocities at between 100 and 600 miles per hour. The speed of the storm cell itself is relatively slow, seldom being more than 20 to 40 miles per hour. The funnel-shaped mass of destructive energy also is somewhat erratic in its course, sometimes bounding upward without touching the ground or winding irregularly in hilly country. In general, the path of these storms in the United States is roughly from southwest to northeast. They seldom travel far, because their violence makes equilibrium precarious. The average distance covered by an individual tornado is only about 1½ miles, although exceptional ones have been known to follow paths over 100 miles long. Courses are somewhat longer over flat, open country.

The global distribution of tornadoes is not well known, because of their small size and local occurrence. They have been reported throughout the world within middle and lower latitudes. Their highest frequency appears to be in the central continental plains east of the dry climates. The United States and Australia have by far the greatest reported number, averaging about 140 per year. Kansas, Arkansas, Iowa, Oklahoma, and Nebraska have the largest number of tornadoes within the United States.

Tornadoes are almost always associated with frontal conditions and with a deep, accompanying cyclonic disturbance. Lapse rates are unusually steep, and generally there is a strong contrast vertically between a thin, warm, humid air mass at the surface and dry, cooler air above. The cooler air aloft may result from a shelving effect, where the upper part of a cold air mass moves ahead of the lower portion, owing to retardation of the latter due to friction next to the ground. The warm, moist air below, once it begins to rise through this "shelf" of cold air, suddenly jumps upward, and the rapid release of heat from condensation adds to the contrast in density between the warm ascending column and the cold upper air. The Coriolis effect, the pressure gradient, and friction turn the rising air into a spiral, which shrinks and increases its angular momentum. The greater occurrence of tornadoes in the central plains of continents east of the midlatitude continental arid regions is explained by the fact that these are the places in which the following features are most likely to be combined.

1. Rapidly moving cold, polar, continental air masses (*cPk*)
2. A relatively thin surface layer of warm, moist, tropical air (*mTk*)
3. A weakly subsident, dry, continental air mass aloft (*cTk*)
4. The absence of rough terrain to destroy the whirling columns by turbulence after they generate

Tornadoes have been known to occur, however, along the intertropical convergence zone in low latitudes.

Two minor storms that are similar to tornadoes but that are smaller and much less violent are *dust devils* and *waterspouts*. The former average about 600 feet in height and about 50 feet in diameter. Their winds are not particularly destructive. Dust devils are formed mainly in hot desert areas, where the

[4] A sudden drop of 34 millibars, or 1 inch of mercury, exerts a force equal to approximately 4.3 pounds per square inch. Applied to a single 30- by 8-foot wall of a frame building, such a pressure would approximate 7½ tons. This is why houses blow apart during such storms.

extreme heating of the bare surface creates unusually strong instability in the lower air. Spontaneous overturning produces the local vertical air columns. They have no accompanying condensation. Waterspouts are tornadoes over water, but they have much less velocity than their counterparts over land. The pendant column consists mainly of water droplets formed as the result of condensation. Only the bottom is sheet water drawn up from the surface. They usually travel in groups and are found principally in the tropics and subtropics.

Much work has been done in the attempt to forecast tornadoes, because of their destructiveness. As yet, however, forecasters can only give warning, a few hours in advance, of general conditions favorable to tornado development; they have not been able to predict the occurrence and trajectory of individual "twisters." It is hoped that "tracking" by mobile radar units flown into predicted danger zones may possibly aid in plotting the course of individual storms. Protective measures are summarized as follows by E. M. Brooks: [5]

> People can protect themselves better by learning to recognize local signs of a tornado and to watch the sky when public forecasts call for severe local storms. If a tornado cloud appears, it is advisable (if time permits) to shut off immediately the electric power and gas supplies and to extinguish all fires (in fireplace, furnace, etc.) so that conflagration will not occur and burn to death someone trapped by heavy debris. The next step is to seek shelter quickly in a tornado cellar, or in the southwest corner of the basement of a frame house, or beside an inside partition on a lower floor of a reinforced concrete or modern steel building, but not in a house with brick walls. In a city, it is generally dangerous to try to get in a car and drive away from an approaching tornado because excessively high winds, often with flying debris and hail, could wreck the car and even kill the occupants. If a person is caught in the open without available shelter, to avoid injury or death he should lie flat in a ditch or culvert, hold on to a fixed object to keep from being blown away, and cover himself, especially his head, to protect himself from missiles.

[5] Reproduced by permission from Edward M. Brooks, "Tornadoes and Related Phenomena," *Compendium of Meteorology*, American Meteorological Society, Boston, 1951, p. 678. Published through the support and sponsorship extended by the Geophysics Research Directorate, Air Force Cambridge Research Center, Air Research and Development Command.

7.27 HURRICANES. Hurricanes are large, violent tropical storms with convergent winds rotating about a low-pressure center. Because of their great size, they are the most destructive storms on earth, although tornadoes are more violent. The diameter of the wind zone at hurricane strength usually is about 100 miles. Wind velocities are upward of 75 miles per hour. Associated features (see Fig. 7.27) include the following:

1. A counterclockwise rotation north of the equator with winds spiraling inward and upward
2. Heavy condensation and precipitation,[6] principally in the quadrants preceding the storm center
3. A central "eye," with cloudless skies and warm, calm air
4. A sudden barometric drop, sometimes as much as 1 inch of mercury within a half hour
5. Isobars that have a symmetrically circular shape, principally during the storm climax
6. Spiraling bands of clouds and thunderstorm centers radiating out from the center like the arms of a pinwheel

[6] The world's record for intensity of rain for a 24-hour period was recorded during a typhoon (hurricane) in the Philippine Islands in 1911, during which time 46 inches of rain fell.

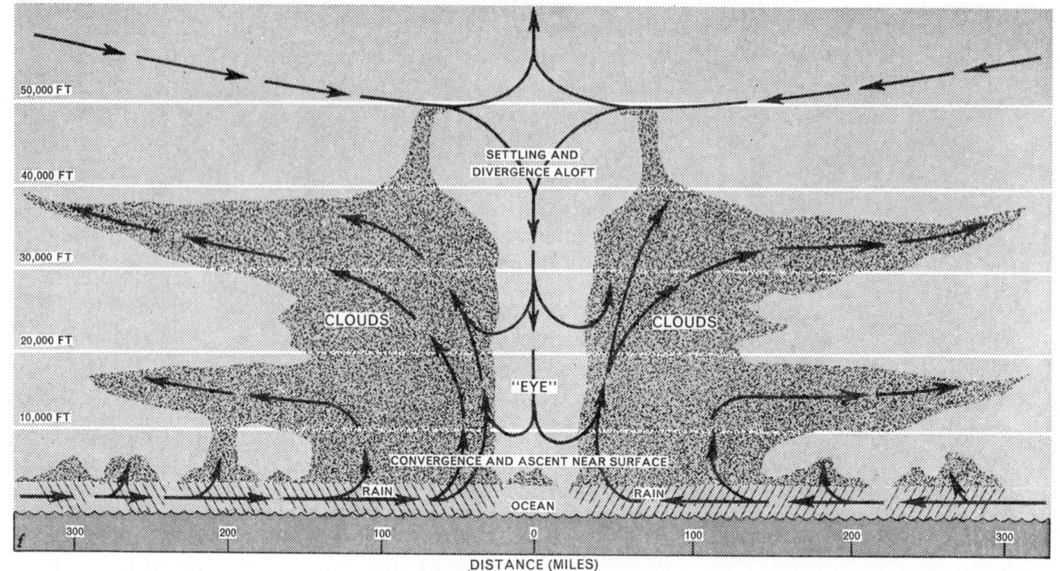

(A) CROSS SECTION OF A HURRICANE

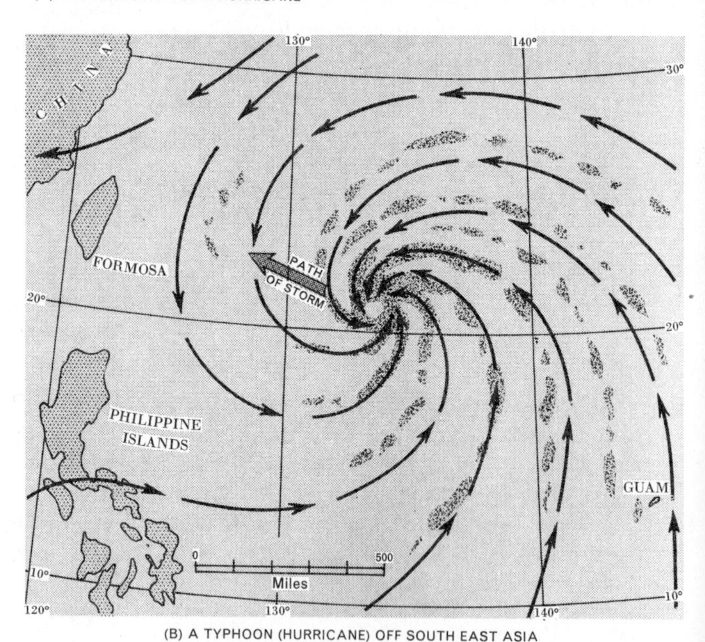

(B) A TYPHOON (HURRICANE) OFF SOUTH EAST ASIA

FIG. 7.27 Typical vertical and horizontal structures of tropical cyclonic storms (hurricanes and typhoons). [After Phelps and Pollard]

7. A surface tongue of unusually warm air preceding the hurricane

The heavy precipitation accompanying hurricanes may result in disastrous floods, such as those associated with hurricane Diane [7] in August, 1955, which devastated valley sections in northeastern Pennsylvania,

[7] Hurricanes noted by the U.S. Weather Bureau are given feminine names in alphabetical sequence: Audrey, Betty, Cora, etc.

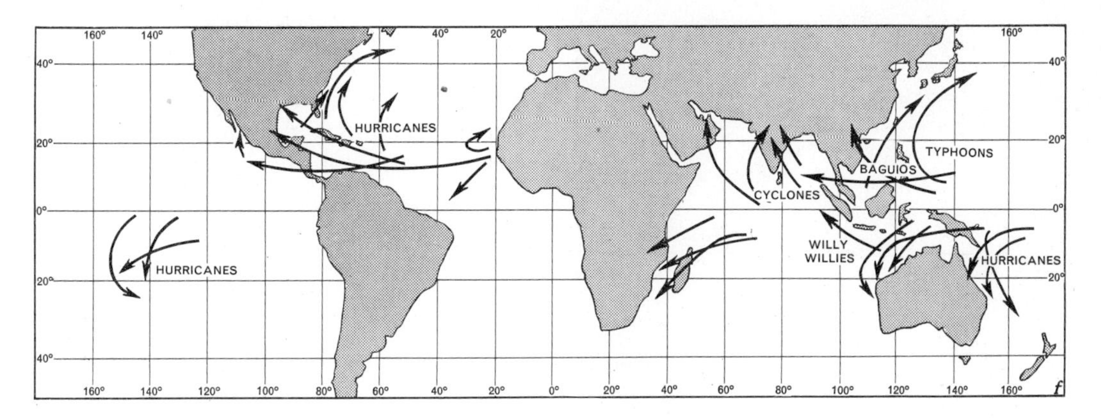

FIG. 7.28 Typical paths of tropical cyclonic storms. [After Garbell]

southeastern New York, and western Connecticut and caused nearly 200 deaths. Diane's winds, at the time of the floods, had diminished to only light gale force (30 to 40 miles per hour).

Hurricanes are found principally in the western parts of oceans between lat 10 and 30°. Some can be found off the west coast of Central America, where they are related to Caribbean atmospheric conditions, and several have been reported in the Bay of Bengal, southeast of India. As indicated in Fig. 7.28, they are absent in the South Atlantic, possibly because the equatorial zone of converging trade winds seldom lies south of the equator there. The two areas where hurricanes are most common are the Caribbean Sea and the Philippines-Formosa-South Japan region in the western Pacific. In the latter area they are generally known as *typhoons* (Chinese, *tai-fung* = big wind). Locally in the Philippines they are termed *baguios,* and in northern Australia, *willy-willies.* Although hurricanes may form during most times of the year, a large proportion of them occur during the late summer and fall months. In the Caribbean Sea–North Atlantic region, they generally occur from late August to the middle of October. In the western Pacific, north of the equator, they are somewhat more frequent during other seasons, but the maximum occurrence is in October and November. South of the equator, March to May is generally the hurricane season.

Evidence now suggests that, although hurricanes develop from tropical cyclones, they are basically the result of conditions in the upper troposphere, in the more or less turbulent upper zone of the tropical easterlies. In this zone there are migrating cyclones and anticyclones somewhat similar to those at the earth surface, although less pronounced. If one of the anticyclonic centers in the upper air happens to coincide in position with the summit of one of the tropical cyclones at the surface, especially those associated with easterly waves, conditions are favorable for the lateral removal of air aloft and subsidence in the center of the cyclonic vortex. These upper-air waves apparently also play some role in steering the course of a hurricane once it is developed, for a low-pressure center usually is observed in the upper air well in front of the storm center.

The hurricane is similar to a pump that removes warm, conditionally unstable air from near the ocean surface and forces it to spiral upward, condense, and liberate heat.

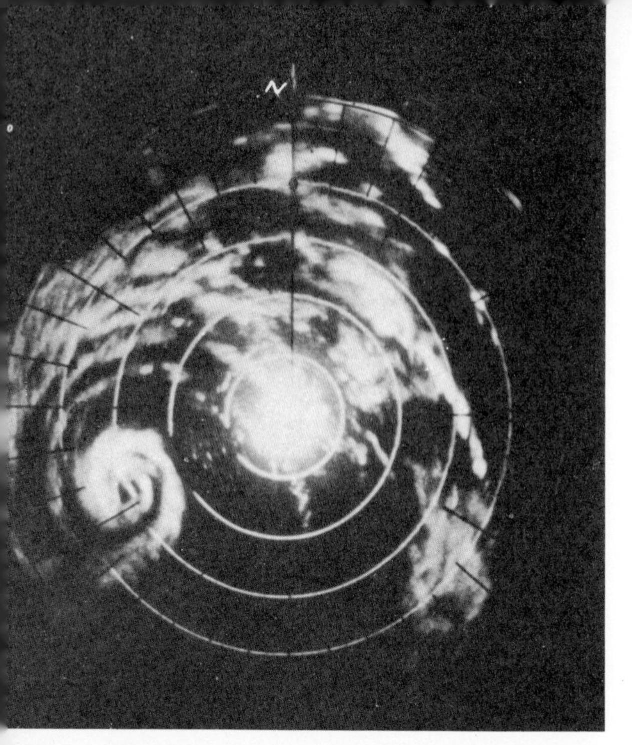

FIG. 7.29 A radarscope photograph of Hurricane "Connie" off Cape Hatteras, N.C., Aug. 12, 1955. Circles are approximately 20 miles apart. Note the spiral arms that extend far out in front of the storm. North is marked by the letter N. The black spot in the center of the hurricane is the "eye" of the storm. The center of the circles represents the location of the observer; thus the hurricane center is about 60 miles to the southwest. [U.S. Weather Bureau]

An extremely warm column of descending air in the center of the hurricane helps to feed warm air into the rising spiral and check the inflow of cold air from the surrounding air that destroys the equilibrium of thunderstorms. Both the strong divergence aloft and the central warm eye appear to be critical in maintaining hurricane equilibrium. The temperature of air in the eye is usually about 15° higher than that of the air outside the rising column and may be as much as 25 to 30° higher. The potential energy of adjacent air masses with such contrasts in temperature is enormous, and this explains why such violent winds can be generated. Little air feeds into the center of a hurricane except at the bottom and the top. The latter generally is at about 40,000 to 50,000 feet above sea level. Hurricanes that move away from the equator and around the flanks of subtropical anticyclones, as many of them do, tend to shrink in size and grow in intensity. This is due to increased deflection owing to the earth's rotation, a smaller vortex, and increased angular momentum. The smaller and more violent the hurricane becomes, the more vulnerable it is to destruction by an interruption in its equilibrium.

The paths of hurricanes, though uncertain, tend to exhibit characteristic patterns—in particular, a curved course poleward and toward the east after leaving an early westward direction. When hurricanes intercept continental coast lines, they soon lose much of their internal generating strength, because of lack of moisture or because of friction with the surface. Since these severe tropical storms are found in the western portions of oceans and tend to curve eastward and poleward, many of them constitute no serious threat to continental coast lines. A depression of lower pressure over the eastern part of the continents between two stationary anticyclones, however, may lead a hurricane in this direction. Such a condition was responsible for the highly destructive hurricanes that passed northward across the eastern United States during the autumn of 1954 and the late summer of 1956. The adjacent anticyclones usually extend to high elevations and thus are able to guide the course of the entire hurricane column.

Hurricanes have been studied perhaps more than any other type of storm, and considerable success has been achieved in following their forward progression by radar plotting and direct observation by planes. Adequate warning, several hours in advance of these storms, has generally been available in the United States. Theoretical projections of

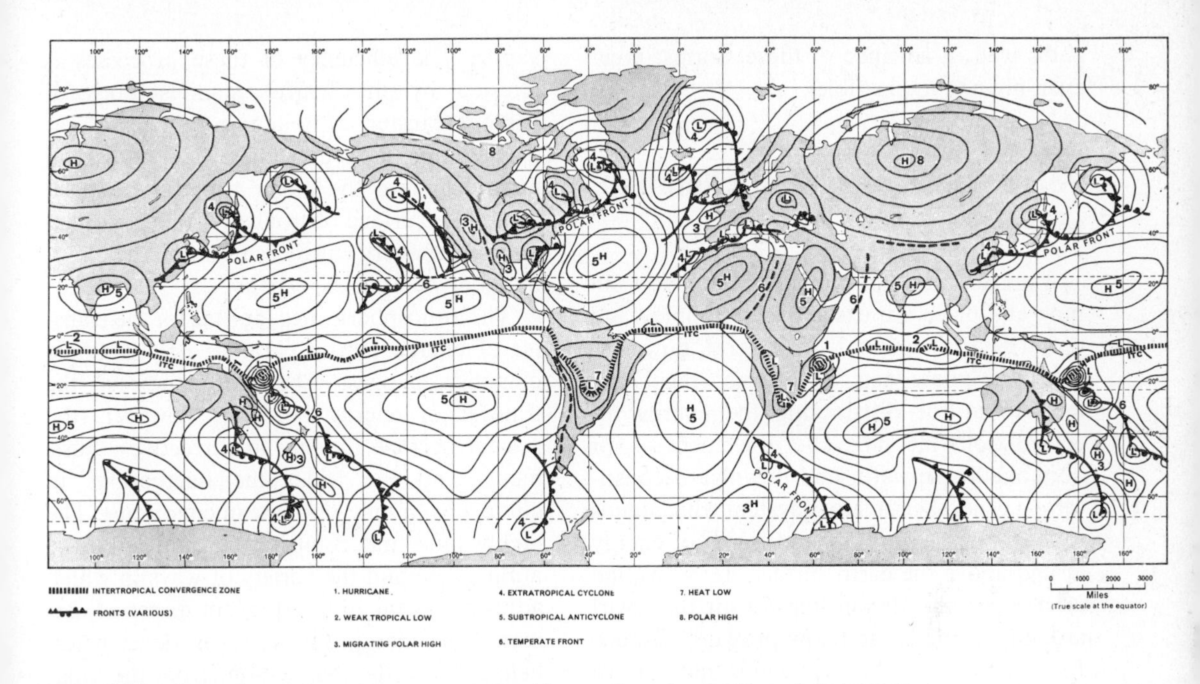

FIG. 7.30 Synoptic weather patterns generalized for northern hemisphere winter season. [After Garbell]

FIG. 7.31 Synoptic weather pattern generalized for northern hemisphere summer season. [After Garbell]

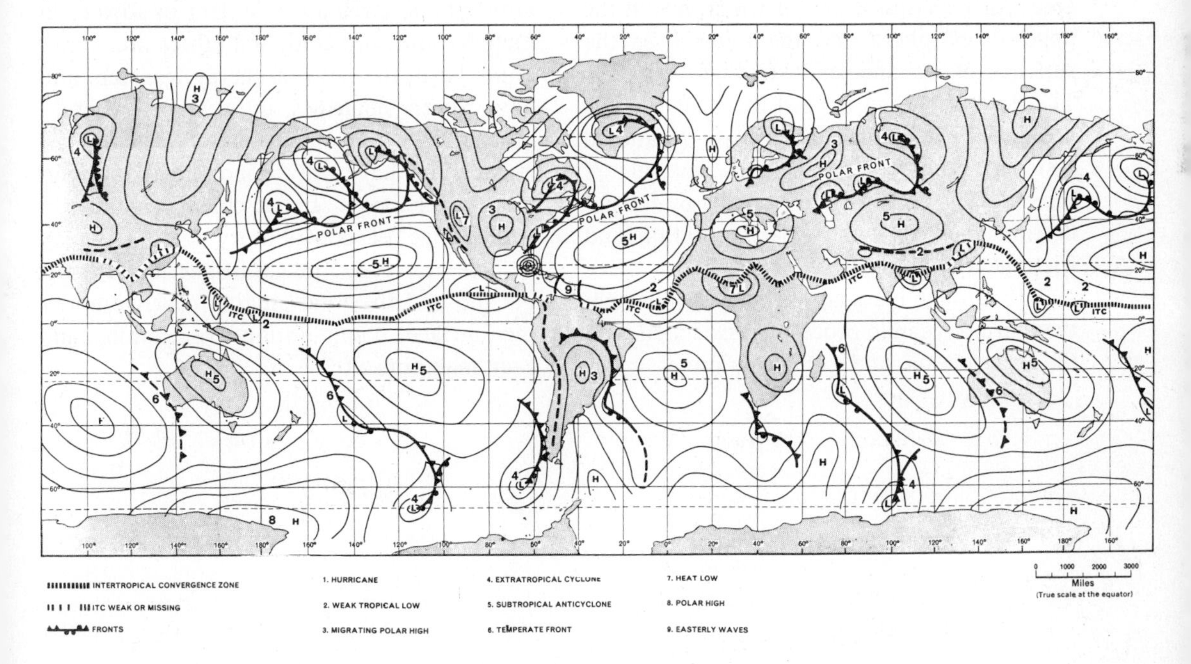

paths well in advance of these storms, however, are not yet possible.

Perspective of global climatic elements

The reasons for climatic differences in time and place are exceedingly complex and not always understood. In general, however, the atmosphere acts as a great regulating mechanism for distributing the energy received from the sun. The movement of air horizontally, upward, and downward constitutes a general circulatory system which tends to level out the receipts and losses of energy at and above the earth surface. Its veins and arteries are the stream lines of air that swirl around the high- and low-pressure centers. Its capillaries are the local winds that remove local energy concentrations.

The general direction of energy flow is away from the low latitudes, where surpluses tend to accumulate, toward the deficiency areas, or heat sinks, one of which lies in the upper troposphere and the other over the surfaces of ice and snow at high latitudes. The flow of energy toward the heat sinks is not direct but involves a series of rotational systems, both horizontal and vertical. A direct flow is prevented principally by the deflection caused by the earth's rotation and friction. The transfer of energy takes place mainly through mass air exchange or through the thermodynamic processes associated with the evaporation and condensation of water vapor. The efficiency of these processes is attested by the fearful manifestations of energy transfer exhibited in hurricanes as they pump immense quantities of warm, humid air into the upper troposphere from above the surface of tropical waters. A small amount of energy also is carried by the circulation of water in the oceans.

The atmospheric mechanisms for the transfer of energy across parallels help regulate climatic changes. The more indirect the transfer of energy becomes, however, the greater become the lags in corrective adjustments and the wider the fluctuations in climate from long-term mean conditions. The highly fluid and compressible nature of the atmosphere and the variety of ways in which adjustments take place prevent direct adjustments of energy surpluses or deficiencies; hence day-to-day fluctuations from the long-run statistical mean are typical.

Some parts of the earth surface are destined to be wet and others dry as the result of their position with respect to the atmospheric circulatory system or to terrain factors. Some are cold, and others are warm. Some lie in the path of energy transfers and have sharp contrasts in weather, whereas others lie within the source areas for air masses and have only minor fluctuations in weather elements. Local climates involve a wide range of contributory factors, which include not only the atmospheric elements but most of the total environment, comprising surface configuration, vegetation, and even man himself.

8

Global climatic patterns

Despite the fluctuations in weather conditions from place to place and from time to time, certain comparable characteristics appear at different scales of observation, enabling climates to be grouped regionally. The climatic classification used in this chapter (see Appendix A for details of simplified system) was developed by W. Koeppen, a German botanist, who recognized that vegetation patterns usually reveal the major gradations of climate. Geiger, a German climatologist, has elaborated the system. The tundra, the tropical rain forest, and the short-grass steppe are obvious reflections of major differences in climate. As a botanist, Koeppen placed the critical climatic boundaries at places where he observed major vegetation changes and defined these areas in terms of mean monthly temperature and precipitation figures. Most of his field work was done in Africa and Europe; therefore the matching of his climatic boundaries and vegetation changes is fairly close in these parts of the world. The two patterns do not agree so closely on the other continents, although there is sufficient correspondence for global presentation. Several slight modifications have been suggested for the Koeppen system. One of these, developed by Glenn T. Trewartha, is reproduced on the rear end-paper of this textbook.

Like any regional classification, the Koeppen-Geiger system is not universally applicable. It utilizes, for example, only the statistics on mean monthly temperatures and precipitation. There is no provision for variations in the strength or constancy of winds, temperature extremes, or the length of the growing season. Data on cloudiness are not considered, and evaporation-temperature ratios are calculated rather crudely. The statistics on which the system is based, furthermore, are not always comparable in terms of the type and position of standardized weather instruments,[1] and the network of reporting stations is not sufficiently close to reveal significant local variations in climatic patterns. Yet, despite these and other inadequacies, the Koeppen-Geiger classification system is easy to use, presents a useful

[1] Weather instruments placed on the roof of a city office building, for example, often will yield considerably different results from those at a municipal airport at the outskirts of the same city. Many weather bureaus have moved from downtown sites to airports, and weather statistics for many American cities indicate this shift in position.

global view, and utilizes climatic data that are easily obtained. It presents a coherent picture and, for our purposes, an adequate one.

The Koeppen-Geiger system utilizes an alphabetical code for generalizing climatic data, using both capital and lower-case letters. Some of the smaller subdivisions are omitted here, but the details of the code are presented in Appendix A. The student should become acquainted with it before proceeding with the present chapter. The principal divisions of this chapter deal with Koeppen's five major world climates, which proceed in sequence from the equator to the poles (at least in the European-African area) and which are designated, respectively, by the first five capital letters in the alphabet. The letter *A* refers to the humid climates that have no winter; the *B* climates are dry; *C* signifies the presence of a mild winter; the *D* climates have a severe winter; and, finally, the *E*, or polar, climates have no true summer.

The *A* climates (humid tropical)

8.1 DISTRIBUTION AND CHARACTERISTICS. The humid tropics include the area straddling the equator that has average monthly temperatures above 64.4°F (18°C) and sufficient rainfall for at least some types of tree growth. Major subtypes are distinguished by differences in the amount and distribution of rainfall, ranging from continuously moist (*Af*), through a short compensated [2] dry season (*Am*), to a pronounced uncompensated dry period (*Aw*). Because of their position in the low latitudes, the *A* climates have no real winter season as far as temperatures are concerned. Daily variations in temperature regularly exceed seasonal changes. The climatic statistics presented in Table 8.1 are based on data from representative weather stations and illustrate each of the three major types of *A* climate.

The *A* climates in general extend from about lat 10° S to lat 15° N on the west side of continents and to about the Tropics of Cancer and Capricorn (lat 23½°) on the eastern sides. The moist *Af* and *Am* subtypes are located mainly within an inner (nearer the equator) zone, with the *Aw* climates

[2] A compensated dry period implies that sufficient rain falls during the wet season to provide moisture for normal tree growth during the dry period. Most trees in the *Am* climates thus do not have to shed their leaves or develop other types of special mechanisms for resisting drought, although some of them may do so. An uncompensated dry season requires such adaptive mechanisms.

TABLE 8.1 Representative climatic statistics for the A climates

	JAN.	FEB.	MAR.	APR.	MAY	JUNE	JULY	AUG.	SEPT.	OCT.	NOV.	DEC.	YEAR
						Penang, Malaya (Af)							
Temp., °F	79.7	80.1	81.3	81.7	81.5	80.6	80.2	79.9	79.5	79.7	79.2	78.8	80.2
Rainfall, in.	3.7	3.1	4.6	7.0	10.6	7.8	8.2	12.6	16.4	16.3	12.0	4.9	107.2
						Manaos, Brazil (Am)							
Temp., °F	80.6	80.4	80.4	80.4	80.4	80.8	81.1	82.0	82.4	82.9	82.6	81.0	81.3
Rainfall, in.	9.2	9.0	9.6	8.5	7.0	3.6	2.2	1.4	2.0	4.1	5.5	7.7	69.7
						Bombay, India (Aw)							
Temp., °F	74.5	74.8	78.0	82.1	84.6	82.4	79.5	78.4	79.4	80.7	79.3	76.4	79.3
Rainfall, in.	0.1	0.0	0.1	0.0	0.7	20.6	27.3	16.0	11.8	2.4	0.4	0.0	79.4

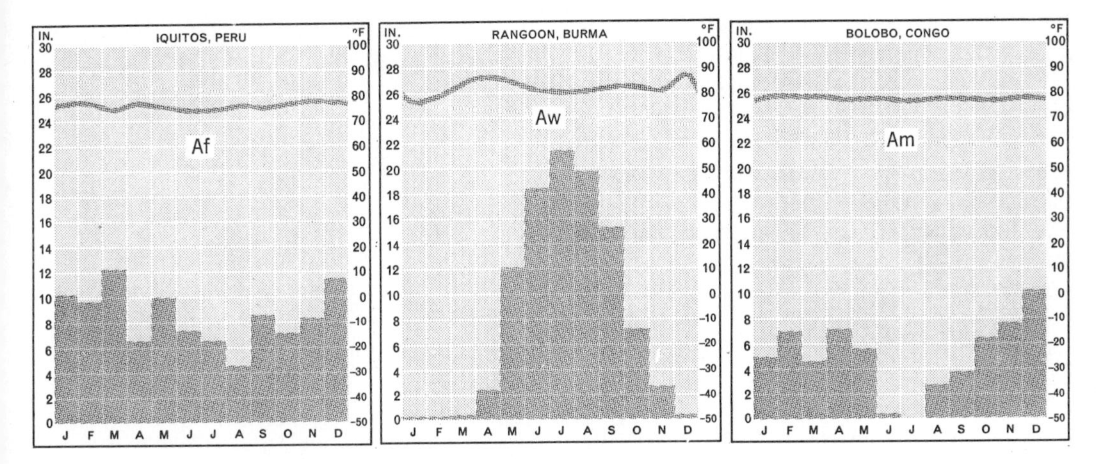

FIG. 8.1 Typical climatic graphs of the A climates. The annual course of average monthly temperatures is shown as the dark upper line. Precipitation is shown by means of the bar graph. [Geographical Review]

occupying an outer or poleward zone, although along the eastern parts of continents the *Af-Am* types may extend to the margins of the *C* climates without the *Aw* transition. This poleward extension along continental east coasts is illustrated by the *A* climates of eastern Brazil, Puerto Rico, eastern Madagascar, and Hainan Island, off the coast of southern China.

THE RAINY TROPICS (AF-AM). The *Af-Am* types have been included together on the world climatic map (see end paper). One of the reasons for this is the widespread intermingling of these two humid climates within the same general area. Slight differences in exposure to winds can suffice to send the minimum mean monthly rainfall amounts either below or above 2.4 inches, the critical boundary between these two types. Most tropical areas experience a short dry season; hence the *Am* type exceeds the *Af* type in total area. The continuously wet (*Af*) climate is more frequently found on low, flat plains near the equator and, throughout the tropics, on mountain slopes that face steady trade winds all through the year. There are widespread variations in the rainfall pattern of these two types. There may be single or double high- and low-rainfall periods, and the driest or rainiest times of year may occur in any month. As a general rule, rainfall tends to "follow the sun"; that is, the highest rainfall period tends to occur in the months when the sun stands highest in the heavens. There are many exceptions to this, however. The rough relationship between sun elevation and rainfall maxima results more from the seasonal passage of the intertropical convergence of the trades (ITC) than from increased solar heating. Indicative of this is the tendency for maximum-rainfall periods to be accompanied by a slight drop in temperature, owing to increased cloudiness. See, for example, the climatic data for Yaoundé, French Equatorial Africa (Table 8.3, p. 251).

Although it should be recognized that weather variations do occur, a typical day in the rainy tropics would have something like the following sequence:

> The early morning hours, shortly before dawn, are the most pleasant. Temperatures generally are in the 70s. Mists hang over the

forest, and the lower temperatures result in relative humidity readings that are near 100 per cent. The sun rises in a cloudless sky, and the mists soon disappear. The first clouds appear about 10 o'clock—small fluffy masses that gradually grow into typical cumulus forms as the day continues. Temperatures climb slowly and reach a maximum, generally in the high 80s, shortly after noon. The first showers are welcome, because of the oppressive heat. They bring only short-lived relief, however, because the sun soon breaks from behind the clouds and the steaming heat returns. Unless there is a distinct breeze, more frequent in coastal areas, perspiration clings to the body and soaks the clothing. Showers increase in frequency in late afternoon, and an occasional severe one is accompanied by thunder and lightning. The most oppressive time of day is in late evening, after sunset, when the humidity begins to rise. Showers tend to become less frequent as night falls, but distant lightning frequently flickers across the sky well into the night.

TROPICAL CLIMATE WITH PRONOUNCED DRY SEASON (AW). The *Aw* climates exhibit strong seasonal contrasts in precipitation, but with only slight temperature variations. The dry season usually occurs in the low-sun period. Rare indeed are the tropical climates that exhibit a pronounced dry period during the summer (*As*) or high-sun season. In the high-sun season, the *Aw* climates have rain mainly in the form of scattered convectional showers, but with occasional periods of stormy weather, usually at the beginning and the end of the rainy season. Temperatures seldom rise above the high 80s during this season, but the humidity is high, usually near saturation during the night and early morning hours. Temperatures are generally higher during the dry season, but they become oppressive only near the end of this period. This is a gaunt, barren time of year, when streams and water holes become dry, the scrawny trees shed their leaves, the dominant grasses wither, becoming brown and brittle and crackling underfoot, and an acrid smoke haze hides distant landscapes. The principal air mass is *mTw* (typical stable, trade-wind air), with pronounced subsidence and a temperature inversion aloft. Africa has large areas of *Aw* climates, which extend to the east coast and straddle the equator in the east-central part of the continent. Unusually wide latitudinal swings in the intertropical convergence zone, together with the high, steep edges of the continent, help to restrict the area of *Af-Am* climates in Africa and to increase the amount of *Aw*.

WEATHER AND AIR MASSES. The weather of the humid tropics appears monotonous to people from mid-latitudes, because of the absence of pronounced temperature fluctuations. Occasionally a polar air mass finds its way into northern Indochina, into the northern Caribbean Sea, or, via the Chaco, into the southern part of the Amazon Basin, but these are exceptional and produce considerable disorder in the daily life of the tropics. There is weather in the tropics, however—plenty of it—although it is measured largely in terms of variations in precipitation, cloudiness, humidity, and wind direction and velocity. Weather variability in the tropics is produced primarily by the interaction of three main air masses: (1) trade-wind air from the subtropical anticyclones, usually designated as *mTw;* (2) air from continental anticyclonic sources, or *cT* air; and (3) neutral trade-wind air (*mT*), or air that is far from its anticyclonic source and that has been modified appreciably in depth by the addition of water vapor and by an increased height or disappearance of an upper-air inversion. This third air mass is developed typically within the *doldrums* and in areas where the trades of one hemisphere have crossed the equator and have penetrated far into the opposite hemisphere in the western parts of oceans or in the low interior plains of continents.

Typical stable trade-wind air supplies the more pleasant weather conditions in the tropics. Temperatures are not oppressive, especially in coastal areas; a breeze is almost always present, and daytime relative humidity is only moderately high. Perhaps the most distinctive feature of trade-wind weather is the cloud pattern, which begins to develop in midmorning. By afternoon the sky appears almost covered with white, fluffy, cumulus clouds with dark bases. The upper-air subsidence which frequently occurs above the trade-wind air is marked by the level at which the higher cumulus cloud tops appear to flatten out and spread laterally. There is a surprising amount of sunlight, indicating that the amount of cloud cover is more apparent than real.

The *cT* air predominates in the *Aw* climates during the dry season. Having recently subsided from upper levels, it is warm and dry. This is desert air, and when the land surface heats under the bright sun, the boundary between the shallow, convectional updrafts and the subsident air aloft may be marked by dust and mirage lines above the land surfaces.

The neutral *mT* air is deep, warm, and moist. Since it is usually conditionally unstable,[3] all that is necessary to induce rain is to raise surface air to the level of condensation, which often is found within 2,000 or 3,000 feet of the surface. The convectional updrafts above a clearing, a plowed field, a cluster of buildings, or some other unequal heating surface may suffice to produce local convectional showers. Because convectional rain occurs most frequently when upward drafts are strongest and when there is the greatest contrast in temperature between the surface and the upper air (steepest lapse rate), such showers are most frequent over land in the late afternoon and evening. Over oceans, however, the convectional showers are more frequent at night (see Sec. 6.22). Exceptionally heavy rainfall occurs where *mT* air is forced to rise over mountains and also where it is involved in cyclonic or occasional frontal disturbances. Such orographically induced heavy rainfall in the tropics is illustrated by the mean precipitation data for Debundja (see Table 8.2), which is located at the foot of Cameroon Mountain, a 13,000-foot volcanic peak that is at the eastern end of the Gulf of Guinea in Africa.

[3] Although conditionally unstable, this air mass is not designated by a *k* in its code classification, since it is not being warmed from below. Its neutral status indicates that its air temperature is approximately the same as the surface over which it is passing. A later refinement in the Bergeron classification uses the additional letters *s* and *u* to indicate, respectively, stability and instability aloft —an important distinction in the susceptibility of an air mass to precipitation.

VARIATIONS IN THE INTERTROPICAL CONVERGENCE ZONE. Additional material on variations in the behavior of the intertropical convergence zone (ITC) is given here, to supplement the discussion in Sec. 7.14, because these variations are extremely important in explaining the seasonal pattern of precipitation from place to place in the tropics. The ITC, which represents the convergence between the trades, may produce heavy convergent lifting along a strip from 1 to 50 miles wide and over 2,000 miles long. Large cyclonic eddies passing along this zone, however, may spread precipitation over a belt 500 to 600 miles wide. In some parts of the world the ITC is more strongly developed and may remain stationary for long periods during a particular season. Its location is influenced largely by the location and strength of the subtropical anticyclones and by the location of the heat lows that tend to develop over the interior of conti-

TABLE 8.2 Rainfall, in inches, for Debundja, Nigeria

JAN.	FEB.	MAR.	APR.	MAY	JUNE	JULY	AUG.	SEPT.	OCT.	NOV.	DEC.	YEAR
8.0	10.9	17.1	17.3	24.8	59.7	64.4	57.7	65.2	45.2	26.6	15.1	412.2

nents. Figure 8.2 shows the shifts in the location of the ITC between January and July. Note that the greatest latitudinal shift occurs over continental areas and in the western parts of oceans. Nearness to the subtropical anticyclones in the eastern parts of oceans south of the equator prevents the ITC from passing south of the equator in this area. Heat lows determine the location of the ITC in the subtropical continental areas. When the convergence is far from the coast and involves fairly dry trade-wind air, it may produce little rain. An ITC usually is found in the Sahara during July, but little precipitation results. In contrast to this, the ITC that is found south of the Amazon Basin during January brings copious rains to the Chaco area. Convergence aids in precipitation only if the air is conditionally unstable.

When the ITC is farthest poleward, usually just after the solstice, the conflicting air masses are likely to present the greatest contrasts in temperature and humidity. Unusually strong and violent thunderstorm activity is present along the ITC at this season, provided that conditionally unstable air is involved. Cyclones are less likely to develop into tropical hurricanes at this time. Near the autumn equinoxes, however, when the ITC lies nearer the equator, the zone is likely to be broader and less violent; cyclonic vortexes are larger, more frequent, and more likely to develop into hurricanes. The rainfall pattern usually is broader and more continuous. Thus the ITC, along with its accompanying cyclonic disturbances, produces definite interruptions in the weather pattern of the tropics as it swings back and forth, bending and straightening and shifting at variable rates of speed. Intense *line squalls,*[4] periods of overcast skies and steady drizzles, and scattered convectional thunderstorms are all associated

[4] A *line squall* is a sudden violent windstorm of short duration associated with a sudden shift in wind direction along the leading edge of a severe thunderstorm.

FIG. 8.2 Seasonal migration of the Intertropical Convergence Zone (ITC). Note that it shifts much farther seasonally over the continents than over the oceans. [After Garbell]

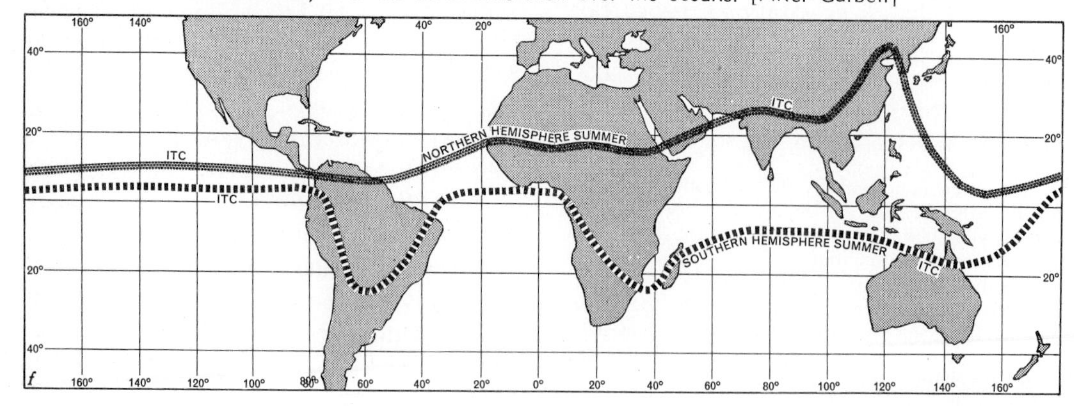

with frontal disturbances. Once the ITC has passed by, normally at the beginning and the end of the rainy season, weather conditions become more regular.

The passage of the ITC is clearly shown by the rainfall regimes of four weather stations in Africa (see Table 8.3). Their locations proceed in order from near the equator southward into the southern hemisphere. Near the equator (Yaoundé) (see Fig. 8.3), there is a double season of rainfall maxima closely following the period of highest sun. Moving southward, the rainfall maxima shift closer to the summer (December-January) solstice, finally becoming a single maximum as the climates shift from *Af-Am* to *Aw*. This shift is not always symmetrical or correlated perfectly with latitude, because of the irregularities, or waves, in the ITC and also because of differences in local exposures to moisture-bearing winds.

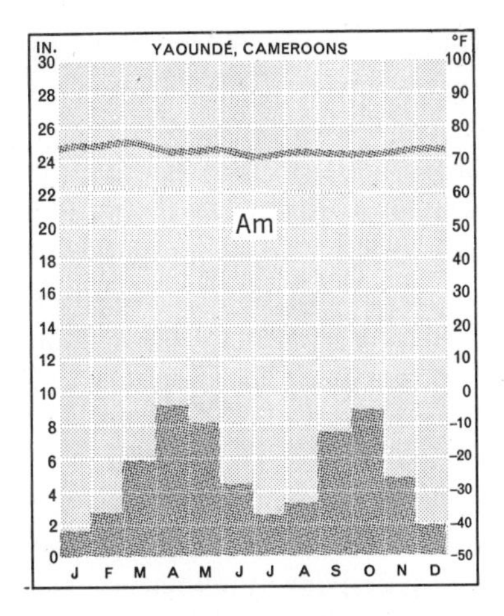

FIG. 8.3 Climatic graph of a weather station near the equator, showing a double maximum of rainfall resulting from the double passage of the ITC near the equinoxes. It should be admitted, however, that such ideal types are not common. [Geographical Review]

8.2 EXCEPTIONS TO THE CLIMATIC GENERALIZATIONS IN LOW LATITUDES.

As might be expected, climatic patterns show noteworthy exceptions to generalizations based on theory. The following are major exceptions to the generalized pattern:

THE NORTH COAST OF VENEZUELA. Although the north coast of Venezuela is well within the latitudinal range of the humid tropics, much of it is desert country. Prevailing winds here are from the east, parallel to the coast, or at a slight angle to it, and the fingerlike extensions of the Andes Mountains produce orographic rainfall, leaving the intervening lowlands dry, as in the vicinity of Lake Maracaibo. The lee, or southwestern, sides of high islands in the Caribbean are dry also. The ITC rarely appears in this area at any season.

TABLE 8.3 Rainfall, in inches, for representative African stations

JAN.	FEB.	MAR.	APR.	MAY	JUNE	JULY	AUG.	SEPT.	OCT.	NOV.	DEC.	YEAR
Yaoundé, French Equatorial Africa (lat 4° N)												
1.6	2.7	5.9	9.1	8.1	4.5	2.6	3.3	7.6	8.9	5.9	2.0	62.2
Luluaberg, Republic of the Congo (lat 6° S)												
7.2	5.4	7.9	6.1	8.1	0.2	0.1	2.5	6.5	6.6	9.1	6.6	60.8
Mozambique, Mozambique (lat 15° S)												
7.9	8.7	7.4	4.4	2.3	1.0	0.5	1.3	0.5	0.1	0.3	4.9	39.3
Bulawayo, Southern Rhodesia (lat 20° S)												
5.9	4.0	3.1	0.7	0.3	0.0	0.0	0.0	0.1	0.9	3.3	5.2	23.6

EASTERN AFRICA. Eastern Africa exhibits several climatic features that differ from what might be expected for its latitude (see Fig. 8.4). North of the equator, for example, the east coast is semiarid instead of humid. The reason for this is that the monsoon winds of the Indian Ocean parallel this coast during both monsoon seasons; hence no importation of moist air is possible. The uplands of Kenya and Tanganyika intercept more rain than the dry Somalia coast, but not enough to make them continuously humid. Their elevation results in temperatures just under the minimum required for *A* climates; thus they are *Cw* climates, without the seasonal temperature contrasts usually found within the *C* group. Such highland *C* climates are also found along the eastern, higher portions of the Brazilian uplands and in smaller mountainous areas throughout the tropics. Nairobi, whose climatic statistics are given in Table 8.4, is illustrative.

MOUNTAINOUS ISLANDS. High, rugged islands in the humid tropics generally produce climatic abnormalities, because of a wide variety of exposures to prevailing winds and because of a drop in temperature with altitude. The high islands of the West Indies and of Indonesia exhibit especially sharp contrasts in seasonal rainfall regimes. Figure 8.5 illustrates some of these contrasts.

SOUTHWEST-FACING COASTS IN SOUTHERN ASIA. Although the southwest-facing coasts of southern Asia have the characteristic wet and dry seasons of monsoon areas, they are exceptionally wet during the summer monsoon season and thus are characterized by *Am* climates instead of the *Aw* that might be expected in their latitude. The exceptional wetness of the summer season is aided by the convergence of moisture-bearing winds—the convergence resulting from mountains lying immediately behind these coasts. Although orographic lifting is confined mainly to the mountain slopes, the convergent effect increases both the thickness of the onshore trade winds and their tendency to produce convectional rain, by raising the level of the trade-wind temperature inversion aloft. Some of the areas on the lee side of these mountains, such as in parts of south-central India, experience unusually dry conditions.

THE NORTHEASTERN PORTION OF BRAZIL. Northeastern Brazil is located along the eastern side of the continent and within 10° of the equator; yet it has an *Aw* climate, with small areas of *BS* (semiarid), instead of the *Af* or *Am* that might be expected. This condition is largely due to the dominance of trade-wind air that is exceptionally stable, owing to subsidence aloft (the South Atlantic subtropical anticyclone is nearby), and also to the fact that the ITC seldom enters this area. It usually leaves the east coast between the mouth of the Amazon and Fortaleza during the southern hemisphere summer season. Fluctuations in this convergence zone, with its attendant cyclonic disturbances, produce highly irregular rainfall conditions in northeastern Brazil from year to year. Farther south, the highlands back of the coast result in higher rainfall for the coastal zone.

TABLE 8.4 Climatic statistics for Nairobi, Kenya (elevation 5,450 feet)

	JAN.	FEB.	MAR.	APR.	MAY	JUNE	JULY	AUG.	SEPT.	OCT.	NOV.	DEC.	YEAR
Temp., °F	63.8	64.7	65.2	63.9	63.4	61.6	58.5	59.3	61.6	64.8	64.0	62.3	63.2
Rainfall, in.	1.9	3.6	4.2	8.9	5.6	2.2	0.9	1.1	1.2	2.3	5.3	2.8	39.9

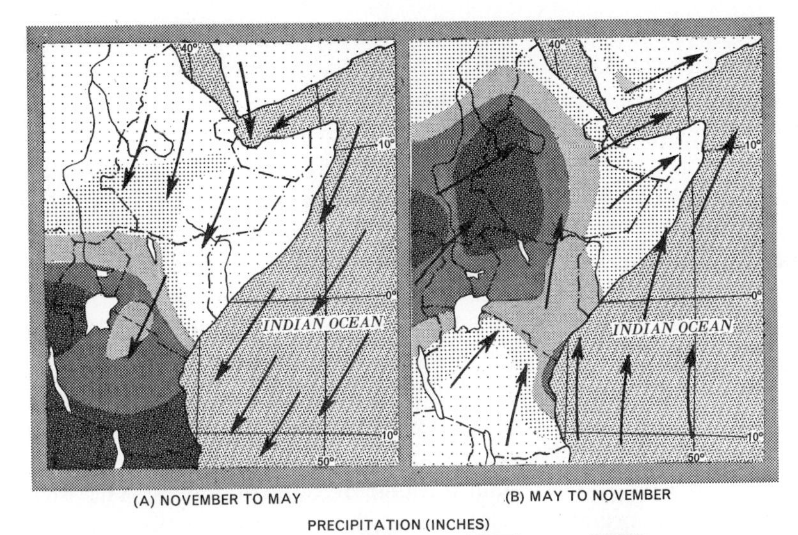

FIG. 8.4 Wind and rainfall patterns in eastern Africa. Note the influence of the Indian Ocean monsoon on wind direction and rainfall along the Somalia coast. Because the winds parallel this coast at both seasons, there is little orographic influence and little convergence.

8.3 PROBLEMS OF HUMAN ADAPTABILITY IN THE HUMID TROPICS. Although much more is known now than before regarding the physiologic adaptability of man in the humid tropics, many of the long-range climatic effects are still inadequately understood. Unfortunately, it has not been easy to eliminate psychologi-

FIG. 8.5 Rainfall patterns on mountainous tropical islands. The seasonal precipitation maps of Java indicate the typically complex rainfall patterns on such islands. The Oahu map shows that mountains in a trade-wind zone may produce extreme contrasts in rainfall within a short distance.

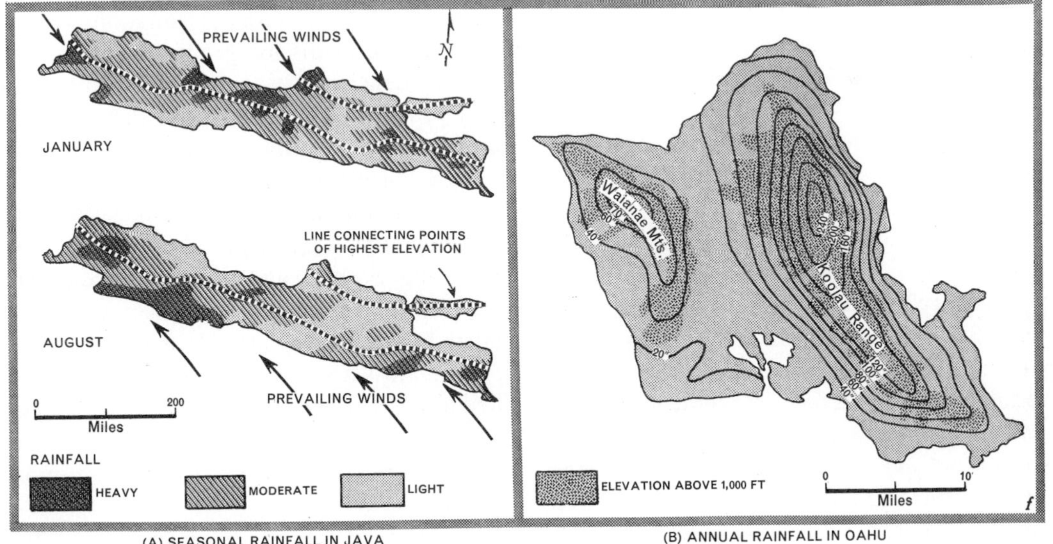

cal and social factors in studies of physiological reactions. Experiments in acclimatization during and following World War II, however, have led to a number of reliable conclusions:

1. Combinations of high heat and humidity can produce actual cell deterioration in the human body, but such combinations are exceedingly rare on earth.

2. Given a reasonable adjustment period, the human body is remarkably capable of adapting itself to increases in skin temperature—through changes in metabolic rate (utilization of oxygen), cooling mechanisms, and various other systemic adjustments.

3. Clothing and diet are highly important in maintaining body comfort in high heat and humidity. Clothing should be loose, absorbent, and kept to a minimum. Constrictive articles of clothing, such as belts, neckties, and garters, should not be worn. They not only restrict capillary blood circulation but check air circulation and provide sites for fungus infections. Alcohol and foods high in fats and sugars should be avoided as much as possible. The more slowly but easily digested starchy foods, fruits, reasonable quantities of proteins, and the various protective foods, such as vitamins, are advised.

4. Regular physical exercise appears to be an important requirement in maintaining body "tone" under conditions of high heat and humidity.

5. Racial differences apparently are of little significance in *physical* adaptability to climate.

The psychological effects of high heat and humidity are significant throughout the tropics. The most important effect is the reduction of the desire for physical activity, and this general physical inertia also affects mental activity. Recognition of the influence of high heat and humidity on the mental and physical comfort of students and faculty was a major factor in moving the campus of the University of Ceylon from Colombo on the coast to Paradeniya in the interior, over 1,000 feet higher in elevation.

Climate has often been blamed for the high incidence of diseases in the tropics. It is somewhat questionable that disease organisms are any more abundant in these areas than in the mid-latitudes, and even if they do happen to be so locally, it is doubtful that this is the result solely of climate. Unquestionably there are types of disease-producing organisms that are found only in the tropics; likewise, there are some that are mainly found in cooler climates. The high incidence of many diseases in the tropics is more the result of low standards of living than of factors of climate. Malaria, for example, is a major debilitating disease in the humid tropics today, but the geographical range of the mosquitoes that act as its intermediate hosts extends far beyond the tropics. It once was a common disease throughout the Mississippi Valley, and sporadic cases of it still appear occasionally.

Poverty is the rule throughout much of the humid tropics, and with it appear inadequate diets, improper sanitation, and a general lack of disease-preventive measures. Dietary deficiencies, particularly of proteins, may produce serious body disorders that are blamed on unknown "tropical viruses." Fungus disorders of the skin are frequently encountered in the tropics, but they often can be avoided by wearing properly aerated footwear and clothing and by taking reasonable preventive measures. Dysenteries, which are taken for granted by many tropical residents, particularly affect newcomers. Such intestinal irritations can be caused by many things besides specific endemic organisms, and sudden dietary changes are among the most common causes.

A final consideration in explaining the

high incidence of disease in the humid tropics is the fact that far less medical attention has been paid to tropical diseases than to those of the mid-latitudes. Tropical medicine is a relatively new field, but it is already yielding fruitful results. It seems feasible to hope that many tropical diseases will be controlled in the future in much the same way as such killers as diphtheria, tuberculosis, polio, pneumonia, and smallpox have been in the wealthier parts of the mid-latitudes.

The variability in the length of the wet season near the outer margins of the rainy tropics is perhaps more significant in human activities than either the direct impact of climate on body functioning or its indirect effects in fostering certain diseases. The *Aw* climates, or those with a pronounced dry season, are notorious as disaster areas. Three such areas stand out in the world: (1) part of the Sudan region of Africa, south of the Sahara, especially northern Nigeria; (2) central and eastern India; and (3) northeastern Brazil. In each of these areas, populations are moderate to dense, standards of living are low, self-sufficient economies predominate, and famines occur periodically. The people of these regions subsist largely by means of agriculture, and crop planting and growth depend on the arrival of the wet season within fairly narrow time limits. The change from the hot, dry period to the wet season in most *Aw* climates comes suddenly with the passage of the ITC. The movement of this zone, then, is extremely critical. It shifts roughly with the more direct rays of the sun, but with by no means the same regularity, since its more immediate regulators are the changes in the position and intensity of the subtropical anticyclones on both sides of the equator. Meteorologists are only beginning to perceive the three-dimensional operations of these great anticyclonic cells, and perhaps when more knowledge is obtained regarding the upper air, they may be able to say something like this to a Hyderabad peasant:

> This season will be a propitious one; the rains will arrive within a day or two of their customary time in June. Plan, however, to preserve somewhat more water in your reservoirs for use during September and October, because rain in that season will be slightly below normal.

Until such long-range forecasting is possible in the tropics or until the respective countries can absorb the economic and social consequences of variations in the movements of the intertropical convergence, dense populations in *Aw* climates will continue to experience difficulties in planning their agricultural activities, and where living standards are depressed, large losses of life due to droughts will continue to occur.

Floods may also cause much damage within these marginal tropical climates. Near the dry margins, stream courses may not be able to hold the abnormally high rainfalls that accompany occasional tropical cyclones or stagnated fronts. Hurricanes are a seasonal hazard in the east-coast areas between lat 10 and 30° (see Sec. 7.33). Throughout the humid tropics, much heavier downpours of rain occur than are usually experienced in mid-latitudes. The copious quantities of water absorbed by hillside soils during typical thunderstorms lead to landslides and mass slumping, especially where the forest vegetation has been destroyed.

The greater number and activity of decay-producing bacteria in the tropics as compared with the higher latitudes result in an additional problem, namely, that of preserving dead organic materials, particularly food, wood, paper, and leather. Food preserving must be done immediately. Wooden structures, such as frame houses, fence posts, and railroad ties, last for much shorter periods than they do in drier or cooler climates. Certain types of wood are much more resistant to decay than others, and impregnation with decay-inhibiting chemicals such as creosote is frequently an effective preventive measure. Galvanized-iron or sheet-aluminum materials often are used for the outer surfaces of more durable buildings. A major benefit received from air conditioning is the preservation of materials within building interiors.

The *B* climates (arid and semiarid)

8.4 DISTRIBUTION AND CHARACTERISTICS OF THE DRY CLIMATES. The dry climates in the world are found characteristically over the eastern parts of oceans, roughly between lat 15 to 30° N and S, extending onto the continents and thence inland and poleward to approximately lat 45 to 50°. They are relatively rare along the eastern margins of continents, although South America (Patagonia) and Africa (Somalia) both have dry east-coast regions. For the most part, deserts are areas where a subsidence of air associated with subtropical anticyclones prevails over an ascendance, where lapse rates and moisture contents are low, and where there is relatively little interaction between contrasting air masses. In some cases (as in Patagonia), the predominant cause for dryness is a position on the lee side of a high mountain range, where there is little opportunity for the importation of moist air. In others, as in the Gobi Desert of Mongolia, the major factor is a low water-vapor content in the air owing to great distance from moisture sources.

Dryness is a relative term, and definitions of what constitute arid, semiarid, and subhumid conditions are subject to various interpretations. The Koeppen classification is based largely on vegetative reactions to dryness. The *B* climates do not permit normal tree growth, and the natural vegetation that is present exhibits specialized characteristics that enable it to resist drought. Dryness is related not only to the amount of precipitation but also to the rate of evaporation, which, in turn, increases with temperature. For this reason, the *B* climates are defined in terms of both precipitation and temperature. Thin or excessively permeable soils may produce local vegetative reactions which are similar to those produced by climatic factors but which are insignificant at global scales of generalization. The term *rainfall effectiveness* is sometimes used to designate the degree to which precipitation is made available for plant growth. Among the variables involved in it, other than the amount and distribution of precipitation and temperature, are the intensity of precipitation, wind velocity, relative humidity, permeability of soils, rate of runoff of surface water, slope, and the type of vegetation cover. It should be noted that these factors are largely local in their influences and therefore are not used in the global Koeppen climatic classification system.

The dry-humid boundary, according to the Koeppen-Geiger classification, is established according to empirical mathematical formulas, which vary according to the seasonal distribution of precipitation. These are shown in Table 8.5.[5] The precipitation of the arid-semiarid (*BW-BS*) boundary is always exactly half the average annual amount at the humid-dry (*A-, C-, D-BS*) boundary. The necessity for separate empirical formulas that

[5] In the Koeppen formulas, *R* equals the total amount of mean annual precipitation at the critical boundary, expressed in either millimeters or inches, depending on whether or not the metric system is used. *T* refers to the average annual temperature, in degree centigrade or Fahrenheit, depending on which formula is used. See Appendix A for illustrations of the use of these formulas.

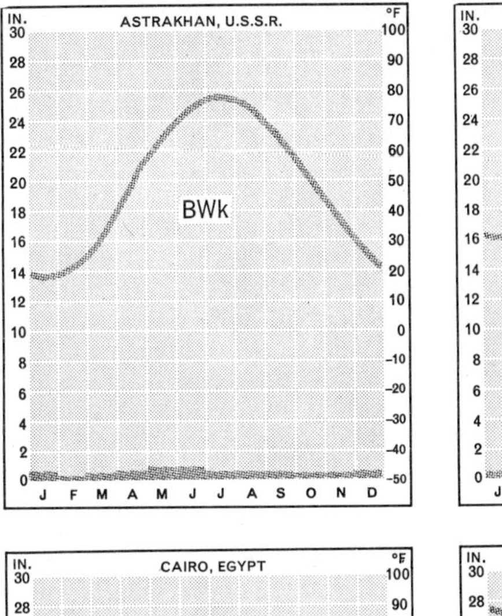

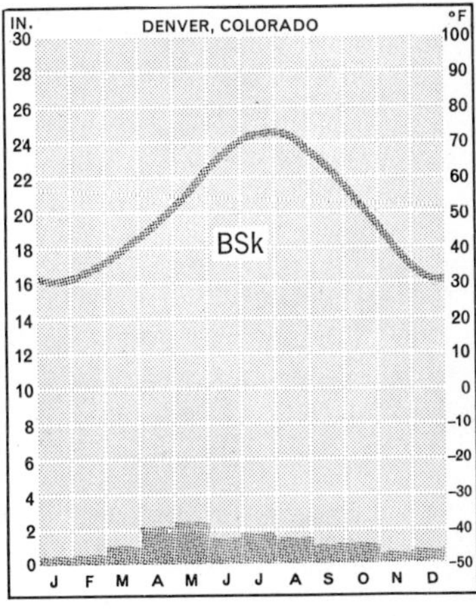

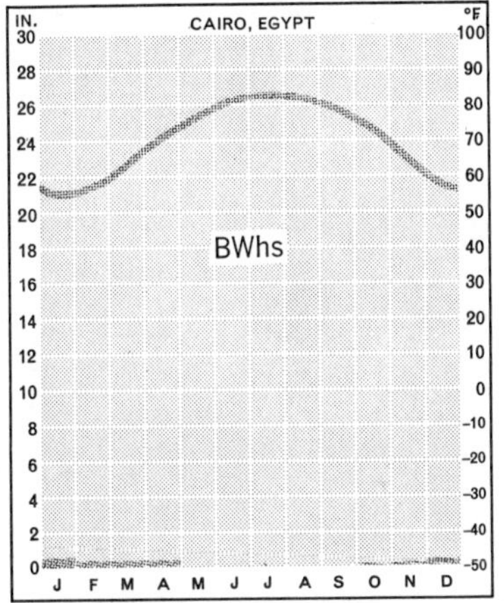

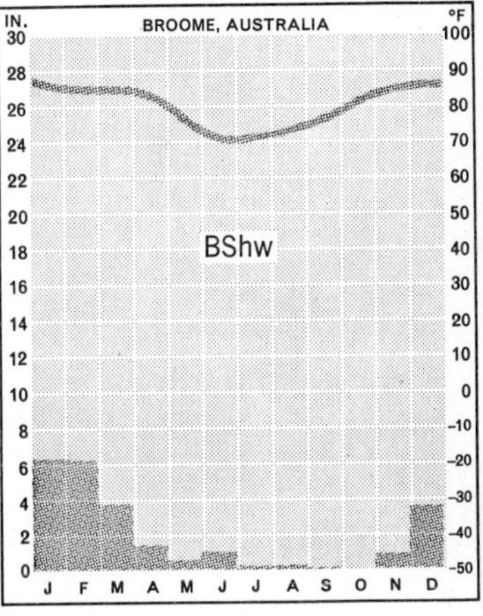

FIG. 8.6 Typical climatic graphs of the B climates. [Geographical Review]

vary according to the distribution of precipitation during the year is mainly due to the evaporation factor. If most of the precipitation occurs during the winter, more of it eventually finds its way into the soil for plant use than if it fell mostly during the warmest time of the year.

Besides the division of dry climates into arid (*BW*) and semiarid (*BS*) types, the Koeppen-Geiger system further distinguishes the hot, dry climates (*h*=*heiss*=*hot*) and the cool, or mid-latitude, types (*k*=*kalt*=*cold*), the temperature boundary corresponding to the 64.4° isotherm for the average annual temperature. Dry climates that have a distinct seasonal variation in precipitation are

TABLE 8.5 Koeppen definition of the B boundary

	CENTIGRADE	FAHRENHEIT
Precipitation evenly distributed	$R(\text{mm.}) = 2(T + 7)$	$R(\text{in.}) = 0.44(T - 19.5)$
70% of precipitation in summer 6 months	$R(\text{mm.}) = 2(T + 14)$	$R(\text{in.}) = 0.44(T - 7)$
70% of precipitation in winter 6 months	$R(\text{mm.}) = 2T$	$R(\text{in.}) = 0.44(T - 32)$

also distinguished (s=summer drought, or w=winter drought). A *BSks* climate, for example, is a semiarid variety with cold winters and a predominance of rain during the winter half of the year. It is, therefore, a midlatitude type. Several varieties of *B* climates are shown in Table 8.6.

Several weather conditions other than dryness are also characteristic of the *B* climates. The small amount of moisture and clouds in the air does little to check both incoming and outgoing radiation; thus there usually are strong contrasts in surface temperatures between day and night. The rapid daytime heating of desert surfaces, which lack the insulating and reflecting capacities of forest vegetation, results in strong convection and turbulence. Even though these updrafts may reach several thousand feet in low-latitude deserts, little rain occurs. A heat haze, dancing and shimmering under the effect of the convection, is a frequent phenomenon near the horizon in level areas. With exceptionally hot desert surfaces, there is an appreciable difference in density of air near the ground and that above 5 to 6 feet. As a result, light rays are bent when passing between the two layers, producing a mirage, an illusion in which distant objects appear to be much closer and the sky seems to be bent below the normal position of the horizon. Palm trees rimming an apparently blue lake in a mirage are not necessarily the hallucination of a thirst-crazed desert traveler.

Wind velocities are likely to be somewhat greater in dry lands than in humid, forested areas, because there is less surface friction. The high temperatures of low-latitude deserts also may create strong pressure gradients about the desert margins. Whenever wind velocities begin to rise, dust swirls into the air. Chronic eye disorders, the result of dust irritation, are common among desert dwellers. Unusually strong winds of gale force produce dreaded sandstorms, which may last for days and which constitute real perils because of the danger of suffocation, loss of visibility, and immobilization. Such storms, however, are localized mainly within the *erg* (sandy) deserts. The smaller quantities of sand carried by strong surface winds in most deserts are responsible for glazing windshields and headlights on automobiles.

Strangely enough, floods are a serious

TABLE 8.6 Representative statistics for the B climates

	JAN.	FEB.	MAR.	APR.	MAY	JUNE	JULY	AUG.	SEPT.	OCT.	NOV.	DEC.	YEAR
Kamloops, B.C., Canada (51° N, BSk)													
Temp., °F	22.9	26.3	37.8	49.8	57.7	63.7	69.5	68.0	58.1	47.5	35.3	28.1	47.1
Rainfall, in.	1.0	0.7	0.3	0.4	0.9	1.2	1.1	1.1	0.8	0.6	1.0	0.9	10.0
Karachi, Pakistan (lat 25° N, BWhw)													
Temp., °F	65.3	68.4	75.0	80.6	84.7	86.8	84.3	82.4	82.0	80.0	74.0	67.4	77.6
Rainfall, in.	0.5	0.5	0.4	0.2	0.1	0.9	2.9	1.5	0.5	0.0	0.1	0.1	7.6
Tripoli, Libya (lat 33° N, BShs)													
Temp., °F	54.0	56.1	59.9	64.8	68.5	74.3	78.8	80.2	78.3	74.1	65.3	57.7	66.2
Rainfall, in.	3.3	1.8	0.9	0.5	0.3	0.1	0.0	0.0	0.5	1.8	2.4	4.7	16.3
Iquique, Chile (lat 20° S, BWh)													
Temp., °F	69.4	69.4	67.6	64.8	62.6	61.2	60.4	60.3	61.2	63.0	65.3	67.5	64.4
Rainfall, in.	0	0	0	0	0	0	0.02	0	0.03	0	0	0	0.05

threat in many dry regions, especially those which have narrow, steep-sided drainage channels. There are few deserts that do not receive occasional precipitation, and the rainfall is likely to be sudden and heavy, especially in low latitudes. Thin soils and sparse vegetation are responsible for a rapid runoff of water. A local thunderstorm miles away in the mountains may result in a flood crest several feet high that sweeps down the dry watercourses without warning.

8.5 THE DRY LANDS OF NORTH AMERICA. The *B* climates of North America conform fairly well to the generalized patterns described in the first paragraph of Sec. 8.4. Along the west coast, the dry climates extend from about lat 20 to 32° N. Some distance inland they extend poleward along the eastern slopes of the Sierra Nevada and the Cascade Mountains, reaching a poleward limit at about lat 52° N in eastern Alberta. The eastern boundary roughly follows the 100th meridian from the United States–Canada border to the Gulf of Mexico, near Corpus Christi, Texas. From here the dry border skirts the coast to about the Tropic of Cancer, thence westward across the Mexican highlands, and around the southern end of the peninsula of Lower California. The true desert (*BW*) is found mainly in the southwestern United States and northern Mexico. Isolated patches of *BW* are found farther north, east of some of the higher portions of the Sierras and Cascades, and in an occasional mountain basin in the Rockies.

There is a wide range of temperatures within the North American dry lands. Death Valley, California, held the world maximum-temperature record for many years at 134°F (now held by El Azizia, Libya, at 136°F), and winter temperatures of –50 to –60°F are frequent over the northern Great Plains. The general precipitation decreases from east to west, there being little change latitudinally. Rainfall effectiveness tends to decrease from north to south because of increased temperature and evaporation. This is the main reason why the southwestern part of the United States is the driest portion of the country.

Parts of the Mojave Desert in southeastern California and southwestern Arizona are rapidly being developed for recreation. The Mojave is near enough to the urban centers of Southern California to be easily accessible, and it offers two important attractions. First, the extremely low frequency of rain assures uninterrupted outdoor sports and plenty of sun for acquiring a tanned skin, an important mark of social distinction in this part of the country. Second, the desert offers a unique and somewhat glamorous environment, which attracts people once its dangers have been minimized by piped water, good highways, motels, and other modern conveniences. These advantages are not duplicated elsewhere in the United States, and exclusiveness has its economic value, particularly for those who can afford the price. The settlements in the deserts of the southwestern United States still are confined, however, to a few concentrated localities, such as the irrigated areas of the Imperial Valley, near Phoenix and Yuma, Arizona, and the sections in the vicinity of the fabulous resort centers of Palm Springs, California, and Las Vegas and Reno, Nevada. Vast areas of the desert still are uninhabited, but even emptiness has its advantages, as indicated by the many testing grounds for atomic energy equipment, rockets, guided missiles, and experimental aircraft located in parts of the dry lands in the western United States.

Like the deserts in many other parts of the world, those of North America are quite frequently interrupted by mountains or high

FIG. 8.7 Strip cropping, a type of dry farming in which part of the area is kept bare and fallow in order to conserve moisture. The cultivated fields here are in wheat. This scene is near Cut Bank, Montana, in the American Great Plains. [Standard Oil Company (N.J.)]

plains. Because of their greater elevation, such topographic features have somewhat higher precipitation and lower evaporation rates than the adjacent lowlands. Some of the mountains of the western United States have two timber lines: a lower, dry one, separating the dry, lower terrain from the timbered slopes above; and an upper, cold one, where low temperatures at high elevations inhibit tree growth. Both timber lines slope northward toward lower elevations, and those on east-facing slopes are somewhat higher than those on the western sides of mountains. The dry timber line varies from about 6,000 feet above sea level in Arizona and New Mexico to 2,000 to 3,000 feet in southern Canada. The cold timber line is generally about 2,000 to 4,000 feet above the dry timber line. Portions of the Colorado Plateau are sufficiently high to have a humid or subhumid climate and to have pine forests instead of the bunch grass or desert brush of lower elevations.

The extensive semiarid plains that border the eastern sides of the Rocky Mountains in Canada and the United States (see Fig. 8.7) have been the scene of an unparalleled attack by mechanized dry-farming [6] techniques on the dry boundary of agriculture. This boundary, which separates the areas of agriculture from those of animal husbandry, has shifted westward irregularly with the introduction of new tools and techniques of modern dry farming, until at several places it lies against the eastern flanks of the mountains. This battle for more intensive use of the dry lands is not without its setbacks, and the abnormally dry cycles that beset semiarid lands exact their toll everywhere through crop fail-

[6] Dry farming is a specialized form of agriculture that utilizes cultivation methods designed primarily to conserve water in the soil.

ures and accelerated soil erosion. The problem of marginality involves not only land settlement but regional living standards and capital gains and losses.

8.6 THE DRY LANDS OF SOUTH AMERICA.

The dry lands along the western coast of South America begin at Cape Blanco (lat 4° S), which marks the change in alignment of the coast line near the Peru-Equador border. The alignment of the coast is largely responsible for the fact that the dry climates extend so far toward the equator. South of Cape Blanco the coast roughly parallels the trades, and cold, upwelling water helps to stabilize air masses. The Andes, furthermore, prevent the importation of moist air from the eastern plains. North of Cape Blanco, warm water from the Equatorial Countercurrent bathes the coast, and the air mass above it is warm and moist as it moves toward the intertropical convergence zone, located somewhat farther to the north. About once every 8 years or so, the ITC shifts farther to the south, producing drastic climatic changes along the Peruvian coast (see Sec. 15.4).

The dry, west coast of South America extends from Cape Blanco to about lat 30° S in middle Chile. The Atacama Desert of northern Chile and southern Peru is one of the driest deserts in the world, and rain has never been recorded at some interior points. This desert, lying in a trough between the coastal hills and the Andes, also is somewhat unusual because of its low winter temperatures, despite its position between lat 15 and 22° S. Drainage of cold air from the Andes settles in the Atacama on clear nights in winter and often sends temperatures well below freezing. The dry west coast of Peru is not so inhospitable as many other dry areas in the world, partly because of the large number of streams that descend the western flanks of the Andes Mountains to supply water for irrigation. The cold water off the coast results in dense cloud and fog banks. Where the cloud zone lies against the slopes of the Andes, the water droplets in the air nourish a sparse grass and shrub vegetation, which, in turn, makes possible a zone of grazing in this region of very low rainfall.

In southern Peru, the dry border passes eastward into Bolivia, and most of the high plains of this latter country are dry and sterile. Nearby subtropical anticyclones with accompanying air subsidence, together with the coastwise direction of the prevailing winds, explain the dryness of the west coast and the high plains in the central Andes area. The clear skies in winter on the Altiplano, as the high Peruvian and Bolivian plains are called, produce rapid cooling at high elevations, and powerful local gravity winds flow down through the valleys and gorges as great streams of cold air. Moist air occasionally penetrates the dry, intercordilleran region across the easternmost divides of the Andes from the Amazon Basin. These moist periods usually occur during the southern hemisphere summer, when the ITC extends into the Chaco district. When this happens, strong surface heating on the Altiplano produces powerful updrafts carrying the moist air high enough to produce thunderstorms.

The dry climates descend the eastern slopes of the Andes in northern Argentina, then cover most of southern Argentina (Patagonia), from Bahia Blanca on the northeast to the Strait of Magellan. Most of the Argentine section of the dry lands is typical "rain-shadow" desert in the lee of the Andes. Wind directions are predominantly from the west, and most of the moisture from the Pacific is dropped on the western slopes of the mountains. Easterly winds here, sometimes brought in by cyclonic convergence, do not result in much moisture, mainly because such air is stable, having been cooled in its lower portions by passage over the cold Falkland Island Current. Such conditions are also more likely during the winter season, when there is less water vapor in the air.

Areas of dry climate lie west of the headlands along the northern coast of Venezuela and in the Dutch West Indies. Explanations for this dry area have already been presented (see Sec. 8.2).

8.7 THE AFRICA-EURASIA DRY LANDS. For present purposes, the land masses of Africa and Eurasia may be considered to be one huge continent. The dry lands of northern Africa extend into the Eurasian continent to form the largest area of arid and semiarid climates in the world. Again the generalized continental pattern asserts itself, for the dry climates begin along the western African coast between lat 15 and 30° N, extend eastward, and thence continue poleward to the northern borders of Mongolia, at lat 50° N. High mountain ranges in central and southwestern Asia interrupt the continuity of this huge dry region, and streams from the more humid mountain summits make possible the many irrigated oases strung along the mountain bases. The dry climates extend almost to the east coast in northern China, because of the topographic barrier of the Chin Ling (Tsinling Shan), a range which extends in an east-west direction a short distance north of the Yangtze River. This range tends to reduce the number of conditionally unstable *mTk* air masses that reach northern China to produce rain during the summer months.

As in North America, the southwestern portion (the western Sahara) of this great dry zone is the driest and warmest. Here the dry, descending superior air (*S*) of the Sahara subtropical anticyclone predominates at ground level during the winter season and at upper-air levels the rest of the year, checking the turbulent convectional summer updrafts, or trade-wind convergences, over the heated desert before they can carry water upward into the rain-making zone. Then too, there is little opportunity for much moisture in the surface air, which either has descended from upper levels or has had its moisture content reduced by precipitation along the continental margins long before it entered this region.

In Central Asia, particularly over Tibet, another subtropical anticyclonic cell can be found, the same one that is located at lower elevations over southwestern China during the winter season. The high mountain ranges and great distance from the sea aid in extending the dry zone northward from the subtropical anticyclonic regions, as does the strong polar anticyclone of the winter season in eastern Siberia. Again, as in North America, the influence of higher latitude in reducing temperatures and evaporation makes the small rainfall more effective for plant growth, and semiarid climates prevail. True deserts in east-central Asia, such as those in parts of Tibet and the Takla Makan Desert of the Tarim Basin in Sinkiang, have their continental dryness accentuated by their position in the lee of some of the highest mountain ranges on earth.

A few scattered dry districts lie apart from the main area of dry climates in North Africa and Asia. Spain, for example, has several areas of semiarid climate, located in the enclosed basins of the Meseta, the general name for the high plains of the interior. Turkey also has areas of dry climate, despite its position between the Mediterranean and Black Seas. A combination of rain-shadow effect and air subsidence is responsible for dryness over the Anatolian high plains, as it is over the interior basins of Spain. The unusual circumstance of a dry climate along the east coast of Africa north of the equator was mentioned earlier (see Sec. 8.2). It is largely the result of dry, subsiding *mTw* air from both hemispheres paralleling this coast during both winter (northeast wind) and summer (southwest wind) under the influence of the Indian monsoon system. The monsoon system of the northern Indian Ocean also accounts for the fact that there is no gradual shifting of the ITC through this region. The seasonal wind reversal takes place suddenly throughout the entire area.

The dry climates in Africa south of the equator are found on the western side of the continent between lat 8 and 32° S. This area is in the subtropical anticyclonic belt and comes under the influence of stable, subsiding airflow from the South Atlantic anticyclone during the southern hemisphere summer season. In the winter season, the continent develops its own high-pressure cell over the Kalahari Desert. The cold Benguela ocean current off the west coast aids in stabilizing the possible summer inflow of air from that direction. The eastern boundary of the dry climates in Africa south of the equator is related closely to the trend in the alignment of the ITC during the December-January solstice season. Southeastern Africa is humid largely because of the moist air from the warm southwestern Indian Ocean which moves toward the cyclonic centers that cross this area from west to east mainly during the winter season.

8.8 THE DRY LANDS OF AUSTRALIA. Nearly all of Australia is arid or semiarid, except for a narrow zone on the north, east, south, and southwest. As on other continents, the desert reaches the west coast in the subtropics, here between lat 18 and 28° S. Typical subtropical anticyclonic subsidence and divergence of air prevail over Australia, although the strong heating of the continent during the summer destroys the high-pressure cell within a few thousand feet of the surface. Only along the northern and northeastern coasts, where the upper-air subsidence is less strong or where there are topographic features to induce orographic rain, can the landward monsoon winds of summer find conditions aloft suitable for continued updrafts and rain formation. Rainfall along the southern and southeastern margins of the continent is the result mainly of cyclonic disturbances along fronts between passing migratory anticyclones or along the leading edges of occasional polar air masses.

8.9 DRY CLIMATES: THEIR RESOURCE SIGNIFICANCE. Although the arid and semiarid climates are generally considered inhospitable to man, they can be preferred environments where water is available from some source other than rainfall. It is noteworthy that many, and perhaps most, of the earliest advanced civilizations developed in the dry lands. Examples are the Egyptian and Babylonian civilizations of the Old World and the Inca and Aztec civilizations of the western hemisphere. When adequately watered and drained, desert soils are unusually productive, because the plant nutrients have not been depleted from the soil by rain washing. Fungus and bacterial diseases are much less common than in humid regions, and the great amount of sunshine provides exceptional conditions for plant growth and for the manufacture of plant starches and sugars. The desert, furthermore, provided a natural protection from invaders, at least in early historic times, before camels and automobiles brought increased mobility. The development of the early advanced civilizations in dry regions undoubtedly was the result of many factors, although a leading role was played by the introduction of irrigation.

Irrigation requires the use of foresight,

particularly in areas like Egypt or Iraq, where early irrigation projects involved the controlled flooding of rivers at critical seasons. The well-known story of Joseph in Egypt, which describes the development and utilization of crop surpluses, a natural corollary of seasonal planning, is a good example of applied foresight. When surpluses in agriculture are developed, manpower can be released for other specialized tasks, and the rewards of labor specialization pyramid. Irrigation likewise necessitates social control to regulate the sharing, distribution, and cooperative management of the water resource, the lifeblood of the social group. This in turn leads to advancements in the societal arts, including both governmental and religious activities. Rising land values in the desert oases led to more precise measurements, and it is not surprising that the earliest principles of geometry, trigonometry, and astronomy were achieved as by-products of land surveying in dry lands.

Today the cultural stimulus to population growth is relatively insignificant in dry lands in comparison with other climatic regions, but desert oases continue to be preferred places in which to live. Horticultural productivity is high, as it has always been, and with growing efficiency of production elsewhere, the low-latitude dry lands are attracting a nonproductive resident population. Some increase in irrigated land is possible, but most of it will require mammoth capital expenditures for the harnessing and efficient utilization of large exotic rivers as a new water supply. The water easily available was appropriated long ago.

Despite the many advantages of oasis living, relatively few dry lands have an available water supply from either surface or subterranean sources, and there is little likelihood of any appreciable expansion. Any increase in the population of the dry lands will have to result mainly from the growth of urban and suburban settlements, with a corresponding decrease in the use of water for irrigation.

8.10 DRY CLIMATES: THEIR RESISTANCE TO HUMAN SETTLEMENT. As indicated in the preceding paragraph, only a small proportion of the desert lands have a water supply available for human use. The absence or scarcity of water is the primary factor in explaining the sparse populations in the dry lands. Even in the oasis areas, however, there are certain environmental drawbacks that counteract the resource significance. In the low-latitude deserts, high summer daytime temperatures are a significant disadvantage. Air temperatures of 110 to 120° are relatively common, as are surface temperatures of 160 to 170°. The maintenance of body comfort requires either the expenditure of considerable energy for air conditioning or the reduction of physical activity. The necessity for the latter explains the common use of the "siesta," or rest period, during the early afternoon hours.

Although crop yields are high, irrigation costs must be added to the normal expenses of agriculture in evaluating the competitive position of dry lands in comparison with humid areas. These costs include the construction and maintenance not only of dams, gates, lifting devices, and distributory canals but also of drainage facilities. Land values and consequent tax rates are likely to be extremely high. With the growing productivity of humid areas under the impact of modern agronomy, irrigation agriculture has been forced into a more and more intensive utilization of the land in areas where a commercial economy prevails.

Another disadvantage in dry regions that depend on subterranean water sources is the difficulty of maintaining adequate reserves of

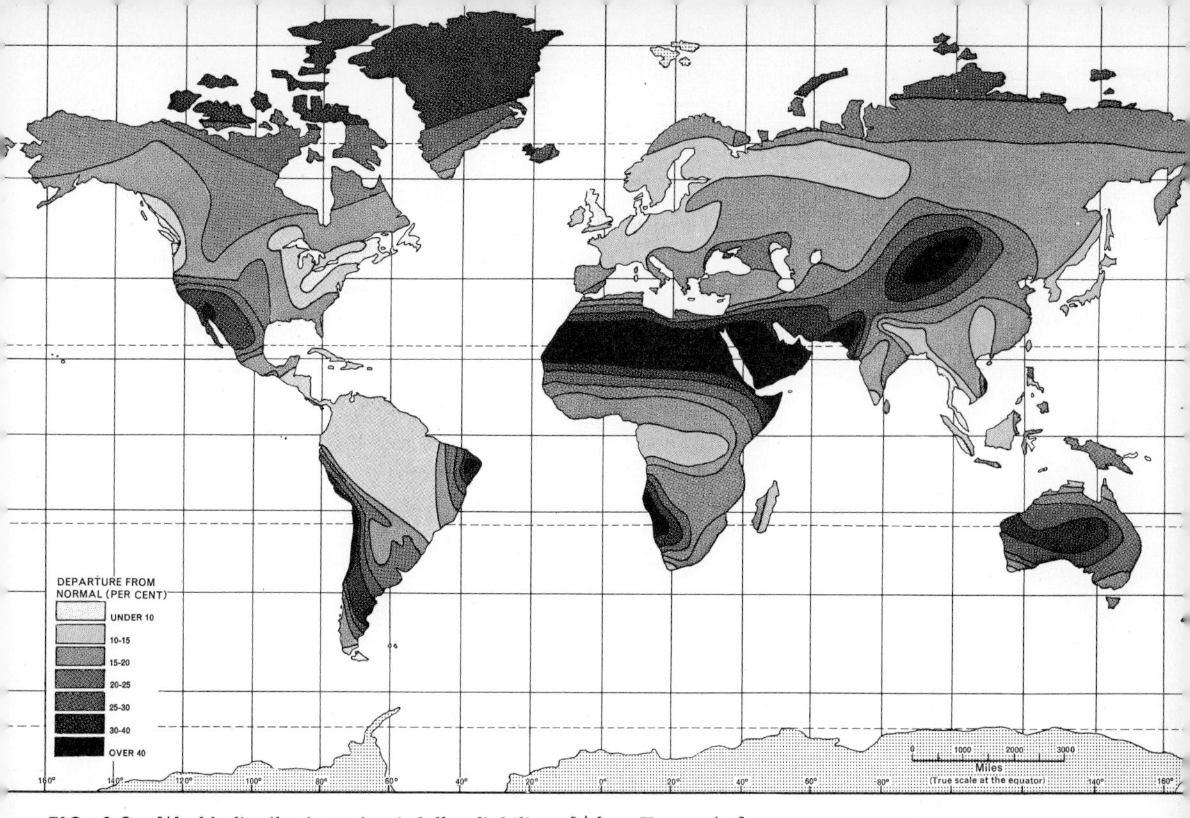

FIG. 8.8 World distribution of rainfall reliability. [After Trewartha]

water in the face of increased economic pressure and the growth of population. Like petroleum, water is a "fugitive" resource, which is able to move from place to place below the surface of the ground. Our legal regulations in the past have generally held that a person is entitled to the use of water on his own land; hence there is little legal basis (under English law) for preventing free competition in the use of subsurface water supplies or restricting the use of such water in order to maintain water levels in wells. Many areas that depend on this type of water supply are threatened with disaster unless the trend toward depletion can be reversed. This factor is discussed more fully in Chapter 14.

A major hindrance to the development of stable ratios of population to land in semiarid regions is the irregularity of rainfall (see Fig. 8.8). Abnormally humid periods are likely to entice settlement beyond the normal limit of stabilized agriculture, and this may lead to disaster when the dry cycles reassert themselves. The semiarid regions of the world have periodically been disaster areas for this reason. Some historians have suggested that the periodic invasions of humid regions by nomadic hordes were correlated with dry cycles in the steppelands of Central Asia.

The *C* climates (humid, mild winter)

The *C* climates, by definition, are humid climates with mild winters, in which the average mean temperature for the coldest month does not fall below 26.6°F. They are divided into several subtypes, distinguished by marked differences in the seasonal distribu-

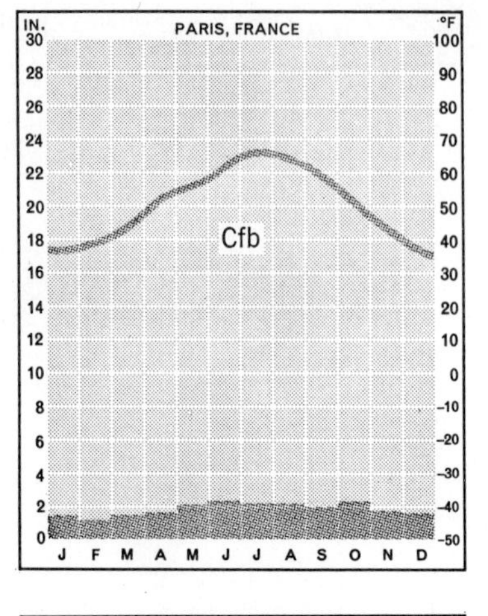

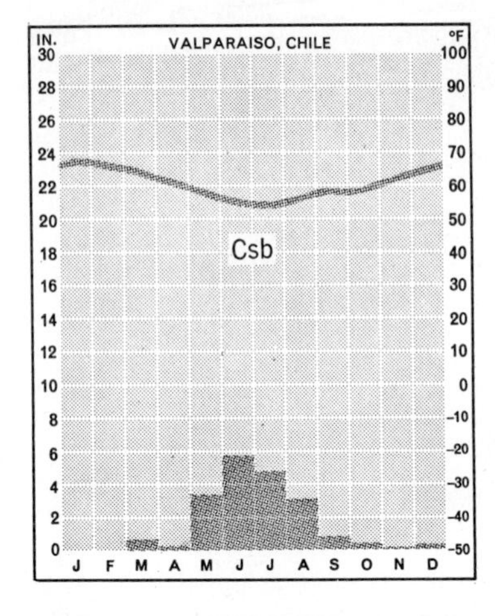

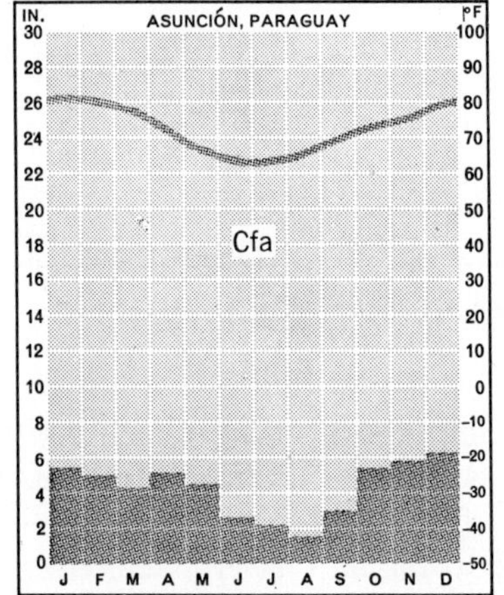

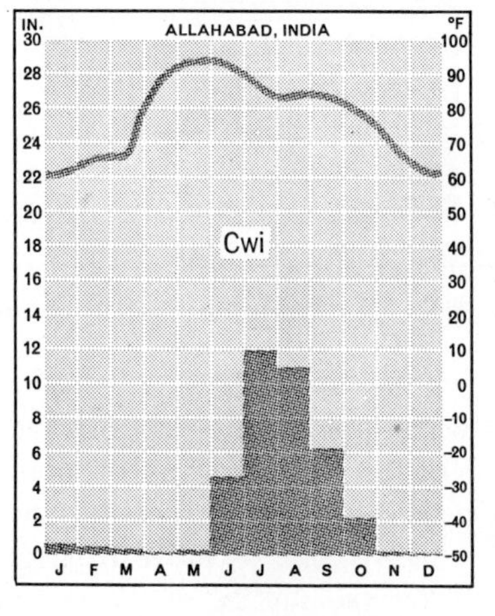

FIG. 8.9 Typical climatic graphs of the C climates.

tion of rainfall and in summer temperatures. Three major subdivisions are considered in this section: (1) the *Cfa-Cwa* types; (2) the *Csa-Csb* climates; and (3) the *Cfb-Cfc* types.

8.11 THE *CFA-CWA* CLIMATES (SUBTROPICAL WITH HOT SUMMERS). The letter *a* in the climate symbols signifies that the mean temperature of the warmest month exceeds 71.6°F. The difference between *Cfa* and *Cwa* climates is that the latter has a pronounced dry season during the winter. From the standpoint of plant ecology, the difference between these two types is not highly significant, since the presence of low temperatures during the winter season forces the curtailment of plant growth processes anyway. Freezing weather can be expected in most of the *C* climates sometime during the winter season, its frequency increasing poleward within the climatic zone. The climatic statistics for Charleston, South Carolina, and Hong Kong presented in Table 8.7 illustrate the *Cfa* and *Cwa* types, respectively.

The most distinguishing feature of the *Cfa-Cwa* climatic group is probably the high heat and humidity during the summer season. Daytime temperatures are above 90° fairly

TABLE 8.7 Climatic data for Charleston, South Carolina, and Hong Kong

	JAN.	FEB.	MAR.	APR.	MAY	JUNE	JULY	AUG.	SEPT.	OCT.	NOV.	DEC.	YEAR
					Charleston, South Carolina (lat 33° N, Cfa)								
Temp., °F	49.8	51.2	57.5	63.9	72.1	78.1	80.6	80.0	76.2	67.0	57.8	51.0	65.4
Rainfall, in.	3.1	3.3	3.4	2.9	3.4	4.8	7.1	6.6	6.0	3.6	2.4	2.9	48.4
					Hong Kong (lat 22½° N, Cwa)								
Temp., °F	59.7	57.7	63.0	70.3	76.8	80.6	81.7	81.1	80.2	76.1	69.1	62.6	71.6
Rainfall, in.	1.3	1.6	2.7	5.4	11.7	15.9	13.8	14.1	9.8	4.9	1.9	1.1	84.3

regularly during the summer months, and nights do not bring much relief. Temperatures are higher here than in the humid tropics, principally because direct rays of solar radiation are combined with long hours of daylight in the summer. Cloudiness also is somewhat less frequent. Summer rains commonly are of the convectional type, consisting of short, heavy showers, resulting from the conditional instability of the *mTk* air masses that pass over the heated land surfaces. The cost of maintaining body comfort,

FIG. 8.10 Average heating degree-days per year in the United States. A heating degree-day is the number of degrees Fahrenheit the mean temperature drops below 65°F in a single day. [After Trewartha]

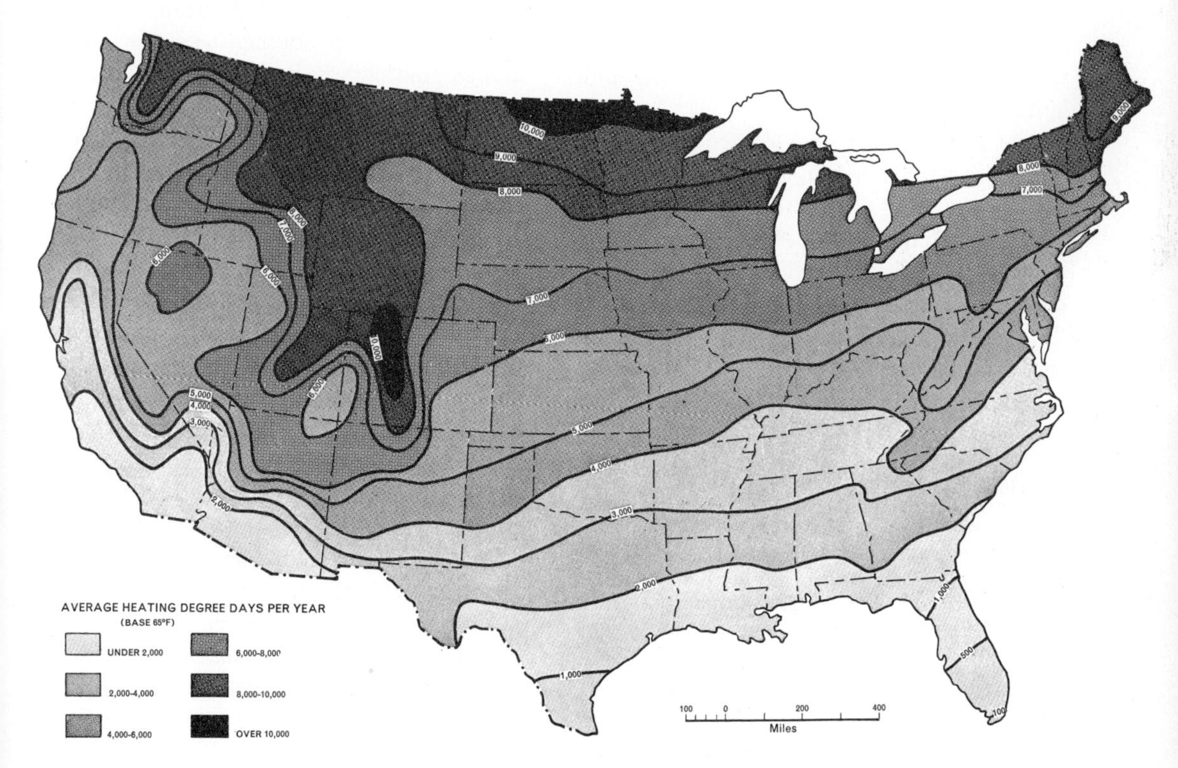

reflected in the large number of *heating and cooling degree-days,*[7] is high, being exceeded only in the *Dfa* climates, which combine hot summers with cold winters (see Fig. 8.10). Snow is rarely a significant obstacle to transportation, although an unusually heavy fall of several inches may block highways for short periods. Although conditions vary somewhat, the *Cfa* regions rarely have a snow cover for more than a couple of weeks. Sleet and glaze are much more troublesome, especially near the poleward margins of these regions, since the freezing line associated with the winter polar front normally shifts back and forth across this climatic zone during the winter months. East-coast areas within this climatic group are likely to experience hurricanes, especially in the autumn months. Tornadoes are fairly frequent on interior plains, especially in early summer. Spring and autumn are delightful times of the year, with warm days and cool nights, and these seasons are long in comparison with the corresponding periods in other midlatitude climates.

The *Cfa* climates are located principally on the eastern sides of continents immediately poleward of the humid tropics, and they normally extend from about lat 20 to 25° to lat 35 to 40°. The extension inland is limited by the *B* climates and by highlands, such as the mountains and dissected high plains of southwestern China. The *Cwa* climates are located mainly in eastern Asia, principally in southwestern China and northern India. Smaller areas include a narrow zone along the northeast coast of Australia and part of the Chaco section of Paraguay and eastern Bolivia. The subsidence and divergence of air associated with the winter subtropical anticyclone over southwestern China and the Himalayas are largely responsible for winter droughts in eastern Asia.

The three largest areas of the *Cfa-Cwa* climatic group include the southeastern United States, eastern Asia, and eastern South America. Less extensive areas are located along the east coast of South Africa and Australia. Small areas of *Cfa* climates which form exceptions to the generalized distribution described above occur in the northeastern Mediterranean Sea area, including the Po Valley of northern Italy, central Yugoslavia, the Hungarian Plain, and southern Romania. These form a transition between the mild winters of the eastern Mediterranean and the severe winters of southeastern Europe, although summers in both areas are hot.

8.12 THE *CS* CLIMATES. The feature that sets the *Cs* group apart from the other *C* types is the pronounced dry season during the summer months. A *Cs* climate, by definition, is one in which three times as much rain falls during the wettest month of winter as during the driest month of summer. Since summer is the major growth period, native plant and farm practices must be adjusted to overcome the deficiency of moisture during this season. Fortunately, the winter precipitation occurs when evaporation is at its lowest; hence much of the precipitation is retained in soils, in subsurface reservoirs, or in the snow fields of adjacent mountains. Water for irrigation is therefore much more available than it is in the *B* climates, which adjoin this group on their equatorward side, and dry-farming practices are highly rewarding.

[7] A *degree-day* is a useful measurement of temperature excesses or deficiencies. It is based on the number of degrees variation in the daily mean temperature from 65°F, taken as a base point of body comfort. A single day with a mean temperature of 46°, for example, is the equivalent of 19 *heating degree-days,* whereas a day's mean temperature of 80° represents 15 *cooling degree-days.* The total number of heating and cooling degree-days for a year is a convenient indication of the requirements for air conditioning (both heating and cooling) in buildings.

TABLE 8.8 Representative statistics for the Cs climates

	JAN.	FEB.	MAR.	APR.	MAY	JUNE	JULY	AUG.	SEPT.	OCT.	NOV.	DEC.	YEAR
					Athens, Greece (lat 38° N, Csa)								
Temp., °F	48.4	49.5	52.2	58.6	66.2	74.3	79.9	79.5	73.4	66.0	57.2	52.2	63.1
Rainfall, in.	2.0	1.7	1.2	0.9	0.8	0.7	0.3	0.5	0.7	1.6	2.6	2.6	15.5
					San Francisco, California (lat 37½° N, Csb)								
Temp., °F	49.4	51.4	52.8	54.3	55.5	57.2	57.3	57.8	59.9	58.9	55.5	50.6	55.0
Rainfall, in.	4.8	3.6	3.1	1.6	0.7	0.1	0.0	0.0	0.3	0.9	2.4	4.5	39.7
					Sacramento, California (lat 38½° N, Csa)								
Temp., °F	45.6	50.2	54.2	58.0	62.9	68.9	72.5	72.1	69.1	62.2	53.4	46.3	59.6
Rainfall, in.	3.8	2.8	2.8	1.5	0.7	0.1	0.0	0.0	0.3	0.8	1.9	3.8	18.5

The two divisions *Csa* and *Csb* represent subtypes that have, respectively, hot summers and cool summers, the latter usually restricted to a narrow coastal zone adjoining cool ocean water. Examples of *Cs* climates are given in Table 8.8.

The *Cs* climates generally are found between lat 30 and 40° N and S on the western sides of continents. Each of the five continents has an area in this climatic group, although the only extensive one is found in southern Europe, bordering part of the Mediterranean Sea. In North and South America, the *Csa* and *Csb* climates are restricted mainly to a relatively narrow zone between the mountains and the sea, though small outlying areas can be found in Idaho and along the western flanks of the Wasatch Mountains in Utah. In Africa and Australia, the continental land masses terminate within this latitudinal zone; hence only the southern continental extremities have *Cs* climates. In southern Europe and in North Africa, the general east-west alignment of the major mountain cordilleras, plus the large interior basin of the Mediterranean Sea, aid in extending this west-coast climatic group well to the east. The continuations into Iran, around the southern margin of the Caspian Sea, and along the western flanks of the central Asiatic mountains are mainly due to mountains. High elevations here reduce temperatures and evaporation sufficiently to make a *Csb* climate out of what is a *BShs* climate at lower elevations. The mountains also cause somewhat greater rainfall.

The *Cs* climates are transitional in several respects. First, they lie in a latitudinal position between humid climates (on their poleward side) and dry climates (on their equatorward side). With the seasonal latitudinal shifting in the angle of solar radiation, anticyclonic pressure cells, wind belts, ocean currents, and frontal disturbances, they experience the typical rainfall regimes of the neighboring climates to the north and south at opposite seasons (see Fig. 8.11). Second, they are transitional in their temperatures, lying between the mid-latitudes and the tropics. Their coastal position likewise produces intermediate temperature conditions. Cold, upwelling water in the Atlantic and Pacific Oceans off these west coasts during the summer (see Sec. 15.16) provides a sharp contrast with the blistering but dry heat a short distance inland. Illustrative of this transition between oceanic and continental temperatures is the sharp contrast in summer temperatures between San Francisco and Sacramento, California (see Table 8.8). The difference between the average mean temperature for July at these two cities is 15°, yet they are only about 80 miles apart. The low mountains between the coast and the Central Valley of California are responsible for this sharp contrast. Daytime temperatures along the highways leading east from San Francisco often may rise 30°F within a distance of 5 miles, where the highways skirt around the ends of the coastal ridges. All areas within the *Cs* climatic group, except the region in Australia, are adjacent to mountains and hence experience the vertical zonation of climates associated with mountainous terrain.

Three weather phenomena which occur occasionally are highly important obstacles in the *Cs* climates. These are (1) polar air masses, which bring freezing temperatures to usually warm lowlands; (2) dry, hot winds descending from desert high plains; and (3) fogs along the oceanic margins. Intensive horticulture is characteristic of most of the fertile lowlands of the *Cs* climates. Near the equatorward margins, winter cropping is an important regional advantage, especially for such subtropical plants as citrus fruits, olives, and figs. Frosts are capable of inflicting great damage within such areas, and they play a major role in determining land-utilization patterns. The dry gravity winds, such as the Santa Anas of Southern California, are not so destructive as the frosts, but they are feared nevertheless. They have been known to wither crops rapidly in the vicinity of mountain passes. Fogs are not only a constant hazard to shipping along the coasts, particularly during the morning hours, but also a hindrance to land transportation along the coastal lowlands. When mixed with smoke in industrial areas, they may be exceedingly unpleasant. Fogs result from a combination of causes, including the development of a temperature inversion by anticyclonic subsidence

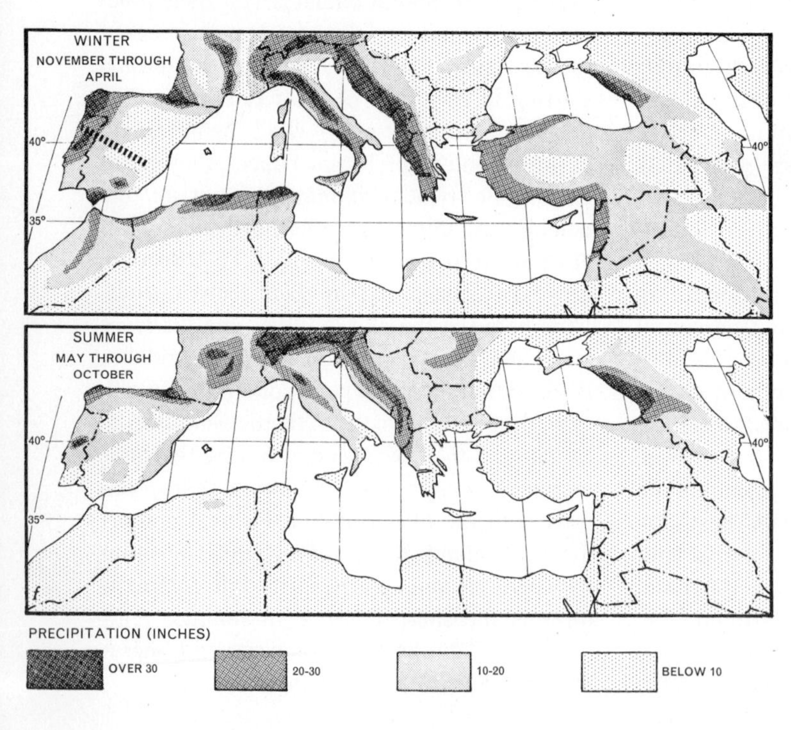

FIG. 8.11 Seasonal variation of rainfall in the Mediterranean Basin. The dry summers and wet winters that characterize most of this basin are clearly shown, especially equatorward of 40° latitude.

FIG. 8.12 Fog coming in from the Pacific through the Golden Gate, San Francisco, Calif. [U.S. Weather Bureau]

above, contact with cold water below, and rapid radiational cooling at night over land. A breeze from the land carries the chilled air out to sea in the early morning hours. Fogs normally disappear during the morning, although a thin cloud sheet marking the inversion boundary sometimes may persist for many days. Coastal fogs are rarely found over the Mediterranean Sea, because the surface water there is unusually warm as compared with the open ocean.

Despite their occasional disadvantages, the *Cs* climates generally have been preferred places for human beings to live. In the United States, for example, the growth of the urban population in California has been one of the major factors in the demographic change in this country during the past three or four decades. Climate, of course, is not California's sole attraction, but there are many indications that it plays a major role. To those who have lived and worked in the snow, sleet, and slush of a northeastern United States winter, retirement in California, or Florida, is something to look forward to. Immigrants to California, however, include not only retired members of the middle class but, among others, many submarginal farmers, who have moved westward from the poorer soil areas of the Great Plains.

Within the *Cs* climates the preferred position for most people is along the coast near the equatorward margin. Here winters are distinctly subtropical, with daytime temperatures in the low 70s. The position adjacent to cool ocean water keeps summer temperatures down. The percentage of clear skies is unusually high, except in the morning hours, and the drizzly, dark days of winter at the poleward margins of the *Csb* climates are rare here. The Southern California coast, between Los Angeles and San Diego, is not the only place in the world where this preferred residential climate prevails. It is also a major attraction of such famous residential cities as Casablanca, Morocco; Valparaiso, Chile; and Capetown, South Africa. The French and Italian Rivieras, on the northern shores of the Mediterranean, have a somewhat similar climate, but here the rarity of freezing weather in winter is the result of the warm Mediterranean and the protection of shielding mountains against the cold polar air masses of northwestern Europe. An occasional *mistral,* however, may provide decidedly unpleasant winter cold spells. The coolness of the Riviera summer is due to its northern position and to air drainage at night down adjacent mountain slopes, not to cool ocean currents as in the other examples above.

8.13 THE *CFB* CLIMATE (MARINE WEST COAST). The *Cfb* climate is humid at all seasons, and there is a low seasonal range in temperature, considering its rather high latitudinal position. It is characteristically located on the western margin of continents, poleward of lat 40 to 45°. In North America, it begins slightly farther north, at about lat 48° N, near the United States–Canada border, and extends to approximately lat 60° N, along the southern coast of Alaska. The island barrier of the Aleutians prevents warm Pacific water from penetrating into the Bering Sea, and cold winter winds from the upper Yukon Valley keep the west coast of Alaska from having mild winters. The south coast of Alaska is shielded from these cold air masses by the Alaska Range. Mountains restrict the *Cfb* climates to a relatively narrow coastal zone in all continents except Europe. In the latter, the plains and low hills of the northwestern section permit the marine influence of the North Atlantic to penetrate inland as far as central Germany.

The principal features of the *Cfb* climate are its mild winters and cool summers, both caused by the dominance of maritime air masses. A highland *Cfb* climate is almost universally found at high elevations in the humid tropics, generally above 5,000 feet, although there are insufficient climatic stations to determine its true extent. These highland *Cfb* climates are important climatic refuges from the hot, humid lowlands nearby. They differ climatically from the west-coast type principally because of the virtual absence of seasons. Usually the yearly temperature varies less than 10°. A related highland climate (*Cwb*) is found in the low latitudes, where an *Aw* climate predominates in adjacent lowlands. Within the region of *Cfa* climates, a drop in temperature resulting from elevation may produce a *Cfb* climate in areas above 1,500 to 2,000 feet, as along the higher portions of the Appalachians.

Characteristic temperature and precipitation regimes for several of the stations within the *Cfb* and *Cwb* climates are given in Table 8.9.

TABLE 8.9 Representative statistics for the Cfb and Cwb climates

	JAN.	FEB.	MAR.	APR.	MAY	JUNE	JULY	AUG.	SEPT.	OCT.	NOV.	DEC.	YEAR
Sitka, Alaska (lat 57° N, Cfb, sea level)													
Temp., °F	31.7	34.1	36.5	41.3	46.6	51.3	54.8	55.5	51.7	45.8	38.2	35.4	43.6
Rainfall, in.	7.6	6.5	5.6	5.5	4.1	3.4	4.2	7.1	10.1	12.2	9.5	9.0	84.8
Wellington, New Zealand (lat 41.5° S, Cfb, sea level)													
Temp., °F	62.4	62.2	61.0	57.4	52.9	49.6	47.5	48.6	51.1	54.0	56.8	60.8	55.2
Rainfall, in.	2.8	2.7	3.1	3.5	4.0	4.2	4.7	3.8	3.1	3.4	2.9	2.8	41.1
Quito, Ecuador (lat 0°, Cfb, elev. 9,350 feet)													
Temp., °F	54.5	55.0	54.5	54.5	54.7	55.0	54.9	54.9	55.0	54.7	54.3	54.7	54.7
Rainfall, in.	4.2	4.3	5.2	7.4	5.0	1.5	0.9	1.5	3.0	3.7	3.8	3.8	44.1
Salisbury, S. Rhodesia (lat 18° S, Cwb, elev. 4,880 feet)													
Temp., °F	69.7	68.8	68.2	65.7	60.6	56.9	56.1	60.2	66.4	70.7	70.7	69.6	65.3
Rainfall, in.	7.5	7.4	4.5	1.0	0.5	0.1	0.0	0.1	0.3	1.1	3.7	5.8	31.9

Note how the marine influence retards the maximum temperatures at Sitka, Alaska, where the warmest month is August. The oceanic influence on winter temperatures is illustrated by the fact that the average mean January temperature at Sitka is about the same as that at St. Louis, Missouri, despite a latitudinal difference of almost 20°. The July temperature at St. Louis, however, is 79°, whereas it is only 55° at Sitka. In exceptional years, the west-coast marine climates (*Cfb*) may experience cold waves, when polar anticyclones over the continental interiors send a tongue or ridge of cold air westward into the west-coast sectors. This is more unusual in North America than in Europe, however, because of the topographic barrier of the northern Rocky Mountains, the Cascades, and the Canadian Coast Range which helps to keep *cP* or *cA* air masses out of the west-coast areas.

Precipitation varies widely in the *Cfb* climates, depending mostly on orographic conditions. Sharp local contrasts can be observed on opposite sides of mountain slopes. Along the coast of British Columbia, the lee side of the mountainous coastal islands generally has an average annual precipitation of between 20 and 25 inches. Mountain slopes on the west coast of Vancouver Island, on the other hand, have more than 100 inches. Similar contrasts are observed between lee and windward positions in the Olympic Mountains of Washington. A pronounced change in vegetation accompanies such sharp precipitation contrasts. The mountainous west coasts of both North and South America are responsible for the fact that precipitation in the *Cfb* climates there is higher than in most comparable climates of western Europe. Norway also has higher precipitation. This is not entirely due to orographic conditions, however, because numerous cyclonic disturbances move along fronts that are pocketed along the coast, especially during the winter season. For this reason, precipitation along these coasts is generally much higher in autumn and winter than in spring and summer. Both winter and summer precipitation is likely to be in the form of slow, drizzly types rather than violent, heavy downpours. Convectional precipitation is rare, the *mPw* air of summer being too stable to produce overturning and the *mPk* air of winter lacking sufficient moisture or sufficiently steep lapse rates aloft to provide heavy precipitation.

Exceptionally heavy snowfalls occur on the adjacent mountain slopes, where orographic influences add to the cyclonic precipitation and where somewhat lower temperatures (as compared with those of nearby lowlands), due to elevation, prevent the snow from melting to form rain. Snow accumulations of as much as 400 inches have been measured on the western slopes of the Cascade Mountains. The lowlands seldom retain much snow on the ground during the winter, because of the relatively mild winter temperatures. Some climatologists have maintained that an average mean monthly temperature of approximately 27° is a critical boundary of snow retention. Although this is only a crude, empirical generalization, subject to many qualifications, it is somewhat useful in estimating snow conditions on a global scale.

Northwestern Europe, excluding the rainy coastal strip of Norway, has a moderate precipitation without pronounced seasonal contrasts, although the immediate coastal areas tend to show a maximum during the winter months. The precipitation is mainly frontal or cyclonic, but the frequency of fronts and accompanying cyclonic waves is much less than in the *Cfb* climates of the western hemisphere. Winter snows occur but seldom stay long on the ground. Warm, moist Atlantic air blowing over a cold, snow-covered land

TABLE 8.10 Climatic data for the Evangelist Islands, Chile (lat 52½° S)

	JAN.	FEB.	MAR.	APR.	MAY	JUNE	JULY	AUG.	SEPT.	OCT.	NOV.	DEC.	YEAR
Temp., °F	47.2	46.6	46.3	44.8	41.3	39.8	37.4	38.6	40.1	41.6	43.0	45.3	42.7
Rainfall, in.	12.8	8.9	12.3	11.6	8.8	8.5	8.9	8.6	7.7	9.0	10.3	9.6	117.0

surface following a winter cold wave produces the heavy winter fogs of the British Isles. As one moves east across Europe, seasonal temperature contrasts gradually increase, until the *Cfb* climates give way to the severe-winter *D* climates of eastern Europe.

Small areas of *Cfc* climate are found in marine positions near the poleward margins of the *Cfb* climates. This type has a fairly mild winter, but its summer is unusually short and cool, with less than 4 months having a mean temperature of over 50°. Examples of this type of climate can be found in parts of the Aleutian Islands and the south coast of Alaska, southern Iceland, the central coast of Norway, and the southern tip of South America. Probably the most unusual example of the marine influence at high latitudes is afforded by the Evangelist Islands, near the western end of the Strait of Magellan, which have an *E,* or polar, climate, despite the fact that the mean temperature for the coldest month is 39°, or about the same as that of Nashville, Tennessee. In no month does the temperature exceed 50°, and mean temperature for the warmest month is only 47°. Almost continuously shrouded in mist and drizzly rains, these islands probably have one of the most miserable climates on earth.

The *Cfb* climate is one of the most favorable types in regard to total expenditures for heating and cooling combined. Air conditioning in summer is rarely necessary, and fuel costs in winter are relatively slight. The growing season is long and free from severe droughts, and in many areas vegetables, winter grains (wheat, oats, or barley), and forage crops are raised during the winter season. Ellsworth Huntington listed it as the most favorable climate for high yields of wheat, and statistics appear to support his hypothesis, although the quality grown in this climate is lower than that of the hard bread wheats of cool, dry regions. Terrain conditions, moreover, are not well suited to the highly mechanized grain agriculture of interior plains. These mild, humid west-coast climates are utilized much more for forage crops and horticulture than for grain production. Grasses do exceptionally well, remaining green for almost the entire year, and small acid fruits such as strawberries and raspberries are prolific.

The *D* climates (humid continental with severe winters)

8.14 THE *D* CLIMATES: GENERAL. The *D* climates include the humid parts of the world that have a summer but that also have a long, severe winter. By definition, this type of climate is one in which the mean temperature for the coldest month is below 26.6° (−3°C) and that of the warmest month is above 50°. It is thus characterized by wide seasonal ranges of temperature, which are the result of continental heating and cooling. Except for a few small spots of *D* climates in the mountains of New Zealand and in the Andes, this group is restricted to the continents of the northern hemisphere. There is insufficient land area at the higher middle

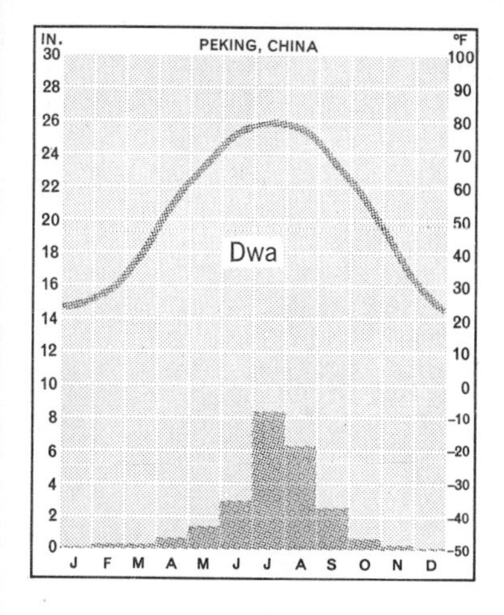

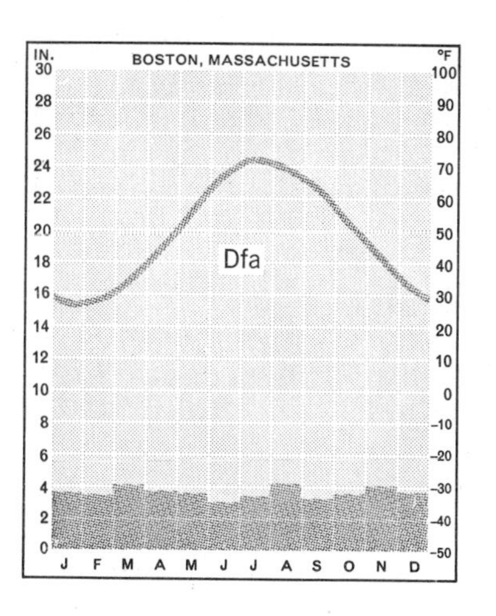

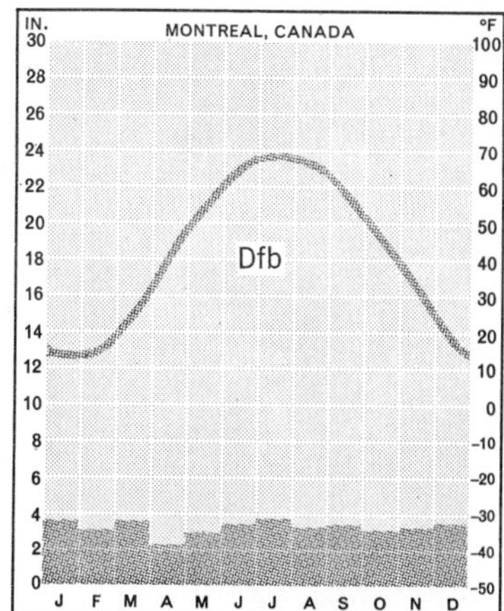

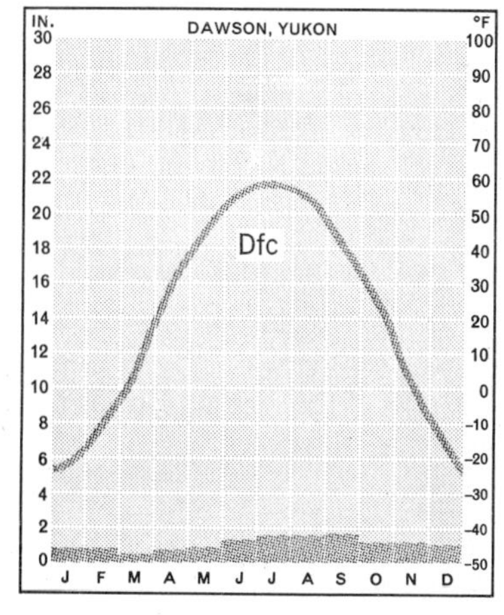

FIG. 8.13 Typical climatic graphs of the D climates. The temperature curve for Boston indicates that it lies close to the C-D boundary. Note the dry winters in Peking, typical of eastern Asia.

latitudes south of the equator to produce wide temperature ranges.

The members of the *D* group are differentiated in the Koeppen code by the degree of summer warmth (*a, b,* or *c*) and by the presence or absence of a winter dry season (*w* or *f*, respectively). The *Dw* climates are found only in eastern Asia, where the Siberian polar anticyclone prevents the importation of moist air during the winter season. The generalized distribution of the *D* climates is from between lat 60 and 70° on the western sectors of the northern hemisphere continents to between lat 40 and 60° on the eastern sides.

8.15 THE *DFA* AND *DWA* CLIMATES (HUMID CONTINENTAL WITH SEVERE WINTERS AND HOT SUMMERS).

The *Dfa* and *Dwa* climates, which are distinguished by the latter's having a pronounced dry season in winter, are characterized by an extremely wide range of seasonal temperatures, with hot summers (warmest month over 71.6°) and cold winters (coldest month below 26.6°). Examples are given in Table 8.11.

The *Dfa* and *Dwa* climates are found immediately north of the *Cfa* or *Cwa* climates in both eastern North America and eastern Asia. They also lie just east of the *B* climates

TABLE 8.11 Representative statistics for the Dfa-Dwa climates

	JAN.	FEB.	MAR.	APR.	MAY	JUNE	JULY	AUG.	SEPT.	OCT.	NOV.	DEC.	YEAR
					Mukden, Manchuria (lat 42° N, Dwa)								
Temp., °F	9.0	14.2	28.4	47.1	60.1	70.7	75.9	73.9	62.1	47.8	30.7	14.7	44.6
Rainfall, in.	0.2	0.2	0.8	1.1	2.2	3.4	6.3	6.1	3.3	1.6	1.1	0.2	26.4
					Chicago, Illinois (lat 42° N, Dfa)								
Temp., °F	25.6	27.0	36.6	47.4	58.4	68.1	74.0	72.9	66.3	54.8	41.5	30.3	50.2
Rainfall, in.	2.1	2.1	2.6	2.9	3.6	3.3	3.4	3.0	3.1	2.6	2.4	2.1	33.0
					Omaha, Nebraska (lat 41° N, Dfa)								
Temp., °F	21.5	24.6	36.8	51.2	62.5	72.0	77.0	74.7	66.2	54.0	38.6	27.1	50.5
Rainfall, in.	0.7	0.9	1.3	2.8	4.1	4.7	4.0	3.2	3.0	2.3	1.1	0.9	28.9

that occupy the interiors of these continents. The southern margin of these climates is located at about lat 35° N in China and about lat 40° N in the United States. In the latter area, the *Dfa* climatic region is widest in the west near the 100th meridian, where it extends from southern Nebraska to the center of South Dakota. It narrows eastward, ending near the western end of Lake Erie. The *Dwa* type predominates in eastern Asia, occupying most of northeastern China north of the Hwang Ho, southern Manchuria, and northern Korea. The drier winter season in Asia is the result of the greater dominance of *cP* air, which originates in the great winter polar anticyclone of eastern Siberia and Mongolia. The smaller size of North America, the deep indentation of the subtropical Gulf of Mexico, and the lesser strength of the Canadian polar highs result in a fairly humid winter season in the upper Mississippi drainage basin.

The distinction between *Dfa* and *Dwa* climates has little significance with respect to vegetation and agriculture. Since the winter season is too cold for active vegetative growth, most plants curtail their life processes, so that it makes little difference whether the precipitation of the winter season is low or high. The difference in amount of snow cover, however, is of some importance. In northern China, the small amount of winter snow leaves cultivated fields exposed to winter wind erosion. The winter season in Peking, as elsewhere on the North China plain, is characterized by an almost continuous dust haze. Although occasional heavy snows occur along winter fronts in the American *Dfa* region, snow does not remain on the ground for any extended period of time. Occasional importations of warm *mTw* air from the Gulf of Mexico during the winter often will remove the snow cover rapidly. Sleet and glaze are troublesome winter hazards in the lower Great Lakes region. Even in the United States, however, precipitation is greater in summer than in winter, and the discrepancy increases toward the west. A comparison of the rainfall statistics for Chicago, Illinois, and Omaha, Nebraska, both of which have *Dfa* weather stations, is illustrative (see Table 8.11). The increased winter dryness of the *Dfa* region west of the Mississippi is aided by the increasing importance of masses of modified *mPw* air from the Pacific Ocean which lose much water vapor during their passage across the mountains and become warm and dry upon their descent into the western Great Plains.

Not only do the *Dfa* and *Dwa* climates regularly exhibit wide seasonal ranges of temperature and precipitation, but there are wide departures from mean figures for temperature and precipitation in both the summer and winter seasons. The primary reason for this is that the eastern interior sections of the northern hemisphere continents are visited by air masses of many types. In the United States, for example, which is the more variable of the two sections, the *Dfa* region may be under the influence of most of the major air masses, including *mP, cP, cT,* and *mT,* which may show varying degrees and kinds of modifications.

The *Dfa* and *Dwa* climates exert some direct influence on patterns of land utilization. As indicated above, the distinction between the two has little bearing on crop patterns, mainly because the winter season is too severe for plant growth and the difference in winter precipitation is therefore not significant. In the United States, where regional specialization has reached a high degree of development, the *Dfa* region is a transitional zone with respect to land use. The lower Great Lakes section, for example, is the area of transition between typical Corn Belt agriculture and the dairy farming of the region that lies to the north. In the Great Plains, the *Dfa* region lies between and slightly overlaps both the spring-wheat region to the north and the winter-wheat region to the south. The severity of winter, accompanied by light snowfall on these plains, hinders the wintering of wheat planted in the fall. The hot summers, conducive to rusts and blights, is a disadvantage to the growth of spring wheat. For this reason, corn is an important grain, although this is not so suitable a corn climate as the *Cfa* region to the south. New hybrid varieties of corn recently have increased the acreage of this crop in the western *Dfa* section. In eastern Asia, kaoliang (a giant millet), wheat (mainly spring wheat), and soybeans are the major crops. Rice is not an important crop, because of the short growing season and the rainfall deficiencies during the summer months.

From the standpoint of human comfort, the *Dfa* and *Dwa* climates leave much to be desired. Homes must have adequate heating in the winters, and summer daytime temperatures frequently rise into the 90s. Rapid changes in temperature occur throughout the year.

8.16 THE *DFB* AND *DWB* CLIMATES (HUMID CONTINENTAL WITH COOL SUMMERS).

The mild-summer variations of the *D* climates (*Dfb* and *Dwb*) are much more extensive than the *Dfa* and *Dwa* types and are found in a broad belt across southern Canada and the northern United States; in central Eurasia, from central Germany into central Siberia; and in eastern Asia, including northeastern Manchuria, the Amur-Maritime District of the Soviet Far East, and northern Japan. The *Dwb* subgroup is found only in eastern Asia.

Winters in the *Dfb* and *Dwb* climates are more severe than in the *Dfa* and *Dwa* types. Minimum temperatures drop to −20 or −30° nearly every winter, and snow usually remains on the ground from 1 to 5 months, depending on the amount of precipitation and the latitudinal position. Summers are pleasant and cool. Mean monthly temperatures in this season do not exceed 71.6°, and there are at least 4 months with mean temperatures above 50°. The statistics reported by the weather stations represented in Table 8.12 are typical.

Continental arctic and polar air masses predominate in the *Dfb-Dwb* climatic region during the winter and summer seasons, respectively. Precipitation generally shows a maximum in summer, because the cold

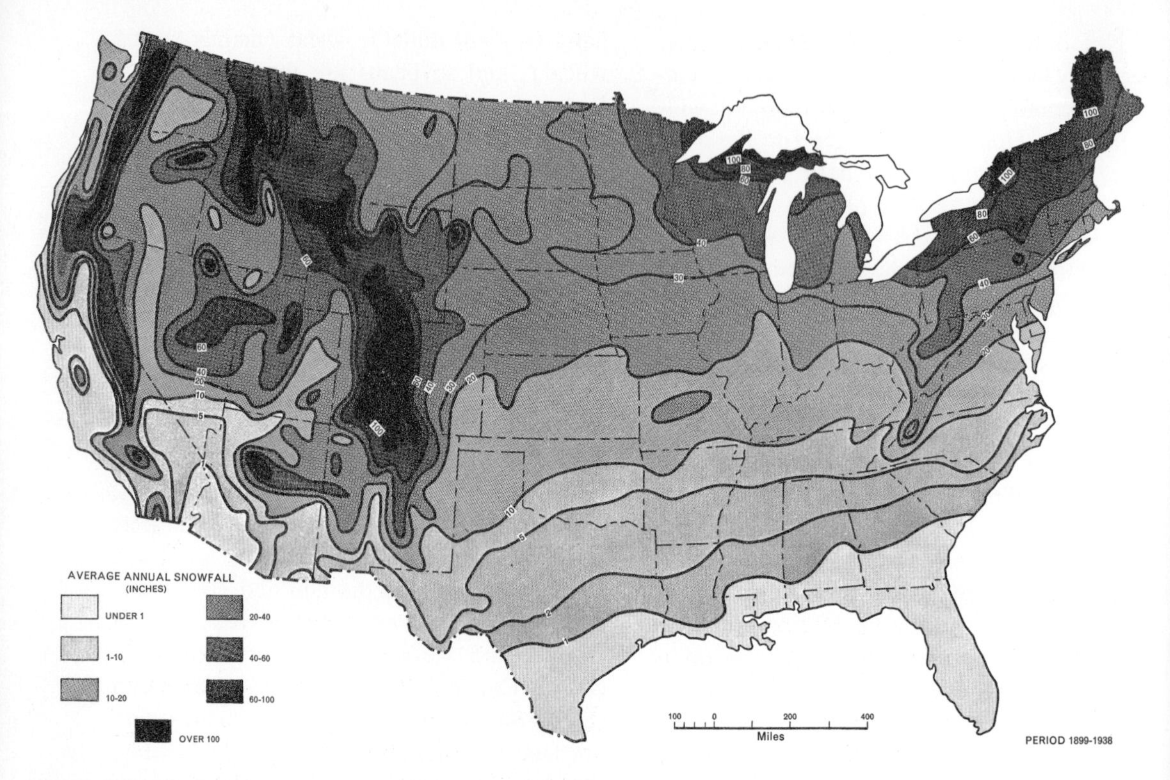

FIG. 8.14 Distribution of snowfall in the United States. The orographic factor plays a major role in influencing the pattern of snowfall. A map of much larger scale would illustrate this point to a much greater degree. Note also the influence of the Great Lakes in producing instability in the polar continental air masses that sweep across them. [U.S. Department of Agriculture]

winter air masses are stable and contain little water vapor. The *cPk* air masses of summer, however, are highly unstable and receive a great deal of moisture from the wet land surface following the melting of snow in early summer. Summer rains often are

TABLE 8.12 Representative statistics for the Dfb-Dwb climates

	JAN.	FEB.	MAR.	APR.	MAY	JUNE	JULY	AUG.	SEPT.	OCT.	NOV.	DEC.	YEAR
Duluth, Minnesota (lat 46½° N, Dfb)													
Temp., °F	10.4	13.3	24.0	38.4	48.0	57.7	65.7	64.6	56.6	45.2	29.4	16.8	31.1
Rainfall, in.	1.0	1.0	1.6	2.1	3.4	4.2	3.8	3.2	3.4	2.5	1.5	1.2	28.8
Vladivostok, U.S.S.R. (lat 43° N, Dwb)													
Temp., °F	7.3	13.8	26.4	39.9	49.1	56.5	64.6	69.1	61.7	48.7	31.1	14.7	40.3
Rainfall, in.	0.3	0.3	0.6	1.2	2.0	2.8	3.0	4.3	4.4	1.8	1.1	0.5	22.4
Moscow, U.S.S.R. (lat 56° N, Dfb)													
Temp., °F	13.6	16.7	24.6	39.4	54.9	61.5	65.7	61.7	51.4	39.9	27.9	18.5	39.7
Rainfall, in.	1.1	0.9	1.2	1.5	1.9	2.0	2.8	2.9	2.2	1.4	1.6	1.5	21.0

likely to be of the heavy thunderstorm variety.

The major economic implications of these *Dfb* and *Dwb* climatic types include the following:

1. High cost of winter air conditioning in buildings
2. High cost of snow removal to maintain surface transportation
3. A short growing season and frost hazards to horticultural specialties
4. Attractiveness of the cool summers as climatic refuges from the heat of the *Cfa* and *Dfa* areas to the south

Air conditioning rarely is needed in summer, but space heating in buildings is desirable over a period ranging from 7 to 8 months. It thus becomes a major item in family budgets. The below-zero winter weather, furthermore, necessitates insulated houses and adds to building costs. Log houses are practical where wood is cheap and plentiful. Frame buildings should be sheathed with insulating material. The cost of lighting houses during the long winter nights is another expensive item, but this is partly counterbalanced by the savings possible during the long days of summer.

The cost of snow removal in areas where motor or rail traffic must be maintained is high, although there are appreciable regional differences in the amount of snowfall (see Fig. 8.14). Areas in this climatic zone that have unusually heavy winter snowfall are described and interpreted in Sec. 6.21.

The growing season in the *Dfb* and *Dwb* climates varies widely, ranging from about 90 to 150 days. The length of the frost-free period is influenced more by the topographic and hydrographic conditions of an area than by its latitudinal position within the climatic region. Specialized horticultural areas are frequently related to low frost susceptibility, particularly for late spring frosts. The specialized fruit areas along the eastern and southeastern shores of the Great Lakes are illustrative. Some of the hardier grain crops, such as oats, barley, rye, and buckwheat, are grown. As in the *Cfb* climates, root and forage crops grow well during the cool, moist summers, being resistant to light frosts. Short-season fruits and vegetables do exceptionally well.

FIG. 8.15 A potato field in Aroostook County, Maine. Long, cool days and short nights during the summer season are especially favorable to the growth of root crops such as the potato in this northern region. [Standard Oil Company (N.J.)]

Despite the high costs of winter space heating and the agricultural limitations of the *Dfb* climates, these areas are well populated. One of the main reasons is the delightful summer season, which has temperatures close to the ideal for body comfort. In the United States and Canada, but also to a certain degree in Europe and Japan, the northern portions of the *Dfb* and *Dwb* regions have important recreational attractions, not only for visitors from the hot climates to the south during the summer but also for winter-sport enthusiasts in winter.

8.17 THE *DFC, DWC,* AND *DWD* CLIMATES (SUBARCTIC).

The *Dfc-Dwc-Dwd*[8] subdivision of the *D* climates is the most extensive of all the groups, covering broad, uninterrupted expanses from Alaska to Labrador in North America and from Norway to Kamchatka in Eurasia. This area closely parallels the region of the northern coniferous forest, that seemingly endless sea of spruce, fir, cedar, larch, and muskeg. This has been described as a country with "10 months' winter and 2 months' bad sleighing." Although every section within this region has at least 1 month with an average mean temperature above 50°, there are invariably less than 4 such months, and frost may occur in any month of the year. The only crops possible without special protective devices are those which will withstand light frosts, such as cabbages, carrots, peas, turnips, and lettuce. These hardy vegetables grow to unusual sizes because of the 18 to 20 hours of daylight during early summer. Although most of the summer is cool, occasional importations of air from the south may send temperatures soaring into the 80s and low 90s for short periods.

Precipitation in these northern regions usually is light, but the low temperatures checking evaporation keep the ground well supplied with moisture. The snowfall is not so heavy as in the *Db* climates to the south, but since less of it disappears through melting or direct evaporation during the winter, a snow cover 2 to 3 feet deep generally persists for 5 to 6 months. Permafrost (see Sec. 12.4), or perpetually frozen subsoil, is a problem in the poleward parts of this group of climates. The southern boundary of permafrost, however, is related more to the texture of the soil material than to average air temperatures.

Winter minimum temperatures in this climatic subgroup are among the lowest ever recorded on the earth surface. An unofficial reading of −108°F was obtained at Oimekon, a small village east of the Lena River in eastern Siberia. For years Verkhoyansk held the world's official record for low temperatures at −90°F, but in 1958 a Russian International Geophysical Year expedition recorded −126°F in Antarctica. Verkhoyansk, located east of the Lena River, has a remarkable range of average mean monthly temperatures, and the mean figures are available for a period that goes back well into the nineteenth century. Its climatic record is given in Table 8.13. The extremely low temperatures in the eastern part of the Soviet Union are caused principally by cold air draining into topographic depressions from mountainous or hilly uplands under excessive radiational cooling on long, clear, calm winter nights. Temperatures elsewhere in the Soviet Union are not appreciably lower than those in northern Canada.

The abnormally low temperatures of the *Dfc-Dwc-Dwd* climates result in a number of problems. Mechanized equipment requires special lubricants, since the customary ones tend to become gummy at −30 to −40°. Also, special clothing is necessary for outdoor wear, largely because the accumulation

[8] Koeppen devised the special symbol *d* to categorize the unusually low temperatures of eastern Siberia. This letter is used when the average mean temperature of the coldest month drops below −36.4°F.

TABLE 8.13 Representative data for the Dwd and Dfc climates

	JAN.	FEB.	MAR.	APR.	MAY	JUNE	JULY	AUG.	SEPT.	OCT.	NOV.	DEC.	YEAR
						Verkhoyansk, U.S.S.R. (lat 68° N, Dwd)							
Temp., °F	−58.2	−47.7	−22.4	8.4	34.7	53.6	59.2	51.4	36.0	5.7	−34.2	−51.7	3.0
Rainfall, in.	0.2	0.1	0.0	0.1	0.2	0.5	1.2	0.9	0.2	0.2	0.2	0.2	3.9
						Churchill, Manitoba (lat 58° N, Dfc)							
Temp., °F	−20.2	−15.6	−3.0	22.4	32.5	42.8	55.5	52.6	42.3	27.3	7.9	−9.0	19.6

of any moisture will rapidly destroy the insulating properties of ordinary outer clothes. Clothing that provides an insulating layer of air between inner and outer coverings is recommended. Steam locomotives have difficulty in maintaining steam pressure, because of rapid cooling and condensation within the cylinders. The tensile strength of metals and other materials rapidly decreases as temperatures drop far below zero, and breakage of structural materials is a constant problem during stress at low temperatures. The increased interest in possible military operations in high latitudes has produced incentives for much research in adaptable materials. Some remarkable achievements have been made in metallurgy, plastics, and silicones (see Sec. 13.20).

As in all polar areas, sunshine on snow produces much eyestrain, and pinkeye (conjunctivitis) is a common and annoying regional malady. Another annoyance of the northern continental areas is the host of bloodsucking insects during the summer, particularly mosquitoes and black gnats. The extensive marshy areas, lakes, and rivers provide ideal incubating areas for winged insects that pass through an aquatic larval stage, and the relative scarcity of animals makes the bloodsucking insects particularly voracious. Fortunately, few of them are carriers of human diseases.

Population is sparse in the *Dc* and *Dd* areas, and it is not likely to increase, except possibly in scattered mining, hunting, and lumbering regions. The greatest pressure for settlement has occurred in the Soviet Union, where there is a continuing effort to force the limit of agriculture northward into this climatic region. Progress has been slow, and for the most part the *taiga,* or northern coniferous forest, remains a wilderness. People are willing to undergo the rigors of this climate only where there are unusual economic opportunities, particularly in mining, and these are for the most part spotty and temporary.

The *E* climate (polar)

8.18 DESCRIPTION AND DISTRIBUTION OF THE *E* CLIMATE.

The *E* climate may be considered to have no true summer. Statistically it includes areas where the mean monthly temperatures do not exceed 50°.[9] An example of the seasonal temperature distribution is shown in Table 8.14, which gives statistics reported by a station near the southern border of the *E* climate.

Except for Antarctica and for high elevations south of the equator, the *E* climate, like the *D* climates, is found only in the northern

[9] Prior to the publication of the latest Koeppen-Geiger climatic map, the *E* climate was subdivided into two types: *ET*, or the tundra type, where the average mean temperature of the warmest month is between 32 and 50°, and the *EF*, or frozen type, where the warmest month is below 32°.

TABLE 8.14 Mean monthly temperatures at Hebron, Labrador, lat 58°N

	JAN.	FEB.	MAR.	APR.	MAY	JUNE	JULY	AUG.	SEPT.	OCT.	NOV.	DEC.	YEAR
Temp., °F	−5.7	−5.1	5.8	18.3	31.5	40.0	47.1	48.1	40.9	31.2	19.8	4.2	23.0

hemisphere. It skirts the northern edges of both North America and Eurasia, extending farther south along the eastern margins of the continents. In Labrador it almost reaches the Gulf of St. Lawrence at lat 52° N. The boundary between the *E* and *D* climates approximates the poleward limit of tree growth, although the depth of the permafrost layer appears to play an important role in determining the details of this vegetation boundary. The most significant feature of the *E* climates is the contrast in length of day between summer and winter. Despite the long daylight period in summer, temperatures do not rise much because of the low angle of the sun's radiation, the large amount of reflection of insolation off snow, ice, or bare-ground surfaces, and the amount of heat that is utilized in melting snow and ice. Daytime cloudiness also is likely to be high during the summer season bordering the Arctic Ocean, thus interfering with incoming radiation. Because of the low temperatures, air masses contain little moisture; thus precipitation is light in both winter and summer seasons.

The *E* climates may not have a true summer in comparison with climates farther away from the poles, but the high-sun period seems a real summer to the few arctic inhabitants. Most of the snow disappears, and an occasional warm, balmy day is experienced. The tundra at this time is a riot of flowering plants, and the great northern rivers break free of their ice. Pack ice moves away from the coast line of the Arctic Ocean, and the open water presages the arrival of the supply steamers to the coastal villages. The dog sleds are replaced by small barges with outboard motors, and houses are aired out for the first time in months. The air hums with hungry insects, and the odor of fresh fish hangs about the settlements. The greatest summer enjoyment lies in taking advantage of the first daylight hours after the winter darkness. Cross-country travel on the tundra is extremely difficult in summer because of the marshy ground, bodies of standing water, and rivers. If travel is necessary, it is generally done by boat. Water dominates the landscape of the plains, despite the light precipitation.

Winter brings darkness and extreme cold, although temperatures are not so low as can be found in some of the more interior positions farther south. The thermometer rarely rises to zero. The snow crunches and rings as one walks on it, and a wreath of condensed vapor marks breath exhalations. The arctic nights are not so dark as those at lower latitudes. The aurora borealis plays back and forth across the sky, and cumulative starlight appears to make surface features dimly visible under the extremely clear skies. Winter gales blow in spells, separated by calm periods. During these gales the air is filled with horizontally flying snow, most of which is blown from the ground rather than derived from fresh precipitation. Visibility is extremely low. Except during these gale periods, winter cross-country travel on the tundra is relatively easy.

Winter gales, mostly gravity winds, are much more frequent over the icecap regions

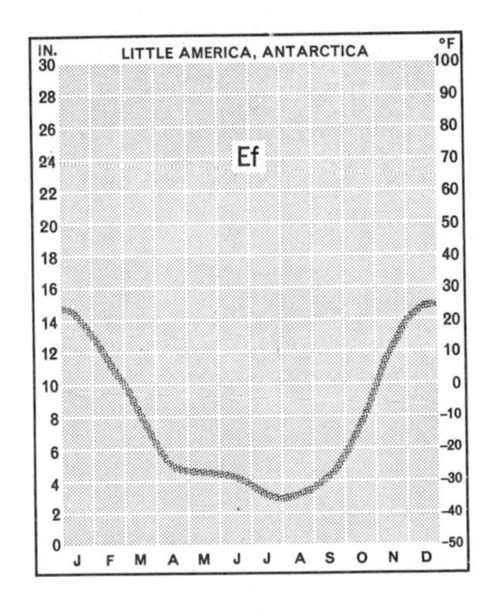

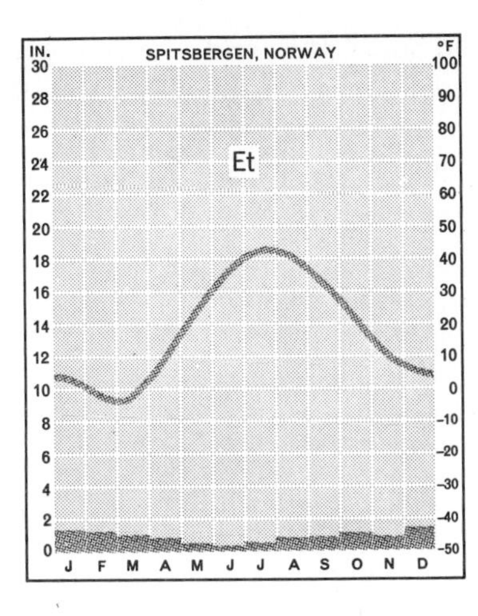

FIG. 8.16 Two extremes of E climates. Only a slight rise in the July average at Spitsbergen (north of Norway) would place it in the D climates. At Little America, on the other hand, none of the monthly averages rises even to the freezing point.

than on the tundra, and "summer" temperatures are much lower. Precipitation consists more of fine ice particles than of true snowflakes.

8.19 THE HIGH-ELEVATION *E* CLIMATES. The *E* climates can be found at any latitude, if a sufficiently high elevation is reached. The mountain *E* climates, like their high-latitude counterparts, begin roughly at the tree line. As might be expected, the elevation of the mountain *E* climates varies with the temperature of the adjacent lowlands as well as with the local lapse rate. Subject to several local qualifications, the *E* climates begin at about 12,000 feet near the equator, rise slightly at lat 20 to 30° N and S, because of higher temperatures and decreased precipitation, then progressively lower in elevation until they reach sea level near the Arctic Circle. The snow line lies roughly about 2,000 feet higher, although its elevation is much more irregular, because of varying precipitation and exposure to insolation. In the northern United States, for example, the permanent snow line lies some 1,500 feet higher on the Rocky Mountain slopes than in the Cascades at about the same latitude. The largest area of high-elevation *E* climates is found in central Asia. Most of Tibet is well above the tree line, and all the major ranges that protrude above its high plains are snow-covered.

The mountain *E* climates are populated to a limited degree, and the permanent inhabitants of this harsh environment probably sought it as a place of refuge. The Indians of Peru, in escaping the subjugation of their Inca and Spanish masters, sought the upper part of the *tierra fria* just below the snow line and, in so doing, gave to the world the "Irish" potato. The tiny, bitter tubers of this native plant provided sustenance in a land that no one else wanted. Barley, the hardiest of all grains, likewise supplies a precarious food supply to permanent dwellers of the high-elevation slopes and plains and may well have been developed from one of the mountain grasses of central Asia. Today it is the staple food for the inhabitants of Tibet and adjacent mountain lands.

The alpine pastures above the timber line have attracted pastoral peoples since earliest times, and throughout the world, flocks of sheep, goats, cattle, yaks, llamas, vicuñas, and alpacas are led up into the mountain meadows during the short summer season.

Where mountains are found adjacent to arid and semiarid lands, the cool, moist alpine regions in the summer are much more attractive than the tundra lands of the latitudinal *E* climates, which are so far from people, so wet underfoot in the summer, and so infested with insects. Only a few specialized groups, like the Lapps and Eskimos, are able to live permanently off the tundra landscape.

9

Principles and factors in plant geography

The great variety of plants that clothe the naked surface of the earth is one of the most interesting and most obvious features of physical geography. All around us can be seen the culmination of eons of plant selection: the forest giants; the lowly microscopic algae that form a scum on stagnant pools; cacti that thrive on meager desert moisture; lichens clinging to bare rock surfaces; carnivorous plants; plant parasites that consume the foods manufactured by other plants, animals, and even man; acid-tolerant plants and salt-tolerant plants; plants that live wholly under water; plants that live wholly underground. These represent some of the different ways in which plants have reacted to widely differing environments.

Much of the material in this chapter and the following one deals with natural processes and associations in the development of vegetation patterns. It should be kept in mind throughout, however, that, although nonhuman factors in the environment of plants are always present, natural vegetation associations or plant communities unaffected by man are exceedingly rare on the face of the earth. To emphasize this point, a separate division has been included in this chapter on the role of man in plant geography. A comprehensive summary of the various ways in which man modifies the plant covering on the earth could not possibly have been included in this chapter. The treatment here, therefore, is meant to be more suggestive than inclusive. It is likely that most readers live in an environment where the human factor is predominant in shaping the local vegetation patterns. Nevertheless, the interested student who keeps his eyes open should be able to observe the influences of the physical environment on vegetation even in the midst of cultivated fields or around the margins of cities.

The arrangement of plants

9.1 PLANT COMMUNITIES. An overall view of the earth and its plant covering reveals that, despite the almost infinite variety of plant forms, distinct groupings of plants appear at different levels of observation. Whether one views the arrangement of plants on an entire continent, within a state or province, on a casual stroll through a

FIG. 9.1 A forest community with hemlock and yellow poplar as the dominant tree types. Rhododendrons and ferns form part of the characteristic ground flora. The photo was taken in the Joyce Kilmer Memorial Forest in the Great Smoky Mountains of North Carolina. [U.S. Department of Agriculture]

neighboring patch of forest, or on one's knees along a fence row bordering a field, distinct groupings of plants will be observed. These groupings of plants are not miscellaneous mixtures of plant types. Instead, they represent plant *communities,* whose individual members share a given environment and often have developed a mutual support in the successful occupation of this environment.

Plant communities vary in size from small local groupings to broad agglomerations that span continents. They are as different from one another as a Chinese peasant village is from an English mill town. There is little in common between the riotous combination of tall grasses and herbaceous plants in a virgin prairie and the soggy, moss-covered, and shapeless forms of the cloud-zone forest on tropical mountain slopes; yet both are distinct communities of plants, developed under widely different environments.

Individual plant types or entire communities may compete with each other for a particular site and react differently to changes in environmental factors. Some groups resist change with stubborn persistence, whereas others are highly sensitive to slight external forces. Continued disruptions of communities often lead to their dissolution, until only traces of their former presence may be observed. Plant communities have a remarkable resilience, however, and after the disruptive factors have been removed, they usually revert to their original form.

There is a decided hierarchy among the individual plant types within a community. In a forest community, for example, trees are the ruling members, and the ferns and low shrubs that dwell on the forest floor represent the lesser members of the plant community. They require less light or less moisture and thus can live on the "crumbs from the table."

The broadest types of plant community are the plant *formations,* comprising the global forests, the grasslands, the desert shrubs, and the tundra. These cover large areas that are closely related to major climatic differences on a global scale. There are, however, great differences within each of these formations. The spruce-fir forests of Canada, the deciduous, oak-hickory forests of the east-central United States, and the broadleaf evergreen forests of the humid tropics are comparable only in that trees form the dominant vegetation forms. There are similar broad differences within the other formations. Both likenesses and dissimilarities of vegetation are present everywhere. Tree growth is a feature common to all forests; yet every local variation in slope, drainage, exposure, and microclimate results in localized differences. A timber "cruiser," in estimating the stand of merchantable timber in a particular forest, is acutely aware of local regional similarities and differences in the arrangement of tree species and ages; yet he usually has only a passing glance for the kaleidoscopic pattern of microflora that changes every foot or so as he strides along his route.

Vegetation communities invariably are arranged in tiers, or stories, reflecting the three-dimensional arrangement of plant environments. A forest, for example, consists of many plants other than trees. It may include the feathery fronds of ferns, thriving in the dampness and shade of the "ground floor." Perhaps it also includes small flowering plants, such as anemones, mayflowers, trilliums, or mandrakes, which find ideal conditions for flowering and fruiting in the short spring season of mid-latitude deciduous forests, before tree foliage reduces available sunshine. A forest may also contain the slender white threads of *mycelium* fungi, interfingering the matting of needles on a pine-forest floor, or clumps of mushrooms, which are able to feed on partially decayed forest litter and are not called upon to manufacture plant sugars from sunlight. In the depth of the tropical rain forest, the lower stories often include tree types that can thrive under different conditions of light or moisture. This arrangement of vegetation into tiers is not confined to forests. Grasslands contain many species of grasses and herbaceous plants that reach varying heights at maturity and represent different selectivities to conditions of light, temperature, and moisture. Similar conditions can be observed in the tundra and among desert plants.

Plant communities are never in a condition of complete stability, although the various elements within an environmental complex always tend to work toward mutual adjustments. The changes that take place in the environmental progression away from or toward relative equilibrium are accompanied by corresponding changes in plant communities. If, for example, a forest is destroyed by lumbering, the struggle for sunlight proceeds from the ground level. Under the open sun, the higher ground-surface temperatures and lower moisture conditions are advantageous to many plants that never had a chance in the competition of a mature forest environment. In time, if left undisturbed, the forest community will once again establish itself—perhaps at first with varieties of trees that are different from those of the relatively stable, or *climax,* types. Eventually, however, these newcomers usually are replaced by the members of the ultimate community.

Not all environmental changes in a forest are as sudden as that associated with lumbering operations. There may be a change in hydrologic (drainage) conditions over several decades, a significant alteration of climate, or extensive gullying over still longer periods of time. Each of these changes, as well as many others of much shorter duration, involves alterations in the forest community, resulting in changes not only in the individual species of trees present but in the groupings of plants within the forest complex.

9.2 PLANT SUCCESSION AND THE ESTABLISHMENT OF CLIMAX COMMUNITIES.

The sequence of plant groupings that progresses from a bare ground surface to a stabilized state in harmony with the total environment is termed *plant succession* (see Figs. 9.2 and 9.3). The following example of plant succession was observed by the author on a garden plot in southern New York State:

> The garden was plowed and harrowed but was not seeded. Within a week or so, the ground was carpeted with small annuals—the weeds that were so troublesome in cultivation the year before. Untouched by the hoe, they grew in profusion. At first the short types covered the ground, but in a few weeks taller varieties made their appearance. Here and there a few grasses took root and spread laterally. By the end of the first summer, the plot was a confused tangle of plants, ranging from lowly purslane to waist-high Compositae. A few scattered perennials appeared, such as dandelions. The perennial herbs and grasses had become more dominant by the end of the second year, and at the end of the third and fourth years they had taken over the garden. Now a definite, storied field community had been established, with goldenrod, Queen Anne's lace, and milkweed as the taller members, grass as the dominant intermediate story, and a ground flora of low vines, including field strawberry, dewberry, and cinquefoil.
>
> Trees and bushes appeared above the herbaceous plants during the sixth and seventh years and consisted mainly of scattered white pine (*Pinus strobus*), clumps of aspen, and willow. The pine rapidly outstripped the others, and from evidence elsewhere in the area it will have established a pine forest within about 20 years. The pine, however, still is not a climax vegetation, and once shade is provided, maple, yellow birch, beech, and elm will become established as an understory, later destined to be the dominants in the climax community.

Widely dissimilar natural environments exhibit great differences in the sequence of plant succession. Not only are the climax communities at the end of the plant succession different, but so also are the stages in the progression toward that climax. A cultivated field, for example, if left to nature for regrowth, will have a much different plant succession in the humid tropics than in Aroostook County, Maine, or on the steppes of Alberta. Likewise, the succession that develops on a sandy soil often will be different from one on an adjacent heavy clay. The succession following a forest fire will be different from one following lumbering or cultivation, even within the same area.

Stages in plant succession may be observed everywhere and are important in understanding the complexity of vegetation patterns. They may be seen along the sides of roads; along fence lines; at the edges of forests; bordering lakes, swamps, and marshes; in old abandoned fields; and on steep, rocky hillsides. If left alone, all these stages will progress toward a relatively long-term balanced state, which is determined principally by climate and surface configuration. Some parts of the world show a greater dominance of stable vegetation communities than others, either because they have more stable physical environments or because man has not been as active in disturbing the vegetation.

Man is especially effective in altering environments, not only the vegetation but other related elements of the landscape. Climax vegetation, therefore, is rare in populated areas. Botanists still are not in agreement as to what the prehuman regional vegetation was in North China, because there are no traces of undisturbed vegetation left in this crowded land, which has had such a long history of human occupancy. Perhaps the most extensive areas of climax vegetation are to be found in some of the great tropical forests or in the unglaciated sections of the northern coniferous forests of the Soviet Union. Both of these regions are now, and always have been, relatively sparsely inhabited.

FIG. 9.2 Plant succession on an abandoned pasture in southern New York. White pine (Pinus strobus) seedlings are among the first trees to follow the tall perennial herbs and grasses. The herbaceous plants shown in the foreground include goldenrod, Queen Anne's lace, and New England asters.

Continental glaciation tends to create unusually complex patterns of plant communities, because of sharp local contrasts in surface materials and in drainage conditions. Also, climatic changes during the 10,000 to 20,000 years since the last major advance of a continental ice sheet may have altered the climax vegetation patterns, although the modifications occurred too slowly to be recognized. Many ecologists today are disclaiming the entire concept of climax communities, on the ground that environments never remain completely stable. For our purposes, however, the concept of plant balances is a useful one, if we keep in mind that there are short-term balances and long-term balances, and that the term *climax* merely refers to a relatively long-term balance with respect to landscape patterns.

Not all forms present in a plant community react in the same way or at the same rate to environmental changes. The microflora, the tiny delicate forms, may change considerably with fluctuations in seasonal weather conditions from year to year, whereas trees in a climax forest may take centuries

FIG. 9.3 Diagram showing typical plant succession on a section of the Atlantic coastal plain in the southeastern United States. The pine probably represents a fire-succession flora. [After Odum]

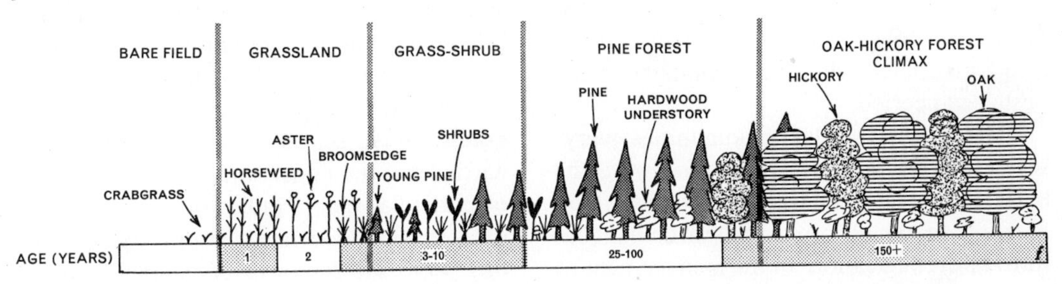

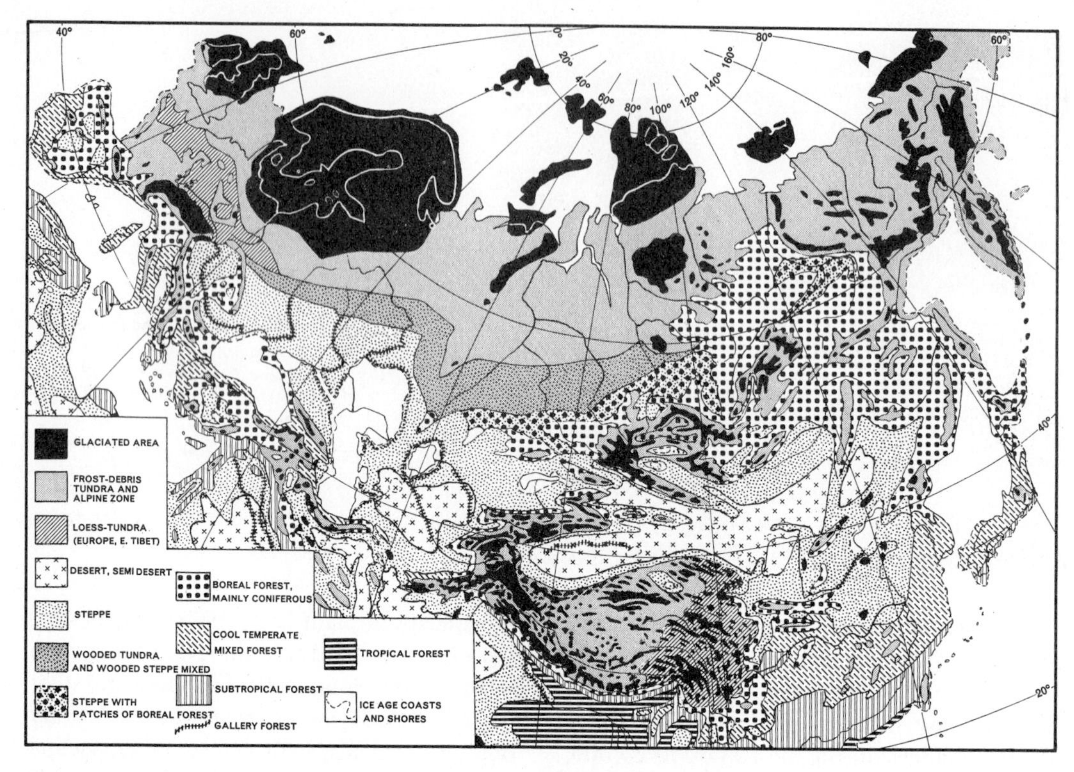

FIG. 9.4 Pleistocene vegetation boundaries. [After Wissmann]

to adjust to the subtle processes of soil development or climatic changes. Because of the varying rate of adjustments within the vegetation communities, some of the larger forms, such as trees, may be *relict* forms, left from a previous climax community. Many plant ecologists believe, for example, that hemlock (*Tsuga*) (see Fig. 9.1), which is a conifer commonly associated with the upland maple and beech forests of the northeastern United States, is a relict form left from the climax forest associated with cooler climates in the postglacial period.

The tendency of plant communities everywhere to assume an equilibrium with the local environment is most useful to man when he seeks to exploit or control particular features of the vegetation. In the management of grazing lands, for example, different plants indicate various stages in the sequence toward, or away from, vegetation equilibrium. This information may be critical in maintaining the range at maximum carrying capacity for animals. Certain weeds in cultivated fields signify a need for drainage to improve crop yields, and others indicate that liming is necessary to check an increase in soil acidity. There are plants in irrigated deserts that indicate increasing or decreasing alkalinity in soils, a critical factor in this type of land utilization. In forest management programs, where selective logging practices are carried on, the appearance or disappearance of particular plant "indicators" may be critical to the maintenance of proper rates of cutting or to the regrowth of valuable species.

9.3 PLANT GEOGRAPHY AND THE PRINCIPLES OF NATURAL DISTRIBUTIONS.

Plants, as elements in the environmental complex, form no exception to the basic principles of natural distributions that were described in Chapter 1. The first principle, that of *infinite variety of forms and areal expression amidst graded likeness,* is beautifully illustrated by vegetation. Botanists still do not have a complete catalogue of plant species on earth, and no perfect duplication has been found within any one species. The variety of plant types is mainly the result of *mutations,* those molecular rearrangements (now believed to be the result mainly of cosmic-ray bombardment) which occur spontaneously from time to time within plant reproductive cells and which are repeated in later generations of plants. Such alterations have taken place since plant life first appeared on earth. Mutations alone, however, do not explain the forms that are now present. The great variety of environments on earth and alterations in these environments create conditions for either the acceptance or rejection of the new forms. Mutations, plus natural selection, result in the kinds of plants that now mantle the earth surface. Because the environment of plants cannot be exactly duplicated in any two spots on the earth surface, neither can the association of plants be exactly duplicated. Differences become apparent if one scrutinizes the area closely enough.

Despite the infinite variety of plant forms and areal differences in plant groupings, graded likenesses in both plant forms and areal groupings also appear everywhere. The reproductive process ensures the continuance of certain basic characteristics; hence the botanist is able to create a systematic classification of plants. A tree may be recognized as a tree; all maple trees have characteristic structures; and despite the many species within the genus *Acer,* each such species can be systematically classified according to form. Likewise, although areal groupings of plants are never exactly alike, similarities can be recognized in widely scattered parts of the world. The recognition and explanation of significant areal similarities and differences in plant communities are the central concerns of plant geography.

The second principle, that *regional similarities grade outward in all directions through transitional zones,* is revealed in plant arrangements everywhere. Examine, for example, the zonal sequence of plant communities bordering a swamp or marsh, and note how the gradual improvement of soil drainage is marked by successive changes in plant groupings. Even such sharp boundaries as a fence line separating a cleared field from a wood lot is not without its sequence of plant communities, reflecting the changes in microclimate and particularly the amount of sunlight available along such a boundary.

Some vegetation transitions can be observed much more easily than others, especially where the dominant types of one plant community are quite unlike those of another in size or form. Also, the place of areal change generally becomes less clear when we are dealing with major plant groupings. The boundaries of the great global vegetation formations, for example, represent unusually wide transitional zones. The long tongues of forest that extend along the watercourses far within the world grasslands and into the tundra, the islands of grass such as the *oak openings* that formerly were found in the forests adjacent to prairies in Indiana and Illinois, the sagebrush that hides the mergence of steppes and desert over hundreds of miles, not only in the western United States, but also in the Soviet Union, are all examples of the broad width of the transitional zone between the formations. On the other hand, the transitions from reeds to sedges, from sedges to bushes, and from bushes to trees along a local marsh-forest boundary may take place within a few feet of one another. Furthermore, the zone which the eye classifies as a zone of sedges contains smaller plant forms that could be further classified to represent still smaller plant regions, and consequently would have sharper regional boundaries. The borders of vegetation regions, regardless of scale, exhibit all the characteristics of transitional patterns, including varying gradients of change, diffusion, interfingering, and enclaves.

The third principle indicates the *continuous alteration of areal associations with the passage of time.* In earlier chapters we noted that land-surface features are altered continuously through various geologic processes and at different rates, ranging from the suddenness of a landslide or volcanic explosion to the slow creep of soil down a slope mantled with forests. We also caught a glimpse of the day-to-day, year-to-year, and multicentury climatic changes that continually take place. Plant groupings are highly sensitive to changes in their environments, and both long- and short-term alterations can be observed. An early frost, an exceptionally dry year, a sudden windstorm—each of these claims its plant victims and thus aids other plants by freeing them from their formerly successful competitors for living space. To be sure, recovery is rapid, but the changes continue. The more lasting alterations are tied to long-range trends, where recovery is less certain. The erosion of an outlet to a swamp or marsh, which results in draining the area, will permanently alter the groupings of moisture-tolerant plants. No plant association in any area ever remains exactly the same with the passage of time.

The fourth and last principle of natural distributions states that *the elements in an environmental complex tend to develop mutual adjustments to each other and to aim toward a relative equilibrium.* Like the other elements, plants of course never reach a complete equilibrium, because of both short- and long-term changes in environments. In the time scale of human endeavor, however, the concept of relative equilibrium is useful and has meaning. Because of the wide range of plant adaptations and their easily observed characteristics, plants make good indicators of changes toward, or away from, relative environmental equilibria. Each of the environmental elements plays some role in determining the characteristics of vegetation patterns, and during periods of relative stability, vegetation patterns reflect the mutual adjustments that are made. Later sections of this chapter indicate the importance of various elements in determining the characteristics of resultant vegetation patterns.

Vegetation itself is not a completely passive element in the environment. The chemical composition of the litter on a forest floor may vary sufficiently to influence appreciably the acidity of underlying soils. The influence of different types of vegetation on the speed of soil erosion is readily observable, and there is growing evidence that forests and grasslands produce different local climatic characteristics, including evaporation rates, humidity, and wind velocities. Belts of trees, termed *shelter belts,* have been planted in semiarid regions in both the United States and the Soviet Union, with varying results in retention of soil moisture. The interrelationship between plant roots and microorganisms in the soil is well known; for example, the nitrogen-fixing bacteria that dwell in nodules on the roots of many leguminous plants, such as clover, alfalfa, and soybeans, convert atmospheric nitrogen into nitrates, which can then be utilized by the plants.

The concept of trends toward relative equilibria in vegetation is perhaps most justifiable in respect to man's relationship to vegetation. Man is extremely active in altering vegetation patterns, because of his interest in utilizing plants for many purposes. From a utilitarian point of view, his own effects on vegetation are far more important than long-run climatic or geologic alterations. For his own welfare, he needs to know whether a particular method of changing vegetation will lead toward, or away from, relative stability.

To illustrate, suppose that a forest in the northeastern United States has been cut and that not a tree remains standing. If left alone, this environment will develop a forest cover, mainly because of climatic conditions and plant competition. Obviously, a forest here represents a more balanced and stable form of vegetation than the low ground cover that immediately follows deforestation. Proof of this is the rapid change in plants that compete with one another for occupancy of the bare site. Suppose, however, that man wishes to reestablish a forest cover without waiting for the natural progression toward the relatively balanced forest community. It is clearly useful for him to know that certain species of trees will thrive and that others will not. It is also important for him to know that, by altering an environmental factor such as drainage, he can produce conditions which will lead toward the establishment of a relatively stable type of forest that yields more valuable kinds of trees.

The major variables in plant geography

9.4 WATER SUPPLY. Among the variety of factors that determine the gross features of vegetation differences on the earth, the most important is the availability of water. Water plays a leading and decisive role in nearly every life process of plants, including germination, growth, and reproduction. It is more than the lifeblood of plants, more than a transporting medium for plant foods and waste products. It enters into the formation of most of the organic compounds of plants. Photosynthesis, or the utilization of solar energy in the manufacture of sugars and starches within green plants, could not take place without it, and even parasitic plants, which do not manufacture such compounds themselves but steal them from others, require water for cell construction and maintenance. When water leaves plant cells, the cells wither and die.

The size of plants usually represents a balance between the intake and outgo of water. Large, tall plants, such as trees, exist in environments where a large intake, mainly through root absorption, is matched by a large outgo, carried on mainly by *transpiration* (exhalation) from leaves and stems. Smaller supplies of water must be matched by decreased outgo; hence plant size must be reduced. In some areas the rate of transpiration is relatively high and the amount of available water relatively low. In desert areas, for example, transpiration rates are high because of strong, steady winds, high plant-surface temperatures, and low relative humidity. In such places, plants must remain small to survive.

The global plant formations represent major differences in moisture balances. Forests occur where plant moisture exchanges are large. Desert shrubs exhibit many characteristics, including small size, which enable them to adjust low intakes to high transpiration rates. The dwarfed vegetation forms of the tundra and alpine associations represent balances that occur between low transpiration rates, which are the result of low air temperatures, and low intakes, resulting from

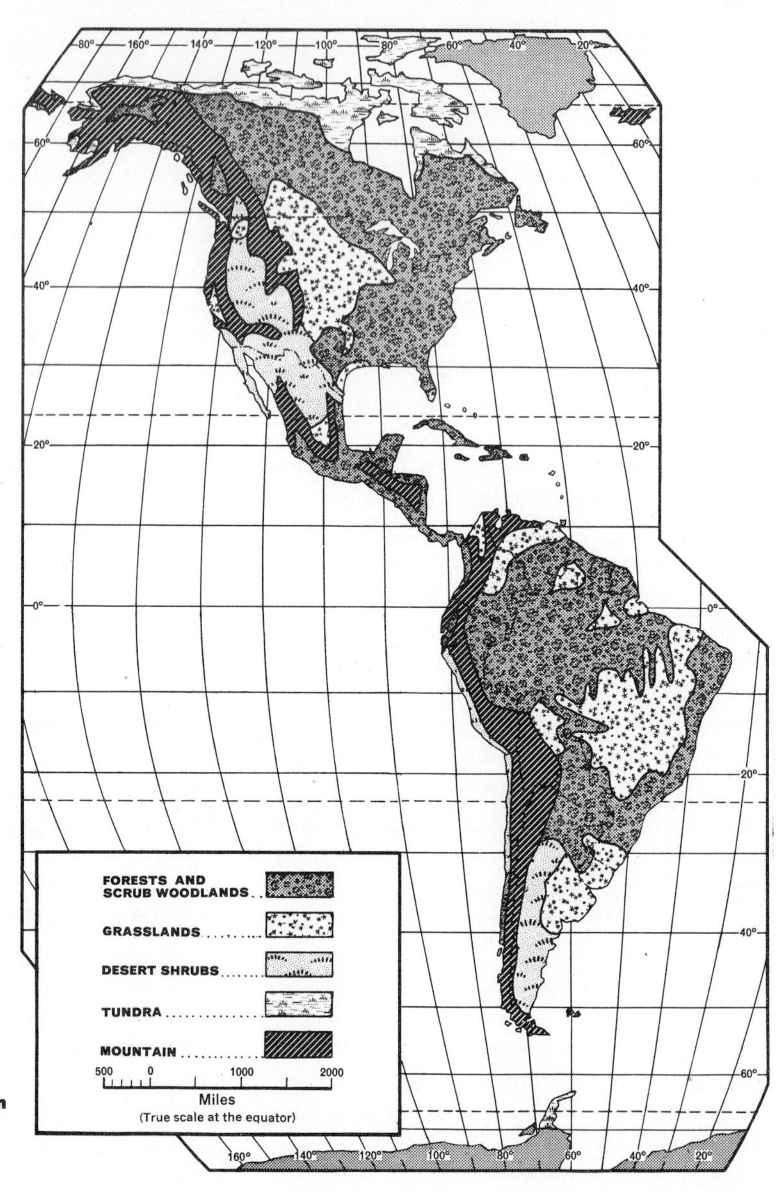

FIG. 9.5 World distribution of major plant formations.

long frozen periods. Natural grasslands appear to develop best under conditions where fairly large intakes of water occur for short periods during the year, particularly during hot periods when transpiration rates are high, and where soil moisture deficiencies frequently occur at other times of the year.

Many of the major subdivisions of the global vegetation formations also reflect plant moisture balances. One of the major subdivisions of global forests, for example, is the type composed of trees that tend to shed their leaves during some season of the year. This characteristic is largely a result of pronounced seasonal climatic differences. In the tropics and subtropics, the deciduous nature

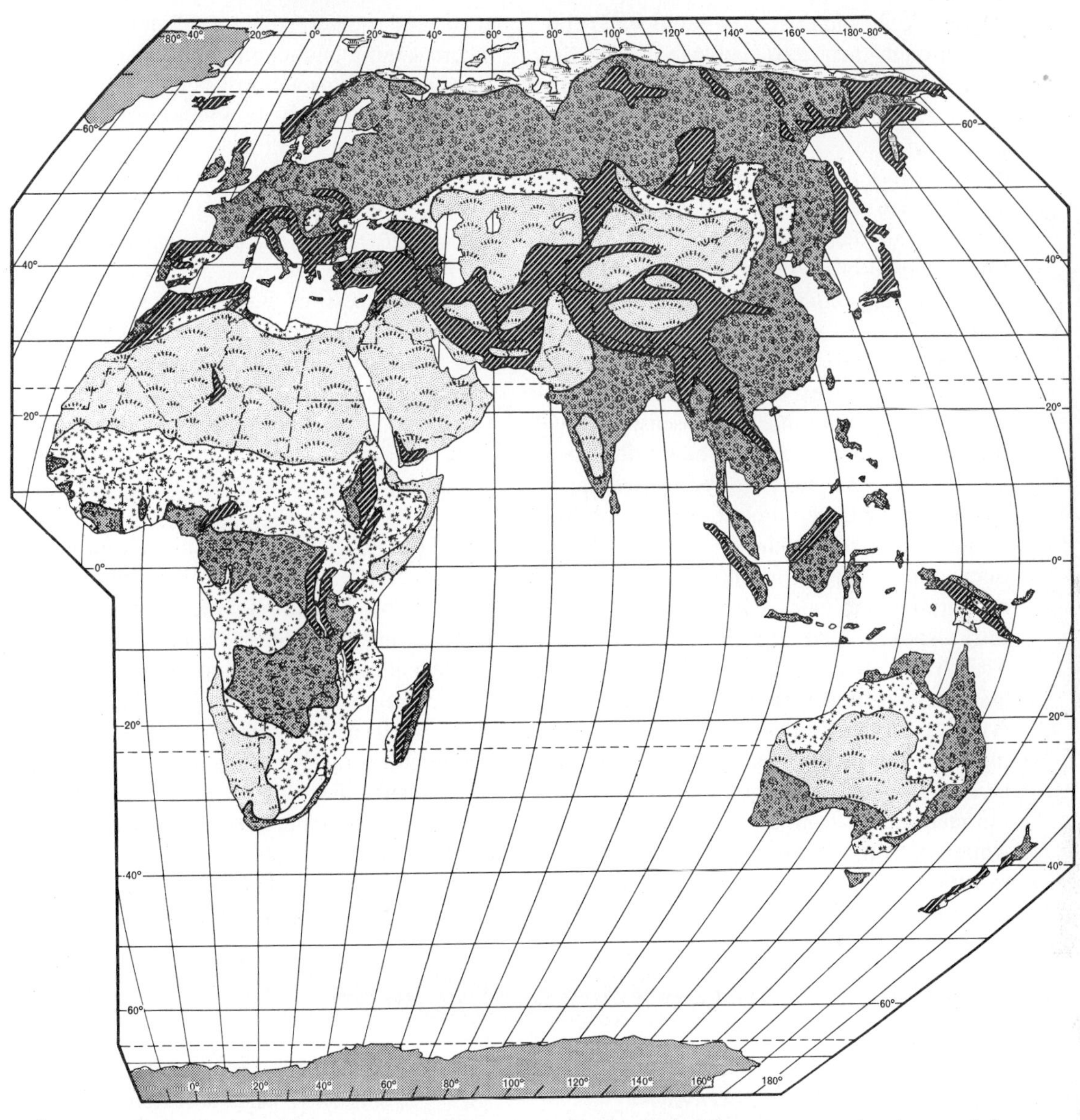

of trees and shrubs is a direct result of alternate wet and dry seasons. Here the abundance of soil water for plant intake and the high transpiration potentials during the humid period favor luxurious tree growth. The dry period, in contrast, supplies insufficient soil water to maintain this lush growth. To compensate, the trees shed their leaves and maintain their life processes at a bare minimum during the dry period.

Winter freezing in the mid-latitudes also produces a deciduous reaction in many trees. In these areas temperature is a decisive factor, but its influence on the deciduous nature of plants operates through the availability of water. In such climates, trees lead a sort of double life. In summer, they pump water rapidly through their cells, behaving much like trees everywhere that have sufficient moisture and heat for rapid growth. In winter, on the other hand, they take on the characteristics of *xerophytes,* or drought-resistant plants. They reduce transpiration to a minimum by shedding all their leaves and retain only a small amount of water within the plant cells, since freezing would cause cell disruption and death.

Needleleaf trees, such as pines and spruces, have many characteristics that enable them to withstand strong seasonal contrasts in moisture balances. The small surface area of the leaves tends to reduce transpiration; yet their large number enables the tree to perform photosynthesis effectively. The thick, pitchy sap of needleleaf trees resists evaporation and quickly heals wounds in the thick, spongy, and highly insulative bark. The shallow but well-developed root system assures that much rain water percolating downward in the soil can be intercepted during the warm season, but since the roots lie at or near frost depth, they cannot absorb too much water from deep in the soil during winter seasons. Because of their moisture-retention capabilities, conifers are also adaptable to highly permeable, and thus droughty, sand and gravel soils of climatic regions where rainfall and temperature would appear to warrant luxurious broadleaf forests.

Moisture is such an important factor in determining plant characteristics that it is the primary basis for several vegetation classifications. The simplest such grouping includes the *xerophytes,* or moisture-deficient plants; the *hydrophytes,* water-loving plants that tolerate an excess of water; the *mesophytes,* which have moderate moisture preferences; and finally the *tropophytes,* which undergo special changes in form to adjust to seasonal variations in moisture utilization. Representative examples of plants in each of these groups are given in Table 9.1.

9.5 TEMPERATURE. Temperature alone is not a significant factor in determining the major global vegetation patterns, although its indirect influence upon water availability through its effect on evaporation rates and the freezing of cell fluids is of primary importance. Cell destruction due solely to high temperatures rarely occurs below 122°F, and some plants thrive in temperatures not far below the boiling point, such as the algae that dwell in the hot springs of Yellowstone National Park. Similarly, low temperatures alone rarely kill plants without the aid of

TABLE 9.1 Classification of plants according to water requirement

TYPE	EXAMPLES
Xerophytes (*xero* = dry; *phyto* = plant)	Cacti, desert junipers, sagebrush, certain bulb plants
Hydrophytes (*hydro* = water)	Water lilies, seaweed, sedges, bulrushes, mangroves, swamp cypress
Mesophytes (*meso* = middle)	Live oaks, mahogany, rubber trees, rhododendrons, and many common field and forest plants
Tropophytes (*tropos* = changing)	Maple, birch, ash, larch, teak, some acacias

freezing water. This does not mean that temperature in itself plays only a minor role in plant characteristics; it signifies only that it is a less important factor than water supply in determining the boundaries of the major plant formations. One eminent plant ecologist has stated that, whereas water balances determine the major vegetation formations, temperature plays the major part in determining the floristic variations within the formations. The *direct* influences of temperature affect rate of growth, fertilization, plant stature, maturing of tissues ("ripening off" in autumn), seed germination, and time of flowering, especially when the latter is combined with length of day.

Every plant has an optimum temperature for each of its various life processes, and in the competition for survival, the optimum temperatures for growth, germination, and reproduction are important assets. Plants also have maximum and minimum temperatures beyond which they cannot survive. Although some plants may survive below-freezing temperatures, they must curtail their normal life processes during such periods; thus protracted freezing temperatures weed out all plants that require extended germinating, growing, and reproduction periods. On the other hand, certain varieties of plants thrive in the short, warm periods of the arctic tundra (see Fig. 9.6) and have remarkably low optimum temperatures for growth and reproduction. The familiar crocus and snowdrop thrive in temperatures that are prohibitive to most garden flowers, and we welcome their bright blooms soon after the snows of midlatitude winters disappear. Although temperature has little direct influence on the boundary between forests and grasslands, it is a highly significant factor in the selection of the particular trees found in a forest and in the association of grasses found in a prairie or steppe.

FIG. 9.6 Mountain Avens (Dryas), a typical arctic flower. The tight, rosettelike clusters and their propagation by budding are typical of many of the arctic plants. [Borge Fristrup; Geographical Review]

The only plants to survive where temperature and moisture conditions show great seasonal contrasts are those that have highly specialized mechanisms for resisting such changes. This is why the number of species within forests increases as one proceeds toward the humid tropics. General growth conditions in the latter are adaptable to a wide variety of trees that differ only in minor respects. Relatively few species of trees, however, have been able to survive the vicissitudes of climatic fluctuations between the long summer days and long winter nights in the forests just south of the tundra.

Temperature differences may influence plants in many ways. The optimum temperature for germination is sometimes well below that of seed production or growth. Lettuce, for example, tends to grow tall and produce seed during high summer temperatures, but it germinates and produces leaves most effectively during cooler periods. Some plants require that their seeds be frozen prior to germination. Others require a special conditioning period in moist soils, with temperatures slightly above the freezing point. Many plants adjust their growth conditions to the fluctuations of temperature between night and day, developing a rhythm (termed *thermoperiodism*) which appears to be essential to their optimum growth.

Everyone who has done any gardening knows that plants differ widely in their sensitivity to low temperatures. Some plants actually suffer cell deterioration at temperatures somewhat above freezing, whereas others may tolerate temperatures far below zero for short periods. The various mechanisms of plants for protection against low temperatures result in reducing the significance of the freezing line as a critical boundary in natural plant geography. Plants that are native to areas where frost occurs have developed tolerances to it and, indeed, may require it for their survival. As was indicated in Chapter 6, the freezing boundary is difficult to define, as is the length of the frost-free period. It appears to be more important as a factor in the broader vegetation patterns. Man is vitally interested in the freezing boundary, wherever it may be, mainly because, in his efforts to produce food and feed by cultivating plants, he is likely to introduce many plants into environments which are not their native habitat. The distribution of peach cultivation, for example, becomes more highly selective topographically as one travels farther north in the United States. This selection usually is accomplished through trial and error, because the factors contributing to success or failure are highly complex. To illustrate, peach cultivation in one area may be prevented because of the high frequency of warm days in the early spring, which results in premature budding and subsequent freezing. Elsewhere it may be related to the absolute minimum temperatures of the winter season, in areas where the temperature is low enough for tree destruction. In both of the above cases, the normal length of the growing season is irrelevant.

The impacts of temperature on plant geography are subtle and complex. In general, however, it appears to have a more direct and determining influence the closer one looks at the vegetation pattern. On a topographic scale, it is ever present as a selector of the individual plant species that one sees about him. The attention paid to microtemperature patterns by large commercial horticultural producers is evidence of this. At the same time, temperature does not determine the gross global patterns. These are outlined primarily by effective moisture balances.

9.6 LIGHT. Light is a form of energy, and most plants require it in their life processes. In burning a ton of coal, one releases the energy of sunlight once captured by plants, bound into complex organic molecules, and later concentrated by compression or consolidation into the free carbon of coal. It takes energy to break apart the bond between carbon and oxygen in a molecule of carbon dioxide. Yet plants must extract this carbon in order to build their tissues and cells and to synthesize their starches and sugars. This is photosynthesis, nature's alchemy, and since light availability is essential to this process, the competition for sunlight among plants plays an important part in the selection of plant types in any given community.

Whereas the intake and outgo of large quantities of water make it possible for plants to grow into tall trees, the competition for light provides the stimulus for vertical growth in forests. Availability of light, therefore, probably is a decisive factor in the arrangement of the storied, or vertical, zonation of plant groupings. Ferns, for example, thrive under conditions of low light availability, lower temperature, and high humidity that typify the deep shade of forests (see Fig. 9.1). Vines have developed specialized mechanisms for climbing tree trunks in order to reach sunlight far above the ground and thus do not require massive size to compete with trees for light (see Fig. 9.7). Certain fungi, such as mushrooms, since they have no *chlorophyll*[1] and do not require photosynthesis, thrive in dark places, free from the competition of green plants.

Latitudinal variations in the length of day and night result in periodic fluctuations in light availability. Many plants adjust their forms to match these seasonal and latitudinal differences, and these changes are termed *phototropism* (Greek, *photo*=light; *tropo*= turning). Seasonal and daily variations in light are highly dependable, because they are controlled by the movement of the earth on its axis or in its orbit around the sun. Many deciduous plants have their triggering mechanisms for budding, leaf shedding, flowering, etc., correlated with seasonal light changes, since they are a far more reliable signal than those supplied by weather or climate, which are subject to wide fluctuations. The flowering of chrysanthemums and dahlias, for example, is controlled by the length of daylight, and florists now are able to force these plants to bloom prematurely in greenhouses, at any time of year, by regulating the length of light-exposure periods.

The long daylight hours in higher mid-latitudes are responsible for abnormal size in some vegetables that can thrive in the moist, cool weather of the short summer season. Root or tuber crops, which are high in starch content, may have enormous yields in these areas, because of the long hours of available light. It is partly for this reason that the major centers of potato cultivation in the United States lie near the northern boundary of the country. Visitors to the subarctic regions of Alaska, northern Canada, and northern Eurasia are always amazed at the enormous size of such hardy, common garden vegetables as cabbages, head lettuce, turnips, and radishes. The land of the midnight sun is not a perpetual wasteland, but its distance from large markets now prevents it from being used for its unique advantages in vegetable cultivation.

FIG. 9.7 Scene in the tropical rain forest near Klamono, Western New Guinea, showing vines and lianas clinging to the tree trunks. [Standard Oil Company (N.J.)]

The influence of intense solar radiation on sugar manufacture by fruits in low-latitude deserts is well known. In these hot deserts, when water can be supplied by irrigation, sugars can be synthesized rapidly and efficiently. The date palm is a splendid example. Even in mid-latitudes, fruits vary in sugar content, depending largely on the number of

[1] *Chlorophyll* is a complex organic compound that is essential to most plants because it acts as a catalytic agent in the formation of plant carbohydrates (starches and sugars). Being a strong pigment, it gives most plants their green color.

sunny days, and the ideal maple-syrup season is one that contains a high percentage of cloudless skies. Opinions differ on the best conditions for growing apples. Some praise the sweetness of apples grown under irrigation in the dry valleys of eastern Washington and Oregon, whereas others prefer the tartness of McIntosh and Winesap apples grown in the more humid northeastern United States.

Like temperature, light is more important in the details of plant morphology and ecology than in the gross patterns; yet it assumes great significance in some features of horticulture and is an ever-present factor in the total environment of plants. Other aspects of its influence are covered later, in the descriptions of global vegetation groupings.

9.7 HUMIDITY AND FOG. The principal effect of atmospheric humidity is its influence on evaporation rates and plant transpiration rates, operating through the mechanism of fluctuations in vapor pressure (see Sec. 6.17). Directly, humidity plays a relatively insignificant role. Small quantities of water may pass into leaf or stem openings following condensation (dew) on plant surfaces, but except for a few desert plants which require only small amounts of moisture, the quantities absorbed are too small to influence plant distributions appreciably. Lichens and some mosses, however, which appear to be able to extract water directly from the air, vary in quantity in proportion to water-vapor content. They are able, therefore, to thrive on bare rock surfaces free of any soil or liquid water.

Fog and clouds on mountain slopes have some noticeable influences on plant geography. The extent of the redwoods (*Sequoia sempervirens*) along the coastal area of northern California, for example, corresponds almost exactly to that of the coastal fogs that drift in from the sea. Water dripping from fog-enshrouded vegetation adds to ground-water supplies. It also tends to reduce incoming solar radiation and thus to lower the surface temperatures of plants. The fog belt along the western slopes of the Andes in Peru supplies water for a narrow zone of short, herbaceous vegetation in this largely rainless area. This vegetation, in turn, supports a distinct zone of pastoral activity. The cloud zones of mountain slopes in the humid tropics result in characteristic moss forests, a most distinctive forest type that appears in widely separated localities in low latitudes. For a description of this unique vegetation type, see Sec. 10.23.

The role of atmospheric moisture in relation to plant diseases is often a limiting factor in the growth of plants. Fungus diseases are especially common in humid areas or in regions where fogs are prevalent. Thus potatoes grown in warm rainy or foggy areas may suffer from late blight, whereas those grown in arid regions under irrigation may be comparatively free from disease infection.

9.8 SOIL. Nearly all plants derive most of their moisture and plant foods from soil; hence soil differences produce variations in plant distributions, particularly on local, or topographic, scales of observation. Soils themselves represent adjustments to a host of environmental conditions; thus the direct influence of soils on plant distributions can rarely be isolated from other factors, such as climate and drainage. Sharp changes in vegetation occur, however, where there are marked differences in underlying rock material and where insufficient time has elapsed for soils to develop an ecological balance with their total environments.

Among the most important soil characteristics influencing the vegetation cover are texture, structure, accessible water content, acidity, organic content, and the chemical composition of the soil particles. The influence of these and other soil properties on vegetation can be touched upon only briefly here. A fuller treatment of these properties is presented in Chapters 11 and 12.

Too little water or too much water for certain types of vegetation may be the result of soil texture. The influence of permeable sands and heavy, tight clays on water supply is clear; therefore this may become a plant geographical factor of considerable importance. Close correlations can be found between the distribution of pine forests and sandy or gravelly soils in the north-central part of the United States, the Atlantic–Gulf of Mexico coastal plain, and the Landes district of southwestern France (see Fig. 9.8), although fire may have assisted in establishing the dominant species. The texture of soils also may influence their temperature. A sandy soil, for example, warms much more quickly in spring than does a clay soil, and hence, by supplying optimum germination conditions, plays a part in the selection of early plants.

The sensitivity of many plants to soil acidity is recognized even by amateur gardeners. Some plants, such as the acid fruits (huckleberries, raspberries, etc.), many conifers, rhododendrons, and some varieties of oak, are acid lovers and require moderate-to-high acidity in soils. Others, such as hickory, maple, and many garden vegetables, do best under conditions of low acidity. Table 9.2 lists the optimum acidity range of several well-known cultivated plants. In this table, increasing acidity is indicated by lower pH values. An explanation of pH, or hydrogen-ion concentration, is given in Sec. 12.1. A pH value of 7 denotes a neutral solution. Values above 7 indicate respective increases in alkalinity.

The physiological effects of acidity on plant growth are mostly correlated with the requirements of different plants for certain critical plant food elements and with the influence of soil acidity on the availability of

FIG. 9.8 A stand of young pines on the sandy soils of the Landes district of southwestern France. This area, like the coastal plain of the southeastern United States, supplies both lumber and naval stores (turpentine and resin). [French Embassy Press and Information Division]

TABLE 9.2 The pH preferences of some common cultivated plants

PLANT	OPTIMUM PH RANGE
Cranberry	4.2–5.0
Cotton	5.0–6.0
White clover	5.6–7.0
Sugar beets	6.5–8.0
Red pepper	7.0–8.5

SOURCE: C. H. Spurway, "Soil Reaction Preference of Plants," *Michigan Agricultural Experimental Station Special Bulletin* 306.

these elements. The content of calcium and other bases in a soil, for instance, usually decreases as the soil becomes more acid.

Soil alkalinity, which refers to low hydrogen-ion concentration in soils, or low acidity, is a characteristic of dry regions. It occurs wherever soluble salts tend to accumulate in the soil, and, like acidity, it results in plant selectivity. Highly alkaline or saline conditions produce toxic effects on most plants, and only a relatively few highly specialized types are able to thrive in such environments. One property that appears to be typical of most salt-tolerant plants is *succulence,* or an unusually high water content within the plant cells. The playa basins of arid regions, which accumulate salts because of poor drainage and high evaporation, show rapid changes in alkalinity about their borders. Concentric zones of plant communities, each with its own degree of tolerance for alkalinity, commonly ring these shallow topographic depressions. Much broader zones of plant forms, corresponding to broader alkalinity tolerances, mark the general transition from arid to humid regions, or from predominantly alkaline soils to acid soils. It is difficult, however, to correlate such broad zones directly to pH concentration, since other variables, such as moisture availability, may be as important.

Cultivated plants that have wide tolerances for alkalinity are of particular value, because of their wide potential geographical range. Alfalfa is grown throughout most of the dry lands of the world mainly because of this property and because of its long root system, which penetrates deep into the ground for water. It also is grown as a highly productive and nutritious forage crop in humid areas in which the acidity of the soil is kept at a low level.

Examples can be found throughout the world to illustrate the influence of underlying materials on the properties of soils derived from them and, in turn, on the vegetation cover. This is an especially important factor in areas of young soils, which are only beginning their general progression toward relative environmental equilibrium. Examples of young soils include those recently developed on alluvium, marine sediments recently uplifted from the sea, recent volcanic deposits, and glacial detritus. Concentric belts of vegetation, corresponding to the belts of marls (limy muds), sands, and clays, are easily distinguished along the Gulf of Mexico coastal plain. Sharp boundaries between types of forest communities mark the change from sandy glacial outwash plains to the heavier soils of morainic belts and from narrow sandy beach ridges to heavy lake clays on former lake plains in many parts of the glaciated portions of North America and Eurasia. Although such borders are the direct result of differences in water availability, this in turn is related to the texture, structure, and composition of the underlying material.

In some areas, such as on the windswept rocky hills of the Scottish Highlands, the rock is so near the surface that there is insufficient soil to furnish anchorage for tree roots. Forests are therefore absent, and small woody plants, such as broom and heather, furnish the permanent ground cover. In the same area, however, on the leeward side of the exposed hill slopes, trees can flourish on soils just as thin, because of the absence of wind stress.

As with the other factors affecting plant growth, the influence of soil can never be completely isolated from that of other variables. Sometimes it plays a dominant role in the selection of the plant cover; in other instances it exerts only a subtle influence and operates through other environmental forces. It is part of the environmental complex which seeks to develop an equilibrium among all its constituent parts.

9.9 DRAINAGE AND SLOPE. Drainage and slope are treated together because they are so intimately related. The importance of water supply to plants has already been treated. Whereas water availability on a continental or global scale is mainly dependent on climatic conditions, local variations are largely the result of drainage and slope conditions. When there has been a heavy rain, less water is left in the soil for plant use on an extremely steep slope than on more gradual slopes. Erosion on steep slopes may remove much of the unconsolidated soil material above the underlying rock, speed runoff, and reduce available soil moisture for plant growth. Conversely, a flat land surface in a humid region may result in excessive water accumulation in soils and require consequent adjustments in the vegetation cover.

The impact on plants of excessive drainage, either horizontally or downward, is similar to that of decreased precipitation. Not all cacti are desert dwellers. The common prickly pear (*Opuntia*) has been observed by the author on thin soils covering steep, rocky hillsides in southern Illinois and Pennsylvania and on sand dunes of the New Jersey coast and the eastern shore of Lake Michigan. All these areas are in humid climates.

Inadequate drainage produces a number of harmful effects on plants that have not developed specialized forms to adjust to it. The most important factor is not the excess of water itself but the lack of aeration. Absorption and the discharge of both carbon dioxide (CO_2) and oxygen are important aspects of plant maintenance, and these do not pass freely into and out of water. The intake of CO_2 and the release of oxygen in plant photosynthesis are well known. Less familiar is the reverse process. Plants require mechanical energy for many purposes—for example, the mechanical force of root penetration. They obtain this energy from the combustion of carbohydrates, in the same way that animals do, except that the quantities are much smaller. Involved in this combustion are the intake of oxygen and the release of carbon dioxide. This process, termed *respiration,* is most noticeable at night, when owing to the lack of sunlight, photosynthesis is not taking place.

Hydrophytes, or plants that thrive under excessive water conditions, have many ways of overcoming inadequate aeration. Most such plants have spongy tissues, or abnormally large intercellular openings, which are capable of storing large quantities of oxygen supplied by photosynthesis. This oxygen slowly decreases in the water during the night and is replenished during the day. In floating forms, these air passages further provide buoyancy, which keeps the top of the plant near the surface of the water. This helps such plants to maintain an adequate source of light. Other plants, such as seaweeds, have extremely slow rates of photosynthesis, extracting dissolved carbon dioxide from the water and releasing oxygen directly. Different amounts of excess water result in varying degrees of adaptation in plants, ranging from completely submerged or floating forms to erect plant types that are occasionally or partially submerged.

The influence of slope on vegetation is not restricted to its effect on the water supply. Temperature and the availability of light may also be related to slope conditions. Mountain regions usually have distinctively different types of plant communities due largely to contrasts in exposure to sunlight. A sunny mountain slope with surface temperatures much higher than shaded slopes may influence plant selection through both light sensitivity and soil-moisture availability. The accumulation and duration of snow cover on mountain slopes may also be related to slope conditions, especially in connection

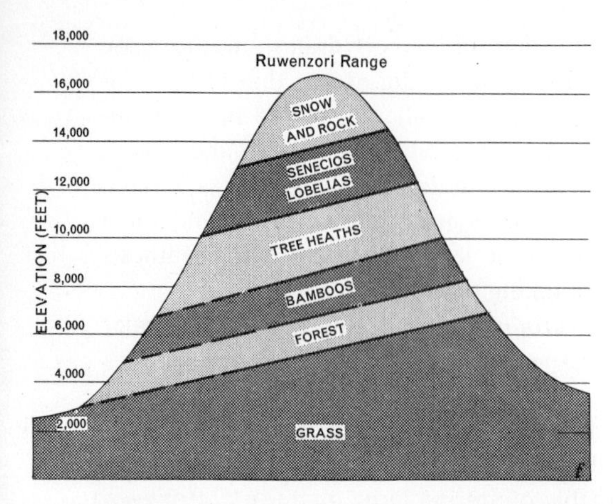

FIG. 9.9 Zonation of vegetation on the slopes of the Ruwenzori Range in Uganda. The greater rainfall of the western (left) side is responsible for the appearance of the zones at lower elevations than on the opposite side. [After Woosnam]

with wind direction and sunshine availability. These in turn affect temperatures, moisture balances, and plant selection. Irregularity of slopes may produce noticeable differences in plant communities in dense forest areas. Sudden changes in slope cause breaks in the continuity of the forest canopy overhead, thus permitting greater light penetration and air circulation and producing a general alteration in humidity and soil-moisture conditions. Steep slopes tend to make the forest crown, or canopy, less regular than on plains. For this reason, forests on steep hill and mountain slopes are likely to have more undergrowth, or lower-story vegetation, than those on flat land, and the plant communities tend to be more complex and varied.

9.10 ELEVATION. Some of the sharpest, most noticeable differences in major plant communities can be observed on mountain slopes, because of differences in elevation. This is especially true of high mountains in low latitudes, where representatives of many of the great global plant formations can be found, arranged in successive zones up the mountainsides (see Fig. 9.9). Such groupings are related primarily to the lapse rate, or the decrease in air temperature with increased elevation above sea level, but factors other than temperature change play a part in the vertical zonation. The timber line, or the upper limit of trees, does not always occur at the same elevation in similar latitudinal positions or even on different sides of the same mountain ridge. Moisture availability, wind direction and strength, and exposure to sunlight are other factors that influence the elevation of vegetation boundaries on mountain slopes. Although such elements result in many local exceptions, mountain vegetation boundaries generally follow the contour of the slopes, and their elevation tends to decrease gradually with increasing latitude.

Experiments in growing plants at different altitudes have yielded much interesting evidence of changes in size and color associated with the alpine environment. The bright light combined with the cool air of high altitudes intensifies the color of flowers and promotes dwarfness. Conversely, alpine plants grown at low altitudes, such as some of the azaleas, fail to develop the brilliant colors seen in their natural high-altitude habitats, and most alpine plants, from the lowly dandelion to the spruces and firs, grow considerably larger and taller at lower altitudes.

One should not assume too close a correlation between the characteristics of mountain vegetation communities and the communities found in broad global zones having comparable temperature conditions. Although the flora high above the timber line may have many characteristics similar to those of tundra communities, the mountain environment produces many dissimilar features. Wind velocities and snowfall, both factors in plant selection, are likely to be much greater on mountain summits than at high latitudes, and the appreciable decrease in air pressure at high elevations leaves its mark on plant characteristics. In low latitudes, seasonal variations in temperature are no more pronounced at high elevations than they are at low elevations; therefore deciduous forests resulting from seasonal low temperatures do not appear at high elevations in the tropics. Conifers, on the other hand, are common members of high-elevation forests at all latitudes, because they can adjust moisture balances to depressed temperature conditions. Mountain slopes, particularly windward slopes, usually have much higher precipitation than do lowland areas, and thus plant relationships to temperature are not always comparable to those which exist elsewhere in the same latitudinal temperature zone. The cloud-zone environments of low-latitude mountains, for example, have few, if any, low-elevation equivalents. Since the totality of environmental conditions at high elevations cannot be reproduced at low elevations, the characteristics of mountain vegetation should be treated apart from those of the great lowland plant formations. Major characteristics of mountain vegetation patterns are discussed in the next chapter.

The role of man in vegetation balances

9.11 GENERAL. It has been stated that there is no such thing as purely natural vegetation anywhere on earth, that man is found wherever plants will grow, and that his presence and abilities, no matter how primitive or sophisticated, have left their mark on the floral landscape. Lest this observation flatter human beings unduly, it should be remembered that the nonhuman members of the animal kingdom also exert their influence on the evolution, maintenance, and distribution of plant communities everywhere. Plant ecologists recognize that plant communities cannot be adequately studied apart from the animal life present in the same area, any more than they can be understood apart from the soil, air, or water conditions in the environmental complex. Microbes decay the forest litter; bees pollinate flowers; earthworms aerate the soil; grazing animals maintain balances between edible and nonedible plants; insects act as food for certain carnivorous plants; and there are many symbiotic, or mutually beneficial, relationships between plants and animals.

Man is a part of the environmental complex of plants, but he plays a much more dynamic role than other animals. He has forces at his disposal for altering vegetation that are far more effective than the feeding habits of animals. Furthermore, his abilities grow with knowledge, since they do not depend on instincts bred into the species of man by millions of years of selection in relatively stable environments. From the humble beginning of gathering wild fruits and roots and taming wild animals that thrived on broad, open grasslands, through the first deliberate planting, to the present-day applications of machine agriculture, controlled plant breeding, and the creation of synthetic growth conditions, man has come a long, long way.

In his attempt to make plants work for him, man has made many mistakes and has suffered unfortunate consequences. His most common mistake has been to demand too much of plants in highly balanced environments, without thought for the future. Sometimes this has been due to ignorance and at other times to pressures beyond his control. Nonliterate human groups, through trial and error, usually developed a mutually beneficial relationship with the particular vegetation communities in which they lived. This was not difficult to achieve so long as man's

FIG. 9.10 Typical migratory-agricultural clearing in the Philippines. Crops are planted haphazardly between the stumps and remaining trees. [R. L. Pendleton; Geographical Review]

relationship to the land was direct; in fact, the environment generally forced human and plant life into equilibrium. In more complex societies, with powerful tools and inanimate energy sources to aid in satisfying human desires and with added knowledge of how to alter many environmental factors, the relationships between man and vegetation become more subtle and more difficult to recognize and to control. The worker on a banana plantation who purchases his food at the company store has a far different relationship to his environment than does a self-sufficient farmer who is living off a tiny patch of cleared land in the adjacent tropical forest.

The succeeding paragraphs of this section are concerned with some of the problems of maintaining natural balances in the face of human exploitation of plant life. Since such problems differ greatly with different environments and with different cultures, the subject cannot be fully treated here. The following discussion merely presents a few of the more prominent problems for illustrative purposes.

9.12 MAINTENANCE OF SOIL FERTILITY WITH CROP CULTIVATION. In a well-balanced plant community, soil fertility is maintained by adding to the soil most of the inorganic plant foods used by the plants during their growth. This is accomplished largely through the decay of the plant material that falls upon the forest floor, but the weathering of inorganic soil particles also results in a small but steady addition of these same chemical materials. Whenever more nutrients are removed than are added by these two processes, soil fertility decreases. Organic material supplied by dead vegetation plays an additional role in fertility by acting as a sponge and retaining water and essential plant food elements which, because of their solubility, would otherwise soon be leached out of the soil. When man removes some of the plant cover for his own food, he must either replace the loss in some way or face declining crop yields. Over the thousands of years of agricultural history, he has found several ways of replacing the nutrients that he takes, but in many situations he has found it impractical or impossible to do so and thus has eventually been forced to abandon his cultivated fields. In a few areas nature periodically restores lost fertility by adding fresh, unweathered material, as in volcanic regions or along the flood plains of rivers. Usually, however, man has had to use foresight in replenishing the fertility of the soil in order to maintain a stabilized system of plant exploitation.

9.13 MIGRATORY AGRICULTURE. One of the simplest and oldest methods of replenishing fertility has been to permit natural regeneration of soil fertility by simply abandoning the land following a decline in fertility. This is the basis of migratory, or shifting, agriculture (see Fig. 9.10). This type of agriculture involves forest clearing by means of girdling trees and burning all dead vegetation except scattered tree boles. Planting usually is done with a pointed stick. Yields are high at first, because of the wealth of nutrients supplied by the ash, but they decline in a few years. Following this, a new clearing in the forest is made, and the process is repeated. This cultivation method is known by many different terms in different parts of the world, including *milpa* (Guatemala), *ladang* (Malaya), *ray* (Indochina), and *taungya* (Burma). Where population is sparse, where forest land is cheap or free, and where regeneration is comparatively rapid, as in some parts of the humid tropics, this procedure can maintain good crop yields and a stable food supply indefinitely. All too frequently, however, this system is abused, sometimes because of overburning and frequently because of overpopulation.

The density of population that can be adequately supported by this cultivation method depends on the initial soil productivity and the length and speed of the regenerative process. In the primitive societies of the humid tropics, the balance between population density and migratory agriculture was at times kept near the optimum by the dual forces of a high birth rate and a high death rate, the latter involving intertribal warfare. The warfare often was the result of territorial violations, which, in turn, were due to the pressures of a growing population and decreasing food supplies. Colonial administrations found to their dismay that the introduction of medical facilities and law and order checked the former controls of population growth and led to the problem of overpopulation. With increasing population pressure, areas of primary (virgin) forest disappeared, the regenerative period of migratory agriculture was reduced, and crop yields progressively declined. Frequent burning and cultivation resulted in the destruction of the forest-regenerative capacities, and the old clearings were replaced by coarse grasses whose sod was too tough for the simple tools to handle.

Today the general tendency is to prohibit migratory agriculture and to attempt to force indigenous peoples to adopt a sedentary life and to practice the more controllable meth-

FIG. 9.11 Air photo showing an extensive area of migratory-agricultural clearings in the Annamese Mountains of Northern Vietnam. Different shades represent different stages of regrowth of vegetation. Little of this tropical forest has remained without having been cleared at some time or other. [U.S. Air Force (MATS)]

ods of crop rotation and fertilization. As a result of the increased competition of sedentary agriculture, mainly on the better soils, and the various government decrees, the remaining migratory agriculturalists have retreated to the most inaccessible areas—usually the steepest, poorest, and least productive parts of the tropical world. This is unfortunate, since the principle of this type of agriculture is still wholly valid. If population can be stabilized at an appropriate level without resorting to high death rates and if deliberate, planned forest regeneration can be practiced without abuse, migratory agriculture may yet prove a useful means of maintaining agricultural stability, and one which may be far easier to control in the tropics than some of the complex fertilizer-oriented crop systems.

9.14 THE FIELD-FALLOW SYSTEM. A second method of maintaining agricultural stability, and one somewhat akin to migratory agriculture, is the *field-fallow* system. This is a form of sedentary agriculture; the farmer does not move to new areas from time to time, but he periodically retires a certain fraction of his acreage from cultivation. Usually the regenerative period is much shorter than in migratory agriculture, and thus regeneration is only partially complete. This system is much more adaptable to the mid-latitudes than to the tropics, because of the greater nutrient-storage capacity of the soils, and it was the basis of the ancient *dreifelderschaft* (three-field system) that was characteristic of much of European agriculture until the seventeenth century. This involved raising grains and root crops on two-thirds of the cultivated land and allowing the other third to stand idle. The fields were rotated every 3 years. Later, with the introduction of animals into the European farm economy, hay crops, forage legumes, and rotation pasture took the place of the fallow period in the crop-rotation plan.

A fallow cultivation method is still widely used in parts of India and in some sections of Africa. With this system, agricultural stability can be maintained, but only on an extremely low-yield basis. It is interesting to note that a low-yield fallow system is employed in many of the great specialized subhumid-to-semiarid wheat regions of the world. Here the fallow period not only provides some regeneration of plant foods but, more important, adds to the reserves of water in the soil. To compensate for low yields, mass-production methods, involving highly mechanized farm practices, are employed; thus per-unit costs are low. Frequently the fallow acres are cultivated but not cropped, in order to keep weeds away and to create a moisture-conserving, mulched surface (see Fig. 8.7).

9.15 THE ORGANIC COMPOST SYSTEM. A third method of providing agricultural stability is the organic compost system. This is the principal method used in much of the Far East, although it is by no means restricted to this part of the world. Very simply stated, this system requires that man return to the fields what he removes—or, more accurately, as much as he can. This involves collecting and treating human and animal wastes, plus unused vegetation in the cultivation process, and utilizing this material as a partially oxidized compost, which is added to the cultivated fields as fertilizer.

With this system, a high level of plant productivity can be maintained for long periods, as evidenced by the continuous cultivation of some parts of China for over 40 centuries. The main difficulty with this form of agriculture is the great expenditure of hand labor that is required, a demand that can be met only by dense populations having a comparatively low standard of living. Recently, however, some interesting experiments have demonstrated that organic compost can be collected and processed by special equipment on a mass-production basis. This new technique may prove to be particularly advantageous in utilizing the efficiency of vegetative growth in the humid tropics. Another disadvantage of the compost system is the spread of human diseases that may result when the compost is not adequately processed. With care, however, this can be prevented, and the danger apparently has been exaggerated.

9.16 INORGANIC FERTILIZATION.

The last major method of maintaining fertility is *inorganic fertilization*. In this system plant nutrients are added in the form of commercial fertilizers, mostly of inorganic origin. The most important constituents are soluble compounds of nitrogen, phosphorus, and potassium. Calcium, as a soil-corrective agent, and small quantities of other elements essential to plant growth are also added. This procedure usually is used in conjunction with selected crop-rotation plans and with green manuring,[2] a process designed to improve the physical state of the soil in order to promote ease of cultivation and the retention of water and nutrients. Legumes, which add to the nitrogen content of soils, also are an important part of the crop-rotation system.

Inorganic fertilization is the system that has received the greatest attention from agricultural scientists, and it is practiced today wherever Western culture has spread. Commercial fertilizers are well-adapted to an industrial economy, and agricultural systems have been able to become stabilized at high yield levels. Essentially the system creates artificial conditions for plant growth, at least with respect to soil environment (see Fig. 9.12). The new, highly productive crop balances, however, are not without their disadvantages. Their security depends largely on the stability of the exchange economy on which they are based; and when maladjustments in the cycle of production and consumption take place, the agricultural stabilization program may likewise become pre-

[2] *Green manuring* refers to the practice of plowing green plants directly into the soil. Such plants decay rapidly and add to the organic content of the soil.

FIG. 9.12 One of the newest techniques for replenishing soil fertility. Field equipment is being serviced with liquid anhydrous ammonia (a nitrogen compound) in Mississippi for use on a cotton farm. [U.S. Department of Agriculture]

carious. With depressed prices, a commercial farmer often will begin his retrenchment by reducing his expenditures for fertilizers, hoping that his plant-food reserve in the soil will tide him over the unfavorable period. Obviously also, a nation dependent on commercial fertilizers for its food supply is more vulnerable in case of military attack.

The new environments created by the use of commercial fertilizers and insecticides present an interesting ecological problem. Although the dangers have been exaggerated by many proponents of organic compost agriculture, inorganic fertilization may upset the delicate balances between plants in their natural habitat and insects and microlife. Such relationships are not fully understood. The roles of soil molds and fungi in relation to plant resistance to disease, for example, are just beginning to be discovered through research into antibiotics. There appears to be no doubt that in some special cases the use of commercial fertilizers has led to an increase in plant enemies. Whether or not science keeps its present lead in its fight to understand and to control the new synthetic plant environments is a matter that remains to be seen.

There are other methods of maintaining plant productivity, including the use of fire ash produced by burning waste vegetation slowly in piles and the use of materials obtained from the sea, such as fish or seaweed, but these practices have a very limited geographic range.

Little has been included here concerning techniques of plant breeding and research into the behavior and pathology of a wide variety of useful plant species. Space permits only a mention of the fact that man is learning how to change not only the environments of plants but also the properties of many plants themselves, in order to make them more adaptable for use. He is discovering, for example, how to make the sugar cane sweeter; the wheat plant more tolerant of drought, rust, and frost; the potato less scabby; the rose more beautiful; the orange seedless; and the apple tree smaller.

Modern man promotes an ever-increasing specialization of the useful plants, and in this lie his greatest strength and his greatest danger. Unless he carefully learns the lessons of ecology as he proceeds, he is likely to find that he has opened a Pandora's box. Some serious results of meddling with the balances of nature already have been experienced—for example, the introduction of the prickly pear cactus (as a forage plant or hedge cover) and the jack rabbit (for game hunting) into Australia, both of which multiplied to serious proportions in this new environment, which did not contain the natural checks of their native habitats. The importation of millions of insects from South America, of a variety that was known to be parasitic on the prickly pear, has checked the spread of the latter. Nature's balances are subtle, but compelling!

9.17 NATURAL BALANCES AND FOREST MANAGEMENT PROBLEMS.

A large part of the world population lives in areas that once were forested. For a long period in human history, it was believed that any area that did not support a natural forest cover was unsuited for agriculture. Contributing to this early avoidance of the humid and subhumid grasslands was the absence of the steel plow, a necessity in removing a tough sod cover. The soft, earthen floor of a forest was much easier to work, but the first step was to remove the trees in the quickest and easiest way possible. Burning has always been a favored method of forest clearing, but it was not always easy to control, especially in the coniferous forest areas and in regions that had pronounced dry seasons. The reduction of forest land in the mid-latitudes, particularly in the eighteenth and nineteenth centuries, accompanied by a rapid increase in population, resulted in growing shortages of wood products. The shortages for a while appeared mainly in highly specialized products, such as tall spars for the masts of ships, oak beams for house timbers and the planking of warships, clapboards for siding, and special woods for wine barrels. Later, the shortages became more general and began to invade the critical field of fuel. The realization came that even the welfare of nations depended on a regular supply of forest products, a supply which for a long time was taken for granted. Public forest reserves were established, and increasing attention was paid to learning the basic principles of forest conservation and management.

Today, forest management is a complex science, which involves a thorough knowledge of plant ecology. Its objective should be *to adjust the plant community and forest practices in a forested area so as to produce a maximum yield adjusted to human needs and the long-run productiveness of the locality*. Many factors are involved in this objective, the most important of which are presented in the following list of pertinent questions:

1. Purpose. Does the forest have both long-range and short-range objectives? Is the objective of the forest site to supply forest products? If so, what kinds? Does the forest furnish protection against soil erosion in critical watershed areas? Is it to be used for recreation or for its scenic and aesthetic appeal? Is it to be used as a laboratory for forest research? Is it to have a multipurpose function?

2. The local balance. What is the local balanced or climax vegetation in the area? Has the balance been reached? If not, what practices, consistent with the purpose of the forest, will lead toward or away from this balance?

3. Adjustment of balance. Can any of the environmental characteristics of the site be altered to produce a new, balanced forest community that will be more consistent with the purpose of the forest than the present balance?

4. The economic balance sheet. What is the capital investment in land, forest, equipment, etc.? What is the annual increase in forest growth? What is the current return in the form of production value? What is the estimated return in the future? What are the current and future demands with respect to avowed purpose? How much investment should be made in ecological improvement programs? When is the most profitable time to cut particular trees?

Not all these factors are investigated by a single person. Some of them are studied by governmental agencies, some by corporation managers, and some by highly trained foresters operating in the field. Still others are determined by public sentiment and taste. Such a forest management program can be developed only in a highly complex and integrated society.

One of the major lessons learned from plant geography is that forest management programs that work well in one area may not be suitable for other areas. A few illustrations will emphasize this point. The periodic burning of dry litter and low brush in the longleaf pine areas of the southern United States has been found to be beneficial and even necessary for the reproduction of the desired species and for more rapid tree growth, but a similar practice could seriously harm other forests. Reforestation of large areas by seedlings of the principal local lumber species may be totally unsuited to areas where such species normally are in a highly mixed, balanced community, but it may be a recommended procedure in areas where the climax forest contains a high proportion of the same type of trees. Reforestation by planting seedlings normally should be used only in areas that will not reforest themselves naturally, because of severe damage resulting from fire, floods, insect depredations, complete elimination of seed producers, etc.

Selective logging [3] is a necessity for a stabilized forest economy in most forested areas. It may, however, be uneconomical and undesirable in such forests as the Douglas fir forests of Washington and Oregon, since these trees commonly thrive best in pure stands of similar size (see Fig. 9.13). Unlike most other climax forest trees (or, more correctly, subclimax), the Douglas fir does not require the shade of other trees for seed germination, but springs forth readily from bare ground. Having an extremely rapid growth, it eliminates most tree competitors other than its fellows of similar size. Standard practices of forest cutting in the Douglas fir areas, therefore, involve the removal of all the trees from a tract of land once they have reached proper size. A few scattered trees may be left as seed producers for natural reproduction, and a neighboring tract of land with trees near maturity is also recommended for reproduction (see Fig. 9.14).

A final illustration involves the relationship between cultures or civilizations and forest management programs. It is customarily assumed that trees should be left to grow to maturity; yet in many densely populated parts of the world, the need for narrow poles to be used in house construction, for thin firewood that does not require splitting, and even for leaves to be used for miscellaneous household purposes may be so urgent that the most beneficial forest management plan would be aimed specifically at a high productivity of young, immature forest stocks. Increases in the production of firewood may have far-reaching consequences; in some areas firewood may be able to replace animal dung as cooking fuel, and the dung, in turn, can be added to fields, thereby raising soil fertility and aiding in the stabilization of the agricultural economy.

[3] *Selective logging* refers to the practice of cutting only scattered trees that have reached a desired size.

9.18 ECOLOGICAL PROBLEMS IN RANGE MANAGEMENT.

The grasslands of the world were the preferred home for grazing animals long before man appeared on earth. These animals were a part of a balanced environmental complex and apparently played an important part in the creation and maintenance of grassland plant communities. The physical characteristics of grazing animals, including hoofs, tooth structure, specialized digestive apparatus, and muscle development for speed, are the result of millions of years of natural selection in grassland environments. Because grazing animals are well suited to grassland habitats and because man has found many of these animals to be valuable as a source of meat, fat, hides, and hair, he has attempted to add as many as possible to the land, particularly in the grasslands he considers useless for agriculture. Before man's appearance, the number of grazing animals was usually regulated partly by their natural enemies, the carnivorous predators; partly by the feeding competition of smaller animals, such as rodents; and partly by the vegetative productivity of the site. When man sought to alter this balance by increasing the population of grazing animals, he found it exceedingly difficult to judge the most efficient carrying capacity of the land, that is, the density of animal population that it could best support. As a result, overgrazing has been the rule throughout most of the semiarid grasslands of the world.

There are a number of reasons why so many of the nonarable grasslands have been abused by man. One is that man's relation to the land in grazing areas is less direct than in agricultural areas. On the open range he is likely to be more interested in the animals themselves than in the subtle changes in vegetation on which the animals feed. Most agricultural crops are harvested annually, whereas grazing animals may take several years to mature; thus the regulation of supply is easier in agriculture than in grazing. Also, far greater areas are involved in pastoral occupations, and thus a much broader diagnosis is required. The manager of a 50,000-acre ranch, for example, cannot recognize the symptoms of declining productivity as rapidly or as easily as a farmer who is cultivating a 40-acre cornfield or a 2-acre rice paddy. Remedial measures on large grazing areas are likewise much more difficult and often more expensive. Finally, the mobility of the animals themselves creates problems in range improvement. How does one keep animals away from areas where regeneration of the plant cover is advisable? Fencing may

FIG. 9.13 Natural regrowth of Douglas fir in former cleanly cut area. Seed trees in the adjacent uncut stands provide the source for reproduction. Note the uniformity in height and density of stand. [Weyerhaeuser Timber Company]

FIG. 9.14 Block cutting in an extensive stand of lodgepole pine, Lewis and Clark National Forest in western Montana. [U.S. Department of Agriculture]

be too expensive over large areas, and in some areas of open range (without private ownership) there is the continual problem of the competitor who has fewer scruples or less wisdom.

Overgrazing has numerous consequences, which influence man's welfare in many ways other than by decreasing the carrying capacity of the range. Increased consumption of edible grasses results in an increase in the number of less desirable plants, including herbaceous annuals and woody perennials. Plants such as the *manzanita* of Texas may develop into an almost impenetrable thicket, ruining the range (see Fig. 9.15). Others, such as the prickly pear and sagebrush, become dominant members of the new plant communities. Continued overgrazing often leads to a destruction of the sod cover, exposing the bare ground to erosion by both wind and water. Accelerated runoff alters the water balance in the soil by lowering the water table; springs dry up, and streams develop a wider range between high and low water, thus increasing the height of floods. The useful life of expensive irrigation and power reservoirs is shortened because of sedimentation. An increase in herbaceous annual plants stimulates the growth of rodents; this in turn increases the number of predators, such as the coyote. Grasshoppers and locusts normally require bare ground for the incubation of eggs; thus, overgrazing may stimulate the swarming of these destructive pests. Yet, despite all the abuses of overgrazing, the range has remarkable recuperative powers and, if left alone for a long enough time, will gradually work itself back to the relatively stable grassland communities it once had (see Fig. 9.16).

Good range management requires a foresighted, balanced evaluation of many factors. It involves consideration of almost the same issues as were discussed under forest management in the preceding section, including purpose, stage of progression toward, or recession from, the vegetation equilibrium, feasibility of altering site factors, and the state of the economic balance sheet. The best range condition for supporting animals is not necessarily at the climax, but perhaps at some intermediate position that can be maintained indefinitely. The recognition of this critical point in grassland plant succession is the ultimate goal of the range manager. This point is never stationary; it differs from time to time and from place to place. The position of the maximum stabilized yield point may be raised toward the climax during periods of high prices and lowered during

FIG. 9.15 Reclamation of brushland in Kerr County, Texas. The area in the foreground was cleared by bulldozer 19 months before, and a good recovery of climax-grass types already has taken place. The thin oak brushland will only support a few goats. [U.S. Department of Agriculture]

FIG. 9.16 The difference between protected and unprotected range. The steppe range soon reestablishes itself once the abuses are checked. [U.S. Department of Agriculture]

periods of low prices. The important objective, however, is to maintain a desired productivity level, measured in terms of the number of animals per square mile and identified by means of plant indicators, which are the individual species of plants that are characteristic of different stages of plant succession.

In grazing, as in agriculture, science is assisting in the effort to increase yields by conducting controlled experiments, introducing new plants and new methods of range improvement, and, most important, providing a clearer understanding of plant reactions to changes in environmental conditions. The need for increasing the carrying capacity of world grazing lands grows with every advance in living standards. Most people like the taste of meat and would eat more if they could afford it. The yield of many grazing regions today is far below what it should be. It can be raised mainly through restraint, ecological knowledge, and the application of foresight. This appears to be simple, but there are strong opposing forces. How does one convince a Navajo that he would be better off by eliminating half of the sheep from which he ekes a bare living? How can the Masai of Kenya be persuaded to give up some of their cattle, which to them are a symbol of wealth and social prestige quite apart from their direct utility? How can livestock be reduced in India, where the lives of cattle are more highly valued than those of human beings? How does one persuade a Western cattleman that the chance of making a "killing," as he did in 1944, with his present stock density is not worth the long-run deterioration of his range?

9.19 FIRE AS A TOOL IN VEGETATION ALTERATION. Fire has always been a significant factor in the human alteration of vegetation patterns. Primitive people used it as a means of clearing agricultural land, as an aid in hunting, as a tactical weapon in both offensive and defensive warfare, as a means of stimulating the growth of new grass for animals, and perhaps merely as an enjoyable spectacle.

Fire has had its greatest impact on vegetation in three major vegetation regions: the grasslands, the deciduous forests, and the coniferous forests. Its abusive use by man, especially in primitive cultures, has led to some noteworthy shifts in the boundaries of some of the great global plant formations. Usually the shift has been at the expense of the more humid vegetation formations; for example, desert shrubs have increased at the expense of grasslands, and grasslands have moved into forested regions.

Grasslands have been the target for intentional burning for thousands of years. Except near the dry margins of the steppes, where grasses struggle with aridity for survival, grasslands are not especially harmed by burning at the end of the growth season. The tropical grasslands (savannas), which lie between the desert and the tropical forests, have a constant smoke haze hanging over them during the dry period (see Fig. 9.17). The rank, coarse, dried savanna grass is symbolic of this hated time of year, when water holes dry up, the heat becomes unbearable, animals are scrawny and ill-tempered, and the grass itself tears the clothes and cuts the flesh. Better a charred landscape; at least it is easier to cross, the fire itself is wonderful to behold, and the people know that the new shoots that will appear a little later will be the greener for it. Near the forest-grassland border, the grass fires slowly nibble at the forest edges, aided in their conquest by the clearings for migratory agriculture or by the efforts of pastoral people who seek to extend their grazing territory. Continued burning in a tropical forest clearing may destroy the regenerative capacity of the forest, so that rank grasses become dominant. Useless for native agriculture, because of the tough sod cover, the grassy openings in the forest are abandoned but are periodically burned, as in the savannas, if even a short dry season is experienced. Thus the forest slowly becomes grassland, and the savannas migrate equatorward. Grasslands created by man, primarily through the use of fire, are found throughout the humid tropics, especially in areas where the population pressure is great.

Many authorities believe that most of the humid grasslands of the mid-latitudes, the tall-grass prairies, are the result of the use of fire by aboriginals. Near the forest-prairie border in Wisconsin and Minnesota, patches of forest cling to the lee sides of lakes, where the sweep of prairie fires was checked. Tongues of forest extend along the stream courses, which usually are entrenched below the general level of the prairies, where there was some protection from the sweep of prairie fires. Distinct ash layers have been found in the soil of the Argentine pampas, indicating that fire has been an active factor there for a long time.

Large areas covered with secondary scrub brush and grass tend to be self-perpetuating through the use of fire. Brush land is of little direct use to human beings, and it is usually resented by local inhabitants. In their desire to destroy it, they use fire without realizing that the brush itself may be a postfire succession. One of the worst areas for brush fires in the United States lies in Southern California. The grass- and brush-covered hills, so familiar to viewers of western movies or television programs, is largely a fire-induced vegetation. The brush reproduces mainly by the suckers of its extensive and well-developed root system. Fire destroys the tops, but not the roots, of these plants; thus the natural competition of other plants is reduced. The fires are unfortunate in many respects; but the brush vegetation helps protect vital watershed areas against too rapid runoff and floods, soil erosion, and silting of water reservoirs, and it provides for a greater retention of rainfall in subsurface reservoirs in this thirsty land.

Wide expanses of less valuable deciduous trees, including birch, aspen, and wild cherry, are found in the northern coniferous forests

FIG. 9.17 Burning the savanna, or tropical grassland. This scene, taken on the llanos of Colombia, could be duplicated on the savannas of many other parts of the world during the dry season. The savanna in this photo is somewhat unusual in that it lacks trees of any kind. [Standard Oil Company (N.J.)]

of Canada and Eurasia. These mark the sites of old fires and appear from the air like huge elongated, light-colored patches on a dark-green quilt. The low branches, resinous leaves, and tangle of fallen trees that characterize the northern coniferous forests are highly inflammable in the late summer and fall months (see Fig. 9.18). In this sparsely populated region, fires may continue to burn for days until quenched by a rainstorm. Lightning and spontaneous combustion, along with the matches of careless human beings, are responsible for igniting them. Burning with exceedingly high temperatures, these northern forest fires consume most of the organic material in the topsoils, leaving them unsuited for reproduction except by specialized fire-succession flora. These fires should not be thought of, however, as being entirely detrimental. The regrowth of grasses, herbaceous plants, berries, and shrubs that follows burning provides cover and food for wildlife, especially deer and other larger animals.

Many conifers are aided by fire in their competition with other plants. The lodgepole

FIG. 9.18 Charred landscape following a forest fire in coniferous forest of the Pacific Northwest. [Weyerhaeuser Timber Company]

pine (*Pinus contorta*) of the Rocky Mountains and the jack pine, or northern scrub pine (*Pinus banksiana*), of the northern United States glacial outwash plains are the best known of several pines that have the unusual property of requiring the heat of a forest fire in order to open their tight cones; thus fire provides for their replacement and improves their competitive position within the postfire succession. The southern longleaf pine (*Pinus palustris*) of the southeastern United States coastal plain has a highly insulative bark that is almost fireproof, and the peculiar arrangement of the terminal buds apparently enables the tree to be virtually defoliated by fire without undergoing serious harm. Fire also seems to assist pine reproduction by providing the bare ground surface necessary for seed germination and by destroying young competitive plants. For a long time pine was believed to be a dominant climax vegetation on coastal-plain sands, but evidence now indicates that oak will replace it if fire is kept away. The periodic burning of longleaf pine forests is standard practice in maintaining and improving this important source of naval stores (turpentine and resin) and rapidly growing timber.

Burning generally tends to exhaust the organic, biological, and chemical resources of the soil. It directly destroys most of the plant remains standing or lying on the surface and also a large part of the plant residues and old root fibers incorporated within the topsoil, leaving only ash and mineral soil material and reducing the soil capacity for retaining water and plant foods. Beneficial soil fungi, along with helpful bacteria, other microorganisms, and insect life, are also destroyed, or at least have their ecological equilibrium disturbed. Minerals and essential chemicals that are ordinarily made available slowly and are normally released only as needed by plants are suddenly rendered soluble by the high temperatures and are rapidly leached out of the soil by subsequent rains. The ultimate result is soil exhaustion and lifelessness, although an apparent effect of increased fertility is exhibited temporarily while the newly released soluble elements are made available to the postfire flora. Burning is generally a wasteful, destructive process, *except in certain special circumstances,* where factors other than soil nutrition seem to justify its use.

9.20 SUMMARY OF THE HUMAN FACTOR IN PLANT GEOGRAPHY.

Man is a comparatively new ecological factor in plant geography, because of his relatively recent appearance on this planet; yet the impact of his influence can be seen throughout the world. Despite the importance of plant life for food and feed, man's modifications of the vegetation cover have not always been to his own benefit. The marks of his abuse are encountered all too frequently. Only in a few regions has he achieved a stabilized balance in his utilization of vegetation growth. He has lowered the carrying capacity of many grasslands by burning and by overgrazing, and he has seriously depleted the world stock of valuable timberland. Eroded, bare, sterile slopes in many humid areas testify to abuses in hillside cultivation. Only in recent decades has he set out to understand the natural balances of vegetation communities and to attempt to control and use them with regard to his future, as well as his present, welfare. Unfortunately, his greatest progress in this direction has been in areas where the pressures for increased plant productivity are not so great.

Notwithstanding the efficiency with which man uses the ax and the plow, the bulldozer and the dragline, his most effective tools for altering vegetation patterns have been fire and livestock. The reduction of the unprincipled use of fire has been the greatest achievement in forest conservation in the Western world. It is hoped that scientific management will bring our ranges to their optimum carrying capacity. The principal reason for the continued abuse of the vegetation cover in the world today is poverty—a poverty that is both a cause and a result of vegetation degeneration.

In the past many peoples maintained a stabilized existence for a long time through a mutually beneficial relationship with the vegetation cover that furnished them food or feed. These older groups developed their balances, not through complete understanding, but through long periods of trial and error. The stabilized plant yields which they accepted were on a low level, far below environmental capabilities. Today we do not accept a position in the balance at such a low productivity level. Through knowledge, we are learning nature's secrets and are beginning to adjust the environmental forces to suit our needs. Until recently it might be said that the natural vegetation balances either accepted or rejected human intervention. Now we are learning how to make the plant world work for us. Plant scientists tell us that we have hardly begun to harness the potentialities of plants for feeding us and that the control of plant environments will eventually have as great an impact on man as did the first domestication of plants.

The classification of vegetation

9.21 PROBLEMS IN THE CLASSIFICATION OF VEGETATION PATTERNS. As was stated earlier, the problems of describing the distribution of vegetation are similar to those encountered in depicting the geography of the other elements of the physical environment. Differences appear at every step, differences that grade into one another and that change with fluctuating conditions, ranging from the daily changes in weather to the slow action of geologic forces operating in cycles of millions of years. Yet, as with the other elements in the environmental complex, similarities can be seen as well as differences, and these make possible regional classifications of plant characteristics. As is pointed out many times in this volume, there are no universally applicable systems of geographic classification. Each system must be suited to the purpose for which it is to be used and to the observational scale that is appropriate to that purpose.

The most widely used systems of classifications of vegetation regions today are based on the plant-community concept, distinguishing between the communities which have reached a relatively long-term stability with the major environmental controls (the climax communities) and those which represent short-term balances (the successional communities). Subdivisions of the climax communities are based on a scale of generalization that ranges from the great global formations to local associations distinguished by the *dominant species* [4] present. Since this is the classification system to be used in describing global patterns of vegetation in the following chapter, no further elaboration of it will be given here.

In describing vegetation patterns on a local, or topographic, scale, classifications that recognize stages in plant succession are most useful. The reason for this is that local variations in slope and drainage are critical in the pattern of plant communities. Thus we

[4] The term *dominant,* as here used, refers to the largest common members of a plant community. In a forest, the dominant species always include trees.

FIG. 9.19 Typical muskeg bogs in the Canadian forest. A close view of this oblique air photo will reveal the zones of different types of vegetation that represent stages in a hydrarch succession. The narrow spires of spruce mark the more advanced stages on somewhat better drained ground. [Royal Canadian Air Force]

may have a *hydrarch* succession, which refers to a sequence of plant communities that characterize the gradation from a bare surface covered with water (as in a lake or pond), through various degrees of poor drainage, to the well-drained upland climax (see Fig. 9.20). Such a complete series is known as a *sere*. It will be noted that any area may undergo a successional shift in either direction; for example, in the hydrarch succession, a site that is poorly drained may become either better drained or more poorly drained. Keeping in mind that a sere represents the complete succession from a bare surface to a climax association, we may note that a simple classification of seres includes the following:

FIG. 9.20 Diagram of a typical hydrarch succession. [After Clarke]

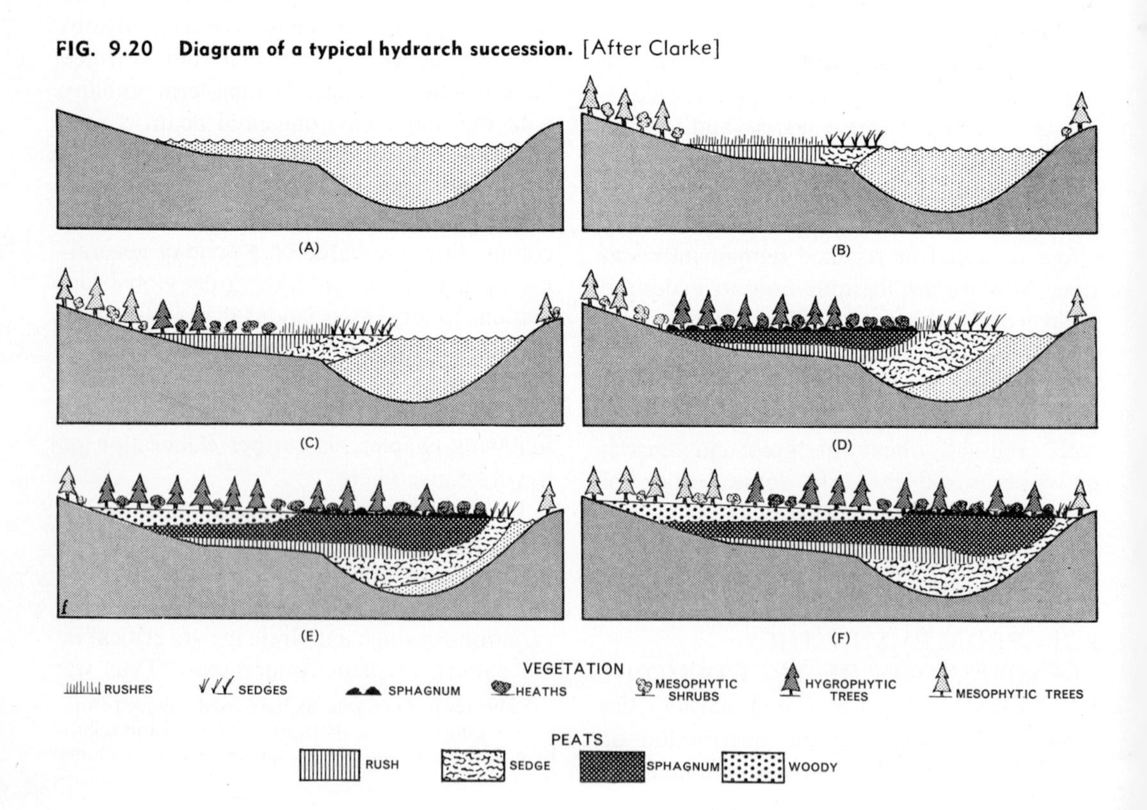

1. *Hydrarch* (a body of open water)
    a. Fresh-water sere: *hydrosere*
    b. Salt-water sere: *halosere*
2. *Xerarch* (a bare, waterless surface)
    a. Rock sere: *lithosere*
    b. Sand sere: *psammosere*

Other types of bare surface on which xerarch seres could develop include gravel, clay, and a burned-out soil following a forest fire. Seres differ widely with different types of climax vegetation, although the plants resulting from the excess or dearth of water may have comparable physiologic characteristics. For example, the swamp plants of the humid tropics often differ markedly in appearance and species from those of higher latitudes, but both may use many of the same mechanisms for overcoming water excesses.

A much simpler classification of plants based solely on water availability is sometimes used. This involves a primary division into four groups: the *xerophytes,* or drought-resistant plants; the *mesophytes,* plants that need a moderate amount of water; the *hydrophytes,* plants requiring an excessive water supply; and the *tropophytes,* plants that undergo periodic changes with respect to water availability. These categories can be divided into as many subgroups as are desired. Usually the subdivisions are based on the morphological characteristics of plants. For example, the xerophytes could be divided into cacti, perennial woody shrubs, needleleaf trees, etc. The major disadvantage of such a classification is that it is difficult to use in showing mixtures of plants, and it does not take into consideration the changes that individual sites may undergo.

Perspective

If one realizes that nearly all the factors catalogued in this chapter operate more or less together to influence plant growth in one way or another, he should have some idea of the enormous scope of plant geography and the amazing complexity of nature. Not only is this subject material immense in breadth, and hence formidable to describe comprehensively, but it is never static. The plant world is in a constant state of change, for it is made up of a living, pulsating complex of unstable variants. The facts of plant life therefore are not of such a nature that they can all be categorically presented in a simple, brief listing. Instead, the various factors seem to work together as a great dynamic system, filled with fluctuations and seeming contradictions, with opposite forces pushing and shoving one another. Plant geography might be pictured as a vast jungle in which science could lose itself; yet this is not the case.

Plant geography is a subject that has developed gradually, along with the various specialized plant sciences. At first a static, descriptive study, it assumed its dynamic character as the biological sciences uncovered some basic facts concerning the substance of living organisms, their habits and potentialities, and their relations with their environments. Plant taxonomy, physiology, pathology, genetics, and a myriad of other ramifications in botanical science are all involved, and it is the task of the plant geographer to bring together many of the contributions of these fields in an attempt to explain the complex pattern of plant life as it clothes the surface of the earth.

In an over-all view, some of the basic points to be observed might be summarized as follows:

1. Plant growth is conditioned by numerous vital factors.

2. These factors are not static, but dynamic and variable.

3. Pressures are exerted upon the plant and upon each other by these factors.

4. One factor may become limiting and temporarily exert a controlling influence.

5. Whenever the pressure of one limiting factor is relieved, some other factor of the complex may assume control and limit the plant; this in turn may be superseded by others, one after another.

6. The factors themselves, however, are not without limitations, for each factor travels in its own special orbit.

7. The plants themselves, in relation to one another, serve as agents in creating part of their own environment.

To illustrate the dynamic nature of plant life, let us say that a plant is inhibited by lack of sufficient water. Such a water deficiency, then, would constitute a limiting factor. Later, with adequate water supplies, there might be inadequate light, or insufficient plant foods, or removal of organic material from the soil by burning—and so on through the long list of environmental factors that may impinge upon plant growth.

Despite all these variables, the circumstances affecting a plant's life are subject to certain laws and rules, enabling plants to grow, thrive, and react in ways that are known and predictable. The end result, therefore, is a fluctuating though orderly system of pressures and demands, controlled by checks and balances, which constantly operate to produce the harmonious but highly diverse results that we see in plant life everywhere.

If one makes a detailed study of the plant growth that can be found on almost any bit of undulating terrain in the humid mid-latitudes, he will observe that each cubic inch of surface soil is occupied by plant life of one sort or another—usually several kinds, living together in a kind of society. In examining this variety at close hand, one can obtain a fair idea of the pressures which are present, the intense competition which exists, and the relative balance which is maintained. One can also recognize the various ecological agents which are focused upon any spot. Actual observation of such conditions in the field will be more effective than volumes of words in giving the student an understanding of these phenomena, which appear at first to be too complicated for the memory to grasp but which in actual operation perform as a successful and orderly process in the total scheme of things.

These complex interrelationships of plants with one another and with their environment are not unlike some situations that exist in human society; they might, in fact, be described by Plato's statement about democracy:

> . . . a charming form of government, full of variety and disorder, and dispensing a sort of equality to equals and unequals alike.

10

Major vegetation regions of the world

The four primary types of vegetation regions of the world, termed *formations,* are the forests, grasslands, desert shrubs, and tundra (see Fig. 9.5). There is sufficient variety within the first two formations to justify a further breakdown into subformations, each of which has sufficient area to be clearly indicated on a world map.

The classification of forests, or the breakdown into subformations, is based on the forms that the vegetation assumes in order to adjust to particular moisture balances. The subformations are as follows:

1. Broadleaf evergreen forest
   a. Hygrophytic (abundance of water) tropical rain forest, or *selva*
   b. Mesophytic (moderate water supply) scrub woodland [1]
2. Broadleaf deciduous forest
   a. Hygrophytic broadleaf deciduous forest
   b. Mesophytic broadleaf deciduous scrub woodland
3. Needleleaf evergreen forest
   a. Hygrophytic conifers with tall trees
   b. Mesophytic low forest (the *taiga*)
   c. Xerophytic (low water supply) scrub woodland
4. Needleleaf deciduous forest
5. Mixed broadleaf deciduous–needleleaf evergreen forest
6. Semideciduous forest (broadleaf evergreen–broadleaf deciduous forest)

The grasslands are divided into the steppe, prairie, and savanna subformations.

Each of the formations and subformations is described in this chapter. A separate division of the chapter is reserved for mountain vegetation, which includes characteristics of several of the formations and subformations but which differs enough from the lowland types to warrant separate treatment. Figure 10.1 shows the pattern of the global vegetation.

Descriptive generalizations of such immense areas as are covered by the vegetation regions described in this chapter must be subject to continual qualification. Exceptions to the generalizations can be found everywhere, if one looks closely enough. The descriptions here are those of climax or near-climax plant groupings. Little can be done with the characteristics of *plant succession* within the scale of our global presentation,

[1] The term *scrub woodland* refers to a sparse tree stand, 20 to 40 feet high, in which a continuous canopy overhead is usually absent but in which trees predominate over grass in the landscape.

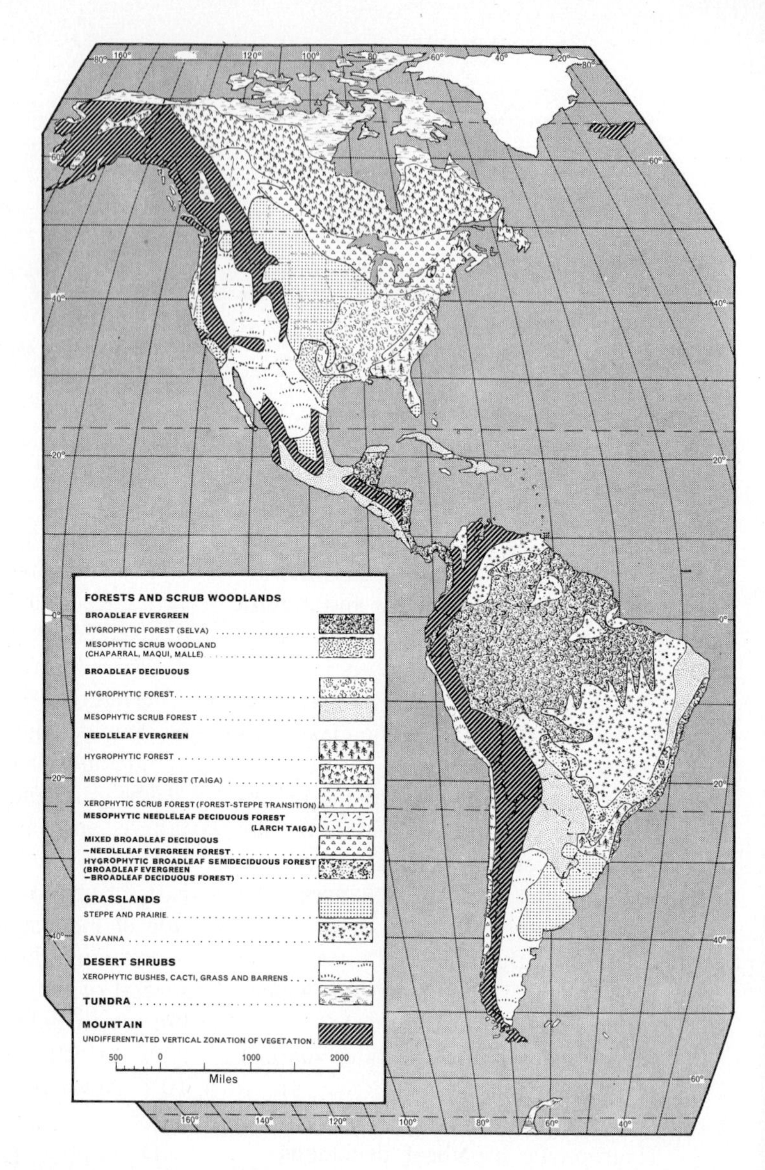

FIG. 10.1 World map of vegetation regions.

but a few of the major implications of succession are noted from time to time to indicate that the processes of vegetation replacement and site alteration are present everywhere.

Our task is not only to portray and to interpret the vegetation patterns but also to indicate their significance to man; therefore, the discussion of each regional pattern is followed by a special section on economic implications.

Broadleaf evergreen forest

10.1 HYGROPHYTIC, TROPICAL RAIN FOREST (SELVA). The high temperatures and rainfall of equatorial areas supply the most ideal climatic conditions for

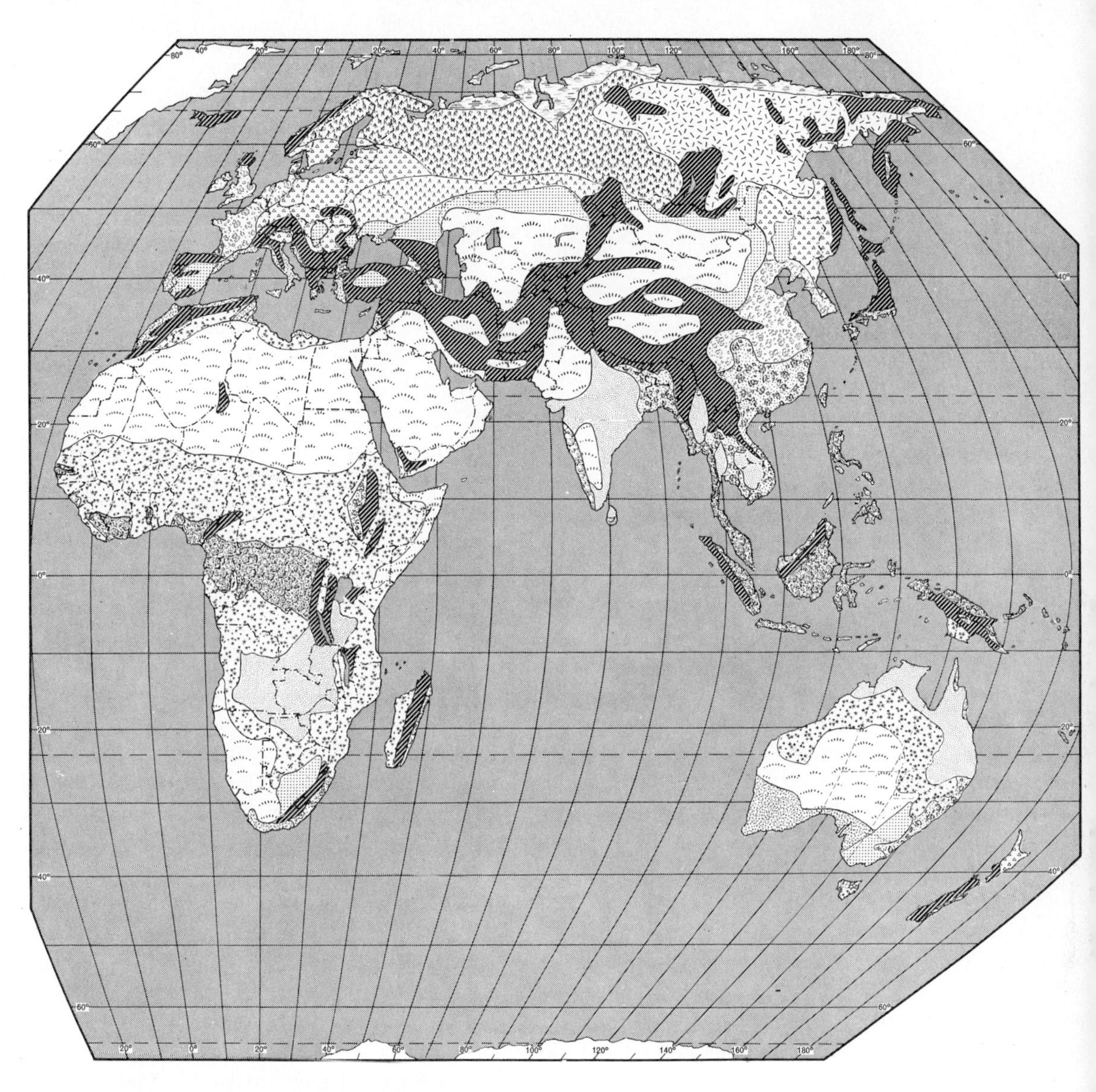

plant growth on earth. Under the stimulus of high moisture intake, high transpiration rates, and competition for sunlight, trees grow tall and straight and form a continuous leafy canopy overhead (see Fig. 10.2).

There is a distinct storied aspect to the selva, or tropical rain forest, with two and sometimes three levels of tree growth. In the upper story, tree heights reach 150 to 200 feet, and branches begin far above the ground. A distinctive feature of the larger trees is their buttressed bases, often in the form of ribbonlike flanges that flare outward, so that from a distance the bases of the trees appear to have diameters of 15 to 20 feet (see Fig. 10.3). These buttressed bases are necessary to support the tall trunks, since tree roots are shallow. The middle story con-

FIG. 10.2 The canopy of typical selva, or tropical rain forest, as seen from the air. The variety of trees is apparent. Location is in the upper Magdalena Valley of Colombia. [Standard Oil Company (N.J.)]

sists of smaller trees, 30 to 60 feet high and only 4 to 8 inches in diameter. These smaller trees are not necessarily younger versions of their giant companions. Many of them are distinct species that have become adapted to this middle level, in which the conditions of light, heat, and moisture are intermediate between those of the forest floor and the canopy overhead. Leaves of trees within the middle story of the forest usually are considerably broader than those of the larger trees. Giant ferns (tree ferns) sometimes abound in the middle story in areas where moisture is especially abundant. The lowest story of the selva includes small seedlings, ferns, and often varieties of climbing bamboos. Mushrooms and other forms of giant fungi are plentiful.

Vines are frequently found in the selva community, ranging from small tendrils of beanlike plants to giant lianas, 3 to 6 inches in diameter, which may hang down from the trees like crooked hawsers (see Fig. 9.7). Equipped with tiny hooks, some of the vines constitute one of the more troublesome features for human beings traveling through the selva. For the most part, however, the relative sparseness of underbrush makes the selva fairly easy to penetrate. *Epiphytes,* or "plants upon plants," which include the orchids, abound in the upper story of the forest, where they find moisture and sustenance in tree crotches and on the more horizontal branches. The more showy members of this highly diverse group of plants are well known in florist shops, but most of them in the selva are small and inconspicuous. Large, brilliantly colored flowers generally are rare throughout the selva. The brilliant flowers seen by tourists in the tropics are more characteristic of human settlements than of natural forests. Another distinctive feature of most rain forests is the presence of many parasitic plants. The most widely distributed of these is the strangling fig (*Ficus*), which may slowly envelop the host tree and literally choke the life out of it.

The species of trees in the rain forest are extremely varied. Whereas ten or a dozen species of trees per acre are common in mid-latitude forests, a hundred or more will often be encountered in the selva. The properties of the trees are as diverse as the species they characterize. There are woods that are extremely hard and so dense that they will not float on water. Others, such as balsa, are light and spongy. There are dark woods and light woods, woods of different colors, straight-grained woods and gnarled woods. Some trees have a milky, thick sap; others contain fluids that are strong irritants and that may even be poisonous. Some trees bear nuts, and others produce fleshy fruits. Contrary to common belief, edible fruits are not abundant in a typical climax selva, despite the great variety of trees. Although there is a striking similarity of forest structure in the humid tropics, diversity is the outstanding characteristic of the trees themselves.

A walk in a climax selva is a unique experience for visitors. A heavy, rank, moldy odor permeates the dimly lit lower story of the forest. There is a surprising amount of bare soil, usually damp and reddish in color. Fallen trunks of dead trees are conspicuously absent. From far overhead comes the raucous clamor of birds and monkeys, interrupted by the shrill piping of tree frogs near at hand.

The largest expanse of undisturbed climax selva in the world is found in the upper Amazon Basin. Thinly populated even today, this area presents an almost unbroken expanse of rain forest 1,000 miles long and 750 miles wide. Elsewhere, however, man has been much more active in his penetration of the tropical rain forests, and, except for Brazil, virgin forest occurs mainly in small, discontinuous areas and in the more inaccessible localities.

FIG. 10.3 A forest giant in the rain forest of Panama. Note the fluted mergence of the trunk and root system and the flared base. The ribbon-like flanges of this tree are about 3 to 4 feet high. [American Museum of Natural History]

10.2 LOCAL VARIATIONS IN THE SELVA. Typical selva vegetation, as described in the preceding section, is developed mainly on well-drained, rolling-to-undulating uplands that have not been occupied by man. Various types of modifications of the selva vegetation occur in the tropics, however, and are sufficiently widespread to warrant separate treatment. All these variations, however, are characterized by typical broadleaf evergreen trees.

SECONDARY RAIN FOREST. Much of the forest land in the humid tropics is in various stages of regrowth following destruction of the climax selva. There is fierce competition among many plants to occupy the site of a forest clearing. The length of time taken to establish the dominance of the giant trees has been estimated at between 100 and 250 years. As a result of migratory agriculture, there are large areas of secondary rain forest in various stages of regrowth in Africa and southeast Asia (see Fig. 9.11).

At first the forest clearings are taken over by a tangled mass of low bushes, vines, ferns, briars, and young saplings. If the clearing was formerly cultivated and not too badly depleted in fertility or too heavily burned, the remains of garden fruits and vegetables often will be found in the tangle, including the spreading vine of the *yam*, the drooping leaves of the *plantain* (banana), and fruit trees such as the *mango, jack fruit,* and *guava.* In southeast Asia, bamboo thickets frequently crowd the assemblage. Gradually the trees become larger, undergrowth thins out, and eventually the selva reestablishes itself.

The vegetation in the early stages of a secondary forest is generally difficult to penetrate, and trails must be hacked out of the tangle. Such vegetation is usually avoided by human beings, and its wide distribution surrounding settled areas probably has helped to establish the erroneous conception that most tropical forests consist of dense jungle growth. A forest is replaced by coarse grasses instead of by secondary forest if annual burning is used consistently to clear away the entering vegetation.

INFLUENCES OF SLOPE AND ELEVATION IN ALTERING TYPICAL SELVA VEGETATION. The true selva is typically developed in well-drained, level-to-rolling interstream areas. In hill and mountain country, steep slopes generally tend to increase the amount of undergrowth and to reduce somewhat the height of the mature forest. Vines and lianas become more plentiful, particularly some of the climbing varieties of bamboos. The sparsest vegetation is generally encountered along the crest lines of narrow ridges, probably because of the lower moisture content of the soil. Most of the native trails are found here. Narrow ravine bottoms have the densest tangles of vegetation.

Selva trees also tend to become shorter as elevation increases, and the general appearance of the forest changes noticeably as one ascends mountain slopes. Above 3,000 to 5,000 feet, tree heights are reduced to 50 to 100 feet, the middle story tends to disappear, and buttressed trunks are much less usual. Vines are not so well developed, and tree ferns (tall, treelike ferns 20 to 40 feet high) become much more abundant. Evergreen oaks are present, but they are quite unlike the familiar deciduous varieties of mid-latitudes, except for the similar appearance of the acorns.

RIVERINE AND SWAMP FORESTS. The rain forest that borders large rivers appears as a solid green wall of vegetation. Such areas contain an abundance of water and some of the most fertile soil in the tropics. The swath of the river breaks the dense forest canopy and thus permits sunlight to reach ground level. Vines grow in rank profusion, extending from the water's edge to the summits of the adjacent forest. No wonder that early explorers in the rainy tropics, penetrating along the waterways, which still are the easiest routes of access, believed that the tropical forest was virtually impenetrable!

The fresh-water swamp forests that develop on the flood plains of rivers, away from the immediate stream banks, differ from the selva proper mainly in having a somewhat denser stand of taller trees and a much larger number of palms as a lower story. Among the latter is the sago palm, particularly abundant in southeastern Asia and Indonesia. The pith contained in the trunk of this palm is high in starch and constitutes a basic element in the diet of some of the peoples in this part of the world.

MANGROVE FOREST. Mangroves (*Rhizophora*) constitute a distinctive type of broadleaf evergreen forest that develops along silty or muddy tidal flats throughout the humid tropics, from Florida to New Guinea. The mangrove is a highly specialized tree that has adapted itself to thrive in ocean salt water. Among its most distinctive features are its aerial roots, which take the form of "knees," as in the cypress, or of prop roots, which protrude laterally from the lower trunks. These aerial roots are highly porous. Mangrove trees may reach heights of 100 feet and have diameters up to 4 feet. The wood, which is hard, durable, and resistant to decay in salt water, is in great demand, and for this reason commercial stands of timber size are rare. It is most commonly used today for pilings and firewood. Unlike the selva, with its great variety of trees, mangrove forests contain only a few species.

Submerged in salt water, the mangrove trees are partly marine and partly terrestrial. The roots frequently form a favored environment for small marine life, and this is one place where one might truly pick a meal of oysters and other shellfish from trees. The combination of mud, water, and the tangle of aerial roots makes mangrove thickets extremely difficult to cross on foot. Tidal channels provide the best access by boat.

10.3 UTILIZATION OF THE SELVA. Nonliterate, nonagricultural people have lived in the selva since early in human history. Some were gatherers, utilizing the great variety of trees to supply them with their needs. Some were hunters as well, such as the pygmies of Africa, who used blowguns with poison-tipped darts to bring down birds or monkeys. Occasionally they also found means of trapping or killing much larger animals, including elephants that found their way into the selva. Fish generally are available in the full-running streams, and the forest supplies unusual tree poisons that, when placed in a pool, have the property of stupefying fish.

A few of the more important tree fruits early became staple elements in the forest economy, and it is believed that the first deliberate planting, the first steps in agriculture, took place in the tropical forest and consisted of inserting roots or shoots of the wild forest plants into the ground, especially the fruits, such as the plantain, mango, papaya, and breadfruit. Some of the plants with tubers or starchy roots were domesticated later and incorporated into native agriculture. Among these were the *manioc* plant (mandioca, or cassava) and the yam. One may wonder what accident led to the discovery that removing the poisonous prussic acid in the manioc root could yield a starchy staple food and the tapioca of commerce. Although there are only a few people in the world today who still obtain their food wild from the tropical forests, many still make a living by gathering certain products that appear in world markets. The best-known of these products include *brazil nuts, tagua nuts* (vegetable ivory), *rattan,* and *dammar,* a vegetable gum. Rubber was once among the important products gathered wild in the Brazilian selva, but it is now almost entirely produced on plantations or synthesized in the industrial centers of mid-latitudes.

The reserves of lumber in the tropical rain forest are vast, but some major disadvantages must be overcome before they can serve as an important source of the world timber supply. At present, the principal commercial woods in the tropics are the hard, durable cabinet varieties, which, because of their great value, justify the required high costs of extraction and transportation. Such woods include mahogany, ebony, rosewood, and many others less well known. The greatest disadvantage of the lumber industry in the tropics is probably the large number of tree species. Since an acre of forest may contain only two or three trees of the type desired, large-scale lumbering methods are hardly practicable. If the forest is clean-cut, there remains the difficulty of handling and marketing such a large variety of woods. Some success has been obtained in planting *djati* (teak) forests in southeastern Asia, but, in general, the slowness of replacement is a distinct handicap. The major market for tropical woods remains in the tropics, where large volumes of a particular wood are not in demand.

Plantation production of tree crops that

once grew wild in the tropical forests offers considerable promise, but even here such products as rubber, quinine, kapok, and gums face serious competition from synthetics. The greatest potential appears to lie in the general field of vegetable oils, including coconut oil and palm oil, which have no serious competitors from mid-latitude oils and fats. Cacao also remains one of the leading plantation tree crops in the humid tropics. Originally the cacao tree was a member of the lower story in the rain forest, and it generally is grown on plantations in the shade of larger trees.

10.4 MESOPHYTIC BROADLEAF EVERGREEN SCRUB WOODLAND.

The mesophytic type of broadleaf evergreen tree vegetation differs markedly from the tropical rain forest, or selva. The trees are relatively low, and a continuous canopy is absent. Such a woodland is found typically in climates that have a mild, moist winter season and a dry summer (*Cs*). The winter rainfall, plus low evaporation, replenishes soil-moisture reserves. The winters do not have sufficiently low temperatures to halt most native vegetation growth; therefore, the principal adjustment of the vegetation is to the heat and aridity of summer.

The distribution of this woodland is mainly poleward of the low-latitude deserts. It is typical of the *Cs* climates but extends somewhat into the *BShs* type (hot semiarid climate, with most of the rain in the winter months). The largest expanse is in the Mediterranean Basin, with extensions into Turkey and Iran along the lower slopes of mountains. Smaller areas are found in Southern California, middle Chile, southernmost Africa, and southern Australia.

The trees of the broadleaf evergreen scrub

FIG. 10.4 Typical chaparral brush and scattered conifers in the San Gabriel Mountains of Southern California. The slight dip running along the side of the mountain slope is the result of slipping along the San Andreas Fault, one of the largest and most active faults in the western United States. [U.S. Geological Survey]

woodland generally have special mechanisms for reducing transpiration. The leaves are small, hard, thick, and leathery,[2] and some are covered with fine hairs. The trunks are gnarled and have a thick, scabby, highly insulative bark. A good example is the cork oak, in which this insulating property is especially well developed. Thorns, waxes, and essential oils are additional features of many such trees. Root systems are well developed vertically and horizontally in order to tap ground water. These root systems also permit propagation by sucker shoots, and when the tops of the trees are destroyed, the young shoots spring up, eventually producing a dense thicket of brush. Such successional thickets are typical features of the landscape today and probably are more extensive than the climax vegetation itself. They are known by various names, including *chaparral* in California, *maquis* in Mediterranean Europe and South Africa, and *mallee* in Australia (see Fig. 10.4).

Another characteristic of the broadleaf evergreen scrub woodland is an understory of low bushes. These include myrtles, laurels, tree heaths, and several small aromatic shrubs, such as rosemary, thyme, oleander, and lavender. Dwarf palms sometimes are also present in the understory.

The most widely distributed genus of trees is the oak (*Quercus*), which is found in this subformation throughout the world. These oaks are evergreen broadleaf trees and thus quite distinct from the deciduous oaks of most mid-latitudes. Eucalyptus, a variety of tree native to Australia, has been introduced into other parts of the world where the broadleaf evergreen scrub woodland is found. It is unique in that it may become a large tree suitable for lumber. Eucalyptus trees more than 150 feet high are found in Australia (see Fig. 10.5). The tree has become popular as an ornamental shade tree in California and along the Mediterranean Sea from Spain to the Middle East. It has an unusual resistance to most local insect pests and diseases.

FIG. 10.5 A grove of eucalyptus in the Snowy Mountains of New South Wales, Australia. These trees form one of the valuable timber resources of the continent. Unlike most of the trees in this vegetation region, the eucalyptus is deciduous. [Australian News and Information Bureau]

Mountains are found in all parts of the world where the broadleaf evergreen scrub forest occurs, with the exception of southwestern Australia. The typical woodland of the lowlands invariably gives way to needleleaf (coniferous) forests on the mountain slopes, as a result of the decreased tempera-

[2] Another term for this vegetation type is *sclerophyll* (Greek, *sclero* = hard; *phyll* = leaf).

tures and increased precipitation characteristic of higher elevations. The conifers include the yellow pine, sugar pine, and redwood of California; the stone, black, and umbrella-like Aleppo pines, cypresses, and cedars of the Mediterranean Basin area; and the Araucaria pine of the central Chilean Andes. In South Africa, practically all of the original needleleaf forest cover has been destroyed, but a few patches of trees similar to the cypress can be found in isolated places above 2,000 feet.

Little of the climax stage of the broadleaf evergreen scrub woodland vegetation remains today. It is highly susceptible to burning during the dry season, and since few of the trees have much economic value, human beings have tended to remove them in order to establish a grass cover more suited to grazing. Grass and brush are much more widespread than in the natural climax vegetation. A few of the trees of the original vegetation have been domesticated. The olive and the cork oak are both members of the original vegetation of the Mediterranean Basin and have become an important part of local agricultural economies. Acorns furnished by the oaks in the scrub woodland supply feed for hogs. Chestnuts are found as part of the native vegetation and are also cultivated in large orchards on the intermediate slopes of southern Europe, particularly in Italy and Corsica.

Grazing is a locally important type of land use in scrub woodland that is unsuited for agriculture. As was noted earlier, both grass and brush thickets tend to form successional stages following the clearing of largely useless woodland trees. Overgrazing of slopes has led to a reduction of grasses in many areas and a dominance of the brush thickets. About the only domestic animal that can browse on such thickets is the goat, which, once introduced, tends to maintain itself on the hardy brush vegetation indefinitely. This is especially true in Mediterranean Europe and the Middle East.

Broadleaf deciduous forests

The broadleaf deciduous trees are those which have broad, flat leaves like those in the selva but which shed these leaves during a particular time of the year. Like the broadleaf evergreen subformation, the broadleaf deciduous vegetation has both true forest and scrub woodland subtypes. The former is found in the humid mid-latitudes, where the leaf shedding is the result of frosts during the winter season. The scrub woodland subtype is found mainly in the *Aw* climates, which are tropical but which have a pronounced wet and dry season.

10.5 HYGROPHYTIC BROADLEAF DECIDUOUS FOREST. Conditions for tree growth in the summer season of the humid, mild-winter mid-latitudes are similar to those in the humid tropics. High temperatures combine with high moisture content in the soils to promote rapid plant growth. Freezing temperatures, even for short periods during the winter season, however, are dangerous to trees that contain large quantities of water in their cells. Most trees in such climates, therefore, withdraw all but a small amount of moisture from their cells, shed their broad leaves, and curtail their life processes. The period of rest varies in length, depending on the length of the frost season. Thus evolve the mid-latitude broadleaf deciduous forests, which reach their culmination in the humid climates with hot summers and mild, short winters (*Cfa*). The generalized location is principally in the eastern parts of continents, roughly between lat 25 and 40°. Smaller areas of this forest type also are found in the humid, mild-winter, cool-summer (*Cfb*) climate, located on the western sides of continents, poleward of the *Cs* climates.

The trees of the humid deciduous forest are typically shorter than those in the selva, usually ranging from 50 to 100 feet in height. The canopy overhead, although continuous, is not so tightly closed as in the selva, and considerably more light filters through to lower levels. The variety of trees is much smaller, and commonly three or four species dominate. For this reason, this forest is frequently divided into communities, termed *associations,* distinguished by the combination of dominant species. The deciduous forest in the United States, for example, includes three major associations: the oak-hickory, the birch-beech-maple, and the oak-chestnut-yellow poplar (tulip tree). The distribution of these is shown in Fig. 10.6.

A distinct middle story of trees, characteristic of the selva, is not present, although younger members of the dominant tree species are found at various heights. A distinctive feature of this forest is the mixture of tree sizes, ranging from tiny saplings to fully mature trees 2 to 4 feet in diameter. The spacing between the trees increases as the trees become larger. The root systems of the deciduous trees are much less shallow than those of the selva, and some of them have taproots which descend far below the surface. For this reason, and also because of the lower tree heights, buttressed bases are not required for trunk support. Lower trunks, as in the selva, are largely free of branches. Decay is not so rapid in this forest as it is in the selva. Scattered windfalls are found throughout the forest, and mounds mark the sites of fallen, partially decomposed tree trunks.

Vines are not nearly so common as in the selva, although they tend to become more frequent toward the equatorward margins. Poison ivy (*Rhus*), Virginia creeper (*Parthenocissus*), and wild honeysuckle (*Lonicera*) are small vines that may cover the lower trunks of trees in some areas.

The ground floor of the broadleaf deciduous forest has a variety of subdominant plants (minor members of the forest communities), ranging from tiny annual wild flowers to perennial bushes. Many of the herbaceous plants that cover the forest floor are arranged in seasonal cycles of dominance, ranging from the early-flowering annuals (such as the spring beauty), which complete their growth cycles under the open sunlight before the leaves open in the spring, through those which are able to thrive under the shade of the trees during the summer (ferns and nettles), to the wild asters, which appear in the late summer and early autumn.

The most spectacular feature of many of the broadleaf deciduous forests is perhaps the brilliant coloration in the early autumn, immediately prior to defoliation. The yellow pigment, *xanthophyll,* is always present in the leaf cell structure, but it becomes visible only when the green chlorophyll begins to deteriorate and disappear in the fall. The red pigment, *anthocyanin,* on the other hand, is produced in association with sugars in the tree sap. Like most plant sugars, it is better developed with greater intensity of sunlight; therefore the scarlet foliage is more brilliant during dry, sunny autumns. It is also chemically influenced to some extent by sudden, chilling temperatures. Individual types of trees differ considerably in the dominance of yellows or reds. The sugar maple (*Acer saccharum*) usually has much anthocyanin in its sap, associated with the high sugar content; thus reds and orange colors predominate in the autumn leaves. The birches, beeches, poplars, and elms, on the other hand, develop mainly yellow hues. Oaks and hickories usually show shades of brown. Certain other

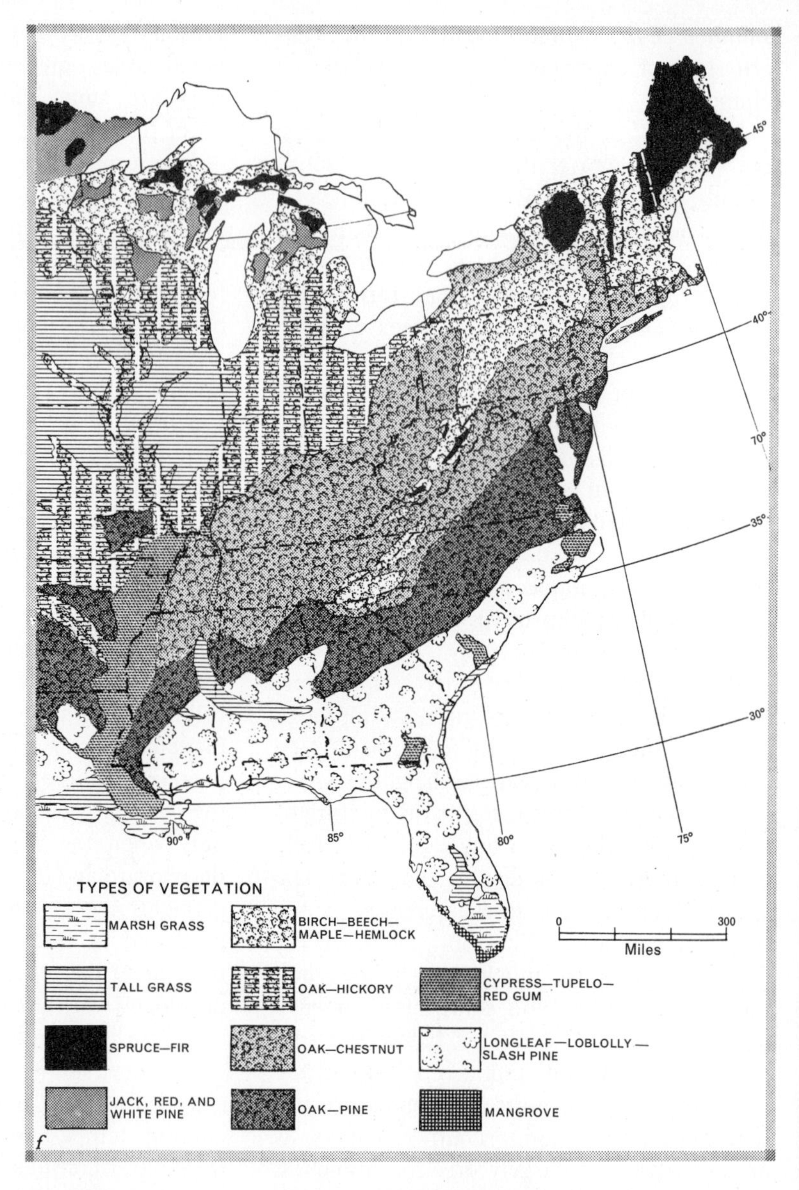

FIG. 10.6 Forest associations in the eastern United States. [U.S. Department of Agriculture; American Atlas of Agriculture]

deciduous trees, such as the willows, do not develop bright coloration, but merely turn a grayish green before falling from the tree. The more brilliant coloration that usually is seen as one proceeds poleward is the result of the greater numerical dominance of sugar maples in the forest associations. The west coast (*Cfb*) deciduous forests usually are not nearly so brilliantly colored as those in the eastern parts of the continents.

The deciduous broadleaf forests of both Europe and Asia have been so modified by man's occupation of the land that few characteristics of the climax vegetation remain. Cultivation has removed much of the natural vegetation on the plains. In Europe, the forests that remain on the hill slopes are carefully tended, and all but the most valuable species of trees have been eliminated. Conifers have been planted in many areas to supply firewood and lumber, because of their relatively rapid growth, as compared to the deciduous broadleaf trees. In China, the need for fuel in this densely populated country has resulted in the removal of even young trees, except in the most isolated parts of the country. This systematic denuding of the hill slopes has continued for such a long time in northeastern China that plant ecologists are not certain what the climax vegetation really is. Reforestation of barren hill slopes has a high priority in China today.

10.6 HYDROSERE SUBCLIMAX[3] ASSOCIATIONS IN THE BROADLEAF DECIDUOUS FOREST. The last stages of the hydrosere in the mid-latitude broadleaf deciduous forest are characterized by vegetation that shows many of the typical features of the climax type, but that differs mainly in the species of trees that are present. In the birch-beech-maple association of the United States, for example, swamp-forest associations usually include red maple, elm, and ash in areas where the ground water has a neutral-to-slightly-acid reaction. Where it is highly acid, however, swamp conifers may be included, such as arbor vitae, larch, or spruce. A dominant swamp tree in the southern part of the United States is the bald cypress, unusual in being, like the larch, a deciduous conifer, or a cone-bearing tree that sheds its needles during the winter season. Associated with the cypress are the gum trees and swamp oaks. Sometimes the subclimax forms of the hydrosere are found on rolling uplands, as in the northern Appalachian uplands, because of poor internal drainage above hardpan soils. Red maple and ash are illustrative dominants in these areas.

[3] The term *subclimax* refers to a plant community that has nearly reached the end of the successional stages in a sere.

10.7 UTILIZATION OF THE BROADLEAF DECIDUOUS FOREST. Broadleaf deciduous forests are utilized principally as a source of lumber, charcoal, and firewood. Most of the trees have a dense, hard wood; therefore the lumber is best suited for furniture, flooring, the interior trim of buildings, and for such miscellaneous uses as wooden utensils, tool handles, and barrel staves. The special qualities of these hardwoods, combined with their nearness to markets and their relatively slow growth, make their lumber expensive. Today most of the furniture hardwoods are thinly sliced and used for veneering on softer, cheaper woods. Particularly prized are walnut, cherry, maple, and oak.

The Appalachian uplands contain the greatest reserves of deciduous hardwood timber in the United States, but farm wood lots supply a considerable quantity throughout the eastern part of the country. The high value of this timber has led to selective logging practices throughout most of the deciduous forest. Large areas are required to yield a steady supply of high-volume production; thus the hardwood lumber industry in the United States is mainly in the hands of jobbers, who contract for the removal of mature timber from a large number of local wood-lot owners, mainly farmers. It has been estimated that between 75 and 125 years is required to replace a clean-cut deciduous forest; so there is little incentive for private ownership of cut-over climax forests. It is likely that there are only a few areas of virgin hardwood forests left in the United States, and these are either in governmental forest reserves or in inaccessible localities. Most of the forest region is in various stages of regrowth, with the mature trees removed as they reach saw-timber size. Culling and thinning of the secondary forest, which aid in speeding the replacement of lumber, afford additional income from firewood, charcoal, or fence posts.

A number of edible-nut trees are included within the broadleaf deciduous forest subformation, but they usually are among the subdominant species. Among these are the *shagbark hickory, black walnut, butternut,* and *chestnut,* but all except the chestnut have too hard a shell to be developed commercially. The American chestnut (*Castanea dentata*), formerly one of the most common trees in this type of forest, was virtually eliminated from the eastern United States during the past century because of the blighting caused by an especially virulent fungus disease. Two other nut trees, the pecan and the tung, are cultivated in extensive orchards along the northern Gulf of Mexico coastal plain, between Texas and Florida. The pecan, a species of hickory, is native to the Mississippi Valley and has been bred and improved until it has become the most important edible nut produced in the United States. The nut of the tung tree, native to southwestern China, yields an oil (tung oil) that is important in the paint and varnish industry because of its rapid-drying properties.

Localized forest by-product industries in the broadleaf deciduous forests of the eastern United States include the maple syrup and sugar industry, centered in the New England states, and the raising of meat-hogs fed on acorns supplied by oak forests in the southern Appalachians.

10.8 THE MESOPHYTIC BROADLEAF DECIDUOUS SCRUB WOODLAND. As one travels away from the rainy tropics, rainfall decreases, becomes more erratic, and tends to show a distinct seasonal deficiency mainly in the winter or low-sun period. Because of this, conditions for tree growth also tend to become more unfavorable. Where a pronounced dry season occurs, daytime surface temperatures become extremely high, and evaporation rates are similar to those in desert areas. Trees become stunted, as compared with those in the selva, and most of them shed their leaves during the dry season. Also, as conditions become less suited for tree growth, grass begins to cover the surface, aided in its competitive struggle with tree growth by man's use of fire. The mesophytic broadleaf deciduous scrub woodland represents a transition between the tropical grasslands (savannas) on one hand and the true tropical forests on the other.

The general appearance of the deciduous scrub woodland is somewhat similar to the evergreen scrub woodland of the *Cs* climates. The principal difference is that nearly all the trees are deciduous. The soils of the *Aw* regions are less retentive of moisture than those of the *Cs* climates, and there is no cool winter season with fairly reliable rainfall and low evaporation rates to store water in the soil for plant use the following summer. The trees cannot obtain enough moisture to support continued tree growth during the dry season, even with various specialized methods of reducing transpiration.

The typical stand of trees in the deciduous scrub woodland varies from an open park or orchardlike cover (see Fig. 10.7) to dense tangles of brush containing occasional grassy openings. The transitions from the deciduous scrub woodland to the savanna, in one direction, and to the true forest, in the other, are gradual. The boundary between the open woodland and the savanna is especially difficult to define, since the only mark of separation is the relative dominance of trees or grass in the landscape. The distinction is somewhat clearer with respect to the forest

FIG. 10.7 Typical "Brigalow scrub," a type of tropical deciduous scrub woodland in Northern Australia. Note the termite hills that abound in such country in both Africa and Australia. [Australian News and Information Bureau]

border, for the continuous canopy of a true forest is absent in a woodland.

The more open stands of the deciduous scrub woodland are composed of trees that are usually between 20 and 40 feet high. There are relatively little undergrowth and relatively few young trees. The influence of fire is evident in the absence of lower branches on the trees and the spreading, flat-topped crowns. Grass fires can sweep through such a forest without having much effect on mature trees. In such a woodland, one seems to be always in the midst of a clearing, with trees becoming closer together in the distance. Usually one can see through the woodland for a distance of about 100 to 200 yards. One characteristic genus of trees in the more open stands of the deciduous scrub forest is the *Acacia,* a flat-topped, sometimes deciduous, thorny tree. The remarkable adaptability of this hardy scrub tree, however, gives it a range throughout the subhumid to semiarid tropics, almost to the desert margin. In Africa and southeastern Asia, clumps of bamboos are found.

The denser stands of this scrub woodland contain small trees and many low, woody, thorny shrubs. The smaller bushes, requiring less water, are more likely to be evergreen *sclerophylls,* which are like the chaparral or maquis of the evergreen scrub woodland of *Cs* climates. They vary in height but are usually under 20 feet. This denser, thorn-bush variety of the deciduous scrub woodland is found in the drier parts of the subformation. Sometimes xerophytic, leafless plants are encountered, including the *Euphorbia,* a giant desert shrub. Acacias are quite common, as in the more open scrub woodland. The *baobab* tree (*Adansonia digitata*) is a noteworthy exception to the bush vegetation. Standing singly, the baobab is a gnarled, twisted giant, apparently ageless, and unaffected by time, fire, or the ravages of insects. It has an enormous girth, often 20 to 30 feet in diameter, but the trunks are low, the branches extending outward a short distance above the ground in irregular, zigzag shapes. The huge trunks frequently are hollow and may be used for shelter and shade. In the Sudan savanna, baobabs are termed *tebeldes,* and their hollow centers are used for water storage.

The world map of vegetation (Fig. 10.1) does not adequately indicate the distribution of this woodland type, mainly because the details of the transitions between the humid forests and the grasslands never have been worked out carefully. Only the larger recognized areas are shown. Unfortunately also, little correlation is possible between climate and this woodland subformation, because in many places dry-season burning has destroyed much of the woodland, replacing it with savanna grasslands. For this reason, the selva passes directly into the savannas, particularly in much of central Africa and in Brazil.

In South America, the two areas of this woodland type shown in Fig. 10.1 include the *caatinga* scrub woodland of northeastern Brazil and the Chaco area of Paraguay and northern Argentina. For the most part the caatinga consists of smaller thorn trees than usually occur in this subformation. The erratic rainfall of this part of Brazil is shown by the presence of cacti among the thorn trees and bushes. The Chaco area is divided between marshy grasslands in the low, flat depressions and typical open scrub woodland just above flood level. Much of this area contains the *quebracho* tree as a member of the woodland association.

In Africa, the largest area of scrub woodland lies in a broad belt extending from central Tanganyika southwestward through Northern Rhodesia into eastern Angola. Patches of it can also be found on the broad interstream areas bordering the Congo Basin and in the northern parts of the Guinea coast countries (Nigeria, Ghana, and the Ivory Coast). Acacias dominate the African open woodland. A considerable portion of peninsular India is in deciduous scrub woodland, and the interior plains of Burma, northeastern Thailand, and west-central Indochina have large areas of this subformation. In Australia, the deciduous scrub woodland corresponds to what is locally termed the Brigalow scrub (see Fig. 10.7), a variety of acacia, which extends along the northern coast and southward within Queensland, excluding a narrow coastal zone of tropical forest.

10.9 UTILIZATION OF THE DECIDUOUS SCRUB WOODLAND.

The deciduous scrub woodland is not a source of lumber, because of the small size of the trees. It does, however, yield a number of valuable products, the principal ones being waxes and gums. In South America, the carnauba palm supplies a hard wax which is used in the manufacture of phonograph records. Gum lacquer and waxes are also important products of this woodland in the lowlands of Laos in Indochina. Sandalwood, an aromatic wood that is especially prized for fine cabinets, has long been sought in the scrub woodlands of the southwest Pacific Islands and in Australia, although little of it remains. Another important product is quebracho bark, from the Chaco area of South America. It has an unusually high tannin content and is used in the tanning of leather.

The open woodland in places offers some possibilities for agriculture or for grazing, but the difficulty of clearing the deep-rooted woody plants is a serious handicap. The brush woodland of Africa also appears to be one of the worst areas for the tsetse fly, a carrier of the dreaded "sleeping sickness." A further hindrance is the unreliability of rainfall in this tropical zone.

Needleleaf evergreen forest

The needleleaf evergreen forests are composed largely of conifers, or cone-bearing trees. These trees are the most widely distributed of the major types of trees and extend from the tropics to subarctic regions. They also are found in widely differing conditions of moisture availability, from the humid west coasts of upper mid-latitudes to semiarid high plains, such as the Colorado Plateau, and from thin mountain soils barely a foot thick to water-saturated swamp soils. The feathery casuarina tree borders the beach strands of many tropical beaches, and the slender spires of alpine firs abut against the timber line of high mountains thousands of feet above sea level. For this reason the conifers, as a type of vegetation, cannot be correlated with any particular climate. For one reason or another, however, large areas of the world are made up almost exclusively of these needleleaf evergreen trees.

The principal features of the conifers include, besides their unique evergreen leaf form and seed cones, a thick, insulative bark; a thick, pitchy sap; a broad, shallow root system; and a tolerance for wide ranges of soil acidity. These properties enable the conifers to become dominant under varying conditions. Their dominance in subarctic regions is mainly due to their resistance to low winter temperatures and highly acid soils. In other areas, tall pines, free of lower branches, are dominant because of their resistance to fire. Sandy and gravelly soils in humid regions sometimes contain conifers as a dominant type of vegetation in an early stage of plant succession because these trees can stand irregular periods of almost complete soil dryness. Their shallow root system enables them to obtain anchorage and nutrient solutions from thin, rocky soils on mountain slopes.

The subdivisions of the needleleaf evergreen forests are based on moisture availability. The first, or hygrophytic, group includes the forests where humid conditions exist for nearly the entire year. These forests are composed of tall trees ranging from 80 feet to 300 feet. The second, or mesophytic, group is found where water is available for only part of the year. This second group also is limited to the forests of high latitudes, where the plant forms are ideally suited to the long periods of low temperatures and frozen soils, snow cover, and oblique solar radiation. The trees in the mesophytic group are not so large as the hygrophytic types, and they are usually less than 80 feet tall. The xerophytic, or drought-resistant, conifers do not cover a large total area, but patches of woodland containing them are found in the semiarid lands of most continents, especially at elevations over 3,000 feet.

All three groups of the needleleaf evergreens are found in mountain areas, and mountain conifers are discussed below under Mountain Vegetation (page 366).

10.10 HYGROPHYTIC NEEDLELEAF EVERGREEN FORESTS. The tall forests of conifers found in the warm humid regions of the world cover broad areas in the west coast *Cfb* climates of North America, South America, and Europe; in the Atlantic–Gulf of Mexico coastal plain of eastern and southern United States; and in widely scattered patches in the low latitudes, including upland plains

FIG. 10.8 Mature stand of trees in a typical west coast coniferous forest. Note the ground flora of large-leafed plants and ferns, adapted to minimum light conditions and high humidity on the forest floor. [Weyerhaeuser Timber Company]

in southeastern Asia, Luzon, northern Sumatra, New Guinea, and southeastern Brazil. The sandy and gravelly coastal plains of Honduras and Nicaragua also have a pine flora, and similar pines are found in places in the West Indies.

THE WEST COAST CONIFERS. Conifers are abundant in many parts of the west coast marine climates (*Cfb*) of the world, including western North America, southern Chile, southwestern France, coastal Norway, and parts of New Zealand.

In North America, the western conifers extend from northern California into Alaska along the coast. At higher elevations, they extend far southward in the Sierra Nevada. Inland, this forest extends to the lower eastern slopes of the Cascade Mountains in the United States (see Fig. 10.8). In central British Columbia and northward, however, the same coniferous forest prevalent along the coast extends eastward to the Canadian Rockies.

The conifers of northwestern North America include several species that are highly important as sources of construction lumber. The most important is Douglas fir (*Pseudotsuga*), whose tall, straight trunks frequently rise over 200 feet above the ground and have diameters up to 20 or 30 feet. Sitka spruce, western hemlock, red and white cedar, and the famous redwoods (*Sequoia sempervirens*) are other important varieties. Farther south, the conifers merge with the mountain conifers of California's *Cs* climate, and western yellow pine and sugar pine become dominant. In the central Sierra Nevada the world's largest trees, the giant redwoods (*Sequoia gigantia*), are found. Throughout the Pacific Northwest region, the conifers are huge. The forests usually are comparatively free of underbrush, although along the western slopes of the Olympic Range in Washington, a rather dense stand of low broadleaf evergreen shrubs and ferns is found, reflecting the constantly wet, dripping, fog-bound environment. The larger trees are covered with moss.

The distinct zonation of different coniferous associations in this region reflects a number of environmental contrasts. The marine belt along the coast supports several species, including Port Orford cedar, red cedar, Douglas fir, the redwoods, and Sitka spruce. Most of the western slopes of the Cascade Mountains and the Canadian Coast Range have a climax of western hemlock and white cedar, with Douglas fir as a fire-succession subclimax. The broad extent of Douglas fir indicates that extensive fires must have occurred frequently throughout this region for centuries. Because of its extraordinarily thick bark, the Douglas fir remains relatively undamaged by ground fires. The long mountain slopes provide updrafts of air and favorable conditions for forest fires, which are extremely difficult to check in these areas, even with modern fire-fighting facilities. Mountain areas also are susceptible to lightning, which was undoubtedly responsible for many of the fires of past centuries that, once started, burned over large areas. Ravine bottoms are less vulnerable to fires which tend to sweep up or along slopes, and these contain the densest stands of the hemlock-cedar association.

Elevation, exposure, and precipitation also play distinctive parts in producing the zonation of associations in the Pacific Northwest (see Fig. 10.10). An entirely different climax association of western white pine, yellow pine, and larch becomes dominant on the drier slopes east of the crest of the Cascades. Lodgepole pine replaces Douglas fir in the fire succession. Spruce and fir are found at high elevations throughout the mountains and, because of the decreased temperatures in such areas, the vegetation resembles that of the northern coniferous forest.

It should be noted that the humid west coast climates, characterized by mild winters and cool summers, do not result exclusively in coniferous forests. Some deciduous forests can be found in the Pacific Northwest, frequently on alluvial soils. These forests also were predominant over most of northwestern Europe centuries ago. Maples (*Acer macrophyllum* and *circinatum*), red alder (*Alnus oregona*), and black cottonwood (*Populus trichocarpa*) are the principal species along the coasts of Oregon, Washington, and British Columbia. Alder in most parts of the world is a small tree, but in the Pacific Northwest it becomes a true forest tree and reaches diameters up to 2 feet. Deciduous forests also are encountered in southern Chile, where the conifers are restricted mainly to the slopes of the Andes.

Some broadleaf evergreens are encountered in the west coast marine climates. The mild, humid winters undoubtedly are responsible for the fact that these usually tropical forms are found so far poleward. They are important parts of the local flora along the

FIG. 10.9 Understory of western hemlock developing beneath a mature stand of Douglas fir in the Willamette National Forest, Oregon. The hemlock is a climax type, while the Douglas fir is a fire-succession type. [U.S. Department of Agriculture]

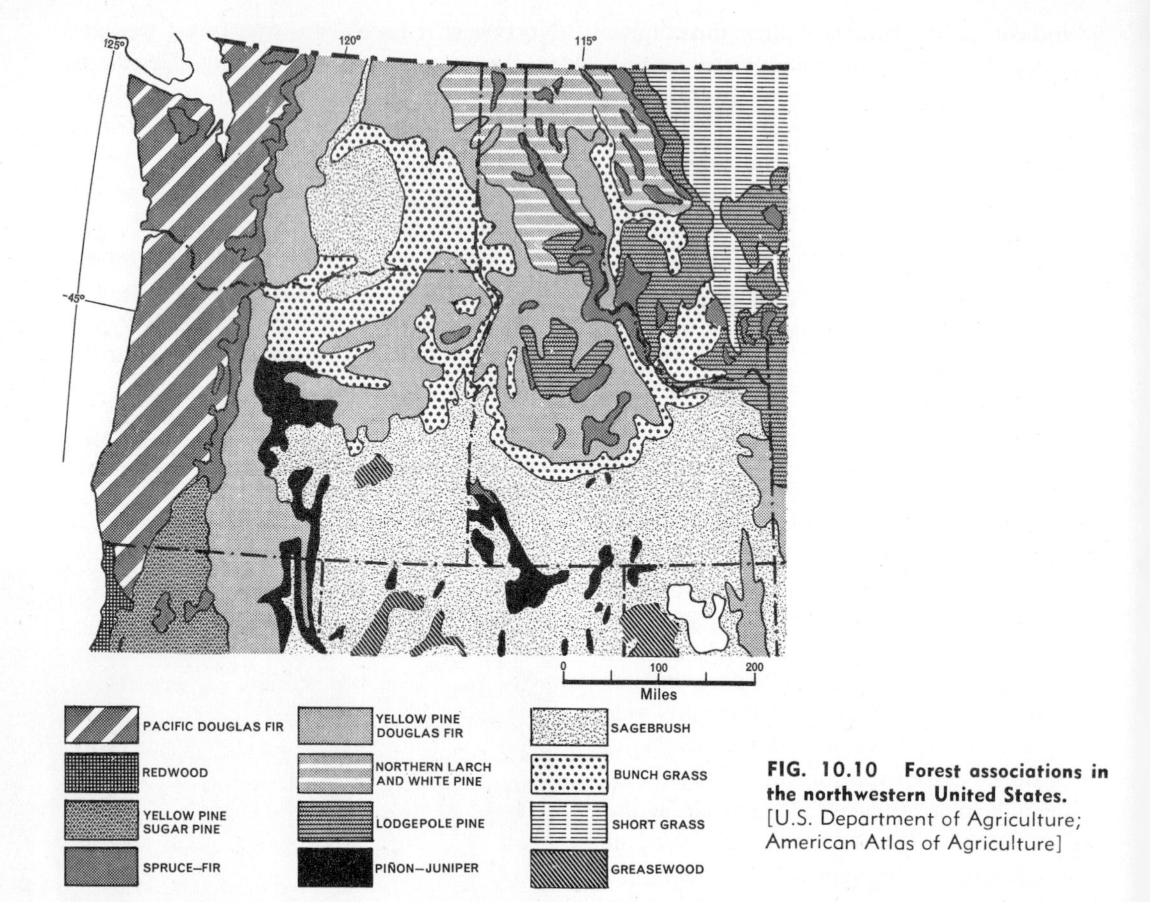

FIG. 10.10 Forest associations in the northwestern United States. [U.S. Department of Agriculture; American Atlas of Agriculture]

immediate coastal area in Oregon, Washington, and southern British Columbia. One of the most interesting members of this evergreen flora is the madrone (*Arbutus*), a broadleaf tree with a scaly trunk, somewhat similar to the sycamore but reddish in color. Usually from 20 to 30 feet high, it may reach 70 to 80 feet and have diameters up to 2 feet. Giant rhododendrons are representative of this flora in the coastal areas of northwestern Europe, and a still more unusual and distinctive feature is the sprinkling of palms that can be found as far north as Scotland.

The reason for the wide variety of tree types in the humid west coast climates is not entirely clear. It may be the result of contrasts in moisture regimes rather than in temperature. The absence of low minimum temperatures may also be more of a factor than the average monthly mean temperatures would seem to indicate. The strong dominance of huge conifers along the northwest coast of North America is also not fully understood. The wide variation in precipitation seasonally, combined with fairly high minimum precipitation averages, may well be a factor.

The west coast conifers afford some of the most concentrated reserves of softwood timber, which is used mainly for construction lumber. Redwood and cedar have unusual resistance to weathering, hence are important for house siding and shingles. Regrowth is unusually rapid in the mild, humid climate of the west coast, and although a great many years are required to replace the full-grown forest giants, trees of saw-timber size generally develop in 25 to 50 years. The large size of the trees and the rough terrain make lumbering in this region a large-scale industry. Scientific forest management is the rule, largely because there is big business at stake. Lumber companies have to be large to operate, and the general long-view approach of corporation management aids in promoting stability and efficiency. The mistakes made in cutting the eastern forests in the United States by "cut-and-run" exploiters are rare in the west. The large area in public-owned forest reserves, in which leased cutting under supervision is permitted, is also helping to stabilize the forest economy of the Pacific Northwest region. Today, despite large-volume cutting, the region is replacing most of the forest wealth that is removed.

THE SOUTHEASTERN UNITED STATES CONIFERS. One of the largest areas of hygrophytic needleleaf evergreen forests in the world is found on the Atlantic–Gulf of Mexico coastal plain, stretching from Cape Cod, Massachusetts, and northern New Jersey, southward into Florida, and thence westward into Alabama and Mississippi. After a gap of about 100 miles at the Mississippi River, it reappears in Texas. This forest area consists almost entirely of species of pine, including southern longleaf and shortleaf pine, pitch pine, loblolly pine, and Jersey scrub pine. The most widely distributed and most valuable species for lumber and naval stores is the southern longleaf, or yellow, pine (*Pinus palustris*) (see Fig. 10.11).

The pines are closely related to the distribution of sandy or gravelly coastal-plain soils. The high summer evaporation rates of this region, combined with the loose, permeable soils, are suited to the xeric (drought-resistant) characteristics of conifers. As was indicated in Chapter 9, burning may have been a major influence in effecting the dominance of many of the pines. A mixed oak-pine forest borders the coastal plain coniferous forest on somewhat heavier soils, and this

FIG. 10.11 Mature southern yellow, or longleaf, pine in Bronson State Park, Texas. Note the absence of undergrowth. Such open forests make fair grazing lands for beef cattle in the south. [U.S. Department of Agriculture]

indicates that the deciduous oaks may be part of the climax vegetation for this region. The same varieties of pine that are dominant on the coastal plain and in the mixed-forest zone can also be found at higher elevations in the Appalachian uplands. Regardless of their successional position, the United States coastal plain pines cover a sizable area, even on a global map. A comparable area of conifers is found in the Landes district of southwestern France, south of Bordeaux. Here too the pines are closely related to the distribution of sandy soils (see Fig. 9.8).

The decay of needles and twigs on the pine-forest floor produces highly acid soil solutions. Where the region is not burned over in the interests of forest management, a particularly abundant, acid-loving, lowerstory flora is found that includes many broadleaf evergreen shrubs, such as the rhododendrons and azaleas. Several deciduous trees and shrubs also may be present.

The pine forests of the southern and southeastern United States constitute one of the most valuable timber areas in the country. The southern longleaf pine is an important source not only of turpentine and resin but also of lumber for both flooring and construction, and its regrowth is rapid. The region has also been important as a major supplier of paper pulp to be used in making kraft paper ever since the introduction of the Herty process for utilizing these resinous woods.

10.11 THE MESOPHYTIC NEEDLELEAF EVERGREEN FOREST (TAIGA). The mesophytic needleleaf evergreen forest, otherwise known as the taiga, or northern coniferous forest, constitutes the largest subformation of all the global forests. It extends across the continents of the northern hemisphere from Alaska to Labrador and from Scandinavia to the Pacific coast of the Soviet Union. Although the general characteristics of the taiga are similar on both continents, the species of trees are different. In Canada, spruce (*Picea*) and fir (*Abies*) are dominant throughout the taiga. The pines (*Pinus*), including white pine, red pine, and jack pine, are found principally in the southern part of the region and appear to be localized types that occur on unusually sandy soils or in fire-succession communities. Arbor vitae (*Thuja*) and larch (*Larix*) are associated swamp conifers. The latter is unique in being a deciduous needleleaf tree. The taiga of Eurasia differs in having a much wider latitudinal distribution of pine, with Scotch pine predominating in Europe and the stone pines in the east. As in Canada, the pine tends to be found on sandier soils or on thin, stony knolls. Spruce is common throughout the Eurasian taiga, as is the fir, and their slender, tapering spires give the northern coniferous forest one of its most characteristic landscape features.

The taiga conifers are not large trees, usually being about 30 to 50 feet in height and having diameters of from 8 to 12 inches at maturity. Tree heights progressively decrease poleward, and those of saw-timber size are found mainly along the extreme southern portions. The forest is remarkably homogeneous with respect to the types of trees present, one or two species dominating over wide areas. The density of the foliage intercepts most of the sunlight; therefore the dark, humid forest floor is suitable only for small herbaceous plants and fungi that require little light. Among these forest-floor dwellers are wintergreen (*Gaultheria*), wood sorrel (*Oxalis*), trailing arbutus (*Epigaea repens*), ground pine (a club moss), and ferns. There are a number of terrestrial orchids, including the beautiful "lady's slipper" (*Cypripedium*). Most of these epiphytes are small and are confined to the ground surface.

Lichens and mosses are abundant and can be found on nearly every tree. The extremely slow decay of dead wood results in a dense tangle of fallen trees, crisscrossed together. Cross-country travel on foot through the taiga is extremely difficult. This is true especially in spruce and arbor vitae swamps, where the trees are close together. Branches begin a short distance above the ground, although some of the larger pine forests have long lower trunks that are branchless.

As is characteristic of forests that have only one or two dominant species, the typical taiga is uniform in height and in density of stand. Seedlings have little chance to grow unless the canopy is broken by the death or destruction of any of the mature trees. Regrowth is unusually slow, being retarded by the long winter season, and it becomes progressively slower toward the north. In the south, about 30 to 40 years is required to develop trees with diameters of 8 to 10 inches. In the far north, along the border of the tundra, fully mature spruce and birches only a few feet high can be found.

Broad interruptions in the continuity of the taiga are formed by fire-succession forest communities, which include such broadleaf deciduous trees as white or paper birch (*Betula alba*), quaking aspen (*Populus tremuloides*), and fire or pin cherry (*Prunus pennsylvanica*). These postfire deciduous enclaves may persist for years because of the slow growth of trees in the northern climates and also because of the destruction of humus in the topsoils. In the Soviet Union, the patches of broadleaf deciduous trees among the conifers are referred to as the white taiga, because of the light-colored leaves and trunks that contrast so markedly with the darker conifers. Spring and fall are threatening seasons in the taiga, because of fire. When dry, the resinous leaves and branches of the conifers are virtual tinder sticks. Unlike the pine or Douglas fir forests in lower latitudes, the typical taiga conifers cannot withstand a ground fire, because their branches begin so close to the ground. In isolated areas, forest fires may burn for weeks.

THE TAIGA BOGS. Hydroseres in the form of bogs are common throughout a large part of the taiga of both Canada and Eurasia. Much of the taiga was glaciated, excluding only the Soviet Union section east of the Yenesei River and parts of central Alaska. Poor drainage, caused by glaciation, resulted in many small swamps, lakes, and ponds. Perhaps the most frequent hydrosere is that associated with the gradual filling of small lakes and ponds with vegetation, producing a typical *muskeg bog* (see Fig. 9.19). All stages of succession can be found in such bogs—the early stages, in which the mosses and feathery cranberry (*Vaccinium*) adjoin the margins of open water; the middle stages, characterized by leatherleaf (*Chamaedaphne*) and Labrador tea (*Ledum*), both of which are coarse, hardleaf, woody shrubs; and finally the later stages, in which the subclimax spruces, firs, and larches begin to establish the forest. Unique among the plants of the bog associations is the pitcher plant (*Sarracenia purpurea*), which has tubular leaves that are adapted to trap insects, which the plant digests as part of its food.

Sphagnum moss usually is present in all the successional stages of the taiga hydrosere. This is a tough, highly acid, stringy moss that is usually grayish in color but is sometimes reddish or light green. Its high acidity makes it virtually sterile to most bacteria; hence it decomposes slowly. Years ago it used to be gathered and sold as antiseptic dressing material for wounds. The growth of a sphagnum moss cover on some of the flat taiga plains following forest fires or clearing often has resulted in "waterlogging," or the establishment of a retrogressive hydrosere. The reason for this is that the moss absorbs precipitation and not only keeps it from evaporating but also prevents it from running off into the subsoil. In time the water content may increase to such an extent that a typical bog is formed. The greater water content and moss growth in the center of the bog cause a slight doming or convex shape to the bog surface. Continued heightening at the center eventually leads to the broadening of the poorly drained area, an invasion of adjacent well-drained forests, tree destruction, and a reversal of the normal successional direction.

THE TAIGA RIVERINE MEADOWS. Flat flood plains of rivers which are flooded periodically are not usually encountered in the taiga of North America, because glaciation interrupted the normal stages in the erosional cycle of streams. In the eastern Soviet Union, however, where glaciation did not take place, such plains frequently are present. The periodic flooding prevents the establishment of forest vegetation, and usually coarse marsh grasses and sedges form strips of meadowland along the stream flats. Narrow equivalents of these can be found in the North American taiga along small streams which are flooded as the result of damming by beavers. Frequently the meadow grasses may grow as tall as a man. When drainage is restored, such meadows usually are replaced by thickets of speckled alder (*Alnus*), prior to the reestablishment of the forest. These alder thickets are notoriously dense and difficult to penetrate, as many fishermen know who have followed trout streams in the "north country."

UTILIZATION OF THE TAIGA. Pines constitute the major source of lumber in the taiga, but they reach sizes suitable for saw timber mainly along the extreme southern margins. The white and red pine lumber of northern New England and the northern Great Lakes states was the source of the massive lumber supplies that were needed in building homes during the settlement of the central part of the United States between 1840 and 1900. Some of these pine forests were magnificent stands of tall, straight-grained softwood trees, 3 to 5 feet in diameter. The indiscriminate cutting of this forest resource and, later, the repeated burning of the pine plains, until their capacity for regrowth was almost destroyed, constitute one of the most unfortunate episodes in the history of American forest utilization. The removal of the fire hazard over wide areas is beginning to produce signs that some of these magnificent forests might once again replace themselves, although probably not for another 75 to 100 years. The greatest reserves of taiga pine timber today lie in the southeastern Soviet Union, northern Korea, and northeastern Manchuria.

The greatest resource of the taiga today is pulpwood, or wood which is destined for paper manufacture. Nearly all the conifers can be utilized in this way, as well as many of the deciduous secondary species, such as aspen. An interesting potential resource of the taiga lies in the possibility of using the softwoods for the production of edible wood sugars by chemical processing. In Norway and Sweden these trees have already become an important source of animal feed, in the form of a molasses syrup produced as a by-product of the paper industry.

10.12 XEROPHYTIC NEEDLELEAF EVERGREEN SCRUB WOODLAND.

An open stand of low, scrubby needleleaf evergreens frequently is encountered at high elevations (3,000 to 7,000 feet) in semiarid regions. Because of the lower temperatures associated with the higher elevations, evaporation is not so great as in the lowlands in such climates, and drought-resistant varieties

FIG. 10.12 Typical juniper-sagebrush association near Montrose, Colorado. The juniper is a type of xerophytic conifer widely distributed in the higher elevations of dry lands. [U.S. Department of Agriculture]

of scrub conifers develop a parklike type of cover (see Fig. 10.12). The tree most frequently encountered in these areas is the juniper (*Juniperus*), and it is widely distributed in the dry uplands of both North America and Asia. Most varieties of junipers are low trees 15 to 30 feet high, but occasionally they are bushlike and form dense thickets. In parts of central Asia, juniper trees may reach heights of 50 to 60 feet. In the southwestern United States, juniper often is associated with piñon pine, another gnarly, low conifer. Low, xerophytic shrubs, like sagebrush and greasewood, also accompany the scrub conifers. In the eastern United States, a variety of juniper (*Juniperus virginiana*), inaccurately termed red cedar in some areas, is often found in pastures and hillsides where bedrock lies a few inches below the surface.

This coniferous scrub woodland is not found over broad areas. Instead, its distribution is patchy, corresponding to intermediate slopes of mountains in dry regions and to some parts of the high plains. In the United States, the largest areas are immediately east of the Cascades and Sierra Nevada in southeastern Oregon and California and in some of the higher sections of the Colorado Plateau.

Because of their low, gnarly, small trunks, these trees are of little value as lumber. The berry of the juniper supplies an oil which is used as a flavoring extract in the manufacture of gin. Piñon pines supply a small edible nut that is in some demand locally in the western United States. Probably the most important use of these scrub trees is as shade for range animals during warm summer days. The juniper-pine areas are favored as summer pasturage for sheep, goats, and cattle, which graze or browse on the low grass and shrub vegetation between the trees.

Needleleaf deciduous forest

Not all needleleaf trees are evergreen. A few of them shed their needles during the winter season. The principal tree of this type is the larch (*Larix*), which has a wide distribution in the northern forest region of North America and Eurasia. In North America, however, the most common variety in the northern coniferous forest is the black larch, or tamarack (*Larix laricina*). It is a swamp tree and is usually associated with spruce in bog associations. Western larch (*Larix occidentalis*), however, is an upland tree of magnificent proportions, growing up to 200 feet or more in height, with a trunk diameter of

FIG. 10.13 Bald cypress (Taxodium distichum) near Lafayette, Louisiana. Note the "knees" that are extensions of the roots above water, and the festoons of Spanish moss, an epiphyte that thrives on the branches and trunks of the trees. Cypress is a common swamp tree on the Mississippi bottom lands and delta. [Standard Oil Company (N.J.)]

3 to 4 feet. It belongs to the giant coniferous forest associations of the Pacific Northwest region. A smaller alpine larch also is found in the western mountains above 8,000 to 9,000 feet. Another deciduous needleleaf tree of North America, and one that grows in an entirely different environment, is the bald cypress (*Taxodium distichum*), a stately tree of the swamps within the Mississippi Valley south of Illinois and along the Atlantic–Gulf of Mexico coastal plain south of Delaware (see Fig. 10.13). This cypress is able to thrive in standing swamp water and is unique in having protuberances on the roots termed "knees," which rise several feet above the ground or water level.

The above deciduous conifers of North America are only subsidiary members of climax forests, or successional species in hydroseres, and hence are not indicated on the global map of vegetation. The only area of this subformation indicated on the map is a large expanse immediately south of the tundra in the eastern Soviet Union. Two varieties of larch (*Larix sibirica* and *L. dahurica*) are dominant species in mature forests within this region, and the evergreen conifers here, such as spruce and pine, are subsidiary to it in the climax association.

The dominance of the larches in the Soviet Union probably is related to the extremely low winter temperatures and to permanently frozen subsoils (permafrost). The larches, by shedding their needles, are able to withstand temperatures from 50 to 80° below zero. These trees also have an extremely shallow root system, which enables them to derive nourishment from the narrow soil zone which lies above the permafrost. Spruce (*Abies*), which has a similar root system, is found along with the larches, but it is more restricted to fertile soils, such as those developed on alluvium in the region. It is noteworthy that the Siberian larch region broadens toward the east, as do the areas where permafrost is found.

The wood of the larches is remarkably heavy and coarse. It does not make good construction lumber, but it is a valuable source of railroad ties, mine props, etc., because of its resistance to decay in the presence of water. Also, except for the giant larches of northwestern North America and those which thrive on some of the more fertile Russian soils, the larches do not become large trees of saw-timber size. The bald cypress wood of the southern United States is especially prized for use in house siding and shingles, because of its resistance to weathering.

The mixed broadleaf deciduous–coniferous forest

The northern coniferous forest, or taiga, merges gradually with the broadleaf deciduous forest along its equatorward margins, producing a mixed broadleaf deciduous–coniferous transitional forest, which is indicated on the world map of vegetation. The mixture of trees may consist either of a combination of broadleaf deciduous and needleleaf evergreen trees in the same forest or of homogeneous patches of one intermingled with areas of the other. Strong contrasts in local environmental conditions, such as soil texture and drainage, generally are responsible for the latter type of mixture. Sandy soils in this transitional subformation, for example, usually support a pine forest cover, whereas the clay loam soils of ridges support a deciduous broadleaf cover with a sprinkling of conifers. Spruce and fir are found mainly in swamps. In the northern United States, the dominant deciduous trees in this mixed forest zone include maple, yellow birch, and beech. The oaks and hornbeams (*Carpinus*), on the other hand, are the most common in Eurasia. It is extremely difficult to generalize the distribution of trees in this mixed forest, because of the variety of species, each of which has its preferred conditions for growth, including site as well as climatic conditions. An interesting complication in the northern United States is the hemlock (*Tsuga*), which is interspersed with the maple-beech-birch association, particularly on cooler, more moist, north-facing slopes. It appears to be a relict of a cooler climatic era.

The world map of vegetation formations and subformations (Fig. 10.1) indicates that the major areas of the mixed deciduous–coniferous forest are found in the northern hemisphere. In North America, the subformation includes New England and the northern Appalachians, most of the area bordering the Great Lakes, and the taiga-steppe transition of northern Alberta and Saskatchewan in Canada. In the latter area, the broadleaf deciduous trees may well be a fire-succession flora. Most of central Europe is within this mixed forest, and it extends across southern Sweden and borders the taiga as far as the Urals. Another large area lies in eastern Asia, in northeastern Manchuria, northern Korea, and northern Japan. The only appreciable areas of this subformation in the southern hemisphere are on the lowlands and coastal hills of southern Chile and in northern New Zealand.

The utilization of this mixed subformation of forests depends on the dominance of the types of trees present. Except for the swamp conifers, the needleleaf evergreens grow much larger than their counterparts in the taiga, and their soft woods are valuable for construction lumber. The deciduous broadleaf hardwoods have uses similar to those described in Sec. 10.7.

The semideciduous broadleaf forest

The semideciduous broadleaf forest is a transitional subformation that borders the broadleaf evergreen forests of low latitudes in many places. Most of the trees in this subformation are broadleaf evergreens, but some are broadleaf deciduous varieties.

Rainfall is the principal climatic variable in the tropics, and wherever a dry period occurs, distinct adjustments are made in the vegetation. If the dry season is short and excessive amounts of rain fall during the rainy period, most plants can pass through the dry period without requiring a leaf-shedding, or deciduous, period. In such areas, however, there are usually some members of the rain-forest community that are more sensitive to drought than others; hence the forest generally contains a sprinkling of broadleaf deciduous varieties. The principal effect of such deciduous trees is to produce interruptions in the forest canopy, so that undergrowth becomes much more dense because of the greater availability of light at some times of year. These semideciduous jungle forests are located on the windward coasts and mountain slopes of monsoon Asia, along the eastern edge of the Brazilian uplands, and in parts of the Guinea coast of Africa. The bamboos are especially abundant in the understory vegetation of these forests in southeastern Asia. Teak is one of the representative deciduous broadleaf trees in the forests of southeastern Asia and is a valuable timber tree.

In the poleward extensions of the humid tropics and along the eastern margins of the continents, broadleaf deciduous trees may be mixed with the broadleaf evergreen types, not because of a dry season, but rather because of the occasional low temperatures during the winter season. Some of these subtropical mixed forests are found in southern China, Formosa, southern Japan, and southern Brazil. A sprinkling of broadleaf evergreen trees in a few areas containing dominantly deciduous forests along the Gulf of Mexico coast in the southern United States indicates that the transition from the rain forest to the subtropical deciduous forest is not a sharp one. Here the live oaks and southern magnolias are green throughout the year and represent the more resistant exotic outliers of the tropical broadleaf evergreens. Were it not for the Gulf of Mexico and the Caribbean Sea, this general area would undoubtedly have a much larger extent of this transitional subformation, such as exists in southeastern Asia.

The grasslands

10.13 THE GRASSES AS PLANT COMPETITORS. Simple, unspecialized forms of life generally tend to have the longest life span, the widest distribution, and the greatest resistance to the cataclysms of nature. Although the grasses are neither the simplest nor the least specialized form of plant life, they are far less complex than trees. Probably the greatest specialization that they have developed is the property of providing mobility for their seeds. Some of the seeds are tiny and light, enabling them to be carried aloft on wind currents.[4] Others have tuftlike appendages which act as tiny parachutes, aiding in their air travel. Still others are equipped with small hooks, which cling to animals and human beings, thus "hitchhiking" rides to distant sites. The grasses, therefore, have an unusually wide geographic range. Combined with the mobility of the seeds is the great durability of the plants, due primarily to the relatively large proportion of the plant structure that lies below ground level, where it can be protected somewhat against the variable conditions of the atmosphere and the exploitive activities of both animals and men.

Grasses have a large variety of forms and, with the possible exception of the *Compositae* (asters) and orchids, have a greater number of species than any other family of plants. This is to be expected, because of the varied kinds of environments in which they are found. This variety can be observed

[4] Grass seeds have been found in air samples taken from an airplane at an elevation of 4,000 feet above the ground.

even among our selected cultivated grasses, ranging from food grasses such as oats, wheat, corn, rice, and sugar cane to the bamboos. Among the properties common to all of them are bladelike, opposite leaves attached to a jointed stem by means of a sheathlike juncture. The roots are finely divided but well developed.

The mobility of grass seeds and the general durability of the plants themselves explain why grasses are found in nearly all environments, from the polar wastes to the equator, from deserts to periodically flooded tidal marshes. Even in the depths of the selva, which offers the most ideal conditions for the dominance of trees, members of the grass family, the bamboos, are found. Only the lichens and mosses, simpler than the grasses, have a wider distribution among the many forms of macroplant life.

Not only are grasses found nearly everywhere, but they dominate the plant covering over about 40 per cent of the land area of the world. The regions included in this 40 per cent are far from uniform with respect to climate, soil, or any other environmental factor. Grass tends to dominate areas that are unsatisfactory for tree growth but that provide favorable conditions for plant growth, at least in the topsoils, for part or all of the year. The conditions that most usually prevent tree growth include dry subsoils, saturated or "drowned" soils, and periodic burning. Grass can thrive under each of these conditions. Where subsoils are dry, grasses can grow and reproduce by utilizing the moisture that penetrates into the topsoil following occasional rains. In marshes, sedges and reeds, which represent the grasses, are among the first plants to send their roots into the saturated soils. Fire destroys most tree growth, but a rapid grass fire during the dry season only destroys the dead grass tops. In climates that will support both trees and grass, periodic burning usually favors the dominance of the grasses.

The grasslands of the world, or the regions in which grass is the prevailing plant form, include the natural grasslands and the culturally induced grasslands. The boundaries between these two types cannot be defined accurately, because of lack of historical evidence, but we at least know that the global natural grasslands have their centers in areas that straddle the boundary between arid and humid regions. Smaller areas where grass dominates are related to early stages in plant succession. Grasses are among the first plants to clothe naked soil surfaces, including (1) the muds that border water bodies, (2) the loose sand at the back of beaches, (3) the first crumbled rock fragments of weathered rock surfaces (where grasses follow lichens and mosses), (4) the fresh ash of volcanic eruptions, and (5) fresh alluvium or glacial detritus. Marshes represent the early, or grass, phase in a hydrosere. Once the marsh grasses have accumulated enough organic detritus, plants of a higher and more complex order inhabit the graveyard of their predecessors. Similarly in the humid tropics, when plant foods are depleted from tropical soils, grass is the main plant form that comes to the sterile, abandoned fields. Asking few favors if left alone, it prepares the way for the reestablishment of the forest cover. It may persist for centuries if periodic burning prevents the restoration of the forest.

An additional environmental feature that favors the dominance of a grass cover is underlying material that consists of soft, pure, permeable calcium carbonate, usually chalks or marls (see Fig. 12.13). Trees apparently do not tolerate soils that are abnormally high in lime, but grass thrives on them. Such soils are relatively rare, but examples include the black prairie soils of north-central Alabama and southeastern Texas and the

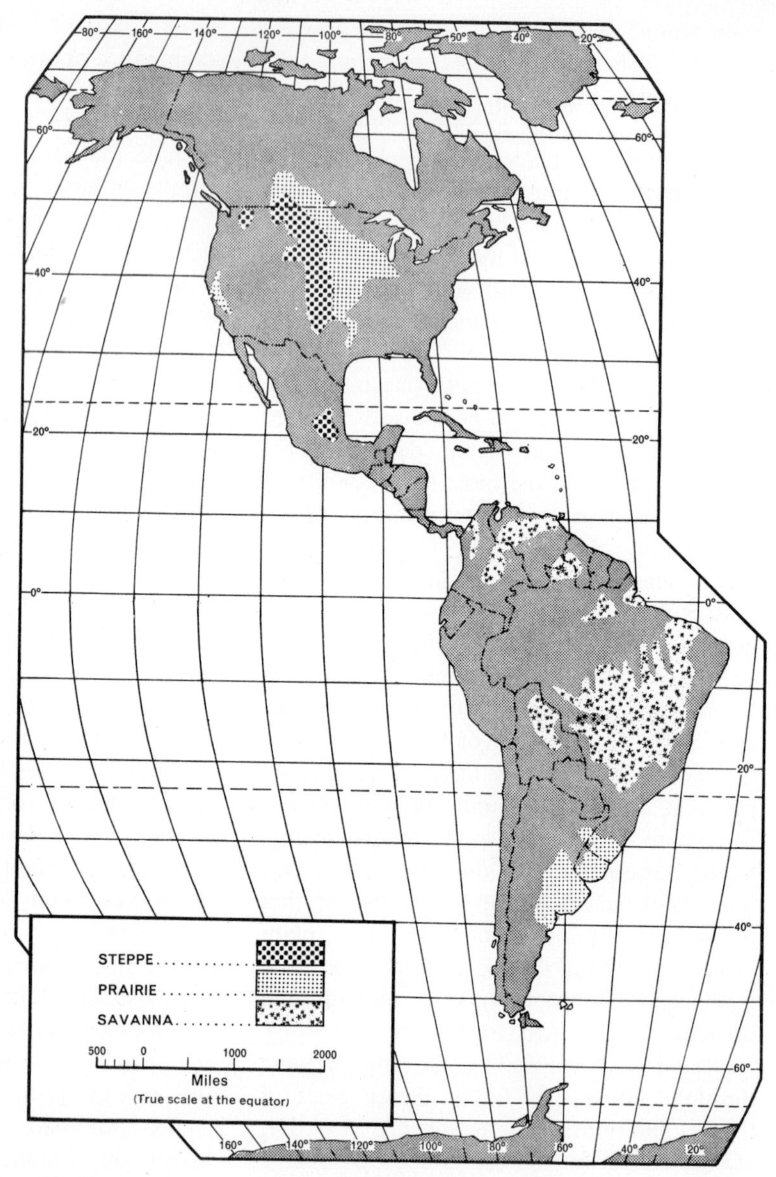

FIG. 10.14 World distribution of major grassland subformations.

chalk "downs" of southern England. These are grassy areas, surrounded by forests on all sides, and their boundaries conform closely to those of the chalks and marls found below the surface.

Excluding the small successional grasslands mentioned above, the global grasslands can be subdivided for study into three main subformations: the prairies, steppes, and savannas (see Fig. 10.14). The prairies include the tall-grass communities that straddle the boundary between semiarid and humid regions in the mid-latitudes; the steppes are short-grass areas located mainly in semiarid regions; and the savannas include the tropical grasslands that are found

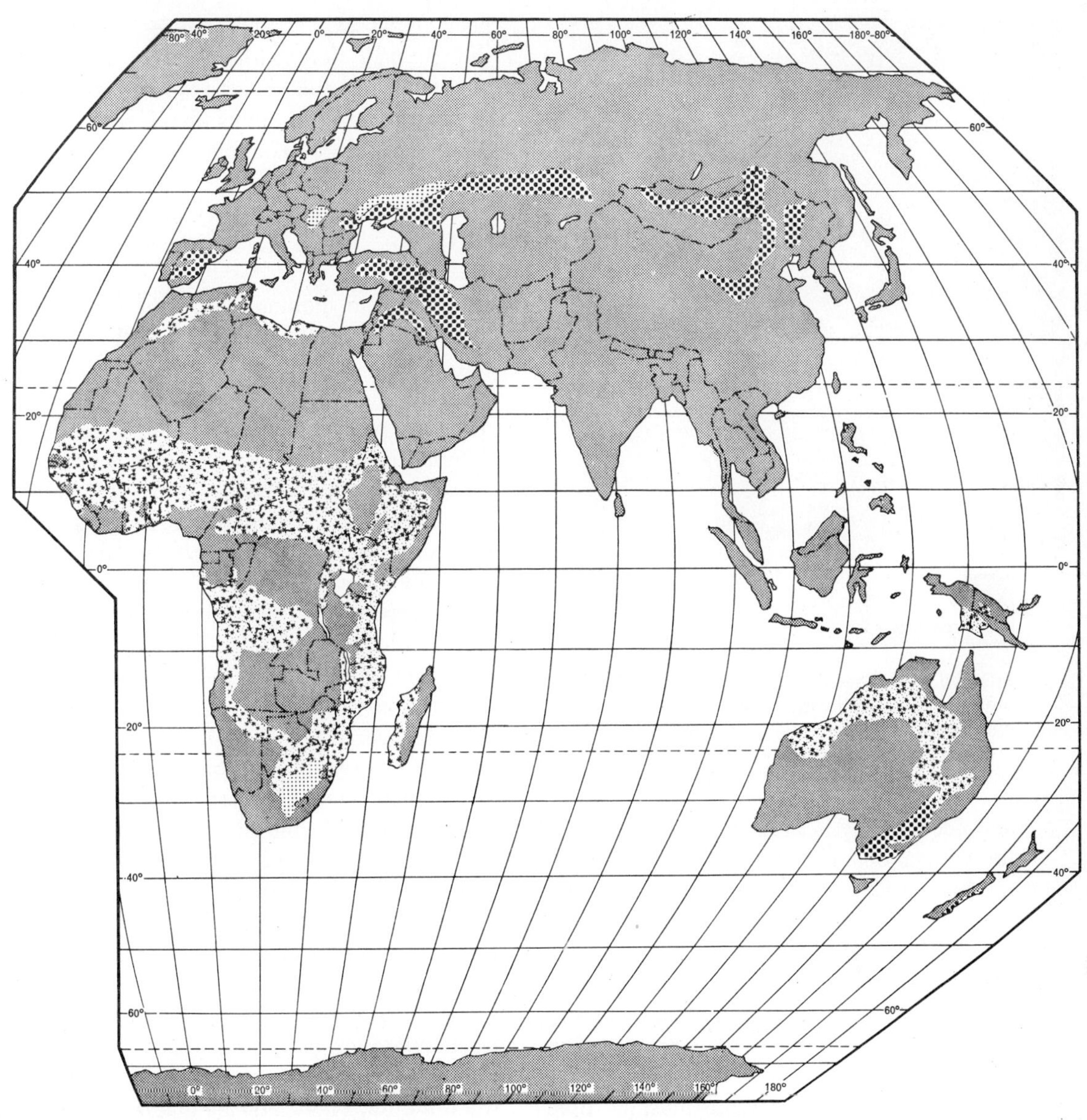

in low latitudes. These subformations are discussed in turn in the remaining divisions of this section. A fourth grassland type, which includes alpine meadows, is treated later, under mountain vegetation.

10.14 THE PRAIRIES. It should be admitted that discussing the prairies of the world today is an academic exercise, because so little of them remains anywhere in the world. Man has appropriated these humid, tall-grass lands as some of his most productive agricultural land. Strips of prairie nevertheless can be observed throughout the "prairie" regions, along the edges of roads and railroads, along fences and hedgerows,

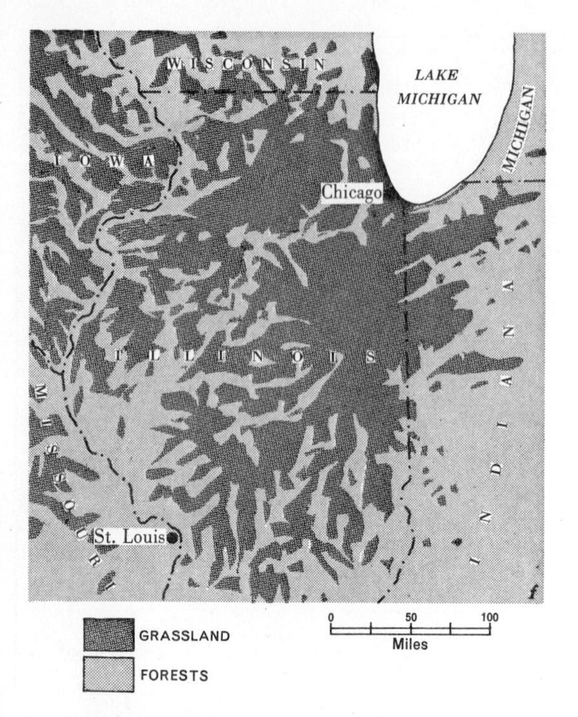

FIG. 10.15 A section of the North American prairie prior to cultivation. Grasslands predominated on the flat-to-rolling interstream areas, while forests were found mainly in the valleys. [After Weaver and Albertson]

and occasionally in areas that are too rough for cultivation. These narrow strips should not be considered identical with the original prairies. Many new species of plants have been introduced, such as bluegrass (*Poa*), which was carried to the United States from Europe. In general appearance, however, these strips are similar to the original cover.

In describing the plant life characteristic of prairies, the same caution must be used as in dealing with any other vegetation generalization. Differences can be found anywhere, and undoubtedly the varieties of plants that inhabit the prairies in Illinois are considerably different from those of the Argentine pampas. Despite such differences, some common characteristics may be noted.

First, the prairies are not, and never have been, great expanses of grasses alone. Although they were without trees, they contained an unusually large variety of nonwoody, herbaceous plants, many with showy flowers. A good example of these in the American Middle West is the wild sunflower (*Helianthus*), appropriately the state flower of Kansas, whose yellow flowers brighten the highway borders during the late summer and early fall months. As in the deciduous broadleaf forest, the flowering herbs are arranged in seasonal cycles of dominance. Each spring, summer, and autumn presents its own aspect, with the prevailing vegetation differing in color and height at each season.

Although the flowering plants are most noticeable, the tall and varied grasses rule the communities. Heights at maturity are generally between 2 and 3 feet, although they occasionally rise to between 5 and 8 feet. A wide variety of grasses are included, but some of the genera have a world-wide distribution, including feather or needle grass (*Stipa*), bearded grass (*Andropogon*), June grass (*Koelaria*), wheat grass (*Agropyron*), and the fescues (*Festuca*). All of these have representatives in the prairies of the United States, Argentina, and the Soviet Union.

The prairies of the world have been without trees during historic times, although stream courses usually were bordered by trees, commonly of deciduous broadleaf varieties (see Fig. 10.15). Trees are seen frequently in the prairies today, however, having been planted for shade or for farm wood-lot use. These indicate that the environment is not entirely unsuited to forest growth.

If trees will grow in prairie environments, why is it that these regions were not forested within historic times? It is likely that there is no single answer to this question. Among the many hypotheses offered by students of the problem are the following: (1) periodic burning by primitive peoples, which enabled the grasslands to intrude into the forest from the adjacent steppes; (2) development of a subclimax grass community perpetuated on glacial detritus in the postglacial period either by burning or by animal browsing; (3) perpetuation of a subclimax grass community by the same processes in a hydrosere succession developed on poorly drained, flat plains; (4) a grass dominance on soil parent material unusually high in lime; (5) maintenance of a grass-herbaceous flora by rare cycles of protracted droughts; (6) a general climatic change toward more moist conditions, which, however, have not yet enabled forests to replace the grasslands, since trees have been held back by animal browsing or by burning. It is likely that all these factors help to explain the existence of some of the prairies of the world. Evidence exists for the influence of fire in most parts of the world, but undoubtedly burning is not the only explanation.

The generalized climatic location of the prairies in the world is along the semiarid-humid boundary in mid-latitudes, usually between lat 25 and 50°. In terms of soil relationships, the prairies follow fairly closely the chernozem and prairie soils (see Chapter 12). They also lie in a transitional position between the steppe grasslands and the deciduous broadleaf forests.

In North America, the main area of prairies is shaped more or less like a triangle, with its apex, pointing east, in the vicinity of west-central Indiana. The western base of the triangle extends roughly along the 98th meridian, from central Texas into Canada, where it trends northwestward as far as central Alberta province. Small outlying areas include the Central Valley of California, the coastal prairies of Texas, and the Palouse country of eastern Washington and Oregon.

The largest prairie region of Eurasia comprises an east-west belt extending from the northern Ukraine, north of the Black Sea, eastward to approximately long 85° E. This is the famous chernozem, or black-soil, belt that is the major granary of the Soviet Union. The Hungarian Plain and parts of the Romanian Plain were prairies prior to cultivation. Much farther east, the central portion of the Manchurian Plain and part of the middle Amur Valley originally had a prairie vegetation. Prairies in South America include the pampas of Argentina, Uruguay, Paraguay, and southern Brazil. The *high veldt* region of South Africa, including all of the Orange Free State and much of southern Transvaal, is a prairie region. No true prairie occurs in Australia, although a large part of eastern New Zealand had a tall-grass–herbaceous cover, similar to the prairies of central California.

Today the prairie regions of the world are utilized mainly for agriculture, especially for grain cultivation. The prairies probably have the most inherently fertile soils in the world. Deep, often stoneless, black with humus, rich in plant nutrients, and highly capable of retaining water and plant foods, they are ideal soils for modern-day agriculture. Their main disadvantage lies in their susceptibility to irregular droughts, particularly along their drier and warmer margins. To early man, however, the sod of the prairies was a handicap, and he avoided it in his search for new farm land.

10.15 THE STEPPE GRASSLANDS. The steppe is synonymous with the short-grass region that borders the desert or lies between the prairies and the areas of desert shrubs in the mid-latitudes. The term *steppe* has been used in various ways. The Russians often use it to designate any grassland of appreciable extent. It also has been used in geographic literature to include all areas of

FIG. 10.16 Typical short-grass steppe vegetation on the Great Plains near Sioux Pass, Montana. [Standard Oil Company, (N.J.)]

short-grass vegetation, including those within the tropics. The definition used here is convenient and less confusing.

The more or less continuous sod cover of the steppe consists mainly of short grasses 6 to 12 inches high, but includes occasional representatives of the taller prairie grasses (see Fig. 10.16). In the United States the short-grass dominants are grama grass (*Bouteloua*) and buffalo grass (*Buchloe*). As in the prairie, herbaceous annuals and perennials are mixed with the grasses, forming cyclical groupings during the year. The variety and conspicuousness of the flowering herbs, however, are not so great as in the prairie. Variations in the percentages of tall grass and short grass can be found throughout the region, sometimes correlated with differences in relief and drainage, or sometimes related to the animals, both domestic and wild, which populate the area.

The ecological position of the steppes is not entirely understood. Plant ecologists are not in agreement about whether the short-grass dominance is a climax vegetation or whether it has resulted from overgrazing by animals that have shown a preference for the taller grasses and have left the shorter varieties behind to establish dominance. If grazing is responsible for the short-grass dominance, was this necessarily the work of domesticated flocks? Most of the steppe regions had large numbers of wild grazing animals, and many of the native rodents, such as the prairie dog, have a preference for the taller varieties of grass. It is likely that the steppes went through cycles of expansion and contraction of short-grass dominance long before man appeared, corresponding in some cases to changes in animal populations and in other cases to changes in climate. Regardless of their successional position, the steppes apparently have been grasslands for a long, long time.

The largest area of short-grass steppe is in the United States, located between the western boundary of the prairie and the foot of the Rocky Mountains. In Eurasia, there are three steppe areas: a narrow strip along the southern edge of the Russian prairies, the region along the eastern margin of the Gobi Desert in Mongolia and northwestern China, and a strip in western Manchuria. Smaller strips of steppe are found along the middle slopes of the great mountain ranges in central Asia.

There are no extensive steppes in the southern hemisphere. Although short-grass areas occur, they are invariably accompanied by desert shrubs. Illustrative of this is the *monte,* a region which borders the Argentine pampas on their dry, western margin—a location where one would ordinarily expect steppes to be found. The dominance of low, xerophytic shrubs gives the monte an appearance quite unlike that of the northern hemisphere steppes.

The utilization of the steppes is confined mainly to grain cultivation and grazing. This clearly is a marginal region for agriculture, and cultivated land has alternately expanded and contracted within the region in accordance with cycles of greater and lesser precipitation, respectively. A great deal of publicity was focused on the problem of wind erosion in the steppe region of the United States Great Plains during the abnormally dry years of the 1930s. Nearly everyone became familiar with the problem, and the general consensus was that man had ruined a large part of the region, partly by cultivating land that should never have been plowed and partly by overgrazing large areas. Notes of travelers in the region in the early nineteenth century, however, indicate that dust storms and excessive wind erosion occurred in the steppe region long before man was active there. Also, some scientists were overly pessimistic about the speed of recovery of the Dust Bowl regions. The moist periods of the 1940s demonstrated how rapidly the steppe can heal its scars.

There does not appear to be any reason for prohibiting agriculture in the steppe, provided that reasonable precautions are taken. Long-range weather forecasting, when improved, will aid immeasurably in planning farming schedules. Farm practices also should be geared to a combination of grazing and dry-farming techniques. In the latter, the emphasis is continually on adding to ground-moisture supplies by checking runoff, reducing evaporation from the soil, and destroying weeds in order to minimize transpiration. Some areas probably will never be cultivated, because of surface configuration or uniquely unfavorable soil characteristics, and should remain as grazing lands, carefully managed so that the density of animal population is geared to fluctuating carrying capacities. Successful utilization of the steppes demands knowledge and foresight.

10.16 THE SAVANNAS. The savannas are tropical grasslands. They differ markedly from the prairies and steppes of mid-latitudes. First, savannas without trees or bushes are exceptionally rare. Second, savannas seldom have a continuous sod cover, but rather a variable spacing of bunch grasses with patches of bare ground between them. Third, nonwoody herbaceous plants are much less common in the savanna plant communities, the grasses themselves are much coarser, and only a few of the dominant genera of the mid-latitude grasslands find representation there.

Savannas differ considerably in general appearance. In some, the grass grows to heights of 8 to 12 feet, but in others it may be only about a foot high. In some areas, the grasses are surmounted by scattered palms, such as the Palmyra palm (*Borassus*), whereas in others the low, umbrellalike *Acacia* thorn trees are found (see Fig 10.17). Patches of scrub thickets—containing such varieties as the chaparral of California, the grotesquely shaped, candelabra-like *euphorbia,* or other cactuslike plants —are another type of nongrassy vegetation on the savannas. Stream courses in savanna regions frequently are lined with *galeria* [5] forests or dense thickets of tall canes or reeds.

Nearly all savannas have pronounced wet and dry seasons, and present a markedly different appearance in each. In the dry season the grass is parched, tough, and brown, and the trees shed their leaves and stand naked under the scorching sun. The advent of the rainy season produces a dramatically sudden change in the landscape that is even more marked than the coming of spring in higher latitudes, because the infirmities of the dead season are not hidden under a snow cover. Trees and shrubs appear to burst into leaf, and the green shoots of grass quickly color the land surface. A general appearance of lushness grows as the rainy season continues, and this has often deceived travelers into making extravagant statements regarding the potentialities of agriculture or animal husbandry in these tropical grasslands.

Students of tropical vegetation have uncovered as many problems in attempting to interpret plant succession in the savannas as have been raised with respect to the prairies and steppes. Some researchers claim that nearly all the savannas were once similar to tropical open woodland or semideciduous rain forest and that they have been transformed into savannas by periodic burning. Others admit that some of them were produced by burning but insist that, over wide areas, the seasonal droughts could never support more than a sparse stand of trees and that a dominance of the coarse grasses is to be expected. All are agreed, however, that the area of savannas is growing at the expense of the tropical forests and woodlands and that savannas have existed for many thousands of years.

The distribution of savannas today is confined largely to South and Central America, Africa, and Australia. Because of their gradual transition to desert-shrub lands on one side and to tropical woodland on the other, maps of savanna distribution may show considerable differences, depending on the judgment and measurements of the compilers. The major savanna areas, nevertheless, have been known and recognized for many years; these include the *llanos* of Venezuela, the *campo* of the Brazil-Guiana uplands, and the Sudan region of Africa. Africa contains the largest single area of savannas, and Shantz, a noted student of African vegetation, estimated that they comprise some 37 per cent of the continental area (see Fig. 10.18). Along with the large areas shown on the world vegetation map, there are scattered small areas of savannas throughout the low latitudes, representing abandoned clearings in the rain forest or tropical woodland in which a grass cover is maintained by burning.

The savannas are utilized in somewhat the same way as the steppes, with grazing as the principal industry and with dry-farming agriculture making some inroads. There are many handicaps to both of these activities, and, in general, the savannas have low population densities. Grazing is hindered by the low nutritional value of the coarse grasses, which are particularly low in phosphorus. Only certain types of animals are capable of digesting these grasses during the dry season and of resisting the high temperatures of the tropics. The major products of the grazing industry are hides and skins. Animal

[5] The term *galeria* signifies a gallery, or corridor, so named because a dense tangle of trees meets over the stream, producing a tunnellike opening below.

diseases, particularly those transmitted by insects, are frequent.

Variations in the length and severity of the dry season are a major disadvantage to agriculture. Yields are also likely to be low because of the poor soil fertility. Here grass does not have the same relationship to soil fertility that it does in higher latitudes. In climates that have a frost season, grass tends to improve the quality of soils for agriculture by increasing the humus content of soils, by adding to the nutrient content (especially calcium), and by generally increasing the retention of water and plant foods. These benefits are related largely to the slowness of decay and to low leaching. In the tropics, on the other hand, fertility is maintained more by a tree cover than by grass, especially if the grass is burned. Trees are able to tap a much greater depth for plant foods than grass and thus are able to return more plant foods to the surface via the decay of leaves and other forest litter. Surface soils are impoverished because of excessive washing during the rainy season; thus grass cannot return much nutrient content to the surface. The rapidity of decay and oxidation prevents the grass roots from adding as much agriculturally valuable organic material to the soil as they do in cooler climates. When the dead surface grass in the tropics is burned, it concentrates its former nutrients into ash which can be made immediately available to plants. The plant nutrients in the ash, however, are subject to leaching by rainfall. Thus the burning of savanna grasses produces a temporary stimulus to plant growth but, over a period of time, results in a progressive impoverishment of soils that were not fertile to begin with.

The grasslands of the tropics do not have the inherently high fertility of the steppes or prairies, where water availability is the critical item in productivity. This does not mean that the savannas cannot be made productive, but if agriculture in these areas is to raise itself above the level of providing a meager subsistence, it must develop special-

FIG. 10.17 Tree savanna along the Magdalena River, Colombia. Note the scattered palms that are typical of savannas in many parts of the world. The savanna here is close to being a tropical scrub woodland. For a more open savanna, see Fig. 9.17. [Standard Oil Company (N.J.)]

FIG. 10.18 Acacia savanna. This photo shows scattered acacias, desert grasses, and karoo bush near Kimberly, Cape Province, Africa. [H. L. Shantz]

ties that, by virtue of their uniqueness, will support the added cost of soil improvement. The alternate wet and dry seasons, combined with high temperatures, appear to be best suited to such products as cotton, sugar cane, grain sorghums, millets, and some of the pulses and beans. Improvement of the pasture grasses and the continued development of a mixed grazing–dry-farming economy seem to be the most suitable goals. Distance from commercial markets restricts most savanna areas today to a self-sufficient basis. When the international price of agricultural products rises and when more of the world can afford to pay such prices, the savannas may come into their own. As yet, however, they are marginal for food production.

A variety of *Acacia,* a thorny tree of the African savanna, yields a gummy exudate when wounded. This material is refined into *gum arabic,* an important ingredient in mucilages and medicinal syrups, etc. It ranks next to cotton among the exports of the Sudan.

Desert shrubs

Nearly all desert surfaces contain some vegetation. There are, of course, a few exceptions, such as active sandy ergs, where the blowing dunes do not remain in place long enough for plants to develop, and windswept, bare rock surfaces, which have no soil to nourish plants; but such areas constitute only a small part of arid regions. In the struggle for life, plants have developed remarkable mechanisms for existing and reproducing under conditions of limited moisture supply. Desert plants consist of five major groups, each of which has a different method of overcoming the handicaps of desert environments: (1) leafless evergreen herbaceous plants, such as cacti; (2) the sclerophylls, or evergreen hardleaf plants; (3) deciduous bushes and shrubs; (4) the ephemerals, or short-lived plants; and (5) the halophytes, or salt-tolerant plants. All five are found in deserts, and their relative proportions depend largely on local conditions.

10.17 THE LEAFLESS EVERGREEN HERBS. The evergreen herbs of the desert, which include the cacti, are succulent, leafless, nonwoody plants that use their stems as breathing surfaces and that are usually equipped with spines to protect them from browsing animals. The lack of leaves results in low rates of photosynthesis; therefore the cacti grow slowly. Their slow feeding habits thus require only shallow and poorly developed root systems. Outer surface cells are hard, waxy, and waterproof, thus protecting the abundant water-storage cells in the interior of the plants. The principal distinguishing features of cacti are related to their high water-storage capacity, which enables them to survive between the infrequent rains. The spines present on many such plants have prevented them from being destroyed by animals, which would otherwise be attracted by the water content of these succulent plants. Cactus flowers, like those of most desert flowering plants, are brilliantly hued. Characteristic forms are highly varied, ranging from low, supine types, such as the prickly pear (*Opuntia*), to the tall, candelabralike *Cereus* and the giant *saguaro* cactus of the Mojave Desert, which may reach 20 to 30 feet in height (see Fig. 10.19).

10.18 THE SCLEROPHYLLS. The *sclerophylls* include the same plant forms that are dominant in the *Cs* climates. They are shrubs and low trees that have leaves and thus are able to grow faster and taller than most cacti, but they must also have elaborate devices for reducing transpiration. Among various of these devices are the following:

1. Dense cell fluids, frequently a milky latex
2. Hard, evergreen, waxy leaf surfaces
3. Insulative and waterproof cork cells in the bark of stems
4. Complex *stomata* (breathing pores) with adjustable openings and various protective devices
5. Phototropism, or the movement of leaves under the influence of light, so as to present edges to the sun

Root systems are unusually well developed in the sclerophylls, and much of the water storage is found there. The most characteristic location for the sclerophylls is along the poleward margins of the low-latitude deserts, adjacent to the *Cs* climates, as in the southwestern United States, northern Mexico, and along the northern borders of the Sahara Desert.

10.19 THE DECIDUOUS SHRUBS OF THE DESERT. The deciduous shrubs are the most widely distributed of the conspicuous desert vegetation. Their leaf-shedding property makes them adaptable to droughts in both high and low temperatures. Growth can be rapid in this group of plants, since they have leaves during moist periods. Root systems are well developed. Many of the various protective properties of the sclerophylls are also found in the deciduous shrubs.

The two most widely distributed representatives of the deciduous desert shrubs are sagebrush (*Artemisia*) and *Acacia*. The former is found mainly in the cooler arid and semiarid regions (see Fig. 10.21), and the latter is a widely adaptable thorn tree and shrub of the low latitudes. In the United States, sagebrush and the creosote bush (*Larrea*) are the most common representatives of the desert deciduous vegetation. The former ranges from northern Arizona and New Mexico northward into central British Columbia and eastern Washington and Oregon, whereas the creosote bush is found in the warmer, drier region to the south (see Fig. 10.10). The creosote bush differs from sagebrush in having an unusually widespread but shallow root system. Like most desert shrubs, these plants become shorter and more widely spaced with increasing aridity. The deciduous desert shrubs encounter considerable fluctuations in their geographic range, interchanging desert environments with steppe and savanna grasslands. A decrease in the grass cover on steppes because of overgrazing, for example, leads to increased soil dryness, even without climatic change, and thus fosters the introduction of desert shrubs. The shrub vegetation, once fixed, is not easily replaced by grass and may persist for many years. This is why sagebrush covers such a large area of semiarid (*BS*) climates rather than true desert (*BW*).

FIG. 10.19 Typical desert vegetation near Phoenix, Arizona. The large cacti are saguaro, whose white, waxy blooms form the state flower of Arizona. [U.S. Bureau of Reclamation]

10.20 THE EPHEMERALS. The ephemerals, or short-lived plants, comprise many diverse types, including grasses, flowering annual herbs, and many tuberous or bulb plants. Most of them are small plants that can exist in dry areas, primarily because they are able to complete their life cycles in a short time. Their seeds, tubers, or corms remain dormant until a moist period stimulates them into germination and growth. After a rainy period, deserts are frequently mantled with a spectacular display of flowers, most of them having brilliant colors and a heavy fragrance. The colors and fragrance aid in insect pollination during the short life span of these plants. A large number of our common garden flowers originated in desert environments; among them are the peonies, some of the irises, lilies, and poppies.

10.21 THE HALOPHYTES. The halophytes, or salt-tolerant plants, are found in association with poor drainage and consequent saline or alkaline soils in dry regions, although some of them are also encountered along seacoasts within humid regions. Most of them are succulent plants; that is, they have many water-storage cells in their stems and leaves, resulting in a thick, fleshy appearance. The fluids within these plants have a high salt content and density, thus balancing the ground water of their environments. When the outgo of water by transpiration exceeds intake, the salt solutions within the plants increase in density to the point where salt crystals are formed. These are forced outward from the plant surface, coating it and giving rise to the descriptive term *salt bush.*

10.22 THE UTILIZATION OF DESERT VEGETATION. Desert vegetation is far from valueless as food for animals, although the carrying capacity of a desert is much lower than that of the grasslands. Feed for animals consists of (1) the bunch grasses, which are associated frequently with the low bush vegetation; (2) bushes and low trees, particularly the tender new tips; and (3) the smaller herbaceous plants. Cattle, goats, and sheep tend to prefer each of these three types of feed, respectively. In many parts of the lower mid-latitudes, desert range is assigned as winter pasturage, supplementing summer pasturage at higher elevations. Since the grasses often have cured into natural hay by this time, summer growth and reproduction are not hindered. Because of the low carrying capacity of desert range, successful ranching requires mobility of herds and large areas for pasturage. Fire is not the destructive agent that it is in the grasslands, because the plants are so widely spaced that there is a large amount of bare ground between them. Overgrazing, however, has seriously altered vegetation balances in many areas.

FIG. 10.20 Clearing sclerophyll brush (mesquite) in Texas. Note the prickly pear cactus (Opuntia) in the foreground. [U.S. Department of Agriculture]

The tundra

The tundra is a vast, treeless expanse bordering the polar margins of the North American and Eurasian continents (see Fig. 3.27). It extends farther south along the eastern margins of these continents, reaching almost to the Gulf of St. Lawrence along the eastern coast of Labrador and as far south as the peninsula of Kamchatka in eastern Asia. Plant growth on the tundra must adapt itself to the following environmental limitations:

1. A short, cool, growing season, usually less than 2 months long, with occasional frosts throughout this season
2. Shallow soils lying above permafrost, or permanently frozen ground
3. Poor internal soil drainage
4. Strong, steady, drying winds
5. Soils having a low nitrogen content

Compensating somewhat for these adverse conditions are the long days of summer and the low rate of soil leaching.

The most outstanding characteristic of the tundra vegetation is dwarfing, or the tendency to produce much smaller varieties of plants than those common elsewhere. This is best exemplified by the trees and shrubs, such as arctic birches, willows, and heaths, which may be only 6 to 24 inches tall at maturity. Wind stress and the shallow soils rarely permit tall trees anyway, but the dwarfing appears to be more a result of extremely low rates of growth, which in turn are due to low transpiration rates and the slowness of protein synthesis for plant tissue development. Except for the first stages of leaf development in early summer, this slow-

FIG. 10.21 Sagebrush in eastern Oregon. Note the wind erosion that has left these desert shrubs growing on mounds. [U.S. Department of Agriculture]

ness of growth holds true even during the long summer days.

The most conspicuous plant forms of the tundra are low, cushionlike woody or herbaceous perennials that reproduce by budding, or from root shoots (see Fig. 9.6). Fruiting, which would be difficult in the short growing season, is thus unnecessary. By remaining short and keeping terminal buds at or near the ground, these plants can take advantage of the protection by snow in the cold winters and the radiation of heat from the ground during the summer months. Wind velocities near the surface also are much reduced.

Lichens, those interesting "double" plants that consist of fungi and algae living together in an ostensibly symbiotic relationship,[6] are found throughout the arctic tundras. Lichens thrive where there are plenty of light and a moderate amount of atmospheric water vapor; they require little else. Free from the close competition of higher life forms, the lichens find a good home in the long daylight summers of the arctic. They reproduce by disjunction; that is, pieces of the colony break off and are carried to a new site. Arctic lichens are distributed widely and take many different forms. *Cladonia,* one of the largest varieties in the tundra, is between 2 and 4 inches high and has a preference for somewhat better drained, sandy soils. Widely misnamed as *reindeer moss,* this pale-green plant is one of the principal foods for arctic browsing animals.

True mosses, such as the sphagnums, are encountered far less frequently in the tundra than in the taiga. According to Berg, a Russian biologist, tundra bogs are by no means so common as was formerly believed, and those which do exist consist generally of sedges (*Carex*) rather than of the sphagnum moss typical of taiga bogs. The sedges are grassy plants with narrow leaves that are triangular in cross section. The water saturation of the tundra subsoils almost everywhere during the warm season, along with an acid environment, is revealed by the wide distribution of plants that are associated farther south with true bogs, such as the arctic cranberry, or cowberry (*Vaccinium*), and the ledums.

The tundra does not always have its customary drab, colorless appearance. Early in the spring, usually in late June and early July, before all the snow has disappeared, the arctic flowers appear (see Fig. 10.22). The display does not have the riot of color that a desert blooming presents, but it is impressive and even more welcome. Botanists who have visited the arctic have often been astonished at the large variety of flowering herbs, particularly those which have tight rosettelike clusters of leaves close to the ground. Among these are the *saxifrages* and *arctic poppies*. Many such plants also have hairy, rather thick leaves that help retard transpiration and insulate against occasional frosts. Grasses are present in the tundra, as they are nearly everywhere on earth. Their most common representatives are the sedges.

The ecological pattern of vegetation is almost entirely related to minute local variations of slope and drainage. There is little difference between the general features of the Alaskan tundra and those of the tundras of Lapland or the Soviet Union. Extremely sharp contrasts in types of plants, however, are found within a few feet throughout the tundra, representing different moisture and temperature regimes associated with variations in snow retention, soil permeability, permafrost depth, or exposure to wind or sun. Since most of this region was covered

[6] It is believed that the fungi are parasitic upon the algae.

FIG. 10.22 Typical tundra near Pond Inlet, Baffin Island. The small mound of earth in the foreground is covered with a profusion of grasses and arctic flowers. [National Film Board of Canada]

with glacial ice a relatively short time ago, environmental balances have not been established except on a local microlevel. Some evidence of plant succession is present, but it is not nearly so clear as in regions to the south.

The southern boundary of the tundra merges with the northern edge of the taiga along a highly irregular line. Isolated clumps of low conifers, mainly larches or spruces, act as outliers of the taiga in the treeless tundra, and long, narrow strips of forest

FIG. 10.23 Zonation of vegetation on the flanks of Kibo, one of the twin peaks of Mount Kilimanjaro, Tanganyika. Changes in the texture of the vegetation is clearly visible, with typical rain forest in the left foreground. [Richard U. Light]

FIG. 10.24 Engelman spruce near the upper timberline in the vicinity of Monarch Pass, east of Gunnison, Colorado. The scene is typical of the high mountain coniferous forests in the Rocky Mountains. [Standard Oil Company (N.J.)]

may penetrate the tundra for 100 to 200 miles along stream valleys. The presence or absence of trees along this boundary is closely related to the depth of the *permafrost* (see Sec. 12.4) layer in the subsoil. Where the permafrost zone lies within 1 or 2 feet of the surface, the water-saturated topsoils will not support trees. Sufficient drainage to avoid soil saturation is therefore a requirement for tree growth in this harsh climate. Trees are encountered along stream valleys, not because of a greater water supply, but actually because of less water. Streams can remove excess surface water, and permeable sands and gravels are more common in valleys. For the same reasons, permafrost consistently lies farther below the surface in valleys.

Except for its utilization in connection with reindeer herding and the gathering of tundra berries such as the cloud berry of northern Scandinavia, the tundra vegetation has no direct economic value. There is considerable potential for increasing the small number of reindeer now herded on the tundra, but a limited market, scarcity of trained herders, and high transportation costs are serious handicaps.

Mountain vegetation

Local relief in mountainous areas is sufficient to produce a vertical zonation of vegetation and a consequent contrast with the adjacent lowlands (see Fig. 10.23). A global map utilizing a classification that distinguishes mountain vegetation signifies only that local differences occur with elevation; no adequate areal generalization can be made here. A few vegetation communities occur in mountain areas that appear to be sufficiently widespread and distinctive to warrant separate description. These include the tropical moss forests, the mountain conifers, and the alpine meadows.

10.23 THE TROPICAL MOSS FORESTS. Moss forests are found throughout the humid tropics, but always within the cloud zone of mountains, which is usually located on the windward slopes and which is nearly always enclosed in cloud mists. It cannot be related to any particular elevation, although it is rarely encountered below 3,500 feet.

The tropical moss forest is a weird type of plant community, quite unlike any other on earth. Compared with their giant neighbors farther down the mountainsides the trees are small, rarely reaching heights over 50 feet and usually remaining under 20 feet. The branches grow straight and stiff, like outflung arms, in order to resist the strong winds that frequently sweep these slopes during thunderstorms. Aerial roots sometimes spring out from the tree trunks and are somewhat reminiscent of those of the mangrove swamps of tropical tidal flats. Tree ferns are scattered throughout. Branches, tree trunks, and the ground itself are heavily mantled with mosses, liverworts, various orchid epiphytes, and ferns of many kinds. The mantle of moss and other plants varies in thickness but is sometimes more than a foot thick. In such cases, it seems as though ground, sky, branches, roots, and moss all merge together. This forest is always wet, and water continually drips from the leaves and branches. Adding to the unearthly atmosphere of the landscape is its quietness. Few birds or monkeys live in this soggy, gloomy sepulchre, and even insects seem to avoid it.

10.24 MOUNTAIN CONIFERS. Conifers not only constitute a large part of the mid-latitude mountain forests but are frequently present at high elevations throughout the world. They are suited to the wide fluctuations in temperature caused by alternate sun and shade in the thin air, as well as to heavy snows and the soil droughts resulting from rapid runoff on steep slopes. Also, because of their wide-spreading, shallow roots, conifers can anchor themselves more adequately in thin soils than can other types of trees. Near the upper timber line appear the firs and spruces (see Fig. 10.24), similar to the dominants in the taiga, but in more open stands. Pines are usually found at lower elevations, below the spruce-fir association. Many of the pines, such as the lodgepole pine (*Pinus contorta*) in the Rocky Mountains and the southern yellow

FIG. 10.25 Not all pines are found in middle to high latitudes. This is a stand of virgin pines in the interior of New Guinea, between Bulolo and Wau. Broadleaf shrubs and bamboos form an understory that is quite unlike that in higher latitudes. [Australian News and Information Bureau]

pine of the Great Smoky Mountains of the eastern United States, are the result of old forest fires. Lightning undoubtedly has been responsible for fires and for the establishment of many of the mountain conifers in these latitudes.

Conifers, especially the pines, are by no means uncommon at fairly high elevations in the tropics. The high plains of northern Sumatra, central New Guinea (see Fig. 10.25), and southeastern Brazil contain pine forests, and pines are found in areas above 3,000 to 4,000 feet in Mindoro and northwestern Luzon in the Philippines and in northern Indochina. The highland pines of the tropics are most frequently located in regions where the adjacent lowlands have a distinct dry season. This is also true of the pines of the Atlas Mountains and the various other mountain areas of *Cs* climates, although the latter locations are more subtropical than tropical.

10.25 ALPINE MEADOWS. Grasses and low herbaceous or woody plants, such as the heaths, often form meadows just above the upper timber line of mountains and are interspersed with forests farther down the mountain slopes. This high-elevation environment has low temperatures, high wind velocities, and soils that alternate between water saturation and drought. Melting snow keeps the ground saturated for much of the earlier part of the summer season, but thereafter the winds dry the thin soils rather rapidly. The wet environment is illustrated by the types of grasses and herbs that are present. The sedges (*Carex*) are by far the most common grasses, and many of the flowering herbs are those which are typical of damp soils at lower elevations, such as the buttercups, marigolds, violets, saxifrages, and poppies. In the upper forest zone, which is usually coniferous, swales and depressions usually are in meadow rather than forest, and this too reflects the influence of water saturation.

The alpine meadows long have been important as summer pastures for animals, especially where a pastoral economy prevails on the adjacent lowlands. This is less often true in tropical regions, because of the difficult forest zones that must be crossed in order to reach the upper timber line. Also, the alpine meadows of the tropics lie at a much higher elevation than do those of higher latitudes.

Above the alpine meadows, and in more exposed sites, the alpine vegetation begins to take on many of the features of the arctic tundra. Cushionlike plants, streamlined by the wind, are frequent, and lichens abound on patches of thin soils and even on bare rock surfaces. Here and there a dwarf tree can be found, bent and blasted by the wind. Wherever snow accumulates, it helps to protect the low vegetation, and shrubs are denser and higher in the hollows, where they are sheltered from the wind. Tiny flowering plants are found growing up to the edges of permanent snow fields and glaciers. The existence of plants in this harsh environment illustrates the general principle that competition for survival among plants is so keen that special adaptations can be found suitable for almost any environment on earth —from the high temperatures of hot springs to the frozen edges of glaciers, from bare rocky surfaces to loose dune sand, from deserts to swamps and marshes, from mountaintops to the continental-shelf zone far beneath the surface of the sea.

11

Soils: their properties and classification

What is a soil? It is clear that soils are a part of the surface mantle of the earth, but when does a mass of broken rock or transported rock material become soil? First, it should be recognized that a soil is a *natural body;* that is, its properties are derived from natural processes. Being a body, it has the dimensions of any solid, including length, breadth, and depth. Perhaps the most distinguishing feature of soils is that their characteristics change with depth. This variation with depth is a reflection of differences in environmental conditions, ranging from free exposure to surface air to varying conditions of compaction, particle size, soil openings, ground water, microlife forms, and other features that appear below the surface.

Let us imagine a thick mass of crushed rock, such as the tailings from the mill of a copper or gold mine. When first deposited, it is not a soil, because (1) it is not a natural body and (2) it exhibits no consistent differences with depth. Let this mass of mine tailings, however, remain exposed to the weather for a long time. Every rain that falls on it will alter the mass somewhat. Some of the finer particles near the surface, for example, will be washed downward, leaving the coarser ones behind. Each shower that trickles downward through the mass will perform some of the chemical decomposition processes that tend to alter mineral substances, changing them into compounds that are more in harmony with the environment than the original crushed stone. Just as an iron bar left out in the open alters in rusting to form the more stable but less useful iron oxide, so too will a host of minerals, which originally were formed in a far different environment far below the surface, alter into new materials.

When does our mass of rock fragments become soil? The answer cannot be given in years, because the process of change is subject to many variables, which are discussed later in this chapter. It is sufficient to state that our mass of mine trailings will develop into soil as soon as the changes in depth become readily observable, that is, when the material develops a vertical profile. In some cases soils develop distinctive properties that are arranged in clearly separated depth zones, termed *horizons;* in others the differences with depth are more gradual.

Many fragmental, or unconsolidated, materials can be found on the earth surface, including beach sand, glacial debris, volcanic ash, marine and lake sediments, loess, and river alluvium. These are not soils, but materials from which soils may be derived. Even solid rock will develop a mantle of soil in time, because the end result of weathering is the production of fragmental solids in a transitional zone between earth and air.

Soils are natural mixtures, composed of representative portions of each of the following zones or spheres that make up the earth:

1. The *lithosphere* (rock sphere), or the inorganic material that forms the earth crust, modified by the weathering processes that prevail at or near the surface
2. The *atmosphere* (air sphere), including both the soil gases that are altered by intimate contact with subsurface liquids and the life gases given off by plant roots and various microorganisms in the soil
3. The *hydrosphere* (water sphere), or the water contained within soil openings in variable amounts and modified through the addition of various substances
4. The *biosphere* (life sphere), or the content of organic material, living and dead, which not only exists within the soil environment but becomes a part of it

All the materials that make up soils are subject to alteration, and each exerts an influence on all the others. Just as vegetation tends to work toward the relative stability of its constituent plant elements, so also do soils, which change more slowly as they become older and develop a relative stability that is a reflection of their total environment.

In summary, *a soil is a naturally occurring body, a mixture of fragmental rock material and varying proportions of gases, water solutions, and organic material, that exhibits differences in chemical and physical properties with depth.* It is "born" when the vertical profile first becomes noticeable. It usually alters rapidly at first, but change takes place much more slowly in later stages, as the soil nears relative ecological equilibrium. Far from being a static mass of material, the soil is sensitive to changes in its environment at any stage in its development.

Like landforms, climate, and vegetation, soils are subject to the basic principles of natural distributions discussed in Chapter 1; that is, they (1) develop an infinite variety of forms areally, yet show degrees of similarity that permit regional comparisons; (2) show transitional changes in border areas between soil regions; (3) alter with the passage of time; and (4) progress toward a relative stability within the total environmental complex.

Soil properties

The most important differences between soils include variations in one or more of the following properties: color, texture, structure, horizons, composition, and depth. Each of these is discussed briefly below.

11.1 SOIL COLOR. Color is one of the more recognizable properties that distinguish soils. Strong contrasts in the color of surface soils are significant features in the comparative geography of continental regions. The bright red and yellow soils of the southeastern United States and the black prairie soils of the Ukraine are quickly recognized, even by the casual visitor. Like the other properties of soil, the color varies not only in different regions but at different depths. Nearly all the soil colors are various mixtures of white, black, red, yellow, or brown. The diagram in Fig. 11.1 shows an arrangement of the dominant soil colors and suggests possible results of color combinations.

A wide variety of organic and inorganic

compounds are found in soils, but only a few of them are responsible for the various color combinations. Among these, the most important are the iron oxides and organic material. Table 11.1 lists the basic colors of soils and the constituents that are mainly responsible for them.

Greenish and bluish shades slightly tint heavy gray clays in the soils of humid, poorly drained regions. As shown in Fig. 11.1, combinations of the constituents listed in Table 11.1 yield various color mixtures; for example, iron (red) and organic material (black to brown), both common soil materials, result in reddish-brown shades, such as chocolate. The effectiveness of the coloring agent varies. A small percentage of iron, for example, may produce a bright red color in soils that contain much higher percentages of aluminum or silica, because the latter are white to colorless. An increase in moisture content tends to sharpen the intensity of soil colors.

A question might be raised about whether or not there is any correlation between soil fertility and color. Black is often regarded as an indicator of fertility, because it is usually associated with a great amount of organic content plus carbonates, both of which supply soluble bases for plant use. Such a generalization, however, is subject to many exceptions. The black alkali soils of desert regions are anything but fertile, and some of the black soils of the tropics have undesirable properties for soil cultivation. The ferrous iron compounds, which are responsible for the greenish- or bluish-gray shades in soils, are associated with water saturation, a characteristic that generally makes the soil undesirable for cultivation. Even here, however, an exception comes to mind, for saturated soils are essential to the mainte-

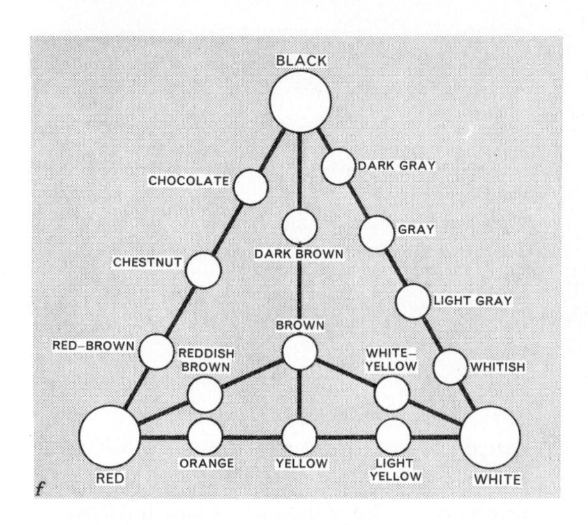

FIG. 11.1 Soil color combinations. [After Zakharov]

TABLE 11.1 Origin of soil colors

COLOR	CONSTITUENT
BLACK	Highly decomposed organic material, usually with associated lime or other carbonates Manganese oxides * Sulfur compounds *
RED	Ferric iron oxides: hematite (Fe_2O_3), turgite ($2Fe_2O_3 \cdot H_2O$)
YELLOW (OCHROUS)	Hydrous iron oxides: limonite ($2Fe_2O_3 \cdot 3H_2O$)
BROWN	Partially decayed, acidic organic material
WHITE	Silica: quartz (SiO_2) Lime: calcium carbonate ($CaCO_3$) Kaolin, bauxite, and other hydrous aluminum oxides and silicates Gypsum: calcium sulfate ($CaSO_4 \cdot 2H_2O$) * Nitrates, borates, and other soluble salts † Certain organic colloids *
GREEN	Ferrous iron oxides *
BLUE	Vivianite (a hydrous ferrous phosphate) *

* Relatively rare soil constituents.
† Rare except in poorly drained dry regions.

TABLE 11.2 Soil textural classes

CLASS	PARTICLE SIZE, MM.
Coarse gravel	Above 2
Very coarse sand or fine gravel	1–2
Coarse sand	0.5–1
Medium sand	0.25–0.5
Fine sand	0.1–0.25
Very fine sand	0.05–0.25
Silt	0.002–0.05
Clay	Below 0.002

nance of productivity in the rice paddies of eastern Asia. Thus we see that color alone is unreliable as an indicator of soil fertility.

11.2 SOIL TEXTURE. Soil texture refers to the relative proportion of different sizes of soil particles. Textural groups must be defined in classifying soil properties either horizontally or vertically. Table 11.2 presents a classification of individual particle sizes used by the Soil Survey branch of the Soil Conservation Service. By far the greatest range is within the clay group, where the particles may be anywhere from 0.002 millimeters to almost molecular size.

FIG. 11.2 Soil texture diagram. The points A, B, and C represent samples taken from three levels in a soil profile in Indiana. The topsoil (A) is thus a silt loam, the lower horizon (B) a clay, and the parent material (C) a loam. The mechanical analysis of this soil profile is given in Table 11.3. [U.S. Department of Agriculture]

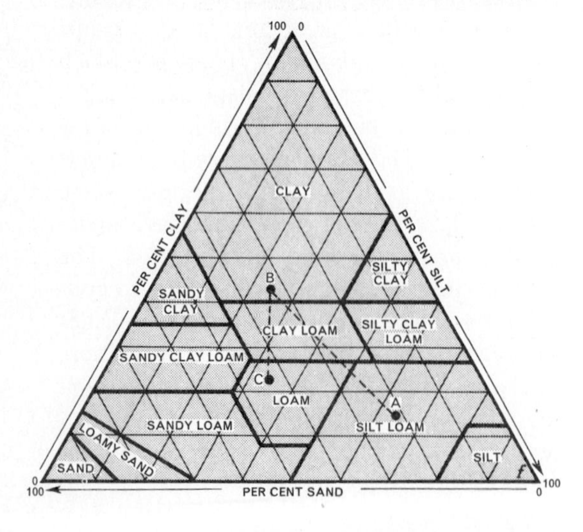

Since soils rarely consist of particles of only one size group, an additional classification is necessary to describe mixtures of particle sizes. The diagram in Fig. 11.2 presents in graphic form the quantitative definitions of the various textural classes used by the U.S. Department of Agriculture. The textural-group triangle shown in Fig. 11.2 also can be adapted to indicate differences in textural grouping with depth, as illustrated in Fig. 11.2. Points *A, B,* and *C* give the quantitative mixtures of particle sizes for the surface, lower soil, and underlying parent material, respectively, for a Miami silt loam from Indiana. The mechanical analysis is tabulated in Table 11.3.

Many factors influence the texture of soils, among them the mineral composition of the parent rock material, the nature and rate of the local soil-forming processes, and the relative age of the soil.

Unqualified statements regarding relationships between the texture of soils and soil fertility should not be made, although texture may be significant in the relative ease of tilling the soil. Sandy soils in humid climates usually are rapidly leached of soluble bases and hence are low in plant foods. They are also likely to have a low capacity for holding soil moisture; therefore they tend to be droughty. By adding much organic material,

TABLE 11.3 Mechanical analysis of a Miami silt loam

HORIZON	SAND, %	SILT, %	CLAY, %
A	21.5	63.4	15.0
B	31.1	25.0	43.4
C	42.4	34.0	23.5

however, some sterile, humid sandy soils have been changed into highly productive ones. Although sandy soils in arid regions have a high nutrient content, because of the small amount of precipitation and leaching, their low capacity for water retention reduces their agricultural value.

Clay soils vary considerably in ease of cultivation and fertility, depending on their chemical composition. Differences in the behavior of the tiny soil particles are discussed later (see Sec. 11.5). Some clays are plastic, sticky, and almost unworkable when wet, and hard and cloddy when dry. Others, however, especially the clay soils of the humid tropics, have a high degree of water permeability and crumble readily when dry.

From the standpoint of tillage, or the workability of the soil, silts and loams are desirable, since they rarely are too loose or too tight for plowing or harrowing. Their fertility varies, however, depending on the quantity and availability of plant foods, water, etc.

FIG. 11.3 An open, crumb soil structure in a prairie soil of McLean County, Ill. This is representative of the prairie soils of the American Corn Belt. Note also the deep black color, indicative of a high organic content. [Standard Oil Company (N.J.)]

11.3 SOIL STRUCTURE. Soil structure refers to the physical arrangement and grouping of individual soil particles. It is developed to some extent in nearly all soils, although it may be absent in loose sandy soils or in extremely plastic clays. The individual particles in the soil almost always are joined in different forms and sizes of particle groupings, and the behavior of a soil is closely related to the size and shape of these structural *aggregates* (see Fig. 11.3). The small clods and crumblike forms of a freshly harrowed, fertile field are illustrative. Some of the most common types of structures are briefly described in Table 11.4.

Soil structure has an important influence on the direction and ease of movement of water in the soil. Many of the usual methods of field cultivation are designed to produce a more desirable type of structure in order to improve conditions of soil drainage, aeration, and availability of plant foods. The addition of lime to a heavy, plastic clay soil, for example, flocculates the fine clay particles into larger structural units. *Flocculation* is the process of uniting the tiny particles of a soil into aggregates. It is comparable to the process of curdling milk. Rolling a freshly seeded field breaks up the aggregates into smaller sizes, thus increasing the number of soil openings and bringing capillary water closer to the surface to aid in seed germination. One of the main reasons for fall plowing is to expose the soil to alternate freezing and thawing, processes which tend to break up the larger clods into smaller structural units and to aerate the soil more thoroughly.

Structure in most soils is better developed in the lower part of the soil than it is at or near the surface, where, indeed, it may be lacking entirely. The reason for this is partly that fine particles tend to migrate out of the upper part of the soil and partly that the

TABLE 11.4 Classification of soil structural units

NAME OF UNIT	SHAPE	SIZE
BLOCK	Irregular, but not elongated	5–10+ cm.
CLOD OR CRUMB	Irregular, but not elongated	0.5–5 cm.
NUT	Clear faces and edges; well-defined aggregates; not elongated	5–20 mm.
GRANULAR	Clear faces and edges; well-defined aggregates; not elongated	0.5–5 mm.
PRISMATIC	Long, vertical axis; edges sharp; sides smooth	1–5+ cm. in diameter
COLUMNAR	Rounded top; flat bottom; sides more or less clearly defined; elongated vertical axis (see Fig. 12.12)	1–5+ cm. in diameter
PLATY	More or less flat, thin, platelike masses	Variable
SHOT	Well-rounded; spherical	2–5 mm.

bases and other flocculating, or coagulating, agents responsible for forming the aggregates are more likely to be found below. Many sandy soils are so deficient in small-sized particles as to prevent the formation of structural aggregates. The sandy soils of desert regions, beaches, and dunes serve as illustrations.

11.4 HORIZON DIFFERENTIATION. Soil-forming processes begin to act at once upon any exposed mass of unconsolidated rock material. Since these processes usually operate from the surface downward, differences in color, texture, structure, composition, and other properties eventually appear at varying depths. These vertical differences, which generally become more pronounced as the soil ages, may divide the soil into zones, known as *horizons*. A vertical section through all the soil horizons constitutes the soil *profile*.

Although all soils exhibit a profile—or morphological, chemical, and biological differences with depth—the separation of the vertical differences into distinct horizons does not always take place. This is illustrated by many humid tropical soils, which may show only a gradual transition, through perhaps dozens of feet, between the surface and the underlying material from which the soil is made. Some students of tropical soils have stated that, when sharply defined horizons occur in humid tropical areas, they usually indicate an interruption in the normal development of soils, such as poor drainage or the presence of a water table within the soil profile.

Distinct horizons in stable, mature soils are best developed in dry regions and in the cool, humid mid-latitudes. Here there is a tendency for material to be removed from the upper parts of the soil and for some of this transported material to accumulate in the lower portions. Three main horizons can be distinguished in such soils and are designated *A, B,* and *C,* respectively, according to depth.

The *A* horizon includes the topsoil, the zone which experiences the greatest loss of material through the mechanical washing downward of fine soil particles by percolating ground water (*eluviation*) and also through the associated process of chemical solution by ground water and its various solvents (*leaching*). Above the *A* horizon there is usually a layer of organic material of variable thickness and at different stages of decay. Subnumerals are used throughout the soil profile to designate noticeable intrahorizon differences—for example, A_1, A_2, B_1, B_2, etc. The numbers increase with depth within the horizons. The organic layer that lies on the surface is often designated as the A_0 horizon.

The *B* horizon, sometimes referred to as the *zone of accumulation,* lies immediately below the *A* horizon and often is separated from it by a sharp, though irregular, boundary. Many of the soluble and insoluble substances washed downward from the *A* horizon are caught and held in the *B* horizon. As a result, the latter accumulates additional soil material with age and, in general, is more compact than the *A* horizon.

The *C* horizon, which lies below the *B* horizon, represents the unconsolidated rock material from which the soil is derived. It exhibits little, if any, vertical differentiation in appearance or chemical composition. If the soil is *residual* (derived in place from solid rock below), there is a gradual transition between the fragmental material in the *C* horizon and the solid rock below. Unlike the sharp boundary that usually exists between the *A* and *B* horizons, the transition between the *B* and *C* horizons is almost always gradual.

The description of a Miami loam given in Fig. 11.4 illustrates how soil properties may vary with different horizons. The Miami soils are typical of well-drained uplands in the lower Great Lakes states and are underlain by glacial till having a high content of pulverized limestone.

The *B* horizons are usually absent in mature humid tropical soils, primarily because there are no sharp changes in the characteristics of the soil solution with depth. The soluble materials taken from these topsoils continue downward and eventually find their way, via ground water, to the rivers and the

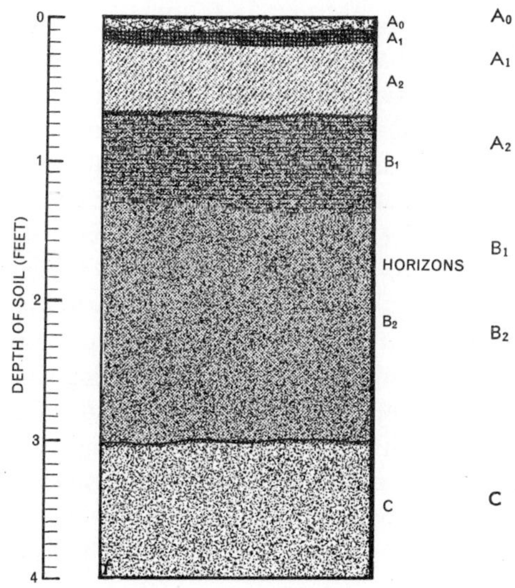

FIG. 11.4 Typical profile of a Miami loam.

A_0 A thin accumulation of forest litter.

A_1 From 1 to 2 inches, dark, mellow loam or humus, containing a high percentage of organic matter, much decomposed and thoroughly incorporated in the soil. The reaction is medium acid.

A_2 From 2 to 8 inches, light-gray, floury, loose loam with a high content of silt and slight development of a platy or laminated (layered) structure. The material crumbles easily into a structureless mass. The reaction is strongly acid.

B_1 From 8 to 16 inches, light-yellow or grayish-yellow loose friable loam, platy in the upper part, becoming granular below. Very acid.

B_2 From 16 to 36 inches, clay loam breaking into irregular angular particles about ½ inch in diameter. The structure particles are brown, but when they are crushed, the resulting soil is yellowish brown. A thin coating of very fine textured brown material on the structure aggregates accounts for their color. When wet, the material is sticky; when dry, it is difficult to crush between the fingers. The reaction is acid.

C Imperfectly weathered, heavy, pale-grayish-yellow calcareous sandy loam or loamy glacial till containing a few stones. The material is variable in color, structure, and texture. It is hard when dry.

FIG. 11.5 Typical podzol profile. Note the light, light, ash-gray mineral A horizon (top 6" on scale) and the darker B horizon. Dark surface material is raw humus. [Charles E. Kellogg; U.S. Department of Agriculture Soil Survey]

sea. In dry regions, however, evaporation alone may suffice to alter radically the concentration of soluble salts or bases in the soil solution and to cause the precipitation of selected substances in a *B* horizon (see the discussion of *calcification* in Sec. 12.11). In cool, humid regions, sharp changes in acidity within the soil profile cause the precipitation of materials in a *B* horizon, particularly iron and aluminum silicates, which are clay fractions whose mobility within the soil is related closely to soil acidity (see the discussion of *podzolization* that is given in Sec. 12.1).

The development of soil horizons sometimes has a profound influence on fertility. Figure 11.5 shows a photograph of a cool, humid region soil with a pronounced *B* horizon. Note that the plant roots are weakly developed within the *A* horizon but that they spread out extensively within the *B* horizon in their search for plant foods and water. In certain circumstances the technique of deep plowing (to depths of 2 to 3 feet) is used to mix *A* and *B* horizons together, thus producing more suitable conditions for cultivation. Sometimes it also is used to break up impermeable *B* horizons, or *hardpans,* which interfere with internal soil drainage.

11.5 INORGANIC SOIL CONSTITUENTS.

Soils are mixtures of minerals, organic material, ground water and its included constituents, and air. Each of these materials may vary considerably in amount and composition in different soils.

The inorganic material in the soil is derived from the mechanical and chemical breakdown (termed *disintegration* and *decomposition*, respectively) of the various minerals of the earth crust. Geologists long have recognized that, although the crust contains nearly all the known chemical elements, only a few of them make up the bulk of it. Table 11.5 lists the eight most common elements in the earth crust, with their respective percentages by weight.

The first four ranking elements in Table

11.5 make up almost 90 per cent of the material in the earth crust by weight. It should be expected that they also comprise a large proportion of the chemical composition of soils. In fact, their percentages are even higher in the soils of humid regions than in the crustal rocks; because when they are brought together in the processes of rock decomposition, they tend to form relatively stable, insoluble compounds. Although their percentages vary somewhat from place to place, the various oxides of iron, aluminum, and silicon form the bulk of soils everywhere, and only traces of the other elements usually are found in soils of humid lands.

The last four of the leading eight elements in the earth crust differ from the first four in tending to form compounds which are soluble in water or associated solvents. They are therefore important in modifying the soil solution and in assisting it in developing the characteristics of the soil profile. Since these soluble compounds in humid regions tend to be washed out of the soil profile via ground water, soils normally contain lower percentages of these four elements than do the rocks from which the soils were derived. The *B* horizons of most soils in dry regions, however, contain high percentages of the water-soluble compounds, because of local concentrations developed within the soil profiles by soil-forming processes.

Wherever chemical processes of rock decomposition are prevalent, as in warm, humid regions, a loose correlation exists between soil texture and mineralogical composition. The larger soil particles, those in the gravel or sand class, are generally fragments of rock minerals that are resistant to the chemical decomposition processes that predominate in the locality. Quartz (SiO_2), for example, usually forms a high percentage of the sand particles in humid soils, not only because it is a fairly common mineral, but, more important, because it is one of the most durable minerals on earth in resisting the attack of common solvents. The small inorganic soil particles, particularly those within the clay size range, are largely mineral particles that were formed during the rock-decomposition processes; therefore they are mostly complex combinations of oxygen, silicon, aluminum, and iron.

TABLE 11.5 Composition of the earth crust

ELEMENT	PERCENTAGE
Oxygen	47.3
Silicon	27.7
Aluminum	7.9
Iron	4.5
Calcium	3.5
Sodium	2.5
Potassium	2.5
Magnesium	2.2
Total	98.1

SOURCE: F. W. Clarke, *The Data of Geochemistry*, U.S. Geological Survey Bulletin 770, 1924.

No such clear relationship can be established within the soils of arid or semiarid regions. Here the processes of chemical rock decay are much slower, because of the scarcity of liquid solvents, and the chemical composition of soil fragments of all sizes depends more on the parent rock material than on chemical weathering processes. Desert sands may be composed largely of quartz, but only if quartz fragments were abundant in the adjacent rocks, as in massive sandstones. They may be composed of many other minerals, especially of the feldspar family, which constitutes a high percentage of the crystalline rocks in the earth crust.

At this point further attention should be paid to the composition and behavior of the finely divided inorganic particles in the soil, most of which, the clays, are the products of soil and rock weathering. A large percentage

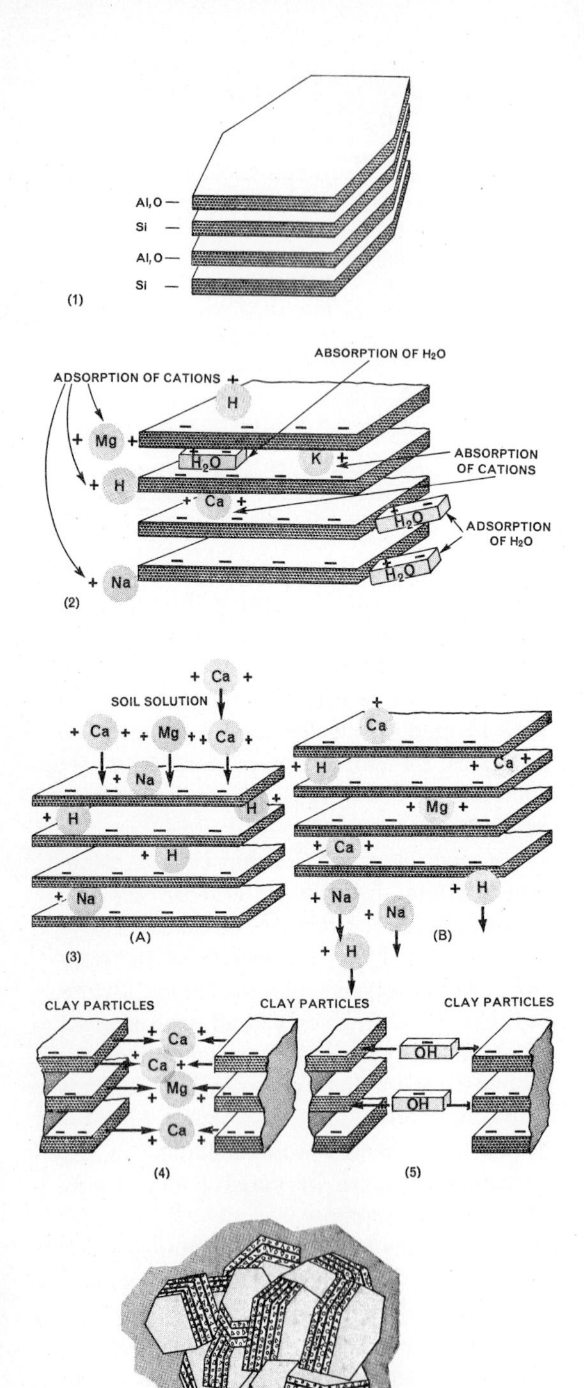

FIG. 11.6 Soil inorganic colloids and their behavior. The sandwichlike arrangement of an individual clay particle is shown in (1). (2) indicates the adsorption and absorption of cations and water molecules. The base-exchange function of clays is shown in (3), where calcium and magnesium ions in the soil solution replace hydrogen and sodium ions in the clay complex. The flocculating action of calcium and magnesium is indicated in (4), where the positive charge of these ions acts as a bridge between adjacent clay particles whose surface charge usually is negative. The peptizing action of hydroxyl (OH) ions is shown in (5), where the negative charge helps to keep the particles separated. A typical clay floccule, or crumb, is diagrammed in (6).

of them are colloidal [1] in nature and therefore have unique properties that influence soil fertility, structure, color, and many other features of soils.

Recent investigations indicate that the clay colloids in soils, instead of being irregular lumps of material, microscopic in size, have a characteristic crystal form, usually consisting of tiny bundles of flakes or sheets and somewhat resembling the arrangement of sheets in a crystal of mica. This flakelike property tends to increase the interfacial

[1] The peculiar physical and chemical properties of colloids are essentially the result of combining the electrical forces of different molecules along *interfaces* (the boundaries of liquid-solid, liquid-liquid, liquid-gas, etc.). A colloidal system is simply a mass which contains enough interfaces to produce a dominance of interfacial properties. If a subdivision of any mass is carried far enough, it may result in a colloidal system. When particles of a substance enter a colloidal system, they often assume physical and chemical properties that are distinctly different from those of the same substance in larger-sized units. Fat globules in milk, for example, rise to the surface and become cream because of their lower specific gravity. When these globules are broken into much smaller droplets of colloidal size (homogenization), however, they become stabilized throughout the liquid. Milk itself is a colloidal system of tiny solid particles in a liquid. The process of coagulation (flocculation) associated with souring or the addition of an acid destroys the former colloidal stability and unites the solids into masses, the curds.

characteristics of the mass, since atoms, ions, and molecules are able to work their way between the tiny sheets of the clay colloids. The colloidal chemistry of soils is a relatively new field of soil science, but it has already revealed that many of the processes responsible for the major differences in soils throughout the world are closely related to the composition and behavior of both inorganic and organic colloids.

Another soil factor associated with the chemical composition of the soil is the *base-exchange capacity*. This is a measurement of the capacity of the soil colloids to exchange base ions (calcium, sodium, magnesium, phosphate, etc.) held by the colloidal particles for others that are found in the soil solution. A high base-exchange capacity indicates that the colloidal soil "bank" is well supplied with various types of base ions and can exchange them for different types of ions from the soil solution. The base-exchange capacity of the soil gives a fairly good indication of its fertility, for the plant foods that roots absorb from the soil solution are largely members of the base-ion group which have been displaced from the colloidal interfaces by less useful ions.

11.6 ORGANIC SOIL CONSTITUENTS. The organic portion of the soil solids, like the inorganic part, includes a wide variety of complex chemical compounds in many physical forms. It is derived from the leaves, roots, and stems of plants and from worms, insects, and the bodies of countless numbers of bacteria, fungi, and other microorganisms that are universally present in the soil. Many of these organisms synthesize various organic compounds in their life processes, and when they die, their decay produces many entirely different substances of amazing complexity. Following the death of a living organism, a long sequence of decay processes is set up. Eventually, through decay or putrefaction, the complex organic compounds are altered into a few relatively simple chemical products, such as carbon dioxide, oxygen, nitrogen, water, the simpler hydrocarbons, and various mineral salts.

The intermediate decay products are termed *humus*. As in the chemical decomposition of minerals, some of the finely divided humus is colloidal in form and behavior. It is primarily this colloidal humus, along with the inorganic colloids, that gives soils their capacity for absorbing and holding moisture and soluble plant foods.

The organic content of soils depends primarily on two factors: (1) the addition of new supplies, dependent largely on the amount and type of vegetation cover, and (2) the rate of decay. Although humid tropical areas generally have a lush vegetative growth, they may have little humus in their soils, because of rapid decay. On the other hand, cold, humid areas, such as the tundras, where the vegetation consists mainly of stunted trees, low bushes, mosses, and lichens, often have soils with a high organic content, because of the slowness of decay. Soils near the boundary between humid and dry climates have a high organic content, partly because the dense grass cover generally adds much dead vegetation annually to both the surface and to the soil profile and partly because dryness tends to decrease the content of many of the decay-producing microorganisms. These tiny forms, like other living things, require water for most of their life processes. Beyond this dry-humid boundary, toward the drier climates, the rate of decay falls off rapidly, but so also does the amount of vegetation, so that there is a general decrease in the amount of organic material contained in the soil.

Associated with the organic content of a

soil is the nitrogen content. This element, so abundant in the atmosphere and so essential to such life processes as fiber building and the manufacture of proteins for tissues, does not easily unite with other elements to form soluble compounds. Most nitrogen compounds in soils are of organic origin; they result mainly from the activity of special bacteria that require organic material on which to feed. Thus most soils throughout the world have a nitrogen content that is roughly proportional to their contained organic material. This explains why desert soils, which are rich in most of the other soluble plant foods, usually are deficient in nitrogen.

Swamps and marshes are favored places for the accumulation of organic material. When the vegetation in a swamp dies, it is often buried below the water level and is thus partially protected from decay, since most decay-producing microorganisms require free oxygen. There are, however, some forms of microlife that can use oxygen from compounds, instead of requiring the gaseous form. These organisms feed on submerged organic material, but they do so slowly and show a decided preference for swamp water with low acidity. Under conditions of high ground-water acidity, the swamp or marsh organic material is brown, fibrous, and not greatly decayed; such material is known as *peat*. Where the ground water is not acid, on the other hand, the resulting material is a jet-black, finely divided bog humus, termed *muck*. When drained and fertilized, this material forms one of our most productive soils for intensive cultivation.

11.7 THE SOIL SOLUTION. The soil solution is mainly a dilute solution of acids, bases, and salts, but it may also carry in suspension tiny colloidal soil particles. It enters the soil profile from either the top or the bottom and either passes through it or remains behind in the small soil openings. Despite its transient nature, the soil solution is a vital part of the soil body. Water itself is a poor solvent for most earth materials, but when combined with acids or bases, it becomes an important agent of rock decay and soil formation. Were it not for the mobility and chemical activities of the soil solution, soil profiles would not develop. The characteristics and the amount of the soil solution are strongly influenced by climate, and it is partly for this reason that many of the major soil-forming processes can be correlated with climatic differences. Plants depend on the soil solution as a source of mineral foods and of the water which is necessary for life.

The quantity of soil fluids contained within the soil may produce many different physical traits in the soil mass. Plasticity, frost heaving, swelling and shrinking, soil flowage down slopes, and many other properties are closely related to water content and its interaction with soil texture and structure. One of the most important factors influencing the quantity of the soil solution is *porosity,* or the total amount of space between the soil solids. This influences the capacity of soil to hold water. *Permeability,* or the relative ease with which the soil solution passes through the soil, is directly related to the size of the soil openings. In general, fine-textured soils have greater porosity but less permeability than those of coarse texture; thus they not only hold more water but retain it longer. Colloidal particles, particularly the organic colloids, likewise greatly increase the water-storage capacity of soils.

Not all of the soil solution is available to plants; some of it is bound to the tiny surfaces of soil colloids by a powerful force, at times reaching the magnitude of 15,000 pounds per square inch. In an aggregate of colloidal particles, as in a clay nodule or crumb, there is a gradual transition between the available water on the outside and the tightly held solution near the center of the colloidal aggregate. The colloids are the storage vaults that keep the soil solution from passing completely out of the soil by percolation or evaporation and that thus provide plants with a supply of water and nutrients to draw upon between rains.

11.8 THE SOIL ATMOSPHERE. The soil atmosphere, another component of the soil, is found in all the openings that are not filled with water. It is a necessary constituent, not only because plant roots and microorganisms depend on it for respiration but also because the included gases, such as oxygen, carbon dioxide, and water vapor, play important roles in the processes of inorganic and organic decomposition. Although soil air and the air immediately above ground usually differ very little in major constituents (nitrogen and oxygen), the following important contrasts should be noted:

1. The soil atmosphere contains 7 to 8 times as much carbon dioxide as does air above the surface, mainly because of the CO_2 released as a result of the decay of organic material concentrated within the restricted confines of soil openings.

2. The relative humidity of soil air frequently is near the saturation point, because of the supply of water contained within the soil. However, the soil humidity will vary somewhat from season to season in areas that have marked seasonal differences in rainfall.

3. The composition of soil air is considerably more variable than that of surface air, because of changes in the activity of microorganisms with seasons and with weather.

4. Temperature fluctuations within the soil decrease rapidly with depth and are considerably less evident throughout the soil profile than above the ground.

11.9 SOIL DEPTH. With increasing age, the soil profile becomes deeper, and where horizons are developed, they generally become more clearly defined. So many factors influence the rate of soil development, however, that it is not possible to measure quantitatively the age of a soil or its degree of maturity solely from its depth. The soil solution can move more easily through coarse-textured soils, such as sands and gravels, than through heavy clays and thus can influence a greater depth over an equivalent period of time. Sandy soils, therefore, tend to have deeper profiles than adjacent heavier-textured soils. In warm climates with heavy rainfall, the rates of chemical reactions, rock decay, and soil formation are greater than in other climates, and some extremely deep soils are found there. Although somewhat unusual, soil depths of over 100 feet have been observed in the tropics.

Soils are likely to be deeper on level-to-undulating terrain than on steep slopes, since the removal of the soil material by erosion checks soil accumulation on steep slopes. The ability of the parent material to resist rock decay, as determined by its physical and chemical properties, also may influence the depth of the overlying soil profile. In summary, then, time, texture, climate, slope, and the composition of parent material are factors that influence the depth of soils.

The variables in soil formation

Soils are a product of their environment, and the different characteristics they show from place to place and from time to time are the result of changes in any one or more of the variables that make up the total environment. Although many factors affect soil development, the basic determinants are parent material, climate, vegetation, slope, hydrography and drainage, microorganisms, man, and time. Any one of these eight elements may exert a dominant influence on the soil properties by which areal differences and similarities are recognized.

11.10 PARENT MATERIAL. Parent material refers to the inorganic rock or mineral material from which the soil is derived. This may consist of broken rock rubble lying directly above the solid rock from which it was formed, or it may be made up of mixtures of rock particles deposited by transporting agents, such as rivers, glaciers, or winds.

The degree to which the parent material influences soil properties (particularly texture, color, and composition) is usually in direct ratio to the newness of the soil. As the soil ages, the influence of the parent material decreases, until the characteristics inherited from the original material may be wholly masked, in some places, by soil properties derived from other factors. The end products of soil formation may bear little resemblance, either physically or chemically, to the original material. On plains that have existed without appreciable erosion for millions of years, such as on some of the Russian steppes, the soils are distributed in patterns that have little relationship to the distribution and characteristics of the underlying parent material. Instead, they correspond closely to climatic patterns or to minor site differences in slope or drainage. Flat-to-undulating land surfaces that have lain undisturbed for long periods of time, however, are relatively rare, because of the general instability of the earth crust. Wherever erosion or deposition is especially active, the processes working toward relative soil stability are interrupted, and in such areas the parent material exerts a significant influence on the overlying soil material.

The persistence of parent-material influences within the soil profile is also related to the composition of the original material. Rocks that have a high quartz content, such as the granites and many sandstones, usually produce sandy soils whose texture and other features will be preserved over a long period of time, simply because of the general durability of quartz in the surface environment. Rocks and minerals containing large amounts of iron or aluminum hydroxide or other chemical compounds that are relatively stable under the influence of soil-forming processes will retain similar properties in the transition from rock to soil. Shale, a soft, sedimentary rock, composed mainly of compacted or indurated clay, usually weathers extremely slowly, and its inherent clay minerals will persist for long periods within the soils that it produces.

11.11 CLIMATE. The three variables of climate that are most significant in soil-forming processes are precipitation, temperature, and evaporation. These factors may influence soils directly, through the rate of chemical reactions, the effectiveness of physical disintegration of rocks, and the amount and characteristics of the soil solution. They may also affect soils indirectly by influencing the quantity and type of vegetation and the microorganisms that are present in the soil environment. The results of climatic influences are more apparent than are the exact processes by which these results are produced.

We have accurate climatic records for only a relatively few score of years; we know that weather is constantly changing, yet no one has been able to isolate climate as a single variable in soil formation, partially, of course, because climate itself is a generalization of many variables. Most of our measurements of climate are inadequate for detailed studies of soil processes. The climate of the soil atmosphere is quite different from that above the ground surface, where meteorological observations customarily are taken. Despite these difficulties, the influence of climate upon soils is unmistakable, and properties that are largely the result of climate have usually been used to classify soil differences on chorographic or global scales of generalization. The global patterns of soils, which correspond closely to climatic patterns, are discussed in the following chapter. Further consideration of the results of climatic differences will be postponed until then.

11.12 VEGETATION. Vegetation affects soils primarily by supplying most of their organic content. Especially important is the organic colloidal material that may be present in the soil profile. Secondly, the chemical composition of the dead plant remains that become incorporated into soils influences the acidity and composition of the soil solution. Finally, the dead organic residue supplies the food for the rich microlife that dwells in the soil and plays a critical role in maintaining soil fertility and in determining the characteristics of profile development. Unlike parent material, vegetation is not an independent variable. It is largely dependent on climate for its most important characteristics; yet, as has been demonstrated, it has features of its own that help influence the details of soil geography.

Some of the principal influences of vegetation on soils can be summarized as follows (see Fig. 11.7):

1. Forests tend to supply more organic material to the surface of the ground than does any other major type of vegetation.

2. Grasslands, although they do not supply as much organic material to the surface as forests do, supply large quantities to the soil immediately below the surface.

3. The content of bases in the leaves and stems of plants varies with different types of plants. Broadleaf trees generally have a higher base content than do conifers (needleleaf trees); hence the derived humus is likely to be less acidic in reaction. Some oaks, however, produce highly acid humus.

4. Forests tend to reduce soil erosion on slopes and hence help to stabilize the soil-forming processes there.

5. The rate and amount of translocation of bases and other plant foods from the subsurface to the surface vary with different types of plants.

6. Forests, by decreasing the velocity of winds, tend to reduce the evaporation of soil moisture and to retain snow cover; these effects, in turn, influence the activities of the soil solution.

7. Forests, as compared with grasslands, tend to have a larger proportion of fungi and a lesser proportion of bacteria among the microlife of their soils—other factors, such as climate, remaining the same. The different activities of such organisms are an important part of soil development.

Where man has appreciably altered the native vegetation of an area, significant changes in soil properties have been observed, often after a remarkably short period of time. Careful measurements of soils in New England, in areas where white pine has followed the abandonment of cultivated fields that originally were covered with virgin, deciduous hardwoods, have indicated noticeable changes in soil profiles within 10 years following the change in vegetation. Sharp local contrasts between prairie and forest soils, each having similar parent material or slope conditions, are observable in many places along the forest-prairie border in Minnesota, Wisconsin, and Illinois.

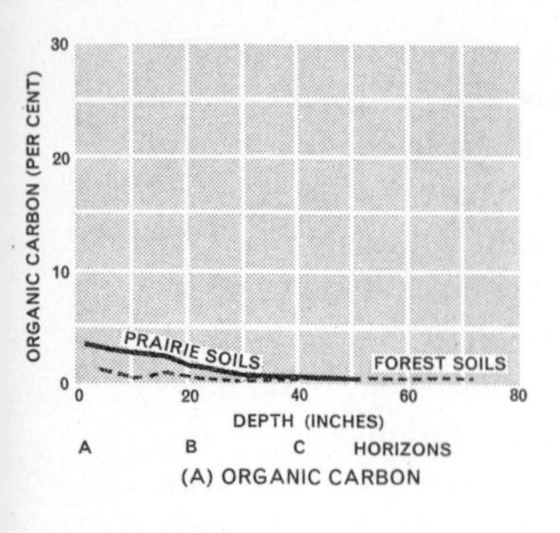

(A) ORGANIC CARBON

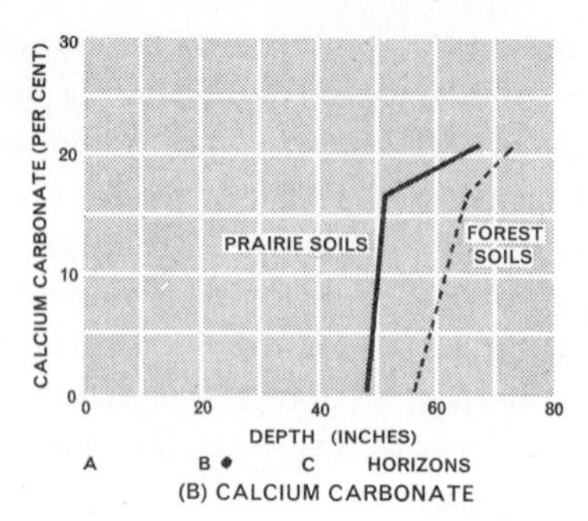

(B) CALCIUM CARBONATE

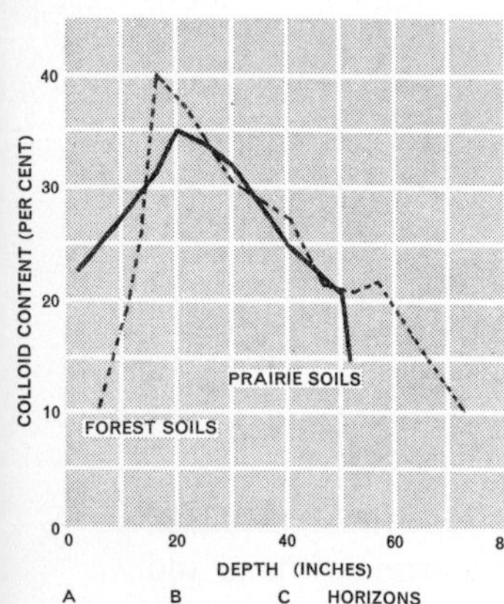

(C) COLLOID CONTENT

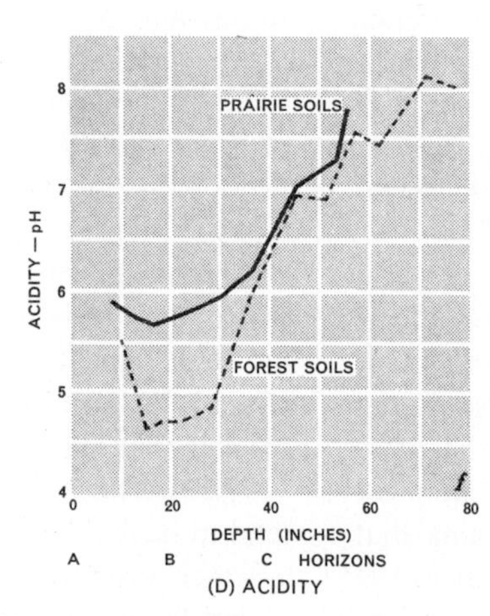

(D) ACIDITY

FIG. 11.7 Comparisons of the soil properties in typical prairie and forest soils in the American Midwest. Note the higher organic and colloidal contents in the prairie topsoils, the higher pH (lower acidity), and the appearance of lime (calcium carbonate) at somewhat shallower depths in the subsoil, as compared with the forest soils. [After Jenny]

11.13 SLOPE. There is a tendency for all loose, unconsolidated material to move downslope under the pull of gravity, the most effective force being exerted on the surface material. This movement, as was observed earlier, tends to retard the development of maturity in soils, or the creation of what we have termed relative soil equilibrium. Any soil profiles found on steep slopes are likely to be thin and poorly developed. On steep slopes that are highly susceptible to erosion, the soil profile may be entirely absent, either because a previous *A* or *B* horizon has been removed or because the fragmental material does not remain in place long enough to develop a profile. Numerous factors other than the degree of slope itself affect the rate of erosion of soil material on slopes. Among these other influences are the type of vegetation cover, the amount of freezing and thawing, the soil texture and structure, the water content, undercutting of the slope by stream action, cultivation by man, and so on.

Slope conditions may alter the effect of climate on soil formation. The influences of a given quantity of rainfall and resultant percolation are reduced on steep slopes, because of more rapid runoff at the surface; hence the rate of profile formation is retarded. The exposure of slopes to sunlight varies, and thus temperature conditions, the action of freezing and thawing, and the rate of evaporation may vary accordingly. On mountain slopes, differences in the degree of exposure to prevailing winds may result in marked differences in precipitation, which, in turn, produce noticeable local variations in soils. In some parts of the world, the lee sides of mountain ranges have a dry climate, with its associated vegetation and soil characteristics, whereas the windward slopes, a short distance away, have contrasting humid conditions and an entirely different type of soil. Many of the features of poor drainage, to be discussed in the section on hydrography, also are related to slope conditions.

As one stands on a slight rise on the undulating or rolling surface of a large, freshly cultivated field in the humid mid-latitudes, he can readily detect the influence of slope on soil characteristics; the effects are particularly striking in areas where special cultivation methods have not been used to check field erosion. In the hollows, the dark, fine, moist topsoil contrasts sharply with the light-colored, coarse underlying material that is exposed on the swells or rises (see Fig. 11.8). Even under a covering of natural vegetation, however, varying slope and drainage conditions produce corresponding profile differences, features that become more marked the more closely the soils are examined.

Soil differences that are related largely to slope conditions are recognized mainly in areal patterns on a topographic scale of observation and presentation, and even here they usually are greatly generalized. At chorographic or global scales, slope as a factor in soil differences must be largely ignored, simply because the variations are too finely distributed to be represented. Most global soil maps show a general category of mountain soils. The areas so designated are large enough to be distinguished easily on such maps, and their classification as mountain-soil regions merely indicates that they have such strong differences in slope, elevation, and exposure that any further soil characterization would be without a great deal of meaning.

FIG. 11.8 Topographic influences on soil types near Dover, Delaware. The dark patches are organic soils, or half-bogs, developed in the slight depressions on an undulating land surface. Field ditches have been dug to drain these depressions. [U.S. Department of Agriculture]

11.14 HYDROGRAPHY AND DRAINAGE.

Soil hydrography refers to the characteristics and distribution of soil water. The importance of the soil solution in the normal development of the profile has already been briefly discussed. Under conditions of poor drainage, the normal development of the profile cannot take place, and certain unique properties appear.

In soils where the ground-water table lies at, or somewhat above, the surface, such as in swamps or marshes, organic material tends to accumulate, because of the limited supplies of oxygen available for decay-producing microorganisms. The thickness of the organic layer varies greatly, depending on such factors as the amount and type of vegetation, the length of time the material has been accumulating, and the fluctuating positions of the water table. Below the organic material, the inorganic soil will also have properties associated with saturation. If the openings between the soil fragments are filled with water throughout the year, free oxidation

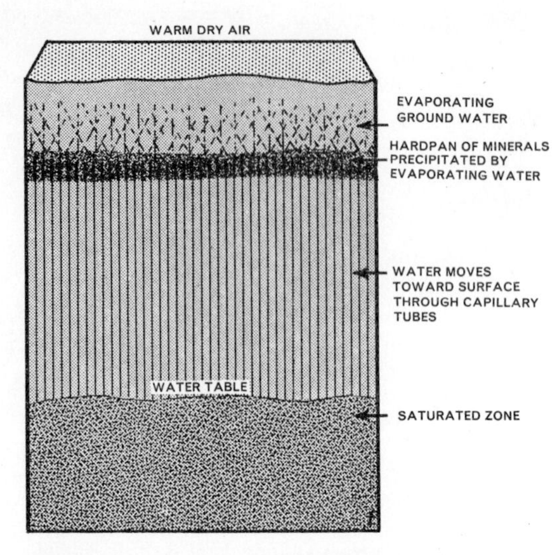

FIG. 11.9 Diagram showing the development of hardpans in soils that have a high water table. In humid regions, such hardpans commonly are composed of iron oxides.

cannot take place, and the soil compounds which are at balance in this environment are usually hydrated oxides. Shades of bluish or greenish gray are frequently seen in the saturated soils of humid areas. Clays are likely to be plastic and heavy. *Anaerobic bacteria,* those which have the ability to extract oxygen from oxides and hence can live in saturated soils, may change ferric oxides (Fe_2O_3) to ferrous oxide (FeO), thus removing the red and yellow coloring from the colloidal particles that have accumulated.

With intermittent or seasonal fluctuations in the water table, the portion of the soil that is subject to alternate saturation and drying develops a characteristic mottling, in which some of the ferrous oxides change into the red or yellow ferric oxides, or, when combined with organic material brought from above, into shades of reddish or yellowish brown. These colors appear along root channels or around the edges of larger openings in the soil, where drying first takes place, and result in the general mottled appearance of such soils.

Where the water table remains fairly constant at some level within the inorganic portion of the soil profile, the upper limit of the water-saturated zone may be marked by a horizon of pronounced deposition. The material brought to this zone may have been carried downward by percolating rain water or carried upward from the water table by capillarity and deposited through evaporation or chemical precipitation (see Fig. 11.9). In humid regions, iron compounds deposited in this zone may form a hard, cemented layer, known as an *iron hardpan.* In the humid tropics, such iron layers in soils are known as *laterites* and are quarried and used for building or paving purposes. In arid regions, wherever the subsurface water has no outlet to a flowing stream, soluble salts may accumulate in the ground water and be deposited at or below the surface as the result of evaporation. The nitrate deposits of Chile are believed to have originated as a subsurface hardpan in this manner.

The ground water drains away slowly on flat land. Various degrees of bleaching, mottling, or hardpan development may occur here, depending on the length of time the soil is saturated with water. Steep slopes, on the other hand, suffer from excessive removal of water, and hence the normal profile development is retarded. The most ideal drainage conditions for the development of relatively stable, normal profiles are found on undulating or moderately sloping terrain.

Like slope, poor or excessive drainage conditions seldom can be treated as significant in interpreting the pattern of soil distributions in global studies. On a topographic scale, however, variations in soil properties may be more closely linked with drainage and slope conditions than with climate, vegetation, or any of the other variables. It is for this reason that most detailed soil surveys on a topographic scale use a classification system in which the properties determined by slope and drainage conditions play a leading role.

11.15 MICROORGANISMS. Wherever organic material exists in the soil, varying populations of bacteria, fungi, protozoa, and other tiny organisms are found that utilize this material as food and become an active part of the soil complex. Larger animal forms, such as rodents, earthworms, moles, and insects, also live within the soil profile and play their part in influencing soil properties.

Perhaps the most important function of the living microorganisms in the soil is to influence the characteristics of the soil solution through their digestive and metabolic activities. In the humid tropics, where conditions for the culture of bacteria and molds are ideal, the large quantities of dead vegetation litter added regularly to the topsoil are rapidly consumed, and the waste products are released into the soil solution. With complete decay, such waste products consist mainly of carbon dioxide plus various mineral salts and bases, the latter having once been among the plant foods taken from the soil solution by the plant roots. A cycle is developed in which bases are absorbed from the soil solution by plant roots and are partly supplied by the decay of organic material obtained from the plants themselves. Some bases also are obtained from the slow, continuous chemical breakdown of inorganic soil particles. The reuse of plant foods supplied as the result of organic decay helps to explain the lush tropical vegetation on soils which contain only small inherent reserves of available bases (low base-exchange capacity). It also explains why the fertility of such soils declines rapidly with cultivation, when the cycle is interrupted by cutting off the normal increment of dead vegetation and the only addition of plant foods must come from rock decay.

In cool, humid regions, where the ground is frozen for much of the year and where conditions are not so favorable for the growth of microorganisms, dead organic material decays less rapidly and thus accumulates on the surface. Fungi tend to predominate over bacteria in such climates and, being less efficient in producing decay, release intermediate decay products, particularly certain types of organic colloids. Many of these organic colloids can be carried by the soil solution, and some have the chemical properties of strong acids. These acidic colloids help leach out bases and iron and aluminum hydroxides from the topsoil, leaving behind a relatively coarse, sterile, bleached, infertile residue high in silica. This basic soil-forming process, which is termed *podzolization,* is discussed more fully in the next chapter.

Many of the major differences in climate and vegetation are reflected in soil differences through the activities of decay carried on by the microorganisms in the soil. These organisms are dependent variables in soil formation, since their activities are largely determined by climatic and vegetation conditions. They represent part of the environmental complex, in which the many forms and forces that are present react with one another and work toward mutual adjustment and stability. Since the global pattern of soils is closely correlated with climatic conditions, the interpretation of areal differences on this scale involves consideration of the role of microorganisms in affecting these differences. The treatment of the major climatic soil-forming processes in the next chapter includes a somewhat more detailed discussion of the activities of these organisms.

11.16 MAN. As human beings increase in number on earth and modify the land surface more and more in serving their needs, they are becoming increasingly significant as an independent variable in soil modification. Cultivation, deforestation, reforestation, irrigation and drainage projects, erosion control, erosion acceleration, and many other human activities produce significant alterations in soil properties and hence change the patterns of soil distribution. So much of the earth surface has been modified by man that completely natural soil conditions are exceptional. A thorough analysis of the human factor in the interpretation of soil differences is far beyond the scope of this volume. It is sufficient to note that, with his increasing knowledge of soil technology, man is now virtually able to alter the soil of any environment to produce whatever properties or qualities he desires. The degree to which he carries out such improvements, however, is generally limited by economic, political, and social feasibilities.

Despite his ability to alter soil properties, man is slowly learning that his uses of the soil are still subject to the inexorable progressions of the environment toward, or away from, relative stability. If he is to have any regard for the maintenance of soil productivity, he must understand the principles of soil ecology and adjust his cultivation procedures accordingly. There are many examples throughout the world to indicate the folly of careless use of soils.

The immense productivity of the reclaimed *polder* lands of the Netherlands and the sterility of the millions of acres of thin, stony, erosion-scoured hillsides in Korea, North China, and many parts of Mediterranean Europe stand as impressive testimonials to the potentialities and destructiveness, respectively, of human intervention in the natural processes of forming soil.

11.17 TIME. All factors that influence soils, as well as soils themselves, are subject to alterations with time. Some soils on ancient erosional plains are subject to change only over long periods of time, whereas others exhibit noticeable alterations in soil properties within a few years. Soils may be considered young if they are just beginning to develop the properties that represent relative equilibrium with the total environmental conditions existing in a particular area. In young soil, changes are rapid. It does not take long for horizons to develop on freshly exposed parent material, and some of the properties of the ultimate soil balance may begin to be recognizable within 50 to 100 years. Studies made of soils that have accumulated on old, abandoned fortress walls in Europe indicate that, over periods of 250 to 300 years, these soils have developed characteristics remarkably like those of the soils overlying the local rock out of which the fortress walls were constructed. Investigations made in the Harvard forest, an experimental area in the Berkshire Hills of Massachusetts, to determine the influence of vegetation alterations on soil properties show significant readjustments of profile characteristics within 20 to 30 years following a change in vegetation.

It is not possible to express soil youth or maturity in terms of years. The rate of change varies with soil texture, with climate, and with age. Because of rapid leaching, loose-textured soils may reach a relative stability or balance in far less time than soils containing a high clay content. The rates of rock weathering, decay of organic material, and chemical leaching of the soil are much greater in the humid tropics than elsewhere.

The task of classifying and mapping soils on a topographic scale is extremely difficult in areas that have undergone the four successive major advances and retreats of continental ice sheets during the past million years. In these areas there is a wide range of parent materials, the slope and drainage patterns in morainic zones are complex and jumbled, and the differences in age of the successive glacial deposits result in appreciable variations in soil depth. In southwestern Wisconsin, for example, the weathered loess associated with the post-Illinoian glacial period (about 200,000 years ago) has reached depths of approximately 8 feet. On similar local parent material of post-Wisconsin age (14,000 to 20,000 years old), unweathered loess is found about 2½ to 3 feet below the surface.

One of the most striking examples of the influence of time on soil morphology is found in the complex series of sand dunes along the eastern shore of Lake Michigan. During the waning stages of Pleistocene glaciation, the water in the Lake Michigan basin stood at several different levels. Dunes were constructed at each lake level. Eventually the dunes were fixed by vegetation, and as they became older, the soils that developed on them became deeper and the *B* horizons more pronounced, particularly in color. The oldest *B* horizons are dark orange, almost chocolate-colored; the sequence that follows with decreasing age is light orange, ochre, light yellow, and, finally, colorless, in dunes of recent origin. The sands are remarkably uniform in texture and composition. The sharp color contrasts are clearly a function of the time taken for the translocation of iron oxides into the *B* horizons of these soils.

Soil classification

In order to describe the distributional patterns of soils, generalizations have to be made which necessarily broaden with the increasing size of the areas to be considered. At any scale of study, certain observable differences in soils must be discarded. The more closely soils are examined, the more differences appear. The soils of no two spots on the earth surface are identical, owing to the variety of both soil properties and the factors responsible for them. Soil classification systems represent generalizations of soil properties in which certain areal similarities are recognized and certain differences discarded as irrelevant to the purposes of the classification involved. In a real sense, the problems of classification of soils are the same as those met in generalizing the distributional features of the other aspects of the physical environment.

11.18 THE GREAT SOIL GROUPS. Late in the nineteenth century, a soil classification system was established which was based largely on soil characteristics that are primarily the result of climatic and biological factors. It evolved from some pioneer work done in soils by a Russian scientist, V. Dukuchaev. His ideas were expanded and applied in Russia by Glinka, one of Dukuchaev's students, by Ramann in Germany, and by Marbut in the United States.

The emphasis given to climate in soil genesis on the part of the Russian scientists is understandable. The soils of the flat-to-undulating plains south of the limit of Pleistocene glaciation in the Soviet Union have remained relatively undisturbed for long periods of time (even measured geologically), and some of these soils have properties quite unrelated to the parent rocks beneath them. The gradual change in soil properties as one passes from the desert, across the steppes, to the taiga, or from arid to humid climates, is clearly observable on every hand. The Russian scientists recognized, however, that the climatic emphasis in soil classification could not be all-inclusive, and they suggested separate categories to include soils whose major properties are the result of local extraclimatic

TABLE 11.6 Soil classification system

ORDER		SUBORDER	GREAT SOIL GROUP
ZONAL SOILS		Soils of the cold zone	Tundra soils
	Pedocals	Light-colored soils of arid regions	Desert soils
			Red desert soils
			Serozem soils
			Brown soils
			Reddish-brown soils
		Dark-colored soils of the semi-arid, subhumid, and humid grasslands	Chestnut soils
			Reddish chestnut soils
			Chernozem soils
	Pedalfers		Prairie soils
			Reddish prairie soils
		Soils of the forest-grassland transition	Degraded chernozem soils
			Noncalcic brown soils
		Light-colored podzolized soils of the forest	Podzol soils
			Brown podzolic soils
			Gray-brown podzolic soils
			Yellow podzolic soils
			Red podzolic soils
		Ferrallitic forest soils	Yellowish-brown ferrallitic soils
			Reddish-brown ferrallitic soils
			Ferrallite soils
INTRAZONAL SOILS		Saline soils of poorly drained arid regions	Solonchak soils
			Solonetz soils
			Soloth soils
		Poorly drained soils of humid regions	Wiesenboden (meadow soils)
			Alpine-meadow soils
			Bog soils
			Half-bog soils
			Planosols (upland hardpan soils)
			Podzolized ground-water hardpan soils
			Lateritic ground-water hardpan soils
		Calomorphic (high-lime) soils	Brown forest soils
			Rendzina soils
AZONAL SOILS			Lithosols (rocky soils)
			Alluvium
			Dry sands

conditions, such as parent material, slope, and drainage.

In the United States, the early soil investigators were interested primarily in the utilitarian aspects of soil differences and thus confined their efforts mainly to studying soil distributions on a topographic scale, in order to assist farmers and farm advisers. The great variety of landforms and surface configurations, the complexity of patterns of underlying rocks, the large area covered by continental glaciation, with all its varied features of drainage, erosion, and deposition, presented the early soil investigators in the United States with a bewildering assortment of soil forms. Their earliest classification system was based on three main variables: parent material, surface texture, and agricultural potentialities. Hundreds of different soils were recognized, recorded, and classified, and as the area covered by the field surveys grew, more soils were added to the list.

The late Dr. Curtis Marbut, of the former U.S. Bureau of Chemistry and Soils, was one of the first outstanding American soil scientists to recognize the importance of studying the evolution of soils as natural bodies, as products of dynamic natural processes and not as static substances whose significance is related solely to their productivity. He was largely responsible for initiating modern soil science in the United States, and he generously acknowledged the contributions and leadership of the Russians in this field. In the course of his research, writings, and teachings, he introduced the Russian soil classification system to the United States, with appropriate modifications. The first application of this classification to the soils of the United States is contained in the monograph *Soils of the United States,* published in 1913 as Bulletin 96 of the Bureau of Chemistry and Soils, under the direction of Marbut and several other soil scientists.[2]

The classification system introduced by Marbut comprises three major orders: the *zonal, intrazonal,* and *azonal* soils. Zonal soils are those whose characteristics are mainly the result of climatic or biological conditions, and there are two major subdivisions: the *pedocals,* or dry-land soils, and the *pedalfers,* or soils of humid regions. *Intrazonal* soils are those whose properties are related more to local drainage conditions or to parent material than to climate or vegetation. *Azonal* soils are miscellaneous unconsolidated materials that have not yet developed distinct soil profiles. Strictly speaking, they are not soils, but soil materials.

The suborders of this classification system include a rough division of vegetation formations within the zonal order and the saline, swamp, marsh, and high-lime soils within the intrazonal order. The units that make up these suborders will concern us most in the next chapter, where we distinguish the patterns of soils on a global scale. These soil units are included in what is known as the *great soil group* and are characterized by basic differences in profile. Many of them are named according to their predominant color. These are mature, or relatively stable, soils; when they represent the zonal order, their characteristics show the influence of climatic and biological factors; when they represent the intrazonal order, their properties reflect a close adjustment to local

[2] The culmination of Marbut's work on soil classification appeared in 1935 in the section on Soils that appeared in the *Atlas of American Agriculture,* a publication of the Department of Agriculture. It is perhaps appropriate at this time to note further that the U.S. Bureau of Chemistry and Soils, which Marbut headed for so many years, no longer exists under this name. Its activities have been merged with those of the Soil Conservation Service, one of the major divisions of the Department of Agriculture.

drainage or slope conditions. Table 11.6 shows the essential details of the classification. Although not shown on the diagram, three additional levels of refinement are utilized in the classification: *series, types,* and *phases*. These finer divisions are related largely to topographic variables, such as parent material, surface texture, and special properties that influence local agricultural use, such as stoniness and steep slopes. For this reason they are not considered further in this text. Their use is exemplified in the many soil surveys published by the U.S. Department of Agriculture.

Soil fertility

Ever since man learned to domesticate plants to provide himself with a dependable food supply, he often has been more consciously concerned with soil differences than with the other features of his physical environment. It is probable that approximately two-thirds of the families in the world today obtain their livelihood by cultivating the soil, and they either bless or curse their fate, depending on how they appraise the particular piece of ground which they cultivate. This appraisal of soil, wherever and whenever it is made, however, is based on human needs and customs; it has no necessary relationship to any one or any combination of the physical properties of the soil itself. Nature is indifferent to the desires of mankind, and all it says is, "Use me as you will, only remember that the rewards or punishments will be earned, not granted." Soil resources and soil resistances are created, not by the properties of soils, but by human desires and drives.

The kinds of soil properties which man finds useful are related to his cultural wants. There is no such thing as an inherently good soil. If we assume that goodness in a soil depends on the per acre production of calorie foods, then we can erect a system of appraising soil properties which is pertinent to this standard. In our own cultural world, monetary profitability is the principal standard for appraising soils, and it may or may not be related to their capacity of producing food or feed. Soils may have value solely as places on which to erect buildings. In such cases, the abstract factor of position may be more significant than the base-exchange capacity. The engineer erecting an earth-filled dam may be far more interested in a soil's plasticity or porosity than in its acidity or organic content, the factors that are often critical in agricultural appraisals. Obviously, an appraisal of soil differences based on standards of profitability alone involves complexities more appropriate to a textbook in economic geography than to the present study in global physical geography; the appraisal here is confined largely to conditions of fertility in agriculture, one of the most elemental types of land use.

Soil fertility, then, relates to the ability of soils to grow plants yielding either food or feed. Soil fertility results from a large number of individual factors which, taken together, might be thought of as a chain. There must be sufficient links in the chain to provide for each of the plant growth requirements, and the total strength of the chain is the strength of its weakest link. A soil may have an abundance of many essential elements of fertility, but if it lacks just one (for example, moisture), such elements have little value for plant growth. Among the most important factors in soil fertility are the following:

1. Mineral plant nutrients. Plant foods consist of chemical elements that are utilized in the synthesis of organic molecules in the plant structure. The most critical elements are *potassium, nitrogen, phosphorus, mag-*

nesium, calcium, iron, and *sulfur.* The first three are needed in larger quantities than the others. Because the soluble ions of these chemicals can be washed out of soils, most humid soils are deficient in the above elements, at least for purposes of intensive cultivation. Phosphorus is a unique element in that its compounds are fairly abundant in soils, but these compounds are stable and resistant to chemical breakdown. The relationship between nitrogen and soil organic material was discussed earlier, in Sec. 11.6.

2. Trace elements. The trace elements are chemicals that are required in minute quantities to perform a variety of functions in plant fertility, including roles as catalytic agents in the complex chemical reactions of plant life processes. The principal trace elements are *iodine, boron, sodium, silicon, manganese, copper,* and *nickel.* They almost always are present in soils in sufficient quantities, since only tiny amounts are required by plants. Occasionally, however, soils are lacking in one or more of them, with the result that plant health and growth are seriously impaired.

3. Water. Water is the lifeblood of plants, since it transports essential elements to the plant cells and removes the waste products of life processes. The requirements of plants for water vary greatly. Lichens, for example, can extract and live on minute quantities obtained directly from the air, whereas swamp trees in the humid tropics may lower the water table by as much as 5 to 6 feet in a year, solely through root "pumping" and transpiration from leaves and stems.

4. Atmospheric gases. Although the composition of the air above the ground remains fairly constant, the composition of the soil atmosphere may change appreciably from time to time and from place to place. Plants obtain most of the essential element carbon from atmospheric carbon dioxide above the surface and use it in synthesizing cellulose, starches, and sugars. Some of the carbon, however, is derived from carbonic acid that is contained in the soil solution and absorbed directly by the plant roots. A supply of free oxygen, which must be available to roots to aid in plant respiration, is also an essential condition of soil fertility.

5. Acidity and alkalinity. Extremes in the concentration of acids and bases may lead to toxic conditions that prevent normal plant growth. The highly acid peat bogs of cool, humid regions support only a specialized type of acid-loving vegetation, such as sphagnum moss and spruce. The saline soils of desert basins indicate that soils can have too large a quantity of some substances which are important plant foods in dilute solutions. The proper level of acidity, appropriate to the plants being cultivated, is an important factor in soil fertility.

6. Colloids. Soil colloids contribute to fertility primarily by serving as reservoirs of plant foods and water that can be released gradually into the soil solution for plant use. Both organic and inorganic colloids perform this function, although the former are much more efficient. Without colloids, soils would soon lose the soluble plant foods that result from the weathering of rock fragments in the soil or from the decay of organic material. Also, without colloids, water in the soil would be found only on its way downward during or immediately following a rain or in the spaces between soil particles below the ground-water table. Under such conditions, plants would find either too much or not enough water.

7. Microorganisms. One of the lesser-known aspects of soil fertility is the interrelationship that exists between plant roots and microorganisms, both fungi and bacteria. Some of the fungi threads penetrate the root stems to form direct connections between

the sap of the plant and the soil solution. They act as miniature extensions of the plant root systems, drawing both water and food from the soil and, in return, utilizing some of the plant's carbohydrates, without having to make the starches and sugars themselves. Some fungi appear to be particularly beneficial in extracting phosphate from the soil. The role of certain soil molds as antibiotics in the control of plant diseases is not yet fully understood, but some authorities believe that it may be important. Some forms of bacteria penetrate root stems to form nodular colonies (especially on the legumes) and, while helping themselves to the plant sugars, extract nitrogen from the air in surplus quantities that can be utilized by the plants. Not all the soil microorganisms are beneficial to plant growth, however; some of them produce serious plant infections.

The numerous factors involved in soil fertility make it exceedingly difficult to construct a world map showing gradations in soil fertility. Most parts of the world exhibit both favorable and unfavorable conditions for plant growth, because of local soil differences. Furthermore, different types of useful, cultivated plants demand quite different environmental conditions. The soil that proves fertile for rice production, for example, has far different properties from those required for the cultivation of white potatoes or maize.

Each of the climatic extremes is reflected in soil-fertility factors. The cool, humid soils are highly acid and likely to be deficient in soluble bases. At the same time, soil moisture is plentiful, and the acid environment is preferred by some useful plants.

The warm, humid soils have low retentive capacities for water and for plant foods, but soil fertilizers produce rapid results, and the climatic conditions are the most favorable to plant growth found on earth.

Dry-land soils have a plentiful supply of most plant foods but are generally subject to periodic deficiencies in soil moisture and, in poorly drained areas, to toxic salinity or alkalinity.

The best-balanced conditions of soil fertility, at least in a natural state, are found in transitional climatic areas, where the favorable factors of one climate tend to balance the unfavorable factors of another. Excluding the young soils of alluvial and volcanic material, which often are fertile because they have yet not been leached of their plant foods, the best soils for general agriculture are mid-latitude soils that lie near the humid-dry boundary. In this intermediate position between cold and hot regions and between humid and arid conditions are found the famous granaries of the world, including the Corn and Wheat Belts of the United States and Canada, the eastern European plains of Hungary and Romania, the Ukraine of the Soviet Union, the plains of northern China and Manchuria, the pampas of Argentina, and smaller areas in southeastern Africa and Australia.

There is no soil on earth whose fertility cannot be improved, and a wide range of corrective practices has been offered by the soil scientists. The problem of soil improvement is largely one of cost accounting. Experience in the United States seems to indicate that, with a few exceptions, investments in improvement pay off more on good soils than on poor ones. We have not yet reached the point of diminishing returns on the application of technology toward increasing soil productivity on inherently fertile soils. Until this point is reached, more and more food will continue to be produced on fewer acres of farm land, and more marginal land will be retired to other, less competitive uses.

One spectacular exception to the above generalization is worth noticing. The sandy coastal-plain soils of northern New Jersey have perhaps the lowest inherent fertility of any soils in the United States, aside from arid regions. Chemical analyses indicate that the Lakewood sand, a common soil type in this area, is composed almost entirely of quartz (SiO_2), one of the most inert minerals of the earth crust. The amount of quartz in the total soil mass in these regions may run well over 90 per cent. Only traces of organic material and mineral colloids are present. Despite such obvious handicaps, some of these sands have been developed into some of the most productive and valuable market garden areas in the country, by gradually increasing the organic content and by supplying immense quantities of commercial fertilizers. This is man-made fertility, and the natural soil is useful only as a physical support for plant roots. The motivation for such expensive practices has been the proximity of metropolitan markets. Farmers in these areas are able to truck fresh garden produce directly to the metropolitan markets of Philadelphia and New York within a few hours. The market gardens are concentrated on sands rather than on adjacent heavier soils, which in their native state are much more fertile, because the former are easier to cultivate and the quantities of water and nutrients supplied to the plants can be better regulated. Such sections represent vegetable factories rather than farms. They illustrate the fact that soil fertility is not entirely a natural resource but can be created and modified by man, provided that he is given sufficient incentive. The human potential for increasing the productivity of soils is enormous, and a treatment of soil fertility solely as a function of nature is incomplete. In Chapter 10, we examined several techniques which man has developed to maintain soil fertility and a suitable balance for plant growth.

Soil erosion

Soil erosion has been one of the most publicized problems relating to the American resource base during the past 30 years, and there has been much controversy about the degree to which man can be blamed for stimulating erosion and about the extent of his responsibilities for halting it. The dramatic rise of the erosion problem within the general framework of the conservation movement in the United States resulted from several factors, including the following:

1. The closing of the land frontier, or the fact that no more land suitable for agricultural settlement in the public domain was available for the asking
2. The establishment of the Soil Conservation Service as an agency for assisting in the public works program during the depression years of the 1930s, as well as its later role as an important division of the U.S. Department of Agriculture
3. The governmental assistance given to erosion-control measures developed on farms and under the supervision of government experts, as an integral part of national-resource planning programs
4. The writings and research on soil erosion by many outstanding specialists, such as Hugh H. Bennett
5. The obvious economic decline of regions where erosion was most acute

Under the stimulus of the general soil-erosion crusade and with the assistance of direct and indirect aid by government agencies, large areas were brought under control programs throughout the United States during the 1930s and 1940s, particularly in the sections most susceptible to erosion. Today erosion still is a serious problem in some parts of the country, but even the uninformed traveler cannot help noticing and being impressed by the preventive and corrective work done in many parts of this country (see Fig. 11.10).

There also has been a growing awareness in recent decades that soil erosion is an international problem. Wherever it occurs throughout the world—on the Navajo Indian reservations of the southwestern United States, the Udi Plateau of Nigeria, or the rocky hillsides of Greece—soil erosion is both a symptom and a cause of overpopulation.[3] It is as much a social and economic problem as it is a physical or engineering one. In most parts of the world with advanced standards of living, the people have recognized their responsibilities for relieving regional economic distress in the interests of national security. One of the most immediate and practical approaches to the rehabilitation of overpopulated agricultural areas within rough terrain is to institute erosion-control measures.

Among the many long-term processes working toward relative environmental stability are those forces of weathering, erosion, and deposition that tend toward leveling all surface irregularities to a gently sloping plain near sea level and toward producing on this surface a soil that is in chemical, physical, and biological harmony with its environment. Such conditions may require millions of years to evolve, and they are seldom achieved, because of the opposing geologic forces of crustal warping that continually operate to interrupt the progression toward stability. Some erosion is as inevitable on sloping land as running water. The significant element in the human appraisal of soil erosion is not the relationship of current erosion rates to the eventual geologic balance but rather the relationship of these rates to the much more immediate and short-term problem of maintaining human well-being. A short-term stability, or equilibrium, is more important than a long-term geologic equilibrium.

[3] The term *overpopulation* is often used loosely. It is applied here to any area in which the standard of living has been lowered by the addition of population, regardless of the techniques, tools, and traditions of the people affected.

Too often erosion has been interpreted as a purely physical problem, challenging man with the clear-cut task of checking as much erosion as possible. Such a view, however, must be considered an oversimplification. Among the questions that have a bearing on the social implications of soil erosion are the following:

1. How much of the erosion within a particular area is the result of human activity, and how much would have taken place anyway under purely natural conditions?

2. Would the investment in erosion control on steep land that is badly eroding and marginal for production yield greater returns if it were applied toward increasing the yield on much more productive acres?

3. At what point would further investments in control measures cease to produce proportionate returns in added yields?

4. How does one determine the comparative costs and returns with respect to different types of erosion control on specific sites? For example, what are the long-run comparative values of storage reservoirs, forest cover, and crop management programs?

5. How large an investment should be made in public programs to convince or to compel farmers to alter or abandon destructive farming practices?

None of the questions listed above can be answered by purely physical measurements or inventories. All involve analytical procedures, which, in turn, depend on many different economic and social variables. We know far more about what soil erosion is, what causes it, and what controls it than we do about how much we should do about it.

FIG. 11.10 Strip cropping and contour cultivation in the Ridge and Valley region of Pennsylvania. The soil in this area is highly productive when it is stabilized against erosion. [U.S. Department of Agriculture]

11.19 TYPES OF SOIL EROSION. Five major types of soil erosion can be recognized: sheet erosion, rilling, gullying, mass wastage, and wind erosion. They are only briefly considered in the following paragraphs, but each has distinctive characteristics that are the result of variable conditions of soil material, climate, and slope.

1. *Sheet erosion* is the mass movement of the topmost layer of soil over a broad area, with surface-water runoff serving as the transporting agent. It is the most insidious and probably the most serious form of erosion, because it occurs largely on gently sloping land, especially where the soil has been cultivated, and also because it often is a slow process, subtle in its development (see Fig. 11.11).

2. *Rilling* is the removal of soil through the erosion of shallow trenches, usually less than a foot deep. It develops much more rapidly than sheet erosion, but it frequently can be underestimated, because the rills can usually be smoothed over in normal cultivation practices.

3. *Gullying,* perhaps the most spectacular

FIG. 11.11 Sheet erosion in a New Jersey spinach field having only a 3 per cent slope.
[U.S. Department of Agriculture]

and most publicized form of soil erosion, excavates linear drainage ways ranging from trenches 2 to 3 feet deep to huge ravines (see Fig. 11.12). There is no mistaking its obvious damage, and its effects tend to be more localized than those of sheet erosion or rilling. Corrective measures may be employed during the early stages. On the other hand, once gullying is well established, it is extremely destructive and difficult to check.

4. *Mass wastage* is the mass movement of unconsolidated material down a slope without the aid of a transporting medium such as running water. In its more sudden occurrences, it may take the form of landslides or slumps. More frequently it is a slow process that is revealed by such indirect evidences as low pressure-mounds and ridges along a slope, the twisting of tree trunks, the slow migration of rock slabs downslope from the ledges from which they were pried loose, or the curling of soil material over road curbs at the foot of a slope (see Fig. 11.13).

5. *Wind erosion,* or the removal of soil material by wind, is encountered mainly, but not exclusively, in the dry regions of the world. Like sheet erosion, it often is subtle in its effects, gradually removing from the topsoil the finer particles that play such important roles in maintaining soil fertility. Dry-land soils that have a high proportion of silts and clays should be carefully cultivated so as to preserve or develop soil aggregates that are large enough to withstand wind erosion (see Fig. 11.14).

11.20 THE HUMAN FACTOR IN SOIL EROSION. All the people of the world, if taken together, could be contained within a cube not much more than ½ mile on a side. The physical space occupied by man alone is only an infinitesimal fraction of the earth surface. For many millions of years prior to man's existence, the earth was inhabited by more animals, larger animals, and animals with larger appetites for plant foods than the animals of today, including man. Yet, at no time in these millions

FIG. 11.12 Severe gullying in Stewart County, Georgia. This is a type of land destruction which is difficult to check once it is well under way. [U.S. Department of Agriculture]

of years had any of the animal forms produced any signifigant alteration in the physical environment, or at least none that was in any way comparable to the changes instituted by human efforts. Man alone, of all creatures on earth, has been able to alter the physical environment appreciably to suit his needs and desires. As long as he had to depend on gathering his food from naturally available stocks (game, fish, fruits, roots, etc.), he could never have the time or the incentive to make nature work for him. The domestication of plants, and thus the beginnings of agriculture, opened the way for an entirely new channel of creative evolution. As yet, the potentialities of controlled plant growth still are far from fully realized, but there are indications of important limitations.

One of these limitations, and a critical one, is the human element involved in handling

FIG. 11.13 Evidences of mass wastage on a slope covered with soil material. [After Sharpe]

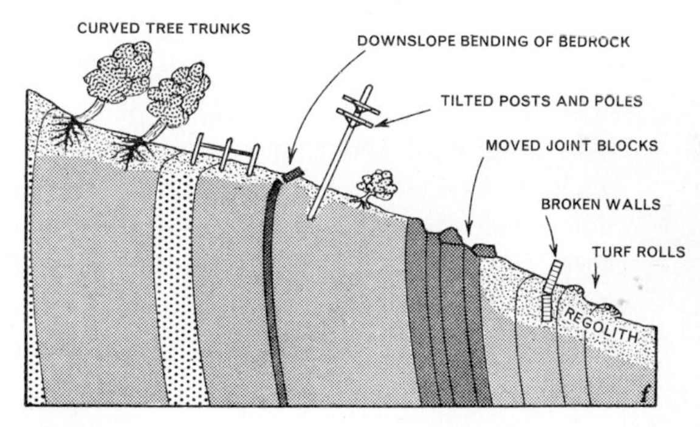

FIG. 11.14 An example of wind erosion in Roosevelt County, New Mexico. Wind erosion has removed soil here to the depth of the man's outstretched arm. The clump of grass has held the soil in place on the mound. [U.S. Department of Agriculture]

the soil base for food production. The overall history of soil management is no credit to man's foresight. Over a considerable part of the earth, the capacity of the soil to produce food and feed has been decreasing steadily. The large gains in population in the world since 1900 have been supported mainly by increases in the productivity of relatively limited areas of fertile, well-managed soils. Part of the decline in carrying capacity in areas of marginal productivity has been the result of the depletion of plant nutrients, owing to the cultivating and harvesting of crops without sufficient replenishment of plant foods in the soil. A much greater factor, however, has been soil erosion, not so much the inevitable type caused by the general lowering of slopes due to geologic processes, but rather the erosion that results primarily from economic pressures and land abuse. Space does not permit a detailed treatment of the human factors in soil erosion, but some of the most important direct and indirect causes are given below:

1. Direct human causes:
   a. Deforestation in the headwater areas of streams
   b. Cultivation on steep slopes
   c. Increasing the acreage of cleanly cultivated row crops, such as corn, cotton, and tobacco
   d. Turning the grain (furrows, etc.) of cultivation down slopes, instead of at right angles to them
   e. Destruction of soil structure through improper cultivation methods, especially in not replacing lost organic material
   f. Overgrazing of pastures and other range areas
2. Indirect human causes:
   a. Growth of farm tenancy and indebtedness, with a consequent increase in carelessness and in exploitive practices
   b. Growing dependence on commercial crops, hindering crop rotation and other corrective practices
   c. Increase in population through reduced death rates in areas of subsistence economies, resulting in greater pressure for more intensive, exploitive cultivation
   d. Political, social, and economic instability, which reduces incentives for conservation practices
   e. Changes in cultural habits—for example, a shift to machine cultivation without adequate safeguards against erosion
   f. Speculative agriculture in marginal areas—for example, gambling in wheat production in potential "dust bowl" areas
   g. Lack of productive surpluses for preventive education, corrective investments, and research programs
   h. Shortsighted attitudes, reflected in such

comments as "What did posterity ever do for me?" and "Here today, gone tomorrow."

11.21 EROSION CONTROL. Both the natural and the human causes for soil erosion presented above indicate that there can be a multiple approach to the soil-erosion problem. Technically, the problem of soil conservation is not difficult. The mechanics and physical methods of erosion control are fairly well known. In fact, nearly all the technical preventive and corrective measures now employed have been known and used for hundreds of years in some locality or other. Some oriental farmers have cultivated highly stabilized slopes for centuries by means of terraces and other devices. The details of physical preventive and corrective measures, including strip cropping, contour cultivation, terracing, gully stabilization, the use of check dams, reforestation, basin listing, mulching, liming, and many others, are given in most standard soil-conservation reference books and thus are not repeated here.

Most examples of serious soil erosion are symptomatic of an unsuitable man-land ratio and are more the result of depressed living standards than a cause of them, although the effect is cumulative. A corollary of this statement is that erosion-control measures are needed most in the areas that can afford them the least. Fully as important as the physical control measures mentioned in the previous paragraph are the steps taken to combat the social, economic, and political pressures that nourish poverty, carelessness, desperation, and ignorance. A land reform program that enables farmers to work their land under a fair and equitable credit or rental system may produce more lasting results than a program of staking out fields for terracing and strip cropping. Soil-erosion prevention and correction require an investment of time, labor, and capital. In many parts of the world, land-tied, debt-ridden subsistence farmers do not have surpluses of anything to invest in a precarious tomorrow.

Moral, ethical, and legal questions are involved in soil-erosion control programs. For example, private ownership of farm land by its operators often has been suggested as an effective means for ensuring incentives for the care of land in areas that have a high rate of farm tenancy. Land ownership, however, may be a financial burden which even capable farmers may feel unwilling to bear. Ownership, moreover, does not automatically guarantee a sound knowledge of soil management. Compulsory soil management programs may be an effective means of checking erosion, but the price paid in terms of regimentation and loss of individuality may be far too high.

Some interesting legal questions relating to erosion have arisen in countries where a landowner is presumably lord of his domain. Does a farm owner and operator, for example, have the right to abuse his own land if, by so doing, he stimulates erosion that spreads to adjoining property? Does a large municipality, dependent on a river source for its water supply, have the right to condemn farm property in the watershed area, not for direct use, but for reforestation purposes, to stabilize runoff and protect its water supply? Does the present population have a responsibility for maintaining the soil resource base for future generations, and if so, is this responsibility only a moral one?

All such questions are immediate, legitimate, and demanding; yet they rarely have been faced squarely. The physical techniques for checking soil erosion involve relatively simple engineering problems; the social implications, on the other hand, are frustratingly complex. That is why we tend to avoid the latter and to pay high prices for the former in areas where the damage is most obvious and the need is great.

Perspective

Soils are natural bodies that develop on the face of the earth as the result of dynamic environmental forces. They are mixtures of inorganic and organic constituents that at all times are sensitive to changes in the environmental complex. Recognition of soil differences, both areally and vertically, is based on such properties as color, texture, structure, vertical zonation, physical and chemical composition, and depth. Acting on the soil constituents are a great many environmental factors, each of which has its own distributional pattern. The major soil environmental factors include climate, vegetation, parent material, living and dead organisms, slope, drainage, and human activities. The length of time that each or all of these factors have operated on an individual portion of the outer surface of the earth is another important variable in explaining what soils are where, and why.

The characteristics of any particular soil at any given time are a reflection of all the environmental factors, but the importance of each factor may vary greatly with time and place. Any one of them may be responsible for the most noticeable features of a particular soil. Profiles, when they first appear, retain many of the properties of the parent material on which they are developed. After long periods of weathering, the factor of climate, with the associated factors of vegetation and other biological forms, rises to dominate the shaping of soil characteristics. Slowly but surely the soil genesis, or evolutionary process, works toward a relative equilibrium between the soil and the total environment. The degree to which the soil reaches this equilibrium depends on the stability of the environmental factors themselves. A change in climate, a paroxysm of the earth crust resulting in rejuvenated erosion or deposition, the draining of a swamp or the creation of a new one, a change in vegetation, or the persistent influence of man as he scratches the surface in search of sustenance—any of these may interrupt the progression of the soil profile toward relative stability.

The geography of soils is as diverse and as challenging as the geography of the other major features in the physical environment of man, and we shall be concerned with the major global features of this geography in the succeeding chapter. Because of the importance of soil as a source of materials for plant growth, soil differences long have received the attention of man. Soil inventories were made 4,000 years ago in Babylonia. Taking inventory of the differences in soils from place to place requires flexible classification systems to make meaningful the infinite variety that can be found upon close examination. Fortunately, the strong motivation to satisfy the ever-increasing demands for more food production can be fused with pedology, the science of soils. In the task of understanding soils, there is ample room for the soil geographer who seeks to portray and interpret areal patterns of selected differences and similarities, whether the patterns are continental in scope or highly localized, reflecting the subtle changes that occur from one side to another within a single cultivated field.

12

The great soil groups of the world

The global pattern of major soil differences presented in this chapter utilizes a classification based on properties that are mainly the result of climatic differences. This system was chosen because climatic data are available in areas where detailed soil surveys have not been made and also because the local soil differences resulting from such factors as slope, drainage, and parent rock material cannot be generalized adequately on a global scale. The climatic soils, or *zonal* soils, as they are usually termed, are presented in this chapter in three main divisions, corresponding to the three major climatic processes of profile development: *podzolization,* the cool, humid process; *ferrallization,*[1] the warm, humid process; and *calcification,* the process associated with dry climates. A section of this chapter is devoted to each of these divisions, covering the development, characteristics, and distribution of the soils in that group and then briefly discussing the effects of poor drainage, which produces distinctive intrazonal soil properties within each climatic division. The regional descriptions given in this chapter are based on the global map of the major soil groups in the world (Fig. 12.1). Note that areas of mountain soils, alluvium, and desert sands are shown separately on this map. These should not be considered zonal soils, but they cover a large enough area to warrant inclusion on the global soil map.

[1] The term *ferrallization,* indicative of the iron and aluminum concentration in tropical soils, has been suggested by some soil scientists, and is used here, as a replacement for the older term *laterization,* which has been subject to much controversy among soil investigators. *Latozation* also has been suggested as a substitute term for the warm, humid, soil-forming process.

The soils of cool, humid regions

12.1 THE PODZOLIZATION PROCESS. The podzolization process prevails in all the cool, humid parts of the world and consists essentially of *soil leaching by highly acid soil solutions.* Although such soil solutions would not burn holes in fabrics—and, in fact, have only a slightly tangy taste—they are exceptionally acidic as soil solutions go,

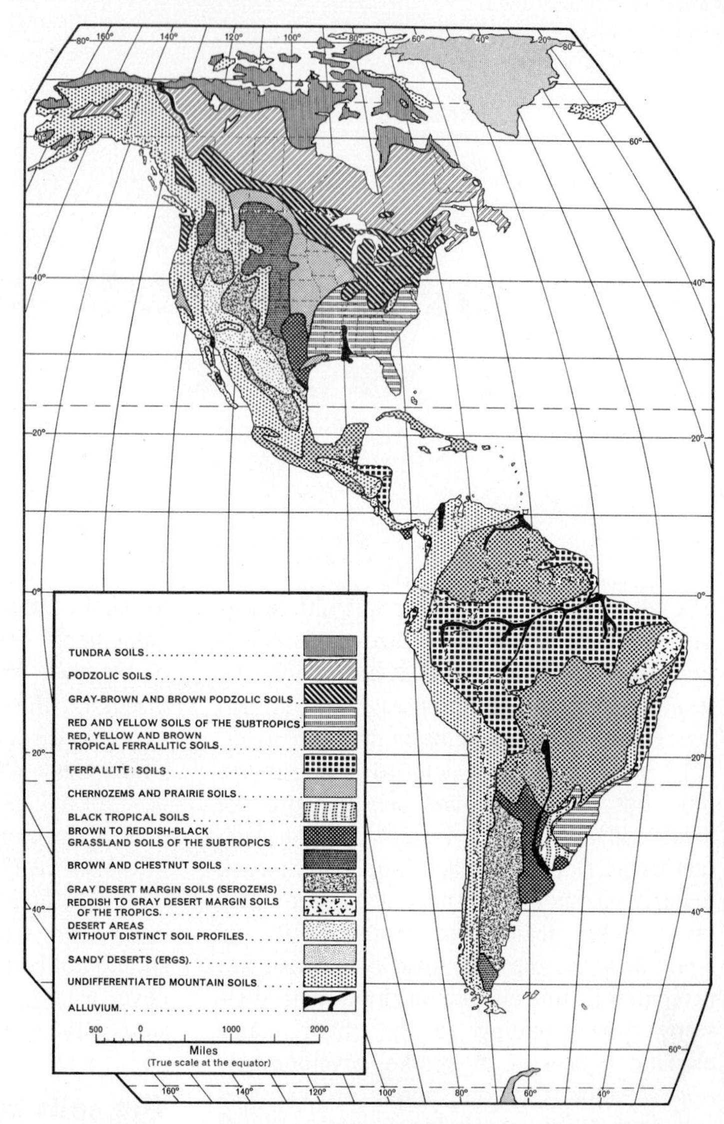

FIG. 12.1 World soil map.

sometimes having a pH [2] as low as 3.5. There is no general agreement among soil scientists about the exact composition of these acidic soil solutions, but most authorities believe that they are organic acids, representing

[2] The pH of a solution refers to the concentration of hydrogen ions (H^+) within it and is therefore a measurement of acidity. A pH of 7 signifies a proportion of 10^{-7}, or the equivalent of 1/10,000,000 by volume. Such a solution is neutral in reaction, because the concentration of hydrogen ions is exactly balanced by the concentration of hydroxyl ions (OH^-), which is also 10^{-7}. A pH of 5, however, signifies a hydrogen-ion concentration of 10^{-5}, or 1/100,000, whereas the hydroxyl-ion concentration is 10^{-9}. Note that the sum of the negative powers must equal -14. With a pH of 5, there is an excess of positive hydrogen ions over the negative hydroxyl ions, and the concentration of the former is 100 times that of a neutral solution. In summary, as the pH drops below 7, the solution is acidic; as it rises above 7, it becomes alkaline in reaction.

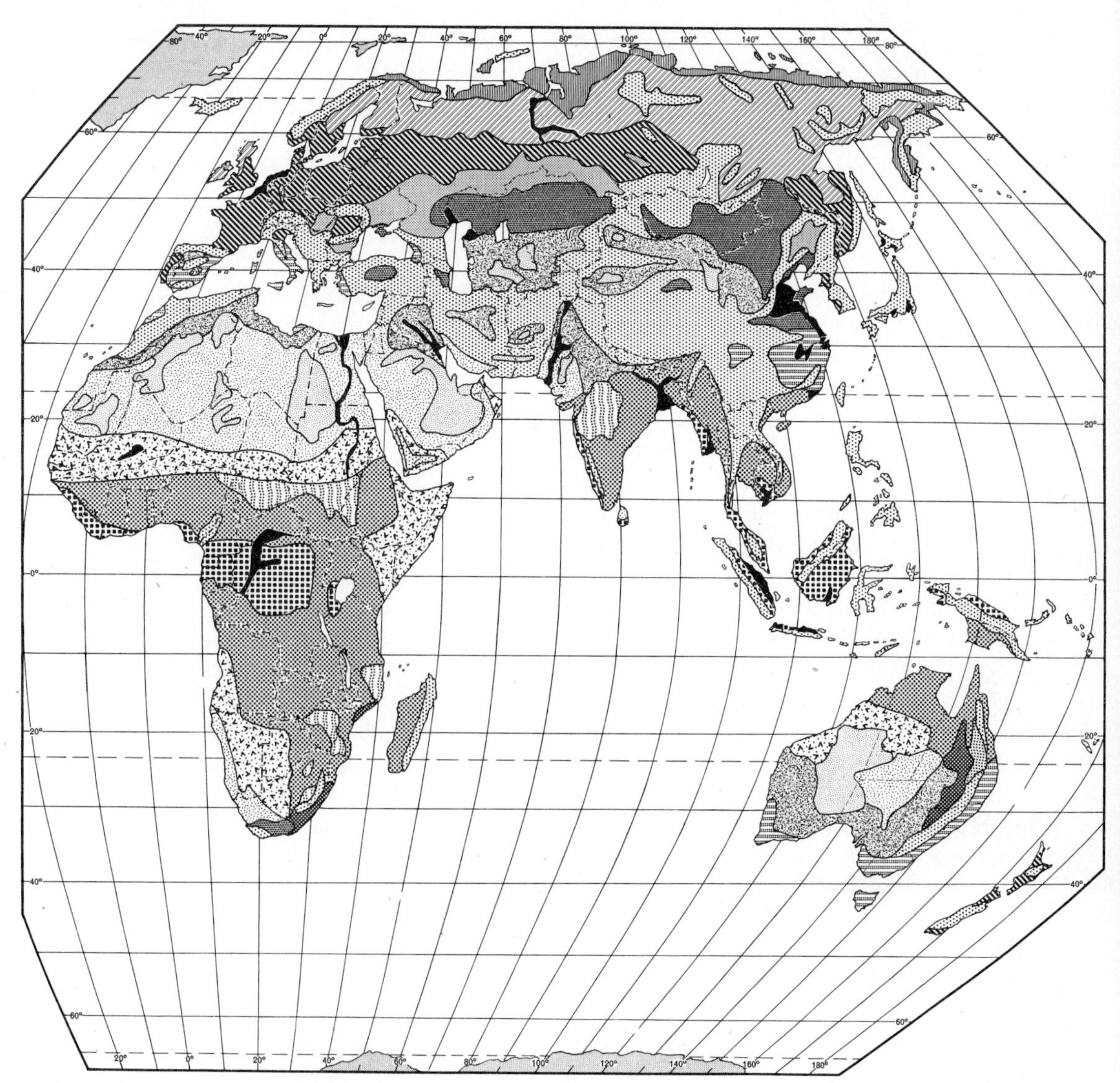

solutions of intermediate decay products. The formation of such organic acids is believed to be related to the slowness of decay in these climates. The quantity and variety of microlife in the soils of these cool climates are not so great as in the humid tropics; the decay process virtually ceases during the long, frozen winters, and fungi tend to be more prevalent than bacteria as decay agents. In the dense pine forests of cool climates, the white threads of *mycelium,* a mold or fungus that feeds on dead forest litter, can usually be found below the top layer of pine needles that cover the ground. Fungi are not so efficient as bacteria in breaking down organic substances, and among the by-products of fungal digestion are the complex colloidal organic compounds that form strong acids in the presence of water. The dark, brownish color (similar to root beer) of the water in swamps, lakes, and rivers in cool climates and in the acid swamps of other regions is caused by some of these organic acids.

Adding to the general acid environment of these soils is the generally acidic residue of the litter derived from coniferous forests, which form the predominant vegetation in the cooler climates. The needles and twigs that fall to the floor of such forests have a low content of bases (P, K, Na, Ca, Mg, etc.) as compared with most other trees and plants. Because such bases tend to reduce acidity when in solution, the coniferous vegetation aids somewhat in the podzolization process. Conifers are by no means necessary for the podzolization process, however, and podzol soils can be found in broadleaf forests as well.

The effect of the availability of bases on podzolization is evident in young soils that have a high content of bases in their parent material. In such soils, the podzolic characteristics develop extremely slowly.

The principal results of soil leaching by highly acid soil solutions can be summarized as follows:

1. Freely soluble bases are withdrawn from both the organic surface layer and the uppermost portion of the inorganic soil body (the *A* horizon).

2. A shortage of structural aggregates (crumbs, nuts, clods, etc.) develops in the *A* horizon, and there is a tendency to produce a loose, powdery, single-grain structure.

3. There is a downward migration of finely divided colloidal particles, including both inorganic (iron and aluminum silicates) and organic colloids, leaving behind a relatively coarse residue, high in quartz and other unweathered mineral particles.

4. The lower *A* horizon is bleached, owing to the removal of iron and organic material, the major soil coloring agents.

5. There is a reduction in the rate of weathering of the remaining inorganic particles in the *A* horizon, since they become coated with a durable, white organic colloid. This appears only in extreme podzolization.

6. Much of the colloidal material removed from the *A* horizon is precipitated in the subsoil, and this produces a heavy-textured *B* horizon with well-developed structural aggregates, a high content of both organic and inorganic colloids, and a color that ranges from reddish brown to yellowish brown.

7. The acidity of the soil environment tends to decrease in passing downward from the top of the *B* horizon.

There are, of course, different degrees of podzolization, but the process consists essentially of the shifting of the colloidal sesquioxides [3] out of the *A* horizon and their redeposition within the *B* horizon.

The key to the entire process appears to lie in the acidity of the soil solution. The highly acid soil solution first tends to remove the easily soluble bases from the topsoil. After this, the mineral particles in the *A* horizon are attacked, and the tiny clay particles (hydrous aluminum and iron silicates) are carried downward, the acid environment keeping them in a peptized, or nonflocculated, state. There is, of course, a limit to the downward movement of these fine clay particles, and they begin to accumulate below. Aiding in the accumulation of clays within the subsoil is a decrease in the acidity of the soil solution. This is caused by three

[3] The sesquioxides include the iron and aluminum oxides. They are thus termed because of the ratio of the metal to the oxygen, which is 1:1½—for example, Fe_2O_3 and Al_2O_3. The sesquioxides rarely occur by themselves in podzol soils but, rather, in a union with silica (SiO_2) molecules within a colloidal lattice, or "sandwich," in which the different atoms make up different layers.

factors: (1) as the distance from the point of supply of organic acids (the forest litter) becomes greater, their effect diminishes; (2) the soil solution is diluted by ground water brought into the soil from below by capillarity; and (3) the ground water from below, having passed through unconsolidated rock material that is unleached, contains a much higher proportion of soluble bases and is much less acid than the soil solution trickling down from above. Once the clay colloids begin to collect in the subsoil, they obtain and hold bases from the ground water brought from below, attract organic colloids, and increase their retentive capacity through flocculation. The acidity of this colloidal complex thus becomes less than that of the soil solution, and the *B* horizon is formed.

Podzol soil properties are found wherever highly acid soil conditions prevail, whether or not the acidity is the result of climatic conditions. If a particular parent material is unusually deficient in bases and a coniferous forest vegetation develops on it, a soil with podzolic tendencies might result even in warm, humid climates. The quartz sands of the Lakewood soil series in northern New Jersey, with their covering of pine or scrub oak, afford a good illustration. Although they do not lie within the humid tropics or even the subtropics, these sterile sands have only minute traces of bases, and the podzol profiles developed on them are reminiscent of the true podzols that are found in much colder climates. Podzollike profiles also have been reported in Indochina and Sumatra, where they occur in soils high in quartz sand. As one nears the typical cool, moist climates, especially in areas of glacial deposition, variations in the parent material play an important role in determining the dominance of podzolic properties. In the northern United States, a glacial till high in lime will exhibit only slight podzolic characteristics, whereas a sandy outwash plain a mile away will have a typical podzol profile. Farther north, however, the podzol profile will develop on any parent material, but it will vary in depth, depending largely on the base content or the texture of the glacial parent material.

12.2 PODZOL SOILS. The podzol soils represent the culmination of podzolization. The word *podzol* is of Russian origin and means "ash soil." (see Fig. 11.5). The gray, ashlike, lower *A* horizon is a strikingly unique feature that readily distinguishes these soils. The Russians early recognized these soils as zonal soils produced in cool, humid climates. In the Soviet Union the podzol soil properties cut across a wide range of parent materials, vegetation cover, and slope conditions. The typical climates of the podzols are characterized by long, severe winters and cool, short summers (*Dfb-Dfc*). Like these climates, the true podzols are concentrated in a broad belt across both North America and Eurasia, south of the tundra. In the United States, podzols are scattered throughout the northern parts of Minnesota, Wisconsin, Michigan, New York, and New England. Farther west, in the Great Plains states, dryness checks the podzolization process, and the southern margin of the podzols runs northward into northern Saskatchewan and Alberta. True podzols can be found in scattered small areas in the southern hemisphere, but not in sufficiently large areas to be indicated on the world soil map.

A typical podzol soil profile is shown in Fig. 12.2.

In their natural state, podzol soils generally are poorly suited to agricultural use. The main handicaps are their deficiency in plant nutrients and the low base-exchange capacity within the topsoil, their high acidity, and the short growing season in the areas

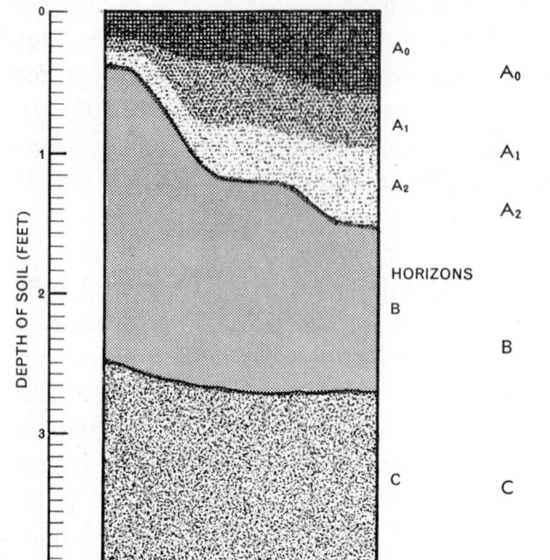

A_0 The humus layer, consisting of from 2 to 6 inches of brown, acidic, fibrous organic material, commonly interwoven with the white threads of mycelium.

A_1 A thin transitional zone, 1 to 3 inches thick, consisting of a mixture of organic and inorganic material.

A_2 The bleached and whitened layer, ash-gray in color; 1 to 6 inches thick; no structure; highly acid.

The boundary separating the A and the B horizons is sharp but somewhat irregular. It tends to deepen with age and with coarseness of texture.

B Generally reddish brown to yellowish brown, lightening gradually downward into the color of the parent material. Definite structure observed, which is usually platy. The top of the B horizon contains the highest percentage of fine constituents. The acidity usually is less than that of the A horizon. Gradually merges with the parent material below.

C The parent rock material.

FIG. 12.2 Typical profile of a podzol soil.

where they are found. Acid fruits, however, such as most types of berries, do well in these soils, particularly with the addition of fertilizers. Despite their low inherent fertility, podzols respond well to improvement methods and can be made highly productive, especially for crops that are able to mature within a growing season of from 75 to 100 days, such as many garden vegetables. The podzols are particularly suitable for root or tuber crops, such as white potatoes and turnips, since the high acid content of these soils hinders many of the scabs and blights which lower yields and quality in less acid soils. Rapidly maturing grains, such as buckwheat and barley, also do well. The erodability of these soils is low.

Improvement of podzol soils for agricultural use mainly involves deep plowing, liming, and fertilizing. The deep plowing mixes the uppermost *B* horizon with the *A* horizon, thus increasing the colloidal content of the latter and making it more retentive of both water and nutrients. The addition of lime not only reduces the toxic effect of high acidity but also flocculates (coagulates) the organic and inorganic colloids, thus creating a favorable soil structure, increasing the base-exchange capacity, and producing a bond to hold plant foods and water within the topsoil. The addition of both organic (green manuring) and inorganic fertilizers is necessary because of the natural deficiencies caused by acidic leaching. Once improved, podzols tend to maintain their fertility and require far less care than do tropical soils. The impressive productivity developed on the Caribou silt loam, a typical podzol soil type in the potato country of northern Maine, shows that the podzols can prove highly valuable for agriculture. The short growing season, which limits the variety of crops grown, and the long distances from markets have been the major factors in the neglect of podzol soils in North America. In northern Europe and the Soviet Union, such soils have been cultivated for centuries, but only by a sparse peasant population. The high cost of podzol improvement evidently has prevented much agricultural expansion within the taiga except in the vicinity of mining or lumbering settlements.

12.3 GRAY-BROWN PODZOLIC SOILS.

This soil group represents a transitional product resulting from podzolization and other major zonal soil processes. Podzolization still is dominant, but its influences are weakened by other factors. The gray-brown podzolic soils are found principally in the mid-latitudes of the northern hemisphere, in an intermediate position between cool, humid; warm, humid; warm, semiarid; and cool, semiarid climates. The two largest areas are in the northeastern United States and in northwestern and central Europe. Smaller areas are in Japan, China, southern Manchuria, the northwestern United States, southern Chile, New Zealand, and parts of southeastern Australia. The characteristics of this soil group vary considerably because of its transitional climatic position. In general, shades of gray, gray-brown, and brown predominate and are the most characteristic feature of these soils. The podzolic tendencies of the group are indicated by:

1. A noticeably finer texture and more pronounced structure in the *B* horizon than in the *A* horizon
2. A somewhat darker color in the *B* horizon than in the A_2 horizon, though the bleaching of the A_2 horizon is not so pronounced as in the true podzols and the ash-gray layer is not present
3. A smaller percentage of sesquioxides in the *A* horizon than in the parent material and a larger percentage in the *B* horizon than in the parent material

Two special varieties of soils that have a distinctive coloration are located in the same general transitional zone as the gray-brown podzolic soils. These include the *gray forest soils* and the *brown forest soils*. Because they appear to be transitional podzolic soils, they are described along with the gray-brown podzolic group. The gray forest soils appear to have been formed as the result of an encroachment of trees upon a cool, semiarid to subhumid grassland, possibly because of a change in climate. The *A* and *B* horizons often are not clearly separated. Small areas of these soils are found along the northern edges of the prairie grasslands in Canada and along the northern margin of the Russian steppes. The brown forest soils appear to be closely related to parent materials high in lime content, such as some of the glacial limestone gravels of the American Middle West and the marls and limestones of France and England. They have a much darker *B* horizon (almost chocolate in color) than is typical of the gray-brown podzolic soils as a group, and the horizons can be much more easily distinguished than in the other soils of the group.

As a group, the gray-brown podzolic soils and the associated forest podzolic soils generally are among the more productive soils of the world for agriculture. Although slightly acid and somewhat deficient in nutrients, particularly phosphorus, they are far more fertile than the podzols and respond quickly to improvement methods. They normally are retentive of plant foods, and natural leaching is slow, because of the relatively high content of clay colloids [4] with a high absorp-

[4] In the transitional belt between the cool, humid and warm, humid climates, the tiny sandwichlike bundles of sheets that comprise the clay colloid crystals largely belong to a group known as the *montmorillonites*. These have unusually high absorptive rates and base-exchange capacities as compared with the *kaolinites*, the group that tends to predominate in humid tropical soils. An intermediate group includes the *illites*. The kaolinite group differs mainly in having a much lower amount of silica in the crystal lattices. The clay colloids appear to develop structural patterns that are in harmony with general environmental conditions, especially with climate and soil acidity.

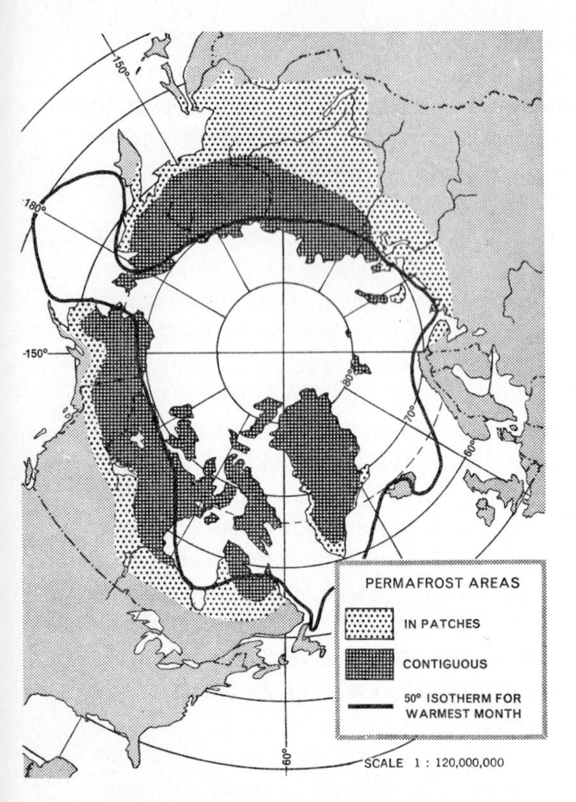

FIG. 12.3 World distribution of permafrost. [After Kimble and Good]

tive ratio. Although the organic content is not high under a forest cover, it may be increased easily by plowing green legumes into the soil. This soil group is somewhat more susceptible to erosion on cultivated slopes than the true podzols but is not so vulnerable as many of the loamy soils of humid, warm climates.

12.4 THE TUNDRA SOILS. Although the tundra soils are listed as a zonal group (see Table 11.7), their major soil properties are related largely to topographic details of drainage and slope. This is not so paradoxical as it may seem, however, since the dominance of the drainage factor is largely the result of the long, frozen winters and the short, cool summers. There are few well-developed profiles in the soils of the tundra, because of the layer of *permafrost,* the permanently frozen ground that lies beneath the surface of the tundra and prevents a continuous downward percolation of water (see Fig. 12.3). The downward movement of water is confined to summer months and to the shallow portion of the soil that lies above the permafrost layer. Complicating the process of tundra-soil formation is the irregular upward movement of ground water in the summer that occurs on low ridges and hummocks and is caused mainly by capillarity replenishing the water evaporated by strong winds at the surface. The low precipitation of high latitudes should also be kept in mind. Ground heaving due to alternate freezing and thawing or to the hydraulic pressure of water or ice confined between a frozen surface and the permafrost zone, especially during the early winter, also tends to cause vertical and lateral movements of soil material, thus interfering with normal soil-profile development.

In the summer months, water normally saturates part of the soil that lies above the permafrost layer. On slopes, this saturated zone may extend to the surface, creating marshes or bogs downslope from this spring line. Many tundra soils thus exhibit the characteristics of poorly drained soils, especially in the lower portions. A dark-gray color, sometimes with yellowish-brown mottling, plus a sticky-to-soupy consistency, is common in these saturated subsoils. If the permafrost zone lies far enough below the surface for the creation of a distinct *B* horizon, the soil generally takes on many of the characteristics of true podzols, although these features are normally evident at shallower depths.

There is no sharp boundary between the tundra and the podzol soil regions. Tongues and islands of the podzols are found far to the north of the generalized boundary. These can be identified easily by the presence of trees, which are normally absent over most of the tundra. The presence of podzol profiles and trees is related more to the distance of the permafrost zone below the land surface than to general climatic conditions. Given approximately similar temperature conditions, the top of the permafrost zone increases in depth with an increase in the textural coarseness of the parent material. This is the main reason why the sands and gravels of arctic river valleys may bear trees, even though the interstream areas are open barrens. Removal of surplus soil water by lateral drainage into the rivers may further aid in lowering the permafrost zone in these valleys.

Knowledge of the properties of tundra soils is of little agricultural use, because of the limitations of climate. It is highly important, however, in overcoming difficulties encountered in engineering projects in the arctic, especially in highway and airfield construction. One of the difficulties met in highway construction is caused by the lateral flow of water in early winter between the frozen topsoil and the impermeable permafrost zone. As the winter season begins, the ground beneath the highways, lacking the insulating cover of vegetation and humus, freezes quickly to permafrost depth. Away from the highway at this time of year, there is a nonfrozen zone, containing water, between the frozen land surface and the permafrost zone. As winter progresses and the depth of freezing gradually increases, the confined ground water may develop considerable hydraulic pressure. Moving toward the highway under pressure, it meets the ice dam beneath the road as is shown in Fig. 12.4. There it may buckle the sides of the road, forcing it upward, and pour forth to inundate the highway area with water, which promptly freezes.

The hydraulic pressure of confined ground water and subsurface ice expansion also cause problems in building construction. Unless heated buildings are adequately insulated from the ground, their sites may act as weak points in the frozen ground cover, and the pressure below, concentrated toward the house sites, may cause damage. Houses have been known to be forced upward as much as 20 feet and finally to be flooded with freezing water gushing forth from beneath the floor. The general hummocky surface of the tundra is due to heaving of the surface by hydraulic pressures from below. The outpouring of water over the ground surface also may produce broad sheets of slush or rough ice, which are hazardous to cross-country travel.

Another major problem along highways is the drainage of subsurface water in the summer months. Because the highways lack an insulating surface, thawing proceeds to a greater depth than elsewhere, and thus the permafrost surface slopes upward away from

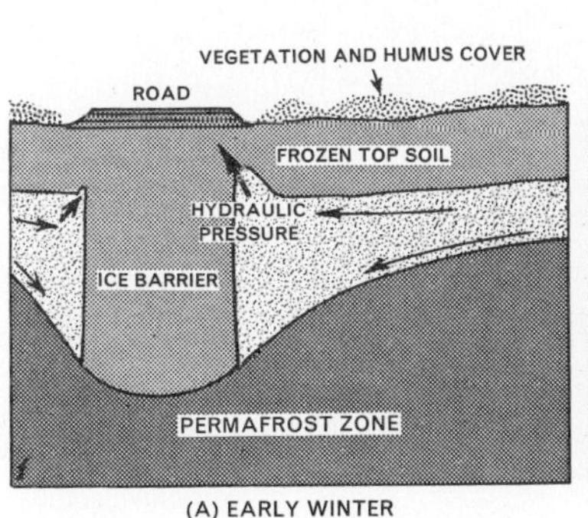

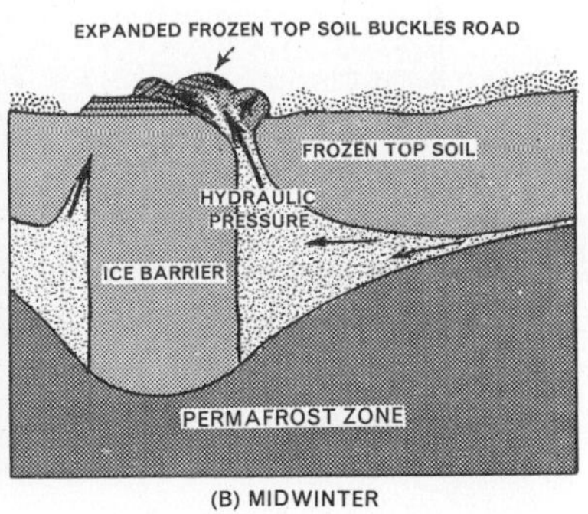

FIG. 12.4 Diagram showing hydraulic action within a permafrost zone and alongside a highway. The ice barrier beneath the road results from rapid freezing, which is due to the lack of an insulating vegetation and humus covering.

the road. Ground water, moving down the sloping surface of the frozen zone, concentrates in the highway area, which, unless properly ballasted, ditched, and drained, may become a continuous line of springs and mudholes. Mud is an almost constant problem in the summer throughout the tundra.

12.5 FEATURES RESULTING FROM POOR DRAINAGE IN COOL, HUMID CLIMATES. The intrazonal characteristics associated with poor drainage are particularly widespread within the cool, humid climates. In fact, in these regions the total area that has inadequate soil drainage to some degree or other is probably greater than that with good drainage. One reason for this is topographic; there are widespread areas of flat-to-undulating plains in the northern parts of the North American and Eurasian continents, and water drains only slowly from such land surfaces. Another and even more important factor is the continental glaciation that covered a large part of these areas during the Pleistocene period. The great ice sheets interrupted drainage patterns in a variety of ways. Lakes, swamps, and marshes are exceedingly common surface features wherever there was significant glacial deposition. The characteristics of poor drainage in the soils of the cool, humid regions, then, are important environmental features that warrant special consideration in regional soil descriptions on a global scale, even though their areal expression is topographic.

The poorly drained soils of the cool, humid climates can be divided into three groups *bog soils, half-bog soils,* and *inorganic soils* (see Fig. 12.5). The bog soils of these regions are similar to those in swamps and marshes nearly everywhere, except that, with a lower temperature and a dominance of podzolization in surrounding areas, the thick organic soils are more likely to consist of the brown, acid peats. Occasionally, however, black muck soils are found, mainly where the ground water contains much lime from underlying porous limestone or from limy glacial tills. Although expensive to drain and fertilize, the muck soils are choice sites for intensive horticulture. Large quantities of fresh vegetables for nearby industrial cities are supplied by the muck gardens of the Great Lakes states, from Wisconsin and Michigan to New York State. In some places, the muck soils have a layer of precipitated white calcium carbonate, or *marl,* immediately below the organic material.

The acid bogs and the mucks of these cool climates can usually be distinguished by their vegetation cover. The peat bogs are likely to bear a covering of mosses, low bushes (such

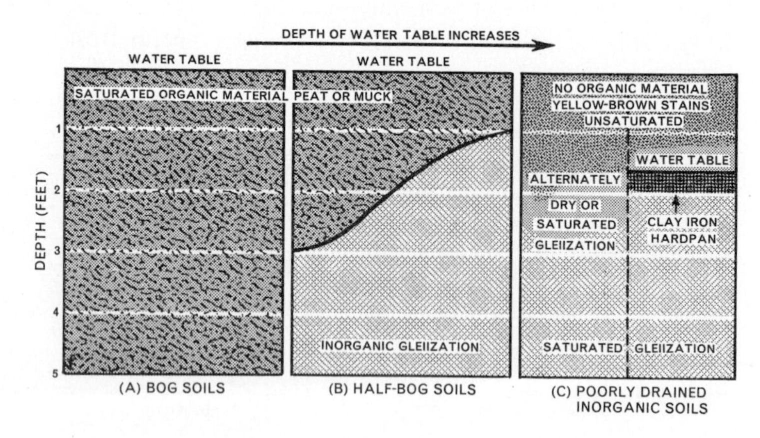

FIG. 12.5 Soil characteristics in bog, half-bog, and poorly drained inorganic soils. [After Jenny]

as *Ledum*), or acid-loving trees, such as the swamp larch (tamarack) or black spruce. Muck soils, on the other hand, which tend to be marshes rather than swamps, are more likely to bear a covering of reeds, sedges, or grasses.

Soils that have a shallow covering (1 to 3 feet) of organic soils above inorganic material are known as *half-bog* soils. They are continually saturated with water, and the lower, or inorganic, part of the soil exhibits typical features of water saturation. Red, yellow, and brown colors are notably absent, and in the usual acid soil environment, the underlying inorganic material is bleached white or gray, in the case of sands, or a steel-gray tinged with light greenish or bluish shades, in the case of clays or silts. These bluish- or greenish-gray clays and silts are known as *glei,* and the process of their formation is termed *gleiization.* This consists essentially of a reduction of oxygen content in the iron oxides under anaerobic conditions and the resultant formation of ferrous iron compounds. The glei clays are likely to be highly plastic and sticky. The half-bog soils normally support a forest vegetation of typical hydrosere subclimax species. Such soils are less easy to reclaim than the deep organic muck soils, even when they are less acid, because ditching is more difficult in the lower, inorganic portion.

The poorly drained inorganic soils exhibit a variety of characteristics, depending on the degree and duration of water saturation, fluctuations in the position of the water table within the soil profile, and the general texture of the soil material. Inorganic soils that undergo alternate saturation and drying usually show a characteristic mottled appearance, with yellowish-brown stains adjacent to the major soil openings in the upper part of the soil. The features of gleiization are found more frequently in the deeper parts of the profiles. Such soils typically occur along the margins of bogs or half-bogs and represent a transitional stage in a hydrologic catena. Mottling of a lesser degree, however, also may appear in flat upland soils of fairly fine texture, because of slow drainage following heavy rains.

Where the ground-water table remains fairly stationary within the soil profile, its position is usually marked by a pronounced depositional layer, or hardpan (see Fig. 11.9). Such soils sometimes are referred to as *ground-water podzols,* because of the concentration of sesquioxides in a distinct layer within the soil. They are of two types: those in which the depositional layer is largely clay, heavily stained with iron; and those which consist almost entirely of iron plus organic colloids. The precipitation of both organic and inorganic colloids from the soil solution is partly the result of a somewhat lower acidity in the saturated zone. Much of the iron, however, is derived from the soluble ferrous iron that is brought to the small capillary tubes from below, precipitated following evaporation, and oxidized by contact with the air. It may form almost a stony layer in the soil. Certain bog iron ore deposits have been formed in somewhat the same manner.

Extensive clay hardpans, such as those found on the undulating upland surfaces in the northern Appalachians, are known as *planosols.* The Volusia and Lordstown soil series are representative. Shales and shaly sandstones lie near the surface in this region and absorb water from the soil only slowly. Water therefore tends to collect within the shallow soils. The normal podzol migration of sesquioxides is reduced to only a short distance, and a claypan containing much iron tends to develop about midway between the surface and the bedrock. In time, this tends to increase the duration of water saturation in the topsoils following rains, so that typical mottled, or glei, features result. Such soils resemble the moor soils of the English or Scottish uplands in many respects. They are difficult to cultivate or reclaim, and most cultivated plants cannot tolerate the long periods of soil saturation. Such soils are best used for forest culture, hay, or pasture. Cultivation tends to accelerate the formation of claypans, but heavy liming can improve drainage somewhat and retard claypan development.

The soils of the humid tropics and subtropics

12.6 THE FERRALLIZATION PROCESS. In passing from cool, humid to warm, humid regions, a different soil-forming process, ferrallization, gradually takes precedence over podzolization. The transition is extremely gradual, and there is much evidence that both processes operate simultaneously within the transitional belt, with one or the other gradually becoming dominant as one travels latitudinally.

Ferrallization involves soil leaching by mildly acid (pH 5 to 7) to mildly alkaline solutions. The reason for the lesser acidity is believed to be the result of more rapid and more complete decay of organic material in the topsoils. Under conditions of intermediate acidity, the silica that is included within the clay fraction of the soil is removed from the clay crystal lattices and transported completely out of the soil via ground water. Soluble bases are likewise removed. As the silica layers are removed from the colloidal iron and aluminum silicate lattices, or "sandwiches," the remaining material alters into iron and aluminum oxides, with varying proportions of absorbed water.

Unlike the mobile sesquioxides of iron and aluminum that are found in the podzols and are carried downward in the soil, the sesquioxides of the somewhat less acid soils of the low latitudes are stabilized (at least above the water table) and tend to accumulate throughout the soil column. The iron oxide molecules, freed from the clay lattice, may unite and begin forming crystals solely of iron oxide (mainly hematite or turgite), in the shape of irregular crusts or nodules. The aluminum oxide, unlike the iron, does not have a tendency to unite with itself to form crystals; rather, it collects as rough masses of hydrated aluminum oxides with varying quantities of clay or iron impurities. The result is *bauxite,* the major ore of aluminum. In summary, ferrallization consists largely of a breakdown of the inorganic clay colloids, the removal of silica and soluble bases from the soil, and a gradual increase in the concentration of sesquioxides throughout the soil (see Fig. 12.6).

Other contrasts between ferrallization and podzolization may also be noted in the development of the soil profile. In the podzol soils, there usually is a fairly thick surface layer of organic matter awaiting decomposition. Such a layer is rare in humid tropical soils, where surface litter is attacked and decomposed as fast as it is added by vegetation. Surface accumulations of organic material in the tropics are almost always the result of poor drainage in bogs.

The general contrast between topsoil and subsoil is not nearly so distinct in the humid tropical soils, mainly because there is no clear development of a *B* horizon, or zone of accumulation, in the well-drained soils. In podzol soils, the strong acid solutions of the topsoil are partially neutralized by the bases and the much lower acidity in the lower portion of the soil profile; the downward movement of both clay and organic colloids is therefore halted, and deposition occurs in the subsoil. In the ferrallitic soils, on the other hand, the sesquioxides remain behind. The silica and bases removed from the topsoil, however, instead of being precipitated in a *B* horizon, are transported completely out of the soil and eventually carried into streams and rivers.

The absence of a pronounced depositional layer in the well-drained tropical soils is mainly the result of the following conditions:

1. The intermediate acidity of the soil solution is not sufficiently high to cause a pronounced downward migration of the clay colloids, and hence such colloids cannot collect to form a compact *B* horizon.

2. The contrast in acidity between the soil solution and the ground water brought from below by capillarity is not sufficiently great to produce a distinct boundary zone where these two fluids meet. Thus the chemical environment deep in the soil is similar to that near the surface. Since silica is mobile in the pH environment of the topsoil, it also is below, and thus it is not precipitated anywhere within the profile.

A major distinction, then, of well-drained humid tropical soils is the gradual transition from the topsoil through to the soil parent material. Depositional features within the profile are more likely to be associated with the top of a high water table (zone of water saturation) or with the earliest stages of soil formation. The principal distinction between topsoil and the lower part of the profile in the ferrallitic soils lies in the degree of accumulation of the end products of weathering, which are generally more abundant near the surface. This difference between layers develops gradually, however, and sharp horizon contrasts are rare under normal drainage conditions.

The insoluble residues in the humid tropical soils include, besides the hydrated oxides of iron and aluminum, other oxides, such as those of titanium and manganese, which are

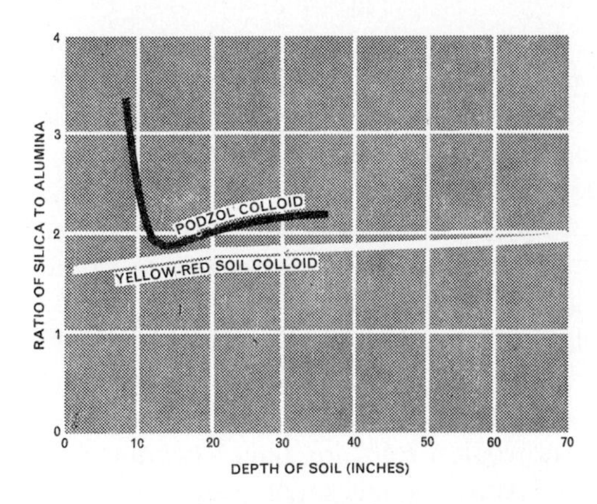

FIG. 12.6 Silica-sesquioxide ratios in clay colloids, representative of podzolization and ferrallization. A ratio of 2 appears to be a reasonable boundary between the two. As one proceeds from cool, humid to warm, humid climates, the silica percentage in the clays tends to decrease, and that of the sesquioxides (aluminum and iron) tends to increase. [After Jenny]

less common but no less durable. Quartz is a durable soil constituent in almost any environment and will accumulate wherever it occurs in large quantities in parent rocks, such as sandstones or granites. There is a great deal of difference in the reaction of silica to weathering when it is in the form of crystalline quartz and when it occurs as separate molecules or layers in the clay colloids.

As stated earlier, the hydrated oxides of aluminum that are concentrated in the soil as the result of ferrallization are identical with bauxite, the principal source of this important metal. It is believed that most of the commercial deposits of bauxite in the world today represent ancient "fossil" soils developed under ferrallization during past geologic periods and preserved from erosion. It is noteworthy that most bauxite deposits are found on ancient erosional surfaces within the tropics or the lower mid-latitudes. As might be expected, bauxite tends to develop above rocks that have a high content of aluminum, such as *syenite,* which is essentially a quartz-free, granitelike rock.

The iron oxides that accumulate within tropical soils are the principal reason for the red coloration of such soils. Both hematite and turgite, the principal oxides associated with ferrallization, are brick-red in color. With the addition of much water, the red color changes to ochre, a yellowish brown. The latter color is derived from hydrated iron oxides, mainly *limonite,* and predominates where tropical soils are almost continuously moist. Although only small quantities of iron oxide are sufficient to color soils, there are areas in the tropics where the parent material contains so little iron that the expected distinctive coloration does not occur, and in such regions the soils may be pink or white.

In young ferrallitic soils, some of the fine clays (prior to desilification) are washed downward by pelting rains and accumulate as a weakly developed hardpan 2 to 3 feet below the surface. This may impede downward percolation, producing greater hydration of the iron residues above, and hence a yellowish color often results. With increasing age, however, the clays lose their silica, the claypan breaks up, the iron compounds above become less hydrated, and red replaces yellow as the dominant color of the topsoil. Red is always an indication that the soil is aerated sufficiently, at least seasonally, to permit fairly complete oxidation of the iron.

No discussion of the process of ferrallization would be complete that failed to take into account the role of microorganisms. Dead organic material decays more rapidly and more completely under conditions of high heat and humidity. Some oxidation of the carbonaceous organic material may take place directly under the effect of high heat and humidity, but most of it is accomplished through the digestive processes of living organisms. Much of the decay is performed by bacteria, which prefer tropical climates and rain-forest environments and which are more efficient than the fungi in breaking apart the complex molecules of organic compounds. Aiding also are many larger soil organisms, including termites, earthworms, moles, and shrews, which contribute to the process of decay by the mechanical shredding of woody material as well as by the chemical action of their own digestive tracts. Although these larger organisms are also present in podzol soils, their activities are confined mainly to the summer months. Moreover, there are undoubtedly more of these larger denizens of the "underworld" in the tropics than in other climates.

The decay process involves the activity of microorganisms in breaking down carbohydrates in order to supply themselves with body energy (a process similar to the breakdown of starches and sugars in the human body). Various nitrogenous materials, such as proteins, also are attacked to supply the nitrogen necessary in body building. The by-products remaining after the bacteria have finished their task consist mainly of carbon dioxide (the result of "burning" carbohydrates); traces of nitric acid or amino acids; waxes and resins, which most microorganisms find too difficult to decompose; water; and various mineral salts. Under podzolization, the decay process is rarely carried this far. Some intermediate decay products in organic colloidal form are present in tropical soils, but they differ from those of cooler regions in being largely colorless and relatively inert chemically. Not much is known of them, but their presence helps explain why even bright-red tropical soils, without apparent humus, sometimes yield appreciable organic carbon during chemical quantitative analyses.

The mineral ash substances or salt residues produced as the result of complete decay are important in the ferrallization process. The reason for this is that they provide the soil solution with bases which tend both to neutralize the weak acids produced by the release of carbon dioxide and to form the hydroxyl (OH) ions that are necessary in the leaching of silica from the mineral clays.

Before discussing the characteristics of the major soil groups developed under ferrallization, it should be emphasized again that exceptions can be found to almost any generalization about such broad soil categories. Furthermore, there are probably more local variations in soil characteristics in tropical areas than in most other areas, because geologic erosion and rock weathering are relatively rapid and thus produce greater differences in slope conditions, greater soil variability because of the age of the exposed surface material, and more rapid deposition of alluvium in valleys and lowlands. Exceptions to the generalized conditions are caused by the variations from the normal that may occur with respect to any one or any combination of the many factors that enter into the natural balance of soil formation. Among these variables are age, parent material, slope, drainage, temperature, rainfall (amount and seasonal distribution), vegetation, microlife, and, of course, man himself. On a global or chorographic scale, the generalizations are more important than the exceptions; the reverse is true on a topographic scale. In mountainous tropical island areas, such as Indonesia and the West Indies, soils are highly diverse, and generalizations are not very meaningful.

12.7 FERRALLITES. The ferrallites include the soils that have developed under ideal conditions of the ferrallization process described in the preceding section. Specifically, these soils have been produced under conditions of high rainfall and largely uninterrupted leaching, by soil solutions ranging in reaction from weakly acid to weakly alkaline, on well-drained plains under 2,000 feet in elevation that have uniformly high temperatures. Sufficient time has elapsed so that comparative stability in soil characteristics has been reached.

The most distinctive property of the ferrallites is the presence of nodules, crusts, or irregular masses of iron and aluminum oxides, which are found throughout the profile but are somewhat more abundant near the surface. Tiny crystals of hematite (Fe_2O_3) can be seen on the irregular surfaces of these masses. The soil color is mainly a dark red, although yellowish-brown shades may occur near the surface, and whites and pinks may predominate at greater depths, especially where the parent material is low in iron-bearing minerals.

In some places as much as 100 to 150 feet of weathered material can be found above the unaltered parent material, and the ferrallitic process operates throughout the entire depth, removing sicila and bases and concentrating the iron and aluminum hydroxides. True ferrallites have little or no surface litter of undecomposed organic material, although the topsoil may contain small amounts of colorless intermediate organic decay products that are scarcely observable in the soils or in the soil solution.

The ferrallites are highly permeable to water, are friable, and do not swell or shrink appreciably with alternate wetting and drying. Following rains, the surface soils dry quickly and may be cultivated much sooner than most mature mid-latitude soils. Because of their high permeability, they do not erode easily, although the rapid intake of water on steep slopes makes them susceptible to landslides, by rapidly increasing the weight of the soil mass. Although they have low plasticity and stickiness, they are slippery when wet. These soils have a rather high content of clays, consisting mainly of kaolinites, which have a relatively low absorptive capacity.

The outstanding agronomic feature of the ferrallites is their low natural fertility. The base-exchange capacity of these soils is extremely low, not so much because of a deficiency of colloids as because of the low base-exchange capacity of the colloids that are present—whether organic or inorganic. The ferrallites may be highly fertile for short periods in a forest environment, because of the nutrients released either by the decay of the small but regular amounts of leaves and twigs that fall to the ground or by the breakdown of previously unweathered rock particles in the soil. However, once the covering of vegetation is removed and the regenerative cycle is interrupted, fertility declines rapidly. Another hindrance to the agricultural use of these soils is the rapid and complete drying of the topsoils following rains. This is not significant in tree culture (bananas, rubber, coffee, etc.), but it may be critical in the cultivation of such shallow-rooted crops as sugar cane, maize, or beans during short dry periods.

When fertilizers are used on ferrallite soils, plants respond quickly. If, however, fertilizers are to prove effective for any length of time, they must be added in greater amounts and with greater frequency than are necessary in most other soils, because of the low retention of the colloidal complex in the ferrallites. In other words, plant foods pass through the soil relatively rapidly. One of the most effective means of increasing the fertility of ferrallite soils is to add both organic materials and soluble bases, especially lime. This may be accomplished by plowing under a green plant cover and then adding a commercial fertilizer or using organic compost.

Figure 12.1 shows the world distribution of ferrallite soils. Comparing this with the climatic map (see end paper), one notices that the ferrallites closely parallel the tropical climates that are continually moist (*Af*). The largest areas are in the Amazon Basin of South America and in west-central Africa. It should be pointed out, however, that even within these areas the total percentage of typical ferrallites is small, since variations from the ideal dominate on a topographic scale, because of interrupted drainage, erosion, immaturity, and unusual types of vegetation and parent material.

Much remains to be learned concerning the evolution and geography of tropical soils. Careful soil surveys are available for only a small fraction of the low latitudes, and soil research has been largely restricted to midlatitudes. In recent years, however, the humid tropics have attracted increased attention because of their growing importance for commercial agriculture. Tree crops seem best adapted to these tropical soils and permit stabilized agricultural programs without large outlays for fertilizers.

12.8 TROPICAL RED LOAMS. The tropical red loams are transitional soils that bear roughly the same relationship to the ferrallites that the gray-brown podzolic group does to the podzols. As their name implies, the red-loam soils are predominantly red, as are the ferrallites. Unlike the latter, however, they generally do not include masses of iron and aluminum hydroxides, and this indicates that the process of removing combined silica from the clays (which essentially is the ferrallization process) has not proceeded so far. For the same reason, the clays are more complex and have a greater absorptive and retentive capacity for water, nutrients, and other clay particles. The red loams thus are more plastic than the ferrallites, swell when wet, shrink and crack upon drying, are much more difficult to cultivate, erode easily, and are more fertile.

The tropical red loams, being a transitional soil group, exhibit many variations in soil morphology, depending on the type of transition. Probably the most usual variety comprises the soils of the rainy tropics that are not so far advanced in the ferrallization process as the ferrallites; they may be considered immature tropical soils, such as develop on volcanic material high in iron or on alluvial materials. As a general rule, the tropical red loams that represent early stages in the development of ferrallites are somewhat darker in color than the true ferrallites, often being a reddish brown. Despite the comparatively rapid tropical weathering, a long period of time is required for complete, or even nearly complete, desilification and the formation of true ferrallites.

Tropical red loams are likely to be found where the underlying material is a shale, because shale, itself a product of weathering, develops mature soil characterstics extremely slowly. Also, the pure, massive limestones of the tropics and subtropics are almost always overlain by red loams. Here the soil parent material is undoubtedly former impurities in the original rock. Massive limestone beds normally are laid down by chemical precipitation in quiet, shallow, warm seas. The fine clay colloids washed into streams from tropical or subtropical soils may settle out of suspension far beyond the silty deltas of these streams and may become incorporated into the lime muds. Following compaction and uplift and the subsequent weathering of the limestone by solution, the clay residues once more become soil material. The residues are red because they were once part of a tropical red-loam profile, as they now become again. Like shales, these red clay impurities are not quickly altered by the ferrallization process. Geologic weathering, or the breakdown of rock material, may well be the most important factor in the soil geography of humid tropical regions.

Red loams also are found in the areas that grade toward the gray-brown podzolic soils of the humid mid-latitudes. Here the incompleteness of the ferrallization process is due more to cooler climates than to a shorter time of development. The bright-red soils of the southeastern United States and China are of this type. They differ from the other tropical red loams in having much shallower profiles, in having a *B* horizon which is slightly more compact and a little darker than the soil above, and in showing definite evidence, upon chemical analysis, of some podzolization.[5] Marbut and others have termed these soils red and yellow podzolic soils (see Table 11.6). In physical properties and in utilization, however, they are much more closely allied to the red loams of the rainy tropics than to the gray-brown podzolic soils. The ratio of combined silica (silica in forms other than quartz) to iron and aluminum oxides is less than 2 to 1, as in most of the tropical red loams (see Fig. 12.6).

Soil scientists have long recognized a special type of soil, termed *terra rossa* (red earth), in the Mediterranean region of Europe and North Africa. Despite the general lack of agreement about its origin, this soil has properties that are decidedly similar

[5] The chemical indications of podzolization include a higher percentage of silica in the *A* horizon and a greater proportion of iron and aluminum in the *B* horizon than in the parent material. An arbitrary boundary between podzolic and ferrallitic soils has been suggested in terms of the silica-sesquioxide ratio in the topsoils. A podzolic soil would have a ratio of more than 2, whereas a ferrallitic soil would have a ratio of less than 2.

to those of the tropical red loams and hence is included in this great transitional group. It is noteworthy that some of the red soils that have developed on the basaltic rocks of southeastern Brazil in the coffee country are termed *terra roxa.* The red loams developed on basalt in southern Indochina also are similar to these soils. The terra rossa soils of the Mediterranean region, however, are formed on limestones.

The red loams that develop over limestone have a definite poleward limit, mainly because, as the podzolization process becomes more dominant, organic colloids unite with the residual clays to produce shades of reddish brown rather than red. The *Brown forest soils* (see Sec. 12.3) of the gray-brown podzolic zone may well be the poleward equivalents of these subtropical-to-tropical limestone soils. Large areas of the tropical red limestone loams are found in southern China, northern Indochina, the Philippines, the West Indies, and northern South America. Some of the red soils that are found in the central United States may be considered to be a transitional type. The Baxter soil series, developed on the limestones of the Highland Rim country of Kentucky and Tennessee, is illustrative, but here podzolization has produced a yellowish *A* horizon overlying more typical red clay loams.

A transition away from the ferrallite soils also develops toward the low-latitude dry regions. In this transitional zone, the ferrallization process decreases as the dry period becomes drier and longer with increasing distance toward the deserts. One of the main effects of a dry period is to produce a reversal in the flow of the soil solution. Under the high temperatures of the dry season, evaporation is at a maximum, and there is an upward movement of water to replace that which is lost in the capillary fringe above the water table. Accompanying this evaporation is a precipitation of materials carried in solution. Some of the materials that are normally removed from the profile during the wet season may therefore be returned during the dry period, including silica and some of the less soluble bases. The former is commonly redeposited in the form of small masses (concretions) of opal or chalcedony, which are translucent varieties of noncrystalline silica. In young tropical soils, where the surface horizon is normally yellowish brown, the occurrence of a pronounced dry period tends to make this upper layer red, more like the subsoil. The production of residual iron and aluminum inclusions in the topsoil, characteristic of the ferrallites, is partially checked because of diminished desilicification. The water in the saturated zone deep within the soil contains small quantities of ferrous (soluble) iron, and this too may be carried into the soil profile during the dry period after oxidation and be deposited, like the silica, within a distinct zone in the soil.

In summary, the tropical red loams include a considerable variety of soils that differ from one another in several details of their morphology and even more in their developmental processes but that nonetheless are grouped together because of their many similarities, especially in color, texture, mechanical behavior (plasticity, permeability, expansion, and contraction), and general adaptability for agriculture. Except for fresh alluvium and some of the black volcanic soils, the red loams are the best soils of the low latitudes and show the greatest promise for agricultural expansion. Although they are too deficient in available phosphorus and nitrogen to be considered naturally fertile, they are easier to improve than the ferrallites. Erosion is the major problem in utilizing the tropical loams, which are probably among the most susceptible soils in the world to this danger. The reasons for this include their high plasticity, their low permeability, their high capacity for water retention, the lack of a protective covering of forest litter, and the intensity of rains in the climatic regions in which they are found. Large areas of tropical red loams in the world have deteriorated, partly from erosion and partly through impoverishment resulting from exploitive agriculture and continued removal of the vegetation cover.

12.9 YELLOW LOAMS. The yellow loams can be found throughout the rainier sections of the tropics and subtropics. They are not indicated on the global soil map (see Fig. 12.1), however, partly because of inadequate soil mapping in the tropics and partly because of their scattered distribution, which is difficult to generalize. The color of these soils, a light yellowish-brown, is derived from *limonite,* a hydrated ferric iron oxide.

The yellow loams are found mainly in areas where iron oxides are being concentrated within the soil profile because of the desilicification process of ferrallization but where the soil does not have much opportunity to dry. This continued wetness may occur in regions where there is almost continuous rainfall, such as along windward slopes in the tropics, or in areas of heavy rainfall where unusually flat terrain results in slow internal drainage without saturation. The yellow loams are especially common in the same general areas where red loams predominate, and some soil authorities believe that a yellowish-brown topsoil is normal for most young tropical soils.

The formation of the excessively hydrated iron oxides in young topsoils is caused by a temporary claypan resulting from a downward washing of fine constituents. Such a compact layer impedes internal drainage but does not prevent it entirely.[6] The yellow loams are extremely rare in any area that has a distinct dry season. In general properties, except for color, the yellow loams differ only slightly from the red loams. Both have only moderate natural fertility and erode easily. In the southeastern United States, yellow loams predominate in coastal-plain areas where the terrain is unusually level and where the water table lies only a few feet below the surface. The Norfolk soil series of eastern Virginia and North Carolina is representative.

12.10 POOR DRAINAGE CHARACTERISTICS OF HUMID TROPICAL SOILS. In some respects, the results produced by poor drainage within the soil profile of the humid tropics are similar to those described for the cool, humid regions. Where the soil is saturated continually with water, the features of gleiization appear. Ferrous compounds producing greenish-blue tints are often encountered, and clays are in a highly plastic state. In the zone where the water table fluctuates, a characteristic mottling occurs, consisting of yellowish or reddish streaks in the larger openings. Organic soils accumulate where the water table stands at, or slightly above, the surface. These organic soils consist of peat or muck, depending on the general pH of the ground water in the area.

Hardpans, or cemented layers within the soil, are much more frequently associated with poor drainage in the rainy tropics than

[6] In the early stages of rock or soil weathering, there may be a higher proportion of fine colloidal clays in the tropics than there is later, when the desilicified iron and aluminum hydroxides are concentrated into crusts and irregular masses. Presumably, with more complete ferrallization, the claypan below the surface becomes perforated, providing for better downward drainage. When this happens, the soils change from yellow to red.

FIG. 12.7 Close-up of a typical tropical laterite, or iron hardpan. Note the slaggy appearance. [R. L. Pendleton; Geographical Review]

in cool, humid areas. The hardpans likewise differ considerably in composition and general appearance. The usual tropical hardpan consists of a porous, slaggy (clinkerlike) layer, containing a high percentage of hydrated iron oxides (see Fig. 12.7). It is predominantly reddish in color, but it is frequently mottled with yellow or violet streaks, and the holes are often filled with whitish aluminum hydroxides. Below the hardpan may be found the characteristic blue-gray glei horizon.

The iron hardpans are soft enough to be cut easily with a spade while they are damp and in the soil, but they harden quickly upon drying. This material has long been used for making building and paving bricks in southeast Asia, and it is from this use that it derived the name *laterite* (Latin, *later* = brick). For many years this material was considered the end product of the warm, humid, soil-forming process, because in many parts of the tropics, erosion had removed the upper soil layers, leaving the more durable laterite at the surface, well above the present water table. It is easy to understand how this conclusion came about, for the laterite layer is similar in appearance to the crusts and inclusions of iron in the mature ferrallitic soils. There is now widespread evidence, however, that the laterite developed as an indurated layer immediately above the water table, particularly on ancient erosional plains, and scientists have therefore abandoned the idea that it is a morphological feature of normal mature tropical soils. Although the terms *lateritic* and *laterization* still are used in much of the soil literature to denote the desilicification process in warm, humid areas, they are now more commonly applied to the process of iron-hardpan formation under poor drainage in the tropics.

Iron hardpans are not restricted to the tropics but are found in cool, humid areas as well, where they are also associated with the evaporation of water from the capillary fringe above a fairly stable ground-water table. They are by no means so common in the latter regions, however, being restricted mainly to sandy areas that are relatively high in iron minerals. Furthermore, in the cooler climates, they are likely to be much darker in color, because of a higher content of organic colloids, and much less porous and slaggy in appearance.

The frequent occurrence of laterite hardpans in the humid tropics probably is due to several factors. The most important is the high iron content that is found in most tropical soils as the result of the general ferrallization process, since iron is a relatively common constituent in the rocks of the earth crust. The iron, made soluble through deoxidation (reduction) by anaerobic bacteria in their search for oxygen in water-saturated soils, is almost always present in the tropical ground water and is available for deposition in the capillary zone. As ferrous iron is precipitated by evaporation above the water table, it oxidizes into the insoluble ferric form and thus becomes stabilized. True laterites do not normally develop in areas of acidic rocks, such as granites, which have only traces of iron minerals.

A further reason for the prevalence of iron hardpans in the humid tropics is the high evaporation rate of ground water in these warm climates, especially during dry periods, and many of the humid tropics do have short dry periods. Some of the best examples of true laterites have developed in the humid parts of southeast Asia, where the monsoon influence provides both heavy rains with copious ground water and distinct dry periods for the evaporation of water above the water table.

A curious phenomenon that sometimes results from the formation of laterites is *pseudopodzolization*. This may occur where the laterite layer has been exposed at the surface because of erosion. The porous, rocky, laterite layer, extremely infertile and frequently barren of vegetation, is soaked by rain water that contains traces of carbonic acid (resulting from the absorption of carbon dioxide during precipitation). Over a long period, this acidic solution, although highly dilute, can remove some of the iron from the exposed rocky hardpan, break down its structure, bleach it slightly, and thus produce a soil that has many of the characteristics of true podzols.

The soils of dry regions

12.11 THE CALCIFICATION PROCESS.

The dominant soil process of dry regions, termed *calcification*, consists of a withdrawal of bases from the topsoil and a deposition of alkaline earths, principally calcium carbonate, within a distinct *B* horizon. Accompanying the deposition of this calcium carbonate is an accumulation of organic colloidal complexes in the upper part of the soil, or the *A* horizon. A collective name for the calcium-accumulating soils is *pedocals*.

The primary reason why calcium, rather than some other base ion, tends to accumulate in the soil is that calcium, like iron, is a fairly common constituent in the rocks of the earth crust (see Table 11.6), especially in sedimentary rocks. Furthermore, when a mixed solution of common salts and alkaline earths is concentrated gradually through evaporation, calcium carbonate is among the first compounds to be precipitated out of solution. The precipitation of calcium carbonate, which is the dominant feature of the calcification process, results not only from the evaporation of downward-percolating

FIG. 12.8 Section of a typical laterite deposit. Note how the laterite zones are related to the movement of ground water. The main laterite zone (3) appears just above the water table (ground-water level) and where iron is deposited following evaporation in the capillary zone. The upper laterite zone (1) may represent a former high-water-table deposit or may be related to the lateral flow of ground water into the surface stream. [After Fox]

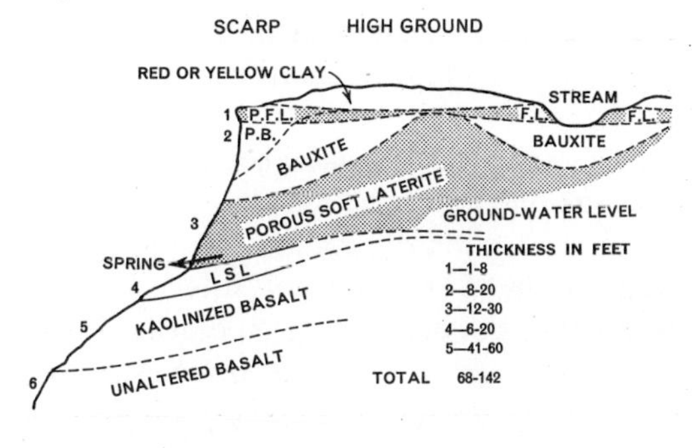

water but also from the evaporation of water brought upward into the soil profile by capillary action. The calcium carbonate may be recognized easily in the soil by its whitish color and its effervescence with the application of acids. With increasing aridity, the lime layer in the *B* horizon tends to decrease in thickness and depth and also to become somewhat more compact. Along the boundary between dry and humid climates, the lime zone may be 3 to 4 feet below the surface. The characteristics of this lime zone vary, but in general, the lime occurs as irregular solid masses or as white coatings on the surface of soil structural units. Occasionally, however, it may form thick, compact, almost stony layers a foot or more in thickness.

Magnesium, another fairly common element in the earth crust, behaves very much like calcium. In fact, most calcium carbonate contains magnesium carbonate as an associated compound. The calcium dominates in the soil, but magnesium might be considered an "unobtrusive companion" in the calcification process. Calcium sulfate is another compound that is precipitated fairly easily following concentration by evaporation, but not quite so soon as the carbonates. This compound, known as *gypsum* ($CaSO_4 \cdot 2H_2O$), thus appears mainly in the drier soils. Whereas only calcium and magnesium carbonates dominate the soil *B* horizons near the humid border of the dry lands, the water-soluble salts (sodium bicarbonate, sodium chloride, calcium chloride, potassium bicarbonate, magnesium chloride, etc.) occasionally appear in the *B* horizons of drier climates, where they are deposited temporarily during dry periods. With adequate drainage, however, they are soon flushed out of the soil during rare wet periods. Like gypsum, these soluble salts become more common in the soil profiles with increasing aridity, but they never constitute important parts of the depositional layer in well-drained soils.

Iron and aluminum silicates (the inorganic clay colloids) form as a result of rock weathering in dry regions, but the rate of their formation decreases rapidly with increasing aridity. They are much less important as coloring agents in dry soils than they are in humid soils, mainly because of the dominance of organic material in the top soils near the humid margins. They are relatively unimportant constituents of true desert soils. If desert soils are red, the color is likely to be the result of iron in the original parent material and not of soil-forming processes. One exception might be noted: with high temperatures in the low latitudes, considerable organic material may oxidize without producing soil humus; therefore, the *A* horizons of tropical grasslands are usually not so dark as those of cooler climates, and the iron present tends to produce shades of chestnut or reddish brown. The physical and chemical activities of the soil colloids show a similar relationship. In the cool, more humid grasslands, organic colloids greatly exceed the clays in water retention and base exchange. In the tropical grasslands, however, the clay colloids perform a larger share of such functions. Both organic and inorganic colloids are rare in true desert margin soils.

Three principal factors explain the high accumulation of humus within the grassland soils of semiarid regions. First, this accumulation is partly the result of a somewhat lower population of decay-producing microorganisms than exist in humid regions. Second, the grasses have an affinity for calcium and transfer large quantities of it from the *B* horizon into the topsoil. This calcium tends to flocculate, or stabilize the organic colloids, preventing them from passing into the soil solution until they are completely mineralized. The darkness of grassland soils indicates both the quantity, or lushness, of the vegetation and the slowness of humus mineralization.[7] Last, a large volume of the grasses and other herbaceous plants is added underground, thus supplying potential humus directly within the soil. Forests normally supply more dead organic material than do grasslands, but nearly all of it is added to the surface of soils. Forest humus, therefore, to be effective within the soil profile, must be transported into it following partial decay. Grassland humus, on the other hand, becomes effective within the soil immediately.

In summary, calcification, as a soil-forming process, develops under good drainage conditions in areas where evapotranspiration exceeds precipitation. It is characterized by the removal of some of the bases from the *A* horizon, the formation in the subsoil of a depositional layer (*B* horizon) of alkaline earths—mainly calcium carbonate—and a stabilization of organic colloids in the topsoils. The process is best developed near the humid margins of the dry lands and weakens toward the true desert. In the latter, mechanical weathering processes, rather than the solvent action of percolating water, determine the major characteristics of the fragmental material mantling the earth surface.

12.12 CHERNOZEMS AND PRAIRIE SOILS. Perhaps the most inherently productive soils in the world are the deep, black soils that straddle the border between the semiarid and subhumid climates within the mid-latitudes. A major soil boundary, separating the pedocals from the pedalfers, runs through the center of this black-soil belt. At the surface, the two sides of the border are indistinguishable in both soils and vegetation. Only in the *B* horizon can be found the deposition of calcium carbonate that distinguishes these two great soil divisions. A touch of acid to the *B* horizon on the pedocal side of the boundary results in strong effervescence, which does not take place on the humid side. From the standpoint of soil management, the two groups of soils are almost identical, since only the topsoils are found within plow depth. Droughts, however, are somewhat more hazardous on the drier side of the border; hence crop patterns differ somewhat. On the global soil map these two groups of soils have been combined into one (see Fig. 12.1), because of the similarity in their surface expression.

The black soils on the dry side of the climatic border are called *chernozems,* a term derived from the Russian word for "black earth." A typical chernozem profile is shown in Fig. 12.9.

There is almost no downward movement of sesquioxides in chernozem soil, since most of them are stabilized in the form of flocculated clay colloids bound together by calcium humates (organic colloids saturated with calcium ions). The pH of the chernozems has a relatively narrow range, usually from about 6.8 in the *A* horizon to 7.5 in the *B* horizon.

The black, humid grassland soils that lack the lime layer are termed *prairie earths.* Their distribution closely follows the distribution of prairie grasses within humid or subhumid regions. Their profiles are similar to those of the chernozems, except that the prairie

[7] This generalization does not always hold true in the low latitudes. In the dry tropics, jet-black soils actually may have lower organic contents than bright-red ones, because, under special conditions, a finely dispersed black substance, probably a complex humate that is in an irreversible, peptized (incapable of being flocculated) state, spreads throughout the profile, coloring it for a depth of several feet. This colloidal material is so finely divided that a relatively small amount of it is sufficient to coat and color the soil particles.

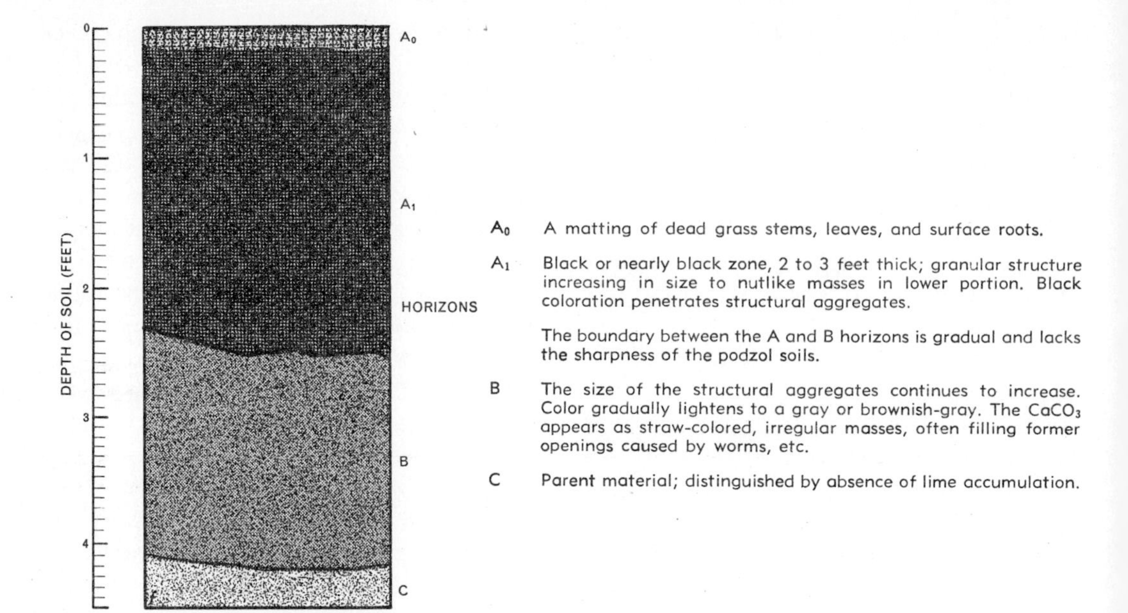

FIG. 12.9 Typical profile of a chernozem soil.

earths lack the deposition of lime in their *B* horizons. There is a gradual decrease in the organic content of the soils with depth, and the *B* horizon is generally a dark reddish-brown. Besides the prairie earths adjoining the chernozems in the United States, Canada, the Soviet Union, Australia, and Argentina, smaller areas of this soil type are found in central Hungary and Romania, central Manchuria, and the grassy highland plains of British East Africa.

Some soil scientists recognize an associated soil group known as the *degraded chernozems.* This group includes chernozem soils that have had at least some of the lime flushed out of the *B* horizon, presumably because of a change in climate that resulted in more humid conditions. In the degraded chernozems, the lime layer gradually moves downward into the lower *B* horizon with increasing precipitation, and may disappear completely. The degraded chernozems develop under a prairie grassland or under a light forest cover, as in the forest-steppe zone of the Soviet Union. The degraded chernozems without a lime layer have a light-colored *A* horizon and are included in the gray forest soils, a soil group mentioned in the discussion of the gray-brown podzolic soils (see Sec. 12.3). Some authorities consider prairie earths to be degraded chernozems, interpreting the prairies as a vegetation relict from a drier period that persists in areas where forest development has been hindered by fire or by animal browsing.

Both the chernozems and the prairie earths are almost completely under cultivation. The chernozems produce a major share of the commercial wheat of the world, and the prairie earths are centers of concentrated grain and animal-feed production. Illustrative of the high inherent fertility of soils on the Illinois prairies is an agricultural experimental plot that has been producing corn continuously without fertilizers for almost 100 years.

12.13 THE BROWN STEPPE SOILS. The brown steppe soils, as defined here, include both the chestnut-brown and the brown soils of the classification used by the U.S. Soil Survey (see Table 11.7). The brown steppe soils represent the dry transition between the gray desert-margin soils on the one hand and the chernozems on the other. Their *A* horizon is lighter in color than that of the chernozems, primarily because of a decrease in the amount of dead organic matter supplied by the vegetation, which, in turn, becomes sparser with increasing aridity. Shades of gray tend to accompany the brown coloration of these soils and to become more pronounced toward the true desert. The chestnut soils grade into the chernozems. The granular aggregates of the chernozems are not present in the steppe soils, which are characterized, instead, by a platy or laminar structure.

Under good drainage, the water-soluble salts are washed out of the topsoils. The alkaline earth carbonates, especially lime, accumulate in the *B* horizons, which are nearer the surface and somewhat more compact than they are in the chernozems. The pH of the *A* horizon is mildly alkaline. Gypsum, or hydrous calcium sulfate, frequently appears as a depositional layer just below the zone of lime accumulation.

The distribution of this soil group is wider than that of the chernozems, because no distinction has been made between the middle- and low-latitude variants. The low-latitude equivalents of the brown steppe soils differ somewhat in being redder in color, owing to the decreased importance of humus and the greater importance of iron as a coloring agent in the soil. Considerably greater differences, however, in both morphology and

FIG. 12.10 A chernozem soil profile. Note the deep A horizon with its dark color owing to included organic material. The B horizon contains much calcium carbonate and is light-colored. [U.S. Department of Agriculture]

utilization distinguish the chernozems from their low-latitude equivalents, and the latter are therefore treated as a special group (sec Sec. 12.17). The brown steppe soils border the desert-margin soils wherever the latter occur.

The brown steppe soils are marginal for agriculture, mainly because of the frequency of severe droughts in the semiarid climate. Dry farming is necessary and has been aided greatly by the introduction of large-scale agricultural machinery and plant breeding.

12.14 THE GRAY DESERT-MARGIN SOILS (SEROZEMS). True soils—those which develop profile differences in depth—can scarcely be considered to exist in truly arid or desert regions. Around the margins of deserts, however, where there is at least some permanent vegetation, though sparse and scattered, the first signs of soil leaching appear. As indicated in Sec. 12.13, gray shades tend to replace the darker brown shades with increasing dryness, because of the decreased vegetation cover. The semidesert soils, where at least the rudiments of profile development are found but where insufficient humus exists for soil coloration, are included within a group known as the gray desert-margin soils, or *serozems* (gray earths).

Extremely little vertical movement of either organic or inorganic material takes place within these gray soils. Calcium carbonate and associated calcium sulfate appear throughout the soil mass, but their zone of concentration is usually within a foot or so of the surface. The soil texture ordinarily is fairly uniform throughout, and neither organic nor inorganic colloids are abundant. The surfaces of these soils in the United States are often covered with a thin, pebbly layer, which is wind-scoured but which helps to protect the loose material below from wind erosion.

The gray desert-margin soils have little agricultural value without irrigation. Like most desert soils, they are deficient in nitrogen, and their low organic and inorganic colloidal content results in a low total base-exchange capacity. The addition of water alone is not sufficient to make the dry-land soils highly productive. There are three important requirements for maintaining high productivity on irrigated desert and desert-margin soils:

1. Great amounts of organic material must be added, to aid in retaining water and plant foods and to increase the base-exchange capacity, thereby checking soil leaching by irrigation water and making the use of fertilizers more effective.
2. The nitrogen content should be increased through the use of alkaline-tolerant legumes or the application of nitrogenous fertilizers.
3. Adequate drainage should be provided for the surplus water not used by plants, to prevent the gradual accumulation of water-soluble salts in the soil.

12.15 DESERT SOIL MATERIALS. Clearly distinguishable soil profiles rarely are observed in the true deserts. Instead, the fragmental material covering the surface is little more than mechanically weathered parent material, which would be capable of developing a soil profile only if there were sufficient water for soil percolation. Crusts, or hardpans, including some of the consistency of concrete, sometimes appear at or near the surface, but they result more from evaporation of soluble salts at the top of a high water table than from a normal process of soil development. Desert hardpans seem to be more common in the loose material of alluvial fans, where there is more opportunity for ground water. The surface material contains a wide range of mineral particles, and the color closely resembles that of adjacent rocks.

A glazed coating, termed *desert varnish,* tends to form on surface pebbles as the result of sand abrasion and the rapid evaporation of rain water, which falls in occasional sudden, short showers. Practically no organic material, of either plant or animal origin, is found within the desert soils. The litter from the few desert plants is insignificant and usually is oxidized at the surface without producing humus.

12.16 BLACK TROPICAL SOILS. The black soils found within the transitional areas between dry and humid climates in the low latitudes are clearly different from the black chernozems and prairie earths of mid-latitudes, despite the similarity in coloration. Their organic content is fairly low, even below that of many of the tropical red loams, and they have a finely granular topsoil. When wet, the black topsoil has a slimy consistency and swells excessively, but it shrinks rapidly upon drying, forming wide, deep cracks. Later it slumps into the cracks, and the upper and lower horizons become mixed. Crusts and layers of calcium carbonate are sometimes present. Little is known concerning the formation of these soils, but although they occur in many different sections of the drier tropics, they are believed to be a feature of interrupted drainage that develops on parent materials unusually high in lime. If so, they are intrazonal, rather than zonal, soils. Their black color probably is due to a finely dispersed, irreversible (incapable of being flocculated) organic colloid or to some type of bituminous material produced from the humus under high temperatures.

The largest areas of these black tropical soils are found on the basaltic lavas of peninsular India and the central Transvaal of South Africa. These lavas have a high content of bases, especially calcium and magnesium. Black tropical soils also have been reported in Morocco, Tanganyika, Indonesia, and Australia. In all the areas where they are found, knolls and ridges rising above the general land surface and underlain by identical parent material tend to develop into red loams. This appears to support the contention that these black soils are intrazonal. Although they are considerably less fertile than the chernozems and prairie soils, they are among the better tropical soils for agriculture. Those of India have provided the basis for the cotton production on the Deccan Plateau, near Bombay. When under cultivation, the black tropical soils are easily eroded by both water and wind.

12.17 REDDISH-BROWN PEDOCAL SOILS OF THE TROPICS AND SUBTROPICS. The reddish-brown pedocal soils are the tropical high-temperature equivalents of the chernozems. Although these low-latitude soils have a deep layer of lime accumulation, they differ from their counterparts of cooler areas in having a reddish-brown instead of a black *A* horizon. Their subsoils normally are reddish, similar in color to the red loams, but a thin yellowish-brown surface horizon sometimes is found. The structural aggregates are slightly smaller than those of the chernozems, and the profiles are not so thick. The higher temperatures tend to increase evaporation, the oxidation of organic material, and the rate of decay. The organic content is therefore lower, and this brings out the reddish color of the inorganic iron oxides. Reddish tropical equivalents of the chestnut-brown and brown soils also are found.

Because of their lower organic content,

these tropical grassland soils are far less retentive of soil fertility than the much darker soils of higher latitudes, but they are still among the better soils of the tropics and subtropics. Their productivity increases with latitude. It is likely that their full capabilities for agriculture have not yet been realized.

Within the United States, representative soils of this group are found in the southern Great Plains, extending from southern Kansas through Oklahoma and Texas into eastern Mexico. Large areas of reddish-brown pedocals also are found on the other continents, straddling the dry, humid boundary standing roughly between lat 10 and 35° N and S.

12.18 FEATURES OF POOR DRAINAGE IN THE SOILS OF DRY REGIONS.

One noteworthy difference exists between the poor drainage in dry regions and that of humid regions. In the latter, there is always a connection between the accumulated ground water and the streams and rivers that flow to the sea—either directly, through surface flow, or indirectly, via subsurface percolation. In dry regions, however, the connections between rainfall, ground water, and stream flow may be interrupted, owing to the excess of evaporation and plant transpiration over precipitation or to the lack of drainage channels capable of removing the occasional water surpluses. Under such conditions the only outlet for accumulated water either at or below the surface is evaporation. A topographic depression that collects water in a dry area, therefore, is similar to the evaporating pan of a furnace or stove, which accumulates a crust of soluble salts following periodic replenishment and evaporation. The general process of salt accumulation is known as *salinization,* and it signifies the deposition of multiple-salt complexes, including the water-soluble salts, instead of just the alkaline earth carbonates, as in calcification.

Far from being scattered phenomena, the features of poor drainage are seen almost everywhere in dry regions, and it has been estimated that approxmately 40 per cent of the soils of arid and semiarid regions are subject to various degrees of salinization.

The salts that enter the salinization complexes in dry regions are mainly derived from solutions accompanying rock and mineral decomposition. Many of the streams that empty into desert basins have their drainage basins in more humid regions, including mountainous borderlands. Large topographic basins, like the Tarim Basin of central Asia, that accumulate the drainage for thousands of square miles usually have extensive salt flats associated with playa-lake deposits. Sometimes, also, the sedimentary rocks that are found in desert regions may contain high concentrations of soluble salts, having once been marine sediments. Some desert basins probably contained large fresh-water lakes at one time, but because of a change in climate or a warping of lake outlets, they lost their outlets to the sea. Such lakes, following evaporation and shrinking, gradually become bodies of salt water. The large salt flats marking the former extensions of Great Salt Lake in Utah and many of the playa basins in Nevada originated in this manner.

Still other basins represent former arms of the sea that have been cut off by crustal warping or by deposition. After the water is evaporated, the sediments remaining have a high content of soluble salts.

A high salt content in adjacent rocks, however, may not be a requirement for salinization. Authorities are not in agreement about whether or not unusual geologic fea-

FIG. 12.11 Solonchak soil near Delta, Utah. The salts, mainly sodium chloride and sodium sulfate, were concentrated in the topsoil as the result of inadequate drainage in an irrigated area. The farm was abandoned 10 to 15 years before because of this salinization. [U.S. Department of Agriculture]

tures such as those described in the previous paragraphs are necessary to explain the abundance of water-soluble salts in dry regions. Some believe that the weathering of nearly all rocks in the earth crust would yield sufficient salt to produce saline soils if sufficient time elapsed for concentration by evaporation. Others believe that chlorine, particularly, is not sufficiently abundant in the solid earth crust to support the latter theory and hence must have been concentrated into sedimentary rocks via marine deposition.

The composition of soluble salts in the poorly drained soils of dry regions varies greatly, although the chlorides and sulfates of sodium, calcium, and magnesium are the most frequently encountered. These may accumulate on the floor of playa lakes and form white, glistening sheets of salt crystals, or they may exist in brine form in permanently soggy soils. Occasionally the salts are precipitated as effluorescent crystals in zones at various depths within the regional soil profiles. The salt accumulation may be found either in the fragmental rock rubble of true deserts or as surface or intraprofile precipitates in the semiarid soils.

SOLONCHAK. A soil that shows definite accumulations of water-soluble salt crystals within the profile is called a *solonchak,* a term taken from the Russian soil literature. The salt layer in a solonchak is not a hardpan, but, rather, a soft, friable zone in which the salt crystals are usually visible (see Fig. 12.11). Sometimes the salt deposition occurs at the surface. Except for the salt crystals within the profile, a solonchak may differ little in appearance from the other zonal soils in the region. Occasionally features of gleiization, indicative of a water-saturated zone, appear in the lower portions of the soil.

Saline soils are significant in the utilization of dry-land areas because many of the salts have a toxic effect on plant growth. Some

FIG. 12.12 Typical solonetz soil. Note the columnar structure, with columns that have rounded tops. [U.S. Department of Agriculture]

desert plants will tolerate and even thrive on high concentrations of sodium chloride or sodium sulfate, but nearly all cultivated plants are highly sensitive to salty soils. Dryland soils often have become salinized as the result of irrigation. Irrigation without adequate drainage tends to raise the groundwater table of dry basins, and if the capillary fringe rises as far as the zone of the soil profile, evaporation will result in the formation of a solonchak. The problems associated with the reclamation of tidal marshes and shallow ocean margins are similar to those in reclaiming saline soils in dry areas. The Dutch have been pioneers in this work, and many of their methods have been applied successfully to irrigation projects in dry regions.

SOLONETZ. Whenever a saline soil (solonchak) has been desalinized (had its surplus salt removed), a distinctive type of soil, called a *solonetz,* results. Such a condition is not so rare as it might seem, since desalinization may result in any of the following ways:

1. A change in climate toward more humid conditions
2. A lowering of the water table, so that salts are flushed out at every rain and the source of supply removed
3. Artificial flushing with irrigation water and with adequate drainage
4. Creation of better drainage through the erosion of an outlet leading from a desert basin

As a result of the flushing of the topsoil and desalinization, several physical and chemical changes are brought about. First, the depositional layer of effluorescent salts is removed. Then the former structure of the soil is destroyed through decoagulation (peptizing) of the colloidal constituents. This is followed by the washing downward of the finer constituents (*eluviation*), producing a more open-textured *A* horizon and a more compact *B* horizon. The latter, in turn, develops a zone of vertical prisms, or columns, an inch or more in diameter and rounded on top. The surfaces of these columns are hard and shiny. The *B* horizon also contrasts with the *A* horizon in being much darker in color, ranging from dark-reddish-brown to black. The entire soil is heavy and sticky when wet and is hard and cracks badly when dry.

This desalinized soil, termed solonetz by the Russians, usually is called *black alkali* in the western United States. Although the acidity of the topsoil is about neutral, the alkalinity increases rapidly with depth. The process of desalinization sometimes is termed alkalinization, because of the tendency for strong alkaline salts, like sodium and potassium carbonates, to form in the soil. These salts, dissolved in water, form powerful hydroxides (lye is a common form of potassium hydroxide), which can disrupt and dissolve the organic residues in the soil and spread them throughout the soil profile. This accounts for the dark color (black alkali). The harmful effects of desalinization—including the destruction of soil structure; the tightening of the subsoil, which makes drainage more difficult; and the addition of exceedingly toxic sodium and potassium carbonates to the feeding horizons of plant roots—must be reckoned with in saline-soil reclamation projects.[8] The loose, open texture of the *A* horizon of solonetz soils also makes them particularly vulnerable to wind erosion.

SOLODI. With a continuation of the desalinization, or alkalinization, process, the soil characteristics change from those of a typical solonetz and become remarkably like those of a typical podzol, but without the overlying layer of raw humus. When such features develop, the soil is termed a *solodi*. The *A* horizon in the solodi is bleached, acid in reaction, high in silica, and low in iron and aluminum oxides.[9] The *B* horizon is more compact than the *A* horizon, accumulates the clay constituents removed from the topsoils, and contains many soluble bases. Eventually vegetation is established, plants begin to transfer bases from the *B* horizon back into the topsoil, and the normal zonal or climatic type is reestablished.

Intrazonal soils

Intrazonal soils are those which owe their distinguishing characteristics to factors other than climate, such as parent material, slope,

[8] An interesting corrective process involves the use of gypsum. The calcium ion in this hydrated calcium sulfate unites with the colloidal particles, causing flocculation. It also displaces other ions such as sodium and potassium, which in turn unite with the sulfate radical of the gypsum and are carried out of the soil with flushing. In this way the colloidal dispersal is prevented, and the newly formed salts are removed while they are in a less toxic form. This is only one example of the results obtained from the relatively new field of applied soil colloidal chemistry.

[9] It is interesting to note at this point that when the pH of the soil solution becomes unusually high (8.5 to 9.4), it produces effects in the soil similar to those associated with strong acids. Silica, for example, becomes stabilized, and the sesquioxides become mobile and are carried downward by the soil solution. The high pH of the solonetz soil solution is the result of the hydroxyl ions associated with the sodium and potassium hydroxides.

FIG. 12.13 Typical dark rendzina soils on meadow lands that are underlain by a permeable white chalk. These smoothly rolling hills are part of the chalk cuesta that constitutes the South Downs of Sussex County, England. [British Travel Association]

or drainage. The total area of intrazonal soils probably exceeds that of zonal soils throughout the world. This fact should serve as a warning in interpreting world maps of zonal soils or studying discussions of zonal soils. In soil geography, the exceptions to the rule are generally more numerous than illustrative examples, but they are also much less mappable on small scales. The intrazonal features associated with poor drainage were covered in the treatment of the zonal or climatic soils, mainly because the characteristics varied with major climatic differences, but the other intrazonal soil characteristics, particularly those related to parent material, are much more difficult to generalize. An extensive treatment of such soils is impractical here, but a few scattered examples are given for illustrative purposes.

One group of intrazonal soils consists of the humid, black variety, known as *rendzinas*. These resemble prairie soils or chernozems at the surface, but they differ in having pieces of lime scattered throughout the profile, instead of being restricted to definite zones. They are found overlying soft, porous limestones, chalks, or marls, and they usually bear a grass cover. Examples are the soils of the Black Belt of Alabama and eastern Texas. They are scattered throughout the world, independently of climate. Some authorities believe that many of the terra rossa soils of the Mediterranean region of Europe and elsewhere (see Sec. 12.8) might be considered red rendzinas, which tend to develop over hard, impermeable limestones rather than the soft, porous varieties of limy parent materials.

Another type of intrazonal soil develops on coarse quartz sand. The extremely low content of bases in the quartz sand, the durability of these mineral particles, and the loose, permeable nature of the soils produce unique properties, regardless of the region in which they are found. Mention already has been made of the intrazonal podzollike soils represented by the Lakewood soil series in New Jersey (see Sec. 12.1).

Bright-red soils well within the zone of podzolization occur over surface hematite deposits in small areas of Northern Michigan and Minnesota and are clearly intrazonal in nature. The soils on the belted coastal plain of Texas change sharply in color, texture, and structure with changes in underlying parent material and should be considered intrazonal soils, even though climatic soil processes can be observed in a close examination of soil characteristics.

Zonal-soil characteristics prevail on the undulating or gently sloping portions of the more stable sections of the earth surface, such as the unglaciated shield areas and some of the broad interior erosional plains. In the continental marginal zones, where crustal instability is strongest, however, and where erosion and deposition produce relatively rapid environmental changes, intrazonal properties are likely to predominate. This is similarly true in areas that have been glaciated. The characteristics of zonal soils appear remarkably soon, however, and may be recognizable, even though the intrazonal properties may remain dominant for a long time. Stability in soil characteristics is a relative term, just as it is in the case of vegetation, climate, and landforms.

Perspective

Three principal soil-forming processes characterize the climatic factor in soil formation. *Podzolization,* which prevails under cool, humid conditions, is essentially a process by which iron and aluminum sesquioxides are transported from the topsoil to a distinct *B* horizon in well-drained, mature soils. *Ferrallization,* developed typically in the humid tropics, tends to increase the proportion of sesquioxides throughout the earth mantle by removing most of the other material, especially combined silica and the soluble bases. There is no pronounced depositional horizon in well-drained soils. *Calcification,* which occurs under conditions of adequate drainage in dry regions, is characterized by the withdrawal of some of the bases from the topsoil, deposition of a carbonate layer in a *B* horizon, and a stabilization of organic colloids in the *A* horizon. Mixtures of properties derived from more than one of these processes within transitional zones result in a wide variety of soil morphological groups.

Unique features of poor drainage are associated with each of the climatic soil processes. In podzolization, the development of ferrous oxides (gleiization) tends to predominate in heavier-textured soils, whereas iron humates (iron plus humus) are more common in sandier soils. In the warm, humid regions, iron depositional layers, or *laterites,* are associated with high water tables. Accumulations of organic soils develop in swamps and marshes throughout humid regions. Poor drainage is marked in dry regions by the accumulation of water-soluble salts.

The human factor in the global environmental complex of soils has not been evaluated in this chapter, although capabilities for soil reclamation and improvement have been briefly discussed in several places. The history of the human factor in soil alteration is an astonishing one, for despite man's increasing dependence on soils as a source of food and his growing knowledge of soil processes, the principal result of his soil-altering activities has been a progressive deterioration of the very soil properties on which he depends most. This has been more the result of need than of any general ignorance or perversity in human behavior. In general, the greatest deterioration has taken place in areas where the food shortages are most acute. Conversely, the greatest improvements are found where the human need is the least. Probably the most harmful effect of human activity on soil properties has been the intensification of erosion on sloping land.

13

Mineral resources

National political and economic strength during the present century depends largely on the ability to command and to utilize mineral resources. From these resources has come the inanimate energy that has released man from much of the physical drudgery that formerly was required of him. From minerals also have arisen the machines, or mechanical slaves, through which inanimate energy is harnessed and put to work. Machinery, utilizing mineral fuels, is extraordinarily more efficient in doing work than man or animals. The surpluses of production resulting from the increased application of inanimate energy and metallic machines have been pyramided by investments in education, research, and inventions. As a result, the per capita material wealth of highly industrialized countries, reflected in their standard of living, has reached heights that would have been unbelievable a century ago.

The rapidly increasing consumption of minerals has led to a growing concern about the adequacy of reserves, and much exploratory work has been done to inventory the world supply of minerals. The distribution of mineral resources, therefore, is much better known now than it was at the turn of the century. The geography of mineral resources is far from a static subject. Changes in technology may create, alter, or destroy specific resource patterns. In order to be considered a resource, a particular mineral deposit must have sufficient utility to warrant exploitation. Whether or not it meets this requirement depends on a great many factors, including the cost of production, the status of technological arts, characteristic cultural demand patterns, and the competition of substitute materials. Because of the complexity of the problem, a quantitative appraisal of resource patterns is largely beyond the scope of this chapter. Instead, the emphasis here is on the locational patterns of the major mineral resource *materials.* We are concerned primarily with the areas that contain minerals of varying abundance and utility, and only secondarily with their importance to man.

13.1 THE GENERAL DISTRIBUTION OF MINERALS. The most notable fact about the global distribution of economically significant minerals is that the total supply is relatively small in comparison with the quantity of all the other mineral materials in the earth crust. Nearly all of the outer covering of the earth is made up of only a few minerals, none of which has much economic importance. The mineralogical composition of

TABLE 13.1 Mean mineralogical composition of 700 igneous-rock samples

MINERAL FAMILY	PERCENTAGE
Feldspar	59.5
Hornblende and pyroxene	16.8
Quartz	12.0
Mica	3.8
Other	7.9

SOURCE: F. W. Clarke, *The Data of Geochemistry,* U.S. Geological Survey Bulletin 770, 1924, p. 33.

a sampling of igneous rocks from scattered locations throughout the world is shown in Table 13.1. Over 90 per cent of the total volume of these rock samples is comprised of only four families of minerals, and each of these groups includes relatively few individual minerals. The feldspars, for example, which constitute some 60 per cent of the crustal rocks, include only eight clearly defined minerals, and one of these, *orthoclase,* far exceeds the others, being the major mineral constituent of granite. The comparative scarcity of the economic minerals adds to their value and makes their patterns of distribution highly important.

A second important fact concerning the location of economic minerals is that many of them, especially the metals, are widely distributed but are generally found in extremely small quantities. High-grade deposits are rare and have been the first to be exploited. Continued increases in the demand for metals have resulted in a shift in emphasis from small, localized high-grade deposits to larger mineralized areas that contain lower-grade ores.[1] This shift, however, has required larger outlays of capital for mining, processing, and prospecting.

[1] An *ore* is a mineral deposit of commercial significance. Many mineral deposits are not ore deposits because their value does not warrant the expense of extraction and processing.

As indicated later, in the discussion of individual minerals, some minerals are closely related to particular kinds of rocks. Many of the metals, for example, are found in igneous rocks. Some, such as tin or tungsten, are found in *siallic* rocks (light-colored igneous rocks of continental masses), and others, such as nickel, occur as ore bodies only in the dark, basic *sima.* Certain minerals are commonly found together in the same mineralized areas—for example, lead and zinc. The fossil fuels, which include petroleum, coal, and natural gas, are almost always associated with sedimentary rocks. Still other minerals, such as copper, appear here and there without any apparent relationship to specific kinds of rocks. No simple generalization can be made regarding the kinds of areas where mineral resources, as a whole, can be found.

For convenience, the following discussion of the distribution of mineral resources is divided into three major parts, dealing, respectively, with the mineral fuels, the metallic minerals, and the nonmetallic minerals.

The mineral fuels

The mineral fuels include two subgroups: the *fossil fuels,* comprising petroleum, natural gas, and coal; and the *nuclear fuels,* which consist largely of the minerals of uranium and thorium. The three fossil fuels are mixtures of carbonaceous materials and differ widely in chemical composition and physical properties. The nuclear fuels include the naturally occurring elements that are being mined to feed nuclear reactors that generate atomic energy or to supply material for atomic weapons.

Although the fossil fuels are alike in being mixtures of carbonaceous material derived from life forms that existed in the geologic past, they differ appreciably from one another in both chemical and physical characteristics. Coal is a simple mixture of carbon, in a solid, amorphous (noncrystalline) state, with various other residues resulting from the incomplete decay of plant material. Petroleum and natural gas belong to a large family of carbon compounds known as the *hydrocarbons*. Petroleum is essentially a mixture of liquid hydrocarbons, whereas natural gas is a mixture of the gaseous members of this chemical family. The hydrocarbons are chain compounds of carbon and hydrogen that have the general formula C_nH_{2n+2}. The four simplest of the hydrocarbons, in gaseous form, are diagrammed below.

As these chain molecules become longer, the hydrocarbons change from gases into liquids and finally into solids at ordinary air temperatures. Paraffin, for example, is a solid hydrocarbon. Natural gas, as it comes from the earth, is usually a mixture of the hydrocarbons illustrated below, but with a decided dominance of methane. Natural gas usually also contains tiny droplets of liquid hydrocarbons, sometimes termed *natural gasoline*. When these included liquids are separated from the gases, they vaporize and ignite readily and, when mixed with somewhat longer hydrocarbons, constitute a high-quality gasoline. Petroleum usually consists of many liquid hydrocarbons along with small quantities of both the gaseous and solid forms. Deposits of natural asphalt, a hydrocarbon that is almost a solid, occur in a few places and consist of a mixture of the extremely long, complex hydrocarbon molecules. The La Brea tar pits near Los Angeles and the tar lake on the island of Trinidad in the West Indies are examples of natural asphalt deposits.

The one factor that makes the carbonaceous, or fossil, fuels of great value to man is their combustibility, that is, their ability to burn. This process involves the union of carbon with atmospheric oxygen and the consequent release of heat energy. The chemical energy bound within the fossil fuels was originally derived from sunlight by living plants. The solar energy was used by plants to split carbon from carbon dioxide in order to synthesize plant sugars and starches that constitute reserve plant foods.

The value of the respective fossil fuels depends largely on their physical differences. Coal is the most abundant of the three and is generally the easiest to obtain. Usually it is also the cheapest, and it is preferred wherever large quantities of heat energy are required and where a long haul from the mines is not necessary. Petroleum is a somewhat more concentrated fuel than coal and, being a liquid, can be more conveniently transported and handled and more easily regulated in a flow combustion system. For these reasons, petroleum is the principal fuel for transportation uses. Along with natural gas, petroleum is also a major fuel for space heating, having the advantages of volume control and low ash and smoke residues. In addition, it has a unique value for lubrication. Because of the large number of liquid hydrocarbons, each with a different degree of viscosity, and the high ignition points of some of these hydrocarbons, the mineral oils are far better than most vegetable oils for reducing frictional wear in the moving

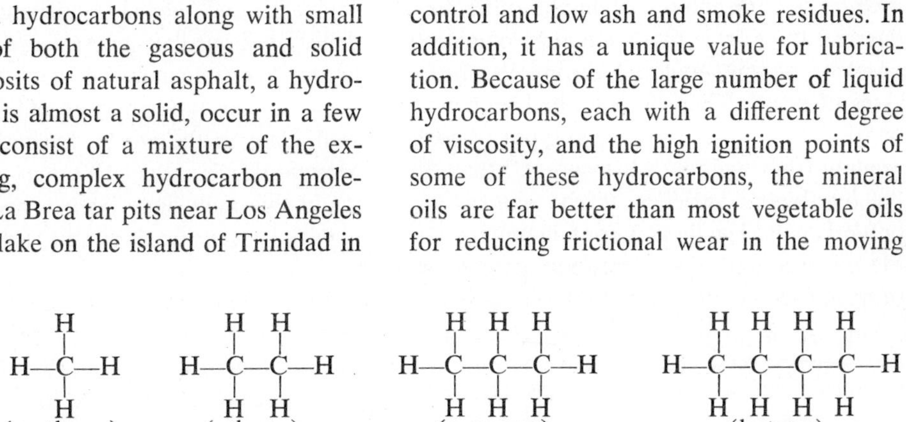

```
    H          H H           H H H            H H H H
    |          | |           | | |            | | | |
  H-C-H      H-C-C-H       H-C-C-C-H        H-C-C-C-C-H
    |          | |           | | |            | | | |
    H          H H           H H H            H H H H
(methane)   (ethane)      (propane)         (butane)
```

parts of machinery. All three fossil fuels are important sources of carbon for the synthesis of many chemical compounds.

Atomic energy is just beginning to be developed as a source of inanimate energy, and it is not yet wholly competitive commercially with the fossil fuels. Like the fossil fuels, the nuclear fuels are used primarily in the production of heat energy. The main advantages of atomic energy lie in the small volume of nuclear fuel required, the slowness of the rate of fuel consumption, and the extremely high temperatures that are produced. It is still very expensive, and the power generating plants now in existence are largely experimental ones. The first applied use has been in the generation of electricity to supply steam motive power in submarines. The bulkiness of the metallic shielding necessary for protection against dangerous radiation makes atomic energy unsuited for most types of transportation; thus it is not likely to be a serious competitor of gasoline and fuel oil. Several nuclear-propelled ocean vessels are in use, and large planes and locomotives are being designed to utilize atomic energy as motive power in the not too distant future.

13.2 COAL. Coal is a brown-to-black mixture of amorphous carbon and other residues resulting from the incomplete oxidation of plant organic material during the processes of decay. There is a gradual sequence, or spectrum, in the recognized types of coal, grading from *lignite,* or brown coal, through the *bituminous* varieties, to the *anthracites,* or hard coals. The lignites contain much volatile material and a relatively low percentage of fixed carbon, and their Btu[2] content is less than 8300 per ton. The bituminous coals have a wide range in heating capacity, varying from 8300 to over 15000 Btu per ton. The proportion of fixed carbon is under 86 per cent. The anthracites have a high fixed-carbon content, ranging from 86 to 98 per cent, and a low percentage of volatile materials. The anthracites are used primarily in domestic heating, because they burn slowly, with a hot flame, and produce little ash and smoke. The bituminous varieties are preferred for industrial use because they burn quickly and still produce much heat. Special equipment is used to handle the ash and soot problem.

Some uncertainty still exists about the exact process of coal formation, but nearly all authorities today believe that coal evolves from accumulations of partially decayed vegetation, deposited in shallow swamps and marshes or at the bottoms of lakes or lagoons. The transformation of these swamp or marsh deposits to coal undoubtedly involves compaction, usually by burial under hundreds or thousands of feet of sediments, but the nature of the subsequent chemical changes is disputed. Certainly a long period of time is required. Swamps and marshes offer the best conditions for the preservation of organic material. If the areas of poor drainage undergo slow progressive subsidence at about the same rate as the accumulation of organic material, considerable thicknesses of the latter may result. The thickest coal seam in the world, located at Fushun, Manchuria, is over 400 feet thick. Originally this may have been a bed of organic material several thousand feet in thickness.

Ideal conditions for the formation of coal existed in the great geosynclinal troughs of the late Paleozoic era, between 200 and 300 million years ago. Prior to that time, vegetation had not yet become established in any

[2] Btu stands for British thermal unit, which is the amount of heat energy required to raise one pound of water one degree Fahrenheit. The rating of these coals is established by the American Society for Testing Materials.

appreciable quantities. Slow, progressive subsidence, in which swampy conditions alternated with sedimentation of coarse erosional material from adjacent highlands, was a characteristic feature of these troughs. The location of coal deposits (see Fig. 13.1) and their geologic age indicate that the major deposits were formed during relatively unstable periods in earth history, when mountains were being formed, the geosynclines were subsiding, and climates were suitable locally for lush vegetative growth. Present-day deposits are only fragments of much larger areas which have been removed by erosion.

Some of the geosynclines which contained coal deposits were subjected to great regional compressional stresses. This resulted in the folding and faulting of the coal beds and increased their compaction. The anthracites were formed in this way. Under such extreme compaction, nearly all the volatile material and moisture were squeezed from the coal, increasing the percentage of fixed carbon. The structure of the anthracite fields of Pennsylvania clearly illustrates this feature (see Fig. 13.2).

GENERALIZED GLOBAL DISTRIBUTION OF COAL. Some of the major features in the global distribution of coal may be summarized as follows:

1. The major deposits are located in the mid-latitudes of the northern hemisphere.

2. Coal deposits are exceptionally rare in the low latitudes, and few are found in the southern hemisphere.

3. The higher-quality coals are generally the older ones.

4. There is a rough correlation between the fixed-carbon content of coal and the quantity and extent of the individual deposit. The coal highest in carbon (anthracite) is found only in small localized areas, and the total quantity is small. Lignites, however, which are at the opposite end of the coal spectrum, are usually found in large seams covering broad areas.

COAL DEPOSITS OF THE UNITED STATES. Correlations between the age, extent, and quality of coal can be well illustrated and explained by a short analysis of the distribution of coals within the United States. The detail of this distribution is shown in Fig. 13.3. The *Appalachian province,* the heart of the United States coal industry, corresponds closely with the *Appalachian geosyncline.* This was a great trough that once extended from Nova Scotia to Alabama and that in places accumulated over 40,000 feet of sediments through progressive subsidence. Interspersed between layers of sandstone and shale are many seams of coal, which become thinner and fewer toward the west, or away from the major axis of subsidence. The plant remains which later formed coal were laid down during the closing periods of the Paleozoic era, roughly 200 to 300 million years ago. Since the higher, or woody, types of plant life did not evolve on earth much earlier than this, these Paleozoic coal deposits are among the oldest on earth. At the close of the sedimentation period, lateral pressure from the southeast crumpled the thick trough sediments into great folds. The folds fade out toward the west. The gradation from high-volatile bituminous coal lying in gently sloping beds in the western part of the Appalachian province, through low-volatile bituminous coal, to anthracite in the northeast is illustrated in Fig. 13.2.

The coal beds of the *interior province* in the United States were formed at the same time as those in the Appalachian province but differ in having been laid down in relatively shallow sedimentary basins, corresponding to persistent "sag" areas in the earth crust. Also, lying in the relatively stable continental interior, they were not subjected

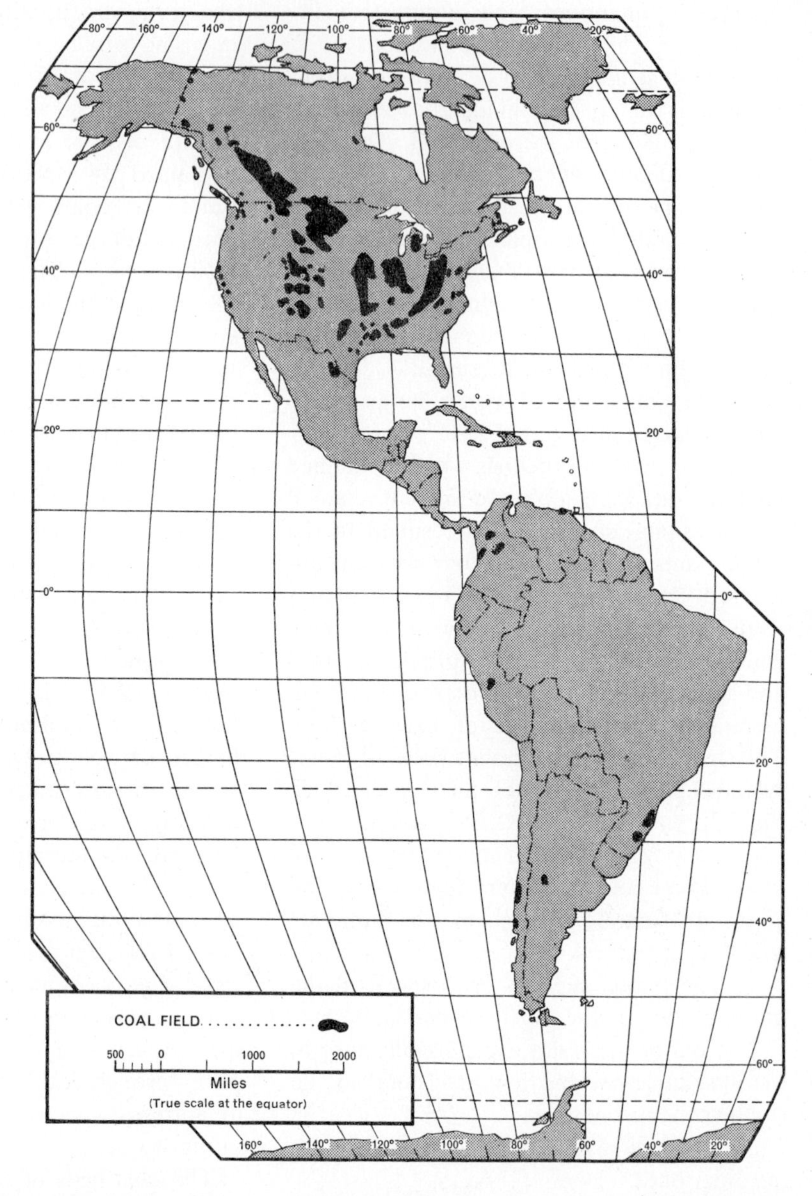

FIG. 13.1 World distribution of coal fields. [After Oxford Economic Atlas of the World]

to the great stresses associated with mountain building. Like the deposits of the western Appalachian province, the coal consists largely of high-volatile, bituminous types. An exception to the above generalization is found in Arkansas. Here, extending in an east-west direction, was another deep geosyncline, termed the *Ouachita trough*. Although much smaller than the Appalachian geosyncline to the east, the Ouachita trough underwent a sequence of events closely paralleling that in the Appalachian geosyncline and at roughly the same time, including the foundering of the trough, compression, folding, and

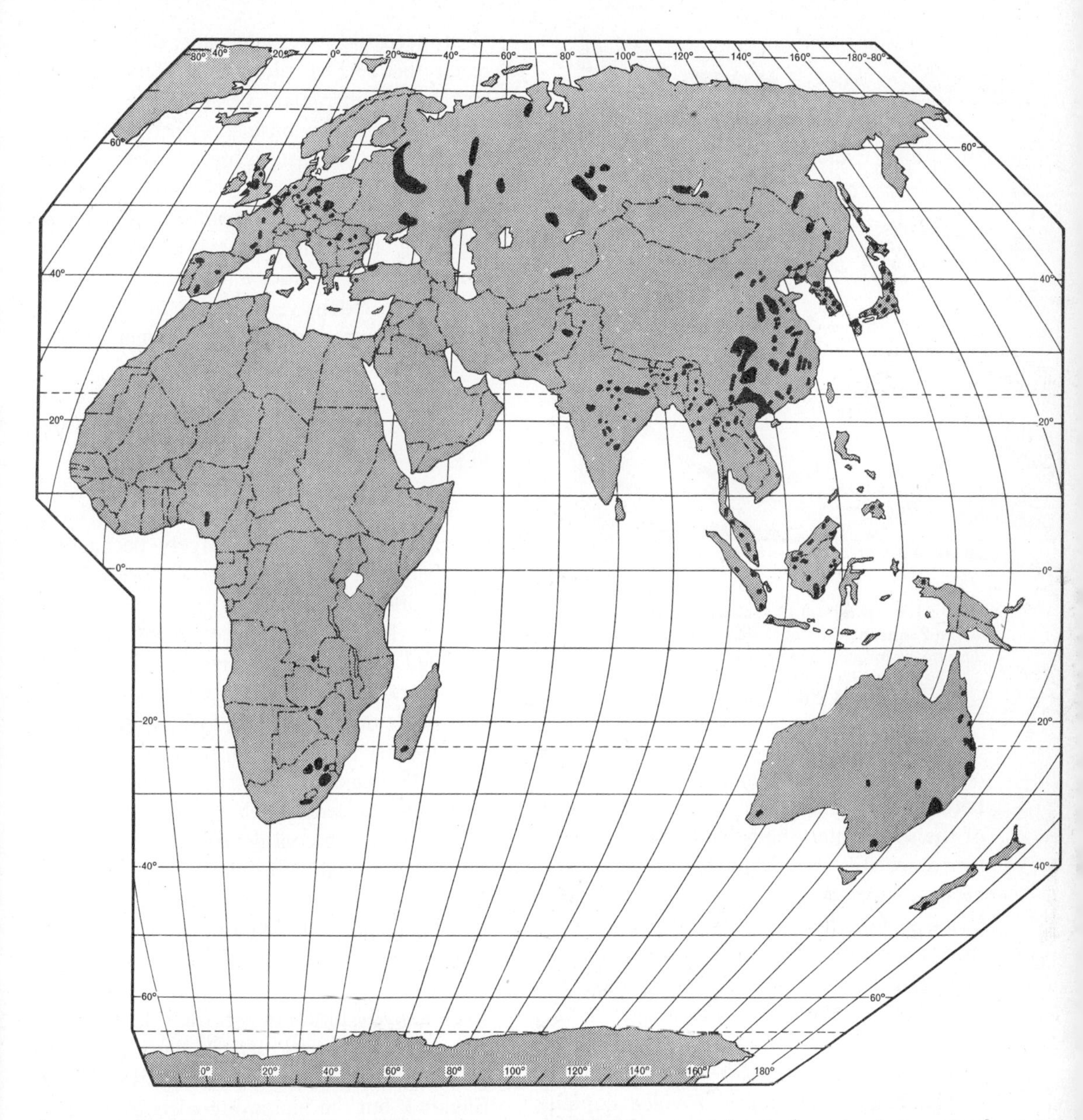

later erosional beveling of the folded strata. Some semianthracite is found in the tight folds of this region and is important for domestic heating purposes in the St. Louis metropolitan area.

The *northern Great Plains province* has some of the most extensive coal beds in the world. These are located somewhat east of the Rocky Mountains, and extend northward from central Wyoming to west-central Alberta in Canada. These deposits are much younger than those in the eastern part of the United States, having been laid down in a huge geosynclinal trough during the Creta-

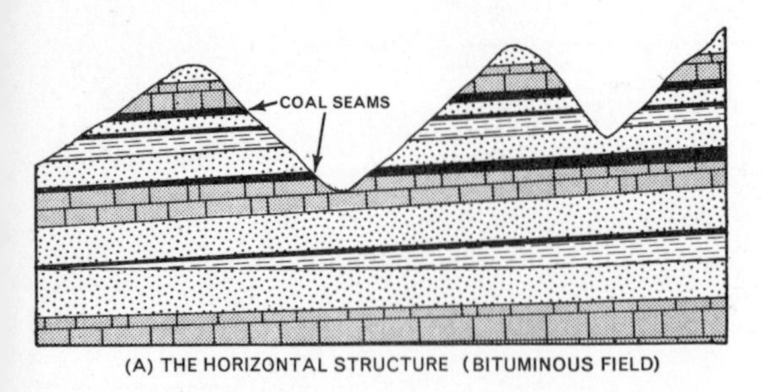

(A) THE HORIZONTAL STRUCTURE (BITUMINOUS FIELD)

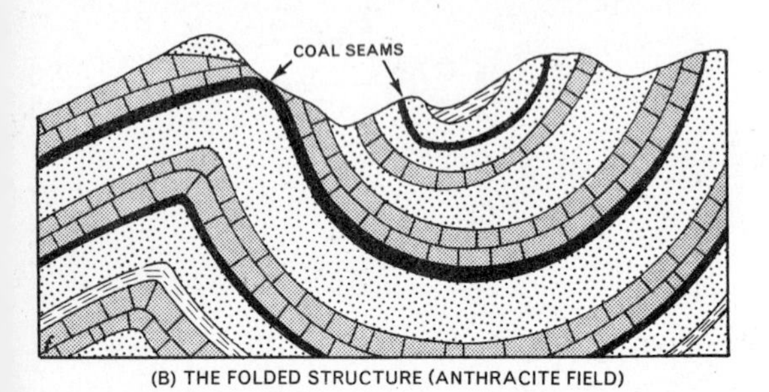

(B) THE FOLDED STRUCTURE (ANTHRACITE FIELD)

FIG. 13.2 Diagram of typical rock structures in the Pennsylvanian coal fields. The steeply dipping anthracite seams are much more expensive to mine than the gently dipping seams that outcrop along the sides of valleys.

ceous and early Tertiary periods, or roughly between 90 and 100 million years ago. Some of the sedimentary beds in which the coal is found are still unconsolidated, never having been compacted or cemented into rock. Lying in huge flat–to–gently dipping strata, these coal beds are of lignite or subbituminous coal. They are rarely mined, since they are unable to compete with higher-quality coals, but they constitute an immense reserve which may someday be important.

The *Rocky Mountain province* contains a large number of unconnected coal deposits formerly laid down in a series of basins of various geologic ages and sizes. Several of the basins were involved in the regional warping during the uplift of the Rocky Mountain cordillera, and hence coal of widely different types can be found. The most accessible deposits are those which reach the surface along the flanks of the high mountain ranges, or along the margins of the sedimentary basins. Such typical positions include the eastern foot of the Colorado Front Range, the margins of the Green River basin in southwestern Wyoming, and an area bordering the ranges in central Utah. The coal beds of the Rocky Mountain province are not so extensive as those in the Great Plains province, but they are much thicker and, in general, of higher quality.

COAL DEPOSITS IN EUROPE. Much of the large industrial growth of northwestern Europe was related to the early development of coal mining. During the early eighteenth century, England turned to coal as a basic material in steelmaking, largely because of the depletion of the hardwood forests used in the production of charcoal. The problem of removing water from coal mines in England led to one of the first practical applications of James Watt's steam engine. The coal fields of England are located in a series of relatively small basins, most of which lie along the flanks of the structural arch of the Pennines, the central belt of hills in the country. Some of the coal deposits, such as those in southern Wales, lie along the coast, and for many years coal could be exported cheaply to ports throughout the world. Coal played an important part in England's global role as a sea power. The English coals consist mainly of bituminous varieties, and some are excellent for use as metallurgical coke. There are still appreciable coal reserves in England, but the increasing costs of production and the outmoded production facilities in many of the mines have been handicaps to the competitive position of the national coal industry.

The greatest coal deposit in Europe, excluding the Soviet Union, lies in the Ruhr Basin of northwestern Germany. This fa-

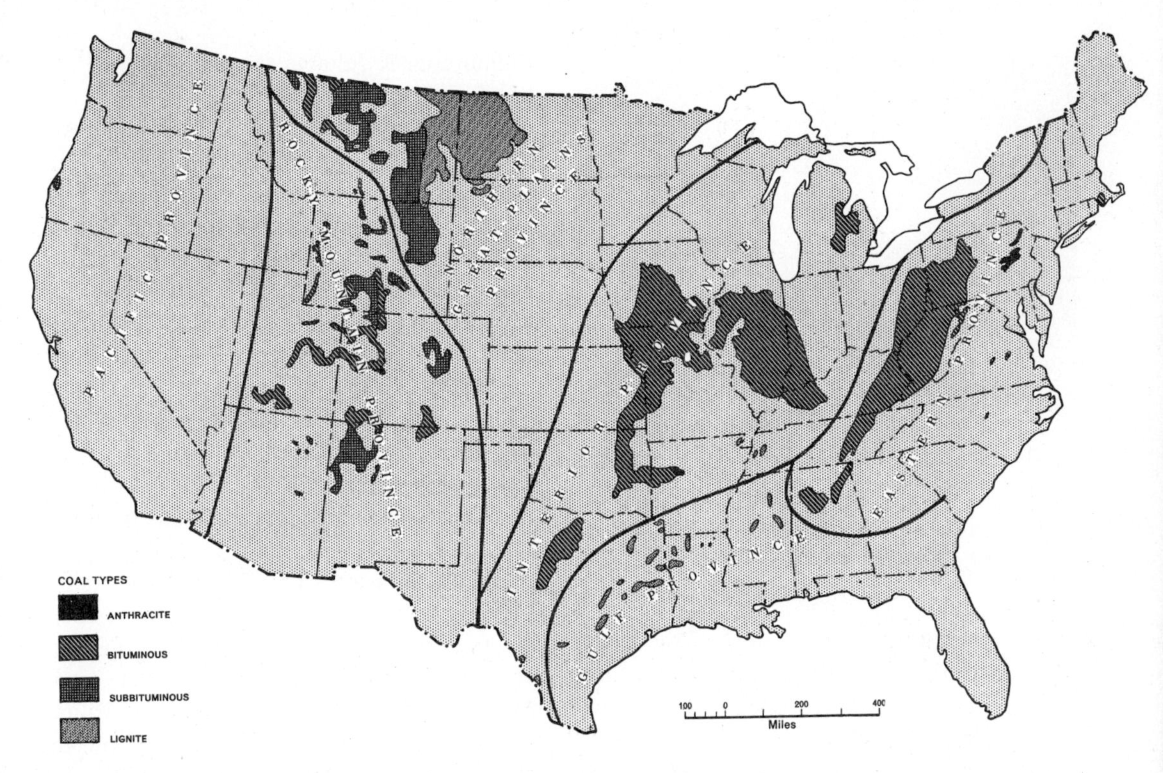

FIG. 13.3 United States coal provinces, showing major coal types. [After Atlas of Mineral Resources of the World]

mous bituminous coal field is especially noted for its excellent coking coal, which has formed the major basis of the steel industry not only in Germany but also in several adjoining countries. The Ruhr ranks as one of the great coal fields of the world. Ruhr bituminous coal also is important in Germany's chemical industry and in the generation of steam electric power. Other bituminous coal fields in western Europe include the Saar Basin and the fields of northern France and southern Belgium. The bituminous coal field of Upper Silesia is an important industrial base for southern Poland.

COAL DEPOSITS OF THE SOVIET UNION. Coal is one of the major industrial assets of the Soviet Union. One of the oldest and still the most important coal field of the country is the *Donetz,* or *Donbas,* area in the eastern Ukraine. It includes a variety of bituminous coals. Ranking second is the *Kuznetz* field of south-central Siberia, near the major steel center of Stalinsk. Both bituminous coal and anthracite are mined in the Kuznetz field. Other major coal fields include the *Karaganda* field, about midway between the Kuznetz field and the Aral Sea; the *Pechora* field, near the Arctic Circle and just west of the Urals; the fields flanking the central Urals; the *Irkutsk* field, west of Lake Baikal; the *Bureya* field, in the upper Amur River area; and reportedly extensive deposits in the upper Yenesei and Lena River basins. Altogether, the coal deposits scattered throughout the Soviet Union are vast, and reserves should be adequate for many decades.

COAL DEPOSITS IN ASIA. China ranks among the world leaders in coal reserves, although

FIG. 13.4 An 8-foot coal seam near Glendive, Montana, showing the sedimentary beds in which the coal was deposited. [M. R. Campbell; U.S. Geological Survey]

production still is far below that of the leading industrial nations. High-grade coking and steam coal, comprising about three-fourths of the Chinese reserves, underlie large sections of Shensi and Shansi provinces in northern China. The Fushun field of south-central Manchuria has one of the largest open-pit coal mines in the world. Small coal deposits are also scattered throughout the sedimentary-rock areas of central and far western China (Sinkiang).

Japan has important deposits of noncoking, good-quality steam coal in northern Kyushu and southern Hokkaido Islands. The Kyushu deposits are difficult to work, however, because of the steeply dipping, thin, faulted seams and the problem of water seepage.

There are also good-quality bituminous coal deposits in India, which are located largely in the Damodar Valley west of Calcutta but also in the central part of the Indian peninsula. The coal of the Damodar Valley is being integrated into a large industrial complex, tied to electrical power and heavy industry. Only a small part of the Indian coal is suitable for metallurgical use, however.

COAL DEPOSITS OF THE SOUTHERN HEMISPHERE. As indicated earlier, there is relatively little coal south of the equator. The largest deposits are found in the Union of South Africa (Transvaal and Natal) and in eastern Australia. Small deposits are also found along the flanks of the Andes in Colombia, Peru, and Chile.

GENERAL GLOBAL RESERVES. Although quantitative figures for coal reserves are subject to many qualifications, based on variable types of coal, differences in accessibility, incompleteness of exploration, and inaccurate estimates, a rough yardstick of reserves is shown in Fig. 13.5. This indicates that the countries having the largest coal reserves are the United States, Soviet Union, China, and Germany—probably in that order. These four nations control approximately 80 per cent of the coal yet to be mined in the world. Because of the nature of coal deposits, data on coal reserves are probably better than those for most other mineral resource materials.

The importance of coal in the economy of nations cannot be overemphasized. Not only is it the principal source of inanimate energy in most industrial nations, but it serves a host of other functions. It has exceeded water power as a source of electric power for many decades, and it is the crucial raw material in most synthetic carbon compounds, from dyes and antiseptics to flavorings and plastics. Coke, a firm, porous mass of carbon formed by driving off the volatile material from certain types of bituminous coal, is essential to the smelting of iron ore. In the future, coal may well have its greatest use in the synthesis of hydrocarbons, when the present reserves of petroleum and natural gas begin to run short. Synthetic gasoline from low-grade coal deposits supplied most of the German war requirements during World War II. Someday coal may supply the world with hydrocarbons.

13.3 PETROLEUM. The origin of petroleum is not so well understood as that of coal, but evidence now indicates that the source material definitely is organic, probably from microscopic sea life (*plankton*) in a shallow marine environment. As in the case of coal, burial of the organic material under thick sediments appears to be required. Some authorities maintain that certain forms of minute plant life, such as diatoms, can form hydrocarbons directly, but other experts believe that the heat and pressure associated with deep burial are necessary for the chemical synthesis of hydrocarbons. Regardless of the exact method of formation, the place of origin is in fine-textured marine sediments, such as clays or lime muds. Many such beds, now compacted into shales and limestones, contain liquid hydrocarbons that are bound tightly within the tiny openings of the rock strata. It has been estimated that more oil is contained within the oil shales of the United States than has been removed so far from oil wells.

As long as the tiny droplets of oil remain within their source sediments, they are scattered, tightly bound to rock particles, and difficult to remove. When these beds are buried under later deposits, however, the resultant pressure may force some of this oil out into more permeable strata. Such strata usually consist of loosely cemented sandstones or granular, porous limestones. Highly shattered and cracked rocks of any kind, however, may contain sufficient openings to permit the passage or storage of oil. Cavernous limestones sometimes contain pools of petroleum, trapped within the openings. Once the oil enters the permeable rock strata, gravity and the hydraulic pressure of

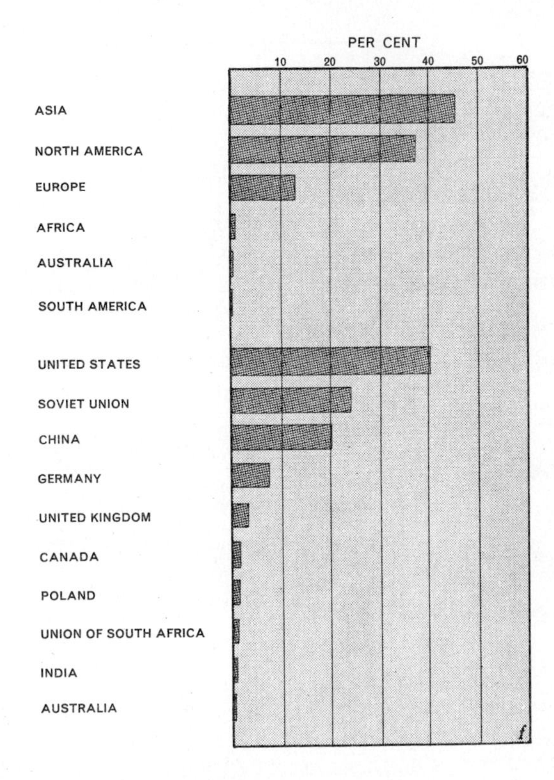

FIG. 13.5 Estimated world coal reserves.

associated water may cause it to migrate laterally for a considerable distance from its point of origin. Although the issue is debatable, some geologists maintain that oil may migrate as much as a few hundred miles from its source.

Somewhere along its path of migration the oil encounters an impermeable rock condition that traps it, preventing further travel. There are several types of oil traps, the most usual of which are shown in Fig. 13.6. As indicated by the percentages, the predominant type is the *anticline,* or simple arch trap, which operates on the same principle as the grease elbow trap beneath a kitchen sink. In order to flow freely from a well, therefore, oil must be located within a porous rock layer and must be prevented from escaping by certain arrangements of confin-

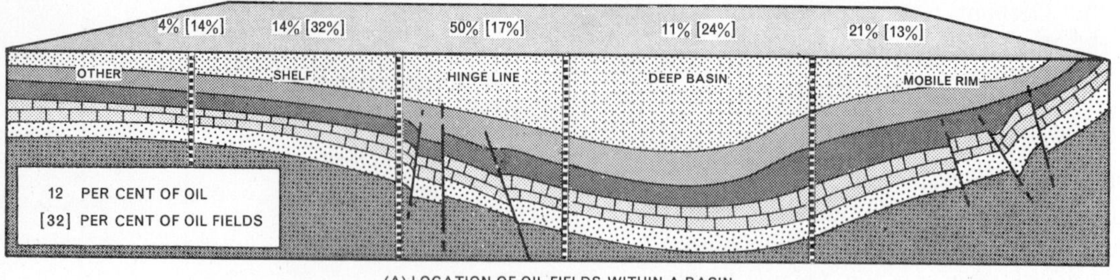

(A) LOCATION OF OIL FIELDS WITHIN A BASIN

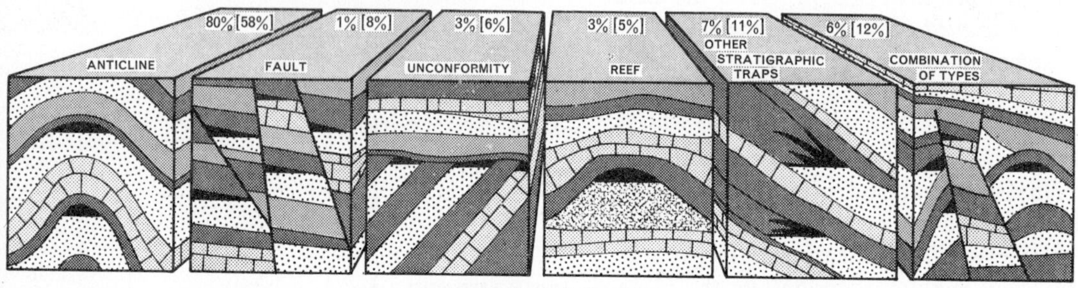

(B) TYPES OF OIL TRAPS

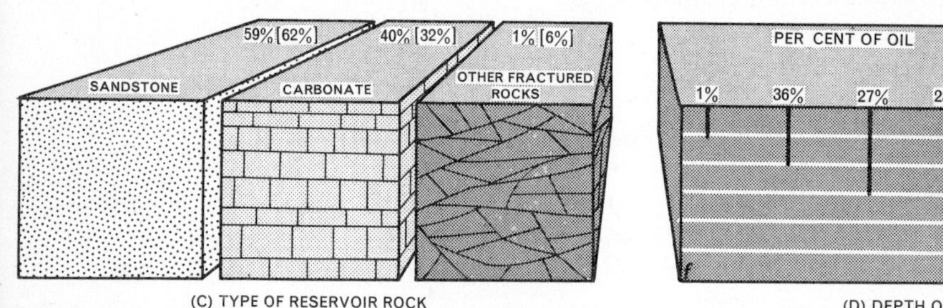

(C) TYPE OF RESERVOIR ROCK

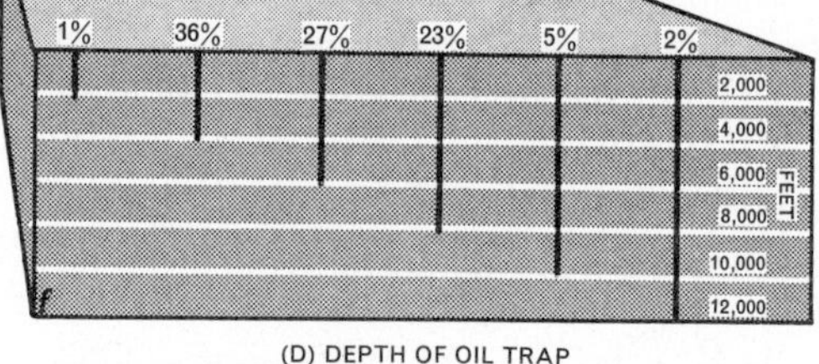

(D) DEPTH OF OIL TRAP

FIG. 13.6 Types and distribution of oil structures. Where two percentages are given, the first refers to the percentage of total oil produced; the second indicates the percentage of individual oil fields located on such structures. These data are composite estimates for oil occurrences throughout the world. [After Krebel, Rodriguez, and Graso]

ing, impermeable rock strata. Note also in Fig. 13.6 that most known oil traps are located along the sides of great geosynclinal troughs, usually at depths between 2,000 and 6,000 feet below the surface. At shallower depths there is a greater opportunity for escape to the surface. At greater depths, the rock strata tend to become more compact, because of rock pressure, and are therefore less permeable.

Although petroleum resources are rather widely distributed over the earth surface, individual oil fields are tiny in comparison with the immense individual beds of coal. The reason for this is that producing wells are restricted to trap structures. Figure 13.7 shows the distribution of oil fields in Texas. Such a scattered pattern is typical of most of the major petroleum-producing areas of the world.

The oil fields of the world are restricted to sedimentary basins containing various thicknesses of sedimentary strata. This does not mean that all of the basin areas shown in Fig. 13.8 contain oil fields. The most likely places within these basins for the occurrence of oil fields are where the strata are composed of marine or near-marine sediments or sedimentary rocks, and where localized flexures or warpings in the earth crust have taken place. Areas of igneous and metamorphic rocks, which make up a large part of the world outside of the sedimentary basins as shown in Fig. 13.8, are highly improbable locations for future oil field development.[3] The areas that contain *currently producing* fields are mainly the great geosynclinal troughs of the world. Note that they border either the continental margins or the great mountain cordilleras. Areas that appear to have large reserves of petroleum, according to a few preliminary test borings, but that have not yet been adequately explored or significantly developed for production purposes include (1) the sedimentary basins that border the Arctic Ocean in Alaska, northwestern Canada, and the Soviet Union; (2) the sedimentary basins east of the Andes in Brazil, Bolivia, Peru, and Argentina; (3) the sedimentary basins that lie on the broader offshore continental-shelf zones. Examples of new producing offshore oil fields are those in the Gulf of Mexico, Southern California, the Persian Gulf, Lake Maracaibo, and the Caspian Sea. These areas are rapidly being developed.

The fact that petroleum is somewhat more widely distributed than coal must be interpreted in the light of several factors. First, petroleum droplets, when first formed, are much more stable and less likely to be oxidized than plant remains. Second, petroleum is able to migrate and hence is not so strictly limited to its original site. The distances involved, however, are uncertain. Third, since tiny marine organisms were probably the first types of life to appear on earth, productive petroleum fields may have a greater age range than coal deposits and may therefore be subject to a wider distribution. On the other hand, because available oil resources are restricted to particular permeable rock layers, there are usually fewer producing strata in a petroleum field than in a coal deposit.

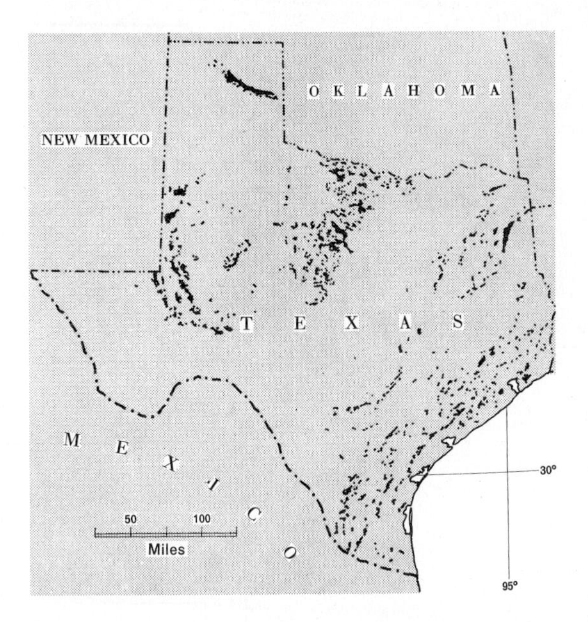

FIG. 13.7 Individual oil pools in Texas. Note the large number of pools and the relatively small surface area of each. This is characteristic of producing areas throughout the world. Groups of pools are termed oil fields. [U.S. Geological Survey]

The distribution of petroleum includes not only the present and potential oil fields but also the shales and other rocks that contain petroleum not obtainable by drilling and pumping. The most important of the latter are *oil shales*. Although these are found in

[3] Porous volcanic lavas and highly fractured igneous rocks have been known to contain petroleum which has migrated there from adjacent permeable sedimentary rocks. Such occurrences, however, are extremely rare.

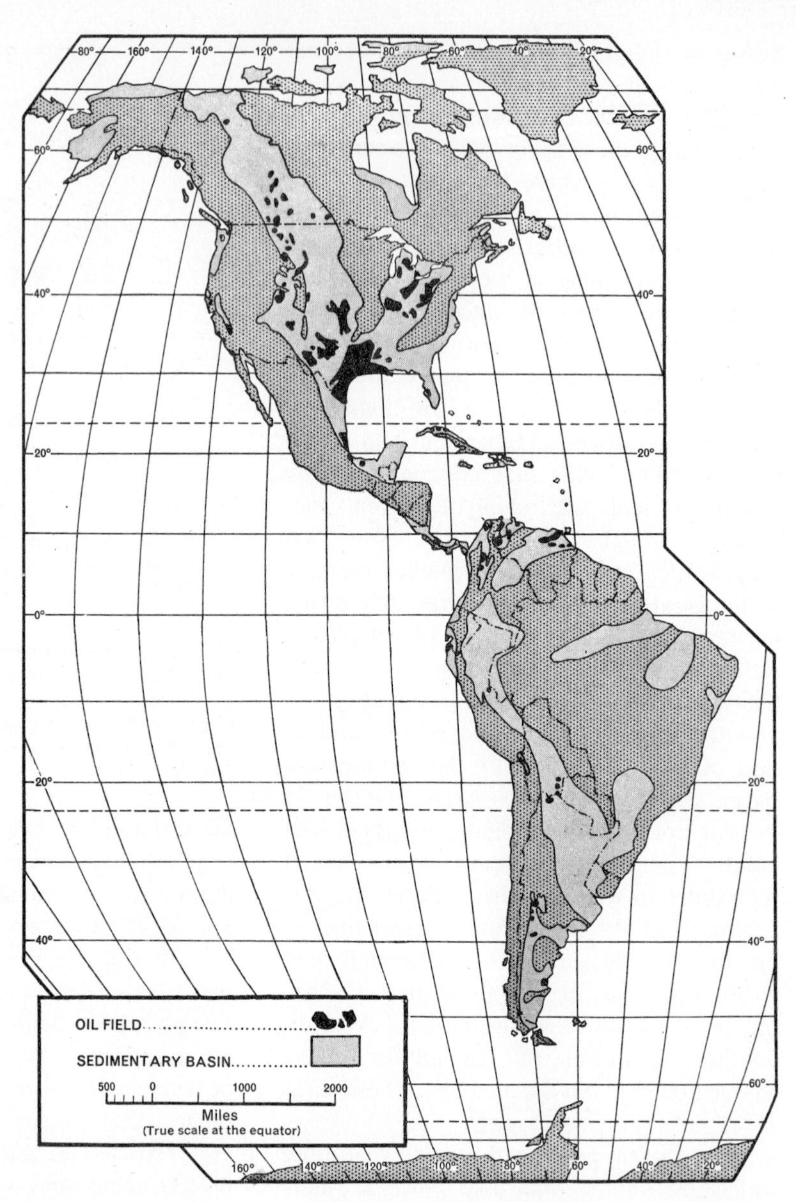

FIG. 13.8 World distribution of oil fields and sedimentary basins. [After Pratt and Good]

many parts of the world, they have not been an important source of oil, mainly because of the price competition of petroleum from wells. In order to obtain the oil from shale, the rock must be quarried, crushed, and heated to drive out the oil. Europe is the principal area for oil-shale utilization, and the Soviet Union, Germany, Scotland, France, Italy, and Czechoslovakia are recovering some oil from this source. Until the development of the new oil-producing area near Yumen in Kansu Province, China, the major source for Chinese petroleum was the oil-shale region near Fushun, Manchuria. Colorado and Wyoming have enormous deposits of oil shale, and the U.S. Bureau of

Mines has been experimenting with techniques for mining and treating them. A private concern in Utah is profitably producing a relatively small amount of oil from shale.

Probably the largest unused single deposit of hydrocarbons in the world is contained within the Athabaskan tar sands, located along the Athabaska River, southwest of Lake Athabaska in eastern Alberta, Canada. These tar sands comprise an enormous deposit of coarse sand partially cemented with heavy hydrocarbons. Estimates of the heavy crude-oil reserves within this single deposit run as high as 100 to 300 billion barrels. Until recently, the high cost of separating the heavy "crudes" from the sands prevented the development of this huge potential resource area. However, a separation plant utilizing a centrifuge process is under way, and a production of 20,000 barrels of crude oil per day is anticipated. The plant is located near Fort McMurray, on the Athabaska River. A small experimental separation plant, formerly run by the government, is now being operated by a private concern in the area.

The nature of liquid petroleum is such that many reservoirs undoubtedly remain to be discovered. Despite the various technical devices, now available for geophysical prospecting, no system yet devised will indicate the presence of petroleum underground. The best exploration methods, such as the use of seismographs (a type of echo sounder), gravity meters (to measure minute differences in gravity), magnetometers (to measure magnetic permeabilities of rock strata), and geologic surveying, will often indicate geological irregularities in the rock strata that may turn out to be structural traps, but whether such traps contain oil can be tested only by well drilling. Moreover, some oil traps, such as the stratigraphic type (see Fig. 13.6), are extremely difficult to locate, even if the best prospecting techniques are used. One of the largest oil fields in the United States, the East Texas field, was discovered by "wildcat" well drilling in an area that apparently lacked suitable trap structures, according to geophysical prospecting.

The immense production of oil in the United States is largely the result of the huge sums of money spent on prospecting and drilling operations. As a rough rule, proved reserves in this country have been maintained at approximately fifteen to sixteen times the current production. Over the past twenty years, well drilling in new areas (wildcatting) has averaged about one producing well to nine dry wells. Of course, the percentage of success is higher in proven fields and in extensions from proven fields. The distribution of productive petroleum fields thus is related closely to the effort expended in finding them, and many countries do not have the necessary capital to sustain the losses resulting from drilling dry or unproductive wells. In 1955, drilling costs in the United States averaged about $50,000 per well, with approximately 56,000 wells drilled. Of that number, 14,937 were exploratory, and only about 20 per cent of these proved to be productive.[4] Prior to 1942, the total number of dry holes drilled by the three major world powers and by the South American countries, collectively, was estimated as shown in Table 13.2.

TABLE 13.2 Number of dry oil wells drilled prior to 1942

United States	252,540
British Empire (prewar)	5,750
South America	2,900
Soviet Union (prewar)	2,650

SOURCE: Wallace E. Pratt, *Oil in the Earth,* University of Kansas Press, Lawrence, Kans., 1942, pp. 40, 65.

A general summary of the oil-reserve situation in various areas of the world is presented in Table 13.3.

In summary, it is probable that the oil industry will discover sufficient petroleum to supply normal demands for several decades. Production and consumption are increasing rapidly outside the United States. The critical reserve point in the United States will be reached when the return from successful exploratory drilling does not match the losses entailed by the drilling of dry holes. In recent years a trend in that direction has been indicated by the fact that fewer barrels of crude-

[4] F. D. Lahee, "Exploratory Drilling in 1955," *Bulletin of the American Association of Petroleum Geologists,* vol. 40, no. 6, p. 1061, June, 1956.

TABLE 13.3 General appraisal of world petroleum resources

AREA	STATUS OF PETROLEUM RESOURCES
UNITED STATES	World's largest producer. Proved reserves continue to be maintained at about 15 times the annual consumption rate. Continued exploration eventually will fail to keep up with the huge consumption. Exploration costs are mounting. The average yield of new wells is declining.
SOVIET UNION	Present production is more than adequate for normal needs, and it is likely that Soviet oil will enter the European markets in increasing quantities. Production in 1956 was more than double the 1950 figure and was reported at 571 million barrels, or about 22 per cent of United States production. Low ratio of production to reserves. The major producing area is in the Middle Volga region.
CHINA	Petroleum is a major mineral deficiency. Some new finds in remote areas of Kansu, Szechwan, and Sinkiang provinces. One-half of 1956 production was supplied by new Yumen field in Kansu. Discovery of major reserves is unlikely. Best future sources appear to be synthetic hydrocarbons from coal and Manchurian oil shales.
CANADA	Should increase its position as one of the great world producers. Large undeveloped reserves are believed to exist in the Mackenzie basin. Rapid new development in Alberta and northeastern British Columbia.
JAPAN	Small production, about enough for lubrication requirements. Petroleum and its products are among the principal imports.
INDONESIA	Ample reserves, mainly in Sumatra and Borneo. This region is a surplus producer for deficient Asiatic countries. The producing areas in western New Guinea are proving disappointing.
INDIA-PAKISTAN	Some oil is produced. More may be found, but the section is not likely to become a major producing area. Principal producing region in India is the upper Brahmaputra Valley in Assam.
AUSTRALIA–NEW ZEALAND	Practically no oil is produced, and major discoveries are unlikely.
THE MIDDLE EAST (IRAQ, IRAN, ARABIA, KUWAIT, ETC.)	Contains world's largest proved reserves. Will be a major producer for many years. This area is the major source for European oil and the rich plum of the international political power arena.
AFRICA	The new finds in southern Algeria and Tunisia indicate a major regional producing potential. Small quantities are produced in Egypt and Morocco. Some possibilities exist along the east coast. New discoveries in Gabon indicate potentialities in equatorial areas.
EUROPE	Romania is the only country with appreciable production. Several small fields are producing in France, Italy, Britain, Netherlands, Germany, Austria, etc., but none of the countries is self-sufficient. Minor finds will continue to be made. Deficiencies should continue.
SOUTH AMERICA	Venezuela is a major world producer. Production and exploration in Colombia are continuing. Reserves are large. Other countries need capital for development. The sedimentary zone east of the Andes should contain undiscovered fields. The first producing well at Nova Olinda, Brazil (1955), proved that the Amazon Basin is a potential oil area. Argentina and the Bolivian and Paraguaian Chaco should find new producing fields.

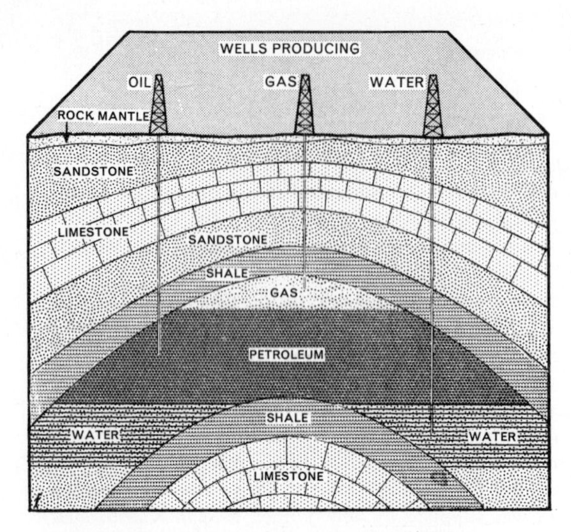

FIG. 13.9 Oil, gas, and water relationships in a typical anticlinal trap. Sometimes a horizontal difference of a few feet in the location of a well means the difference between a gas well, a petroleum well, or a water well.

oil reserves are being found for each new oil well completed. The major features of the distribution of petroleum are related to the great sedimentary basins of the world, concentrated along the margins of the unstable zones of the earth crust. Again, as in the case of coal, the northern hemisphere is blessed with a disproportionate share of the world's petroleum. The specific distribution of producing petroleum fields, however, is closely related to the pattern of oil exploration and investment in potential oil-producing zones.

13.4 NATURAL GAS. Natural gas is formed, and therefore distributed, in much the same way as petroleum, differing only in being a gas rather than a liquid. Gas and petroleum often are found in the same field, with the gaseous hydrocarbons occupying a position in the rock traps nearer the surface (see Fig. 13.9). Where there is a large amount of rock pressure against both the oil and the gas, much of the natural gas may be dissolved in the liquid—in much the same way as carbon dioxide is confined in a bottle of soda water. When a high-compression gas and oil field is reached by drilling, the pressure forces the oil and gas to the surface together and may produce violent "gushers." Such wells have been known to produce several thousand barrels of oil per day for short periods. Natural gas may occur by itself, however, without associated petroleum.

Natural gas, being lighter and more mobile than liquid petroleum, is found over a wider area. The volume of the gas also is considerably greater. Some rock strata may have conditions of porosity and permeability favorable to the migration and trapping of natural gas, but not petroleum. Broad, shallow warps in the rock structure, for example, may contain gas and no oil. In areas such as these, the principal hydrocarbons are commonly of the "dry" type, with a predominance of methane and ethane. The gas associated with oil wells, on the other hand, commonly has high proportions of the "wet" gases, propane and butane. Where gas and oil exist together in the same trap, as shown in Fig. 13.9, the surface boundary separating oil wells and gas wells may be extremely sharp.

For a long time natural gas was only an annoyance to oil producers in the United States. Occupying a large amount of space, it could not be easily stored, and if released into the air, it could constitute a serious fire hazard. It frequently was burned at the wells, and for many years the oil fields that had associated gas were vividly marked at night by the glow of the tall flares of burning gas, visible for miles. Natural gas was a valuable fuel for areas located a short distance from the producing fields, but the cost of transportation prevented its use elsewhere. Pipelines later proved to be ideal for the shipment of natural gas, particularly following the introduction of welded-seam pipe, which permitted the transmission of gas under high pressure.

The general popularity of natural gas for urban household use and for industrial uses that require careful regulation of flame heat (as in the manufacture of glass) has led to an enormous increase in natural-gas production and pipeline construction, and in 1956 all but two states (Maine and Vermont) in the United States were being served by gas pipelines. In 1957, the consumption of natural gas in the United States amounted to about 10 trillion cubic feet, almost five times greater than it had been 20 years earlier. A further explanation for the increase in consumption is the popularity of liquefied petroleum gas, or natural gas that has been compressed into liquid form. This makes possible the use of household gas in rural homes. Although utilized primarily for house heating, liquefied petroleum gas also has significant uses in the chemical industry, notably in the manufacture of synthetic rubber. In addition, it is used for flame cutting and for propulsion of industrial tractors and lift trucks. Some taxicab fleets have had their motors adapted for burning liquefied petroleum gas as a motor fuel. In 1956, almost 850 million gallons of liquefied petroleum gas was used as motor fuel.

Approximately one-third of the natural gas produced in North America is derived from oil wells, with the remainder supplied by gas wells. The continental interior fields, ranging from the coast of the Gulf of Mexico far into Canada, have huge gas reserves, with Alberta and northeastern British Columbia as the main areas of recent development. Proved reserves in Alberta alone are reported to be in excess of 40 trillion cubic feet. A trans-Canada gas pipeline, 2,150 miles long, extending from Alberta to Toronto was scheduled for completion in 1958. Another 30-inch gas line, 650 miles long, from Alberta to Vancouver, British Columbia, was completed in 1957. Plans have been made to connect Canadian gas fields with California.

Natural-gas production outside North America is relatively limited. Venezuela ranks next to the United States and Canada, with a total of about 1 trillion cubic feet in 1956. Venezuelan consumption, however, is relatively small, and a large part of the gas is returned to producing formations to maintain pressure or is burned at oil fields to avoid dangerous accumulations.

The Soviet Union claimed a production of 483.8 billion cubic feet of natural gas in 1956, or roughly one-fortieth that of the United States.[5] The 1960 goal was reported to be 1.4 trillion cubic feet. Pipelines serve most of the larger cities of the western Soviet Union. Production formerly was mainly from the Caucasus and Baku areas. A new field near Bukhara, in the Uzbek Republic south of the Aral Sea, however, now is the leading producer. A large part of the Polish production is being routed to the Soviet Union.

The most important producer in Europe, excluding the Soviet Union, is Italy. The shortage of other mineral fuels has made the natural gas of the Po Valley a critical item in the industrial economy of northern Italy, and 157 billion cubic feet was produced in 1956. Small quantities of gas are being produced in most of the other European countries.

The low production and consumption outside North America, the Soviet Union, and

[5] The general estimates of natural-gas production in this section were obtained from the Aug. 15, 1957 issue of *World Oil.* Accurate statistics, however, are difficult to obtain, because of the large number of small producers and consumers scattered throughout the world.

FIG. 13.10 The Calder Hall atomic energy plant in England. This is the forerunner of four such plants, and was completed in 1956. It not only produces over 60,000 kilowatts of electric power, but also produces plutonium for the military program. [British Information Services]

Venezuela are related largely to the inadequate development of markets, gas fields, and pipelines. In areas where natural gas is abundant, as in the Middle East, custom and the lack of gas-using equipment hinder the growth of a significant domestic market. In other areas of high potential markets, gas is not available in sufficient amounts to stimulate the manufacture of gas appliances. National border restrictions hinder the construction of transcontinental pipelines. At present, much of the surplus gas in the Middle East is being injected back into the ground for storage in suitable empty trap reservoirs. A new development is the liquefaction of natural gas by chilling, and subsequent shipment by large, refrigerated tankers. The first shipment of such liquefied gas from Ras Tanura in Saudi Arabia took place in 1961.

13.5 ATOMIC ENERGY AND THE MINERAL FUELS OF NUCLEAR FISSION.

The development of atomic energy has introduced a new source of inanimate energy for human use and has created a demand for a new type of mineral fuel. Although the first application of atomic energy produced through nuclear fission was for destructive purposes, research indicated that fission could be controlled and that an immense amount of heat energy could be released from a relatively small quantity of nuclear "fuel." *Nuclear fission* consists of splitting the nucleus, or core, of an atom. In this disruptive process, the energy which formerly held the nucleus together is released in the form of powerful radiant energy having short wavelengths. This short-wavelength radiation is capable of generating much heat and is the energy source in atomic energy power plants, which harness this heat in the production of steam and electric power.

Shortly before World War II it was discovered that a particular *isotope*[6] of uranium, U^{235}, was especially susceptible to fission

[6] An *isotope* is one of two or more kinds of elements that have the same number of electrons and protons and similar chemical properties but that differ in atomic weight, because of the number of neutrons in the atomic nucleus. The atom of the simplest of all elements, hydrogen, for example, consists of a single, positively charged proton in the nucleus and an encircling, halolike negative charge. Occasionally, however, extra neutrons may join the nucleus, forming isotopes of hydrogen having a greater atomic weight. *Deuterium* and *tritium* are, respectively, the "twin" and "triplet" isotopes of hydrogen and form what is sometimes known as *heavy water* when combined with oxygen in the water molecule.

when exposed to the bombardment of subatomic particles. It was further discovered that the particles released in this fission, especially neutrons, could in turn induce further fission in adjacent atoms and that a chain reaction of cumulative fission would release large quantities of powerful short-wavelength radiant energy, provided that a critical mass of this isotope could be brought together. The atomic bomb was the first applied result of this discovery. The underlying principle of atomic power plants is the same as that of the bomb, except that the cumulative action is controlled, or dampened, thus releasing the energy over a longer period of time and reducing the violence of the fission.

The principal fission fuel, U^{235}, is a natural element, occurring wherever uranium is found and always in about the proportion of 1 part of U^{235} to about 140 parts of U^{238}. Separating it, however, has proved to be a long, difficult, and costly process. The separation of plutonium is about as difficult as that of U^{235}.

Atomic fission as a commercial source of energy has had to await the solution of many problems, including shielding against dangerous radiation, the high cost of extracting fission "fuel," the disposal of radioactive wastes, the development of new metals to withstand high heat and corrosive action in atomic reactors, and the discovery of new "moderating" materials to slow down particle velocities and thus act as brakes in the chain-reaction process. Of these, the most serious drawback has been the great cost of separating U^{235} from uranium ores in order to obtain fission fuel. This cost has been reduced somewhat by the discovery that with a properly controlled nuclear reactor, or atomic "furnace," fissioning U^{235} can create plutonium out of the more stable and abundant U^{238} (ordinary uranium), thus supplementing its own fuel. This type of furnace is known as a *breeder reactor*. Next it was discovered that *thorium* (atomic weight 232), an element two to four times as abundant in the earth crust as uranium, could be altered in a reactor to a new and rapidly fissioning isotope of uranium (U^{233}). Both uranium and thorium, therefore, are potential atomic energy fuels, capable of generating enormous quantities of heat energy within the controlled environment of a nuclear reactor.

A new type of thermonuclear energy, termed *fusion energy,* has been announced by British and American scientists. Though

FIG. 13.11 Anaconda's Jackpile Mine, a multi-million-ton deposit of uranium-bearing sandstone ore located on the Laguna Indian Reservation between Grants and Albuquerque, New Mexico. [The Anaconda Company]

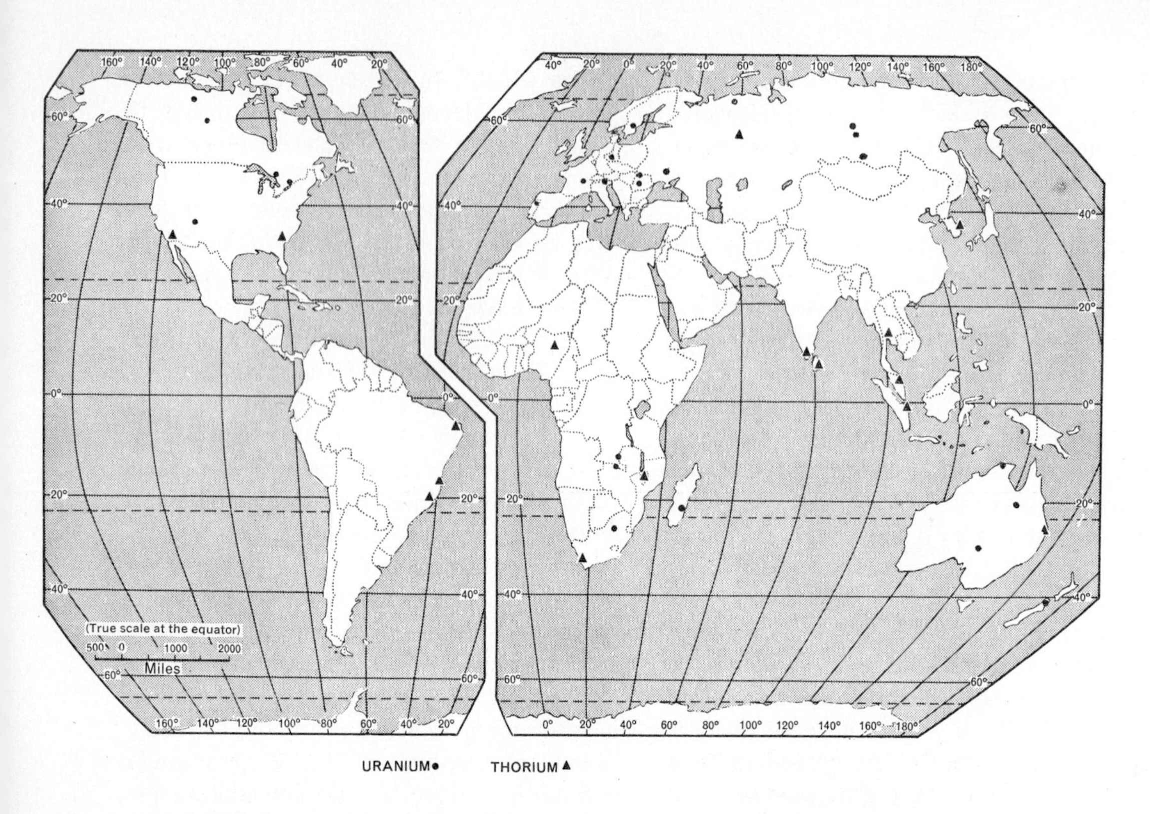

FIG. 13.12 World distribution of uranium and thorium. [After Oxford Economic Atlas of the World]

still far from perfected, it has untold possibilities, and if and when the difficult problems of generation and control are solved, it will provide almost unlimited amounts of radiant energy. Even more startling is the fact that the basic raw materials are mainly deuterium and tritium, isotopes of hydrogen that are available in immense quantities in the ocean. The process of generation consists of fusing the nuclei of these two hydrogen isotopes together to form helium nuclei. Energy is released in the act of fusion. This is essentially the same process that generates the energy in the sun and the uncontrolled energy of a hydrogen bomb. If such a process could be controlled, and deuterium and tritium could be separated from sea water on a practical basis, it might well make the mineral fuels, both fossil and nuclear, relatively insignificant.

13.6 URANIUM. Uranium, which is currently the major mineral source for atomic energy, is rather widely distributed on earth and is considered to be about as abundant as copper. Much of it, however, is scattered in small quantities throughout many rocks, and high-grade deposits of commercial importance are relatively rare. Since it is radioactive, its presence within 12 to 18 inches of the surface can be discovered by special instruments that can detect the emission particles and radiation. The high value of uranium has stimulated prospecting, and important new discoveries are being made every year.

Uranium occurs in a variety of natural forms, but three types predominate: (1) the pure crystalline mineral *uraninite,* or uranium oxide; (2) *pitchblende,* a black, amorphous form of uraninite; and (3) *carnotite,* a lemon-yellow uranium oxide which usually contains associated potassium and vanadium. The first two are found mainly in crystalline rocks, whereas carnotite is found mainly in coarse sandstones.

The global distribution of uranium is closely related to the distribution of lightweight continental rocks, such as granite, and the sedimentary rocks derived from them. For this reason, the uranium minerals are found mainly in the crystalline shields and in the intruded granitic cores of mountain cordilleras. Uranium is exceedingly rare in areas of basic, dark-colored volcanic rocks. The borders of continental shields appear to have more uranium than the central portions. Sedimentary rocks containing uranium of commercial importance are mainly coarse-textured sandstones of continental, rather than marine, origin, especially those which contain some carbon derived from organic material. For some reason, uranium that has been concentrated as the result of weathering and erosion has an affinity for carbon. Such deposits are most common in the sedimentary rocks bordering mountain areas, especially in many of the high plains areas of the world. The distribution of producing uranium deposits is shown in Fig. 13.12. The major producers include the Skinkolobwe area of southern Republic of the Congo; the Port Radium mines on Great Bear Lake, Northwest Territories, Canada; the Joachimsthal district bordering Czechoslovakia and Germany; the Colorado Plateau in southwestern Colorado and southeastern Utah; and three new Canadian areas: one in the Beaverlodge region of Saskatchewan, another at Bancroft, Ontario, and the third and largest of all at Blind River, Ontario.

13.7 THORIUM. Thorium, like uranium, is radioactive; therefore it can be located fairly easily with instruments that will detect the emission of subatomic particles. Until the discovery that thorium could develop fissioning U^{233} in a breeder reactor, it had much less value than uranium, and the search for thorium ores was not so determined as for uranium, although several important deposits were located during the course of uranium prospecting. The major mineral of thorium is *monazite,* which is heavy and durable and hence tends to accumulate in sands and gravels derived from the weathering and erosion of igneous rocks. High-grade vein deposits are rare, since monazite is usually scattered through the crystalline rocks. Placer deposits thus constitute the major source. Until recently, production was slight and was utilized mainly for experimental purposes. Its production and use in atomic energy programs have greatly increased since 1955. At present most of it is obtained as a by-product of heavy-mineral separation of beach sand in the search for tin and rutile, the latter being an important source of titanium. The major deposits and producing areas include the east coast of Brazil, the coastal sands of southern India and Ceylon, and the placer tin deposits of Malaya and Indonesia (see Fig. 13.12). Some rich veins of monazite have been located in Colorado, Idaho, and South Africa. In the United States, the major source is the placer stream deposits of Idaho. The general location of thorium deposits thus is in placer stream or coastal sediments bordering the edges of crystalline-rock regions, principally in rocks of the lightweight, continental types, such as granite.

The metallic minerals

Since it is obviously impossible to cover the distribution of all the metals and their minerals in this section, the discussion here is restricted to the most important metallic minerals, along with some lesser-known metals that are growing in significance with our rapidly developing technology.

Generalizations covering the abundance, distribution, and association of the metallic elements are always subject to qualification, but some recognizable relationships between such features and the chemical behavior of these elements can be indicated. In general, the elements of lowest atomic weights are the most abundant. Also, elements having similar chemical properties tend to be found together; for example, the platinum metals (platinum, osmium, and iridium) almost always occur together; so do the rare earths. Calcium and magnesium frequently are within the same carbonate, oxide, or silicate minerals. The frequent coexistence of many nonmetallic elements also supports the above generalization. Note, for example, the associations of iodine, bromine, and chlorine; the inert gases in the atmosphere (helium, argon, neon, etc.); and sulfur and selenium.

The low-density continental rocks with a high silica content have by far the largest proportions of the rare earths, the alkalies, and the many associated elements, including fluorine, tin, tungsten, molybdenum, uranium, thorium, and boron. The heavy, dark-colored rocks low in silica have the largest

FIG. 13.13 World distribution of copper, tin, lead, and zinc. [After Oxford Economic Atlas of the World]

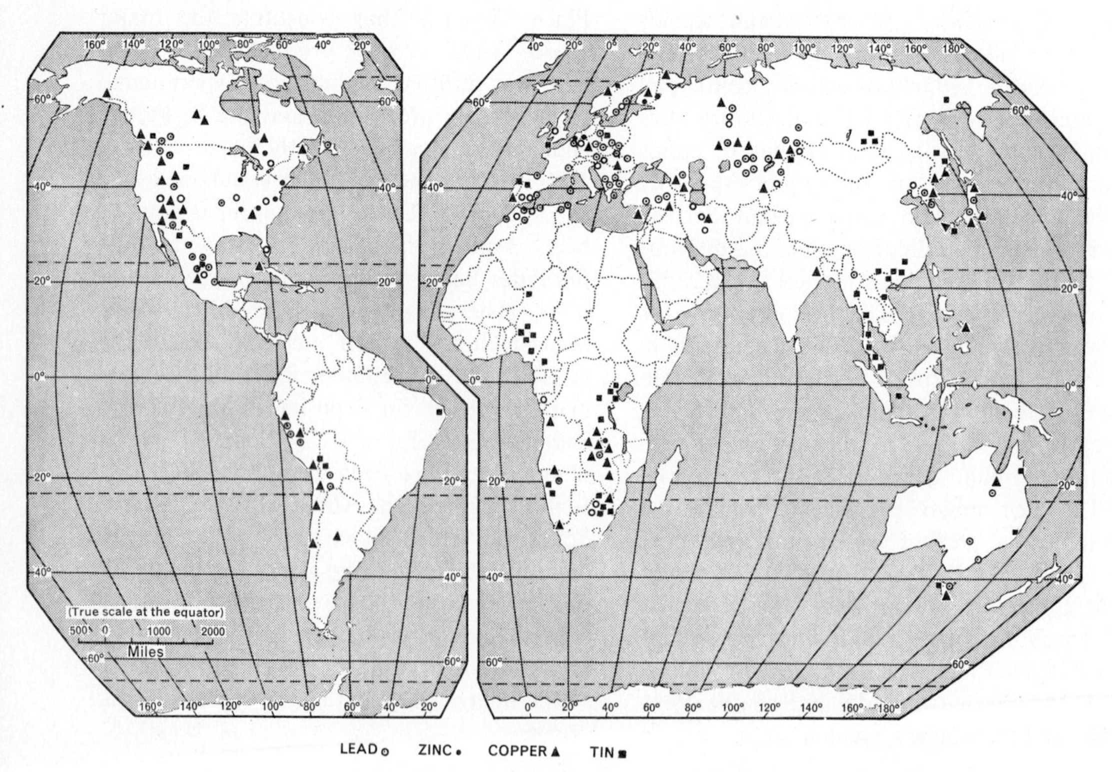

FIG. 13.14 The E. W. Davis plant of the Reserve Mining Company at Silver Bay, Minnesota. This plant, which enriches low-grade iron ore (taconite) from the Mesabi iron range, has a rated capacity of 3,750,000 tons of beneficiated ore per year. Note the typical Great Lakes ore carrier in the foreground. [Reserve Mining Company]

concentrations of the alkaline earths and such metals as iron, magnesium, nickel, cobalt, titanium, chromium, manganese, and those of the platinum group.

Some metals are widely distributed, and others are restricted to highly localized areas. Gold, for example, although not an abundant metal in comparison with many others, is found in a wide variety of rocks belonging to many geologic ages and is scattered throughout the world. Nickel is found in small quantities in nearly all dark-colored basic rocks low in silica, but commercial quantities occur only in a few scattered localities on earth.

Some parts of the earth are especially blessed with mineral resources, whereas others are veritable mineral deserts. This is especially true of the metallic minerals. Figure 13.13 shows the major producing areas for several metallic minerals. Some areas contain a variety of metals, and others contain unusually large concentrations of a single mineral. Such areas might be regarded as *metallogenic* regions. Some of the world's most important metallogenic regions include the Republic of the Congo–Northern Rhodesia area; the Ural Mountains district of the Soviet Union; the central Rocky Mountains, Arizona Highlands, Coeur d'Alene, and upper Great Lakes districts in the United States; the Hartz Mountains of southern Germany; the Sudbury, Nipissing, and Noranda districts of Canada; the Andes of Chile, Peru, and Bolivia; the Broken Hill district of New South Wales in Australia; and the Bawdwin district of Burma. In some of these districts, individual mines operate primarily to extract a single metal, but in the refining process a number of subsidiary metals may be produced as by-products. Several of the scarce but valuable metals are produced in this way.

13.8 IRON. Iron is more abundant in the earth crust than any other metal except aluminum. It is almost universally present in dark, basic igneous rocks. Such rocks, however, rarely contain sufficient iron for mining, and the principal ores occur mainly where the iron has been concentrated by weathering and depositional processes. The only major producing areas of *magnetite,* a black, magnetic, and crystalline oxide of iron, which is found mainly in igneous rocks, are the Adirondack district of northern New York State, the Kiruna district of northern Sweden, and the Urals of Russia.

By far the most important mineral of iron is *hematite,* a reddish oxide that usually occurs in sedimentary beds, where it was concentrated by deposition and weathering. In some cases other forms of iron oxide were precipitated from solution in swamps and lakes. Bog iron forms rapidly under suitable conditions. The Clinton hematities of the Appalachian region and the iron ores of Luxembourg were deposited in a shallow marine environment.

Most high-grade hematite ores are accompanied by extensive low-grade deposits. Techniques of beneficiating, or enriching, the leaner ores by preliminary processing have been developed and have greatly added to the potential iron ore reserves of the world, especially in the mining districts where the supply of high-grade iron ore is beginning to run short. The generally widespread distribution of iron deposits of low-to-moderate iron content in the world and the large size of some of the newly discovered high-grade deposits indicate that the global re-

FIG. 13.15 World distribution of iron ore and bauxite. [After Oxford Economic Atlas of the World]

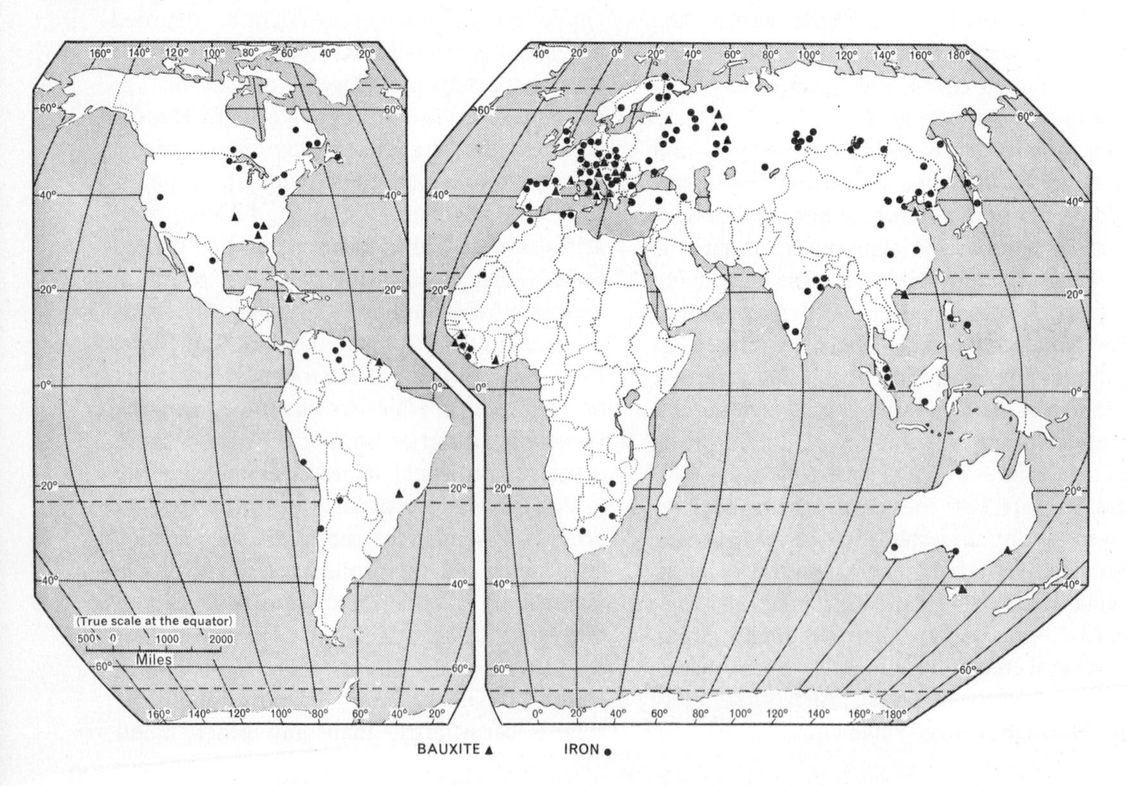

TABLE 13.4 Major world iron ore deposits

AREA	LOCALITY OF IRON DEPOSITS
UNITED STATES	Mesabi district, Minn.*; Northern Michigan and Wisconsin*; Birmingham, Ala.; Adirondack Mts., N.Y.
SOUTH AMERICA	Minas Gerais, Brazil; Cerro Bolivar, E. Venezuela; Tofo, N. Chile; San Felipe, Cuba
AFRICA	Liberia; Sierra Leone
CANADA	Knob Lake, Quebec-Labrador; Steep Rock, Ont.; Wabana, Newf.
EUROPE	Kiruna, Sweden*; Ovieto-Santandes, Spain; Lorraine Field, France-Luxembourg*; Belgium
SOVIET UNION	Krivoi Rog, S. Ukraine*; Urals*; Stalinsk, Siberia*; Kerch, Crimea
MANCHURIA	Anshan*
INDIA	Singhbhum* (Bihar and Orissa); Salem (Madras); Drug district (central provinces)

* Major producing area.

serves of this strategic mineral will be adequate for a long time.

Figure 13.15 shows the distribution of the major deposits of iron ore in the world. Table 13.4 indicates those which have unusually large reserves of workable ore.

13.9 ALUMINUM. Aluminum, next to steel, is our most important structural metal. Its main advantages lie in its strength and low specific gravity, the latter only 2.9 times that of water. It also is a fairly good conductor of electricity and hence can be used for high-voltage power lines, where the greater weight of copper, a better conductor, requires many more supporting towers. Aluminum's main use as a structural metal is in the transportation industry, especially in the construction of aircraft, railroad cars, and truck bodies. About 20 per cent of the aluminum produced in the United States goes into such nonmetallic materials as aluminum salts for the chemical industries.

Bauxite is the principal ore of aluminum. It is an amorphous, earthy mass, predominantly composed of hydrated aluminum oxide but also containing varying proportions of silica and iron. Bauxite results from the desilicification of syenites or of shales and clays of high aluminum content or is precipitated from ground water in tropical soil hardpans or in cavities within limestones.

Although aluminum is the most abundant metal in the earth crust, there are not many high-grade ore deposits. This is illustrated by the fact that nearly 95 per cent of the United States production is derived from two small areas that together total only about 15 square miles in Saline and Pulaski Counties, Arkansas. Smaller amounts for nonmetallic uses

TABLE 13.5 Bauxite production, 1904-1939

COUNTRY	TONS (APPROX.)
France	13,000,000
United States	10,000,000
Hungary	4,000,000
Italy	3,400,000
Surinam	3,230,000
British Guiana	3,000,000
Yugoslavia	3,000,000
Soviet Union	1,200,000
Dutch East Indies	820,000
Greece	680,000

SOURCE: R. B. Ladoo and W. H. Myers, *Nonmetallic Minerals*, McGraw-Hill Book Company, Inc., New York, 1951, p. 84.

are produced in Alabama, Oregon, Washington, Georgia, and Tennessee. A concerted search for this vital resource, stimulated by the great demand for aluminum during World War II, led to the discovery of large reserves of low-grade ore in Georgia and Oregon. As in the case of iron ore, our domestic reserves of aluminum ore have been increased by beneficiation processes, which involve the treatment of low-grade bauxite deposits to produce a more usable residue. As yet, however, bauxite beneficiation is not particularly efficient, and the United States is by no means self-sufficient in this mineral resource. If a process can be developed for removing combined silica from aluminum clays or shales cheaply, the United States and the rest of the world will have an unlimited supply of aluminum ore.

The foreign sources of bauxite also are concentrated in a relatively few locations (see Fig. 13.15). According to a rough estimate by Litchfield, about 98 per cent of the world production between 1904 and 1939 was supplied by only ten countries (see Table 13.5). Since 1939, the United States has been the world's leading producer, followed by Surinam and British Guiana, both of which produce mainly for the United States. Russian production has also increased greatly. Note in Table 13.5 how many of the producing areas lie in the tropics and lower mid-latitudes. The bauxite deposits of the Mediterranean region are associated with terra roxa soils (see Sec. 12.8), which are highly weathered reddish clays derived from limestones. The bauxite deposits of the tropics are mainly of ferrallitic origin. The Arkansas deposits are ancient residual deposits derived from underlying syenites. The largest reserves of bauxite are now in Hungary, the Gold Coast, and the West Indies (Jamaica and Haiti). The deposits on Jamaica are believed to be the largest in the world. New deposits undoubtedly will be discovered in the vast expanses of unprospected tropical forests. It now appears that, although local shortages may occur, world resources of bauxite will be adequate for many years to come.

13.10 COPPER. Copper is somewhat unusual among the major metals, because it occurs in nature in so many different mineral forms—as a native element and in various compounds, including oxides, silicates, carbonates, and sulfides. The distribution of copper, like that of gold, does not appear to be related to any particular type of rock. The largest ore bodies, however, are formed as the result of secondary enrichment of copper-bearing rocks due to leaching by ground-water solutions. Most of these large ore bodies, therefore, are found fairly near the surface. Copper deposits are irregularly scattered throughout the world.

Copper lies at the heart of the entire electrical industry, because of its cheapness and its excellence as a conductor of electricity, being exceeded in the latter property only by silver. It also is an important constituent of brass. The rapid expansion of the electrical industry during the past 15 years has led to intensive exploitation of copper reserves throughout the world. As a result, copper probably will be among the first metals to become seriously depleted on a global scale. Nearly all the major industrial countries of the world, including the United States and the Soviet Union, list copper as one of their critical metallic deficiencies.

The hilly upland section of southeastern Arizona, which lies south of the Colorado Plateau and extends into New Mexico, comprises the major copper province of the United States. For some reason, the crustal rocks in this area contain an unusually high concentration of this important element. Copper deposits of many different types and geologic ages are found within this metallogenic province and have yielded copper ores for many decades. It is interesting to note that the largest copper discovery of the twentieth century within the United States was made at San Manuel, Arizona. Other major copper districts within the United States include the Bingham, Utah, district and Butte, Montana.

One of the few large reserves of copper in the world is found in the Republic of the Congo–Northern Rhodesia metallogenic province of Africa, mainly in Katanga and adjacent areas. Canada has important producing deposits in several parts of the country, including the Flin Flon district of western Manitoba; Noranda in western Quebec; eastern British Columbia where the famed Brittania mine is located; and northern Newfoundland. Copper also is an important associated metal in the Sudbury, Ontario, nickel deposits. Despite Canada's large production, reserves are not believed to be great.

The South American copper deposits have been worked for many years. The rich Chuquicamata deposit (see Fig. 13.16) on the western slopes of the Andes in northern Chile is not only believed to be the largest producing copper ore body in the world but is also thought to have larger reserves than

FIG. 13.16 Open-pit workings of of the Chuquicamata copper mine, Chile, one of the largest and richest copper ore bodies in the world. Such open-pit workings are typical of large-scale mining operations throughout the world. [The Anaconda Company]

any other deposit. The Cerro do Pasco mine in central Peru is another major producer.

The principal producing copper deposits of the Soviet Union formerly were located in the central Urals. Two new producing areas in Kazakhstan, however, have replaced the Urals as the major suppliers of this strategic metal. These are Kounrad, near Lake Balkash, and Djezkazgan, some 300 miles to the west.

Japan is one of the few industrial countries in the world that is self-sufficient in copper, but deposits are small and scattered, and reserves are not believed to be great. The availability of copper in Japan has been an important asset to the electric power and electrochemical industries of that country.

Accurate statistics on copper reserves are impossible to obtain. The major reason for this is that copper undoubtedly is in short supply throughout the world, and few producing nations wish to release accurate estimates of their reserves. A similar situation exists with respect to lead and zinc. New discoveries of copper undoubtedly will be made, but they are likely to be low-grade deposits, which will be difficult and costly to locate and will necessitate expensive plants for processing.

Few high-grade ores of copper exist in the world today. The Chuquicamata ores of Chile average about 2 per cent copper, but most deposits are far below this. The average content of copper in ores mined throughout the United States is about 0.9 per cent, and some of the largest mines are profitably handling ores that run below 0.5 per cent.

13.11 TIN. Tin is an unusual metal in that it is one of the oldest known to man but is found in exploitable quantities in only a few widely scattered locations. Its principal uses include the plating of steel and the production of various alloys, mainly solder and bronze, the latter being an alloy of tin and copper. Because the principal minerals of tin are heavy and durable, they are usually obtained from placer (stream gravel) deposits. It was in such gravels that primitive man must have found tin and recognized it as an unusual material. One of the oldest producing areas in the world is in Cornwall, at the southwestern tip of England. Tin ores were mined there and formed an important item in commerce long before the Christian era. The Phoenicians virtually monopolized the tin trade for centuries.

The global distribution of tin (see Fig. 13.13) is related closely to large granite intrusions, large masses of lightweight crystalline rock that worked their way toward the surface when in a molten state. The tin was originally deposited as vein or fissure fillings near the top or surface of the granite magma reservoirs. The general distribution of tin is similar to that of tungsten, and the two metals are sometimes found together. The major world deposits are in placers, found in southeast Asia, including Malaya, Burma, China, Thailand, and Bangka and Billiton Islands. Important deposits also are found in Bolivia. The Bolivian mines, which exploit vein deposits, were developed rapidly during World War II when supplies from Japanese-held southeast Asia were withheld from markets in the United States and northwestern Europe. The Republic of the Congo and Nigeria are now producing areas. World reserves appear to be adequate for several decades.

13.12 THE FERROALLOYS. These include the metals that are combined with iron to produce a variety of steels. Among the most important are (1) *manganese,* which aids in reducing the oxygen and sulfur content of steel and adds to the quality of toughness; (2) *chromium,* used mainly to produce corrosion-resistant stainless steels;

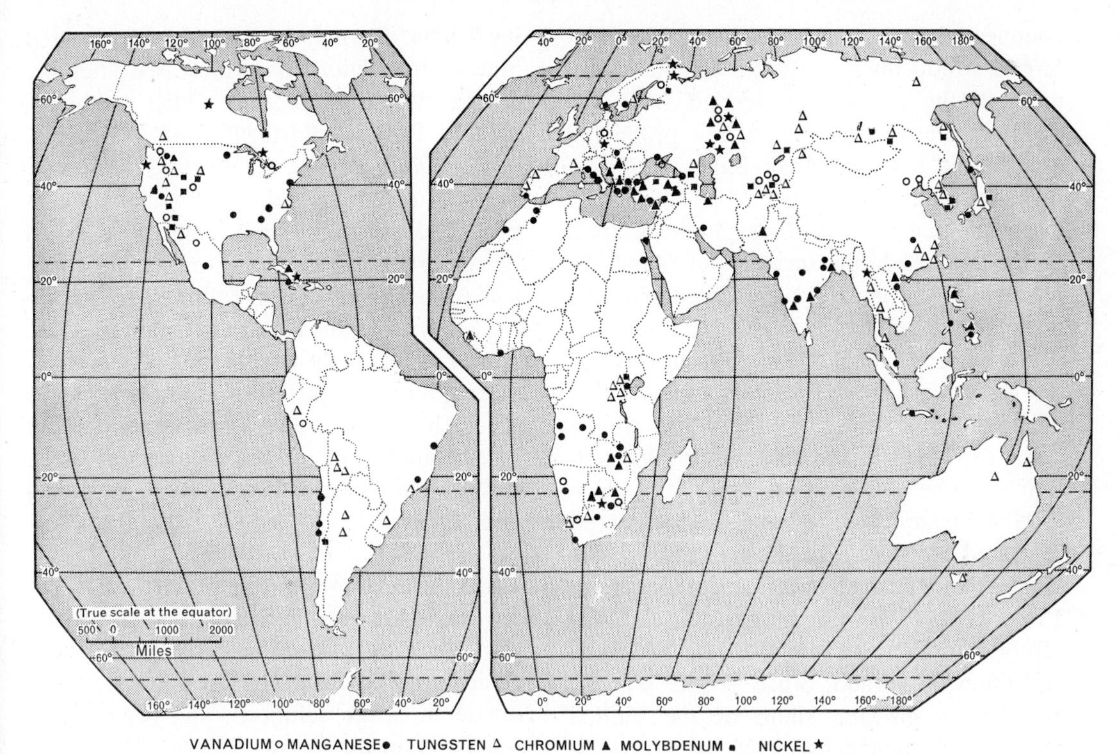

FIG. 13.17 World distribution of ferroalloys. [After Oxford Economic Atlas of the World]

(3) *nickel,* which also is used in stainless steel and other durable alloys; (4) *molybdenum,* which is used to produce a heat- and corrosion-resistant steel and which can serve as a substitute alloy material for nickel or tungsten; (5) *tungsten,* used mainly for preserving hardness under high temperatures, a necessary property of drill bits, combustion engines, etc.; (6) *vanadium,* which gives steel great strength, durability, and resistance to shock. The world distribution of several of these ferroalloys is show in Fig. 13.17.

Manganese is required in greater quantities than the other ferroalloy metals, but reserves appear to be considerably greater. It is a fairly abundant element in the earth's crust, and it tends to accumulate in residual soils similar to those which contain iron and aluminum oxides and silicates. Manganese ores are found in both sedimentary and igneous rocks. Huge reserves are located in the Soviet Union, India, Ghana, Brazil, and South Africa. Although the United States has large undeveloped reserves of low-grade manganese, it currently imports nearly all the manganese it requires.

Chromium, like nickel, occurs only in the dark, heavy, basic rocks. Its commercial ores are much more widespread than those of nickel, however, and global reserves appear to be ample for many years. The largest amounts come from the Ural area of the Soviet Union, Turkey, Southern Rhodesia, Cuba, and South Africa. The Philippine Islands contain some of the largest reserves.

Nickel, although fairly abundant in the basic igneous rocks (sima) of the crust, is mined in only a few localities, since ores of commercial quality are exceedingly rare. The largest producing country is Canada, with most of the production derived from the Sudbury, Ontario, district. A new producing area in the Mystery-Moak Lakes region of northern Manitoba is reported to be a major discovery that may rival the Sudbury area. Normally Canada produces about four-fifths of the world supply. New Caledonia, the Soviet Union, Cuba, Finland, and the island of Sulawesi (Celebes) in Indonesia produce the remainder. Proved reserves indicate that nickel ores, like those of copper, are rapidly being depleted. Fortunately, other alloy materials can be used as substitutes.

Molybdenum has perhaps the most concentrated production of the ferroalloys. The United States normally produces all but about 15 per cent of the world supply, and until recently, most of this came from a single mine at Climax, Colorado. Since World War II, however, a growing share of the United States production consists of the molybdenum recovered as a by-product of copper mining. Molybdenum is not a particularly critical ferroalloy, because there are satisfactory substitutes, but it is especially advantageous to the United States, which not only has plenty of it but is deficient in most of the other ferroalloy minerals. Its prime value lies in its versatility, since a small quantity of molybdenum imparts to steel many of the qualities that would otherwise have to be derived from other alloys.

Tungsten has a general rock association similar to that of tin, but it is much more widely distributed, many new deposits having been discovered during the past 2 decades. Aiding in the new discoveries was the use of ultraviolet lamps, since *scheelite,* one of the major tungsten minerals, tends to fluoresce, or glow in the dark, when exposed to ultraviolet radiation. The major producing areas lie in countries of eastern Asia, including China, Burma, and Korea. The United States production has increased notably during the past 2 decades. Other producers include Bolivia, Portugal, and Argentina.

Vanadium occurs mainly in sedimentary rocks of secondary origin, although some is produced in Peru from vein deposits in igneous rocks. The leading producing country is the United States, followed by Southwest Africa, Finland, and the Union of South Africa. Since only small quantities are required, reserves appear to be ample for some time. The major United States deposits occur in the sandstones of the Colorado Plateau and in the phosphatic shales of Wyoming and Idaho.

13.13 LEAD. Lead is usually, but not always, associated with zinc, and frequently with silver as well. Most lead and zinc deposits are the result of precipitation from low-temperature solutions, and occur as irregular vein or cavity fillings. The veins, pockets, and lenses of the ore are found in many types of rock. Large, massive, low-grade lead ores are exceedingly rare. For this reason lead is fairly expensive to mine, and global reserves appear to be comparatively small.

The high specific gravity of lead and the perfect cubic crystal form and cleavage of its principal mineral, *galena* (lead sulfide), attracted attention early in history. Its general versatility, softness, high density, low melting point, and resistance to corrosion have made it a useful metal, and for many of its uses no suitable substitute for lead has been found. Today it is utilized primarily in sheathing for underground or undersea cables, noncorrosive collapsible tubing, solder, storage-battery plates, shielding against radioactivity, ammunition, and type metal.

The major producing area in the United States is the Flat River district of southeastern Missouri, where lead occurs as a large ore body near the surface and where, uniquely, it is found with only small amounts of other sulfide ores as accessory minerals. The tri-state district of southwestern Missouri, northeastern Oklahoma, and southeastern Kansas is another major producer. Here, however, zinc is an important associated metal. The Coeur d'Alene district of northern Idaho produces lead in association with silver and zinc ores, and this metallogenic region continues into southeastern British Columbia. The famous Sullivan lead, zinc, and silver mine is located near Kimberley, British Columbia.

North America far exceeds any other part of the world in lead production, with the United States, Canada, and Mexico as major world producers (see Fig. 13.13). Australia, Germany, the Soviet Union, Yugoslavia, and Burma also are important producers.

13.14 ZINC. The principal mineral of zinc is *sphalerite* (zinc sulfide), a resinous-looking substance that is almost always found associated with lead sulfide ores. Like lead, zinc has had a long and illustrious history. It is an essential constituent of brass, which dates back to Roman times. Its major uses today are for galvanizing iron and steel and as an alloy material in brass and other zinc-base metals. Most photoengraving and lithographing plates are made from sheets of rolled zinc. It also resembles lead in that there are few satisfactory substitutes for zinc in its major uses. Along with copper and lead, zinc should be listed as one of the metals that is in critically short supply, from the standpoint of global reserves. An indication of this is that most countries have tight security regulations governing the information released on reserves.

The largest single zinc-mining area in the world is the tri-state district of Oklahoma, Kansas, and Missouri. Production has greatly decreased there, however, and there are indications that reserves in the district are not large. The Broken Hill district of New South Wales, Australia, is another great zinc-producing area. Canada ranks among the world leaders in production, and the main source areas are Kimberley, British Columbia, and Flin Flon, Manitoba. The metallogenic region of Upper Silesia along the former Polish-German border is the principal European producer. The United States is the leading world producer, followed by Canada, Germany, Australia, and Mexico, in roughly that order. Data on the production and reserves of the Soviet Union are not available.

13.15 MAGNESIUM. A relative newcomer to the group of structural metals, magnesium can be alloyed with aluminum to make a metal (*duralumin*) that is both lighter and stronger than aluminum. Duralumin is therefore used mainly in the aircraft industry. Magnesium metal also has important military uses for flares and signal rockets. When ignited in the presence of oxygen, it burns with a brilliant white flame. Magnesium salts are important in the chemical, pharmaceutical, and photographic industries.

Magnesium is abundant in the earth crust, in both igneous and sedimentary rocks. It usually is associated with calcium and iron in most dark, basic rocks and is a common constituent in many limestones. Such magnesium limestones are termed *dolomites*. The three major commercial sources of magnesium are (1) *magnesite,* a carbonate formed from the alteration of magnesium silicate rocks by ground water containing carbonic acid; (2) *natural salt brines,* which are pumped from subsurface salt deposits; and (3) *sea water*. Extraction of the metal from each of these three sources involves expen-

FIG. 13.18 Typical salt-brine well near Midland, Michigan. Such salt brines supply products other than sodium chloride. Among these are magnesium salts, from which magnesium metal can be obtained. [Dow Chemical Co.]

sive processes. Were it not for the difficulty of separating the metal from the oxide, magnesium alloys undoubtedly would have a far wider use than they now do.

Reserves of magnesium are enormous, and the oceans of the world could supply the present demand for an indefinite period. The Soviet Union is the leading producer of magnesite, and other large deposits of this magnesium mineral are found in Manchuria, Korea, Austria, and Canada. The principal United States deposits are in Washington, California, and Nevada. Salt brines from Michigan subsurface salt deposits are the major source of magnesium in the United States. Several plants extracting magnesium from sea water are also in operation in California, Texas, and New Jersey.

13.16 GOLD AND SILVER. The two principal precious metals, gold and silver, are unique in that a special arbitrary value is placed on them by cultural and political groups. Both of these metals attracted the attention of man early in history. Silver and gold occur in nature as unusually heavy, pure metallic elements and hence contrast strongly with the adjacent rock or mineral material in which they are found. Pure native silver, however, is relatively rare. Being soft and malleable, gold and silver can be shaped easily into various forms. Gold has been prized especially because it is a relatively inert metal that does not unite easily with other elements. It does not form oxides; thus its bright yellow color does not become dulled by corrosion. Neither gold nor silver is abundant in the earth crust, and the scarcity and easily recognizable properties of these metals led to their early ornamental use and to their high value as means of exchange. Gold and silver have been considered symbols of wealth by most cultural groups throughout recorded history, and thus man has been powerfully motivated to discover and develop deposits of these precious metals.

Gold has an unusually wide distribution in the world (see Fig. 13.19), though the estimated quantity in the rocks of the earth crust is relatively low. Traces of it can be found in most types of igneous rocks. Commercial deposits consist mainly of narrow veins, or lodes, where it usually is associated with quartz. Most of the past production of gold has been from placer deposits, where grains and nuggets of this heavy and inert metal have been concentrated by stream erosion and deposition. The relative ease of working placer deposits, however, has led

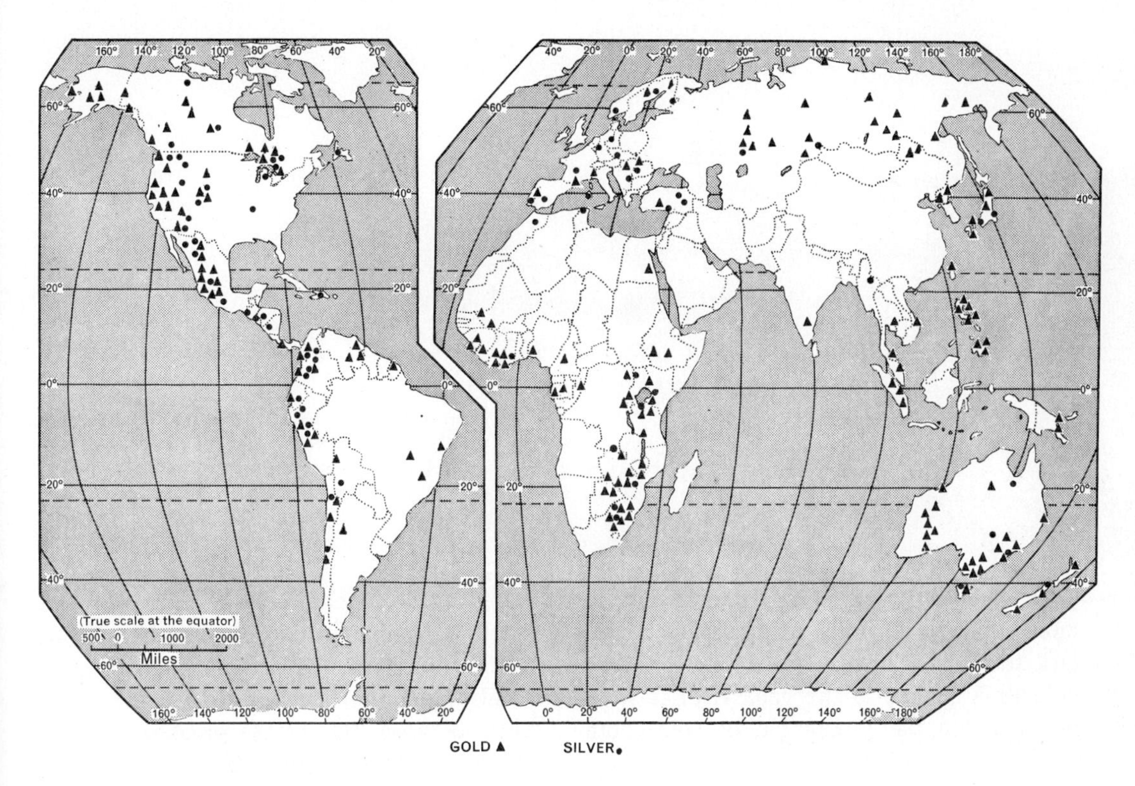

FIG. 13.19 World distribution of gold and silver. [After Oxford Economic Atlas of the World]

to the depletion of most high-grade ore deposits of this type (see Fig. 13.20). Lode and vein deposits are more difficult to locate and to work, but new discoveries are made periodically. As with many other minerals, the major production today is from large deposits of low-grade ore.

The world's leading producing area for gold is the Witwatersrand district near Johannesburg, in the Union of South Africa, where the gold occurs in a mass of conglomerate (cemented gravel). It is believed that this deposit represents an ancient Pre-Cambrian placer deposit. Canada ranks second to South Africa in gold production and derives its main supply from vein deposits within the igneous rocks of the Canadian shield, northeast of Lake Superior. The Porcupine and Timiskaming districts of northeastern Ontario are the principal producers. In the United States, the largest single mine is the Homestake Mine in the Black Hills of South Dakota, where the gold occurs in narrow threads, or veinlets, thoroughly penetrating a large rock mass. The entire intruded rock mass constitutes the ore body. Placer deposits in the gravels along the western flanks of the Sierra Nevada continue to supply gold, as they have for over a hundred years. Gold is mined in many parts of the Soviet Union, but the principal areas currently producing are the placer gravels of the Soviet Far East and the lode deposits of the Angara shield, east of Lake Baikal.

Gold production throughout the world today is influenced in large measure by the

FIG. 13.20 One of the largest goldmining dredges in Alaska. This placer deposit is located near Fairbanks. [R. E. Wallace; U.S. Geological Survey]

price of gold, which is regulated by law in most countries in order to provide a monetary standard. Either a rise in the price of gold or a decline in the general price level will increase the production of gold, both areally and quantitatively.

Silver has a more concentrated distribution than gold and can be produced more cheaply. This has made it increasingly more difficult for governments to use this metal as a supplement to gold in a monetary base. Political considerations have maintained the price of silver within the United States, but a quota system prevents more than a given quantity from accumulating in the monetary reserves. Although such artificial controls have tended to restrict the use of silver for nonmonetary purposes, the metal is not employed exclusively for money and ornamentation but is also utilized in other ways, primarily in special electrical apparatus (silver being the best conductor for electric current of all the metals), photographic film, and various chemical compounds. A large part of the world silver supply finds its way to the Orient, where for centuries it has had a preferential value as negotiable wealth and is displayed in many forms to indicate social prestige. In many countries, silver is a popular form in which to place marriage dowries.

Silver deposits are not so widespread as those of gold. By far the greatest reserves are concentrated in the western hemisphere (see Fig. 13.19), where nearly all the deposits occur along major continental structural lines. The alignment that follows the mountain cordilleras from eastern British Columbia, across the United States, through Mexico and Central America, and along the axis of the Andes in South America has been termed "The Great Silver Channel." This general belt has produced all but a small part of the world supply of silver. Today most silver is produced as a by-product of lead, copper, zinc, and gold mining, since silver often occurs in mixtures within the sulfide ores of the first three. Minor deposits are found associated with sulfide ores in the metallogenic districts of Broken Hill, Australia, and Bawdwin, Burma. Japan, Germany, and Austria also produce some silver. Mineral reserves of silver are less promising than those of many other metals, and future production will probably consist more and more of the by-product type. Fortunately, the metal is not critically important in modern industry.

The nonmetallic minerals

Variety is perhaps the most outstanding characteristic of the great family of nonmetallic minerals. They differ widely in nearly all types of physical properties, and most of their important uses are related to the extremes in such properties. Heavy nonmetallic minerals, such as *barite,* are valued for their high specific gravity, which is needed in the development of flushing muds used in drilling oil wells. In contrast, *sepiolite,* one of the lightest of all minerals, with a specific gravity less than that of water, has a small and highly specialized use in the manufacture of pipes for smoking tobacco, where it is better known as *meerschaum.* The nonmetallic group also includes a large number of refractory minerals that have varying degrees of resistance to heat or to electrical conduction. *Asbestos,* or rock wool, has value primarily because its noninflammable, heat-resistant, fibrous, flexible crystals can be woven into fabrics. Unusually hard and unusually soft minerals each have their uses.

Many nonmetallic minerals are more important for their chemical properties than for their physical characteristics. The entire chemical industry depends far more on the nonmetallic minerals than on the metals.

FIG. 13.21 Laying refractory bricks for a series of "checkers." Heat from combustion gases is absorbed by these bricks and later used to heat intake air in a regenerative process, an important fuel-saving device in the steel industry. The combination of various nonmetallic mineral substances in various forms to withstand the high temperatures in metallurgical processes is a major industry in itself. [Steelways, American Iron and Steel Institute]

Sulfur and chlorine compounds are illustrative. Also included in the nonmetallic group are the fertilizer minerals, especially the salts of nitrogen, phosphorus, and potassium, which are becoming vital in the maintenance of food production. Finally, the group includes a long list of mineral substances used as construction materials, such as gypsum, limestone, marble, and slate.

Some of the metallic minerals have nonmetallic uses. Hematite, for example, is not only a source of metallic iron but also an important source of a reddish pigment used in paints. Ilmenite and rutile, the major minerals of titanium, also supply titanium oxide, which is used as a dense white pigment in paints. Bauxite, the major source of aluminum, is also used as an abrasive. Most metals form salts and various other compounds that have important nonmetallic uses.

The distribution of the nonmetallic minerals cannot be generalized adequately because of their great variety and the wide range of their chemical properties. The remainder of this section is devoted to nonmetallic minerals that are among the most important for human use, but the list is by no means inclusive.

13.17 THE FERTILIZER MINERALS.

The principal fertilizer minerals are the mineral salts of nitrogen, phosphorus, and potassium. Their world distribution is shown in Fig. 13.22.

NITROGEN. The least available of the fer-

FIG. 13.22 World distribution of nitrates, phosphates, and potash. [After Oxford Economic Atlas of the World; U.S. Department of Commerce]

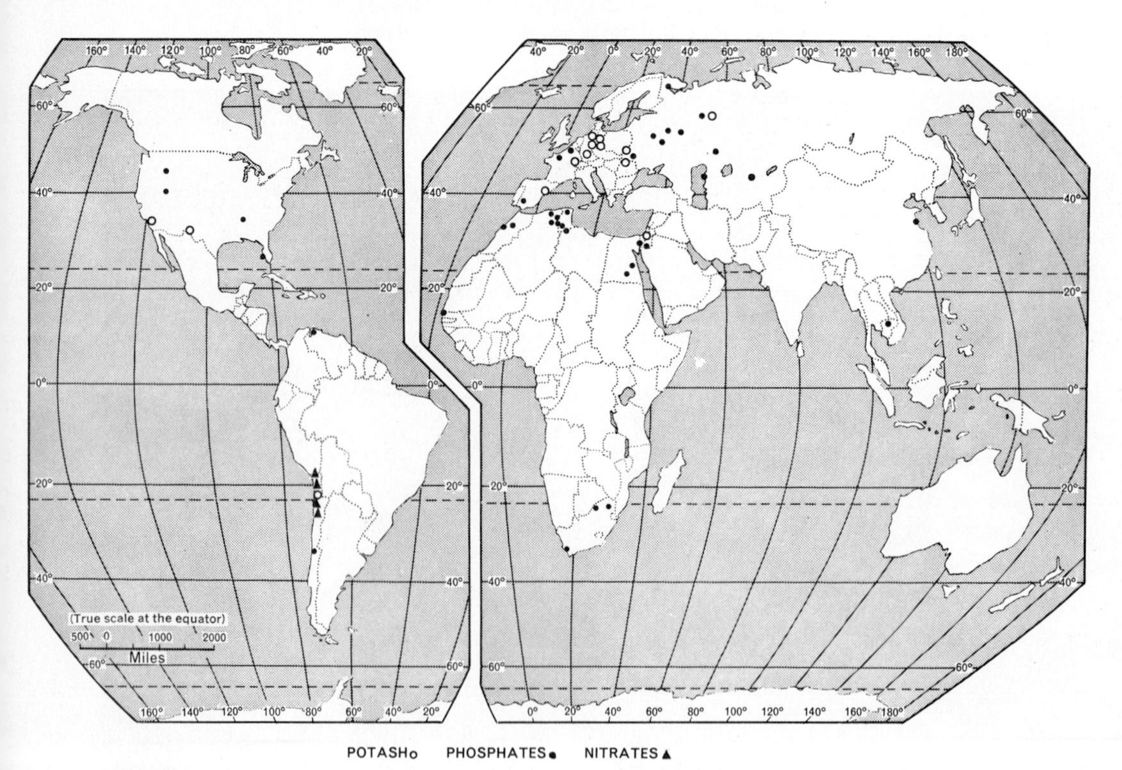

tilizer minerals in natural form are the compounds of nitrogen, despite the large quantity of the element in the atmosphere. Adding to the fertilizer value of this element, which is needed by plants and animals to form proteins, is its importance in the manufacture of explosives. Nitrogen's scarcity as a natural salt is primarily due to the fact that it is a relatively inert gas that does not unite easily with other elements. Living organisms, especially the soil microbes, have been responsible for the synthesis of most nitrogen salts and have added these to soils for later plant use. The nitrogen salts are soluble in water; therefore about the only place that they can accumulate as exploitable deposits is in desert areas. Such deposits are not common even here, however, because deserts are not favored environments for life of any kind. The most important nitrate deposits in the world are found in desert hardpans within the Atacama Desert of northern Chile, where they are comprised largely of sodium nitrate, the famous Chilean saltpeter of commerce (see Fig. 13.23). Guano deposits, or accumulations of bird manure, are minor sources of nitrogenous fertilizers and are still produced on some of the dry nesting islands off the coast of Peru.

FIG. 13.23 Drilling into the desert hardpan that comprises the sodium nitrate deposit of the Atacama Desert in northern Chile. This hardpan, or "caliche," is sometimes as hard as concrete. [Grace Line]

High prices for the natural nitrate fertilizers led to a search for other sources, and two synthetic processes for producing nitrogen compounds were developed near the beginning of the present century. The first involves recovering ammonia (a nitrogenous hydroxide) from by-product coke ovens. The other consists of electrolytically combining atmospheric nitrogen into various compounds by several methods. Today the synthetic production of ammonia by combining atmospheric nitrogen with hydrogen dominates the nitrogen fertilizer industry, and mineral nitrates supply only a small fraction of the growing world demand. The major requirement for synthetic nitrates is cheap electric power.

PHOSPHORUS. In contrast to the nitrogen minerals, those of phosphorus are abundant and widespread and occur in a variety of forms. Some are found in igneous rocks, and others are formed in sedimentary rocks as the result of both organic and inorganic processes. The most abundant mineral of phosphorus is the crystalline, or igneous, mineral *apatite,* which is a calcium phosphate. Over much of the world, however, apatite is not used as a source of commercial phosphate, because of the competition of sedimentary phosphate rock, which is easier to obtain and requires much less processing to make the phosphorus available in soluble form for plant use. In the Soviet Union, however, phosphate fertilizer is obtained almost exclusively from apatite, most of which comes from the Kola Peninsula, adjacent to northern Finland. Global reserves of apatite are believed to be enormous, and the United States and Canada both have huge tonnages of it.

Phosphate rock, which is by far the most important commercial source of phosphorus, develops in sedimentary rocks through alteration of animal remains, including bone material and guano (bird excreta). It is widely distributed, but high-grade deposits are localized. North Africa, including Morocco, Algeria, and Tunis, is the largest general producing area. Other important high-grade deposits are found on several small tropical islands in the Pacific and on Curaçao Island in the West Indies. The major supply of phosphate rock for the United States is derived from phosphatic limestone pebbles that have weathered out from a soft limestone in Florida. Tennessee, South Carolina, Kentucky, and Arkansas also produce some. Large reserves of low-grade phosphate rock are known to occur in Wyoming, Montana, Idaho, and Utah, and these western states are currently supplying about one-third of the national production.

POTASSIUM. Potassium, like phosphorus, is an abundant element in the earth crust, but most of it occurs in complex silicates, such as the feldspars, from which it is exceedingly difficult to extract. Potassium salts constitute an appreciable part of the salt content in sea water, and the major commercial deposits have been laid down in ancient seaways or basins that were separated from the sea by crustal movements. Here the salt was concentrated by evaporation, and these deposits were later buried under sediments. The world's largest deposits are found in structural basins of Permian age, a geologic period characterized by large crustal movements and wide climatic extremes. Three of these Permian basins, each of which contains important beds of potassium salts in its sedimentary strata, are as follows:

1. Central and northern Germany. Near Stassfurt, the beds are fairly near the surface, and mines in this area have made Germany the leading producer.

2. Eastern European Soviet Union. This basin is west of the Urals and north of Molotov. The producing beds lie well within 1,000 feet of the surface.

3. Eastern New Mexico–West Texas. This potash basin at one time was a low portion of a large seaway that lay east of the Rocky Mountains and extended from Canada to the Gulf of Mexico. The major potash salt beds lie near Carlsbad, New Mexico.

Other potash salt deposits of more recent origin occur near Mulhouse in southern Alsace; northwest of Barcelona in Spain; the Dead Sea basin near the Israel-Jordan border (see Fig. 13.24); and in the portion of the southwestern Soviet Union taken from Poland following World War II. Small deposits are found in many of the desert salt flats throughout the world. The Searles Lake playa in southeastern California supplies a considerable portion of the United States production of potash, together with several other salts. Asia is a relatively small producer of potassium, because the place of mineral fertilizers is taken largely by organic compost. As the Asiatic nations industrialize, more inorganic fertilizers are likely to be produced and used.

13.18 SULFUR. Sulfur is one of the most important elements in the chemical industry, mainly because it is easily obtained, and is the basic material for the production of sulfuric acid, the cheapest and most useful acid for industrial chemical reactions. It also is important in the synthesis of many sulfides and sulfates, chemical compounds that have broad industrial applications, from the mak-

FIG. 13.24 Salt evaporation pans near S'dom on the Dead Sea in Israel. The white material shown here is carnallite, a potash salt and a valuable fertilizer. [Israel Office of Information]

ing of paper to the production of medicines.

Sulfur is obtained from two basic sources: deposits of pure native sulfur, and from metallic sulfides such as pyrite, which is a common sulfide of iron. Some native sulfur is found in most active volcanic areas, where it collects in and about volcanic vents as a residue from hydrogen sulfide fumes. The largest native sulfur deposits, however, are formed as the result of the alteration of gypsum (calcium sulfate), a rather common salt that frequently occurs adjacent to rock salt.

The United States and Mexico contain the largest reserves of native sulfur in the world, and these occur in connection with salt domes along the Gulf of Mexico coastal plain (see Fig. 13.25 and Fig. 13.26). Some of

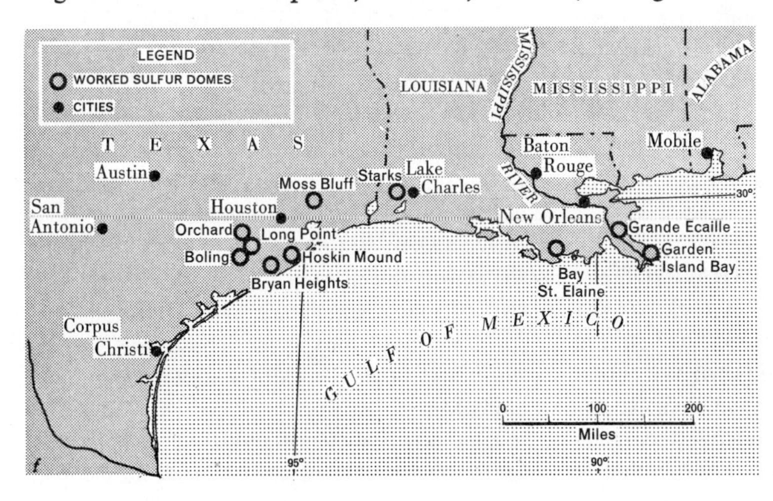

FIG. 13.25 Location of sulfur deposits being worked in association with salt domes along the Gulf Coast of the United States. The association of sulfur and salt has aided in the growth of the chemical industry along this coastal region. Such structures are also located in parts of eastern Mexico.

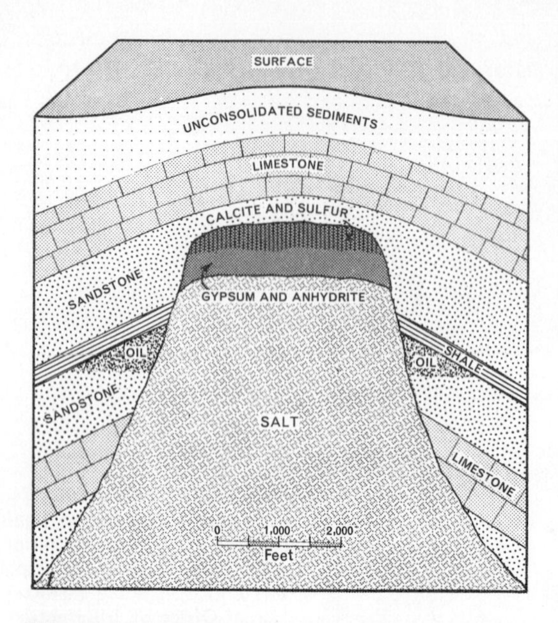

FIG. 13.26 Diagram of a typical salt dome with associated sulfur and petroleum.

the sulfur beds, although localized, are as much as 100 feet thick. The sulfur is obtained by forcing hot water and compressed air down a drill pipe into the sulfur-bearing formation. Molten sulfur is forced to the surface, where it is collected and solidified in huge vats. Italy mines sulfur-bearing sedimentary rock, and Japan and Chile both produce native sulfur from volcanic rocks. Elsewhere, sulfur is derived mainly from pyrite or as a by-product in the refining of sulfide ores of several other metals, including copper, nickel, lead, and zinc. Global reserves of sulfur appear to be sufficient for a long, indefinite period.

13.19 SALT (SODIUM CHLORIDE). Common salt, which occurs in rocks as the mineral *halite,* is a leading element in the chemical industry. Its best-known use, however, is as an important condiment in flavoring foods, a use that has always been universal. Its value in the chemical industry lies in the large number of compounds of either sodium or chlorine. Its greatest use is in the general field of alkalies, such as soda ash, which is basic to such important industries as glass and soap manufacturing. Salt is one of the most widely distributed minerals; it not only exists in large quantities in sea water but occurs in vast sedimentary rock strata covering hundreds of thousands of square miles. It is also found in desert playa-lake beds and in salt brines confined within permeable sedimentary beds, such as sandstones. The extraction of salt from most of the above sources has been practiced since early human history.

Most salt produced today is derived either from mines or wells tapping sedimentary rock-salt beds or from the solar evaporation of sea water. The latter process is particularly useful in arid regions. The world production of salt is based largely on the volume of industrial requirements and population, but the quantity available can be considered virtually inexhaustible. In the United States, the world's leading producer and consumer, salt brines pumped from subsurface salt beds are the major sources. The principal producing states are Michigan, New York, Louisiana, Kansas, Ohio and California.

13.20 NEW NONMETALLIC INDUSTRIAL ELEMENTS OBTAINED FROM MINERALS. Modern industrial research programs are continuing to develop new uses for nonmetallic minerals and for chemical elements that hitherto have held only academic interest. There is a long list of these, but the present discussion covers only two of them, which are briefly treated here for illustrative purposes. These are *germanium* and *silicon,* both of which are chemical elements.

GERMANIUM. Germanium is one of the more spectacular of the recently developed materials, because of its remarkable applications in the relatively new electronics industry. Its current importance is due to the fact that it is intermediate between a metal and a nonmetal. Along with pure silicon, germanium is a semiconductor of electric current and, when mixed with an impurity in exactly the right proportion, develops the property of modifying electric currents passing through it. Thus it operates in much the same manner as a rectifier or amplifier tube in a radio set, and small quantities of such germanium alloys are able to substitute for bulky vacuum tubes in many types of electronic assemblies, with a great resultant saving in space, expense, and energy. Wafers of germanium alloy used for this purpose are called *transistors,* and they are being used widely in hearing aids, miniature radios, guided missiles, and automatic computers. The cost of purifying germanium is high, and in 1956 it was selling for $400 per pound. It seems well worth the price, however, since a pound of germanium will make over 2,000 transistors. At present the element is either obtained as a by-product of zinc refining or recovered in the chemical treatment of flue dusts in coke by-product ovens. Nearly all zinc ores have germanium as an associated element, and some ores of the Belgian Congo are reported to have as much as 7.8 per cent germanium oxide.

SILICON. Silicon is a chemical element that, like germanium, is midway between the metals and nonmetals. It should not be confused with *silica,* which is the usual name for the chemical compound silicon dioxide and which is, in its natural crystalline form, the mineral *quartz.* In 1956, pure silicon was selling for $380 per pound, which indicates the difficulty of isolating this exceedingly abundant element from its oxide. The first separation was made by fusing quartz sand and coke together in the high temperature of an electric furnace to form a silicon-carbon compound which had unusual hardness and durability and became a leading synthetic abrasive, under the trade name Carborundum.

During World War II, research led to the synthesis of an entirely new group of silicon compounds, termed *silicones,* which are chain compounds somewhat similar in structure to the hydrocarbons but which consist of a combination of silicon and oxygen atoms instead of hydrogen and carbon. The silicones, which have the property of adding both chemical and physical stability to various other materials, have had wide applications—for example the preparation of special lubricants designed for use under extremely low temperatures and in the manufacture of rubber that will retain its elasticity under both high and low temperatures.

One of the most recent developments in the use of silicon lies in the electronics industry, where it is used to produce transistors similar to those made of germanium. Although germanium seems to work better for this purpose at normal air temperatures, it loses its property as a semiconductor as the temperature increases, becoming worthless for this purpose above 100°C. Silicon, on the other hand, can function over a far greater range of temperatures and thus is useful for electronic control systems that are likely to encounter high temperatures, as in high-velocity guided mssiles and in high-speed machine-tool controls. Silicon is produced today mainly in countries having facilities for advanced chemical research. The raw material, quartz, can be found nearly everywhere.

13.21 THE COMMON ROCK RESOURCES. There are several rock materials that have a great resource value to man, yet are not usually considered minerals;

these include quarried stone, gravel, sand, and clay. The total value of these products throughout the world, although never determined, probably exceeds that of all the mineral products combined. Some parts of the world utilize such rock materials much more than others, but there are few areas that do not use them in one way or another.

There are many types of *quarried stone,* including cut stone for building purposes, crushed stone for road ballast or the manufacture of concrete, flagstones for pavements, marble or granites for monuments or decorative stone, limestone for various purposes, and slates for roofing or blackboards. *Limestone* probably is the most important quarried stone, partly because its relative softness and smooth texture make it easy to shape and cut and also because its chemical composition (calcium carbonate) makes it valuable in the manufacture of cement and in the chemical industry. It is found throughout the world. *Granite* probably is the most widely distributed of any single rock type. It constitutes most of the rock in the crystalline, igneous-rock shield areas. It is less useful than limestone, however, because its hardness makes it difficult to shape or crush. In the humid tropics and subtropics, granite crumbles rapidly because of rock decomposition. In cooler climates, however, it is an exceptionally hard, durable rock that is used for cemetery monuments or for street paving blocks. *Sandstones* that are cemented with iron oxide or silica are used for building purposes, and those which are relatively free of iron are used as a source of silica for glassmaking. Because of their special properties, *slate* and *marble* have had a long history of use. Slate is valued for its tendency to split along smooth cleavage planes, and marble (crystalline limestone) is prized because it polishes and cuts easily.

Sands and *gravels* are used widely in combination with cement to form concrete for construction purposes. Some pure quartz sands are used for glassmaking, whereas other fine-textured sands are used in the construction of molds for metal castings and as abrasives. Although both gravel and sand, which are found associated with alluvial, coastal, and fluvioglacial deposits, are common throughout most of the world, serious shortages are developing in many local urban areas, because of heavy exploitation, especially for hard-surfaced road construction. Because of their relatively low value and high bulk, sand and gravel cannot be shipped far. In some areas both sand and gravel are being produced by stone crushing.

One of the principal uses for clays, fine sands, shales, and other earth materials is in refractories. These are substances that will withstand high temperatures, yet can be molded and fixed into many shapes. Furnace linings, porcelain and enamel wares, molds for castings, and many kinds of insulators are examples. Clays and shales also are widely used for pottery, tile, and brick manufacture. Although both clay and shale are widely distributed, suitable deposits for use in high-grade potteries are rare. The most valuable deposits are those which are relatively free of iron, although techniques for removing the iron prior to molding and firing have been developed. Probably the major use of clays is simply as sun-dried mud, or adobe, which is a building material used throughout the world in arid and semiarid climates.

Although there are dozens of minerals, exotic and otherwise, that are obtained only at great expense and effort and that are utilized in many sophisticated ways, they have not displaced the simple rock and stone materials that have been useful to man since long before recorded history. Undoubtedly rock and stone will continue to be important resource materials far into the future. Their distribution is widespread and their variety is great, but they have their greatest regional importance where wood is scarce and expensive. It is interesting to note that the most imposing monuments of modern cultures—the skyscrapers, factories, and superhighways—as well as the most enduring monuments of ancient cultures—the pyramids, temples, and fortifications—are constructed out of the same simple rock and stone materials.

Perspective

The geography of minerals is a complex subject, and the distributional patterns and their interpretations are still incompletely known. The distribution of some minerals is related to structural and chemical processes deep within the earth interior, whereas other minerals exhibit the marks of environmental relationships common to all other features on the earth surface. Some minerals bear the determining stamp of climate, and others are related to sequences in geological weathering or to local conditions of drainage. Still others are relatively uninfluenced by surface phenomena and appear to be as stable at the earth surface as when they were first synthesized deep within the earth crust. The position of the latter minerals may change, but their properties remain constant. It is clear, however, that, on a geological time scale, the distributional patterns of most minerals do change. Minerals come and go and are altered and shifted around. They seem stable only in relation to the shortness of human life.

Minerals may be affected by various features of the environment, but they also play a role in determining environmental characteristics. The soils, vegetation, and various life forms of an area often exhibit the marks of the underlying mineral deposits. This relationship has been exploited in mineral prospecting, in which valuable deposits of minerals such as iron, copper, and cobalt have been located from the air by noting subtle changes in the coloring of vegetation or soils. Minerals are also a major factor in determining the suitability of environments for human use and occupation. Man is becoming increasingly dependent on the exploitation and use of minerals, and mineral accessibility has become a critical factor in national development.

The meaning of mineral patterns alters far more rapidly than the patterns themselves. Resources are created by man according to his wants and techniques. Minerals themselves can be considered as "neutral stuff," the materials out of which resources are created. Our pattern of mineral resources, therefore, is altered by the new developments arising from the research programs of industrial chemists and metallurgists, by new mining techniques, and by changes in cultural patterns throughout the world.

The apparently insatiable appetite of modern industry for minerals continues to grow. Some minerals are beginning to show signs of depletion, and others are only coming into use. No part of the world is free from the scrutiny of man in his search for mineral wealth. If future generations are to be successful in maintaining or increasing the general living standards of the world population, they will have to recognize and guard against the danger of appraising minerals as static elements in the environment. Wise use involves the interdependence of areas, the development of substitute materials, and strenuous efforts to anticipate and provide for future shortages.

The minerals of the world are both concentrated and scattered. Some are common, and others are rare. The countries having large territorial areas usually have a wide variety of minerals and an abundant supply of some of them. The large nations are therefore likely to be the mineral-rich nations, and those with great political and economic potentials. No nation is completely self-sufficient, however, and through the caprices of geological processes that were operative long before man appeared on earth, some important deposits of strategic minerals were bestowed on small, politically weak nations. If a proper relationship is to exist between men and minerals, it must lie far above the petty jealousies of nations. Such a workable balance involves a stable interrelationship of the entire human race and the marshaling of human efforts everywhere.

14

Water resources

Fresh water is one of our most precious basic resources. Although it is a renewable resource, or one that is replenished following use, great differences occur in the quantities available to man from place to place on the surface of the earth. Man's demand for water has increased continuously, reaching a peak in the modern era, owing to the new industrial and urban demands. Increasing demands on our water supply have focused attention on this vital part of our resource base. The problem of supplying fresh water for human use is not uniquely modern, however, and it has played an important role in the rise and fall of nations since antiquity.

In this chapter, the emphasis is on the water-supply problems in the United States, because of the greater availability of data. Similar conditions can be found, however, in many other parts of the world. The scope of our modern demands on water may be suggested by the fact that in 1957 the United States used about 200 billion gallons per day,[1] or about 1,250 gallons per person. About half of this amount is available for reuse. A breakdown of the major uses of water in the United States is given in Fig. 14.1.

There is no substitute for water in the living cells of plants and animals; therefore, regional deficiencies in water constitute the most completely limiting environmental factor affecting the distribution of life forms. We have seen the importance of water in the global arrangement of vegetation in Chapter 9, and it plays a major role in the geography of climates, soils, landforms, and surface configurations. The occurrence of water on earth is subject to the same basic principles of natural distributions as the other elements in the natural environment: it varies in its modes of occurrence; it varies in quantity and quality from place to place and from time to time; it tends toward relative stability in establishing relationships with other elements in the environmental complex; and

FIG. 14.1 Uses of water in the United States. [U.S. Geological Survey]

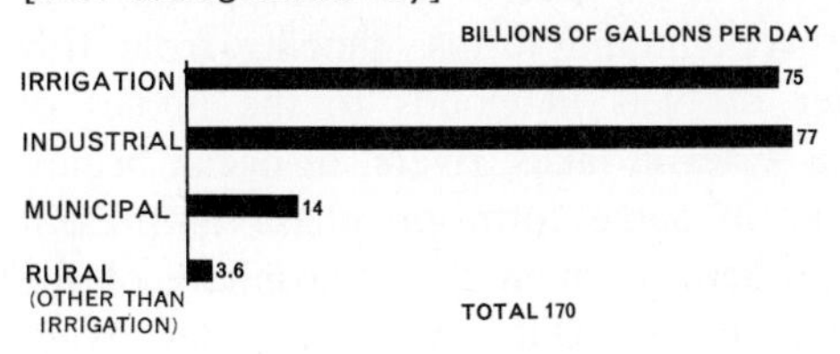

[1] The annual consumption at this rate, or about 73 trillion gallons, would cover the State of New York to a depth of about 6 feet and would equal about 17 per cent of the total surface runoff in the United States.

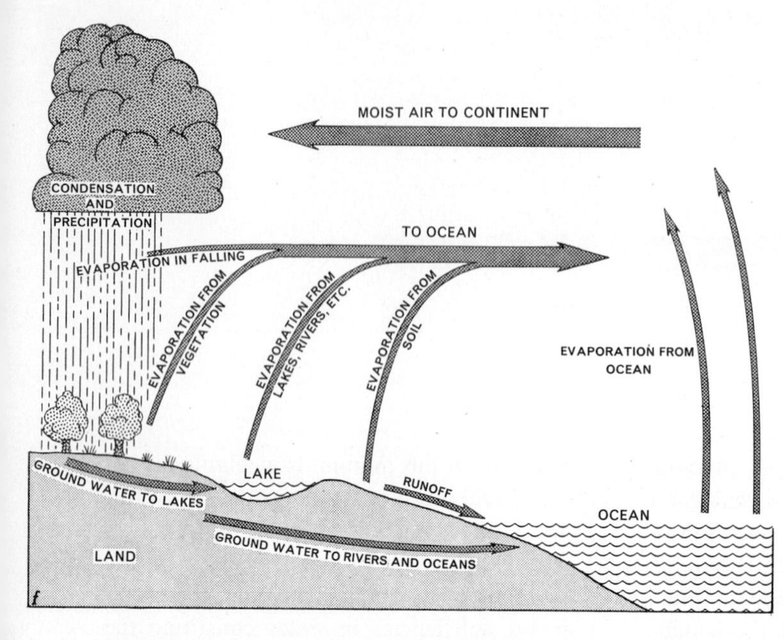

FIG. 14.2 The hydrologic cycle.

its areal patterns exhibit transitional features.

The interaction of fresh water and the other major natural environmental factors has been discussed in other chapters. In this chapter we are interested in water primarily as an independent environmental element and as a resource, particularly with respect to its availability and patterns of distribution. The various qualitative differences in water for human use and changes in the dynamics of water appraisal are also discussed.

The distribution of water

Water is found in nature in a solid phase, as ice or snow; in a gaseous phase, as invisible water vapor in the atmosphere; and in several liquid forms, ranging from tiny water droplets in clouds to the bodies of fresh water in lakes, rivers, or ocean brines. Water in some form or phase is present everywhere, even in the atmosphere of the driest deserts. Differences in water availability, however, make the geography of water resources an influential factor in the distribution of population.

14.1 THE HYDROLOGIC CYCLE.

The ultimate reservoir for the global water supply is the oceans, and probably all the water in the world was contained within this reservoir at one time or other and will return to it sometime in the future. The circuit of water as it is evaporated from the oceans, precipitated to the continents, and eventually returned to the oceans via rivers and streams is known as the *hydrologic cycle* (see Fig. 14.2). An understanding of its mechanics helps to clarify the reasons for variations in water availability throughout the world.

Approximately 97 per cent of all the water on earth is contained in the oceans and seas, and if we were to add to this the amount locked within the continental ice sheets of Greenland and Antarctica, the percentage left to be considered in our treatment of water resources would be small indeed.

Nevertheless, this remaining 1½ per cent or so plays a dominant part in sculpturing the portion of the earth surface that rises above the oceans and in shaping the life forms that dwell thereon. The water that leaves the ocean takes many different routes and encounters many detours, "blind alleys," and short cuts along the way. Perhaps it would be more appropriate to speak of many hydrologic cycles, some of which are long and complex, whereas others are short and direct.

The first stage in the hydrologic cycle is evaporation. By far the largest amount of evaporation occurs over warm tropical ocean surfaces, although it takes place everywhere to a certain degree. The process of evaporation is more than a simple transfer of water from a liquid to a gaseous phase. As indicated in Chapter 6, evaporation is an essential part of the major global heat-energy transfer in the low latitudes (see Sec. 6.14). The climatic factors that influence evaporation, including temperature, relative humidity, and absolute humidity, also were treated in Chapter 6. The temperature factor is of the utmost importance in determining the capacity of air to evaporate and to hold water vapor. Air at 70°F, for example, will hold about 150 times as much water vapor as air at minus 30°F. This is why the warm ocean surfaces are the major starting point in the hydrologic cycle.

The second step in the cycle involves condensation and precipitation, which were discussed in Chapter 6. Precipitation is the most important single factor in both the hydrologic cycle and the geography of fresh-water resources. In general, areas having abundant precipitation in the form of rain have abundant resources of fresh water. The distribution of precipitation is influenced by many factors, and the reader is referred again to the chapters dealing with climate for a treatment of this important subject. When rain falls directly into the ocean, the hydrologic cycle is terminated abruptly.

FIG. 14.3 Factors influencing the movement of surface water into the ground.

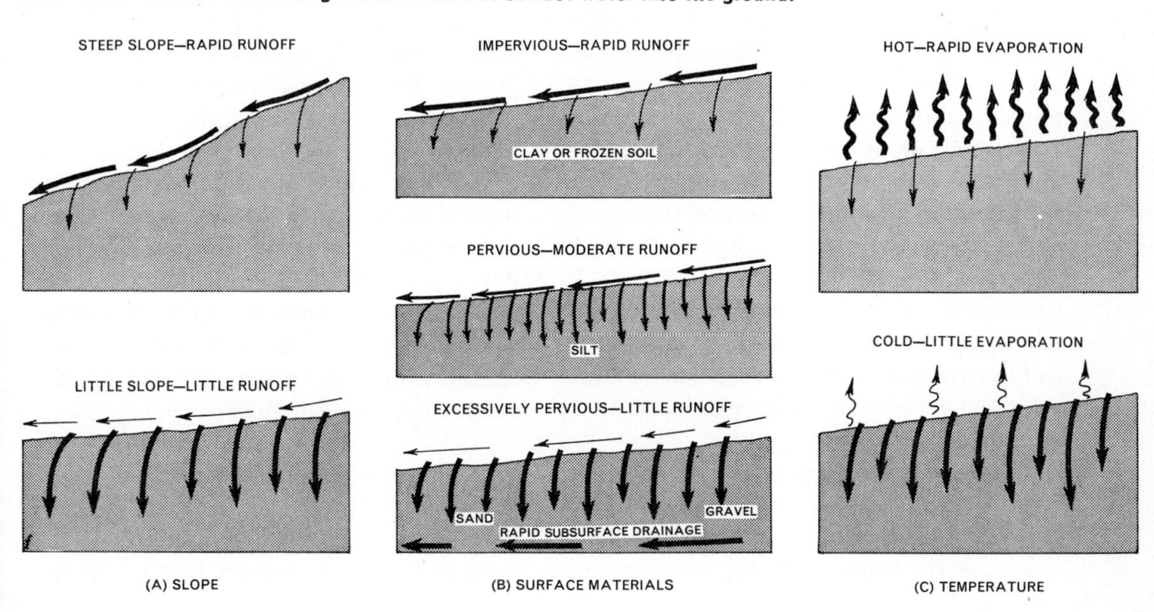

When precipitation occurs on the continents, however, the course of the cycle is diverted into several different channels (see Fig. 14.2).

Part of the precipitation that reaches the earth surface flows as surface water into streams and rivers and eventually completes the cycle upon reaching the ocean. This portion of the cycle is known as *runoff,* and it constitutes one of the major sources of fresh water for human use. Not all the runoff flows immediately to the sea to complete the cycle. There is some evaporation from the surface of streams, and where the runoff is temporarily detained in large lakes, evaporation may represent a sizable proportion of the original runoff.

A second portion of the precipitation sinks into the ground, where its course in the hydrologic cycle is greatly slowed or even interrupted. This underground water may be involved in many long detours before it eventually returns to the sea. Some of it may work its way into adjacent streams via springs or river-bed seepage. Some of it may be reevaporated from soils, and some may be absorbed by plants and released into the air as vapor through the process of transpiration. Some of it may be locked within mineral substances for indefinite periods through chemical combination, and some may penetrate deep into the earth along permeable rock strata, to be confined there for thousands or even millions of years.

Interior basins may intercept both runoff and underground water. If the climate is sufficiently arid, evaporation may make it impossible for enough water to accumulate to form an outlet to the sea. In such a case, evaporation may be the sole means of escape.

A third portion of the precipitation may be in the form of snow, which may linger a few days before it melts and returns to its course in the cycle or which may become incorporated into the mass of a continental ice sheet, such as that of Antarctica, and have to wait centuries before it returns to the sea.

The various circuits in the water cycle are shown diagrammatically in Fig. 14.2. The following subdivisions of this section are concerned, respectively, with the three major routes that water may take following its precipitation upon the land surface: (1) evapotranspiration, or the return of water to the atmosphere; (2) runoff; and (3) ground water.

14.2 EVAPOTRANSPIRATION.

The return of water from the land to the atmosphere by direct evaporation and through transpiration by plants can be considered as a bypass, or detour, in the progression of the hydrologic cycle. *Evapotranspiration,* as this return of water to the atmosphere is termed, may be of great significance in the study of water resources, since it reduces the supply of fresh water added to the land by precipitation and thus curtails the amount directly available to man. When evapotranspiration exceed precipitation, the fresh-water supply becomes insufficient for plant growth. The *potential evapotranspiration* of an area, when determined, is a much better indicator of aridity than precipitation alone or simple temperature-precipitation ratios, such as those used in the Koeppen classification of climate. Careful research by Thornthwaite and others has produced an empirical formula whereby an index of potential evapotranspiration can be obtained, utilizing readily obtainable figures of precipitation, temperature, and length of day.[2]

[2] Those interested in the determination and application of potential evapotranspiration are referred to C. W. Thornthwaite, "An Approach toward a Rational Classification of Climate," *Geographical Review,* January, 1948, pp. 55–94.

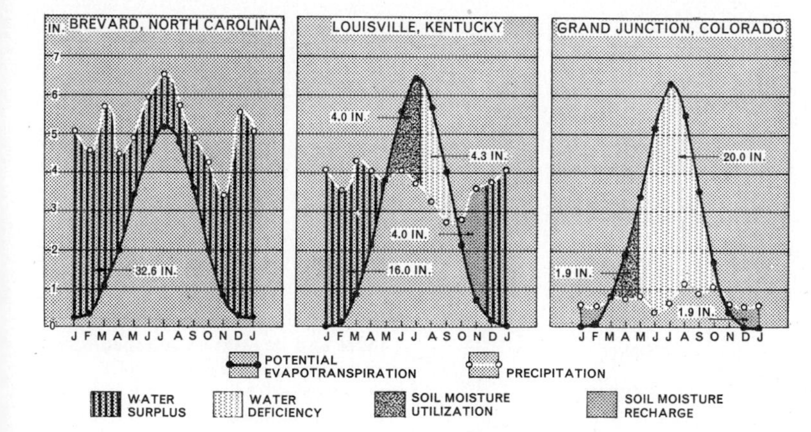

FIG. 14.4 Precipitation and potential evapotranspiration at three selected stations in the United States. [After Thornthwaite]

The use of the potential evapotranspiration index can be illustrated by the three charts shown in Fig. 14.4. The chart for Brevard, North Carolina, shows that precipitation exceeds potential evapotranspiration in every month; thus there is a surplus of water in every month for runoff and for the replenishment of reservoirs both above and below the land surface. The chart for Louisville, Kentucky, indicates that precipitation exceeds potential evapotranspiration during the months between October and May and that during this period a total surplus of 16 inches of rain is available for runoff or ground-water addition. During the summer months at Louisville, however, a deficiency of 8.3 inches of precipitation exists, 4 inches of which [3] is offset by water stored in the soil during the wet season, leaving a seasonal total deficiency of 4.3 inches, occurring in July, August, and September. In October and November, the water supplies in the soil at Louisville are recharged with water totaling 4 inches, after which surpluses once more appear. As indicated in the chart for Grand Junction, Colorado, the water reserves in the soil never become fully recharged, and no surpluses occur in any season for surface runoff. Agriculture must be supplemented by irrigation at nearly all times of the year.

Evaporation and transpiration for the most part detract from the fresh-water resources of the world and are therefore important factors in the water resource base. Under certain unusual conditions, however, atmospheric moisture may constitute a reserve of available water for direct or indirect human use. Mention already has been made of the grazing zone along the western slopes of the Andes in Peru, which is maintained by a sparse vegetation based on unusually heavy dew.

14.3 GROUND WATER. Water which seeps into the ground following precipitation may have several destinations. Some may evaporate on its way through the soil; some may be intercepted by the molecular attraction of soil particle surfaces; and some may be "pumped" out of the soil by plants and transpired into the atmosphere. Most of the subsurface water, however, will continue downward until it is stopped at a zone where the openings have already been filled with

[3] The figure of 4 inches is the average amount of water that can be stored within soils and within the reach of plants. Unusually coarse-textured soils would tend to reduce this figure, and heavy clays would raise it.

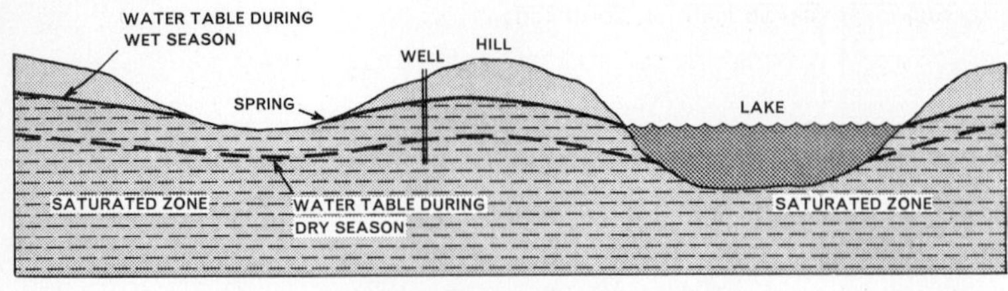

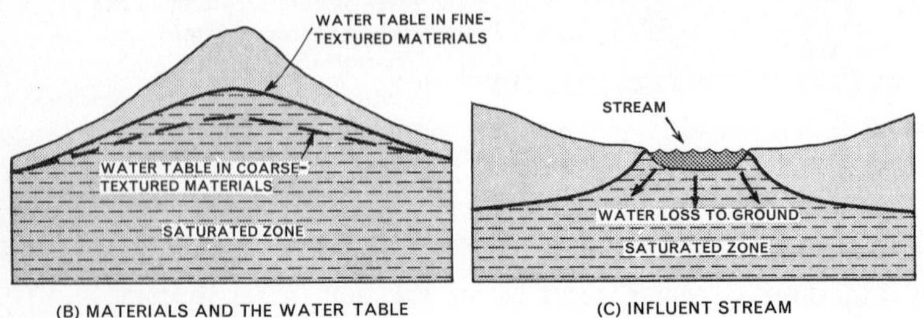

FIG. 14.5 Diagram of a water table and its relation to topography and surface materials. In (C), the stream lies somewhat higher than the water table on each side; hence it loses water to the ground below.

water. Once within this saturated zone, the water is termed *ground water,* and the upper limit of the saturated zone is known as the *water table* (see Fig. 14.5). The total quantity of water stored below the surface as ground water is many times the amount in surface reservoirs, such as lakes and swamps. Not all of it, however, is suitable for use, and the quantities available vary greatly from place to place.

The most common deterrent to the use of ground water is its content of dissolved solids, principally the water-soluble salts. The U.S. Public Health Service does not consider ground water potable if it contains more than 1,000 parts of dissolved solids per million, and it recommends using water that has less than 500 parts per million. Table 14.1 indicates some of the implications of soluble mineral contents in water.

TABLE 14.1 Implications of dissolved solids in water

IMPLICATIONS	MINERAL SOLUTES IN PARTS PER MILLION
Toxic limits of boron to plants	1–3 (boron)
Most rain water	Under 16 (total soilds)
Soft domestic water	Under 50 (total solids)
Hard domestic water	100–200 (total solids)
Recommended upper limit for domestic use	500 (total solids)
Recommended upper limit for rice irrigation	600 (total solids)
Recommended upper limit for general irrigation	700 (total solids)
Absolute limit for irrigation	1,200 (NaCl; less for other salts)
Upper limit of human tolerance (drinking)	4,000 (NaCl; less for other salts)
Upper limit for cattle use	9,400 (NaCl; less for other salts)
Upper limit for sheep use	15,600 (NaCl; less for other salts)
Mean salinity of sea water	34,000 (total solids)

The areas shown in Fig. 14.6 as having very hard water have ground-water supplies that contain more than 2,000 parts of dissolved solids (of all kinds) per million. Such water has decided disadvantages even for most industrial purposes. Four general types of area are likely to have ground water that contains objectionable proportions of dissolved solids: (1) arid and semiarid regions, where salts are concentrated in soils by soil-forming processes; (2) areas underlain by porous limestones or other soluble sedimentary rocks; (3) unconsolidated sediments having high lime contents, such as marls or glacial tills; and (4) low-lying coastal zones that lie within the tidal influence of salty or brackish water.

The availability of ground water varies widely from place to place. The most important single factor in the availability of ground water is the amount and size of openings in the earth material lying below the surface. In order to be an effective source of water, a subterranean water-bearing horizon must be able not only to hold much water but also to replace water rapidly as it is removed. Fine-textured clays, for example, are dismissed as important sources of ground water, even though their total water content may be high, because the tight molecular hold and friction along the tiny surfaces of the clay particles will not permit water to move freely. Sands and gravels that have large openings between the rock particles are ideal types of reservoirs for available ground-water supplies. Water not only can leave such *aquifers*

FIG. 14.6 The quality of ground water in the United States. [After U.S. National Resources Board]

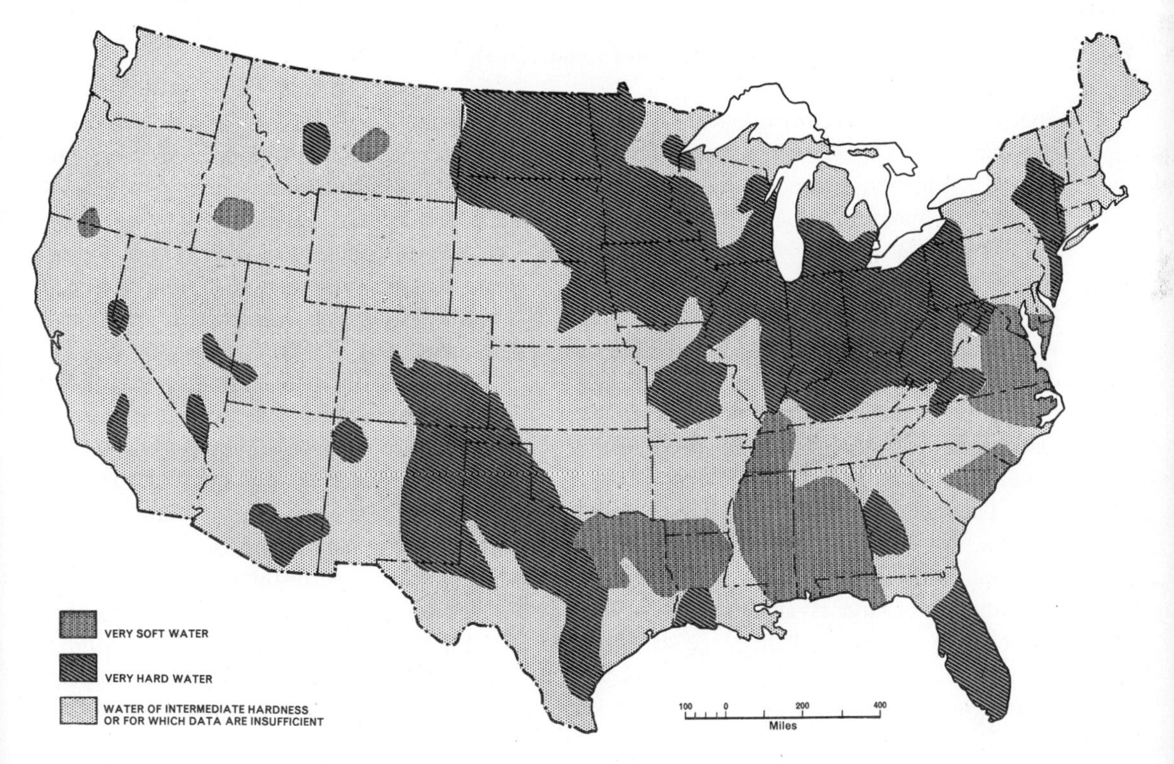

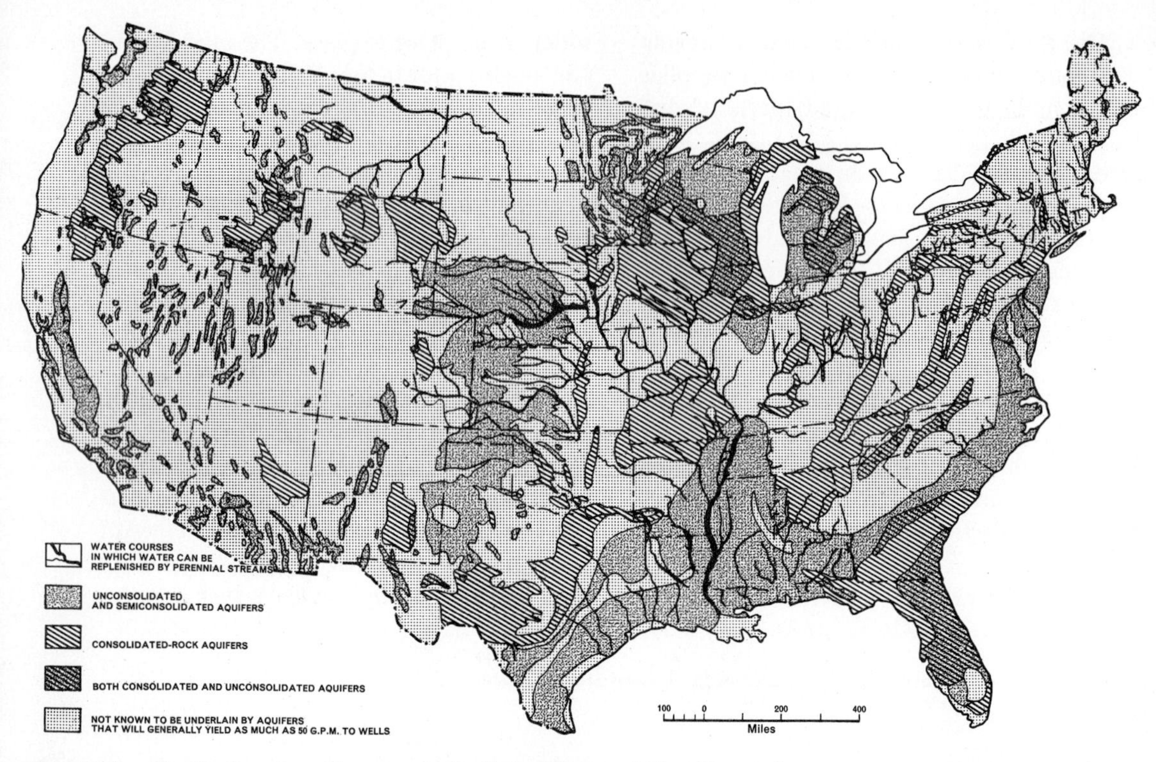

FIG. 14.7 Distribution of aquifer types in the United States. [After Thomas]

(permeable, water-bearing strata) rapidly but can enter quickly to replace the withdrawals. Further, since this water is less exposed to mineral surfaces, it tends to have a lower content of dissolved solids than relatively impermeable porous strata. It has been estimated that nearly 80 per cent of the well water produced in the United States is derived from loose or slightly consolidated gravels and sands. Figure 14.7 indicates the distribution of the following three major kinds of aquifers in the United States:

1. Unconsolidated material along watercourses. An example of the unconsolidated material that develops along watercourses is the alluvium of large river flood plains. Wells in the valleys of some of the large streams in the northeastern United States have yielded huge flows. A single well at Wallingford, Connecticut, yields 5 million gallons per day, despite a depth of only 80 feet. Much of the water from such sources is recent surface runoff and hence is likely to have a much lower content of dissolved solids than ground water from wells tapping deeper ground water that has been in the ground for years.

2. Unconsolidated and semiconsolidated strata. Examples of unconsolidated and semiconsolidated strata include coastal-plain sands and gravels, glacial outwash plains and drainage channels, young sediments of the Great Plains, and some of the alluvial-fan strata of the western states.

3. Consolidated-rock aquifers. In order to qualify as good aquifers, consolidated rocks must have sufficient openings to permit the easy passage and retention of water. Ex-

amples are the cavernous and fractured limestones of some of the southern states, the porous basaltic lavas of the Columbia and Snake River plateaus, and some loosely cemented sandstones, such as the Dakota and St. Peter sandstones.

Only about half of the United States has suitable ground-water resources. Similar conditions can be found over much of the world. High quality, potable ground water is a valuable resource, and one that should be managed carefully.

The amount of available ground water varies greatly in different parts of the world. The most important factor is the availability of suitable aquifers. In the crystalline-rock areas of the world, ground water is confined mostly to a relatively shallow veneer of soil or transported sediments, such as glacial debris or alluvium. This is partly why surface waters, including rivers, lakes, and swamps, are prominent landscape features in such areas. Deep, highly permeable, unconsolidated sediments, on the other hand, may contain huge reserves of ground water.

Other hindrances in the use of ground water as a resource include (1) the high pumping costs of obtaining water from deep aquifers; (2) occasional local pollution in shallow ground-water supplies; (3) low permeability in aquifers, resulting in slow pumping rates and slow recharge; (4) objectionable odors, caused by a high content of sulfur or certain types of organic material.

The utilization of ground water is high, despite the general limitations resulting from solutes and the localization of suitable aquifers. Where ground water is accessible and sufficiently fresh, it usually is much preferred to surface runoff, and it constituted approximately 17 to 20 per cent of the total amount of water consumed by human beings in the United States during 1950. Its advantages include an even flow, the lack of any necessity for elaborate storage reservoirs, short vertical transportation rather than long horizontal haul, even seasonal temperatures, and considerably less danger from pollution. In some areas, expensive municipal water-softening plants are used to overcome objection-

FIG. 14.8 Diagram of a Ranney well, designed for obtaining high-volume withdrawals of water from river-valley gravels. Such wells also can be used to discharge surplus water into subsurface aquifers for use during dry periods. Wells such as this may supply several million gallons of water per day. [The Southwestern Ohio Water Company]

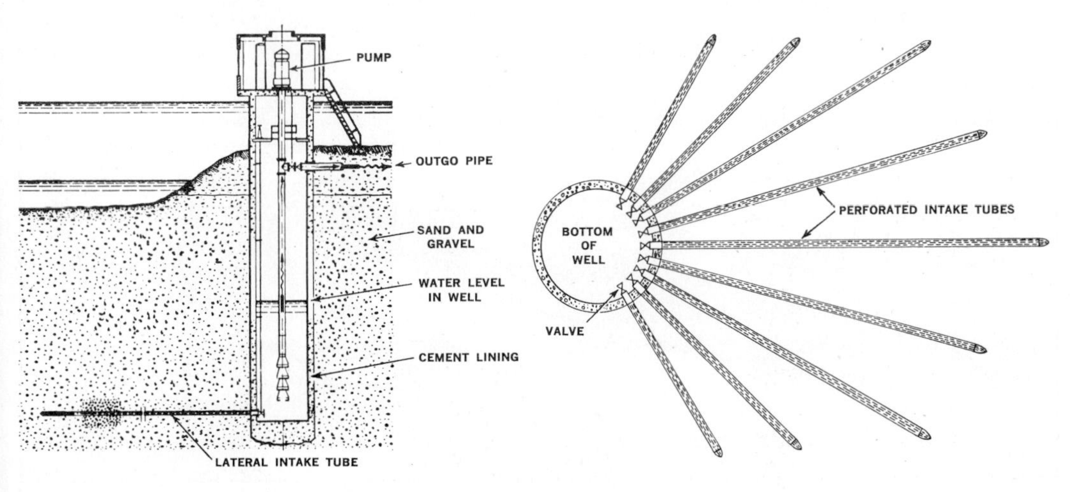

able mineral salts, so that the benefits of ground-water resources can be utilized.

A characteristic feature of ground water is the sharp differences that often can be found within short distances. These differences may be related to the quality of water, the rate of discharge, or the height of the water table—all of which are important in appraising the water resource base of an area. Irregular ground-water patterns are not surprising, since aquifers usually consist of sediments and the conditions of sedimentation may change rapidly within a short distance. Wells dug or drilled into a sedimentary zone may intercept a rapidly flowing aquifer, or they may encounter much clay or silt a few feet away in the same horizon, resulting in an appreciable reduction in water yield and increases in the degree of salinity.

Figure 14.5 shows different conditions that may influence the local depth of the water table. The water table rarely is a flat surface, despite the tendency for water to seek a level. In general, the water table tends to follow the general slope of the land surface, but at a somewhat shallower gradient. Irregularities in the water table, which roughly tend to parallel surface slope conditions, are likely to be greater in fine-textured earth material than in more permeable sands or gravels, because of the greater friction to flow caused by the small soil particles. The water table fluctuates with variations in the ground-water supply. In rainy periods it rises nearer the surface, but in dry periods or under conditions of excessive pumping, it may drop to lower levels. Wherever it intersects the land surface, a line of springs may be found. Topographic depressions below such spring lines are filled with water to form lakes or swamps. The water level in these depressions represents a rough continuation of the water-table surface above ground level. Irregular deposits of glacial

FIG. 14.9 Diagram of water spreading. [Remains of a Byzantine system, Negev, Israel; Israel Exploration Society]

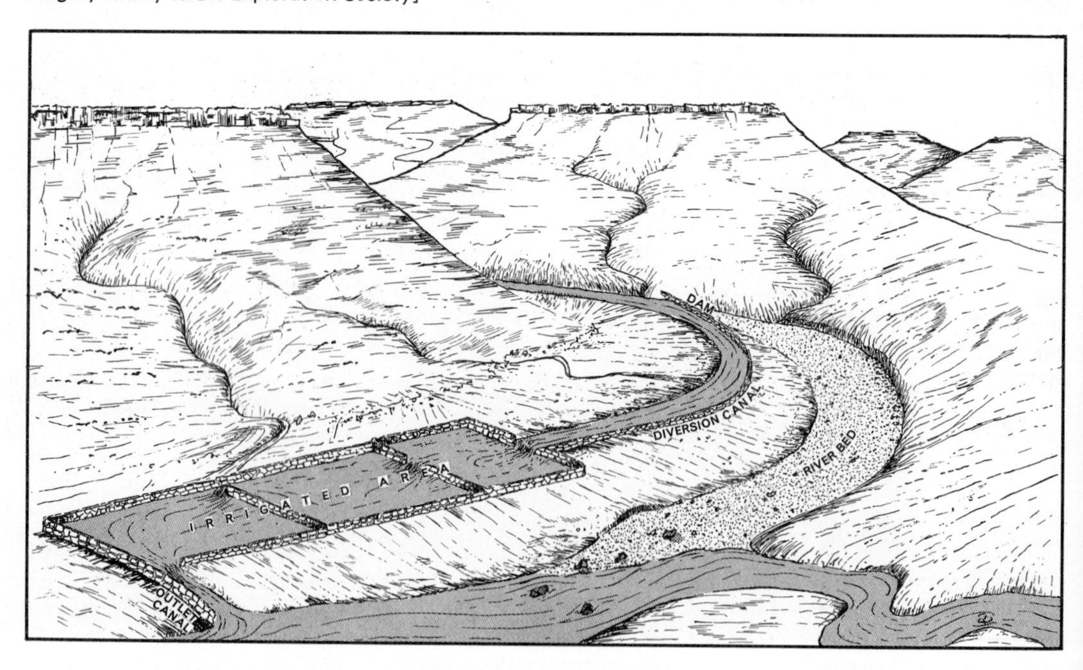

FIG. 14.10 Water spreading to increase subsurface water supplies near Sonora, Texas. [U.S. Department of Agriculture]

clays and outwash sands and gravels may produce complex water-table patterns in areas of glacial deposition.

Underground reservoirs are replenished not only by precipitation moving directly downward through the soil but also by water derived from streams and rivers. A river whose channel lies above the water table (an *influent* stream) generally loses much of its water by alluvial absorption along the bed of the stream, until the water table is raised to stream level. Recharge of an aquifer by stream flow, however, may be slowed by the deposition of fine silts in the stream channels. Heavy rains in an interstream area having a highly permeable subsurface may cause the water table to rise rapidly, creating flowing streams in valleys that are supplied almost entirely by ground water (*effluent* streams). Because of friction, however, the sensitivity of water-table fluctuations to surface stream behavior, or vice versa, decreases with distance from the stream and with the decreased permeability of the underlying material.

One of the major problems in areas that depend largely on ground-water resources for their water supply is to increase ground-water reserves by retarding the runoff of surface water. An ancient system, used thousands of years ago to approach this problem in the Negev Desert in southern Israel, involves *water spreading,* or the forcing of floodwater out of the stream channels in wadis, or dry river beds, through the use of check dams, deflection dikes, retaining walls, and special spillways. Figure 14.9 shows an example of such a system. This method, which has recently been revived, is highly recommended for use in the stream beds of dry lands throughout the world, particularly where water-table levels have been dropping steadily because of excessive pumping (see Fig. 14.10). Another solution to the problem of replenishing ground-water reserves is artificial recharge, which involves pumping water from streams into wells or shafts during high-water periods. This method is now employed in several places in the United States and is likely to be more widely used in the future.

Artesian systems are important types of ground-water reservoirs. An artesian system

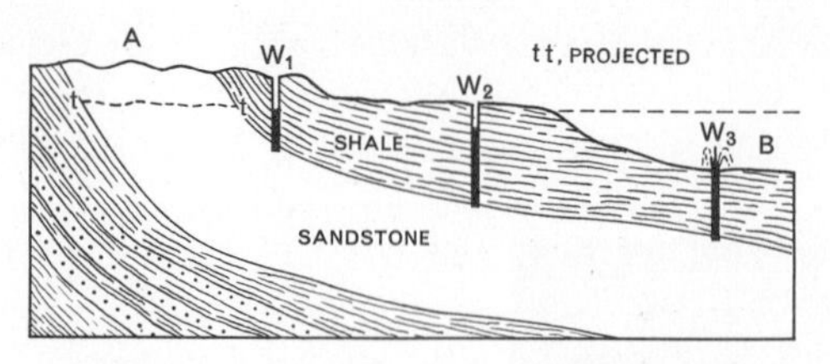

FIG. 14.11 Diagram of an artesian system. Water from the intake area A saturates the sandstone layer up to the water table (t-t). Hydrostatic pressure forces the water into the wells (W_1, W_2, W_3). W_3 is a flowing artesian well; the others would require pumping. [Gilluly et al.]

essentially consists of a sloping aquifer whose lower portion is confined within relatively impermeable beds; the result is a closed water system with accumulated water pressure (see Fig. 14.11). When the aquifer of an artesian system is tapped by drilling wells through the "cap layer" at a point below the intake level, the hydrostatic pressure, or "head," forces the water to rise in the drill tube. Water may, but usually does not, flow out to the surface. The following conditions must be met in any artesian system:

1. A catchment, or source area, where water is able to enter the aquifer
2. A sloping, permeable aquifer
3. Confining, impermeable layers above and below the aquifer to prevent the escape of water
4. A blocked lower portion of the aquifer
5. A well or outlet through the impermeable cap rock at a point lying at a lower elevation than the catchment area

Despite these requirements, artesian systems are relatively common throughout the world where a sloping land surface is underlain by sediments of differing permeability. Artesian wells constitute important water sources because of the great capacity of some of the larger systems, the low pumping costs (eliminated in flowing artesian wells), and the constant, uncontaminated flow. A disadvantage of some artesian systems is the high content of dissolved salts. Large artesian systems, although relatively rare, are particularly important in arid regions, because they may conduct water from more humid source areas many miles away.

One of the largest artesian systems in the world is found in the east-central portion of Australia, where permeable beds of sand and gravel carry water westward for over a hundred miles from a source area in the humid, eastern part of the continent. Another famous artesian system underlies a large part of the Great Plains of the west-central United States. Here a highly porous and permeable sandstone, known as the *Dakota sandstone,* lies at the surface near the base of the Rocky Mountains and the Black Hills and slopes gradually underground in an easterly direction. It conducts some of the surface runoff of these upland areas far to the east—into Nebraska, Kansas, and the Dakotas.[4]

Small artesian systems can be found in interior basins throughout the world, many of them in desert areas, where they are associated with sloping alluvial fans or plains. The sloping beds of coastal plains likewise may contain artesian systems. The artesian systems of Long Island in New York State and the coastal lowlands of Southern California are examples. The sloping plains at the foot of high mountain cordilleras usually contain artesian systems, the best-known of which include those along the foot of the Pyrenees in southern France, along the flanks of the Atlas Mountains in Morocco and Algeria, and along the northern margin of the Po Valley at the foot of the Alps.

[4] The water within the Dakota sandstone has too high a salt content to be suitable for irrigation, although it is valuable for livestock and ranch use. The relatively small surface exposure of the sandstone indicates that much of the water contained in this aquifer to the east may have been derived from sources other than the foothill areas.

Artesian systems do not provide an unlimited supply of water, and excessive pumping may lead to depletion of the artesian reservoir. Coastal-plain artesian systems have been irreparably harmed in some places because excessive pumping has enabled sea water to back into the aquifers from the offshore zone. Water pressure in the aquifers normally keeps such salt water out. Once salt water occupies an artesian aquifer, it is extremely difficult to remove, since its density is greater than that of fresh water.

14.4 RUNOFF.

Runoff is the portion of the water surplus (precipitation minus evapotranspiration) that is removed by surface drainage via streams or rivers. It constitutes the most important single source of fresh water for human use and plays an important role in balancing the water cycle by removing water surpluses and recharging the ocean basins.

An appreciable part of runoff, and generally the most usable portion, is derived from ground water that discharges into streams or lakes whose beds lie below the water table. Precipitation that does not enter the ground usually runs off the surface quickly and is responsible for the high-water periods of stream flow. Although this surface flow is of much shorter duration than water from subterranean sources, it usually comprises the major part of the total runoff. Such surface runoff often is turbid and charged with suspended soil particles. Once water has been removed from the surface following rains, however, streams adjust their volume of flow to the height of the water table, and the resulting runoff from subterranean sources is clear and relatively steady. Although the runoff supplied from underground sources contains more soluble material than surface runoff directly following precipitation, it is generally fresher than well water. With respect to salinity, stream water is almost always suitable for human use. Streams that contain water that has been used for irrigation in arid regions, however, may have high salt contents. The Pecos River at Carlsbad, New Mexico, has been known to have a water-soluble salt content of over 2,000 parts per million.

Despite the regulating effects of ground-water increments, runoff regimes show wide areal and seasonal differences. Regional climatic differences in precipitation and evapotranspiration produce widely divergent runoff patterns. Regional quantitative differences in runoff, however, are usually several hundred times greater than the differences in precipitation between the same areas. The reason for this is that the surface runoff over broad areas tends to be concentrated into stream or river channels. In the wide variety of runoff patterns, three major classes of stream-flow regimes may be recognized: (1) streams with fairly constant flow; (2) streams with unusually wide fluctuations in flow but with low minima; and (3) streams with wide fluctuations in flow and with high minima.

Constant-flow streams, the first of the three types indicated above, are particularly useful as water-supply sources. Also, where suitable gradients are found, such streams are especially favorable for hydroelectric power development, since developmental projects can be easily planned for maximum efficiency where the flow is reliable. Constant-flow streams are associated with the following runoff conditions:

1. Discharge from large lakes. Lakes act as storage reservoirs, thus leveling the discharge rate. Example: the St. Lawrence River.

2. Discharge of large rivers that have complementary seasonal regimes among their tributaries. Example: the middle Amazon

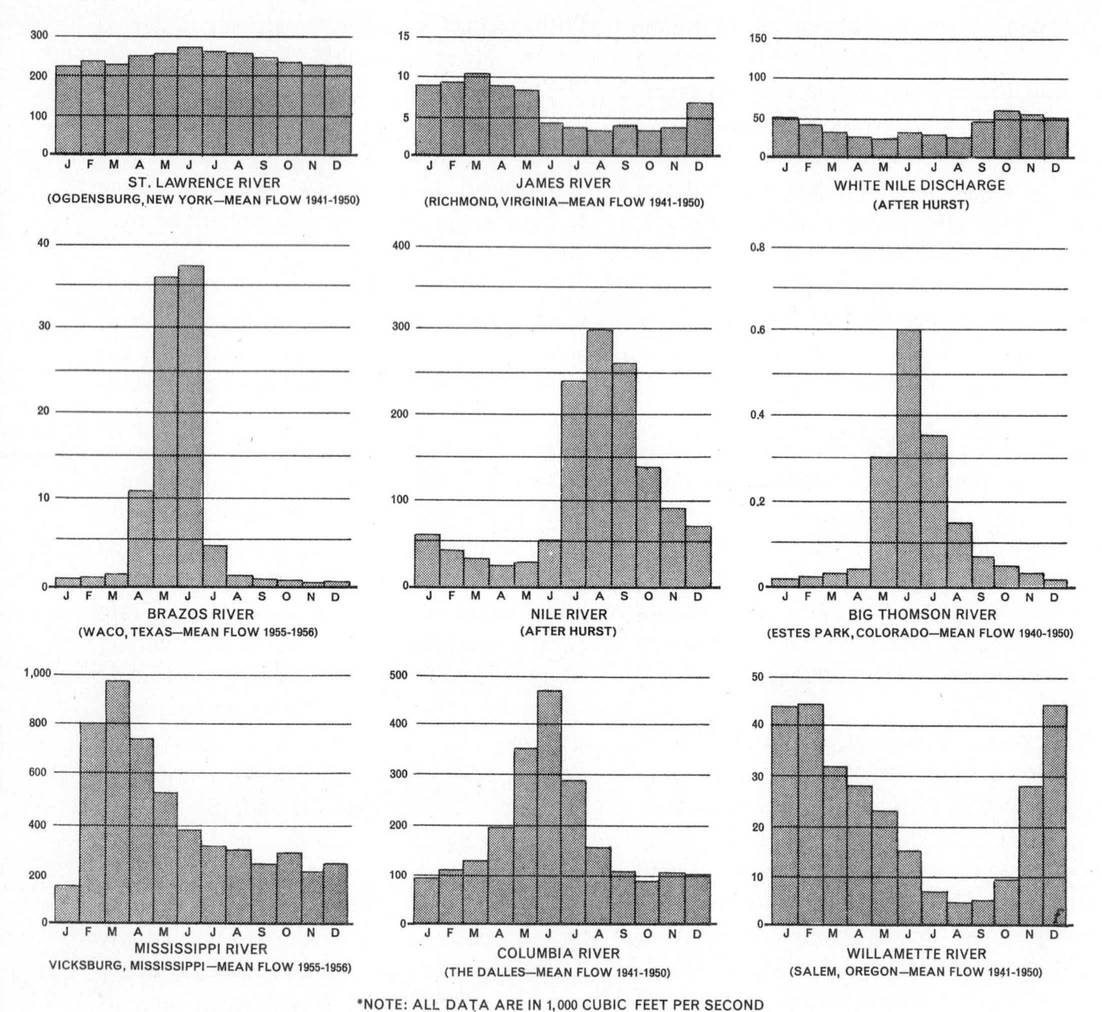

FIG. 14.12 Graphs of stream-flow regimes for selected rivers.

River, below the confluence of the Rio Negros.

3. Discharge of streams in the cool, humid marine climates of the mid-latitudes, with small seasonal ranges of precipitation. Examples: stream regimes in Ireland and New Zealand.

4. Large areas having unusually permeable soils in a humid region with a moderately even seasonal distribution of precipitation. Example: the James River and others of the Atlantic coastal plain of the United States.

The second group, streams with wide variations in flow but with relatively low minimum discharges, are related to the following conditions:

1. Areas with wide fluctuations in precipi-

tation, such as the monsoon regions, the borders of the humid tropics, and the west coast Mediterranean regions with dry-summer climates (*Cs*). The pronounced low-water periods of such streams tend to promote water storage and irrigation through reservoir construction. Examples: the San Joaquin, the Orinoco.

2. Arid regions with exotic streams from adjacent humid regions. Examples: Nile, Indus, Colorado.

3. Dry regions of mid-latitudes with streams from nearby mountains having much summer melt water from snow fields and glaciers. Examples: the upper Arkansas and North Platte Rivers in the United States; the upper Brahmaputra (Tsang-po) of Tibet.

The third group, streams with wide variations in flow and relatively high minimum discharges, constitute important navigable waterways and are valuable as sources of water supply, but flood hazards are frequent. Such streams are found in the following types of areas:

1. Areas where there are wide fluctuations in precipitation but where water deficiencies do not occur in any season throughout the drainage basin. Examples: Yangtze, Mississippi.

2. Humid mid-latitude and subarctic regions, where the rapid spring thawing of winter snows produces high maximum discharges. Examples: Ob, McKenzie, Columbia.

The increasing number of pronouncements about threatened water shortages may appear at first to be unduly alarming. Only about 17 per cent of the total runoff in the United States is used as a source of water for irrigation, industry, and domestic consumption. A considerable part of this diverted portion, furthermore, is released following use and thus cannot be considered as ultimate consumption. Despite these facts, however, the consumption rate is a justifiable cause for concern, primarily because most streams in humid areas have wide fluctuations in flow and usually 50 per cent or more of their discharge takes place during short periods of high water. The problems of reducing these peak flows are difficult to resolve. Although peak flows can be leveled to some extent by checking surface runoff in watershed areas through various agricultural and forest practices, meteorological abnormalities can never be avoided. The retention of peak floodwaters usually involves costly reservoir construction. Since, moreover, most floodwater is surface runoff, which has a higher sediment content than ground water, the effective duration of retention dams is likely to be reduced because of sedimentation.

Despite the low ultimate consumption rate of surface runoff, especially in humid regions, the reuse of water may not always be as practical as might appear. Irrigation water once used in dry areas frequently contains too much dissolved salt to be used again without treatment. If river water is used for industrial cooling purposes or for waste discharge, the resulting deterioration in the quality of the water may render it unsuited for reuse for a long distance downstream, unless it is subjected to an expensive reconditioning process. Increased public legislation prohibiting industrial pollution of important streams, however, is tending to increase the trend toward reuse.

The difficulty of utilizing runoff efficiently is well illustrated by the problems involved in harnessing the large exotic rivers of arid lands. Such rivers as the Nile and the Indus have been used for irrigation for thousands of years, and water is more precious in Egypt and India than in most other parts of the world; yet a surprisingly small part of the total runoff of these rivers is utilized. It has been estimated that only about 10 per cent of the total stream flow of the Indus River is used for irrigation, and even if the most ambitious plans for harnessing the Nile were to be completed, they still would leave about half of the flow (including subsurface percolation) unused. In general, the largest streams have the lowest proportion of their total flow in use. Unfortunately, also, runoff is most difficult to control in arid regions, where it is most needed. The reasons for this are that the runoff in such areas usually is composed of a roily, turbulent flow, with only a small proportion derived from ground water, and that stream flow regimes are likely to be more irregular.

14.5 SNOW AND ICE AS SOURCES OF WATER SUPPLY. A portion of the water included in the global hydrologic cycle is diverted and temporarily detained in the solid state. Large quantities of it may be withheld from the global circulation for hundreds, and perhaps even thousands, of years, as in the icecaps of Greenland and Antarctica. Whether or not these great ice masses represent a periodic adjustment of global thermal balances on a multi-million-year basis is not entirely clear, but they do represent a sizable fluctuation in the hydrologic cycle, sufficient to withhold some 150 to 200 feet of water from the ocean basins. The great icecaps, however, have little direct effect on global water reserves, although they exert some indirect influence by affecting precipitation patterns. Much more important are the smaller quantities of snow and ice that mantle the summits of mountains in more habitable latitudes, and that clothe a large part of the land surface within the higher mid-latitudes during the winter months. Snow and ice constitute an important part of the water resource base, since they contribute their melt water to both ground water and runoff.

The significance of snow and ice in the water resource picture is largely the result of their ability to serve as reservoirs; that is, they store water during winter periods, when it is less in demand, and release it gradually to streams or to ground-water reservoirs during the early part of the growing season. This function is especially valuable in the mountain areas adjacent to west coast Mediterranean climates (*Cs*), which have mild, rainy winters and dry summers. The retention of the heavy orographic snowfall of the mountain winters and the release of the contained water during the dry summers, for irrigation or for a fresh-water supply, are of utmost significance to the adjacent lowlands. The delayed runoff also makes it possible to forecast summer runoff quantities through careful methods of snow measurement and inventory (see Fig. 14.14). Such predictions greatly aid in the efficient utilization of summer runoff. Crop management plans, hydroelectric generating schedules, flood warnings, and allotments of irrigation water all can be planned in advance to ensure maximum use of the water supply.

Although its effect on water resources is less spectacular than that of mid-latitude mountain snows, the snowfall of the higher mid-latitude lowlands also serves man by filling ground-water reservoirs during the spring season, by replenishing municipal reservoirs prior to the heavy-drain periods of summer, and by postponing summer periods of water deficiencies beyond the critical growth periods for crops.

The ratio of snow to liquid water varies considerably, but an average ratio of 10 : 1 is normally used for the conversion of fresh snowfall to water. Occasionally, sublimation [5] of tiny ice crystals in cold, clear air

[5] *Sublimation* is the transfer of water directly from a vapor phase to a solid phase, or the reverse, without an intervening liquid stage.

FIG. 14.13 An air view of a small portion of Antarctica—a vast reservoir of ice and snow, and an appreciable detour in the hydrologic cycle. An estimated 1.5 per cent of the total world water is tied up in ice and snow. [Finn Ronne; Geographical Review]

may produce extremely light snow, with densities as low as one-fiftieth that of water and a water content of only 2 per cent. With great depth, alternate freezing and thawing, and wind drifting, the density of snow may increase appreciably over that of a fresh fall. Estimates of the water content of winter accumulations in critical areas are made by weighing standard volume samples of snow over prescribed routes. Predictions of later runoff that were based on these snow surveys have been remarkably accurate and useful.

As in many other types of natural balance, both within and outside the water cycle, conditions of disequilibrium in snow accumulations occur which lead to corrective adjustments. When snow accumulations at high elevations become so great that they cannot be removed through evaporation or melting and cannot be retained on slope surfaces, there is likely to be a mass movement of snow or ice downslope. If the surplus increases slowly, as it may when there is a gradual reduction in average temperatures, the increase in accumulated mass and consequent potential energy may lead to the formation of mountain glaciers and the slow transfer of excessive ice masses to lower elevations. Sudden increases in snow accumulation, however, may produce much more rapid and spectacular readjustments through the action of avalanches.

The snow line, or the line of permanent snow cover in mountain areas, does not lie at a consistent elevation. In polar areas, the snow line is at sea level, and it slowly rises as the latitude decreases. In New Guinea, glaciers and snow fields are higher than 15,000 feet above sea level. In northern Peru, the snow line is at about 16,000 feet. In the dry areas of southern Peru, it lies at about its highest point in the world, roughly between 19,000 and 20,000 feet. In central Asia, it lies near 18,000 feet. Local variations in the snow line are caused by differences in precipitation, steepness of slopes, and exposure to winds and sunshine.

FIG. 14.14 A snow-survey crew measuring the weight of a snow sample in the Northern Rocky Mountains, near Ketchum, Idaho. [U.S. Department of Agriculture]

FIG. 14.15 Intensified land use resulting from irrigation in a semiarid climate. This photo shows horticultural land use in the Paonia Project, near Grand Junction, Colorado. [U.S. Bureau of Reclamation]

The use of water for irrigation in dry lands

Water is most precious where it is in short supply, and it has always been at the very roots of human existence in the dry areas of the world. Not long after man discovered how to domesticate plants, he learned that applying water to desert soils paid unusual dividends in crop yields. Once this lesson was learned, the great hydraulic civilizations were born, stimulated into greatness by the subtle effects of such diverse factors as (1) water distributional requirements; (2) the necessity for planning and executing public works programs; (3) the accumulation of agricultural surpluses for trading purposes and for overcoming agricultural bondages; (4) cyclical variations in water supply, which demanded the use of foresight (e.g., the Biblical tale of Joseph in Egypt); (5) the development of legal systems involving water rights; and (6) various engineering and mathematical problems connected with water diversion and land division. It is noteworthy that nearly all the great civilizations of antiquity were agricultural hydraulic civilizations that developed either in dry lands or in regions that had a pronounced dry season. The deaths of such civilizations, furthermore, were frequently linked with failures to maintain the intricate social, political, and mechanical systems that were necessary to support the complex balances between water supply, salt accumulation, and food supply. From earliest times, population numbers in the dry lands have pressed close to the limits that can be supported by the fresh-water supply. In short, deserts are attractive places to live, but the extent to which they are occupied is determined almost solely by the quantity of fresh water. In discussing water supply for irrigation in the dry lands of the world, we first describe the kinds of places where water for irrigation is found, then mention some of the methods used to utilize natural supplies effectively, and deal lastly with some of the problems of increasing available supplies.

14.6 WATER SOURCES IN ARID REGIONS. The principal sources of irrigation water in arid regions include (1) exotic rivers, (2) subterranean aquifers, (3) mountain streams near the heads of alluvial fans, (4) wadi bottoms, and (5) erg basins.

EXOTIC RIVERS. Exotic rivers are those which flow into arid regions from distant humid areas. Examples include the Nile, Tigris-Euphrates, Indus, Colorado, Amu Darya, Syr Darya, and Orange Rivers. Such rivers constitute by far the largest type of desert oasis, or water source, and the first three mentioned above have supported millions of people for centuries. As was indicated earlier, only a relatively small part of the total runoff in exotic streams is used, and the possibility of more efficient utilization offers the greatest hope of adding to the irrigated acres in dry lands. Reasons for the present low utilization rate include the high seasonal variations in flow, the enormous volume of water at floodtimes, the high cost of control structures on large rivers, and the high sediment content during high-water periods. Another great hindrance to the expansion of irrigation on some exotic rivers is the incised nature of their valleys. The Colorado River, for example, is useless for irrigation along much of its length, because of the canyon in which it lies. There is insufficient level land at the bottom of the canyon for appreciable cultivation, and the cost of lifting the water to the Colorado Plateau level thousands of feet above would be prohibitive. Such streams are usable only in segments.

In exotic streams that flow on broad flood plains, such as the Nile, the alluvium beneath the river channel contains a large volume of ground water that is slowly percolating toward the river mouth. Little of this river-bed ground water has ever been tapped in any of the great exotic rivers of the world, because the cost of pumping is much greater than the cost of obtaining water from the surface stream itself or its distributary canals. If such rivers could be diverted into new channels and a cheap source of inanimate power could be developed for pumping, large increases in irrigated land would be possible. The water is there; regulating it and using it effectively are largely technical and economic problems.

SUBTERRANEAN AQUIFERS. Subterranean aquifers are valuable sources of ground water in desert areas, but they are decidedly limited, both in extent and in the quantity and quality of water supplied. The more valuable ones include coarse gravels and sands that slope away from mountain ranges, where precipitation is greater. Artesian systems are particularly desirable, because hydrostatic pressure tends to reduce pumping costs from deep-seated aquifers. Among the more significant disadvantages of well-water sources in arid regions are (1) the cost of lifting water, (2) the likelihood of high salinity in ground water derived from distant intakes, (3) the difficulty of adjusting withdrawals to hidden and uncontrollable replenishments, and (4) the difficulty of controlling withdrawals of such a "fugitive" resource as ground water. This final point is illustrated by the attitude of users in areas of extensive underground aquifers, who tend to argue, "If I don't pump it, someone else will."

Modern techniques of well drilling and pumping have increased the ease of ground-water withdrawals, and serious depletions of subterranean sources have taken place throughout the world in dry areas supplied from such sources. Despite these obstacles, wells continue to be important sources for water supply in arid regions. The more important dry regions for well-water sources include the High Plains of the United States east of the Rocky Mountains, Southern California, and Arizona, the great artesian basin of east-central Australia, and the hamadas of the western Sahara and central Arabia.

HEADS OF ALLUVIAL FANS. The simplest and easiest means of obtaining water for irrigation in desert regions consists of diverting water from mountain streams as they leave their upper canyon courses onto the heads of alluvial fans in desert basins (see Fig. 14.16). The fans are sloping; thus gravity conducts the water to where it is needed. The main obstacles to the effective use of such water are the rapid absorption in the highly permeable sediments of alluvial fans and the irregularity of flow, particularly in low-latitude deserts, where mountain rainfall is likely to be in the form of sudden downpours followed by rapid runoff. Dams for the retention of floodwater, however, are much less costly than those on the large exotic rivers and have greatly added to the available water supply.

Alluvial-fan oases fed by water from snow-capped mountains are especially attractive sites, because of their relatively regular, year-round water supply. The hindrance of high soil permeability is sometimes eased by lining diversion ditches or canals and by using shallow subsurface tunnels with lined bottoms (see the description of *kanats* in Sec. 14.8). The high permeability of fan sediments is a decided advantage with respect to drainage conditions. If irrigation water has an outlet from the soil, accumulations of salt, a danger that threatens dryland irrigation throughout the world, will not develop.

Mountain streams are rarely able to supply irrigation water for large areas; hence alluvial-fan oases cover only a small part of desert basins. Such oases are strung like beads on a string along the foot of the huge mountain ranges in central Asia, flanking the Andes in Peru and northern Chile, and along the eastern foot of the Cascades in Washington and Oregon. The flanks of the Atlas Mountains of North Africa are dotted with them. In the Central Valley of California, nearly every stream that enters the basin from the Sierra Nevada has a reservoir at the head of its alluvial fan, serving several purposes—for irrigation, urban water supply, flood protection, recreation, and hydroelectric power generation.

DESERT WADIS. Desert wadis almost always have thick accumulations of sand and gravel in their beds. These watercourses have long been sources of ground water, which is reached by shallow wells. Genesis 27:17 states: "And Isaac's servants digged in the valley, and found there a well of springing water." Although the supply of water in such sources generally is small, it is easy to obtain and is suited to simple types of desert agriculture. Wadis on the hamada platforms of the Colorado Plateau, the western Sahara, and southern Argentina have been used for this purpose for centuries. Mention already has been made of the techniques of water spreading used by early cultural groups to replenish ground-water reservoirs in the wadi bottoms of southern Israel.

ERGS. Ergs, or sandy deserts, are frequently among the least habitable places on earth, but in some places, where they are found covering shallow desert basins or drainage ways, the sand protects the inflow of water from evaporation, thus forming a thick aquifer that lies near the surface. Several low drainage ways in the great Sahara ergs are oases that support a considerable local population subsisting on date palm cultivation. The description of the erg oasis of the Souf in southern Algeria by the French geographer Jean Brunhes is one of the classic landscape studies in geographic literature.

14.7 IRRIGATION.

Irrigation accounts for a major portion of the total amount of water diverted for human use throughout the world. In the United States, for example, almost half of the total water use in 1950 was for irrigation; furthermore, because of the relatively small percentage of irrigation water that can be reused, irrigation accounts for about 80 per cent of the ultimate water consumption in the country. In the dry lands of the world, it is almost the sole basis for supporting population, although there are a

FIG. 14.16 Irrigation works developed by the Mormons along the flanks of the Wasatch Mountains. The narrow irrigation ditch on the right, still in use after more than 90 years of service, diverts water from within Logan Canyon and distributes it over the slope of an alluvial fan beyond the mouth of the canyon. The concrete retaining wall was added in later years. [U.S. Bureau of Reclamation]

few scattered pastoral groups and occasional settlements that are based on mineral production.

The history of irrigation is as old as our written records. In the eastern hemisphere, irrigation probably developed about the fourth millennium B.C., and in the western hemisphere, about 2,000 years later. The hydraulic civilizations of the past have generally flared into brilliance and later subsided into mediocrity. Irrigation systems have varied from extremely simple types to highly elaborate, balanced systems of public works, organized and integrated by complex social and political groups. In historic retrospect, the simpler types have proved to be the most permanent, and the dry lands of the world have many ruins of aqueducts, canals, terraces, and settlements, the "bones" of cultures that were unable to pay the price of discipline, effort, or vigilance necessary to maintain a precarious but highly productive and rewarding living in an inhospitable environment. The irrigation methods used in any locality are the result of either the characteristics of the water source itself or the stage of the technological arts in the area involved.

One of the most critical problems of dry-land irrigation is that of maintaining a proper salt balance in the soil. Just as continued replenishment of water in a furnace evaporating pan will lead to salt incrustation, so will the addition of water to desert soils, unless special precautions are taken, which include the use of the proper amount of water and provision for sufficient soil drainage to remove surplus salts. If too much water is used, ground water may be rapidly evaporated from above a raised water table, leaving salt deposits in the subsoil. If too little water is used, it will be evaporated in the soil, leaving its salt content behind (see Fig. 14.17). Heavy-textured soils are particularly susceptible to damage by salt accumulation. This is one of the reasons why sandy loam soils are preferred for irrigation development. Salt probably is the worst enemy of irrigation projects, and many areas of formerly productive land have been abandoned because of it. Saline soils can be reclaimed by extensive flushing with fresh water and by the use of sulfur or gypsum (see Sec. 12.18), but only at considerable expense.

The process of irrigation includes the following steps, although some of those listed may be omitted, depending on local circumstances.

1. Lifting water. Lifting water may be derived from a well, from a river, or from a diversion or irrigation canal. Basin flooding and some types of diversion systems do not require this.

2. Transporting water. Water must be channeled from the water source to the point of use via canals or aqueducts.

3. Grading and terracing. The cultivation site must be prepared so that the force of gravity can be efficiently utilized in the application of water.

4. Field preparation and ditching. The topsoil must be in proper tilth to absorb water quickly, yet not be susceptible to excessive evaporation. Field ditches must be prepared so that gravity will distribute the water to the plants.

5. Timing of water distribution. Not too much water, not too little water, the right time of day or the proper seasonal adjustment to conform to plant needs—all these are necessary.

6. Drainage. Drainage is one of the most important, but too often neglected, aspects of irrigation. It is as important to drain water away from irrigated fields as it is to add it. Many fields have had to be abandoned because of the accumulation of water-soluble salts in the soil resulting from inadequate drainage.

14.8 METHODS OF IRRIGATION.

The following paragraphs describe some of the principal methods of irrigation. These include basin flooding, diversionary canals, wells, and storage dams. Each of these involves unique problems in maintaining an adequate water supply for cultivation.

BASIN FLOODING. The system of basin flooding, which was typically used in ancient Egypt, has been aptly described by Hurst as follows:[6]

> The basin system of irrigation was used throughout Egypt until towards the middle of the nineteenth century and is still carried on in Upper Egypt on about 1,000,000 acres. In this system the land is divided into basins of from 1,000 to 40,000 feddans (acres) by the construction of a longitudinal bank, as near the river as it can safely be placed, and cross-banks between this bank and the edge of the desert. When the Nile rises, water is let into these compartments through short canals with regulating sluices, flooding the land to a depth on the average of from 1 to 2 metres. The water is held there for from forty to sixty days and after the river has fallen sufficiently is drained back again. During this time it drops its silt and this process, repeated for thousands of years, has formed basins of which the surface is so perfectly graded by the deposition of the silt that it drains completely leaving no pools behind. In the basin area the villages are on mounds above flood level and become islands when the basins are flooded, so that in many cases a village can only be reached in a boat.

The basin compartments usually are in series of four or five, with a short canal connecting the river with each series. One of the major advantages of the basin system was the regular replenishment of fertility resulting from the annual deposition of silt from the floodwaters. The main disadvantage was the dependence on the stream flow pattern of the river. Abnormally low flood crests or an

[6] By permission from H. E. Hurst, *The Nile*, Constable & Co., Ltd., London, 1952, pp. 38–39.

FIG. 14.17 Land abandonment resulting from increased salinity in the San Simon Valley, Boulder Canyon Project, Nevada. [U.S. Bureau of Reclamation]

unusually retarded high-water period could be dangerous to agriculture.

DIVERSION CANALS. Diversion canals, a suitable irrigation method for both alluvial-fan and exotic-river areas, were widely used in early times, as they are today. Records indicate that such canals constituted the predominant irrigation system in Babylon as early as 2000 B.C. In Egypt, on the other hand, extensive irrigation from diversion canals began only in the early part of the nineteenth century.

In the diversion canal system, water is diverted from a flowing stream by a network of distributary canals. On alluvial fans, or on rivers that have noticeable gradients, the canals are simply graded slightly above the level of the terrain which is to be irrigated, and they maintain a slope less than that of the river itself. On large rivers, such as the Nile, where the gradient of both the river and the land is slight, the river level must be raised slightly in order to provide the canals with sufficient height at the intake to permit gravity distribution toward the fields. This is done by means of low dams, or *barrages*.

The deposition of silt within the canals is a problem often encountered in diversion canal irrigation, and formerly was overcome by a laborious dredging process. Today diversion points are usually equipped with sedimentation pools for removing most of the solids before the water enters the irrigation canals. Elimination of these solids, however, has necessitated increased expenditures for fertilizers.

KANATS.[7] Kanats constitute an ingenious, but laborious, system of water diversion for irrigation on alluvial fans. They consist of tunnels, dug a short distance below the surface, which lead down the slope from near the apex of alluvial fans. The floors and lower sides of the tunnels are usually lined with packed clay or mortar. The sides are left open, permitting water to seep in from the water-bearing sands and gravels in which these tunnels are excavated. Covered openings, like gigantic manholes, are spaced regularly along the top of the tunnels, permitting removal of water and ingress for repairs. The major advantage of the kanats, in comparison with surface canals, is that they distribute water farther down the fan slopes and permit much less loss from evaporation or seepage.

[7] *Kanat,* or *qanat,* is the term used in Iran. In the western Sahara, the corresponding term is *foggara.*

FIG. 14.18 A good example of a diversionary canal and ditch system in the Crow Creek Project, Montana. Good equipment and a well-planned irrigation system make it possible to irrigate a 25-acre sugar beet field with only five hours of actual labor in changing siphons. [U.S. Bureau of Reclamation]

WELLS. The simplest and the oldest irrigation systems were supplied from wells, including shallow ones dug in wadi bottoms or in the valley bottoms adjacent to exotic rivers, as well as the deeper ones dug or drilled into artesian or other aquifers.

The large variety of tools and techniques developed in different parts of the world to lift water from wells is a testimonial to the ingenuity that man has evidenced since early in human history. Among the lifting tools are the *shadoof,* or well sweep, which uses the principle of a counterbalanced lever; the Archimedian screw lift; the windlass; and the many varieties of water wheels. It is believed by some that the first use of the wheel (thought to have originated in northwestern China) may have been to lift water.

In any well system of irrigation, care must be taken not to withdraw ground water at a rate which exceeds inflow. An indication of this is, of course, a drop in water level within the wells. This was not a serious problem when water lifting was done slowly, by means

FIG. 14.19 Sprinkler irrigation near Yakima, Washington. This type of overhead irrigation is admirably suited to rolling or undulating land surfaces. [U.S. Bureau of Reclamation]

of the animate energy of animals or men, and when the increasing height of lift soon eliminated marginal users. Today, however, with high-capacity electric or diesel pumps operating in easily drilled tube wells, groundwater sources can be "mined" of their supply as thoroughly as an ore deposit.

In most well irrigation systems extreme variations in withdrawal capacities and in the quality of water are likely to occur within short distances. Watercourse wells, or those which tap wadi bottoms, are particularly susceptible to such local variability in flow and quality. This feature is related largely to differences in the permeability of the underlying sediments.

STORAGE RESERVOIRS. Reservoirs which impound waters for gradual irrigation use are more usual along the humid margins of dry lands and also in areas where surplus capital is available for construction. The growth of international credit facilities, especially for reconstruction financing, has stimulated the construction of reservoirs which can be used for several purposes in addition to irrigation, and this helps defer costs which would be difficult for agriculturalists to bear alone.

One of the major difficulties of using storage reservoirs in arid regions has been the excessive loss of water through evaporation. This is important both in the large, shallow reservoirs that might be practical along large exotic rivers and in the smaller reservoirs built in critical watershed areas. An interesting approach to this problem has been experimentation with the use of protective liquid films. One of the most promising is cetyl alcohol, which apparently is harmless to plants and animals and has been able to reduce pond evaporation by as much as 30 to 50 per cent. In countries that have large seasonal extremes in rainfall, such as India, small artificial storage ponds, or "tanks," are used for irrigation purposes, and the efficiency of these water sources could be appreciably increased by the use of such protective liquids.

SPRINKLERS. One of the newest systems of irrigation is the use of sprinklers, which add water to fields in much the same way as rain does. Some sprinkler systems operate by means of surface and overhead pipes that have perforations to permit the release of water under pressure. Others utilize a rotating nozzle that releases water under pressure and thus sprinkles an area within a radius of about 30 feet. The sprinkler system of irrigation was greatly aided by the development of cheap, lightweight aluminum pipe, which can be easily disconnected into sections and carried to different parts of the area to be irrigated. The use of this system makes the laborious work of ditching, leveling, grading, and water control unnecessary (see Fig. 14.19). The amount of water added can be much more easily controlled, and evaporation losses are much less than they are in open irrigation ditches, provided that the spray is not too fine. The sprinkler method is particularly advantageous in areas where labor is scarce and expensive. It also may be practicable in hilly terrain that is not suited to canal or ditch irrigation. This last use is illustrated in some of the irrigated fruit orchards on the lower slopes of hills in eastern Washington and British Columbia.

14.9 FRESH WATER FROM SEA WATER. The constantly increasing demands for fresh water and the mounting costs of providing water in water-deficient areas have attracted much attention to the most abundant natural reservoir of water—the oceans. Processes for separating fresh water from salt water have been known for many years and have been used successfully under special conditions. The main problem lies in performing the task cheaply enough to supply massive quantities of fresh water at rates roughly comparable to those for present supplies. If the cost could be reduced to below 50 cents per 1,000 gallons (1957 price levels), such a method would have important implications throughout the world. In 1950, the Congress of the United States, under the Saline Water Act, set aside 2 million dollars per year for 5 years to finance a study of the problems involved in the extraction of fresh water from salt water. During this period, the program produced some highly promising results, despite the fact that costs in 1957 remained above $1 per 1,000 gallons. Continued improvement in the efficiency of several widely differing processes appears to indicate that this major technological problem is near solution. The following are among the various processes that are being studied: [8]

1. Distillation by solar energy in broad, shallow, glass-covered pans, a new and highly refined version of windowpane condensation.

2. An ion-exchange filter chamber, involving a one-way passage of salt ions through a plastic membrane, driven by an electric current. This appears to be more practical for the treatment of brackish water than for the extraction of salt from sea water.

3. A condensing still utilizing a rotating drum and involving the rapid transfer of heat by spreading hot sea water into a thin, turbulent film by centrifugal compression, thus greatly increasing the efficiency of vaporization. This seems, at present, the most promising method for distilling sea water.

4. A multistage still, in which the latent heat of condensation released in condensation chambers is used to aid evaporation in adjoining vaporization chambers.

5. A modification of the Claude process, used in French West Africa, in which energy developed from the temperature differential between upper and lower ocean levels is being used to develop a vacuum system of flash evaporation.

6. Separation of fresh water from salt water by sudden and controlled freezing.

Commercial distillation of sea water is in use today in many places in the world—for example, at some of the naval bases on small Pacific islands and for small specialized com-

[8] For an excellent summary of the many new processes, see Davis S. Jenkins, "Fresh Water from Salt," *Scientific American*, pp. 37–45, March, 1957.

munity use in the oil fields of Arabia, in the Bahamas, and in Egypt. Distilled water flows in domestic plumbing on Curaçao, an island off the north coast of Venezuela, but it is expensive. Householders have to pay $4 per 1,000 gallons for the privilege of watering their lawns with distilled water, and even this cost is supported by a government subsidy. The distilled water is mixed with a certain proportion of saline water to make it more palatable. Such installations are found only under unusual conditions and must be supported by unique local economies. Large installations, however, would undoubtedly be able to provide distilled water at a lower cost, and it now appears that the industrial use of treated brackish water is within practical limits and may well be the first mass utilization of some of the new techniques. Such installations would be applicable mainly to the treatment of ground water having high salinity values.

The mass utilization of sea water will probably have to await not only further refinements in distillation techniques but also the application of cheaper power sources. There are many indications, however, that the oceans will gradually take on added importance as a source of fresh water and that the distillation plants now in existence will continue to multiply and grow larger as processing costs become lower.

Irrigation in humid regions

The use of water to irrigate cultivated fields is not restricted to arid and semiarid regions. Somewhere between one-third and one-half of the total population of the world derives its major caloric intake from rice, nearly all of which is produced as paddy, or wet-field, rice. The acreage of irrigated rice land undoubtedly far exceeds the total acreage of irrigated land in dry regions. In the last few decades irrigation water also is being used to increase yields of many other crops in humid regions. Both rice irrigation and non-rice irrigation in humid lands are discussed in succeeding paragraphs.

14.10 RICE IRRIGATION. Most of the paddy rice in the world is grown in areas that have large surpluses of water, either resulting from high rainfall or from large stream runoff that is easily diverted for field use. In such areas, rice rarely has much significant competition from other uses of water. Paddy rice requires that about 6 inches of water be retained on the fields during nearly all of its growing period. Taking into consideration the large quantity of field water that evaporates under the high temperatures of the principal rice-growing areas and the constant slow lateral drainage which is necessary to avoid stagnation, the total water volume thus used is huge. For this reason, a large part of the rice is grown in areas where the water from large, permanently flowing streams can be diverted for field use. The delta plains of eastern and southern Asia are ideal. Some paddy rice, however, is found in areas of exceptionally heavy precipitation, in areas where groundwater supplies are used (as in southwestern Louisiana and Arkansas), and in areas where rainfall can be impounded into reservoirs or tanks.

The major problems of water supply in rice cultivation are not related so much to the total quantity of surplus runoff available as they are to engineering problems in water distribution and to irregularities in the timing of seasonal changes in precipitation. The utilization of stream flow for rice irrigation requires a complex, carefully engineered system of irrigation, methods for raising water from ditches to fields, and adequate provisions for drainage. On most of the delta plains of eastern and southern Asia, only a relatively small part of the stream flow is diverted from the great rivers, such as the Yangtze, Mekong, and Irrawaddy, for rice cultivation. Increases in rice acreages in such areas require huge capital outlays for dams, or barrages, to raise the water level and for aqueducts, or canals, to distribute the stored water over a greater area. Also needed is a cheap source of power to operate small, simple lift pumps to move water from canals onto fields. Labor thus released could be used to extend areas of cultivation and to improve methods of cultivation. In many rice-growing areas far more labor is expended in handling water than in the cultivation processes.

Many of the rice areas in Asia have strong seasonal contrasts in rainfall. Fluctuations in the movement of the intertropical convergence zone and in the "breaking" of the monsoons may be vital to the success or failure of the rice crop. This is especially true in those areas which depend on rainfall instead of stream flow for their source of water. Rice yields may be greatly reduced by the arrival of the dry season only a week or so ahead of schedule or by the retardation of the rainy season. Such factors are one of the main reasons for the comparatively low rice yields in the Philippine Islands. Except for the ingenious hydraulic engineering feats of some of the mountain tribes on Luzon, most of the lowland rice is grown on "naturally irrigated" land and not under the more controllable system of stream irrigation. The same is true of much of Indochina and Thailand. Irrigation projects could probably be used more effectively to raise crop yields on existing cropland than to increase the acreage of cultivated land. The major water problem of rice culture is more one of water control than of water supply. The fact that Japan has one of the highest yields of rice per acre in the world is partially due to the comparative ease with which water can be diverted by gravity and controlled across the gently sloping plains that lie at the ends of mountain valleys.

Irrigated rice is grown under highly mechanized cultivation techniques in the United States, including parts of central California, the coastal region of Texas, the Mississippi delta of Louisiana, and the bottom lands of southeastern Arkansas. The hydraulic engineering of many of these fields involves an elaborate system of dikes, ditches, pumps, and drainage gates. The cost of production has been lowered until it compares favorably with that in some parts of eastern Asia. These techniques have also recently been adapted to rice cultivation in parts of the West Indies.

The highly mechanized rice cultivation of the United States has not been free of water-supply problems. In both Arkansas and Louisiana, the immense quantities of water used are obtained from ground-water aquifers by means of large-capacity pumps. Because of the compact subsoil, which aids in retaining water on rice paddies, there is little recharge of the aquifers from the paddies, and most of the surplus water drains into ditches and rivers and is thus lost for aquifer replenishment. The underground reservoirs are being depleted rapidly, and the present rate of replenishment is inadequate to balance withdrawals. In the Lake Charles, Louisiana, area, there is a further threat of increased salinity from old ground water deep in the aquifer.

14.11 NON-RICE IRRIGATION IN HUMID LANDS.

A recently expanded use for water in the humid eastern part of the United States is in the irrigation of land for pasture or for high-value agricultural crops, such as fruit, tobacco, and vegetables. Even more recent has been the increasing use of irrigation for such general field crops as corn and cotton in areas that undergo short but critical dry periods during the growing season. Figure 14.4 indicates that Louisville, Kentucky, tends to have moisture deficiencies during the summer months. A relatively small amount of water added to fields during such periods may make the difference between success and failure in highly competitive commercial farming ventures. This expanding use of water represents part of the general trend in American agriculture to maximize the yield per acre on highly productive soils without increasing labor requirements. The most common type of irrigation used is the sprinkler system.

Florida is the leading state in the eastern United States for this type of irrigation, although several other states have shown substantial increases in recent years. In the past, irrigation has not been a seriously competitive use for water in the eastern part of the country. A considerable increase in this type of water use is contemplated, and several states are in the process of revising their legal statutes with respect to water rights, anticipating legal difficulties stemming from this new type of competitive use (see Sec. 14.14).

Industrial and urban uses for water

The supply of water for urban or for industrial uses presents distinctly different problems from those associated with dry-land irrigation. One essential difference is that irrigation is responsible for a much greater ultimate consumption of water but for a smaller immediate consumption. In most urban and industrial uses, water merely deteriorates somewhat in quality, and only

FIG. 14.20 Moving aluminum pipe for an overhead sprinkler irrigation system, Bristol County, Massachusetts. Not all irrigation is restricted to dry regions. The system shown here was used to keep a dairy pasture green during a summer season. [U.S. Bureau of Reclamation]

a relatively small amount is actually removed from the potential supply. The sewage discharged by our great cities and factories may be transformed into fresh, pure water more easily and more economically than the salt-laden water that manages to find its way into drainage channels following arid-land irrigation use. This is why irrigation is responsible for about 80 per cent of the ultimate consumption of water in the United States. This does not mean, however, that the urban and industrial pressures on water supply are minor. On the contrary, in many cases they may be much more important economically than the problems of supplying water for arid-land irrigation, mainly because of the large populations involved, the massive supply systems that must be created, and the large investments that are made.

The basic water problem in urban and industrial areas is that of providing a concentrated and constantly increasing supply of pure, fresh, cool water—high-quality water—and having it available in large quantities for use at any time of the day or year.

The implications of this supply problem take many forms. The individual consumer sees the problem in terms of mounting water bills—as part of the price he pays for having a lawn to water or an outdoor pool. He weighs the values and finally agrees on the new price. The urban water commission is concerned largely with the technical engineering aspects of the problem—with new aqueducts and treatment facilities, new mains and pumping stations. The industrial planner sees the water-supply problem mainly in national terms and takes it into consideration in deciding where to build a new plant. Today, for many industries, the cost of an adequate water supply is a major item in plant location. Finally, the water-supply problem presents perplexing difficulties for governments, which must attempt to resolve equitably the inevitable conflicts over priorities with respect to competing uses. These are new problems, for which local laws often have no precedents.

14.12 GROWTH OF INDUSTRIAL USES. Industry is the largest single immediate user of water today in the United States (irrigation being a greater ultimate consumer), as it is in most countries where industrial and urban ways of life prevail, and its consumption of water is increasing at a rapid rate. A relatively few industries, mainly of the heavy or producer-goods type, are the major users. A recent survey of some 3,343 industrial concerns indicated that only 5 per cent of this number was using some 75 per cent of the water consumed by the total group.[9] Among the heavy users are the industries that require large quantities for cooling—for example, the petroleum refining, petrochemical, and metal processing industries. Atomic energy plants and plants for hydrogenating coal, both of which are likely to be important newcomers to the industrial scene, will be particularly thirsty members of this group. Another group consists of the heavy industries that require large quantities of water for washing or for removal of wastes, such as the paper and pulp industries, the mineral beneficiating plants, the tanneries, and a wide variety of chemical industries. The rapid growth of steam-electric plants has placed this industry at the top of the list of water consumers, and the new high-pressure boilers used in such plants require water with an unusually low content of dissolved solids. The processing of foods and beverages also requires relatively large quantities of Grade A water.

The problem of mounting industrial demands has thus far been met primarily by regarding such uses of water as temporary bypasses in the water cycle and by ensuring that the water is returned to runoff for further use following treatment. The proportion of water vaporized in industrial processes is small, even in heat-transfer mechanisms. With mounting water costs, it soon may become more economical for industry to reuse water that it has treated through aeration, cooling, and purification than to purchase fresh supplies. Local and state regulations prohibiting the pollution of streams also have aided in extending the development of industrial water reuse.

The geography of industrial water use today is largely related to the location of the heavy users. Within the United States, one of the most critical industrial water-shortage areas lies in Texas and in parts of Oklahoma, where the use of water in the petrochemical industries and in refining not only has actively competed with irrigation and municipal use but also has lowered ground-water

[9] *Water in Industry,* National Association of Manufacturers and the Conservation Foundation, New York, 1951, p. 10.

reservoirs to dangerous levels. Fortunately for the United States, the major heavy industries in the country lie adjacent to some of the greatest and best sources of water supply in the world, namely, the Great Lakes and the Mississippi-Ohio River system.

14.13 WATER FOR CITIES. One of the striking features of the increasing consumption of water has been the growth of water use by urban residents. In the United States, the municipal consumption of water, exclusive of private industrial use, was approximately 95 gallons per capita per day in 1900. This rose to about 145 gallons per day during the 1950s.

There appears to be a rough correlation between the size of cities and the per capita consumption of water; furthermore, the more complex the urban life and the higher the standard of living, the more water people use. It has been estimated that prior to World War II, the per capita urban use of water in New York, Philadelphia, Baltimore, Chicago, and Detroit amounted to 155 gallons per day, as compared with 39 gallons per day for London, Paris, Vienna, Edinburgh, and Berlin. The most important reason for the disparity in consumption is that water-using household appliances are far more prevalent in the United States, where there is a higher per capita income, a greater volume and variety of such appliances offered for sale, and many more inducements for their purchase. The increase in suburban living has also led to higher water consumption. Lawns to be watered, back-yard gardens to be sprinkled during hot evenings, shower baths following recreation, automobiles to be kept clean—these are the large water users of the increasing American urban middle class.

In most parts of the United States, as well as in the rest of the world, the increase in municipal consumption of water has not resulted in serious water shortages, mainly because the largest cities lie within humid regions. Only three sections of the United States show consistent shortages for municipal use: Southern California; the arid southwest (including New Mexico, Arizona, and Nevada); and the southern Great Plains, from the Gulf Coast of Texas to central Colorado. In California, where urban population, industry, and horticulture have all greatly increased, the water needed to supply the growing demand must often be obtained from distant sources. Los Angeles, for example, draws water from such far-off locations as Mono Lake, 350 miles distant; Owens River, 285 miles away; and Parker Dam, on the Colorado River in Arizona. The longest aqueduct now in use is the one which taps the Colorado River at Parker Dam and distributes water to some twenty-six cities along its total length of 450 miles, including such large metropolitan areas as Los Angeles and San Diego (see Fig. 14.21).

The cities of Albuquerque, New Mexico, and Phoenix, Arizona, contemplate continued strict rationing of water for both industrial and irrigation use and have little hope for greatly expanded supplies. Dallas, Texas, in the midst of a drought cycle in 1956, was busily importing poor-quality water from the Red River 80 miles away and mixing it with less salty supplies. The shortages in the west are illustrated by municipal water rates. In Dallas, Denver, Oklahoma City, and Phoenix, water rates run between $2 and $3 per 1,000 cubic feet, or between 27 and 40 cents per 1,000 gallons. These rates are about double those in the large eastern cities. Heavy pumping of ground water by the cities of the Texas Gulf Coast to match the rapid urban growth in this area not only has forced attention to distant surface waters but has begun to reduce the quality of local

FIG. 14.21 A portion of the second, or parallel, aqueduct leading from Parker Dam on the Colorado River and supplying water for the Los Angeles metropolitan area. [U.S. Bureau of Reclamation]

supplies, because of salt-water infiltration into the ground-water aquifers.

In the central plains of the United States city water supplies based on streams or lakes are subject to shortages during unusually dry periods. (The municipalities located along the larger rivers and the Great Lakes are exceptions.) For this reason, some cities have increased their reservoir capacities far beyond their normal needs, whereas others have increased their withdrawal of ground water during dry periods, diluting it, if necessary, with fresher surface water. The principal water-deficiency problem in the American Middle West is the summer shortage of the cool water needed for industrial purposes. Industries in such cities as Louisville and Cincinnati are seeking ground-water sources in order to avoid using the tepid, polluted Ohio River water, which would require expensive reconditioning.

Competition for the control and use of water in the areas surrounding large cities is another problem associated with municipal water supplies. In humid areas, the increasing impoundment and withdrawal of runoff invariably meet opposition. Local residents object for many reasons, including the decreased supply available for recreational use, inundation of valuable farm land, enforced resettlement, and altered local tax structures. The City of New York has been under almost constant litigation with respect to its expanding water supply system. Competition also involves the needs of other expanding municipalities, and this problem tends to increase as the control of water passes farther toward the headwaters of major drainage basins. Our legal system is undergoing considerable modification in the attempt to define proper equity in the distribution of water. The necessity of obtaining water from the upper Delaware River watershed for New York City has resulted in compromises among the states of New York, Pennsylvania, and New Jersey, as well as New York City itself, in the allocation of runoff.

With the growing concentration of population in cities, water supply becomes one of the most vulnerable points in the general pattern of national security. As reservoirs become larger, as aqueducts become longer, and as the systems become more centralized, they all become more vulnerable. The history of elaborate water supply systems does not support an optimistic view of their permanence. The downfall of several great civilization centers in the past was aided by the vulnerability of their water supply. Good examples include the Roman cities, the cultural centers of Ceylon during the first millennium, and the ancient Mohan-Jo-Daro civilization of the Indus Valley in India. The modern threat of radioactive pollution resulting from fallout following a thermonuclear explosion provides an important stimulus to the development of less vulnerable systems and alternative emergency sources. Sea-water distillation facilities and emergency ground-water supplies may be able to make important contributions in this respect.

The problem of treating the water discharge of municipalities also is important in the water-supply problem. Purification of most sewage is expensive, although not difficult, and is practiced by most cities in the United States that do not have safe natural outlets for this material. In future decades, industrial atomic energy may be much more important than it is at present, and the disposal of radioactive wastes would cause difficult problems in handling municipal sewage. In some areas today, the increase in water temperatures caused by industrial cooling constitutes a problem difficult to resolve. One of the major reasons for industrial dependence on ground-water supplies in the eastern United States, despite an abundance of surface water, lies in the high temperatures of the latter during summer periods. Likewise, the heavy use and reuse of water for cooling purposes may appreciably increase the temperature of river outlets. The Mahoning River in eastern Ohio has its water temperature raised many degrees as the result of the repeated use of water by the steel industries that line its banks. At times the water temperatures may reach over 100°F, interfering sharply with the customary processes of sewage disposal. A recommended solution for the problem of warm surface water for industrial or municipal use is to pump river water during the winter into subsurface reservoirs and to remove it during the summer season.

14.14 THE LEGAL ASPECTS OF WATER USE.[10]

One of the main purposes of the laws enacted by responsible governments is to reconcile the conflicting claims of individuals. Litigation associated with the conflicting uses of runoff and ground water and the establishment of laws defining water rights are about as old as legal systems themselves. One of the oldest legal docu-

[10] Acknowledgment for several of the ideas in this section is gratefully given to Edward Hamming for his excellent, concise article on this subject: "Water Legislation," *Economic Geography*, vol. 34, no. 1, pp. 42–46, January, 1958.

ments in existence, the *Code of Hammurabi,* prepared by a king of Babylon who reigned from about 1955 to 1913 B.C., deals with regulations concerning the disposition of irrigation water. Historically, the doctrines governing water rights in humid lands have evolved quite differently from those developed in dry lands. Whereas the former were based on a philosophy of abundance, the latter were dictated by a philosophy of scarcity. For centuries these two legal doctrines worked well in resolving conflicting claims within their respective territories. Today, however, as the requirements for water grow in both humid and arid regions, the traditional doctrines are being questioned. Many eastern states of the United States are in the process of revising the ancient legal principles that have been handed down for centuries.

The water code of humid regions is known as the principle of *riparian rights.* Basically, it states that a person who owns property adjoining a stream is entitled to consume a certain amount for household use, etc. (termed *natural use*), provided that this amount does not deny such use to others. If, however, the riparian owner diverts more than this amount, he must eventually return such water, undiminished in volume and unimpaired in quality. Originally this principle was designed to maintain navigability, to regulate the flow for water power or other nonconsumptive uses, and to prevent pollution. Uses which could appreciably diminish the flow or deteriorate the quality were thought to be wasteful and unessential. In the case of ground water, the traditional riparian rule, derived from English common law, gave the owner of land a clear title to the water below the surface, under the same principle that gave him ownership of the soil and subsurface minerals. In a sense, this is contradictory to the surface riparian doctrine, because it does not recognize the flowability of ground water. Presumably, excessive users of water were to obtain their supply from ground-water sources and not from surface supplies.

In arid regions, irrigation is a prime consideration in the use of flowing water, and riparian rights are not appropriate. Here the basic principle is one of *appropriation,* or "first come, first served." If a person develops an irrigation system that puts stream water to beneficial use, he is entitled to that use as long as he desires. He cannot, however, withhold water from someone else if such water is not in use. An existing use of water, furthermore, cannot be placed in jeopardy by a new use; for example, a person may not dam a stream and use it for irrigation if, in so doing, he would diminish the flow below the amount required for existing water diversions downstream. Usually the *appropriated rights,* as the dry-land doctrine is called, are established by statute; for example, John Jones obtains legal title to the right to withdraw 0.01 acre-foot of water twice each day from River *Z;* or City *X* establishes a title to remove 100,000 gallons of water per day from a particular river. The user, furthermore, need not own property adjoining the stream. At present, the states of Montana, Idaho, Wyoming, Colorado, Utah, Nevada, Arizona, and New Mexico are governed by the appropriated-rights doctrine.

States that have both humid and dry regions within their borders (such as the Pacific coast states and those along the 100th meridian) have in the past amalgamated both types of water-rights doctrines, and there is a definite trend toward this direction in many of the eastern states. The principal objective now appears to be to fix by statute a system of priorities for the use of water when there are conflicting claims. When there is no competitive use, the rights to water should be acquired easily. The competing claims for the use of water from the Colorado River on the part of ranchers in the Colorado headwater areas, cottagers on Lake Mead, the City of Los Angeles, the irrigators of the Imperial Valley (both American and Mexican) are illustrative of the need for a modification of both riparian and appropriated-rights doctrines. In the humid East, conflicts between municipal, industrial, recreational, and agricultural users are clogging the courts, which do not have sound, equitable legal doctrines to guide them in settling such claims. The social and political regulations which man has developed to govern the utilization of his physical environment must be continually reevaluated.

Nonconsumptive water uses

Man utilizes water in several ways that do not tend to diminish or deteriorate its quantity or quality. Among these nonconsumptive uses are hydroelectric power, recreation, and navigation. Factors aiding or hindering such utilization are irregularly distributed and are responsible for the distributional patterns of these uses.

14.15 THE USE OF WATER POWER FOR ELECTRICITY. Not all of the energy imparted to water vapor in the process of evaporation is released in the form of latent heat upon condensation. Some of it is retained as potential mechanical energy, which is later released in the form of kinetic energy as rain descends upon the surface and works its way down the stream channels toward the oceans. This kinetic energy of running water is expended in various ways, but principally in friction, in transporting sediment, and in sculpturing the land surface. The harnessing of this continually recurring source of inanimate energy took place early in history with the development of the water wheel, a device which was probably first used to lift water for irrigation. For many centuries water power was, along with wind power, the major source of inanimate energy, and it played an important part in the early development of the Industrial Revolution. The direct transfer of mechanical energy from stream flow to a machine via a wheel, axle, and gears, however, had definite limitations, and water power never reached a proper flexibility of use until the discovery of the modern turbine, electric generators, and power transmission lines.

Electric power is one of our most versatile forms of energy, mainly because it can be easily and quickly transformed into different types of energy, such as light, heat, mechanical motion, and chemical energy. This versatility has become exceedingly important with the multiplicity of uses for inanimate energy in our industrial economy. The principal limitation of electric power is that it cannot be transmitted economically via power lines for more than about 200 to 300 miles without supplemental power intakes. The distance of transmission is roughly proportional to the voltage (current pressure) carried. Long-distance transmission requires not only massive power lines with huge supporting towers but large power generating stations as well.

A thorough analysis of the distribution of developed hydroelectric power facilities is an exceedingly complex task and one that lies beyond the scope of this text. Among the many factors involved—apart from the purely natural ones, such as river regimes, gradients, and site characteristics—are the competition of steam-electric installations, the regional demand for electric power, multiple-use river-development plans, available capital to cover installation costs, com-

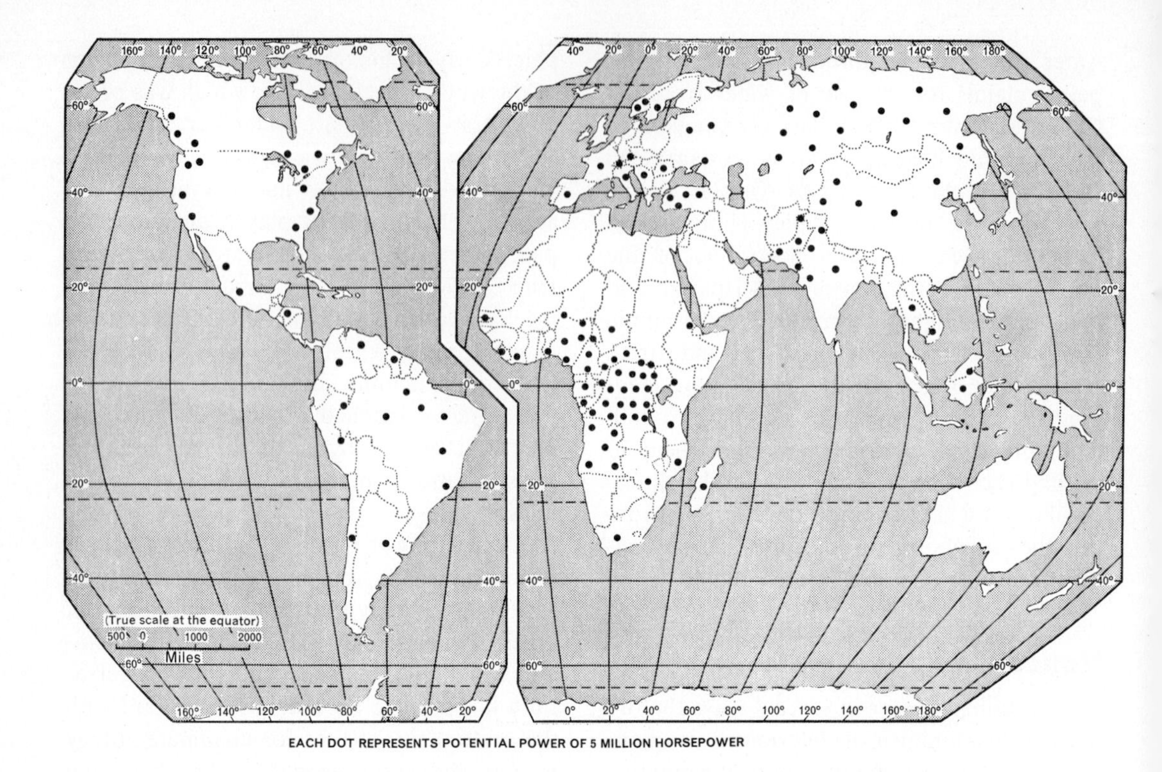

FIG. 14.22a World distribution of potential water power. [After Woytinski and Woytinski]

petition with other water uses, and public-utility policies and tax structures. Atomic and nuclear power constitutes a new item in the electric power field, but although it will undoubtedly influence the future pattern of hydroelectric power development, its implications are as yet unclear.

The physical factors favoring or hindering hydroelectric power generation are pertinent to our treatment of the geography of water resources. Figures 14.22*a* and *b* show the distribution of both potential and developed hydroelectric power in the world. It will be noted that there is little correlation between the two and that each has a highly irregular distributional pattern. The most favorable physical factors for hydroelectric power generation include the following:

1. A large, regular flow of water, aided by even seasonal distribution of precipitation, natural storage reservoirs such as lakes, and a large drainage basin containing much ground water
2. Steep stream gradients
3. Suitable dam and reservoir sites, which are often necessary to ensure a firm flow of power and which involve the following factors:
   a. A strong, impermeable rock base for dam anchorage, free of fractures or openings
   b. Valley constrictions to reduce length of dams
   c. Suitable watertight impoundment basins to store water
   d. Low sedimentation rates

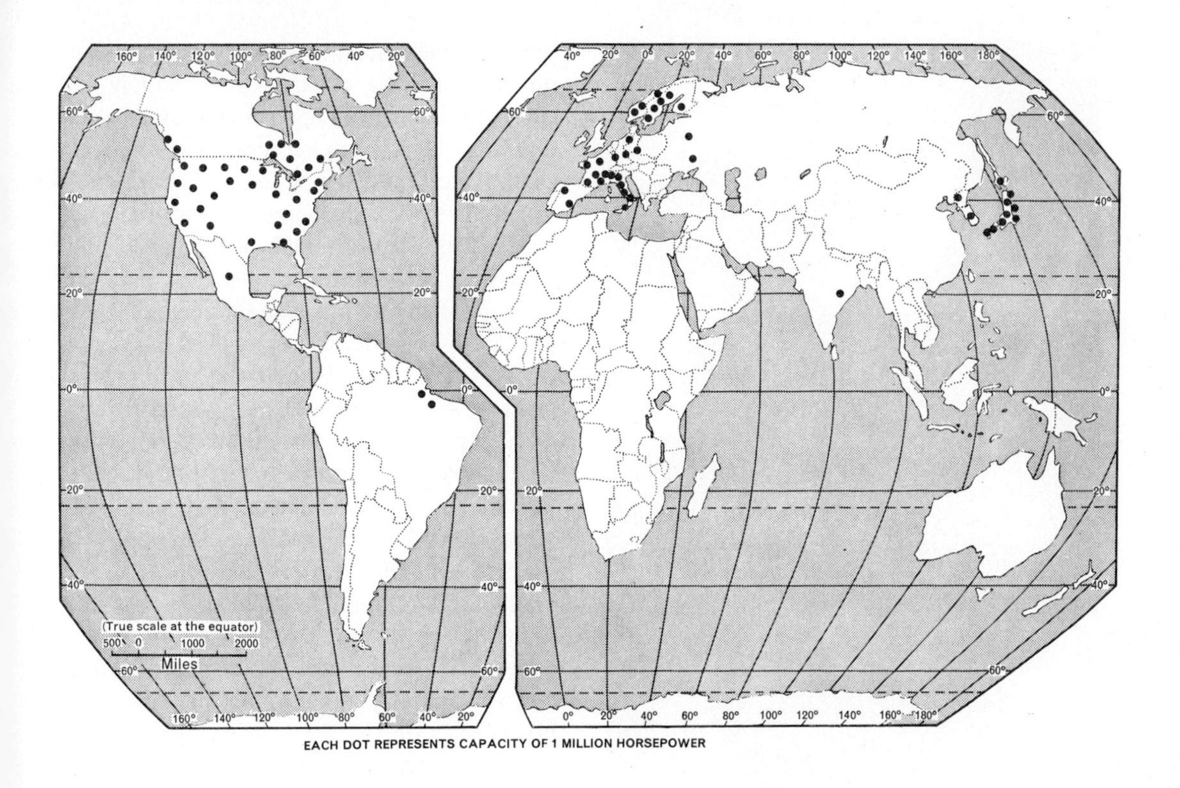

FIG. 14.22b World distribution of developed water power. [After Woytinski and Woytinski]

4. Possibilities for complementary uses, including irrigation, municipal water supply, flood protection downstream, improvement of navigation, and recreation

The total potential power of a site is related mainly to the amount of water, its regularity of flow, and its fall. If the flow is exceedingly regular, as at Niagara Falls, dams and reservoirs are unnecessary to ensure dependability. The rated capacity of a site thus will vary, depending on whether or not a reservoir is necessary, and/or feasible, to raise the minimum flow. Hydroelectric power installations are expensive and generally must be used at or near capacity. They should not be permitted to lie idle during low-water periods. Rating the potential capacity of a hydroelectric site thus involves consideration of the general feasibility of such control structures as dams and reservoirs.

In examining the world pattern of potential hydroelectric power (see Fig. 14.22*b*), several points are worth noting. The humid tropical interior of Africa contains the greatest potential of any area, largely because of the combination of heavy, regular rainfall and the steep descent of the great rivers, such as the Congo, Niger, Zambezi, and Nile, as they leave the interior high plains and hill lands of the continent. Lack of industrial markets leaves these great African water power potentials largely unused.

In South America the greatest potentials are found around the margins of the Brazilian and Guiana highlands, along the eastern

FIG. 14.23 A dam on the Tignes River in the French Alps. Although these French mountain streams are not large, the long fall from their mountain sources make them valuable for the generation of hydroelectric power. [French Embassy Press and Information Division]

sides of the Andes in Ecuador and Peru, and in southern Chile and Argentina. The Amazon River does not have the potential of the African rivers, because of the low elevation of much of its basin. A large number of power sites of smaller capacity, however, are located along the margins of the Amazon Basin. Like many of the power sites in Africa, these interior South American sites lack markets for their power. The principal developed facilities are found in eastern Brazil and in parts of western Argentina. Also important among the potential water power areas in the world are the margins of the great glaciated shield areas of Canada, Scandinavia, and the Soviet Union, largely because of the regulating effect of lakes and marshes, the many generating sites, relatively clear water, and the series of short, steep slopes that mark the descent from broad upland areas. Canada and Scandinavia both have large power installations.

Most of the high mountain areas, such as the Sierra Nevada, Cascades, Rocky Mountains, Andes, Alps, Himalayas, and the east-central Asiatic ranges, have good hydroelectric power sites, despite limited drainage areas. A high fall can compensate for a relatively low volume of stream flow, and smaller streams often are much more suited to development than the larger ones (see Fig. 14.23). The mountain ranges near major industrial areas have had the greatest development of hydroelectric power. India, China, and southeast Asia have many undeveloped power sites on the great rivers that descend from the interior highlands of central Asia. High seasonal fluctuations in flow, large volumes to control during high-water periods, and high sedimentation rates make these rivers difficult to develop without huge engineering works. However, increased needs for inanimate energy, supplemental uses of water for rice irrigation, and flood-control requirements explain the many developmental projects that are either in progress or being planned for this area.

In general, the developed hydroelectric power sites in the world are concentrated in industrial areas that are characterized by one or more of the following factors: (1) a deficiency in mineral fuels; (2) a fairly high standard of living; (3) accessibility to capital for public works; and (4) suitable physical requirements for hydroelectric power generation. Table 14.2 lists the developed hydroelectric capacity of the ten leading nations in the production of this type

TABLE 14.2 Installed capacity of electric power utilities, in thousands of kilowatts

COUNTRY	YEAR	THERMAL PLANTS	HYDROPLANTS
United States	1950	64,176	17,675
Canada	1946	381	7,909
Italy	1950	1,200	6,744
Japan	1950	3,984	6,559
France	1950	8,360	6,100
Sweden	1949	1,022	3,388
Norway	1949	113	2,784
West Germany	1950	5,021	1,880
Soviet Union	1947	no data	1,600 †
Spain	1950	607	1,529

SOURCE: W. S. Woytinsky and E. S. Woytinsky, *World Population and Production,* The Twentieth Century Fund, New York, 1953, p. 969.
† United Nations Bulletin of Statistics, June, 1948.

of power. These are responsible for about 85 per cent of the total world production.

A close examination of the electric power industry within the larger countries listed in the table above would reveal a complex pattern of interrelationships between water

FIG. 14.24 The Shipshaw spillway at the Isle Maligne power station on the Saguenay River near Arvida, Quebec. This power station produces 540,000 horsepower of electrical energy for the Arvida aluminum plant. This is another resource of the Canadian shield region. [National Film Board of Canada]

FIG. 14.25 Ullswater, one of the lovely glacial lakes in the lake district of western England. This is one of the famed vacation areas in England. These lake basins were scoured by mountain glaciers radiating from a high upland. Note the U-shape of the distant valley. [British Travel Association]

power and steam power. Steam power predominates in areas where the fossil fuels are abundant and cheap, but hydroelectric power supplants it in many other regions. Often the two are linked together in the same area, with water power handling the steady demand and steam power supplying the peak demands. A large volume of steam power, for example, is produced at Niagara Falls, New York, despite the unusually favorable conditions for hydroelectric power.

The need for electric power is expected to increase greatly, and good hydroelectric power sites undoubtedly will continue to be developed. Most sites that are capable of producing large amounts of electric power and that are near urban and industrial areas have already been developed. It is probable, however, that new massive installations will be constructed in isolated areas and that the power produced will not have to be transported but will be used by industries that are attracted to the site—industries that require large amounts of cheap electric power, such as the metal refining and electrochemical industries. The new hydroelectric power plant at Kittimat in northern British Columbia is a good illustration. The Volta power project along the upper Niger in Africa is an indication that the trend is world-wide.

The competition of steam power resulting from advances in the perfection of coal combustion and the steam turbine, as well as the indicated potentials of nuclear energy, may slow the rate of hydroelectric development in the future, but as long as water flows downhill, it will represent a constantly renewed source of inanimate energy to serve man's demands. Since the generation of hydroelectric power represents a nonconsumptive utilization of water, it does not actively compete with most other claims on the water supply.

14.16 WATER FOR RECREATION.

Satisfying man's recreational and aesthetic desires is another nonconsumptive use for fresh water. The increased productivity of machines has led to shorter work weeks and longer paid vacations. As a result, the recreation industry, catering to people having increased leisure time, has become one of the most important income producers in many parts of the industrial world, and lakes and streams play a central role in this new type of enterprise, particularly in the continental interiors. Fishing, waterfowl hunting, swimming, boating, and aesthetic appreciation of scenery are among the major attractions, and large lakes provide climatic refuges during hot summer periods. The physical qualities of water bodies for recreational use do not appear to be as important in the use patterns of this resource as the social and economic factors of accessibility and living standards.

Lakes generally are more intensively used for recreation than rivers, and lake resort centers are famous throughout the world. Among the most famous lake resorts are Lake Placid in New York State, Lake Tahoe in California, Lake Louise in Alberta, Canada, Lake Geneva in Switzerland, Lake Como in the Italian Alps, Lake Nahuel Huapi in Argentina, Lake Malaren in Sweden, and Lake Chuzenji in Japan. The thousands of lakes located in the glaciated areas of the northern United States, southern Canada, and northern Europe offer summer enjoyment and recreation to millions of people every year.

In some cases the recreational requirements of water bodies conflict with other uses. Municipal water reservoirs do not permit swimming, and the damming of streams for power or water supply sometimes interferes with fishing and scenic sites. Pollution by industrial and municipal water uses is a major limitation on the recreational uses of streams near urban areas, where such recreation is most desired. In the United States the growing importance of a pure water supply for both urban and recreational use has resulted in many state and local ordinances against stream pollution.

14.17 INLAND-WATER NAVIGATION.

The use of inland waters for navigation depends largely on cultural patterns. It is inappropriate to label waterways as navigable solely on the basis of such physical factors as depth and width. Inland waters may be important for carrying people and commodities, even though they have many physical handicaps, if they are in areas where labor is unusually cheap and plentiful and where overland transportation facilities are inadequate. In isolated areas of China, for example, rafts and shallow boats are often used on streams only 2 to 3 feet deep. Dragging small cargo craft over bars and shallows is frequently necessary, but the labor involved is still less than that required for overland hauling. In the humid tropics the difficulty of constructing and maintaining highways and railroads in the past has emphasized the importance of waterways as routes of travel.

The large, deep inland lakes and rivers of the world long have been, and will continue to be, important arteries of travel and commerce. The Great Lakes comprise the finest and most heavily used inland waterway in the world. Not only is it an excellent water route from a physical standpoint, but it lies adjacent to a highly industrialized region that requires large amounts of bulky raw ma-

FIG. 14.26 Coal barges being pushed along the Ohio River. Large tonnages move cheaply along this important interior waterway. [Steelways, American Iron and Steel Institute]

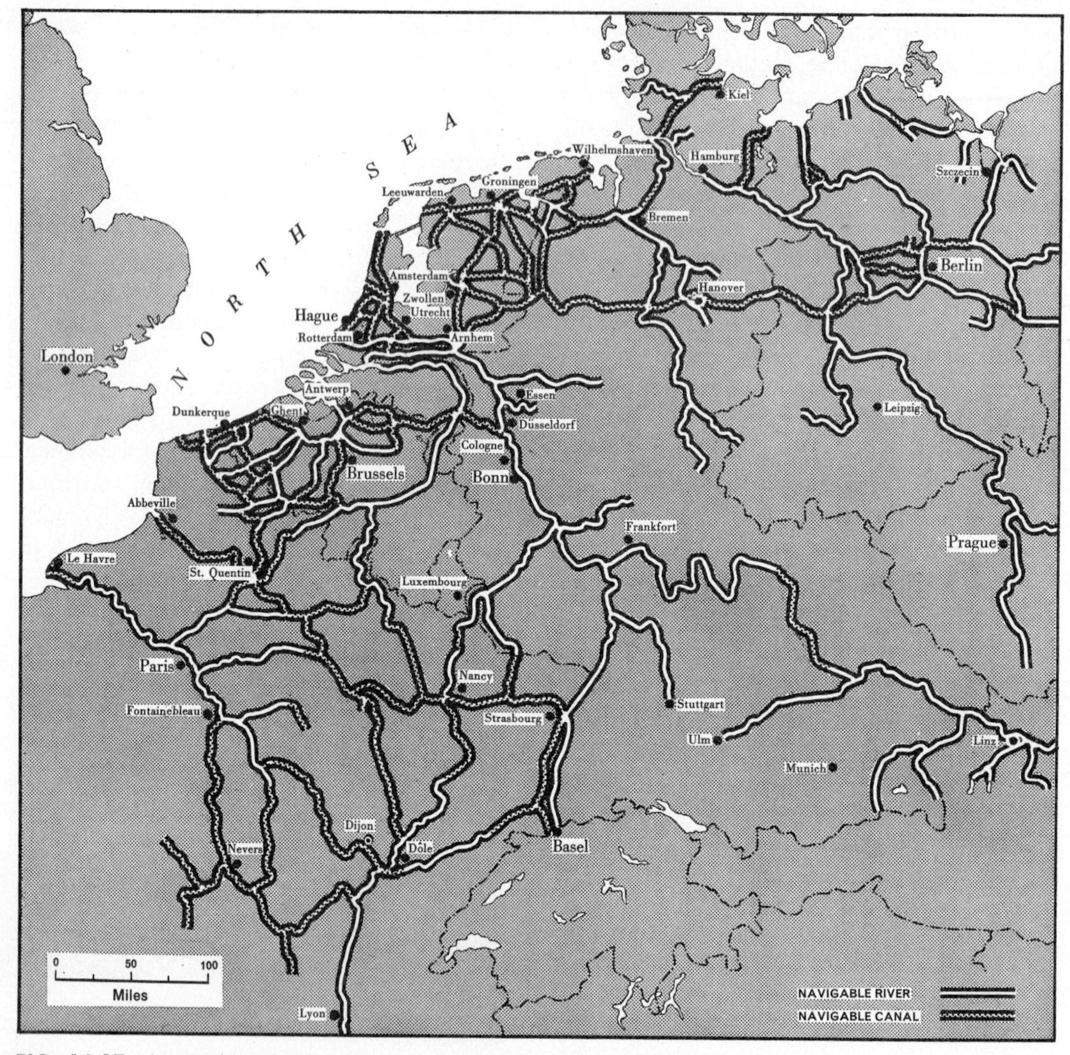

FIG. 14.27 Navigable inland waterways of northwestern Europe. This amazing network of waterways, suitable for bulk shipment of commodities by barge, is of vital concern to the industrial complex of Europe.

terials, the type of cargo best suited for water transport.

The Mississippi-Ohio River system, although much longer than the Great Lakes and lying in the central part of the United States, cannot compare with the Great Lakes in terms of tonnage hauled. The efficiency of any water body for navigation today depends largely on the size of the vessels that can use it and the demand for traffic. Rivers, unless they are unusually wide, deep, and slow-moving, are not especially good carrier routes. Water transportation is most competitive with land transport when large, bulky cargoes are involved; hence the more efficient railroads and highways become, the larger must be the bulk carriers on waterways. River transportation thus has tended to decrease in relative importance, and the large rivers have had a better competitive position than small ones. The greatest disadvantages of rivers as traffic routes include (1) slowness; (2) indirect trajectory, large rivers being likely to meander on their flood plains; (3) variations in channel depth due to sedimentation, resulting in possible delays due to grounding; (4) irregularity in volume and its effect on velocity and depth; (5) obstacles such as falls or rapids, which necessitate expensive locking facilities or land bypasses; and (6) stoppage of shipping during the icebound winters, which affects most middle- and high-latitude streams. Also, many rivers that might otherwise be favorable for traffic have their courses aligned in unfavorable directions. The Mississippi undoubtedly would have had a much larger traffic use if it flowed from west to east. The large Russian rivers that flow into the Arctic Ocean are admirable waterways for navigation, but they are aligned disadvantageously.

The large rivers of Europe, such as the Rhine, the Elbe, and the Danube, are extensively used for barge transport. Supplementing these is a network of canals which binds most of the north-south rivers with lateral waterways (see Fig. 14.27). Many of these canals in Germany follow glacial drainage lines or spillways excavated during the waning stages of continental glaciation. The availability of waterways, both natural and artificial, has been a great advantage to the heavy industries of France, Belgium, Netherlands, Luxembourg, and Germany. The Soviet Union also has connected its major rivers in the west with lateral canals, so that bulk cargoes can be shipped by barge to most of the heavy industrial centers.

The densest network of waterways in the world, not excluding the canal system of the Rhine delta, is found in eastern China on the delta of the Yangtze River (see Fig. 14.28). Although the canals are not large and although they are also utilized for rice irrigation and for drainage, they replace roads over wide areas and are used by small boats. In commenting on these waterways, Cressey[11] makes the following observation:

FIG. 14.28 Network of waterways in Kiangsu Province, China, and north of the delta of the Yangtze. This has long been one of the flood hazard areas of China. Few surface roads can be found in this region and nearly all travel is by boat. [U.S. Air Force (MATS)]

> In one measured mile, which appears representative, they have a total length of 27.8 miles, with an average spacing of 380 feet. . . . The mileage in this part of the delta [Yangtze] may thus approximate 150,000 miles, and for the region as a whole there may be a quarter to half a million miles of navigable waterways.

The differences in utilization of waterways for navigation in the world well illustrate

[11] George B. Cressey, *Asia's Lands and Peoples,* McGraw-Hill Book Company, Inc., New York, 1951, p. 122.

the importance of cultural factors in the meaning, or significance, of the physical environment. The maze of small canals on the rice delta plains of eastern Asia, with their traffic of tiny, poled sampans; the European canals, with their narrow barges loaded with coal, iron, steel, or chemicals; the bridgeless Amazon River, with both passenger and cargo traffic carried in vessels ranging from ocean freighters to dugout canoes and serving a roadless region; the Erie Canal, with its large powered oil tankers and wheat barges plying between Buffalo and New York; and finally the Great Lakes, whose immense lake vessels (one launched in June, 1958, is 729 feet long) carry upward of 75 million tons of iron ore and over 400 million bushels of wheat in a single summer season—all these waterways transport people and goods from place to place, serving the needs of the time and the situation.

Perspective

Water is man's most valuable resource. Necessary for plant, animal, and human life, it blesses some areas with its presence and blights others with its absence or unbounded surpluses. In its eternal cycle from sea to land and back again, it halts here, plunges there, flowing over the land and through the land. As rain or snow or invisible vapor, it is subject to the vagaries of climate and weather, testing man's ingenuity in predicting its behavior and planning for critical shortages. Here and there it is detoured from its course for days, centuries, or even thousands of years, captured in a pool or a porous rock layer, or bound within a mass of glacial ice. Like other aspects of man's physical environment, it adjusts its presence to the subtle pressures of its companion features in the environmental association and, in turn, places its own stamp upon the others.

The availability of fresh water, being a biological determinant, perhaps is the most important factor in outlining the oekoumene, or habitable part of the earth surface. In areas where its availability is marginal, man's fortunes have waxed and waned, not only with the cyclical nature of precipitation, but also with human intervention in delicate water balances. The desert margins of the world are dotted with the ruins of civilizations that perished because of water-supply failures, both natural and man-made.

Today the marginal position of adequate water supply has moved toward the humid regions, toward the areas where unlimited water supply hitherto has been taken for granted. The thirst of cities and factories continues to increase, partly because of the growing population and partly as the result of the technological arts, which have found new ways to use water in adding to man's comfort and in satisfying his wants. As the consumption of water increases in areas of marginal water supply, man is forced either into deficit withdrawals or into reliance on distant sources. Dependence on the former only postpones the time of abandonment.

Fortunately our knowledge of the behavior of water in the air, on the ground, and in the ground is increasing rapidly, and through careful water planning and the prospective new energy sources and techniques at man's disposal, it may someday be possible to alter the water cycle in such a way as to make it work for us without dangerous maladjustments, instead of adjusting our lives to conform to its caprices during its wanderings about the surface of the globe. Meanwhile, water balances are just as vital to man and his works today as they were to primitive man centuries ago. The relationship may be more indirect and intricate now, but it continues to play a vital part in human welfare.

15

The realm of the sea

Thus far in this text we have been concerned with the physical characteristics of the solid outer surface of the earth, or the lithosphere, and the gaseous envelope of the atmosphere that surrounds it. The emphasis on these is warranted, because both are intimately associated with the drama of human life. Consideration of the realm of the sea, however, deserves treatment in the descriptions and interpretations of physical patterns on earth, partly because this realm comprises 71 per cent of the surface of this planet and partly because it is becoming increasingly important in human affairs.

Our understanding of the oceans always has lagged far behind our knowledge of land areas, and many misconceptions about ocean characteristics are still prevalent today. Among such mistaken ideas are the beliefs that the floors of the oceans are broad, level plains, that the major ocean currents flow as smooth, regular streams, and that the ocean depths are largely barren of life. Research in oceanography encounters many obstacles, including the high cost of research vessels and equipment, the variable nature of the mobile fluid on or within which to carry out investigations, and the difficulty of raising funds for projects that do not appear to have immediate, practical utility. The problems of generalizing the changes in the atmosphere from place to place and from time to time are somewhat comparable to those of describing and explaining the geography of oceans. The available data on the latter, however, are much less complete.

As oceanographers continue to add to their store of knowledge concerning the realm of the sea, it seems clear that the total picture is becoming more complex and that the oceanographic generalizations continually must be refined and subjected to more qualifications. Far from being a homogeneous environment, the oceans at times exhibit a kaleidoscopic array of differences perceivable in area and depth—differences that change every hour if they are examined closely enough.

The increasing importance of the oceans to the welfare of mankind can be illustrated in many ways. As stated in Chapter 14, bulk cargo finds its cheapest transportation on water, and with the growing economic interdependence of countries throughout the world, the seas are becoming the arteries of the global, economic circulatory system. The pressures for supplying food continue to tax man's ingenuity as the world population continues to grow. The sea, although long a source of human food, has seldom been considered a medium for controlled food production; yet it presents opportunities that may be relatively no more challenging than those faced by the early domesticators of land plants and animals.

The sea someday may be much more important than it now is as a source of industrial raw materials and fresh water. Nearly all the chemical elements now useful to man are contained in sea water, although most of them are in minute proportions. Some of the compounds, such as the chlorides, bromides, and iodides, already are being extracted. Metallic magnesium for our aircraft and calcium chloride for our roads are being obtained from ocean brines. Finally, the oceans constitute a major factor in the mechanics of heat distribution over the earth surface, and although the details are not yet clear, studies of the behavior of the oceanic circulatory systems may yield information useful to long-range weather forecasting over continental margins.

The principles of natural distribution in the sea realm

15.1 THE PRINCIPLE OF VARIETY OF FORM AND AREAL CHARACTERISTICS. The realm of the sea cannot be considered a simple environment except in one respect—the presence of sea water, which is not only a highly interesting, carefully balanced solution, whose chemical ionic proportions remain almost unchanged everywhere, but an almost universal solvent, whose exact proportions have never been determined precisely or synthesized in chemical laboratories. Except for this one remarkable property of proportional chemical equilibrium, which is discussed more fully later, the sea realm is perhaps as varied as the continental surfaces. The ocean floor has relief features that, though lacking the fine etching of erosion on land, exceed the continental cordilleras, canyons, and basins in scale and grandeur. Variations in temperature, pressure, life forms, currents, and availability of light are associated with different depths. Anyone who has watched waves pound against the coast has noticed that no two of them have exactly the same form or behavior. The plant and animal life of the sea exhibits a variety that continually challenges the marine biologist to expand his classification systems. Yet, despite all this variety, which becomes greater with closer examination, the forms and phenomena are not haphazard but show gradations of similarities that yield to classification systems. Whereas no two waves are exactly alike, wave frequencies, heights, depths, and internal water motions are subject to physical laws that are predictable on a reasonably generalized basis.

Wide areal differences accompany the variety of forms. Position rarely was a serious problem to the wise skipper of a Gloucester fishing schooner before the days of radar and loran, even when he was becalmed in a thick fog. Noting the color of the water and the direction of its drift, casting the sounding lead to determine depth, examining the bits of bottom mud that clung to the weight as it was withdrawn—all these revealed his approximate location. The sonic depth gear of a transoceanic liner (see Fig. 15.1) today plots accurate profiles of the sea bottom along the ship's course, and captains and navigators learn to recognize the landmarks, which serve as navigational aids to supplement the more traditional devices. The vastness of the oceans and the difficulties of plotting and charting the detailed differences away from continental margins or islands have been responsible for a dearth of oceanic maps (except for navigational charts) on other than global scales. On land, the surface is readily visible, and the observer soon recognizes that the forms about him are infinitely varied. The sea observer, on the other hand, requires special apparatus to observe and record the subtle differences from place to place. Human eyes were made to see in air, not water, and man requires special breathing apparatus, weights to counterbalance the buoyancy of water, and artificial light to illuminate the dark depths, in order to explore the sea realm. Those who have visited the sea bottom have found it a never-ending source of new discoveries. Sea water itself, although remarkably homogeneous in its ionic proportions, varies considerably in such properties as salinity (salt content per volume), temperature, color, gas content, viscosity, and density.

Generalizations of areal differences and similarities can be made in presenting a regional geography of oceans, just as the wide variety of areal differences on land can be grouped into regions at different scales. The broad regional differences at sea were recognized at an early date. The Sargasso Sea, a section of the North Atlantic, with its clear, blue water and floating masses of distinctive seaweed, was feared by many early navigators as a region of forbidding evil, a marine limbo or sinister graveyard, capable of snaring and holding forever any vessel that entered its borders. Such fears were unwarranted, although sailing vessels faced the possible danger of becoming temporarily becalmed, but the distinctive characteristics of this area stamp it as being a region apart from the surrounding seas. Pytheas, an early geographer from Massilia (now Marseilles), sailing on a Phoenician trading vessel centuries before Christ, noted with wonder the unusual properties of the ocean near Thule, the northern end of the world (presumably in the vicinity of the Orkney Islands). He described the green, slimy consistency of the sea water and the persistent fogs in this northern region and marveled at this outer periphery of the world, where sky, water, and solids seemed to fuse. The special nature of the Gulf Stream, the most marked of the great ocean "rivers," with its distinctive coloration, temperature, salinity, and life forms, marks the stream as a distinct ocean region.

FIG. 15.1 Watching the fathometer on board the atomic submarine Nautilus as it cruises beneath the ice in the Arctic Ocean. This is an important navigational instrument for surface vessels as well as for submarines. [U.S. Navy]

15.2 THE PRINCIPLE OF TRANSITIONAL BOUNDARIES. The regional boundaries established in the ocean can rarely, if ever, be considered fixed lines. What constitutes the edge of the continental shelf? Where is the boundary between continents and ocean basins? Where is the boundary between the Atlantic and Arctic Oceans? What is the lower limit of sunlight penetration? Where are the limits of the Peruvian, Quroshio, or Gulf Stream Currents? Boundaries can be arbitrarily established for all these regions of the sea, but their determination is always based on some definition, and almost always such definitive properties will be found to be transitional in nature.

Some boundaries in the realm of the sea, however, have much sharper transitions than others, just as some topographic boundaries on land are clearer and more easily defined than others. The sharpest boundaries in the sea are those associated with ocean currents. When fluids of different densities are merged, they tend to develop fairly sharp boundaries. Color lines often can be observed separating masses of water having marked temperature contrasts, e.g., those between the warm, blue Gulf Stream and the cold, green Labrador Current. Even here, however, the separation is more apparent than real, and the investigators have learned that such color lines can be deceiving. A certain amount of mixing through diffusion and turbulence always takes place, and interfingering, enclaves, and scattering can be observed along many of the apparently clear-cut current boundaries.

The relief features on the ocean floor tend to be more sharply defined than those on land. The active processes of subaerial erosion and weathering are not present, and in the quiet waters below the limit of surface wave action, constructional landforms resulting from crustal deformations of volcanic activity are preserved for millions of years. The Hawaiian Islands represent the summits of an enormous volcanic ridge that rises from the ocean floor some 15,000 feet below. Many cliffs and escarpments 3,000 to 4,000 feet high can be found, representing the accumulation of thousands of years of crustal slipping along great rupture lines. Above water, many of these sharp prominences would have been removed, or at least subdued by erosive and depositional processes.

Despite the sharpness of such topographic features as those mentioned above, gradations in the ocean are the general rule, and boundaries shown on oceanic maps should be considered as zonal transitions, useful in generalizing the differences from place to place.

15.3 THE PRINCIPLE OF ENVIRONMENTAL DYNAMICS. The oceans, being composed of a mobile fluid, are subject continually to changes brought about by environmental alterations. The surface zones constantly are being altered by fluctuations in heating, by the buffeting of winds, and by internal turbulence. Changes in precipitation, in tidal action (caused by changes in lunar and solar relationships), and in the melting of antarctic or Greenland icecaps—all produce changes in the behavior patterns of ocean currents. The patterns of organic life also undergo periodic shifts in dominance and location. Witness, for example, the swarms of microscopic algae, veritable clouds of life forms, that suddenly appear at times in tropical seas, coloring the ocean for thousands of square miles, and then vanish as suddenly as they come. Note also the change in location of schools of surface-feeding fish that lead their human pursuers a merry chase and make commercial tuna fishing as much a search operation as a catching process.

Changes in the course of such currents as the Gulf Stream continually take place. In its reactions to both external and internal forces, this great ocean "river" twists and turns, swirls and splits, accelerates and slows. Even the center of the great eddy in the midst of the North Atlantic is far from a static environment, despite the absence of the strong currents found in bordering areas. Observers have noted the rapidly changing designs in the arrangement of the masses of sargasso weed, whose long streamers seem to shift positions as if obeying a series of commands.

The ocean bottoms are not subject to the variety of sculpturing that is characteristic of land surfaces, yet the surface features of the ocean floor undergo great changes from time to time. The immense trenches that can be found along many of the ocean margins are particularly weak sections of the earth crust. Dislocations of the crust within ocean areas tend to be more frequent and to have a greater amplitude than most of those on the continents. The large number of breaks that have occurred in submarine cables indicates that the sea bottom is far from being terra firma, especially around its margins. Sediment brought to the ocean rim by continental rivers significantly alters the marginal zone, as is evidenced by the complexity of sequences in sedimentary rocks that now lie exposed for examination on continental land surfaces. Waves and currents rework the material brought to the coastal zones by rivers, and the details of the coastal margins may be altered noticeably during a single severe storm.

The characteristics of the oceanic environments, therefore, are changing continually, as are those of the terrestrial realm. The major features of ocean floors, like those on the continental surfaces, are only relatively stable in the time continuum. The weather and climatic changes in the atmosphere have counterparts in the short- and long-term changes in the sea itself. The sensitivity of land plants and animals to changes in temperature, precipitation, and soil fertility can be matched by the sensitivities of marine organisms to variations in temperature, oxygen content, and nutrient availability. Regional changes do not always take place at the same rate, however, and just as there are relatively stable environments on land, so too there are relatively stable portions of the sea realm.

15.4 THE PRINCIPLE OF ENVIRONMENTAL EQUILIBRIA. In discussing the various elements in the physical world of continental areas, such as climate, vegetation, soils, and landforms, we indicated that, in every area, these elements tend to adjust their individual characteristics so as to trend toward an environmental equilibrium. This principle can also be observed throughout the realm of the sea, and major changes in any of the environmental factors that characterize ocean areas will set in motion adjustments toward new balances.

One of the most spectacular changes in the sea environment that can be used to illustrate associated readjustments is the periodic arrival of El Niño (The Child), a warm, surface current off the coast of northern Peru (see Fig. 15.2). Normally, the coast is bathed by the comparatively cold Peruvian Current. Enriched by a flood of chemical nutrients brought to the surface by upwelling water, this cold current is an exceedingly fertile area for microscopic sea organisms; these serve as food for larger sea animals, which, in turn, lure countless thousands of fish-eating birds. Approximately once every 7 years, and shortly after Christmas, from which it gets its name, the warm El Niño turns the corner of Cabo Blanco, the westernmost point of Equador, and flows southward as a narrow surface current along the Peruvian coast. Mixing with the cold, fertile water, the relatively sterile, oxygen-deficient El Niño causes havoc among the organic life by suffocating the teaming microorganisms, whose putrefaction creates toxic conditions that poison larger fish. The hydrogen sulfide produced by the putrefaction has sometimes tarnished the lead in the paint on ship bottoms to a black color, producing the

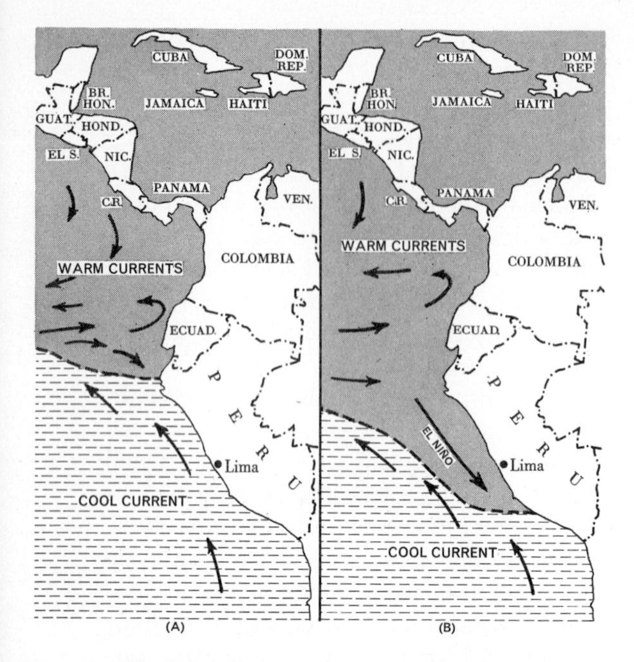

FIG. 15.2 El Niño, the warm current that occurs every seven years or so off the Peruvian coast. As shown in (A), the warm equatorial current normally does not pass the westernmost extremity of South America.

phenomenon known as the "Callao Painter" that so mystified seamen in these waters. Patches of water tinted unusual shades of pink, orange, brown, and red can also be found, marking the swarms of dead organisms. Dead fish are washed ashore, and their odor fouls the atmosphere for miles. The sea birds leave their favorite haunts, and native fishermen and guano collectors curse the elements. Even climatic changes take place. Deluges of rain beat down on the normally arid coastal zone, causing floods and severe erosion. Coastal dwellers, in their mud-walled huts, a type of housing characteristic of desert lands everywhere, obviously do not welcome these torrential downpours. The severity of the rains varies somewhat from period to period. The cause of El Niño is not certain, but many authorities believe that it results from an abnormal southward shift in the position of the subtropical oceanic anticyclone and the intertropical convergence zone. The high rainfall of the El Niño period also can be explained by this abnormal shift southward in the intertropical convergence zone.

El Niño represents an unusually sudden and spectacular alteration of environmental balances, but many other, more subtle adjustments take place in different parts of the ocean. Changes in salinity occur with variations in precipitation, evaporation, and the melting rates of the glaciers that adjoin the oceans in high latitudes. Also, as is discussed later in greater detail, the sea serves as a gigantic mechanism that aids in regulating temperature conditions throughout the world. Finally, minute changes in the content of dissolved gases and in the local availability of nutrients produce sympathetic changes in plant and animal growth patterns, in much the same way as short- and long-term climatic changes affect terrestrial organisms.

The configuration of the ocean floors

The development of echo-sounding apparatus, or *sonar,* for ocean vessels (see Fig. 15.1) has simplified enormously the task of plotting the shape and configuration of the ocean floors. Although the total picture is by no means clear, the major features are rapidly being sketched in. The following broad generalizations can now be made:

1. The continents are almost always bordered by a continental-shelf zone of variable width, which slopes gradually down to between 300 and 600 feet, beyond which there is a steep descent to much greater depths (see Fig. 15.3).

2. Major irregularities in the ocean floors,

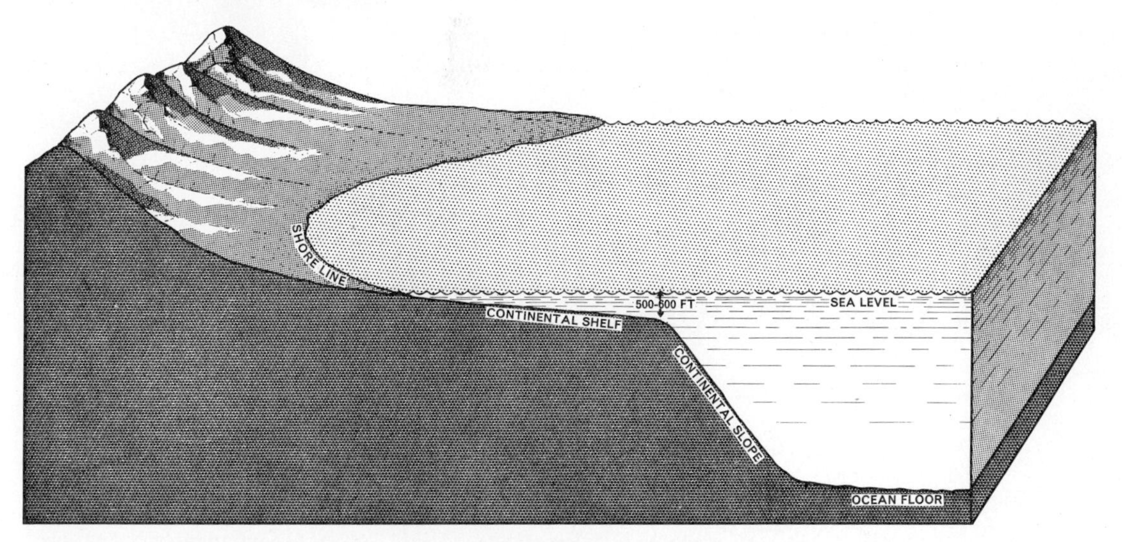

FIG. 15.3 Typical profile of the continental-shelf zone.

including huge ridges or submarine mountain ranges and deep trenches thousands of feet deep, are aligned roughly parallel to the continental outlines.

3. Longitudinal submarine ridges tend to divide the ocean basins into great troughs, with a rough alignment from northwest to southeast or from northeast to southwest. Transverse east-west ridges break such troughs into distinct basins. The bottoms of the troughs and basins generally lie at depths between 12,000 and 18,000 feet.

4. Most of the deep trenches lie adjacent to the outer margins of the continental-shelf zone.

5. Extremely steep-sided, isolated peaks, or pinnacles, termed *sea mounts,* or *guyots,* rise from the ocean floor at many places but are especially common along the seaward margins of the great trenches.

Some of the most distinctive features of the sea bottom are discussed in the following sections of this division.

15.5 THE CONTINENTAL-SHELF ZONE. The terrace which borders the continents is a persistent feature that is absent only in those few places where high mountains border the coast, as along parts of the west coast of South America. It has an average width of about 30 miles, although in places, such as off the north coast of Siberia, west of Borneo, and off Patagonia, it may extend 300 miles or more offshore. The slope of the continental shelf is remarkably slight, generally less than 1 per cent. The *continental slope,* on the other hand, which is the outer slope of the shelf, or terrace, has a steep descent, as much as 45 per cent in places. The depth of the break in slope, or the boundary between the shelf and the continental slope, usually lies between 300 and 400 feet, although in some places it is nearly 600 feet below sea level.

A unique feature of the continental shelf is the deep, steep-sided submarine canyons which cut into its outer margins. In profile, they resemble the canyons that entrench the high plains of continents (see Fig. 15.4). The submarine canyons are generally located opposite the mouths of rivers and almost always end on a small, flat plain in the ocean

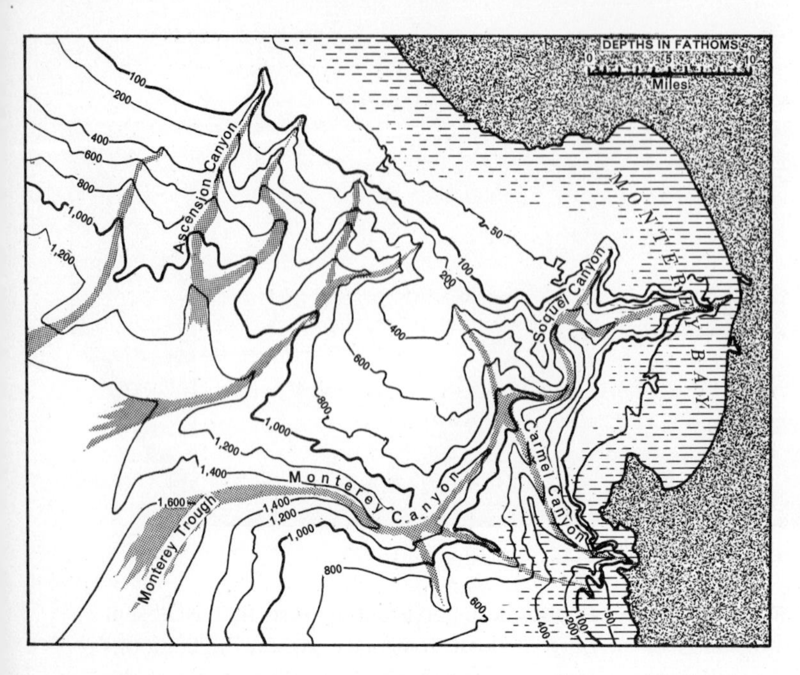

FIG. 15.4 Bathymetric map of the submarine canyons off the coast of California. Such canyons are found in many places along the continental-shelf zone bordering the continents. [After Sverdrup]

depths. Such characteristics led investigators to believe at first that the canyons resulted from river erosion at a time when the entire continental slope was above water. There is little evidence to support such an extreme shift in sea level, however, and the most accepted hypothesis today is that they are the result of scouring by turbidity currents, or avalanchelike movements of coarse, sandy sediments, brought to the edge of the shelf by streams and currents and periodically shaken loose down the outer slope by earth tremors. Hundreds of miles long in places, and often over a mile deep, the submarine gorges are major gashes in the flanks of continents. Knowledge of the location of these canyons is important in locating suitable routes for submarine cables. Mass slumping of erosional detritus in the canyons off the Colombia coast in the Caribbean has broken the same cable seventeen times since 1930.

The continental-shelf zone is undoubtedly the most important part of the ocean floor with respect to resource use. Most of it is well within the depth zone of light penetration, and it contains good conditions for both the fixed and floating types of plant life. Enriched by nutrients brought to the shelf by rivers and, in some areas, by upwelling currents from the depths beyond the shelf, the plant life of the shelf zone forms rich "pastures" for the animal life of the sea. The major commercial fisheries of the world are located here.

The composition of the floor of the continental shelf differs widely from that of the ocean depths. Most of the material is derived from continental erosion and includes sands, silts, and clays. Sediments here have a wide range of colors, including red, green, blue, black, brown, and white. The greenish shades predominate and are due mainly to the mineral *glauconite,* a complex silicate mineral that contains iron and potassium. The variations in composition of the shelf floor are largely the result of different patterns of sedimentation, currents, and depth. The continental shelf off the east coast of the United States, for example, is unusually sandy and contains only small quantities of muds and other fine-textured sediments, because the streams that enter the ocean along this coast are relatively clear. The Gulf of Mexico, on the other hand, has a broad shelf that is mainly of clay and silt. The ocean currents in the Gulf cannot remove the material as fast as it accumulates off the mouths of the Mississippi and Rio Grande Rivers.

The sediments covering the continental shelf are wedge-shaped, with the thickest part of the wedge near the outer edges. As the weight of the sediment increases with the growth of the shelf, subsidence generally takes place, creating conditions similar to those associated with the development of geosynclines, in which subsidence matches sedimentation. Organic material, trapped in the subsiding shelf zone, may be altered into hydrocarbons. The continental-shelf zones, therefore, are attracting attention as potential source areas for petroleum and natural gas, especially where there has been rapid sedimentation of clays and silts. Geologic evidence indicates that the continental-shelf zones nearly everywhere are of relatively recent origin, dating roughly from the end of the Lower Cretaceous, or about 100 million years ago. Whether or not the present shelf terrace masks older terraces remains to be discovered.

15.6 THE OCEAN TRENCHES. Deep gashes scar the ocean floors near the margins of the continents, where the crust of the earth is the least stable. Compared with surface depressions on the continents, these trenches are huge. The bottom of the Tonga-Kermadec trench northeast of New Zealand, for example, lies some 15,000 feet below the general level of the ocean floor, and its total length is about 1,200 miles. Like most of the other trenches, it has precipitous sides. Many of the trenches attain about the same general depth, roughly between 30,000 and 35,000 feet below sea level. Most of them also are V-shaped, with rocky bottoms free of sediment. A few, however, exhibit flattened bottoms, which may be the result of sedimentation over long periods.

The ocean trenches undoubtedly are the result of crustal movement. They lie in the zones of greatest earthquake activity, and volcanoes often are found nearby. Measurements indicate that sharp contrasts in gravitational pull occur in the vicinity of these huge chasms, indicating strong contrasts in the density of the rock below. Other careful observations have shown that the discharge of earth heat at the bottom of the trenches is less than one-half the average for the earth surface as a whole. On land, such downwarped areas would be filled rapidly by erosional debris. In the sea, however, they tend to remain as chasms for a long time, even geologically speaking.

The geographic pattern of the ocean trenches shows a large number around the margins of the Pacific basin, especially in the west. The Arctic Ocean is believed to be relatively free of them, although, until recently, there has been little careful surveying of the ocean bottom in the Arctic. The Atlantic Ocean has three or four trenches, and there is one in the Indian Ocean. The trenches are found especially in the vicinity of volcanic islands or volcanic continental margins. Knowledge of their precise locations is essential in plotting routes for laying transoceanic cables. They also constitute important "landmarks" in the sea-bottom topography and thus serve as an additional navigational aid for vessels equipped with sonic depth-finding apparatus.

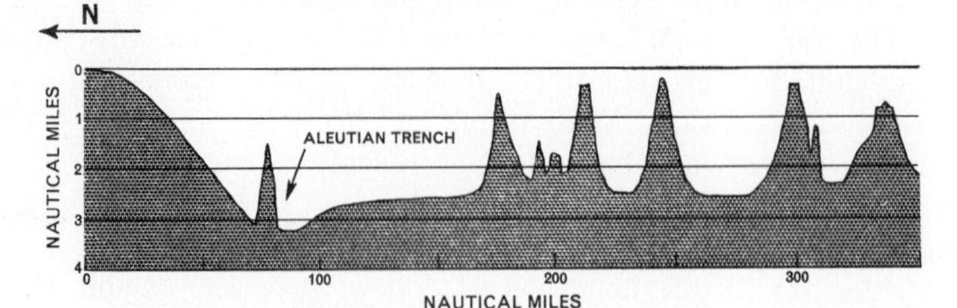

FIG. 15.5 Diagram of sea mounts and guyots off the Alaskan coast. [After Dietz]

15.7 SEA MOUNTS AND GUYOTS. Other unique landforms of the ocean realm, having no counterpart on the continents, are *sea mounts,* and *guyots.* These are isolated, extremely steep-sided pinnacles that rise abruptly several thousand feet above the floor of the ocean. Guyots differ from sea mounts in being flat-topped and appear to have been truncated, as if someone had lopped off their summits with a gigantic saw. It was believed at first that they were relatively rare features, but careful submarine topographic mapping has revealed large numbers of them (see Fig. 15.5). They appear to be most prevalent in the vicinity of the deep ocean trenches, especially on the oceanward side of the trenches. Guyots have been observed, however, in many parts of the Atlantic and Pacific Oceans. They are not found on the continental shelf but rise directly from the ocean deeps. Most of the coral islands in the Pacific, such as the Tongas, Gilberts, Tuamotus, and Marshalls, are guyots that have been surmounted by coral growth.

Both guyots and sea mounts are believed to have been volcanic peaks that were protected from erosional destruction by their submarine position. The flat summits of guyots are the result of erosional beveling either above or near sea level by wave and stream action at a time when they stood much higher. At present the summits of most guyots lie 5,000 to 6,000 feet below sea level. Subsidence may have been due to the gradual accumulation of volcanic material and the resulting weight on the crust below. Gradual subsidence could have been matched by coral growth, resulting in the coral caps on many of the guyots in tropical waters. Only a few of the sea mounts in the oceans are islands. Many of the submerged ones have a capping layer formed of accumulations of tiny snow-white calcareous (limy) shells, like frosting on a cake.

158.8 SUBMARINE RIDGES. Not all mountain cordilleras are confined to the continental surfaces. Soundings have revealed that the Pacific, Atlantic, and Indian Oceans all have long, irregular ridges that compare with the cordilleras of the continents in both height and length. Although the submarine ridges are usually found far within the ocean basins, their alignment, for the most part, is roughly parallel to the edges of the continental blocks, indicating some relationship to the arrangement of primary global crustal features. The predominant direction is northeast-southwest or northwest-southeast, although some ridges trend almost east-west. The submarine ridges thus tend to divide the oceans into a series of great troughs, which, in turn, appear to play a significant role in channeling the movement of deep ocean water.

The best known of the submarine ridges is the mid-Atlantic ridge (see Fig. 15.6). Soundings a century ago revealed the presence of this ridge, but only recently has its total extent been realized. Approximately 10,000 miles long, it follows the middle Atlantic from about lat 60° N to 50° S, then recurves eastward toward the Indian Ocean. A few high peaks extend above sea level, including the Azores, St. Paul Rocks (northeast of Natal), Ascension Island, and Tristan de Cunha Islands. The S curve in its middle section, between Brazil and Africa, is a noteworthy feature, indicating its relationship to the factors that shaped these continental land areas, whatever they may have been. On the average, the ridge ranges in height between 5,000 and 10,000 feet above the floors of adjacent basins. There is only one gap along the entire length of the ridge, and this is a deep, narrow trench near the equator, termed the Romanche trench.

The Indian Ocean also has a central submarine ridge. It extends from India southward toward Antarctica, but it is considerably lower and somewhat wider than the mid-Atlantic ridge. In the Pacific, the ridges are less continuous and tend to be aligned in a northwest-southeast direction. They are more numerous in the western part of the

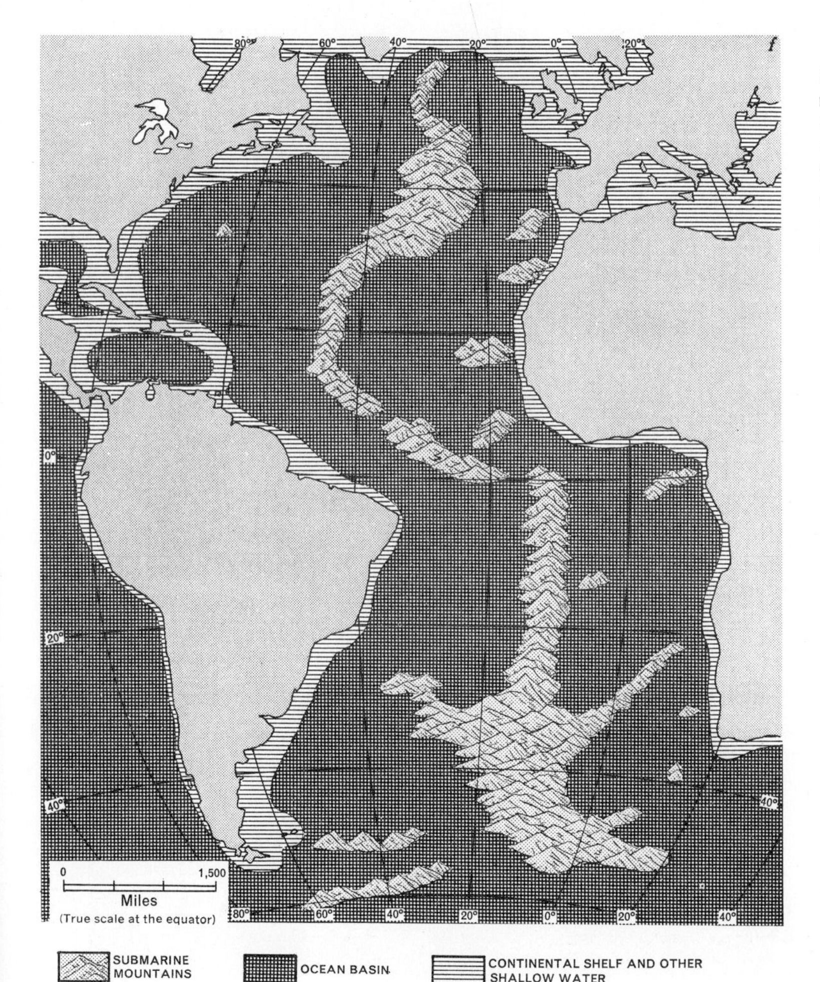

FIG. 15.6 Location of the mid-Atlantic ridge. Some investigators believe that this ridge represents a former junction of the Americas, Europe, and Africa, and constitutes a section that remained after the pieces drifted apart. [After Strommel]

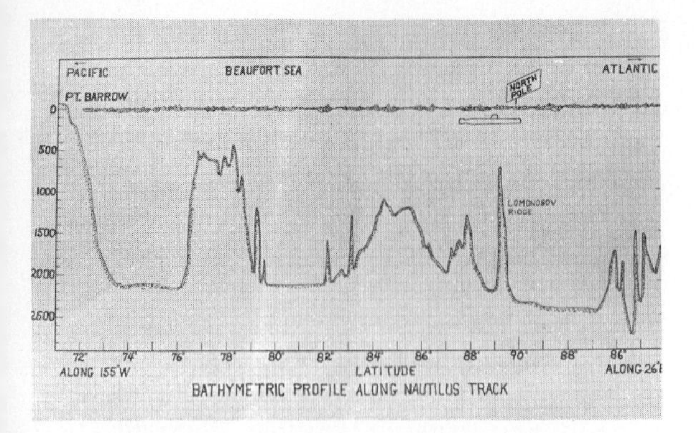

FIG. 15.7 Ocean bottom profile taken along the track of the atomic submarine Nautilus during its transpolar voyage. The Arctic Ocean shows irregularities along its bottom similar to the other oceans. Depths to the left are in fathoms. The Lomonosov ridge is a long ocean ridge that almost crosses the Arctic Ocean. [U.S. Navy]

ocean. Recent investigations in the Arctic Ocean have revealed similar ridges there (see Fig. 15.7). One of these, the Lomonosov ridge, almost bisects the entire ocean basin.

15.9 OCEAN PLAINS. Apart from the continental-shelf plains, featureless flat plains are not nearly so common on the ocean floor as was formerly believed, primarily because the ocean depths do not undergo the gradational processes found on the continents. Sedimentation tends to smooth out minor surface irregularities, but throughout most of the oceans beyond the continental slope and away from the major ridges, the rate of such accumulation is exceedingly slow. All the irregularities resulting from crustal disturbances, including fault escarpments and volcanic outpourings, are preserved indefinitely, because the normal processes of erosion on land are not present. Wave action is confined to shallow depths, generally within a few hundred feet of the surface, and strong currents are absent in the ocean depths. Nevertheless, a few broad, flat plains can be found. One of these lies in the western part of the North Atlantic, between Bermuda and the mid-Atlantic ridge, and there is another southeast of Ceylon in the Indian Ocean. Smaller plains are found within the various basin areas of the Pacific. The irregularity of the ocean floor is well illustrated in Fig. 15.8, which shows a profile of the bottom across the North Atlantic.

15.10 OCEAN-FLOOR SEDIMENTS. The composition of the ocean floor beyond the continental shelf varies widely from place to place. Muds and sands of terrestrial origin predominate and exhibit, immediately beyond the continental slope, the same variety of colors and compositions as those within the shelf zone. Sedimentary layers are unusually thick along the flanks of some of the great ocean ridges. Thousands of feet of them, for example, are found along the mid-Atlantic ridge. Such great thicknesses of sediment, however, are not the rule over most of the ocean floor.

The deep sea basins are mantled with a comparatively thin veneer of various types of sediment that were derived from several

FIG. 15.8 A surface profile across the North Atlantic. Wide, flat ocean floors are relatively rare in most of the ocean basins. [After Heezen]

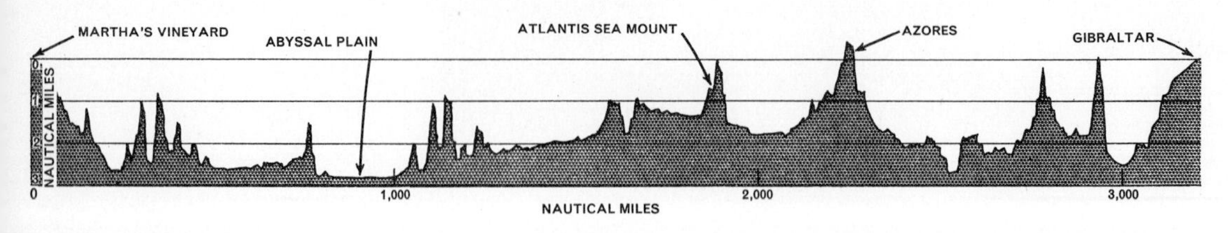

different origins. Over wide areas this veneer consists of organic oozes, composed mainly of the tiny, calcareous shells of microorganisms in the lower latitudes and of the lacy, siliceous remains of other microorganisms in the high latitudes. Other broad areas are covered with a fine red clay, especially in the deepest basins of the North Pacific and in other areas where the surface waters are relatively barren of life. This red clay differs considerably in chemical composition from that produced by the weathering of continental rocks. Some of it may represent meteoric dust gathered from outer space over millions of years or volcanic dust that has settled out of the atmosphere following unusually severe explosions.

Properties of sea water

Geographic differences above the sea bottom, within the realm of the ocean itself, consist mainly of differences in the chemical composition, color, density, salinity, and movement of sea water. Each of these properties is discussed below with respect to areal patterns and interrelationships.

15.11 CHEMICAL COMPOSITION. One of the most remarkable features of sea water is the fact that the relative proportions of the major chemical nongaseous elements (usually in the form of ions) remain relatively unchanged throughout the oceans. This appears to be true regardless of variations in density, salinity, or temperature. These proportions are presented in Table 15.1.

Many other elements are present in sea water; in fact, about fifty of the known elements have been detected in it, and traces of others have been found in the remains of sea organisms, evidence that such elements were present in the water. The amounts of the contained elements, other than those listed in Table 15.1, are so small that it is extremely difficult to determine their proportions. Although the proportions of major constituents are remarkably consistent, there is considerable evidence that

TABLE 15.1 Major soluble constituents of sea water

IONIC PROPORTIONS		MOLECULAR COMPOSITION (*analysis of unevaporated residue*)	
Chlorine	55.04%		
Sodium	30.61	Sodium chloride	77.76%
Sulfate (SO_4)	7.68	Magnesium chloride	10.88
Magnesium	3.69	Magnesium sulfate	4.74
Calcium	1.16	Calcium sulfate	3.60
Potassium	1.10	Potassium sulfate	2.46
Bicarbonate	0.41	Calcium carbonate	0.34
Bromides	0.19	Magnesium bromide	0.22
Boric acid	0.07		100.00%
Strontium	0.04		
	99.99%		

SOURCE: The data on ionic proportions are from H. V. Sverdrup, Martin W. Johnson, and Richard Fleming, *The Oceans,* Prentice-Hall, Inc., Englewood Cliffs, N.J., 1942, p. 166. Reprinted by permission of the publisher. The data on molecular composition are from Dittmar, quoted in R. E. Coker, *This Great and Wide Sea,* University of North Carolina Press, Chapel Hill, N.C., 1947, p. 79.

some of the minor constituents vary in amount from place to place and from time to time and that the quantities present affect the distribution and characteristics of organic life in the sea. Nitrates and phosphates, for example, are important to marine life just as they are to land animals and plants; yet only traces of these minerals can be detected in sea water. The fertility of ocean waters is not solely a function of light, oxygen, carbon dioxide, and temperature. The most fertile sea acres are found where water is brought to the surface from the depths and where phosphatic and nitrogenous nutrients accumulate on the bottom following the ultimate decay of dead organisms. Although the sea contains only small proportions of the minor constituents important to organisms, the total quantities are large, because of the immense volume of the sea. Iodine, for example, is present in sea water in the proportion of only 0.000005 per cent, yet in 1 cubic mile, there are some 590 tons of it. Table 15.2 shows the number of tons of various chemical elements present in a single cubic mile of sea water, assuming an average salinity of 34,048 parts per million.

Sea water is a nutrient solution containing nearly all the elements needed by organisms. Except for the nitrates and phosphates, the chemical nongaseous elements are available in fairly abundant supply everywhere in the sea. Furthermore, it now appears that biological activity in the sea is responsible for helping to maintain the proportionate balance among the various constituents. Some microorganisms have a high preference for silicon, whereas others prefer calcium for the construction of their shells or hard parts. Kelp and other seaweeds use unusually large

TABLE 15.2 Composition of sea water by elements,* in tons per cubic mile

Element	Tons	Element	Tons
Chlorine	223,766,608	Arsenic	118–236
Sodium	124,507,966	Iron	24–236
Magnesium	14,996,371	Manganese	12–118
Sulfur	10,422,006	Copper	12–118
Calcium	4,715,800	Zinc	59
Potassium	4,480,048	Lead	47
Bromine	764,324	Selenium	47
Carbon	330,109	Cesium	24
Strontium	147,265	Uranium	18
Boron	54,212	Molybdenum	6
Silicon	236–47,154	Thorium	6
Fluorine	16,505	Cerium	5
Nitrogen	118–8,253	Silver	3.5
Aluminum	5,895	Vanadium	3.5
Rubidium	2,358	Lanthanum	3.5
Lithium	1,118	Yttrium	3.5
Phosphorus	12–1,180	Nickel	1.2
Barium	589	Gold	0.07
Iodine	589		

SOURCE: H. V. Sverdrup, M. W. Johnson, and R. Fleming, *The Oceans,* Prentice-Hall, Inc., Englewood Cliffs, N.J., 1942, pp. 176–177.

* Proportions are based on 11,789,650,000 tons of water per cubic mile. Gases are not included.

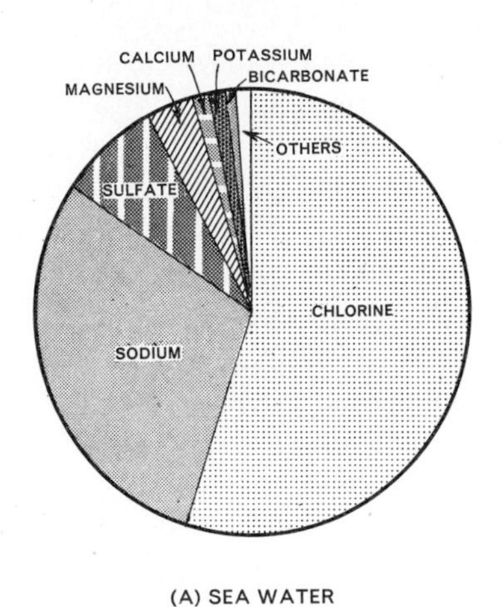

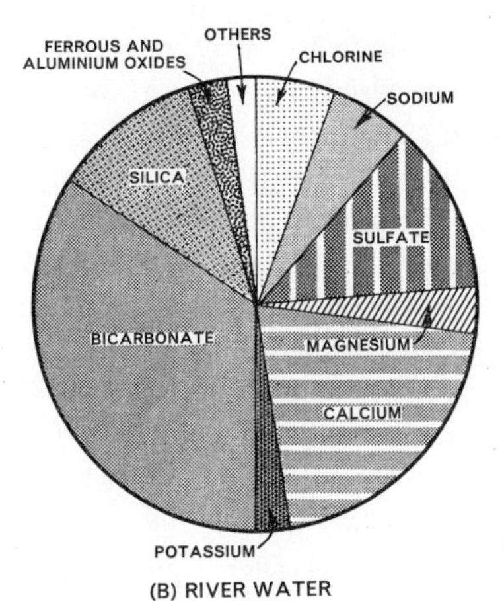

FIG. 15.9 Comparison of ionic contents in sea water and typical river water. [Data from Sverdrup et al.]

amounts of potassium and iodine in their tissues. Other biological processes probably play a part in removing iron, silica, and potassium from sea water to form the complex mineral substances, such as glauconite, which cover broad areas on the sea bottom. Some such processes must exist, for the rivers that bring solids to the sea have quite different proportions of chemical elements than sea water. Sodium and chlorine ions, for example, are much less important soluble materials in river water than they are in the sea, whereas the bicarbonate, sulfate, calcium, and silicate ions are among the leading dissolved solids in most river water (see Fig. 15.9). The question of the origin of chlorine in sea water is open to considerable debate.

The dissolved gases in the oceans are not subject to the same degree of proportional equilibrium as are the solid elements. The principal gases include oxygen, nitrogen, and carbon dioxide. Minute quantities of the inert gases argon, helium, and neon have been detected, and under the special conditions of organic decay associated with oxygen deficiences, hydrogen sulfide and ammonia may be found. Of the gases, by far the most important for organic life in the sea are oxygen and carbon dioxide, just as they are for terrestrial organisms. Factors influencing the content of these two important gases include the following:

1. Temperature. Sea water in contact with the air tends to maintain a definite proportion of the atmospheric gases. This proportion tends to increase as the temperature decreases. Cold water holds more of the gases than warm water; hence cold surface water, upon warming, tends to lose some of its gas content, just as a warm bottle of soda loses its "sparkle" when the cap is removed. Conversely, warm surface water flowing into high latitudes absorbs oxygen and carbon dioxide from the air upon cooling.

2. Salinity. When surface sea water becomes more dilute, it holds more oxygen and carbon dioxide. Excessive evaporation, which produces a higher salinity, results in losses of these gases.

3. Biological activity. Photosynthesis by plants tends to decrease the carbon dioxide content and increase the oxygen content. Respiration by the marine fauna, on the other hand, has an opposite effect. The formation of calcium carbonate shells by organisms also removes carbon dioxide from

the water. In other instances, an increase in hydrogen-ion concentration (increased acidity) tends to dissolve calcium carbonate, releasing carbon dioxide into the water. Animals and plants complement each other with respect to the intake and release of oxygen and carbon dioxide, just as they do on land.

4. Turbulence and mixing. The mechanical influences of waves and currents tend to alter the gas content of ocean water. This helps explain why life activity in the surface water varies widely from time to time. Warm surface water in low latitudes has its gas content increased appreciably during stormy periods, because of the frothing of breaking waves. The mixing of colder water from below increases the capacity of the surface water to hold the added gases. Surf similarly tends to increase the gas content in coastal waters. Corals thrive best in the aerated zone of heavy surf in tropical seas. All these factors operate in various degrees in different parts of the ocean to create distinctive environments for sea life. Although most areas vary in their content of dissolved gases, local equilibria tend to be developed, maintained by long-range conditions of both sea and air.

The surface ocean areas beneath the subtropical anticyclones of the atmosphere are the true deserts of the sea, mainly because of their extremely low content of gases. Under the high heat and cloudless skies, the surface waters are heated, evaporation concentrates the salinity, and both oxygen and carbon dioxide are released into the air.

At the other extreme are the oceans of high latitudes, where the chilled surface water takes in oxygen and carbon dioxide from the air in much the same way as a sponge absorbs water. During the long summer days, the surface water teems with tiny life forms, which thrive in these waters, since there is not only much oxygen for microanimal life but also carbon dioxide for microplant forms. These organisms also find an abundance of nutrient minerals, brought to the surface by the overturning of water (vertical currents) during the previous winter season. The rising of deep water and the subsidence of surface water during the high-latitude winters are caused by an increase in density at the surface, which is the result of the chilling and freezing of surface water. The atmospheric gases absorbed by sea water in high latitudes may be the same gases that were released by the water in the subtropics and brought to the seas of high latitudes by winds. The cold polar water, moving into the depths of the ocean as it passes equatorward, brings life-giving oxygen to the grotesque animal life of the ocean deeps.

In some isolated basins, especially in those which are adjacent to continents and which are prevented by a shallow sill or ridge from receiving an inflow of deep, oxygen-rich bottom water from the open ocean, an unusual and lethal environment may be created. In the depths of the Black Sea or, as Kuenen reports, in some of the seas adjacent to Indonesia, dead organic material drifts down from above and remains for long periods, since the lack of oxygen keeps it from being consumed. This putrid mass eventually breaks down through the action of certain specialized types of bacteria, and hydrogen sulfide gas is generated. This gas is highly toxic to sea organisms, and thus these murky depths are lifeless, a death trap to any unsuspecting sea creatures that enter. It is believed that many of the black marine shales that are now exposed on the continents and that have a notable scarcity of fossil forms may have originated under such conditions. The few fossils that are found in such shales usually are composed of iron sulfide (pyrite, or fool's gold), the sulfur being obtained from hydrogen sulfide, and the iron from the muds brought in by streams. In the open ocean, however, such conditions of toxic putrefaction are exceedingly rare. The polar waters bathe the sea floor in all latitudes, bringing oxygen with them.

15.12 COLOR. Color is the most striking characteristic that distinguishes one region of the ocean from another. Color is by no means unrelated to other properties of the sea. Pure sea water is blue for the same reason that a clear sky is blue, that is, because only the short, blue wavelengths of light are scattered by the constituent molecules of air or water. Whenever tiny foreign particles are added, however, the color of both the sky and the sea changes.

Next to blue, green is the most common sea color. It is now believed that the various gradations between blue and green are the result of mixtures of microorganisms that are themselves colored either yellow or green. Green is a sign of organic fertility in sea water, whereas deep blue is the color of the ocean "deserts." Cobalt blues predominate in the open water of middle- and low-latitude seas. The contrast between the blue Gulf Stream and the green Labrador Current off the east coast of the United States is striking. Shallow water near shore is normally greenish in color, even in the tropics, because wave action increases the gas and nutrient content of water and thus makes possible a greater organic population. There is a remarkable color contrast between the green water of coral lagoons bordering tropical islands and the deep blue of the open sea beyond the outer line of breakers.

Colors other than green or blue, though far less common, are also encountered. Yellowish water, resulting from clays and silts brought to the sea by large rivers, can be found in several places. The Yellow Sea off North China is appropriately named. Mention already has been made of the unusual colors produced by concentrations of certain types of algae in the description of El Niño off the Peruvian coast (see Sec. 15.4). Red, or rather a rust shade, is a common color. It is caused by a sudden flare-up in the population of tiny single-celled organisms. This phenomenon, which is restricted to subtropical and tropical seas, has given the Red Sea its name. Spanish explorers named the Gulf of California the Vermilion Sea for the same reason. The red coloration also has been observed along the Florida coast. In general, however, the greens and blues greatly predominate, with the greens in waters of high latitudes and shallows and the blues in the deep open waters of middle and low latitudes.

15.13 DENSITY. Differences in the density, or specific gravity, of sea water, that is, its weight relative to that of an equivalent volume of pure water at 0°C and at atmospheric pressure (at sea level), constitute one of the factors influencing the global circulation of water, just as the pressure of air is involved in horizontal airflow. The two most important variables involved are temperature and salinity.

Increases in the density of sea water are caused by the cooling, evaporation, or freezing of surface water. Decreases in density are the result of surface heating, precipitation, the discharge of river water, or the melting of icebergs. When surface water has its density increased, it tends to subside to greater depths until it reaches a density equilibrium, whereupon it spreads laterally. The cooling of water at high latitudes and the warming and freshening of water in the tropics thus produce a large circulatory system. The cold polar water has a greater density than any other ocean water; thus it forms the major bottom water at all latitudes. This

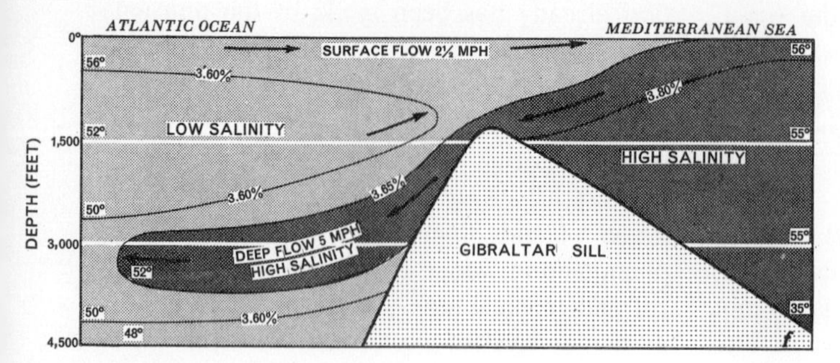

FIG. 15.10 The flow of water through the Strait of Gibraltar. The outflow of dense, high-salinity water from the enclosed Mediterranean Sea takes place along the bottom of the strait. This outflow is more rapid, but lower in volume than the surface inflow. [After Kuenen]

is why water at great depths, even near the equator, is rarely above 40°F.

Excessive evaporation, causing an increase in salinity, produces density differentials. A definite bottom flow of cool, highly saline water moves out of both the Mediterranean and Red Seas, because of the excess of evaporation over precipitation within these sea areas. Subsidence of water within the Mediterranean also is caused by winter cooling. The current moving out of the Mediterranean has been traced for hundreds of miles into the Atlantic (see Fig. 15.10), where it spreads out at a depth of about 6,000 feet. Replacing it is a surface inflow of low-salinity water through the Strait of Gibraltar.

The circulation of water resulting from density patterns is not rapid and is in no way comparable to the surface currents driven by winds. The flow along the bottom, for example, is for the most part extremely slow and irregular.

15.14 TEMPERATURE. The temperature of sea water varies between about 29 and 84°F. Below 29° the water either freezes at the surface, thus protecting the water immediately below from excessive radiational cooling, or subsides to lower depths because of an increase in density. Above 80°, evaporation is an effective means of reducing surface temperatures. Ocean-water temperatures, therefore, do not vary nearly so much as air temperatures, either with latitudinal distribution or with diurnal or seasonal changes. Day- and nighttime temperatures rarely differ by more than about 1°, and seasonal differences are usually less than 10° for most oceanic positions.

The distribution of surface temperatures in the oceans is influenced by several factors, the most important being the pattern of ocean currents, the latitudinal variation in solar heating, the upwelling of water, and the melting of icebergs. Figure 15.11, which shows the distribution of temperature *anomalies,* or gradations above or below the normal for the particular latitude, indicates several important nonlatitudinal controls. Note, for example, the negative anomalies (colder than normal) off the west coasts of continents in the subtropics. These are due largely to upwelling cold water. (The reason for the upwelling is discussed later, in connection with ocean currents.) Other negative anomalies can be observed off the northeast coasts of North America and Asia and off the southeast coast of South America. These are the result of polar water moving toward the equator and being deflected against the eastern sides of continents by the earth's rotation, before dipping beneath warmer water heading poleward. The low temperatures off the northeastern coast of the United States are maintained during the summer by the melting of icebergs from Greenland. The surface water that encircles the world south of Africa, South America, and Australia is also somewhat colder than is expected for the latitude, because of the continual addition of cold antarctic water along its entire length. Irregularities in the supply of icebergs from the antarctic icecap produce some variations in the temperature of this water from year to year.

Warm surface currents, heading poleward and being deflected toward the east by the earth's rotation, bring positive anomalies to the west coasts of continents poleward of lat 40°. Temperature anomalies also are likely to occur in continental seas, such as the Mediterranean, the Red Sea, the Persian Gulf, and the Yellow Sea, although the anomalies here tend to be reversible, that is, positive (warmer) in summer and negative in winter.

Temperature patterns are notably different at different depths. For the most part, the great surface currents, with their distinctive temperatures, are confined to the top 1,500 feet or so of the oceans. In the Middle Atlantic, the entire warm central portion is underlain by much colder water between 1,500 and 4,000 feet below sea level. Distinct layers of water of different temperatures also occur in places. Some of these cold and warm layers may be traced for thousands of miles. At depths below a mile, ocean waters everywhere are generally near 32°F.

15.15 SALINITY. Measurements of salinity are relatively easy to make, because the proportions of the major salts in the

FIG. 15.11 Average annual ocean temperature anomalies in degrees centigrade. Positive anomalies indicate temperatures that are greater than the average for the particular latitude. [After James, Markus, and Sokalsky]

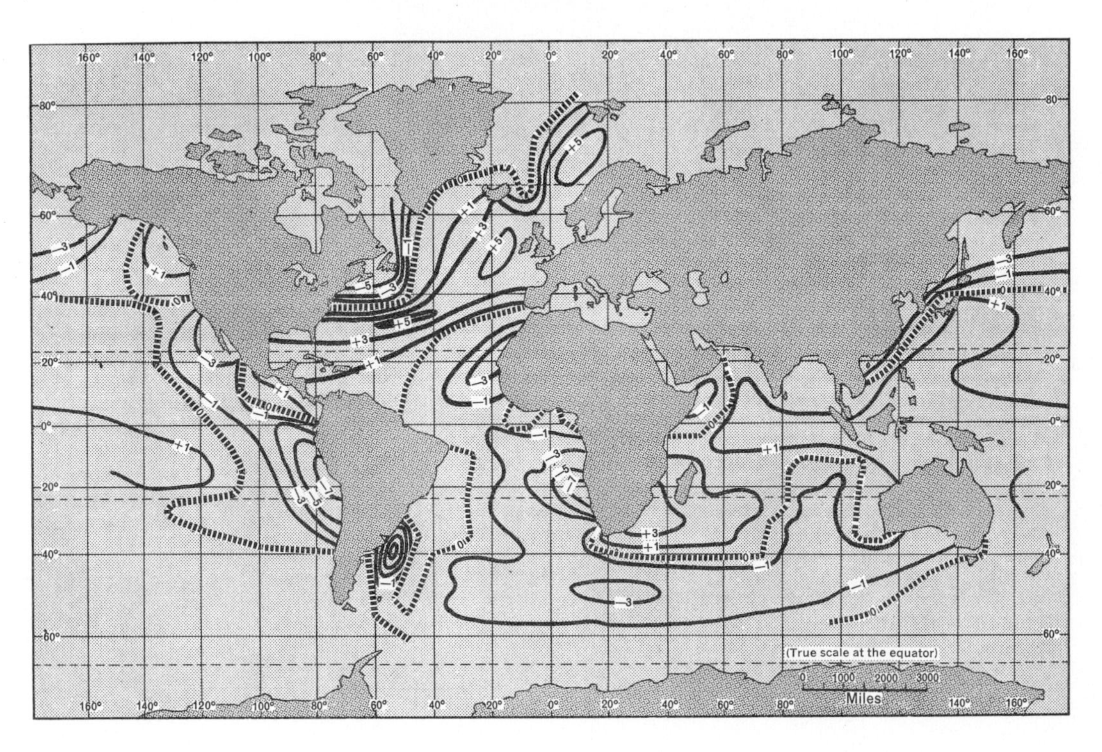

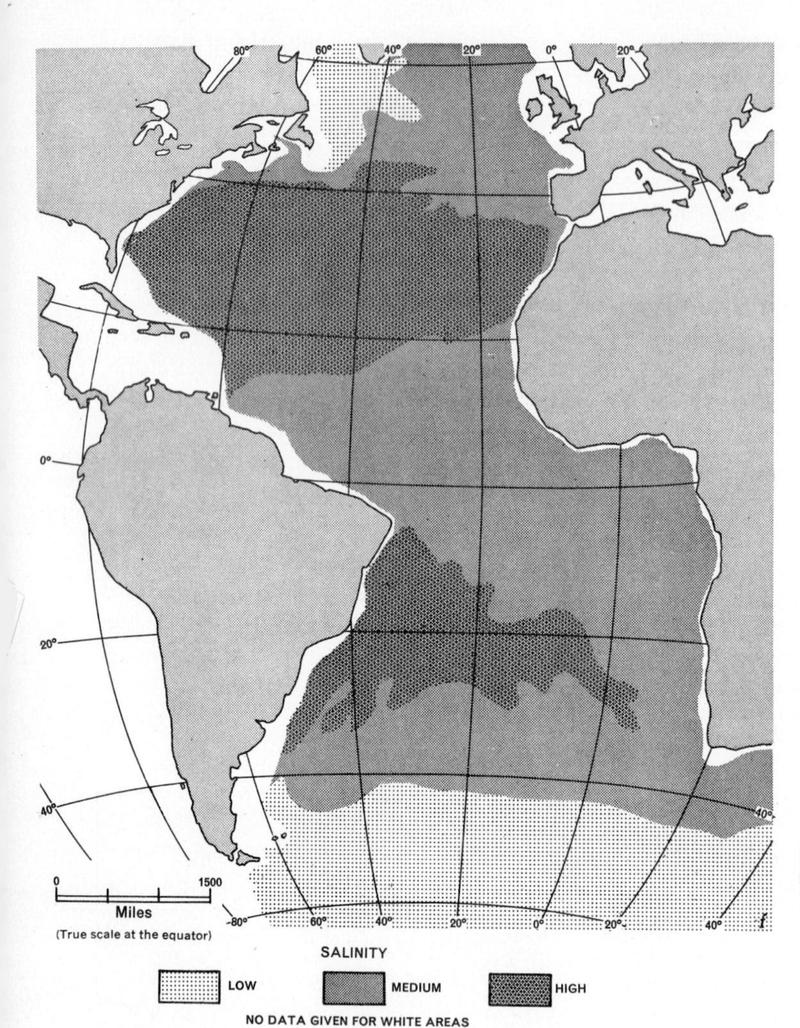

FIG. 15.12 Distribution of ocean salinity in the Atlantic. [After Strommel]

ocean remain nearly constant; thus it is necessary to determine the quantity of only one of the major elements, usually chlorine. As was indicated in Sec. 15.13, salinity tends to be increased by evaporation and by the formation of sea ice. It is decreased by precipitation, the discharge of rivers, and the melting of sea ice and icebergs. Since accurate measurements of the speed and direction of ocean currents and the temperatures of great depths are difficult to make, variations in salinity, which are easily measured, constitute an important means of identifying particular ocean currents. In the open ocean, the salinity range is rather small, generally varying from about 3.4 to 3.7 per cent. The oceanic average is about 3.48 per cent, or, more precisely, 34,482 parts per million. The Baltic Sea, with its influx of river water and restricted connections to the Atlantic, varies widely in salinity, and a minimum salinity of only about 0.9 per cent has been observed during the spring season. The Red Sea, on the other hand, with its excessive evaporation, has produced salinities of over 4 per cent.

The highest salinities in the open ocean generally occur near the surface in the middle latitudes (see Fig. 15.12). Deep water is considerably less saline. Polar water is generally of low salinity, which helps explain the lower salinity of bottom water in the oceans. Near the equator, salinity figures for surface waters drop below those of the subtropics, because of increased precipitation. The influence of salinity on water density, and thus on the general global circulation of ocean water, is not appreciable. The influence of high salinities on density patterns within the subtropical anticyclonic areas, for example, is partially neutralized by the high temperatures.

The oceanic circulation

All the oceans are included in a gigantic circulatory system that is relatively simple in its over-all pattern but extremely complex in detail. In general, the circulation comprises a huge convectional heat-transfer system that carries tropical heat energy via surface flow into high latitudes, where it gives up this heat to the air or diffuses it by mixing with colder water. The cooling produces an increase in density, and the cold polar water finally returns to the tropics, mainly by way of the ocean depths. The pattern of the surface ocean currents thus presents only a portion of the entire circulation system. The speed of movement within the system varies widely, ranging from as much as 5½ miles per hour (excluding local tidal currents) to an almost imperceptible drift. The slowest movement is along the bottom, and the most rapid is located at the surface in the western parts of the oceans. Probably every molecule of water in every ocean has made the round trip between the tropics and the polar seas and has alternately visited the surface and the ocean bottom. Scientists now believe that this round trip takes a long time; estimates range from 300 to 600 years. As indicated below, there are many possible detours on such a trip.

One such detour, which is prominently reflected in the pattern of surface currents, is within the huge rotating cells, or *gyres,* whose centers are found in the subtropics (lat 20 to 30°) of each of the major ocean basins, both north and south of the equator. The operation of the North Atlantic subtropical gyre is described in detail in the next section and may be considered as typical of the others. The northern hemisphere gyres, like the anticyclones within the atmosphere, rotate in a clockwise direction, whereas those south of the equator rotate in a counterclockwise direction. The surface flow in each of the gyres is relatively shallow, usually lying within 1,500 feet of the surface.

15.16 THE NORTH ATLANTIC SUBTROPICAL GYRE. The North Atlantic gyre, like the others, is oval-shaped, with its major axis oriented in an east-west direction and with its center toward the western part of the ocean basin (see Fig. 15.13). It is generated mainly by three factors: (1) the convective flow of less dense, warm surface water away from low latitudes; (2) the deflective effect of the earth's rotation, which turns the flow toward the right; and (3) the pressure of prevailing winds on the surface. The speed of rotation varies considerably in different sections of the gyre. The most rapid flow is along the western side, where all three of the causal forces are working together. In the western North Atlantic, this current is the Gulf Stream, which attains a speed up to 5½ miles per hour. Aiding also in this speed is an injection of water from the Gulf of Mexico through the Florida Strait, caused

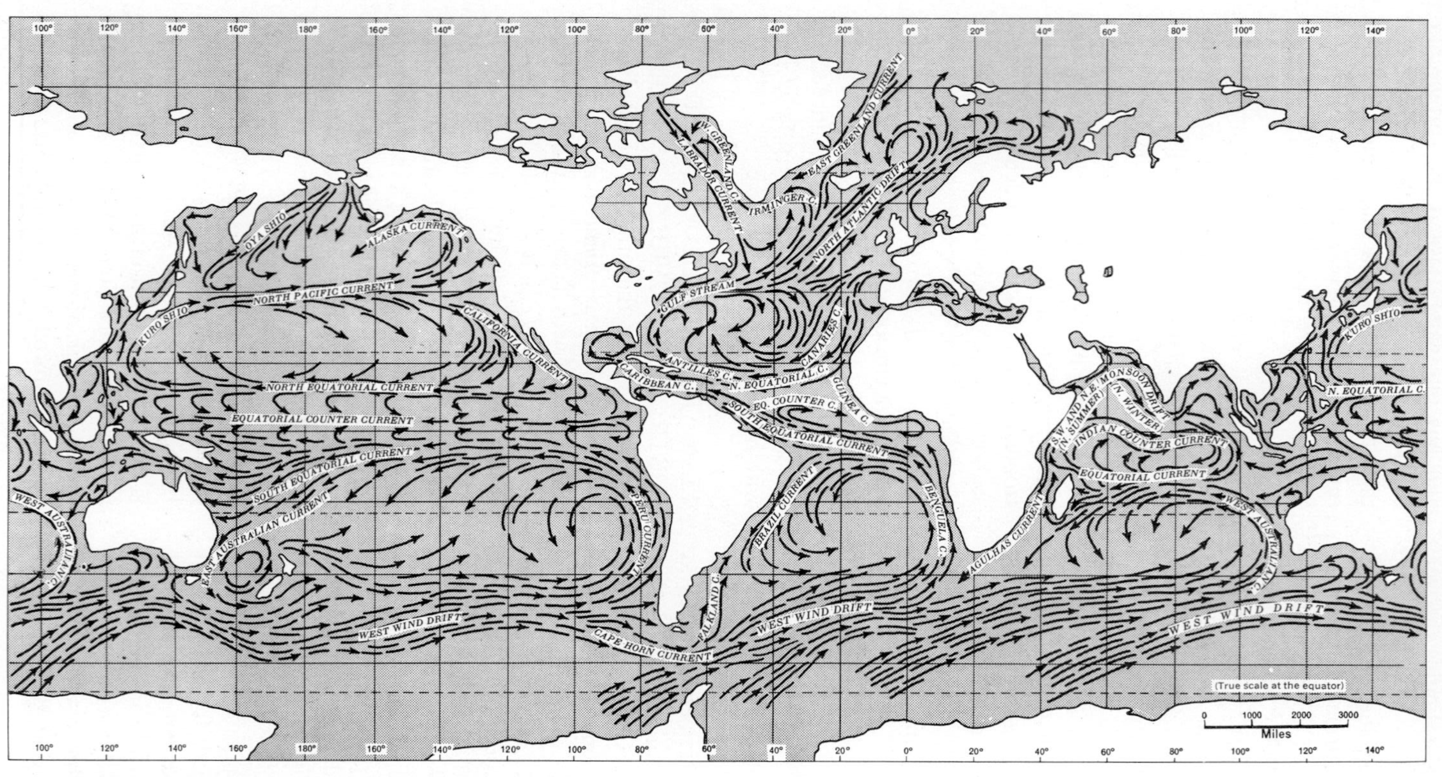

FIG. 15.13 Major surface ocean currents of the world.

by the somewhat higher level of the Gulf of Mexico waters.

The Gulf Stream often has been likened to a gigantic ocean river. At times, for example, it is subject to irregular meanderings, or loops, some of which may be 100 to 200 miles in diameter. These are most frequent in its course after it leaves the coastal area near Cape Hatteras. These loops appear suddenly, and occasionally one of them may be broken from the main stream, thus introducing large quantities of Gulf Stream water into the ocean areas on either side (see Fig. 15.14). The flow of the Gulf Stream appears to be similar to that of a jet, and it has been compared to the jet stream within the atmosphere. It is not a single flow, but a series of long, narrow filaments of Gulf Stream water separated by strips of water that occasionally may be moving in an opposite direction. The movement of water within the Gulf Stream, like that of all ocean currents, is a *turbulent* flow.[1] The volume and speed vary considerably. Fluctuations in the behavior of the entire gyre are magnified in the flow of the Gulf Stream, and research is being carried on to determine whether fluctuations in the flow are indicative of broad changes in global weather patterns and hence might be used for long-range weather forecasting. Another interesting feature of the Gulf Stream is the slope of its surface, which is toward the west and which varies directly with the speed of the current. The Gulf Stream is much slower and broader and less distinct east of about long 50° W. In this area it is known as the North Atlantic Drift. Off northwestern Europe, the flow of the gyre splits, some of it

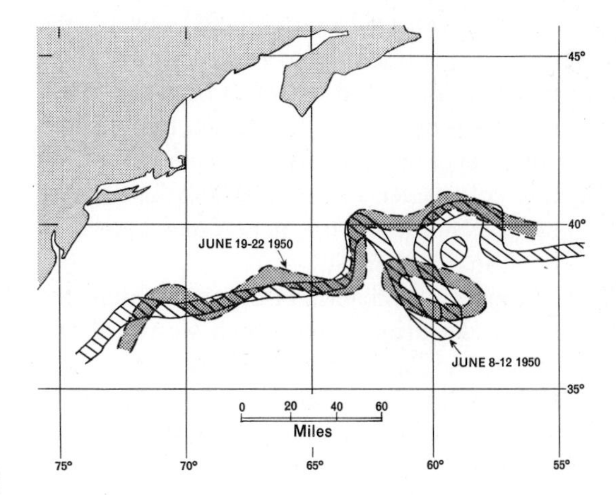

FIG. 15.14 Shifts in the trajectory of the Gulf Stream. Note how a great meander or loop broke away from the main stream during the period of observation. [After Munk]

heading northward toward the Norwegian Sea and the Arctic Ocean, some of it entering the English Channel toward the North Sea, and the remainder turning southward toward Spain and the Canary Islands.

The southward flow on the eastern side of the gyre is the slowest part of the marginal circulation of the gyre, principally because there is a loss of angular momentum when the water curves toward the equator. In this sector, as in the other subtropical gyres, a new feature enters the picture, namely, the addition of cold water due to upwelling from below. The cause of this upwelling is believed to be the movement of surface water offshore under the influence of wind pressure. A principle of oceanic flow, termed Ekman's law, states that *water tends to move at an angle of 45° to the right of the prevailing wind direction in the northern hemisphere, and to the left in the southern hemisphere, the amount of deflection increasing somewhat with velocity and decreasing with depth.* Since the prevailing wind direction along the coasts bordering the eastern side of the gyre

[1] *Turbulent* flow contains a varying proportion of irregular speeds and directions on the part of different included masses of water. It thus is quite unlike a smooth *laminar* flow, or a flow of liquid in which layers of the liquid move smoothly without appreciable local variations in direction or speed.

is roughly parallel to, or slightly toward, the coast, the surface water moves offshore. The incoming slow drift of water from the north is not strong enough to replace the offshore flow; hence water must rise from below. As this cold water in the North Atlantic gyre moves southwestward, it becomes known as the Canaries Current.

Under the influence of the trade winds, the Canaries Current moves both westward and toward the center of the gyre. Since the effect of Ekman's law is to force surface water toward the center throughout most of the gyre's margin, the center becomes a shallow dome with sloping edges. Movement toward the center of the gyre is balanced by gravitational and centrifugal forces which tend to shift water outward. It is believed by some that variations in the position and strength of the subtropical anticyclones tend to affect the flow pattern of ocean water around the margins of the gyre, both by altering wind patterns and by changing the size and shape of the domed center. Changes in the shape and the slope of the dome also can determine the amount of water to be discharged into the currents that surround the gyre and the amount discharged from these into either the equatorial or high-latitude areas.

The flow of water along the southern margin of the North Atlantic gyre is westward and is termed the North Equatorial Current. Cool at first in its eastern sector, this water gradually warms in its course westward. In the western part of the Atlantic, the North Equatorial Current is deflected northward by the northeastern coast of South America and also by the earth's rotation. Joining it is some water from the South Atlantic Current which is split and driven northward by the wedge shape of eastern Brazil. Near the West Indies most of the warm equatorial water flows northward as the Antilles Current. Some of it, however, enters the Gulf of Mexico, where it tends to raise the sea level of the Gulf, forcing a gravity flow outward between Florida and Cuba.

With the large addition of water flowing into the western parts of all oceans in low latitudes, the level of the oceans there becomes somewhat higher than toward the east. Gravity thus tends to pull water eastward in the zone between the trade winds or between the subtropical gyres of opposite hemispheres. This eastward current is known as the Equatorial Countercurrent. It is weakest in the Atlantic, because of the narrowness of this ocean area and also because of the wedge shape of eastern Brazil, which tends to divert the water northward or southward without as much "piling up." Miniature gyres are formed on each side of the Equatorial Countercurrent, between the westerly countercurrent and the two easterly equatorial currents. The behavior of these gyres is much less regular than that of the major subtropical gyre in the North Atlantic basin. The Equatorial Countercurrent is especially well developed in the Pacific. The countercurrents, like the subtropical gyres, shift north and south with the seasons.

The center of the North Atlantic gyre is known as the Sargasso Sea. Essentially a domed area of relatively "dead" water, it has only fitful, variable surface currents, which are generated by the weak, changeable winds associated with the subtropical anticyclone that normally lies over it. Water occasionally is added from the outer slope of the dome, particularly during storm periods, and there is a slow subsidence within, caused by the growing density resulting from evaporation. A considerable amount of potential energy is stored within the dome of the gyre, and it has been estimated that, if the wind were to stop, the circulation of water around the gyre would last for some 3 years. The subsidence within the center of the gyre spreads at an intermediate level below, because it cannot match the density of the cold water below 4,000 to 5,000 feet (at this level it encounters deep water from the South Atlantic). A brilliant ultramarine color is characteristic of the Sargasso Sea. The sterile, inhospitable waters harbor little life except for the masses of floating weeds and their associated life forms. This is truly an oceanic desert region. Pieces of driftwood and other flotsam, caught within the gyre and enmeshed by the Sargasso weed, gave rise to the ancient notion that this was the graveyard of lost vessels, a haunted place to be avoided.

15.17 THE OTHER SUBTROPICAL GYRES. The other subtropical gyres match, in general, the behavior of the North Atlantic gyre. They are indicated in Fig. 15.13. Exceptions may be noted in the northern Indian Ocean and in the South Pacific. In the northern Indian Ocean, the peninsular wedge of India and the seasonal shift in the monsoon winds result in a double gyre within the Arabian Sea and the Bay of Bengal, respectively. These bodies of water have opposite rotating gyres which reverse direction seasonally; the Arabian Sea rotates clockwise in the summer and counterclockwise in the winter, and the Bay of Bengal has an opposite regime. Apparently there is little upwelling of cold water within the eastern sides of these gyres. The other exception is in the South Pacific, where there is a tendency to develop a double gyre, one in the east and one in the west, possibly aided by the deflective effects of the Tuamotu Archipelago and a large series of coral seamount islands and reefs. The North Pacific gyre is much larger and more elongated than those in the other oceans.

15.18 THE PATTERN OF SURFACE CURRENTS IN HIGH LATITUDES. As noted earlier, the general circulation of water carries warm water into high latitudes and, after it has been cooled, returns it to low latitudes. The warm surface water is injected into the waters of high latitudes along the poleward margins of the subtropical gyres, but the manner in which this is accomplished is quite different in the northern and southern hemispheres. The difference is caused primarily by the configuration of the continents.

In the northern hemisphere nearly all the warm, saline water from the mid-latitudes reaches the high latitudes via the northeastern Atlantic. Only a small amount enters directly from the Pacific, because of the topographic barriers of the Aleutian Islands and the northwestern coast of North America. The subsidence of water resulting from cooling in the far north is slow and irregular. For this reason, there is a considerable surface outflow to match the large surface inflow brought to the arctic regions by the North Atlantic Drift. The great rivers of Eurasia also add their share to arctic waters. The major outflow takes place in Denmark Strait, between Greenland and Iceland. Subsidiary outflows occur through Davis Strait and the Bering Sea. As the outflow moves southward, the deflection of the earth's rotation turns the arctic waters toward the west, thus creating the East Greenland Current and the Labrador Current in the Atlantic and the less marked Oya Shio (or Kamchatka Current) in the northwestern Pacific. The complex pattern of surface currents in the far northern Atlantic, between Norway and Greenland (the Norwegian Sea), is indicated in Fig. 15.13.

The general movement of the antarctic surface currents is from west to east around the Antarctic Continent. This is termed the Circumantarctic Current. It is driven principally by the strong westerly winds associated with antarctic cyclonic disturbances (the "Roaring Forties"). Immediately next to the continent, however, a narrow current flows westward at the surface and may be generated by the gravity winds blowing off the continental ice sheet. As the Circumantarctic Current flows eastward, the earth's rotation tends to give it a northward direction; thus there is a general convergence of water within the West-wind Drift, the southern rim of the subtropical gyres. Unlike the Arctic Ocean, the Antarctic Ocean has no strong localized surface inflow or outflow currents. Instead, the inflows and outflows are distributed all along the length of the convergences (see Fig. 15.15). Only where the tip of South America extends into antarctic waters is there a pronounced flow northward, which forms the Falkland Islands Current and brings cold water to the east coast of Patagonia. The mechanics of interchange between warm and cold surface waters in far southern oceans thus is much less localized than in the Atlantic and operates either through eddying along the convergence boundaries (see Sec. 15.20) or through vertical movements (upwelling or subsidence). This may explain why the outflow of both bottom water and deep water from the antarctic is much greater than the subsurface outflow from the far north. Antarctic water, for example, can be traced far into the North Atlantic at depths below a mile.

15.19 SUBSURFACE OCEANIC DRIFTS. The pattern of water movement below the surface layers of the oceans was conjectural for a long time, principally because there were no suitable instruments for measuring it but also because subsurface drift is, for the most part, exceedingly slow, lacking the push from surface winds. Careful measurements of salinity and temperature have been used to identify types of water originating in different areas. Water from the Mediterranean, from the subtropical-gyre subsidences, from the arctic and antarctic—each has its own identifying properties. The deep waters are channeled by major irregularities on the ocean floor. Deep, cold water from the antarctic region, for example, does not enter the eastern Atlantic directly, because of the barrier formed by the mid-Atlantic ridge, although it may be identified well into the northern hemisphere within the western Atlantic.

In 1957, a joint American-British oceanographic expedition, studying features of the Gulf Stream, discovered the existence of a pronounced current flowing equatorward off the foot of the continental slope in the western Atlantic. Although this deep current has a velocity of 2 to 8 miles per day, which is much less than that of the surface Gulf Stream, it is far more rapid than any estimates of bottom-water flow elsewhere in the North Atlantic. Aiding in the discovery was an ingenious float that uses an ultrasonic transmitter to reveal its position while maintaining itself at a predetermined depth. It is believed by Stommel that this localized equatorward bottom flow is largely the result of the Coriolis effect. The equatorward flow of high-latitude water is deflected to the right in the northern hemisphere and to the left in the southern. Being intercepted by the continental slope off the east coast of North America, this flow of water is concentrated into a distinct current that parallels the continental slope. If the theory is correct, a similar equatorward current should be found off the east coast of Africa, along the Tonga-Kermadec trench in the western Pacific, and off Brazil and Argentina. There should also be a weak current off Kamchatka and Japan.

Another newly discovered subsurface current occurs in the equatorial portion of the South Pacific. It flows eastward at a depth

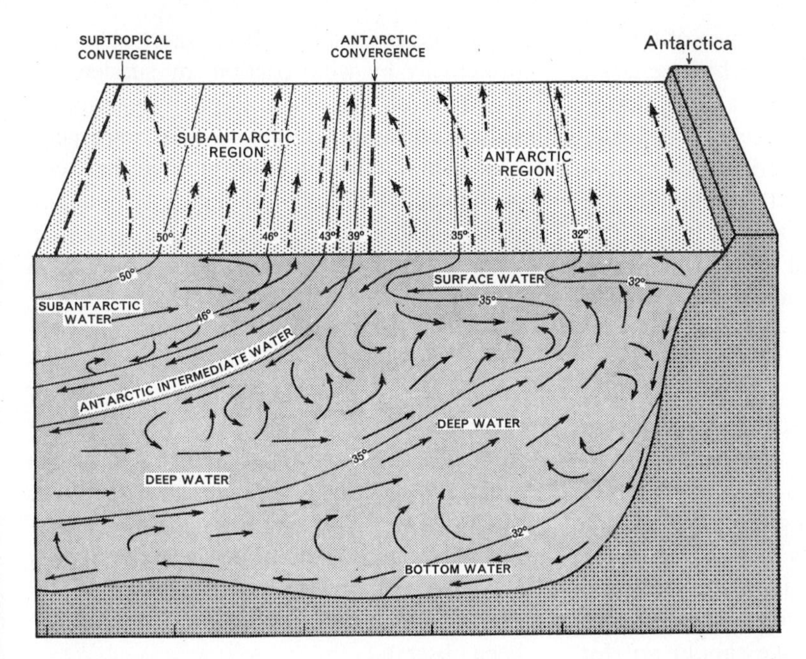

FIG. 15.15 Subsurface water movement off Antarctica. Vertical movements of water are common in high latitudes. [After Sverdrup et al.]

of 100 to 800 feet and is about 250 miles wide. Its speed is surprisingly great for a subsurface flow.

The global pattern of subsurface movement is complex, because of the factors of rotational deflection, topographic deflection and channeling, local subsidences and upwellings, and density differentials with depth. The movements are away from source areas of subsidence and toward the areas of upwelling. The centers of diversion include (1) high-latitude areas of excessive cooling; (2) the convergences, or boundaries between converging currents; (3) the centers of the subtropical gyres; and (4) the subtropical adjacent seas [2] with restricted access to the oceans. The high-latitude source areas produce most of the deepest bottom water, whereas the drifts at intermediate levels originate in the other source areas. Vertical currents, both ascending and descending, are most frequent in high latitudes and during the winter, owing to the rapid overturning of water caused by surface chilling and the formation of ice.

The complexity of movement in the ocean depths is illustrated by the schematic diagram of Fig. 15.15, which shows the movement and temperature of ocean water in a sector of the antarctic.

[2] The term *adjacent sea* refers to partially enclosed bodies of water adjacent to the continental margins. The Mediterranean, the Red Sea, and the Gulf of Southern California are examples.

15.20 CONVERGENCES. Convergences are ocean areas where surface waters of different origins and densities merge. They might be likened to the fronts separating different air masses. Invariably the denser of the two masses is diverted downward. Because they separate two dynamic, fluid masses, the convergence zones fluctuate in position and in sharpness and frequently show wavelike irregularities and many other features of atmospheric fronts. Stresses tend to develop along these boundaries, and there is considerable transfer of energy from one mass to another. The best known of the convergence boundaries is that which separates the Gulf Stream from the cold Labrador Current off the northeast coast of the United States. This has been described by some as the "cold wall" of the Gulf Stream, although its changeable nature belies the use of this term, for the word "wall" implies a smooth plane surface, which definitely is not present.

Waves and tides

On a global scale, waves and tides are merely microfeatures on the surface of the seas, but they sometimes play an extremely important role in human affairs. We are concerned here mainly with the characteristics of the larger forms of these two types of water movement. In minimizing the less spectacular forms, however, we should not forget that the tiny ripples on the ocean surface do more to drive the major surface currents in the global seas than do the huge storm waves and that a variation in sea level of even a few inches, caused by fluctuations in the tide, may be of paramount importance in the passage of a trading schooner through a coral reef or in the berthing of a huge liner.

The dynamics of waves and tides are exceedingly complex and properly belong within the field of physics. Here we shall consider only the most elementary and basic factors that are involved in their actions and that help to explain their distributional aspects. Attention is focused more on the description of their patterns than on cause and effect.

15.21 SOME CHARACTERISTICS OF OCEAN WAVES. The following are some of the most significant features of ocean waves. The diagrams in Fig. 15.16 illustrate the terms used as well as some of the characteristics mentioned in the following.

1. Ocean surface waves are generated principally by wind friction, by sudden dislocations of the sea bottom, by submarine volcanic eruptions, and by tidal influences.

2. The motion of water particles in waves is confined within approximately *wave depth,* which is about one-half the *wave length.* In most waves, the water particles describe a slow circular or elliptical orbit.

3. The height, length, and speed of ocean waves caused by wind increase with the volcity, steadiness, duration, and *fetch*[3] of the wind.

4. The highest waves are found in the Antarctic Ocean. These are frequently as much as 40 or 45 feet high. Average maxima elsewhere are about 35 feet. The highest wave ever measured was 110 feet.

5. Wave lengths up to 1,000 feet have been observed.

6. Wave velocity may be as much as 1½ times wind velocity.

7. Waves tend to break or overturn when the included angle between the windward and leeward sides becomes less than 120°. Oversteepening, followed by breaking, is caused, first, by continued wind friction on the windward side, and second, by suction at the crest, downward pressure on the trough by eddying, and finally, by bottom friction in shallow water.

8. Wave damage and erosion are caused mainly by breaking waves, particularly when the overturning is sudden.

9. The pattern of waves in the open sea is highly irregular in all directions, with a wide variety of wave sizes and shapes, but regularity increases toward shallow water.

10. When waves leave a generating area of high winds, they travel for long distances, decreasing slowly in height, increasing in velocity, and becoming more regular in shape

[3] Wind *fetch* is the horizontal distance over which the wind blows.

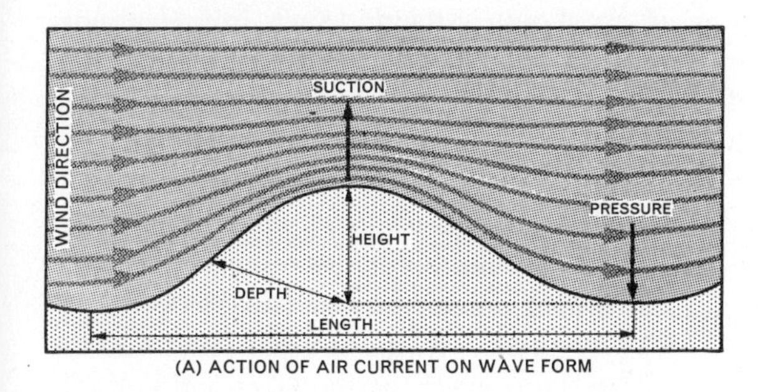

(A) ACTION OF AIR CURRENT ON WAVE FORM

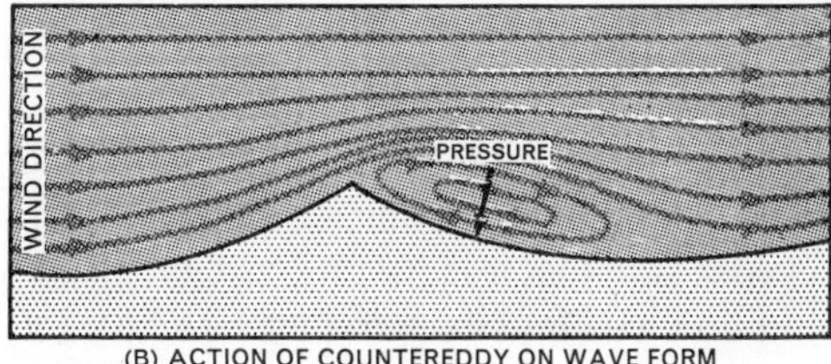

(B) ACTION OF COUNTEREDDY ON WAVE FORM

FIG. 15.16 Typical wave forms caused by the passage of wind over a water surface. Note how the upward motion of the air stream creates suction at the crest of the wave, while the downward flow on the lee side creates downward pressure on the water surface. Eddying oversteepens the lee side as shown in (B). [After Kuenen]

and period. Such waves from distant sources are known as *swells.* The wave length of swells has been known to reach two-thirds of a mile.

11. An unusual type of oscillatory wave, known as a *seiche,* is frequently encountered in bays and shallow, narrow lakes. It is somewhat similar to the waves produced in a shallow basin of water by rocking it slightly. Tides are the usual, but not exclusive, generating force.

The waves that are responsible for most of the damage along coast lines are those generated by storms and those produced by sudden dislocations of the sea bottom. The latter are termed *tsunamis.* The largest tsunamis have been generated by gigantic submarine volcanic eruptions. Krakatoa, a volcano located on a small island between Java and Sumatra, erupted in 1883 in a cataclysmic explosion. Some 2½ cubic miles of rock material was pulverized and thrown into the air. The island was split apart, and on one side, where there had previously been part of a mountainside several thousand feet high, was a stretch of ocean a thousand feet deep. The gigantic waves produced by this explosion were reported to be 100 feet high. Although these waves rapidly decreased in height as they passed outward, they were detected on the opposite side of the earth. The global encirclement took less than 36 hours. The recession of water following such gigantic destructive waves is generally as destructive as the initial impact, because nearly everything loose along adjacent coasts is swept into the sea. It has been estimated that about 35,000 people were drowned in the Krakatoa eruption. Such sudden destructive waves are sometimes called "tidal waves," but the term is inappropriate, since tides have little to do with them.

The damage to seacoasts caused by severe windstorms often is more the result of a rise in sea level than of the large waves themselves. The piling up of water along coasts undergoing severe storms is partially caused by wind friction but also by abnormally low atmospheric pressure. An increase in sea level of only 2 or 3 feet may prove disastrous along gently sloping shore lines if it is accompanied by large incoming storm waves. A good illustration of this effect is afforded by the disastrous floods that occasionally occur along the flanks of the English Channel when severe storms coincide with unusual tidal maxima. A large amount of dike construction work is being done by both the

Dutch and the English to wall off low-lying coastal areas from the sea (see Fig. 15.17). Water levels along the northern coast of Friesland have been known to rise as much as 18 feet. Along low coasts such as this, storm-wave surges at high water levels may cause enormous damage. Salt-water inundation of valuable agricultural land usually requires years of reclamation work.

15.22 DISTRIBUTIONAL ASPECTS OF LARGE WAVES. The incidence of large waves varies considerably throughout the ocean areas of the world. The most consistently stormy ocean area in the world, and the area that has the highest average waves, is the great band of water known as the "Roaring Forties," which encircles the globe in the southern hemisphere roughly between lat 40 and 60° S. Waves are consistently high here because there are no continental masses to break the fetch of the wind, because many severe cyclonic storms ripple along the boundary between antarctic and maritime Pacific air, and also because there are few islands upon which to dissipate wave energy. Regular swells from this stormy sector produce almost continuous high surf on exposed south-facing coast lines in the southern hemisphere. The high surf along the southern side of the Indonesian arc and the Guinea coast of Africa is illustrative.

Another stormy ocean area with high waves is the North Atlantic, but here the high waves are generated mainly during the winter and are associated with the cyclonic disturbances moving eastward from Newfoundland to northern Scotland. Surf is particularly heavy at this season along the entire northwestern coast of Europe, because the fetch is greatest in this direction.

Hurricanes and typhoons bring occasional high surf and high water to the eastern coasts of continents between lat 15 and 40°, except in the South Atlantic. Such storms usually reach a seasonal maximum in the autumn. Islands and continental coast lines exposed to long fetches of trade winds in the subtropics are also likely to have steady, moderately high surf.

The distribution of the tsunamis, the sudden waves caused by crustal dislocations, is closely related to the unstable parts of the ocean floor, where earthquakes and volcanic eruptions take place. For this reason, they occur most frequently along the margins of the Pacific Ocean, although they are not unknown in parts of the Atlantic and Indian Oceans.

15.23 TIDES. The rhythmic changes in sea level, termed the tides, form one of the most interesting of all the ocean phenomena. The flooding and ebbing of ocean waters along coast lines have long attracted man's attention and have been important in the lives of coastal dwellers in many ways—from the creation of tidal flats that have made shellfish easily obtainable since early times to the berthing of large ocean liners in modern ports. The periodicity of tides, though relatively simple in some coastal areas, is exceedingly complex in others, and accurate predictions of tidal occurrences had to await the accumulation of records obtained from tidal gauging stations throughout the world over a period of many years.

The most important cause of tides is the gravitational attraction of the moon. The point on the earth surface nearest the moon experiences the greatest gravitational pull, and at this point the attraction of the moon works against that of the earth itself. Theoretically, a person standing at this point weighs slightly less than he would if the moon were not present. The lunar gravitational pull, however, is extremely small, amounting to only about a nine-millionth that of the earth, owing to the smaller mass of the moon and to its distance from the earth (approximately 240,000 miles). As Kuenen has noted, a man's weight would vary only by the equivalent of one drop of perspiration. Nevertheless, despite its relative weakness, the lunar attraction has an appreciable effect on the large mass of the earth and its ocean waters, and it creates a distinct bulge in both. The ocean waters are more susceptible to warping than the solid crust of the earth, because, being fluid, they yield more easily to displacement. Careful measurements, however, indicate that the lunar pull affects the solid crust as well, and tidal bulges ranging from 9 to 12 inches have been observed in the interior of continents.

The tidal bulge on the earth at the point nearest the moon is matched by another at the antipode, or the point on the earth farthest from the moon (see Fig. 15.18). This opposite bulge is due to the comparatively low lunar gravitational force acting at this greater distance (greater by approximately 8,000 miles). Every particle of material in or on the earth is warped in position slightly in the direction of the moon's gravitational attraction. The amount of warping decreases with increased distance from the moon. The crust of the antipodal position, therefore, lags behind the rest of the earth in tidal warping, and the result is an apparent bulge. Actually, it is not a matter of the antipodal bulge being pulled out from the earth but of the earth being pulled away from the bulge.

In summary, the ocean waters at the point nearest the moon form a tidal bulge because they experience the greatest lunar gravitational attraction. At the antipode, another tidal bulge occurs because the moon is farthest away at this point and the lunar attraction is weakest. The zone midway between the two bulges, the intermediate position between the gravitational deformation on one side of the earth and the apparent bulging resulting from inertia (resistance to change in motion) on the other, is marked by a trough of low sea level, or low tide. This trough would encircle the globe if the oceans were continuous.

DIURNAL TIDES. As the earth rotates on its axis, every point on the earth surface is nearest the two bulges twice each day. This produces two high tides and two low tides every 24 hours, or a change in tide approximately every 6 hours. If the moon's orbit around the earth were exactly in the equatorial plane of the earth, there would be no difference in the range of *daily tides* at any one place (disregarding the effects of shoreline configuration, etc.). The moon's orbit, however, generally is oblique to the earth's

FIG. 15.17 System of groynes and sea wall used to stabilize the coast of southern England against marine erosion. This view is near Dymchurch, Kent. [British Crown Copyright]

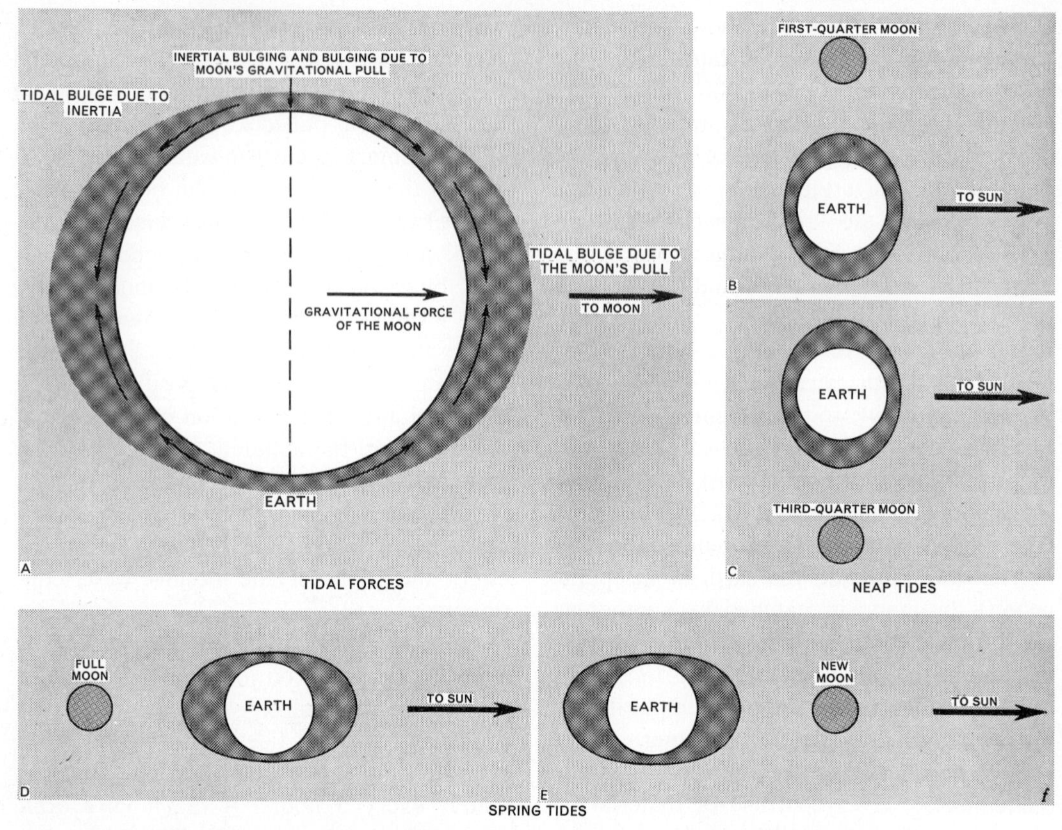

FIG. 15.18 Tidal forces. The influence of the moon alone is indicated in A. In B and C, the sun and the moon are pulling at right angles to each other, hence the low neap tides. The higher spring tides occur at new or full moon, when the pull of the sun parallels that of the moon.

equatorial plane, and this obliquity changes slightly; hence points on the earth surface vary in their nearness to the respective tidal bulges, and therefore the heights of the two daily high tides (see Fig. 15.19) also vary. Sometimes, and in some places, one daily high tide may be so much stronger than the other that there appears to be only a single daily high tide.

The time of occurrence of daily tides changes each day, owing to the moon's motion in its orbit around the earth. Because the moon rises approximately 45 minutes later each day, each of the two daily high tides occurs about 20 minutes later than the corresponding high tide of the previous day.

FORTNIGHTLY TIDES. A noticeable variation in the range between the daily high and low tides takes place according to the phases of the moon. The highest range occurs during the full- and new-moon phases. The tides during these two phases are known as *spring tides,* an unfortunate choice of terms, because such tides have no relationship to the spring season. The lowest fortnightly tidal range (or the difference between high and low tide) occurs during the first and third quarter-phases. The tides during these low-range periods are known as *neap tides* (neap = scanty).

The cause for these fortnightly changes in the range between high and low tide is the sun's gravitational attraction. Although the sun is many thousand times larger than the moon and the earth combined, it also lies some 400 times farther away than the moon; consequently its gravitational pull is only about one-fifth that of the moon. The effect of the sun is most noticeable in comparing the tidal range of periods when the sun and moon are "pulling" together (as in the full- and new-moon phases), with the tidal range when the two are pulling at right angles to each other (as in the quarter-phases). The solar influence is diagrammed in Fig. 15.18. A slight variation in spring and neap tides also can be noted, depending on the relationship between the plane of the moon's orbit and that of the earth's ecliptic. The highest spring tides occur during solar and lunar eclipses, when the earth, sun, and moon are exactly in line.

EFFECTS OF SHORE-LINE CONFIGURATION ON TIDES. In their daily journey around the earth, the tidal bulges undergo many changes that are brought about by the shape and configuration of coast lines. An incoming tidal bulge may be channeled and concentrated by widemouthed and tapering estuaries that open directly toward it. The Bay of Fundy, for example, has spring tides that range up to 50 feet (see Fig. 15.20). In such areas, where there is rapid shoaling near the mouth of an estuary, the incoming tide may move up the estuary and develop a steep wavefront, known as a *tidal bore*. The most famous are those in the Bay of Fundy, Hangchow Bay in China, and the lower Amazon River. In Hangchow Bay, the bore may be as much as 20 feet high and may proceed up the estuary at a speed of as much as 12 miles per hour. Marco Polo called attention to this unique phenomenon. *Tidal currents,* resulting from the channeling of tides, can be hazardous to navigation in the vicinity of islands or narrow straits. The junction of tidal currents from

FIG. 15.19 Influence of the angle of the moon's ecliptic on the periodicity of tides. In (A) the moon's ecliptic and the earth equatorial plane are in the same plane, and the daily tidal period everywhere follows two high tides and two low tides, each 6 hours apart. More frequently, however, the moon's ecliptic, as in B, is inclined somewhat to the earth equatorial plane, thus producing irregular tidal periods that vary with latitude. Note the similarity between this and the effect of the declination of the earth axis on the length of day and night (see Fig. 2.5).

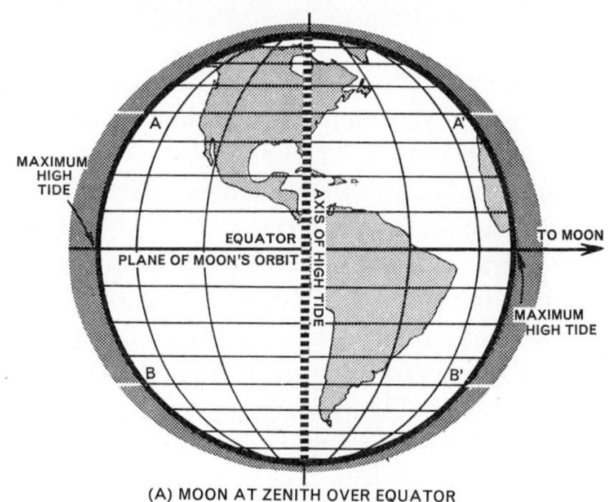

(A) MOON AT ZENITH OVER EQUATOR

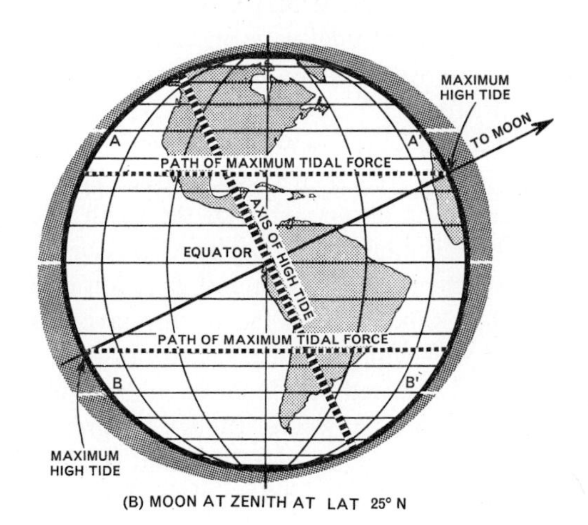

(B) MOON AT ZENITH AT LAT 25° N

FIG. 15.20 Removing fish from nets at low tide in the Bay of Fundy. The high tidal ranges in the area create many problems, but perhaps none as unusual as this. [National Film Board of Canada]

opposite directions sometimes produces areas of especially turbulent water known as *rip tides* or *tidal falls*. The navigational charts of waters in the vicinity of many Pacific islands note such areas as hazards.

Tides sometimes reflect from shore lines, producing a complex pattern of "echo" tides. The exposure, or angle, of the coast line is reflected in variations in tidal periods. Coast lines that are highly irregular, such as in the Indonesian archipelago, may have tidal patterns that differ widely in both time of occurrence and range within short distances. The complexity of tidal patterns caused by shoreline configuration is illustrated by the tidal chart for the North Sea in Fig. 15.21.

Several other factors influence tidal patterns to a greater or lesser degree. These include the Coriolis effect of the earth's rotation, variations in atmospheric pressure, and the changeable strength and direction of prevailing winds. Of all the factors involved in tidal behavior, the easiest to predict are those associated with lunar or solar positions. These alone, however, though of great importance, may be overshadowed locally by conditions of site and weather. There is no substitute for accurate tidal observations, accumulated over many years.

The geography of life in the sea

The total volume of life in the sea is much greater than that on the continents, partly because of the greater area involved and also because life forms can be spread throughout the entire volume of the oceans, without being restricted to positions on or near the bottom. The greatest advantage of the ocean environment to both plant and animal life, however, is the general uniformity of sea water as a nutrient solution. Whereas the rocks, soils, and soil solutions of the terrestrial surfaces vary widely in chemical composition, nearly all the elements needed in organic cell synthesis are available everywhere in the sea. This does not mean that sea water is a perfect nutrient solution. If it were, organic life would crowd the ocean space. Limitations to organic expansion are caused mainly by local shortages of a relatively few critical chemical materials, and variations in the quantities of these substances are the major factor in determining regional differences in the characteristics and abundance of sea life. The most important of such substances are oxygen, carbon dioxide, phosphates, and various nitrogenous compounds. Other factors limiting organic development include light availability (mainly for plants), salinity, temperature, and the presence of toxic materials, such as hydrogen sulfide.

Since sea water constitutes a generally suitable environment for cell growth and maintenance, it supports large quantities of tiny, relatively simple, and unprotected organisms. Life probably began in the sea and was conditioned in its evolution by the sea environment. It is interesting to note at this point that the solutes present in the body fluids of all animals, including human blood, contain roughly the same proportions of mineral salts as are found in sea water, although, of course, much more diluted. We may well owe the saltiness of our tears to the sea-water environment where the mysterious beginnings of life on earth may have occurred. With the exception of fish, marine animals require little energy to maintain a proper chemical concentration within their cells and body fluids.

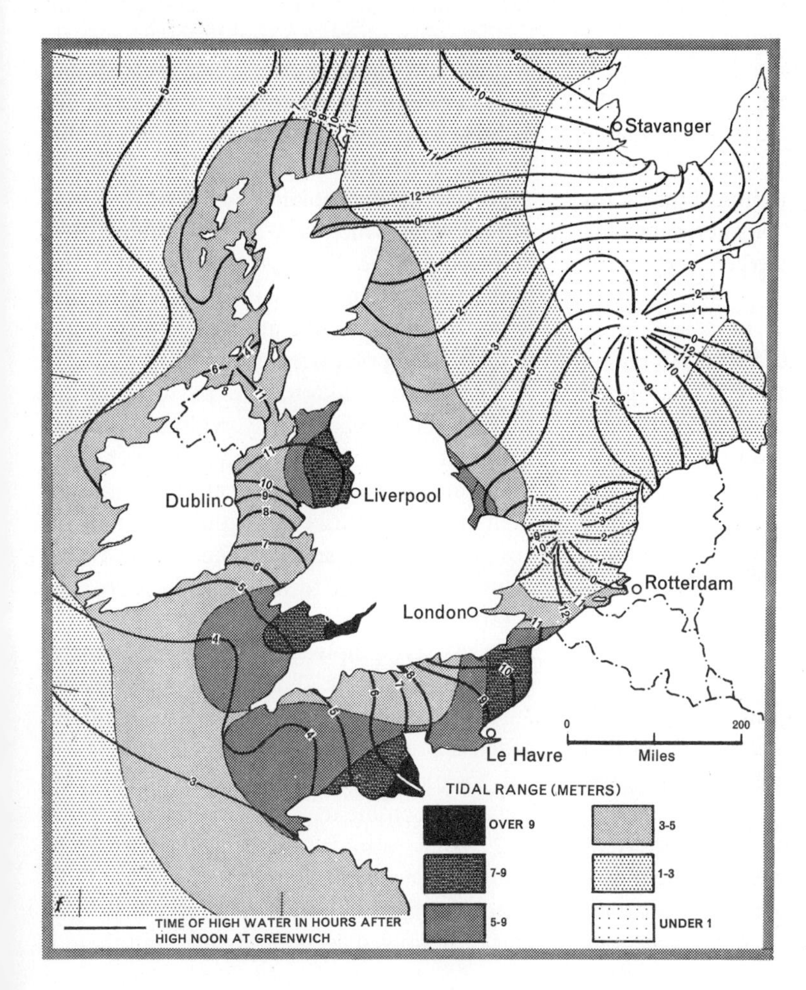

FIG. 15.21 Detail of tides in the North Sea. [After Chapin]

The microorganisms, particularly the single-celled plant forms, are the basis on which most of the animal life in the sea depends. They constitute the "pastures" on which the animal life feeds, either directly or indirectly. The distribution of most organic life in the sea, therefore, is closely concerned with factors favoring or hindering the availability of the microplant world. Since such microplants require both sunlight and carbon dioxide for photosynthesis in forming their carbohydrates (the storehouse of energy), these tiny plants do not thrive in the black depths of the sea. Life exists in these depths, however, and includes fish and bottom scavengers that feed on one another or on the slow rain of dead organisms that drift downward from the upper layers of the ocean. Food for animals is thus available throughout nearly all of the sea, but in varying amounts. The major limiting factors for sea animals are the supply of microplant life and the availability of oxygen, which is needed for respiration.

15.24 MICROPLANT LIFE IN THE SEA. The boundary between microplant life and microanimal life is broad, and several of the algae (plants) and protozoa (animal), both of which are tiny single-celled organisms, have debatable positions in either the plant or animal kingdom. The most common representatives of these tiny organisms are the floating or drifting types. Since they comprise the basic food on which most other sea life depends, it is appropriate to learn more of their forms and ecology. Collectively, the floating microplants are termed *phytoplankton.* The nonfloating plant types include various bacteria.

Diatoms are the most abundant variety of phytoplankton. These are microscopic algae, comprising hundreds of varieties, shapes, and forms. They often bear tiny, siliceous (glassy) protective cases, especially in cold water. They can be found throughout the ocean surface layers but thrive best in cold, polar waters. Since the tiny protective glass cases are relatively insoluble, they accumulate on the sea bottom as a fine siliceous mud, termed *diatomaceous ooze.* This material is especially abundant in the far northern and the far southern Pacific Ocean, down to depths of 12,000 feet. Another group of tiny plants (or protozoa) consists of the *dinoflagellates,* free swimmers that move about by waving a flagellum—a whiplike appendage from which they derive their name. They prefer warmer waters than do the diatoms and sometimes multiply so rapidly as to give the water a rusty appearance. Their shells, if any, are composed of cellulose, hence decompose rapidly following death. For this reason they do not form bottom deposits. A group of even smaller microplants includes the *coccolithophores,* which are mainly yellowish in color and have limy protective plates that make up bottom oozes in areas where lime is not dissolved. They are widely distributed in all but the polar oceans.

The phytoplankton, the pastures of the sea, are contained mostly within the upper 250 feet or so of the ocean. They have a phenomenal capacity for multiplying, and their numbers are close to the limit that the environment can support. The highest concentrations appear to be found in four characteristic locations:

1. Areas of upwelling water. In areas of upwelling water, an abundant supply of nutrients is brought to the surface and maintains a dense population of phytoplankton. Typical locations are off the subtropical west coasts of continents.

2. High latitudes. Especially during the summer season, when the days are long, the waters of high latitudes contain a high content of dissolved carbon dioxide, and there is

an abundance of nutrients that were brought up from below by the water overturning during winter.

3. Coastal waters. Nutrients are added to coastal waters by continental streams, and waves and currents keep the water agitated and aerated.

4. Convergences of cold and warm water. The mixing of warm water with cold appears to stimulate the reproductive rate of the phytoplankton.

The small plant forms are least abundant in the blue waters of the subtropical gyres, which are characterized by high salinity, few nutrients, and a low gas content. Although the microlife of polar waters is extremely abundant during the summer months, this population falls off rapidly in winter, owing to the small amount of sunlight for photosynthesis and also to the covering of pack ice, which checks absorption of gases and further checks light availability.

The major nonfloating microscopic plant forms include bacteria, which are scattered throughout the sea but which are concentrated mainly in the bottom muds, where they decompose the waste organic debris collected there from above. Little is known of these miniature "garbage disposal" plants, but it is believed that they play an important role both in providing food for tiny animals and in maintaining the organic cycle, by releasing phosphatic and nitrogenous nutrients in the organic decay process and making them available once more for plant use. In this respect they are similar to the soil bacteria of terrestrial environments. The waters of the bottom provide the bacteria with the oxygen necessary for the oxidation, or decay, of organic material. The bacteria may also be involved in some way in the formation of hydrocarbons. Certain types can extract oxygen from chemical compounds, instead of obtaining it directly from sea water, and these are responsible for the generation of ammonia and hydrogen sulfide gas in the stagnant basins of some seas.

15.25 MICROANIMAL LIFE (ZOOPLANKTON) IN THE SEA.

The next step upward in the hierarchy of organism size consists of the microanimals that are collectively termed *zooplankton.* This group comprises many varieties and sizes, from microscopic forms to types measuring ¼ to ½ inch in diameter. The zooplankton are much larger proportionately, however, than most of the phytoplankton upon which they feed. A finely meshed net will usually collect many of them. The total aggregate volume of each zooplankton variety is inversely related to size, as is true of nearly all organic life in the sea. This phenomenon has been termed the *size pyramid,* in which the tiny organisms form the broad base, both in terms of numbers and in aggregate volume, and the relatively rare large forms lie at the apex.

The individual forms that comprise the zooplankton vary not only in size but also in structure, ranging all the way from tiny protozoa, or single-celled animals, to small representatives of the higher orders of the animal kingdom, including worms, mollusks, and shrimplike crustacea. Three great groups of animals comprise the bulk of the zooplankton: the Radiolaria, the Foraminifera, and the Copepoda. The first two are protozoa, or single-celled animals. The Radiolaria are microscopic bits of protoplasm that are similar to the diatoms in that they develop a protective outer shell of silica. Tiny openings perforate the siliceous coverings and form exquisite patterns (see Fig. 15.22). These openings enable protoplasm "arms" to protrude in search of nutrients and oxygen. The Foraminifera are similar, except that their shells are made of calcium carbonate instead

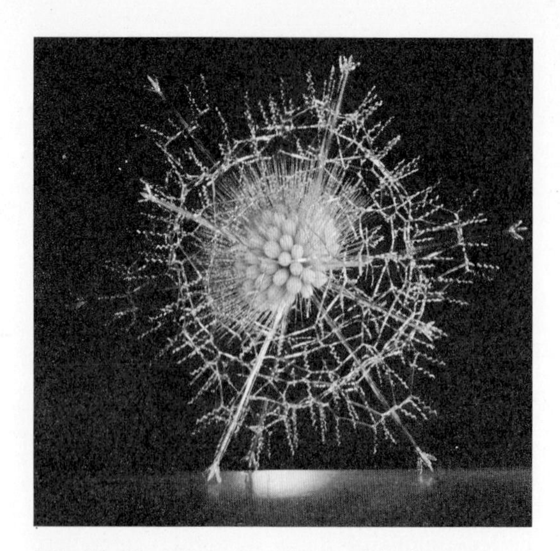

FIG. 15.22 Photo of a glass model of a type of Radiolaria. This differs from the Globigerina in being much smaller, and in having an exquisite, lacy skeleton composed of silica instead of lime. Radiolaria are especially abundant in the waters of high latitudes. [American Museum of Natural History]

FIG. 15.23 Photo of a glass model of Globigerina, a variety of marine protozoa. The needlelike forms represent the pseudopodia, or protuberences, of protoplasm, emerging from openings in the calcareous "shell." These tiny shells, like microscopic golf balls, form much of the bottom sediments in some parts of the ocean. [American Museum of Natural History]

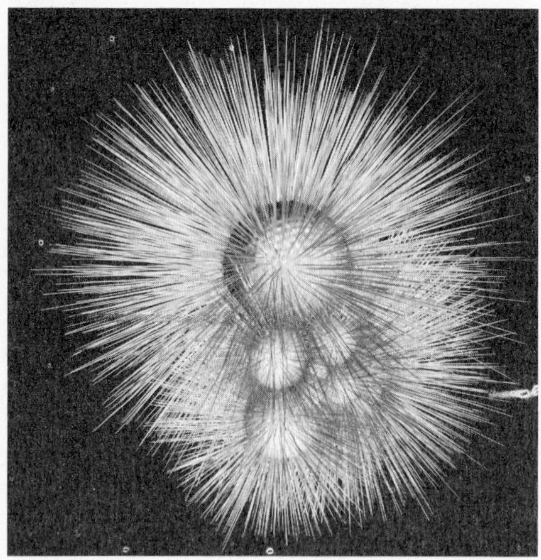

of silica (see Fig. 15.23). They are usually more abundant than the Radiolaria, and their lime coverings form bottom sediments over broad areas, especially in the eastern Atlantic, southern Pacific, and Indian Oceans. Some chalks of continental areas were once foraminiferal oozes. The Copepoda are by far the most dominant of the zooplankton that are large enough to be seen without a microscope. They are generally from 1 to 4 millimeters long and have an oval-shaped body, protected by a segmented body case, and a taillike appendage. They have a wide range of habitats, from shallows to ocean deeps, and have a wide diversity of form.

The densest populations of zooplankton favor the same areas as the phytoplankton. They are not, however, confined to surface layers, and deep-dwelling forms are found that apparently feed on bottom bacteria or on the dead material that sifts down from above. Also, unlike most of the phytoplankton, many of the zooplankton forms have means of locomotion, hence can shift position independently of currents and drifts. A vertical shifting of zooplankton layers has been observed, and there are complex variations in the density of these layers. Such layers tend to move toward the surface during the night and to descend during the day. These layers puzzled the operators of echo-sounding devices for a while during World War II, because they produced distinct echoes when they intercepted the projected sound impulses. The zooplankton assemblages are highly sensitive to changing environmental conditions, and their distribution patterns are continually being altered.

The zooplankton are the major food supply for most of the larger animals in the sea, although there are many predators that feed on other large animals. Even some of the largest whales depend on these tiny animals to satisfy their enormous appetites; as they dash through zooplankton-rich waters with mouths agape, they collect bushels of small animals in the fine straining apparatus that lines their jaws.

15.26 THE MACROPLANT LIFE IN THE SEA. The larger plant forms in the sea never developed the complexity of form and structure that characterizes the larger members of the terrestrial plant world. They did not have to, for life is easy for marine plants, at least with respect to obtaining food, and the environment rarely is subject to wide and sudden extremes. In the shallow waters where light, carbon dioxide, oxygen, and nutrients are all available, plants can grow to large sizes without developing any specialized functions other than an anchorage on the bottom and the flexibility to withstand movements of currents and storm waves. For this reason, the larger plants belong almost exclusively to the algae, the lowest and simplest of the plant groups.

Brown algae are the most abundant of the larger plant forms. *Kelp* is one of the best-known representatives. The long, waving, greenish-brown stalks of kelp may be as much as 100 feet long. *Rockweed* is another brown alga that is usually found near shore. The only brown alga of the open sea is the sargasso weed, a highly branching plant marked by small air bladders that are attached to the stems and enable the plant to float (see Fig. 15.24). It is found attached to rocks in the shallow waters of tropical seas, and it is believed that most of the masses of sargasso weed in the central Atlantic originated in such shallow tropical waters. Once adrift, *Sargassum* apparently is able to thrive and multiply. Except for this unusual floating, shifting weed, the brown algae are restricted to shallow water. Like most other algae, they are most abundant where a constant supply of nutrients is made

FIG. 15.24 Sargasso weed from the Gulf Stream. The globules, about 1/4 inch in diameter and resembling berries, are air bladders that enable the plant to float. [Victor Slocum; American Geological Society]

available. Huge forests of kelp are found adjacent to areas of upwelling water, such as off the coast of Southern California.

The red algae form the other major group of seaweeds. They grow on the ocean bottom in deeper waters of the continental shelf than do the brown algae. Some varieties have the ability to synthesize calcium carbonate from sea water. These calcareous algae play an important role in maintaining a balance between acidity and alkalinity in coastal waters. Great fossil masses of this alga form some of the limestones in the marine sedimentary rocks of continental interiors.

Another sea plant is eel grass (*Zostara*), which is confined to relatively shallow waters of the continental shelf. It is important because it constitutes a food supply for fish.

15.27 THE MACROANIMAL LIFE IN THE SEA. The animal life in the sea that is larger than the zooplankton exhibits a great complexity of form and structure, unlike the large plant types. The variety of habitats and the active competition for survival have resulted in a wide range of forms and habits. The larger marine animals are found nearly everywhere, except for a few stagnant basins. Some, like the fishes, are free swimmers with a wide range of mobility. Others, like the crinoids (sea lilies), sea anemones, and adult corals, are permanently attached to the bottom and wait for food to come to them. Other bottom dwellers, such as starfish and mollusks, have a restricted mobility and slowly seek their food by crawling on the sea floor. The various mechanisms for defense and attack are amazingly varied. Space does not permit even rough generalizations of this complex fauna, and the reader is referred to standard texts on marine biology for such information.

The distribution of the macroanimal types is almost as varied as the types themselves. Each type of fish and each sea animal has its preferred environment, and the zoogeography of the sea is almost as complex as that of the continents. The densest fish and shellfish populations, however, are found wherever the basic microlife is most abundant. These include the waters of most continental-shelf zones, the west coast areas of upwelling water, the mixing areas of cold and warm water, and the summer "pastures" of high-latitude seas.

The sea realm and its resources

The sea is a bountiful storehouse of riches for those who understand it and can take advantage of its largesse. Its food potential has scarcely been touched, although, at the same time, the stocks of certain types of food fish have been seriously depleted over wide areas. We have not yet found a way of utilizing zooplankton directly as food, and it is unlikely that it ever can be made appetizing without much processing, because of its slimy consistency and "fishy" taste. It seems reasonable to expect, however, that some sea pastures, like the terrestrial grasslands, can be made to yield far more under cultivation than they ever do in their natural state. Experimentation in sea cultivation has already begun, and narrow sea inlets in both Scotland and Norway have been isolated and artificially treated with nutrients to stimulate the growth of phytoplankton, zooplankton, and the larger fauna. The reaction has been phenomenal. Such efforts, however, are still in the experimental stage, and private capital is reluctant to invest in sea farming, except for such highly priced items as pearls, oysters, and clams. Whatever man does along this line will always be insignificant, however, in comparison to the processes that go on within the vastness of the open sea.

In addition to its value as a source of food, the sea storehouse reveals other startling possibilities. The inorganic constituents of sea water form a virtually inexhaustible supply of many chemical elements. Salt has been taken from it for centuries, and magnesium metal and calcium chloride are being extracted in increasing amounts. When the problems of volume control and mass production can be solved and when the metallic ores of mines begin to run short, this aspect of marine resources will increase in importance.

The sea has long been investigated as a source of inanimate energy. Attempts have been made to harness the energy of tides, but thus far only on a relatively small scale. The wide temperature differential in tropical seas between water at the surface and at depths of a few thousand feet indicates that heat pumps could be developed to generate electric power, and the French have been carrying on experiments along this line in the Gulf of Guinea. Undoubtedly also, large reserves of petroleum and natural gas still remain to be discovered in many parts of the continental shelf. All these energy sources are as yet of only potential significance, and their development requires new techniques, new tools, and huge outlays of capital.

The potential of the sea to supply fresh water where this vital material is in short supply has already been discussed (see Chapter 14). As an immediate source of material resources, however, the ocean is most important in supplying marine food for human beings.

Perspective

The realm of the sea is distinctly different from that of the continents, and its apparent homogeneity is deceiving. Those who sail the seas are prone to ignore the subtleties below the surface and to emphasize the comparative uniformity at their own scale of observation. The ancients regarded ocean water as the universal fluid that surrounded the home of man, a barrier placed there by the gods to keep man in his proper place and to separate him from the divinities. It has been a relatively short time since the breadth of the ocean was first spanned and only a few decades since its mysteries began to unfold. We know now that the sea is a far more hospitable environment for plants and animals than was previously believed and that the variety of natural landscapes on land can be matched by those in the sea. The unique regional landforms of the ocean produce a complex pattern of giant mountain ranges, deep trenches, numerous isolated pinnacles, long valleys, canyons, basins, and plains. The circulation of the atmosphere has its counterpart in the movement of ocean waters (although the latter is less variable), which, like the air, transport heat from the surplus equatorial areas to the deficient high latitudes. The broad, average patterns of fluid motion, density, and temperature, as well as the short-term fluctuations, can also be likened to certain weather phenomena on land. In the sea, as in the atmosphere, "weather" can be observed best along the boundaries between opposing currents, the sea convergences. The sea and air climates are unquestionably linked, and important changes in one produce sympathetic alterations in the other.

FIG. 15.25 A new source of income from the sea. Recreational fishing for salmon is a major regional industry in the Pacific Northwest. This is a salmon that did not get away. The scene shown here is at Finlayson Arm, Vancouver Island, B.C. [Government of British Columbia]

Vegetation is also present in the sea, in volumes unmatched on land, and those who wish to spend hours observing marine plant life under a microscope will discover a wonderful variety of form, despite the relative simplicity of function. The plant world of the sea, like that of the land, has its deserts and its prolific jungles and supports a large and varied fauna, arranged in a complex spectrum of three-dimensional regional differences. The surface materials of the sea bottom, although quite unlike terrestrial soils in origin, form, and function, likewise show distinct geographic patterns, reflective of the adjacent topography, the life of the area, and the depositional processes at work.

Man is just beginning to utilize the mineral, energy, and food resources in the vast realm of the sea, and as his requirements increase, he undoubtedly will pay more attention to this part of his environment, especially as the supplies of terrestrial resources become depleted. He has already begun to have an effect on the ecology of marine life, particularly with respect to the selected withdrawal of chosen foods from the bottom zone of the continental shelf and the reduction in number of the marine animal giants—the whale, the seal, and the sea otter. It is heartening to note, however, that some of the best examples of international cooperation have been agreements among nations to curb the unbridled exploitation of these and other marine organisms.

The geography of the sea, which was long considered a purely academic study, is now becoming a matter of concern in the world of everyday economics. Tribute is due the many pioneering oceanographers for their contributions to the understanding of areal patterns and marine dynamics within the realm of the sea. Enlarged public support for oceanographic research is needed to resolve the many questions whose answers are still hidden beneath the waves.

STUDY QUESTIONS

CHAPTER 1

1. Define geography. How does physical geography fit into the general objectives of geography?
2. Explain the statement that geography is the science of space, whereas history is the science of time. Develop this analogy.
3. Compare and contrast the objectives of physical geography with those of the other earth sciences.
4. What are the principal elements in the natural environment of man? Why is it inappropriate to eliminate the human factor in purely physical geographic studies?
5. Suppose you were asked to make a map of 1 square mile of forest. What factors would you consider in making such a map?
6. What are the four principles of natural distributions? Explain and give examples to illustrate each.
7. What is meant by the "scaled orderliness" of nature?

CHAPTER 2

1. Explain why the linear value of a degree of latitude is almost exactly twice that of a degree of longitude at lat 60° N.
2. Can a careful measurement of the angle of elevation of Polaris ever enable one to obtain a true latitudinal position without adding or subtracting an amount equal to all or part of its apparent orbital diameter? Explain.
3. On the summer solstice (June 21), at noon, sun time, an observer measures the sun to be exactly 67°15′45″ above the northern horizon, and he also notes that his London chronometer reads 9:15 A.M. What is his latitude and longitude?
4. As the vertical "rays" of the sun migrate back and forth between the Tropic of Cancer and the Tropic of Capricorn during the course of a year, does this progression take place at a uniform rate? Explain. Also explain why the solstices and equinoxes do not occur on exactly the same date every year.
5. Explain the use of the military grid in locating points on a map. Give an example of interpolation using such a grid.
6. How large is a piece of property that carries the following designation: N½/SW¼/NW¼ of Sec. 23, T46N—R24W?
7. In using the map of isogonic lines shown in Fig. 2.14, in what direction will a compass needle point at New York City? At Seattle, Washington? At Charleston, South Carolina? Why do such maps usually carry a date?
8. In airplane navigation, why is it almost impossible to follow the shortest possible course between two points? What do these considerations require of the navigator?

9. Is the boundary between oceans and continents a line or a zone? What is *mean sea level,* and how is it determined?
10. What procedure would you follow if given an assignment to prepare a map showing the distribution of elk in Yellowstone National Park? Describe both field and cartographic procedures.
11. If a map scale is 1:1,000,000, approximately how many miles are there to the inch? Why are such map ratios always incorrect to a certain degree with respect to linear scale measurements?
12. Using Table 2.1, select an appropriate projection for each of the following uses:
    a. A map that will indicate the towns and cities covered by airline distance zones from a central point
    b. A weather map of the United States
    c. A map showing the world distribution of forest land
    d. A navigational map from which compass bearings may be plotted from one point to another
    e. An atlas map of Africa
    f. A map of a small city
    g. A world map of temperatures (area not important)
    h. A pictorial representation of the earth for use with a news story
    i. A base for large-scale topographic mapping

CHAPTER 3

1. Distinguish among structure, process, and stage in the development of landform characteristics, and give an example of each.
2. Use the characteristics of stream valleys to illustrate the statement that perfect symmetry rarely is found in landform shapes. Explain. Can you think of any exceptions?
3. Explain why the large African rivers have longitudinal profiles that differ from those of most streams.
4. Why are there so few areas in the world that are typical of old age in the erosion cycle of streams in humid regions? Is there any evidence that such areas existed in previous geologic time?
5. Outline the major characteristics of areas in youth, maturity, and old age in a humid area dominated by stream erosion.
6. Give some reasons why typical karst topography is not found in all areas underlain by limestone. Why have karst areas so few surface streams? Why do military commanders fear offensive operations in areas of karst topography?
7. Explain why roads, settlements, and major surface features often have crescentic areal patterns on the flood plains of large rivers.
8. How and why do talus slopes in dry areas differ from those in humid regions?
9. Why are flash floods a regional hazard in arid regions?
10. What are some of the terrain obstacles to cross-country automotive travel in the Sahara?
11. Give some reasons why irrigated alluvial fans frequently have a zonal distribution of land-use patterns.
12. What hindrances to cultivation, apart from the shortage of water, are likely to to be found in desert basins?
13. Why are there so many offshore barrier-beach islands along the east coast of the United States and so few along the west coast?
14. Describe a typical atoll. Where are atolls found? Why?

15. Examine the map of continental glaciation and explain the major irregularities in the border of the glaciated area in the northern hemisphere.
16. What factors explain the wide variety of soils in glaciated areas?
17. Contrast the dominant processes of rock weathering in polar areas with those in the humid tropics.
18. Explain why several large areas of basaltic lavas are found in the vicinity of the great rift valleys or grabens in eastern Africa.

CHAPTER 4

1. Define the following: local relief, mountains, hills, and plains.
2. Why are coast lines considered to be poor boundaries between continents and ocean basins?
3. What consistencies are exhibited in the pattern of continents and ocean basins?
4. Describe the global distribution of mountains in less than twenty-five words.
5. Explain the similar global distribution of earthquakes, volcanoes, and high mountain cordilleras.
6. Give several advantages and disadvantages of mountain lands for human settlement.
7. Explain the statement that the productive rewards of mountain lands rarely remain within such regions. Illustrate.
8. Explain why all densely populated areas are located on plains but not all plains are densely populated. Explain the apparently paradoxical fact that Japan is a densely populated, mountainous country.
9. Present a short, generalized summary of the global distribution of plains. What exceptions to your generalizations can you find?
10. Study a topographic map of a section of high plains. What features illustrated on the map indicate disadvantages for human settlement?
11. Give some reasons why hill areas often are problem areas with respect to human settlement and living standards.
12. Identify the principal shield areas in the world.
13. Contrast the appearance of the hill countries of northern Ontario, West Virginia, southern China, central Pennsylvania, and eastern Brazil. Explain the characteristic terrain in each.

CHAPTER 5

1. What are the elements of surface configuration?
2. What is the difference between area slope and local relief? Give an example to illustrate that an area may have a large amount of area slope, yet only moderate local relief.
3. Give specific examples to show how each of the following might influence the effect of slope on transportation:
   a. Tariffs
   b. Available capital
   c. Political decisions
   d. Climate
   e. Standards of living
4. How do curves and grades influence the capacity of highways for traffic volume?
5. Why does most of the worst damage resulting from soil erosion take place in areas of low-to-moderate slope rather than in areas of steep slope?
6. Give two methods of finding the elevation of a particular site.
7. Why should one check his automobile radiator before entering a mountainous region?

8. Give several reasons for the existence of swamps and marshes, and give illustrations of each.
9. Why are intrusive igneous rocks more coarsely crystalline than the extrusive types? Which of the two are more widely distributed over the world?
10. What kind of rocks contain most of the metallic ores? Explain.
11. What kind of rocks contain most of the fossil fuels? Explain.
12. Locate the major areas in the world that are underlain by extensive basaltic lavas. Why are such rocks desirable for agriculture in the tropics? Why are they of somewhat less value in higher latitudes?
13. Give some economic uses for each of the major rock groups. Which is the most important and why?
14. What is loess? Where is it found, and how was it formed?
15. Give several reasons why alluvial soils generally are favored for agriculture. Locate several of the largest areas of alluvial soils in the world. Locate some alluvial-soil areas that are sparsely populated. Explain.

CHAPTER 6

1. What areal differences in temperature have you observed in the vicinity of your home community? Have these local differences resulted in any observable differences in the landscape? Explain.
2. Would a square piece of metal placed exactly at an angle of 60° to the sun's radiation receive the same amount of solar energy during 1 hour of exposure on January 1 as it would on July 2? Why or why not?
3. Where would an observer see the sun in the sky at midnight at the North Pole on the June solstice? Theoretically, where would an observer at the Arctic Circle see the sun at the same moment? Why are cabbages that are grown in high latitudes so much larger than those grown elsewhere?
4. Tables 6.2 and 6.3 give data for the northern hemisphere. Would Table 6.2 be appreciably different if the data were for the southern hemisphere? Explain. What differences would you expect to find in Table 6.3 if it presented data for the southern hemisphere?
5. Explain why a cloudy day in summer is likely to be cooler than a clear day and why a cloudy night is generally warmer than a clear night.
6. Why does a clear sky have a deeper blue color near the zenith than near the horizon at midday? Why do sunsets and sunrises have so many shades of red and orange, and why are desert sunsets usually so brilliantly colored?
7. Give examples of the conditions under which solar radiation may be changed into (*a*) heat energy, (*b*) chemical energy, (*c*) electrical energy (*d*) terrestrial radiant energy.
8. What is the difference between the lapse rate and the adiabatic rate? If the air temperature at sea level is 70°, what would it be above the same locality at an elevation of 15,000 feet, assuming a normal lapse rate?
9. Give several reasons why afternoon temperatures in July are much higher in Dallas, Texas, than in Panama.
10. Assuming the specific heat of ice to be 0.5, the heat of fusion of water to be 80 calories per gram, and the vaporization of water to be 540 calories per gram, how many calories would be required to change 20 grams of ice at −20°C to water vapor at 100°C?

11. The highest mean figures for relative humidity in the world are in low latitudes, yet the highest seasonal figures at high latitudes occur in winter rather than summer. Explain this apparent paradox.
12. What roles do evaporation and precipitation play in stabilizing temperatures on the earth surface?
13. Explain why winter precipitation in mid-latitudes tends to be more frequent but less intense than summer precipitation.
14. Explain why rain in the tropics usually occurs in showers, and why these are most frequent on land in the afternoon and over oceans at night.
15. Why is hail restricted to summer periods in mid-latitudes? Why is sleet normally a warm-front type of precipitation?
16. Explain why Mediterranean Europe has dry summers and humid winters.
17. In dry areas, why are there so many years of below-average rainfall and so few years of above-average rainfall?

CHAPTER 7

1. An atmospheric pressure of 1,026 millibars is the equivalent of how many inches of mercury in a barometer?
2. Explain the process whereby an air mass that increases in temperature decreases in atmospheric pressure. Explain why the subtropics, which have some of the highest temperatures on earth, also have some of the most pronounced anticyclones.
3. Why are most deserts windier in the daytime than at night?
4. Do the zones of pressure centers shift position latitudinally more over continents than over oceans during the course of a year? Give specific evidence for your answer from the seasonal maps of pressure, and explain.
5. Why are there more cyclones and anticyclones in winter than in summer? Why does the northern hemisphere have more of them than the southern?
6. Why is the atmospheric pressure unusually low near Iceland during the winter season? Why not during the summer?
7. Why is the atmospheric pressure lower in Iran during July than it is in the Belgian Congo during the same month?
8. If one-half of the air is found below 18,000 feet, would one-fourth of it occur below 9,000 feet? Explain.
9. Why are geostrophic winds rare in the low latitudes?
10. What difference is there between the wind spirals around an oceanic anticyclone and those over a continent? Explain.
11. Why does most meridional flow of air take place near the surface of the earth?
12. How do we know that a heat sink must be located in the upper air?
13. Are the winds likely to be stronger at the summit of Mount Mayon in the Philippines or on Mount Fujiyama in Japan? Explain.
14. Examine the seasonal maps of pressure and air stream lines. Does most of the meridional flow take place over continents or over oceans? Explain.
15. Explain why trade-wind air normally has an upper-air temperature inversion. What influence does this have on the stability of the air mass?

CHAPTER 8

1. Why are most of the Koeppen temperature unit boundaries expressed in frac-

tions of a degree, such as 64.4° or 71.6°?

2. Give the two principal reasons why the *A* climates extend farther poleward along the east coasts of continents than along the west coasts.
3. Explain why the west coast of Madagascar is so much drier than the east coast.
4. What is the ITC and what role does it play in the distribution of precipitation through the year within the humid tropics?
5. In the Koeppen-Geiger system, a humid month is defined as one with at least 2.4 inches of precipitation in the *A* climates or as one with at least 1.2 inches in the *C* and *D* climates. Explain.
6. Locate Bombay, Hyderabad, and Madras on a map of India. From your knowledge of Indian monsoons, grade these in order of their total mean annual precipitation. Use a world map of average annual rainfall to check your answer.
7. A weather station has 70 per cent of its precipitation in the 6 summer months, with a mean annual total of 30 inches, and its mean annual temperature is 60°. Using the appropriate Koeppen formula, determine whether the locality has a humid, a semiarid, or an arid climate.
8. What is rainfall effectiveness, and what factors may influence it? Which of these are considered in the Koeppen definition of aridity?
9. Would a *BShs* climate be more likely to be found to the north or to the south of the Sahara Desert? Explain.
10. List some of the advantages of living in a desert oasis.
11. What is the Koeppen climate of New Orleans, Louisiana? In general position, where in Asia would one find a comparable climate? Where in South America?
12. What part of the United States has a climate roughly comparable to that of Naples, Italy?
13. If a retired British civil servant wished to emigrate to the part of Canada where the climate would be most like home, where would he find it? What difference would he observe in this same area?
14. Using climatic criteria only, which of the following cities would be your first choice for a branch sales office of a company selling room air conditioners? (*a*) San Francisco, (*b*) Tokyo, (*c*) Casablanca, (*d*) Paris.
15. Which of the following would you select if the product were a lightweight, waterproof topcoat? (*a*) Chicago, (*b*) Montreal, (*c*) Vancouver, British Columbia, (*d*) Madrid. Explain.
16. Explain why Trondhjem, Norway, at lat 63½° N, has a *C* climate, whereas Peking, China, at lat 40° N, has a *D* climate.
17. Explain why the snow line in the Rocky Mountains of Montana is higher than it is on Mount Ranier in the state of Washington.

CHAPTER 9

1. What is a plant community? In what way may a fern aid a tree beneath which it grows? How may the tree aid the fern?
2. What are the four global plant formations? Which is the most extensive?
3. What is a *plant succession?* Find evidences of one in your local area and briefly describe its stages.
4. What is a plant indicator? Find some indicators in your locality for each of the following: (*a*) Soil acidity or alka-

linity, (*b*) poor drainage, (*c*) inadequate soil moisture.

5. Give some specific illustrations to indicate how vegetation patterns conform to the principles of natural distributions.
6. Briefly explain the relationship between the water balance of plants and plant size.
7. List as many properties as you can that show how plants adapt to seasonal deficiencies of water.
8. What are some properties of plants that live in or on water?
9. Why are there so many more species of trees in the tropical forests than in the forests of northern Canada?
10. Why are fruits usually sweeter when grown under desert irrigation?
11. What is the difference between transpiration and respiration in plants?
12. Describe and illustrate the principal ways in which man has learned to stabilize his agricultural productivity.
13. Explain why most of the semiarid grasslands in the world have suffered progressively from overgrazing.
14. What are the principal harmful effects of fire on tropical and subtropical soils and vegetation? Explain why some authorities consider fire a major factor in delineating the boundaries of the global plant formations.

CHAPTER 10

1. What types of tropical forest have dense underbrush? Explain.
2. What are the principal handicaps to commercial lumbering in the tropical forests? What commercial products are obtained from them?
3. Describe a typical selva.
4. Why is it so difficult to find close correlations between the boundaries and climate of the deciduous scrub woodland?
5. The *Cs* and *Aw* climates both have characteristic types of scrub woodland. What principal difference is there between these two?
6. Contrast the types of vegetation that are encountered as one passes poleward out of the rainy tropics on the western side of continents with those encountered passing poleward on the eastern sides.
7. Explain why the semideciduous forest is much more extensive in Asia than in North America.
8. How do the typical trees of the selva differ in form from those of the broadleaf deciduous forest?
9. Describe the vegetation transitions encountered as one proceeds north, east, south, and west from the broadleaf deciduous forest in the central Appalachian area of the United States.
10. What genus of conifers is typically adapted to a position in a fire succession? What features do these trees have to give them this advantage?
11. What is the typical shape of taiga conifers? Explain.
12. Contrast typical lumbering operations in the Appalachians and the Cascade Mountains. Explain.
13. What is the general global location of the prairies, or humid grasslands? If you wished to see a typical prairie, where would you search in the state of Illinois?
14. What are some of the handicaps to the utilization of the tropical savannas for grazing or for agriculture?
15. Give an example of each of the major subdivisions of desert vegetation.
16. What advantages do the "cushionlike" plants have in a tundra or high-elevation environment?

17. What are lichens, and why are they usually the first plant forms to cover a bare rock surface?
18. Give several examples of the relationship between simplicity of structure and the geographic range of plants.

CHAPTER 11

1. What is a soil?
2. Why is it impossible for solid rock to remain indefinitely in this state at the outer surface of the earth?
3. How long does it take soils to form?
4. A pail filled with marbles or shotgun pellets holds exactly as much water as the same pail filled with billiard balls. Can you explain why a pail filled with clay usually holds much more water than a similar pail filled with sand?
5. Travelers have reported large areas of light-pink soils in parts of the Amazon Basin. What would be the most logical explanation for such a color?
6. What are colloids? What are the two major groups of colloids in soils, and what functions do they perform?
7. What is meant by the regenerative cycle of fertility in the humid tropics?
8. Give some reasons why the soils of central Illinois have such a high content of organic material in their profiles.
9. Explain why the four most common elements in the earth crust should be found in even greater proportions in humid soils, while the next four in rank show greater proportions in dry soils.
10. Why are black muck soils found mainly where the ground water contains much lime in solution?
11. What criteria would you use to distinguish the depth of weathering in a soil?
12. The soils of flat upland areas often exhibit a characteristic mottled coloring of grays, yellows, and browns. Explain this.
13. What is a ground-water table? Why does it profoundly influence soil characteristics when it appears within the soil profile?
14. In a local area, where would be the most logical place to find a soil that best typifies the zonal great soil group predominant in the region?
15. Distinguish among zonal, intrazonal, and azonal soils, and give an example of each.
16. From field observation prepare a detailed description of a local soil profile.
17. Explain the following statement: "It is unfortunate that the tsetse fly should constitute the most influential factor in erosion control within Africa."
18. Explain why periods of cultural change or fusion often are accompanied by soil instability.
19. Explain why hill lands generally suffer more from erosion than do mountain lands.
20. Why is soil erosion in China more of a social than an agricultural problem?

CHAPTER 12

1. What are the three great zonal processes of soil formation, and with what climates are they associated?
2. Briefly describe the process of podzolization.
3. What are the physical and chemical properties of clays, and how are these related to soil formation?
4. What role is played by microorganisms in podzolization? What role is played by vegetation?
5. What is the difference between podzol and podzolic soils?

6. What are the advantages and disadvantages of podzol soils for agriculture?
7. What is glei, and how does it develop?
8. Ferrallization has been described as being more a geologic process than a soil-forming one. Explain this statement and reconcile it with the text treatment of ferrallization as a soil-forming process.
9. Why is there no well-developed *B* horizon in well-drained ferrallites?
10. What is meant by the silica-sequioxide ratio, and why is it a useful chemical determinant of podzolization and ferrallization?
11. Why do red colors prevail in humid tropical soils? Explain the yellow soils in the tropics.
12. What is a laterite, and how is it formed?
13. In what kinds of places does one find the better tropical soils for agricultural use?
14. Describe the process of calcification and the soil characteristics that result from it.
15. Explain why calcium rather than sodium is the most common base ion in well-drained dry soils.
16. Why are Texas soils that are exposed to 20 inches of precipitation redder than North Dakota soils that have the same amount of precipitation?
17. What is the difference between salinization and alkalinization?
18. Explain why many irrigation projects have ruined land for further agricultural use.
19. What limitations and qualifications should always be read into a world map of the great soil group?
20. Do the zonal, intrazonal, or azonal soil properties dominate in the area where you live? Explain and give an example of each in your area.

CHAPTER 13

1. Explain the seemingly paradoxical statement that a copper deposit may be too high a grade to be mined profitably.
2. Why are most emeralds and rubies found in stream gravels? Why is gold, but not iron, found in commercial quantities in stream gravels?
3. Explain why petroleum has a wider global distribution than coal.
4. In what general types of areas would it be logical to prospect for uranium? For thorium?
5. Explain why coals of higher rank generally are older and less abundant than coals of lower rank.
6. Why is it said that the location of proved petroleum reserves is related to the distribution of living standards?
7. Explain why there is such a low consumption of natural gas in northwestern Europe.
8. What metals appear to be in shortest supply in the world?
9. What technological development altered the iron ore reserve situation in the United States?
10. Why has there been such an increase in the world consumption of copper? What element can be substituted for it? Why is not more of the latter used?
11. Contrast the global reserves of lead with those of magnesium.
12. Why are mineral nitrates so rare in nature?
13. Explain the statement that the common rocks have far more economic value to man than the common minerals.

CHAPTER 14

1. What is the hydrologic cycle? Trace several paths taken by water in completing the cycle.

2. What is evapotranspiration, and what factors are involved in this process?
3. What are the advantages and disadvantages of ground water for use by human beings?
4. How can we add to our ground-water reserves?
5. Describe an artesian system.
6. Why is such a small percentage of runoff in exotic streams used for irrigation?
7. Explain why snow has sometimes been termed the "poor man's fertilizer."
8. Why have the subterranean aquifers suffered severely because of water exploitation?
9. Explain why the salt balance is a critical problem in the maintenance of successful irrigation in dry lands.
10. Egypt early developed basin flooding as its principal type of irrigation, whereas Babylon utilized diversion canals. Examine a regional physical map of the two areas and give a possible explanation.
11. What advantages do sprinkler irrigation systems have over other types?
12. What is the current status of the process of extracting fresh water from salt water?
13. Explain why the yields of rice per acre often can be correlated with water control.
14. Explain why quality and not quantity is the major problem of municipal and industrial water supply.
15. What is the difference between riparian and appropriated water rights?
16. What factors are challenging the riparian-rights doctrine in the eastern part of the United States?
17. Explain the major global distribution of potential hydroelectric power.
18. What factors influence the navigability of a waterway?

CHAPTER 15

1. Give specific illustrations of the principles of natural distributions as applied to the oceans.
2. What are the major topographic features of the ocean floor?
3. What general differences are there between the topography of the ocean floor and that of the continents? Explain.
4. What types of sediments are found on the ocean floor? How do they differ from those on the continental shelf?
5. What is meant by the proportional equilibrium of sea-water ions? What are some of the minor constituent elements of sea water that appear to vary somewhat in their proportions?
6. Explain and illustrate how organisms help maintain chemical balances in the ocean.
7. What factors influence the content of oxygen and carbon dioxide in sea water?
8. Why are corals more prolific on the outer, or seaward, side of a coral reef?
9. Explain why the Gulf Stream is blue and the Labrador Current is green.
10. Explain why there is a surface westerly current and a bottom easterly flow of water in the Strait of Gibraltar.
11. How much variation is there in the salinity of sea water? What factors influence this?
12. Explain the doming of water within the great ocean gyres.
13. Identify and locate the principal ocean currents in the world. Distinguish the relatively warm and cold currents.
14. Explain the upwelling of water along the subtropical west coasts of continents. Why are these excellent areas for deep-sea fishing?
15. Describe the principal features of the Gulf Stream.

16. Contrast the general pattern of currents in the high latitudes of the northern and southern hemispheres.
17. Give several reasons for the complexity of tidal periods.
18. What factors are most important in determining whether a particular sea environment is a fertile area for marine life?
19. Locate the ocean "pastures" and "deserts" and explain.
20. What are some of the potential ways in which the resource value of the oceans may be increased?

APPENDIX A

Details of a Simplified Koeppen-Geiger System of Climatic Classification

A CLIMATES

Humid or subhumid, with no winters; no month with a mean temperature below 64.4°F (18°C)

For examples of the *A* climates, see the list of climatic stations, page 590.

Subtypes:

- *f* = at least 2.4 inches (60 millimeters) of rain in every month
- *m* = at least 1 month having less than 2.4 inches of rain; dry season compensated (see Table 1 below for boundary between *m* and *w* or *s*)
- *w* = uncompensated dry season during the low-sun period
- *s* = uncompensated dry season during the high-sun period
- *g* = highest temperature occurring before summer solstice
- *w′* = rainfall maximum in autumn
- *w″* = double maximal rainfall periods

TABLE 1 Determination of Am-Aw or -As boundary

ANNUAL RAINFALL, IN.	RAINFALL OF DRIEST MONTH, IN.	ANNUAL RAINFALL, IN.	RAINFALL OF DRIEST MONTH, IN.
40	2.34	59	1.58
41	2.30	60	1.55
42	2.26	61	1.51
43	2.22	62	1.47
44	2.18	63	1.42
45	2.14	64	1.38
46	2.10	65	1.34
47	2.07	66	1.30
48	2.02	67	1.26
49	1.98	68	1.22
50	1.94	69	1.18
51	1.90	70	1.13
52	1.86	71	1.10
53	1.82	72	1.06
54	1.78	73	1.02
55	1.75	74	0.98
56	1.70	75	0.94
57	1.66	76	0.90
58	1.63	77	0.86

TABLE 1 Determination of Am–Aw or -As boundary (continued)

ANNUAL RAINFALL, IN.	RAINFALL OF DRIEST MONTH, IN.	ANNUAL RAINFALL, IN.	RAINFALL OF DRIEST MONTH, IN.
78	0.81	89	0.37
79	0.78	90	0.34
80	0.74	91	0.29
81	0.70	92	0.26
82	0.66	93	0.22
83	0.61	94	0.18
84	0.58	95	0.14
85	0.54	96	0.09
86	0.50	97	0.06
87	0.46	98	0.02
88	0.42		

B CLIMATES

Arid and semiarid climates

Subtypes:

BS = *semiarid.* The *BS*-humid climatic boundary corresponds to the following formulas:

1. Precipitation mainly in summer (70 per cent in summer 6 months) $R = 0.44(t - 7)$
2. Precipitation mainly in winter (70 per cent in winter 6 months) $R = 0.44(t - 32)$
3. Precipitation evenly distributed (neither 1 nor 2) $R = 0.44(t - 19.5)$

In the above formulas, R = mean annual precipitation in inches, and t = mean annual temperature °F.

BW = *arid.* The *BW-BS* boundary is exactly one-half the figure for the *BS*-humid boundary, as determined from the formulas above or from Table 2 below.

The following lower-case letters are used with the *BW* and *BS* climatic symbols:

h = mean average annual temperature above 64.4.[1]

k = mean average annual temperature below 64.4°F

k' = warmest month below 64.4°F

w = winter dry season; 70 per cent of the precipitation in summer 6 months

s = summer dry season; 70 per cent of the precipitation in winter 6 months

[1] Some climatologists have recommended the use of 32°F for the coldest month as a better boundary between the hot and the cold dry climates (h and k), especially in North America.

TABLE 2 Average annual precipitation along the BS-humid boundary (based on Formulas 1, 2, and 3 above)

AVERAGE ANNUAL TEMPERATURE	70 PER CENT OF RAIN IN WINTER	EVEN DISTRIBUTION	70 PER CENT OF RAIN IN SUMMER
32	0.0	5.5	11.0
33	0.4	6.0	11.5
34	0.9	6.4	11.9
35	1.3	6.9	12.3
36	1.7	7.3	12.8
37	2.2	7.7	13.2
38	2.6	8.1	13.6
39	3.1	8.6	14.1

TABLE 2 Average annual precipitation along the BS-humid boundary (based on Formulas 1, 2, and 3 above) (continued)

AVERAGE ANNUAL TEMPERATURE	70 PER CENT OF RAIN IN WINTER	EVEN DISTRIBUTION	70 PER CENT OF RAIN IN SUMMER
40	3.5	9.0	14.5
41	3.9	9.5	15.0
42	4.4	9.9	15.4
43	4.8	10.3	15.8
44	5.3	10.8	16.3
45	5.7	11.2	16.7
46	6.1	11.6	17.1
47	6.6	12.1	17.6
48	7.0	12.5	18.0
49	7.4	13.0	18.5
50	7.9	13.4	18.9
51	8.3	13.8	19.3
52	8.7	14.3	19.8
53	9.2	14.7	20.2
54	9.6	15.1	20.6
55	10.1	15.6	21.1
56	10.5	16.0	21.5
57	10.9	16.5	22.0
58	11.4	16.9	22.4
59	11.8	17.3	22.8
60	12.3	17.8	23.3
61	12.7	18.2	23.7
62	13.1	18.6	24.1
63	13.6	19.1	24.6
64	14.0	19.5	25.0
65	14.4	20.0	25.5
66	14.9	20.4	25.9
67	15.3	20.8	26.3
68	15.7	21.3	26.8
69	16.2	21.7	27.2
70	16.6	22.1	27.6
71	17.1	22.6	28.1
72	17.5	23.0	28.5
73	17.9	23.5	29.0
74	18.4	23.9	29.4
75	18.8	24.3	29.8
76	19.2	24.8	30.3
77	19.7	25.2	30.7
78	20.1	25.6	31.1
79	20.6	26.1	31.6
80	21.0	26.5	32.0
81	21.4	27.0	32.5
82	21.9	27.4	32.9
83	22.3	27.8	33.3
84	22.7	28.3	33.8
85	23.2	28.7	34.2

For examples of *B* climates, see the list of climatic stations, page 590.

C CLIMATES

Humid or subhumid climates with mild winters; temperature of the coldest month above 26.6°F (−3°C), but below 64.4°F (18°C); temperature of the warmest month above 50°F

Subtypes:

- *f* = no pronounced dry season; difference between wettest and driest months less than required for *s* or *w;* precipitation in driest month of summer more than 1.2 inches
- *s* = summer dry season; at least three times as much precipitation in the wettest month of winter as in the driest month of summer; precipitation in driest month of summer less than 1.2 inches
- *w* = winter dry season; at least ten times as much rain in the wettest month of summer as in the driest month of winter
- *a* = hot summers; temperature of the warmest month above 71.6°F (22°C)
- *b* = cool summers; temperature of the warmest month below 71.6°, but with at least 4 months above 50°F
- *c* = cool, short summers; 1 to 3 months above 50°F
- *g* = warmest month occurring before the summer solstice
- *t′* = warmest month in autumn
- *x* = maximum rainfall in spring or early summer; dry period in late summer

For examples of the *C* climates, see the climatic statistics, page 590.

D CLIMATES

Humid and subhumid climates with severe winters; coldest month below 26.6°F[2] (−3°C); warmest month above 50°F

Subtypes:

- *f, s,* and *w* defined as in the *C* climates; *a, b,* and *c* defined as in the *C* climates
- *d* = temperature of the coldest month less than −36.4°F

E CLIMATES

No summer; warmest month below 50°F (10°C)

[2] Some climatologists have suggested that the isotherm of 32° for the coldest month forms a more adequate boundary between cold and mild winters than the Koeppen boundary of 26.6°.

World Climatic Station Records

TABLE 3 Mean temperature (degrees Fahrenheit) and precipitation (inches) for selected climatic stations (by continents) The location and Koeppen classification of the following stations are given on pages 590 and 591

STATION	JAN.	FEB.	MAR.	APR.	MAY	JUNE	JULY	AUG.	SEPT.	OCT.	NOV.	DEC.	YEAR
						Africa							
1	56	57	60	65	70	75	78	79	77	74	67	59	68
	0.9	0.4	0.4	0.2	0.1	0	0	0	0	0.1	0.5	0.7	3.8
2	57	59	60	63	65	67	68	68	68	67	63	59	63.7
	2.2	1.5	2.2	0.7	0.6	0.1	0	0	0.2	1.3	2.4	2.0	13.2
3	49	50	52	56	61	68	73	75	70	64	57	52	61
	4.0	2.6	3.3	2.0	1.7	0.7	0.1	0.1	1.2	3.4	4.1	4.0	27.4
4	71	74	83	92	94	94	89	86	89	89	81	71	84
	0	0	0.1	0	0.3	0.9	3.5	2.8	1.1	0.4	0	0	9.0

TABLE 3 Mean temperature (degrees Fahrenheit) and precipitation (inches) for selected climatic stations (by continents) The location and Koeppen classification of the following stations are given on pages 590 and 591 (continued)

STATION	JAN.	FEB.	MAR.	APR.	MAY	JUNE	JULY	AUG.	SEPT.	OCT.	NOV.	DEC.	YEAR
5	81	82	82	82	81	80	79	78	79	80	81	81	81
	0.4	0.3	1.2	4.1	11.5	20.0	35.6	36.6	28.5	12.6	5.1	1.4	157.2
6	70	73	79	86	91	91	88	86	88	87	80	72	83
	0	0	0	0	0.1	0.3	1.6	2.2	0.7	0.2	0	0	5.1
7	81	82	83	82	82	79	78	78	78	79	81	81	80.5
	1.1	2.1	3.7	5.7	10.5	18.7	10.7	2.8	5.3	7.8	2.6	0.8	71.6
8	75	76	85	88	87	81	79	78	79	81	81	76	80
	0	0	0.1	1.8	2.5	4.5	6.2	10.6	5.0	1.3	0	0	32
9	79	80	79	78	79	78	76	76	77	77	78	78	78
	4.1	3.5	4.1	5.6	6.2	6.1	6.3	6.3	6.3	6.6	2.6	9.3	66.9
10	64	65	65	64	63	62	58	59	62	65	64	62	63
	1.9	3.6	4.2	8.9	5.6	2.2	0.9	1.1	1.2	2.3	5.3	2.8	39.9
11	71	70	69	66	61	57	57	61	68	72	72	72	66.5
	5.9	4.0	3.1	0.7	0.3	0	0	0	0.1	0.9	3.3	5.2	23.6
12	70	70	68	63	59	56	55	56	58	61	64	68	62
	0.7	0.6	0.9	1.9	3.8	4.5	3.7	3.4	2.3	1.6	1.1	0.8	25.3
13	79	81	78	76	72	69	68	69	71	74	76	79	74.5
	15.0	14.3	17.8	12.0	9.8	14.4	13.2	8.5	7.1	5.3	3.9	9.6	130.9
14	81	81	80	78	76	74	73	74	74	76	79	81	77
	3.3	2.1	4.8	11.9	7.4	1.1	1.7	1.1	1.1	1.2	2.9	2.7	42.3
						South America							
15	54	55	54	54	55	55	55	55	55	55	54	55	55
	4.2	4.3	5.2	7.4	5.0	1.5	0.9	1.5	3.0	3.7	3.8	3.8	44.1
16	71	73	73	70	66	62	61	61	61	62	66	70	66
	0	0	0	0	0	0.2	0.3	0.5	0.5	0.1	0	0	1.8
17	79	79	80	81	81	80	81	81	82	82	81	80	81
	7.9	4.6	7.2	6.0	11.1	11.7	9.9	6.5	3.1	2.9	6.7	11.1	88.7
18	78	77	77	78	78	78	78	78	79	79	80	79	78
	7.6	13.3	17.0	17.8	11.8	9.1	2.3	2.8	0.6	0.5	0.6	2.6	89.6
19	81	81	81	80	77	75	76	78	82	82	82	81	80
	9.8	8.3	8.3	4.0	2.1	0.3	0.2	1.1	2.0	4.5	5.9	8.1	54.6
20	78	78	77	74	71	69	68	69	70	71	73	76	73
	5.0	4.5	5.3	4.2	3.2	2.2	1.7	1.8	2.6	3.3	4.1	5.5	43.3
21	74	72	69	61	55	50	49	51	55	60	66	71	61
	3.1	2.7	4.4	3.5	2.9	2.5	2.2	2.5	3.0	3.5	3.1	3.9	37.2
22	83	81	77	70	64	58	58	60	68	73	78	81	71
	2.8	3.2	4.6	1.6	0.6	0.2	0.2	0.1	0.6	1.5	2.1	3.3	20.8
23	64	63	61	58	56	52	52	53	54	57	60	62	58
	0	0	0.9	0.1	2.7	6.0	5.3	3.4	0.4	0.5	0.3	0	19.6

TABLE 3 Mean temperature (degrees Fahrenheit) and precipitation (inches) for selected climatic stations (by continents) The location and Koeppen classification of the following stations are given on pages 590 and 591 (continued)

STATION	JAN.	FEB.	MAR.	APR.	MAY	JUNE	JULY	AUG.	SEPT.	OCT.	NOV.	DEC.	YEAR
24	59	58	54	48	41	35	35	38	43	49	53	56	47
	0.6	0.4	0.3	0.6	0.6	0.5	0.7	0.4	0.2	0.4	0.5	0.8	5.9
25	62	60	58	53	50	45	46	46	48	52	55	59	53
	2.6	2.9	5.5	9.3	15.7	17.2	16.3	13.7	8.4	5.5	5.0	4.4	106.3
26	47	47	46	45	41	40	37	39	40	42	43	45	43
	12.8	8.9	12.3	11.6	8.8	8.5	8.9	8.6	7.7	9.0	10.3	9.6	117.0
						Europe							
27	39	40	42	47	53	59	63	62	57	50	44	40	50
	1.9	1.7	1.8	1.5	1.8	2.0	2.4	2.2	1.8	2.6	2.4	2.4	24.5
28	41	43	47	53	58	64	68	68	64	55	47	41	54
	2.5	2.0	2.3	2.5	2.8	2.8	1.9	2.0	2.6	3.6	3.1	2.7	30.7
29	42	42	44	47	52	57	60	60	56	50	46	43	50
	2.3	1.9	1.9	1.9	2.0	2.0	2.6	3.0	1.9	2.7	2.7	2.5	27.4
30	50	52	54	58	60	67	70	71	68	62	56	52	60
	3.5	3.4	3.5	2.9	2.0	0.8	0.2	0.2	1.5	3.1	4.5	4.1	29.7
31	45	47	51	57	64	71	76	75	70	62	53	46	60
	3.2	2.7	2.9	2.6	2.2	1.5	0.7	1.0	2.5	5.0	4.4	3.9	32.7
32	31	34	39	47	57	63	66	64	58	49	40	34	48
	1.5	1.3	1.7	1.4	2.0	2.0	3.1	2.2	1.8	1.8	1.6	1.7	22.2
33	24	25	31	40	51	60	63	60	52	42	33	26	42
	1.1	1.1	1.3	1.3	1.7	1.9	2.9	3.5	2.3	2.6	1.9	1.7	23.2
34	26	31	41	52	62	70	72	72	63	53	40	31	51
	1.3	1.1	1.6	1.7	2.5	3.5	2.7	2.0	1.6	1.7	1.9	1.6	23.1
35	18	18	25	37	49	58	63	60	51	40	30	22	39
	0.9	0.8	0.9	0.9	1.7	1.8	2.7	2.7	2.0	1.7	1.4	1.2	18.8
36	14	17	25	39	55	61	66	62	51	40	28	18	40
	1.1	0.9	1.2	1.5	1.9	2.0	2.8	2.9	2.2	1.4	1.6	1.5	21.0
37	38	39	43	51	63	72	77	77	71	62	51	44	57
	1.3	0.9	0.8	0.8	0.6	0.3	0.2	0.2	0.8	1.2	1.2	1.2	9.5
38	39	39	43	51	61	69	75	75	66	58	48	43	55
	1.8	1.6	1.6	1.3	1.1	1.5	1.3	0.9	1.4	1.7	2.0	3.0	19.9
						Asia							
39	50	54	61	70	81	90	94	94	88	78	63	53	73
	1.2	1.3	1.3	0.9	0.2	0	0	0	0	0.1	0.7	1.2	7.1
40	65	68	75	81	85	87	84	82	82	80	74	67	78
	0.5	0.5	0.4	0.2	0.1	0.9	2.9	1.5	0.5	0	0.1	0.1	7.6
41	78	80	82	84	83	78	77	77	78	79	79	78	79
	0.3	0.2	0.6	3.2	9.5	35.0	29.8	15.3	8.4	10.3	4.9	1.1	118.6

TABLE 3 Mean temperature (degrees Fahrenheit) and precipitation (inches) for selected climatic stations (by continents) The location and Koeppen classification of the following stations are given on pages 590 and 591 (continued)

STATION	JAN.	FEB.	MAR.	APR.	MAY	JUNE	JULY	AUG.	SEPT.	OCT.	NOV.	DEC.	YEAR
42	75	77	79	84	89	88	86	84	84	81	78	76	82
	1.1	0.3	0.3	0.6	1.8	2.0	3.8	4.5	4.9	11.2	13.6	5.4	49.6
43	65	70	79	85	86	84	83	82	83	80	72	65	78
	0.4	1.1	1.4	2.0	5.0	11.2	12.1	11.5	9.0	4.3	0.5	0.2	58.8
44	53	57	69	81	89	93	89	87	85	76	63	55	75
	0.9	1.0	0.8	0.5	0.7	1.4	5.1	4.7	2.3	0.3	0.1	0.4	18.1
45	75	77	81	85	82	79	79	79	79	80	78	76	79
	0.2	0.2	0.3	1.6	12.0	18.0	21.4	19.9	15.3	6.9	2.8	0.4	99.0
46	78	78	79	80	81	80	80	80	79	80	79	78	79
	9.7	7.1	7.3	7.8	6.5	7.0	6.7	7.8	6.9	7.9	10.1	10.4	95.1
47	82	81	81	81	80	79	78	78	78	80	81	82	80
	7.5	9.2	6.8	3.3	3.0	0.8	1.0	0.8	1.4	0.8	2.0	4.2	40.8
48	81	81	81	79	79	78	77	78	78	79	80	81	79
	5.1	4.6	5.2	11.3	19.8	24.6	23.1	15.9	9.1	6.2	4.4	5.4	134.8
49	79	79	79	79	79	78	77	78	79	80	81	81	79
	15.7	14.8	8.7	2.5	1.2	0.4	0.2	0.1	0	0.8	3.4	10.0	57.8
50	77	77	80	83	83	82	81	81	80	80	78	77	80
	0.8	0.4	0.8	1.3	4.4	9.3	17.3	16.0	14.3	6.7	5.2	3.0	79.6
51	69	67	74	80	83	85	84	85	81	78	73	70	78
	4.0	4.8	1.8	2.4	3.6	2.8	3.4	4.0	16.2	26.3	22.4	10.2	102.0
52	69	74	82	89	88	85	85	85	83	82	76	69	81
	0.1	0.1	0.2	1.1	5.8	5.5	3.3	4.6	5.7	4.7	1.6	0.4	33.2
53	60	59	63	70	77	81	82	82	81	76	69	63	72
	1.3	1.8	2.7	5.3	12.0	15.8	14.0	14.6	9.7	5.1	1.7	1.1	85.1
54	38	39	46	56	65	73	80	80	73	63	52	42	60
	2.0	2.3	3.5	3.7	3.5	7.3	6.0	5.7	4.4	3.2	2.1	1.4	45.1
55	49	50	58	67	74	79	82	84	76	67	59	50	56
	0.6	0.8	1.4	4.0	5.5	7.1	5.6	5.1	5.8	4.5	2.0	0.9	43.4
56	40	41	48	61	71	78	83	83	75	65	53	43	62
	1.8	1.9	3.8	6.0	6.5	9.6	7.1	3.8	2.8	3.2	1.9	1.1	49.6
57	23	28	39	55	68	76	77	76	67	54	38	27	52
	0.1	0.2	0.2	0.6	1.4	3.0	9.4	6.3	2.6	0.6	0.3	0.1	24.9
58	37	39	44	54	62	69	76	78	71	60	50	41	57
	2.2	2.8	4.4	4.9	5.7	6.5	5.3	5.7	8.7	7.4	4.2	2.1	59.9
59	23	22	32	37	44	50	58	63	59	50	39	29	42
	1.3	1.0	2.2	2.9	3.7	3.7	3.8	4.3	5.5	3.8	3.3	2.3	37.8
60	8	14	30	47	60	70	76	74	61	48	29	14	44
	0.2	0.3	0.7	1.1	2.2	3.4	5.8	5.3	3.3	1.5	0.9	0.2	24.9
61	30	34	46	58	68	76	80	76	66	54	45	36	56
	1.8	1.4	2.6	2.6	1.1	0.5	0.1	0.1	0.2	1.1	1.4	1.7	14.6

TABLE 3 Mean temperature (degrees Fahrenheit) and precipitation (inches) for selected climatic stations (by continents) The location and Koeppen classification of the following stations are given on pages 590 and 591 (continued)

STATION	JAN.	FEB.	MAR.	APR.	MAY	JUNE	JULY	AUG.	SEPT.	OCT.	NOV.	DEC.	YEAR
62	3	4	14	37	58	67	71	67	56	38	20	9	37
	0.5	0.2	0.4	0.4	0.8	0.9	1.1	0.4	0.6	0.6	0.6	0.8	7.3
63	−6	−1	13	33	46	58	63	59	46	31	13	−1	30
	0.6	0.5	0.4	0.6	1.2	2.3	2.9	2.4	1.6	0.7	0.6	0.8	14.5
64	−58	−48	−22	8	35	54	59	51	36	6	−34	−52	3
	0.2	0.1	0	0.1	0.2	0.5	1.2	0.9	0.2	0.2	0.2	0.2	3.9
65	−3	4	16	32	48	59	64	60	49	32	14	3	31
	0.7	0.6	0.7	0.8	1.3	2.7	3.5	3.2	1.5	1.4	1.3	0.9	18.6
66	−13	−5	6	21	32	42	53	54	47	28	4	−7	22
	0.1	0.1	0.1	0.2	0.5	1.1	0.5	1.8	2.1	0.7	0.2	0.2	7.5

Australia and Oceania

STATION	JAN.	FEB.	MAR.	APR.	MAY	JUNE	JULY	AUG.	SEPT.	OCT.	NOV.	DEC.	YEAR
67	72	71	69	64	59	54	52	55	59	63	67	70	63
	3.7	4.2	4.8	5.6	5.1	4.8	4.8	3.0	2.9	3.2	2.8	2.9	47.9
68	66	67	65	61	57	53	52	52	55	57	60	64	59
	2.7	3.0	3.0	3.4	4.4	4.9	5.0	4.2	3.6	3.6	3.3	2.9	43.9
69	74	74	70	64	58	53	51	54	57	62	67	71	63
	0.7	0.7	1.0	1.8	2.8	3.1	2.7	2.5	2.0	1.7	1.2	1.0	21.2
70	73	74	71	66	60	56	55	56	58	61	65	71	64
	0.3	0.3	0.7	1.7	4.9	6.6	6.4	5.6	3.3	2.1	0.8	0.6	33.3
71	83	82	77	68	60	54	53	58	65	73	79	82	70
	1.8	1.7	1.2	0.7	0.7	0.6	0.4	0.4	0.4	0.7	1.0	1.6	11.1
72	84	83	84	84	82	79	77	79	83	85	86	85	83
	15.9	13.0	10.1	4.1	0.7	0.1	0.1	0.1	0.5	2.2	4.8	10.3	61.8
73	86	85	85	83	76	71	70	72	77	81	85	86	80
	5.0	6.4	3.8	1.4	0.4	1.2	0.3	0	0.1	0	0.9	3.5	23.0
74	67	67	65	60	54	50	48	51	54	57	61	64	58
	1.9	1.8	2.2	2.3	2.2	2.1	1.9	1.8	2.4	2.7	2.2	2.3	25.6
75	71	71	71	73	75	77	78	78	78	77	75	72	75
	3.7	4.3	3.8	2.3	1.9	1.1	1.3	1.5	1.5	1.9	4.2	4.1	31.6
76	81	81	81	80	80	80	80	80	80	81	81	81	81
	11.5	11.9	17.9	14.0	19.8	15.8	15.5	13.8	13.6	11.4	14.0	17.3	176.5

Central America

STATION	JAN.	FEB.	MAR.	APR.	MAY	JUNE	JULY	AUG.	SEPT.	OCT.	NOV.	DEC.	YEAR
77	80	80	80	81	81	80	80	80	80	80	79	80	80
	3.7	1.6	1.6	4.3	12.4	13.3	16.0	14.7	12.5	15.1	20.7	11.4	127.3
78	61	63	66	66	68	66	66	66	66	65	63	61	65
	0.3	0.2	0.5	1.3	5.6	11.5	8.0	8.0	9.2	6.7	0.9	0.2	52.4
79	55	57	61	64	65	64	62	62	61	59	56	54	60
	0.2	0.2	0.5	0.7	1.9	3.9	4.5	4.6	3.9	1.6	0.5	0.2	22.8

TABLE 3 Mean temperature (degrees Fahrenheit) and precipitation (inches) for selected climatic stations (by continents) The location and Koeppen classification of the following stations are given on pages 590 and 591 (continued)

STATION	JAN.	FEB.	MAR.	APR.	MAY	JUNE	JULY	AUG.	SEPT.	OCT.	NOV.	DEC.	YEAR
80	71	72	74	76	79	80	82	82	81	79	75	73	77
	3.0	1.5	1.7	1.7	5.1	5.6	4.3	4.3	5.0	7.0	3.2	2.4	45.0
81	75	77	79	80	82	82	83	83	82	79	76	74	79
	5.1	2.6	1.6	1.5	4.1	9.1	9.6	8.5	9.4	11.0	10.2	6.3	79.0
82	58	62	68	73	79	82	82	83	78	71	64	57	71
	0.5	0.5	0.7	1.1	1.2	2.3	2.1	2.0	4.4	2.4	1.3	1.0	19.5
North America													
83	68	68	70	74	77	80	82	82	81	78	72	69	75
	2.5	1.8	2.2	3.0	6.2	6.9	5.4	6.2	8.3	8.4	2.9	1.7	55.6
84	54	57	63	69	75	81	82	82	79	71	62	56	69
	4.3	4.2	4.7	5.2	4.6	5.9	6.4	5.8	5.0	3.3	3.1	4.8	57.3
85	50	52	58	65	73	79	82	81	77	68	58	52	66
	2.9	3.2	3.4	2.8	3.3	4.7	7.2	6.6	5.1	3.2	2.3	2.8	47.6
86	32	35	45	56	66	75	80	78	71	59	46	36	57
	2.3	2.4	3.5	3.8	4.4	4.4	3.5	3.5	3.2	2.9	2.8	2.5	39.3
87	35	36	44	54	65	73	77	75	68	57	46	37	56
	3.4	3.0	3.6	3.3	3.7	3.9	4.4	4.3	3.7	2.9	2.6	3.1	42.0
88	31	31	39	49	60	69	74	73	67	56	45	35	53
	3.6	3.5	3.8	3.3	3.3	3.5	4.2	4.4	3.5	3.4	3.1	3.3	42.9
89	23	24	32	45	57	66	71	69	62	51	39	29	47
	2.8	2.2	2.9	2.2	2.8	2.9	3.1	3.8	2.5	2.7	2.5	2.6	32.1
90	21	22	30	39	48	55	60	61	56	48	37	26	42
	3.6	3.2	3.7	2.8	3.0	3.0	3.1	2.9	3.1	3.6	3.5	3.4	38.9
91	25	27	36	47	57	67	73	72	65	54	40	29	49
	1.9	1.8	2.7	2.8	3.6	3.5	3.1	3.1	3.2	2.6	2.4	2.0	32.9
92	8	12	25	43	55	64	71	68	58	45	28	15	41
	0.4	0.5	0.9	1.5	2.2	3.4	2.3	1.8	1.3	1.0	0.6	0.5	16.4
93	22	26	38	52	62	72	77	75	67	55	39	27	51
	0.7	0.9	1.3	2.6	3.6	4.7	3.7	3.1	3.1	2.1	1.2	0.9	27.9
94	31	33	39	48	57	67	73	71	63	52	40	33	50
	0.5	0.5	1.1	2.0	2.3	1.4	1.6	1.4	1.0	1.0	0.6	0.6	14.0
95	45	50	56	64	72	81	82	80	75	64	52	45	64
	0.5	0.4	0.3	0.3	0.4	0.6	1.7	1.6	1.2	0.8	0.5	0.5	8.8
96	52	56	61	68	76	85	90	89	83	71	60	53	70
	0.8	0.8	0.7	0.4	0.1	0.1	1.0	1.0	0.9	0.4	0.6	0.9	7.7
97	55	56	58	60	63	66	71	71	70	66	62	57	63
	2.9	3.3	2.7	1.0	0.4	0.1	0	0	0.2	0.6	1.1	2.9	15.2
98	50	53	54	56	57	59	59	59	62	61	57	51	56
	4.6	3.7	3.1	1.5	0.7	0.1	0	0	0.3	1.0	2.4	4.4	21.9

TABLE 3 Mean temperature (degrees Fahrenheit) and precipitation (inches) for selected climatic stations (by continents) The location and Koeppen classification of the following stations are given on pages 590 and 591 (continued)

STATION	JAN.	FEB.	MAR.	APR.	MAY	JUNE	JULY	AUG.	SEPT.	OCT.	NOV.	DEC.	YEAR
99	46	50	54	58	63	69	73	73	69	63	54	46	60
	3.7	3.0	2.6	1.5	0.8	0.1	0	0	0.4	0.9	1.9	3.0	17.9
100	39	43	48	52	58	62	67	67	62	55	47	42	54
	6.1	5.3	4.5	2.8	2.2	1.6	0.5	0.6	1.8	3.3	6.1	7.0	41.9
101	32	34	36	41	47	51	55	55	52	46	38	35	44
	7.6	6.5	5.6	5.5	4.1	3.4	4.2	7.1	10.1	12.2	9.5	9.0	84.8
102	−20	−13	−13	−2	22	35	41	38	32	16	0.3	−15	10
	0.1	0.4	0.2	0.3	0.3	0.3	0.9	0.9	0.5	0.7	0.3	0.4	5.3
103	5	10	23	40	51	57	61	59	50	41	25	14	36
	0.9	0.6	0.7	0.8	1.8	3.2	3.4	2.4	1.4	0.7	0.7	0.8	17.4
104	−23	−11	4	29	46	57	59	54	42	25	1	−13	22
	0.8	0.8	0.5	0.7	0.9	1.3	1.6	1.6	1.7	1.3	1.3	1.1	13.6
105	6	8	20	36	47	57	63	60	53	42	28	14	36
	0.7	0.6	0.9	1.5	2.0	2.7	3.6	2.9	3.1	2.2	1.3	0.9	22.5
106	10	11	22	36	51	61	67	64	56	43	30	16	38
	3.7	3.1	3.2	2.4	3.2	3.9	4.1	3.9	4.0	3.5	3.6	3.4	42.1
107	23	22	28	35	43	51	59	59	54	45	37	29	40
	5.4	5.1	4.5	4.2	3.6	3.5	3.7	3.6	3.8	5.4	6.1	4.9	53.8

LOCATION AND CLASSIFICATION OF CLIMATIC STATIONS

Africa

1. Port Said, Egypt (*BWhs*)
2. Mogador, Morocco (*BSks*)
3. Algiers, Algeria (*Csa*)
4. Timbuktu, French West Africa (*BWhw*)
5. Freetown, Sierra Leone (*Amg*)
6. Khartoum, Sudan (*BWhw*)
7. Lagos, Nigeria (*Amg*)
8. Wagaduga (Ouagadougou), French West Africa (*Awg*)
9. New Antwerp, Belgian Congo (*Afw"*)
10. Nairobi, Kenya (*Cw*)
11. Bulawayo, Southern Rhodesia (*BShw*)
12. Capetown, South Africa (*Csa*)
13. Tamatave, Madagascar (*Afw"*)
14. Dar es Salaam, Tanganyika (*Aw*)

South America

15. Quito, Ecuador (*Cfb*)
16. Lima, Peru (*BWhs*)
17. Georgetown, British Guiana (*Afw"*)
18. Belem, Brazil (*Am*)
19. Cuyabá, Brazil (*Awg*)
20. Rio de Janeiro, Brazil (*Am*)
21. Buenos Aires, Argentina (*Cfa*)
22. Santiago, Argentina (*BShw*)
23. Valparaiso, Chile (*Csb*)
24. Santa Cruz, Argentina (*BWk*)
25. Valdivia, Chile (*Cfbs*)
26. Evangelist Islands, Chile (*E*)

Europe

27. London, England (*Cfb*)
28. Bordeaux, France (*Cfb*)
29. Dublin, Eire (*Cfb*)
30. Lisbon, Portugal (*Csb*)
31. Rome, Italy (*Csa*)
32. Berlin, Germany (*Cfb*)
33. Oslo, Norway (*Dfb*)
34. Bucharest, Romania (*Dfa*)
35. Leningrad, U.S.S.R. (*Db*)
36. Moscow, U.S.S.R. (*Dfb*)
37. Baku, U.S.S.R. (*BSks*)
38. Yalta, U.S.S.R. (*Csa*)

Asia

39. Baghdad, Iraq (*BWhs*)
40. Karachi, Pakistan (*BWhw*)
41. Calicut, India (*Amg*)
42. Madras, India (*Awg*)
43. Calcutta, India (*Awg*)
44. Lahore, Pakistan (*BShw*)
45. Rangoon, Burma (*Amg*)
46. Singapore (*Af*)
47. Port Moresby, Papua, New Guinea (*Aw*)
48. Amboina, Ambon Island, Indonesia (*Af*)
49. Koepang, W. Timor (*Aw*)
50. Manila, Philippine Islands (*Aw*)
51. Hué, Viet Nam, Indochina (*Ams*)
52. Mandalay, Burma (*Awgw''*)
53. Hong Kong, China (*Cfwa*)
54. Shanghai, China (*Cfa*)
55. Chungking, Szechwan, China (*Cwa*)
56. Hankow, China (*Cfa*)
57. Peiping, China (*Dfa*)
58. Tokyo, Japan (*Cfa*)
59. Nemuro, Hokkaido, Japan (*Dfb*)
60. Mukden, Manchuria (*Dwa*)
61. Tashkent, U.S.S.R. (*BSks*)
62. Semipalatinsk, U.S.S.R. (*BSk*)
63. Irkutsk, U.S.S.R. (*Dfc*)
64. Verkhoyansk, U.S.S.R. (*Dwd*)
65. Tobolsk, U.S.S.R. (*Dfc*)
66. Okhotsk, U.S.S.R. (*Dwc*)

Australia and Oceania

67. Sydney, New South Wales, Australia (*Cfa*)
68. Auckland, New Zealand (*Cfb*)
69. Adelaide, South Australia (*Csa*)
70. Perth, Western Australia (*Csa*)
71. Alice Springs, Northern Territory, Australia (*BWhw*)
72. Darwin, Northern Territory, Australia (*Awg*)
73. Broome, Western Australia (*BShw*)
74. Melbourne, Victoria, Australia (*Cfb*)
75. Honolulu, Hawaii (*Aw*)
76. Jaluit Island (*Af*)

Central America

77. Colon, Panama (*Amw'*)
78. Guatemala City, Guatemala (*Cw*)
79. Mexico City, Mexico (*BSkw*)
80. Havana, Cuba (*Aww'*)
81. Belize, British Honduras (*Amw'*)
82. Monterrey, Mexico (*BShw*)

North America

83. Miami, Florida (*Amw'*)
84. New Orleans, Louisiana (*Cfa*)
85. Charleston, South Carolina (*Cfa*)
86. St. Louis, Missouri (*Cfa*)
87. Washington, D.C. (*Cfa*)
88. New York, New York (*Cfa*)
89. Rochester, New York (*Dfb*)
90. Eastport, Maine (*Dfb*)
91. Chicago, Illinois (*Dfa*)
92. Bismarck, North Dakota (*Dfb*)
93. Omaha, Nebraska (*Dfa*)
94. Denver, Colorado (*BSkw*)
95. El Paso, Texas (*BWk*)
96. Phoenix, Arizona (*BWh*)
97. Los Angeles, California (*Csb*)
98. San Francisco, California (*Csbt'*)
99. Sacramento, California (*Csa*)
100. Portland, Oregon (*Csb*)
101. Sitka, Alaska (*Cfbs*)
102. Point Barrow, Alaska (*E*)
103. Edmonton, Alberta, Canada (*Dfb*)
104. Dawson City, Yukon Territory, Canada (*Dfc*)
105. Port Arthur, Ontario, Canada (*Dfb*)
106. Quebec, Quebec, Canada (*Dfb*)
107. St. Johns, Newfoundland (*Dfb*)

APPENDIX B

Reference Reading List

CHAPTER 1

Davis, Darrell Y.: *The Earth and Man,* The Macmillan Company, New York, 1947. *The first chapter of this general geography text contains a concise summary of the development of geography as an organized body of knowledge. Recommended to students for supplementary reading.*

Dickinson, R. E., and O. J. Howarth: *The Making of Geography,* Oxford University Press, New York, 1933. *A small book, easily read, and useful as a condensed summary of the history of geographic thought to the modern period.*

Dohrs, F. E., L. M. Sommers, and D. R. Petterson: *Outside Readings in Geography,* Thomas Y. Crowell Company, New York, 1955, pp. 1–25. *Three excellent short excerpts on the nature of geography are included in this collection of geographic articles and essays.*

Hartshorne, Richard: *The Nature of Geography,* The Association of American Geographers, Washington, D.C., 1939. *A definitive treatment of the history of geographic thought from the middle of the eighteenth century. Recommended only for teachers or advanced students.*

James, Preston E., and Clarence F. Jones (eds.): *American Geography: Inventory and Prospect,* Syracuse University Press, Syracuse, N.Y., 1954. *A comprehensive book surveying the status and nature of American professional geography, written by representative leaders in the field. The first two chapters are recommended particularly for those interested in a careful view of regionalism and its role in geographic philosophy.*

Kimble, George H. T.: *The Way of the World,* George Grady Press, New York, 1953. *An interesting and readable series of lectures on the field and functions of geography in the world today.*

CHAPTER 2

Balchin, W. C. V., and A. W. Richards: *Practicat and Experimental Geography,* John Wiley & Sons, Inc., New York, 1952. *An interesting little book dealing with various methods of clarifying three-dimensional aspects of the earth globe for beginning students. Especially valuable to teachers of geography in elementary and secondary schools.*

Chamberlin, Wellman: *The Round Earth on Flat Paper,* The National Geographic Society, Washington, D.C., 1947. *A small book designed to clarify the properties, functions, and construction of some of the more widely used map projections.*

Deetz, H., and O. S. Adams: *Elements of Map Projection,* U.S. Coast and Geodetic Survey Special Publication 68, 5th ed., 1945. *One of the standard reference works on map projections for cartographers. Contains instructions, tables, and critiques for most of the major map projections.*

Greenhood, David: *Down to Earth,* 2d ed., Holiday House, Inc., New York, 1951. *A readable, well-illustrated volume of maps, mapping, and map making. Highly recommended as supplementary reading for beginning geography students.*

Johnson, Willis E.: *Mathematical Geography,* American Book Company, New York, 1907. *An old, but valuable reference book on various mathematical applications in geography. Particularly useful for its treatment of the variables in earth-sun relationships.*

Lobeck, A. K., and W. J. Tellington: *Military Maps and Air Photographs,* McGraw-Hill Book Company Inc., New York, 1944. *A useful reference volume on military maps, the military grid system, and the interpretation of air photographs, with special emphasis on terrain features.*

Raisz, Erwin: *General Cartography,* 2d ed., McGraw-Hill Book Company, Inc., New York, 1948. *A thorough reference book on the history of cartography, the analysis of map projections, and cartographic art.*

Robinson, Arthur H.: *Elements of Cartography,* John Wiley & Sons, Inc., New York, 1953. *One of the standard introductory textbooks in cartography. Concise, yet most adequate in its treatment.*

CHAPTERS 3, 4, and 5

Bradley, John H.: *Autobiography of Earth,* Coward-McCann, Inc., New York, 1935. *A semi-popular account of the evolution of the surface features of the earth. Excellent supplementary reading for students.*

Croneis, C., and W. C. Krumbein: *Down to Earth,* University of Chicago Press, Chicago, 1936. *An introductory text in physical geology that is unusually readable in its presentation. Recommended for students as supplementary reading on processes of landform development.*

Gamow, George: *Biography of the Earth,* The Viking Press, Inc., New York, 1948. *An interesting, popular account of the history of the earth planet from its origin to the development of life. Chapters 6 and 7 are of particular interest.*

Lahee, F. H.: *Field Geology,* 5th ed., McGraw-Hill Book Company, Inc., New York, 1952. *The standard manual for the interpretation of landforms in the field. Useful mainly to teachers.*

Leet, L. D., and S. Judson: *Physical Geology,* Prentice-Hall, Inc., Englewood Cliffs, N.J., 1954. *One of the newest and best of the introductory textbooks in physical geology. Deals with the processes of landform development.*

Lobeck, A. K.: *Geomorphology,* McGraw-Hill Book Company, Inc., New York, 1939. *An excellent reference book on the description and interpretation of landforms. Particularly well illustrated.*

Longwell, C. R., A. Knopf, and R. F. Flint: *Outlines of Physical Geology,* John Wiley & Sons, Inc., New York, 1955. *A widely used introductory text on the processes of landform development.*

Pough, Frederick H.: *A Field Guide to Rocks and Minerals,* Houghton Mifflin Company, Boston, 1953. *A useful manual for beginners in the recognition of rocks and minerals in the field.*

Sharpe, C. F. S.: *Landslides and Related Phenomena,* Columbia University Press, New York, 1938. *A classic treatise on the movement of material down slopes. Comprehensive, yet readable.*

CHAPTERS 6, 7, and 8

Blair, Thomas A.: *Weather Elements,* 3d ed., Prentice-Hall, Inc., Englewood Cliffs, N.J., 1948. *An introductory textbook in meteorology. Suitable for student reference.*

———: *Climatology, General and Regional,* Prentice-Hall, Inc., Englewood Cliffs, N.J., 1942. *An introductory summary of global climatic patterns and their analysis.*

Brooks, C. E.: *Why the Weather,* Harcourt, Brace and Company, Inc., New York, 1935. *A popular explanation of weather phenomena. Excellent for supplementary student reading.*

Byers, Horace Robert: *General Meteorology,* McGraw-Hill Book Company, Inc., New York, 1944. *One of the standard texts in meteorology. Especially valuable for those with a background in physics and mathematics.*

Clayton, H. W.: *World Weather Records,* Smithsonian Miscellaneous Collections, vols. 79, 90, 105, Smithsonian Institution, Washington, D.C., 1927, 1934, 1947. *A collection of climatological statistics.*

Compendium of Meteorology, American Meteorological Society, Boston, 1951. *A compendium of articles reviewing the current status of knowledge concerning the science of meteorology. Compiled by specialists.*

Donn, William L.: *Meteorology with Marine Implications,* McGraw-Hill Book Company, Inc., New York, 1951. *An elementary, nontechnical meteorological reference book. Recommended for student reference.*

Garbell, Maurice A.: *Tropical and Equatorial Meteorology,* Pitman Publishing Corporation, New York, 1947. *A useful, nontechnical reference for more than tropical meteorology. Well illustrated with diagrams.*

Haurwitz, Bernhard, and James M. Austin: *Climatology,* McGraw-Hill Book Company, Inc., New York, 1944. *A useful review of global climatic patterns. Recommended for student reference.*

Kendrew, W. G.: *The Climates of the Continents,* 4th ed., Oxford University Press, New York, 1953. *Useful for descriptive material on world climatic patterns, arranged by continents. Analysis of patterns is weak and outdated.*

Koeppen, W., and R. Geiger: *Handbuch der Klimatologie,* Gebruder Borntraeger, Berlin, 1930 and later (5 vols., not completed). *Most of this is in German, but some is in English. It is the most detailed and accurate global climatology available.*

Petterssen, Sverre: *Introduction to Meteorology,* McGraw-Hill Book Company, Inc., New York, 1941. *A condensed and simplified version of the author's "Weather Analysis and Forecasting," a classic introduction to the science of meteorology.*

Trewartha, Glenn T.: *An Introduction to Climate,* McGraw-Hill Book Company, Inc., New York, 1954. *A particularly valuable textbook in elementary climatology. Readable and well illustrated.*

CHAPTERS 9 and 10

Berg, L. S.: *Natural Regions of the U.S.S.R.,* The Macmillan Company, New York, 1950. *Excellent descriptions and photographs of vegetation and floristic characteristics for this huge country. A wealth of detail on general ecological relationships. Soils, zoogeography, and landform characteristics also are treated regionally. Can be of value to both the specialist and the generalist.*

Cain, S. A.: *Foundations of Plant Geography,* Harper & Brothers, New York, 1944. *An advanced treatise on the principles of plant ecology. Recommended for those with a botanical background.*

Daubenmire, R. F.: *Plants and Environment,* John Wiley & Sons, Inc., New York, 1947. *An especially good reference book on the influence of various environmental factors on the form, function, and evolution of plants.*

"Grass," *The Yearbook of Agriculture, 1948,* U.S. Department of Agriculture. *A particularly good reference volume on various aspects of grassland ecology and management. Mainly concerned with grasslands of the United States.*

Hardy, M. E.: *The Geography of Plants,* Oxford University Press, New York, 1920. *An itinerant description of vegetation characteristics of the world by continents.*

Hill, A. F.: *Economic Botany,* 2d ed., McGraw-Hill Book Company, Inc., New York, 1952. *A standard reference book on the economic uses of plants. Especially well illustrated.*

Klages, Karl H. S.: *Ecological Crop Geography,* The Macmillan Company, New York, 1949. *A good reference book on the environmental factors that influence crop patterns. Global in treatment, but emphasis is on the United States.*

McDougall, W. B.: *Plant Ecology,* 4th ed., Lea & Febiger, Philadelphia, 1949. *Particularly recommended as an elementary reference book in plant ecology. Suitable for both student and teacher.*

Merrill, Elmer D.: *Plant Life of the Pacific World,* The Macmillan Company, New York, 1946. *An interesting small volume dealing with various aspects of the tropical Pacific flora. Includes general descriptions of major plant communities as well as common species. Originally designed as briefing material for military forces operating in the Pacific area.*

"Natural Vegetation," *Atlas of American Agriculture,* sec. E, U.S. Government Printing Office, Washington, D.C., 1924. *This section of the atlas contains a classic description of the major plant associations of the United States.*

Newbigin, Marion I.: *Plant and Animal Geography,* Methuen & Co., Ltd., London, 1936. *One of the classic volumes on plant geography. Of particular value to geographers.*

Shantz, H. L., and C. F. Marbut: *The Vegetation and Soils of Africa,* American Geographical Society Research Series, no. 13, New York, 1923. *A classic work on the vegetation and soils of Africa. A summary of descriptive work done prior to 1920.*

"Trees," *The Yearbook of Agriculture, 1939,* U.S. Department of Agriculture. *A reference volume on forest descriptions, problems, and management, with special emphasis on those of the United States.*

Weaver, John E.: *The North American Prairie,* Johnsen Publishing Co., Lincoln, Neb., 1954. *An excellent treatment of the North American prairie, its morphology, ecology, and history. Contains remarkable grassland photographs.*

———, and F. E. Clements: *Plant Ecology,* 2d ed., McGraw-Hill Book Company, Inc., New York, 1938. *One of the standard textbooks in plant ecology. It particularly stresses the processes of plant succession, stabilization of climax communities, and the importance of plant indicators.*

CHAPTERS 11 and 12

Ayres, Quincy C.: *Soil Erosion and Its Control,* McGraw-Hill Book Company, Inc., New York,

1936. *A technical book emphasizing the engineering aspects of soil-erosion control.*

Bennett, Hugh H.: *Elements of Soil Conservation,* 2d ed., McGraw-Hill Book Company, Inc., New York, 1955. *The most outstanding reference book on soil erosion, its characteristics, causes, remedies, and distribution. Excellently illustrated.*

Bushnell, T. M.: *The Story of Indiana Soils,* Purdue University Agricultural Experiment Station Special Circular 1, June, 1944. *A description of a topographic system of soil classification as applied to the soils of Indiana.*

Jenny, Hans: *Factors of Soil Formation,* McGraw-Hill Book Company, Inc., New York, 1941. *A useful reference book with excellent illustrative material on the major factors in soil formation, including time, parent material, topography, climate, and organisms.*

Joffe, Jacob S.: *Pedology,* 2d ed., Pedology Publications, New Brunswick, N.J., 1949. *An excellent and up-to-date summary and critique of the basic research in soil science, with special emphasis on Russian contributions. Designed for the advanced student of soils, but much of the descriptive material can be followed with profit by the general student.*

Kellogg, C. E.: *The Soils That Support Us,* The Macmillan Company, New York, 1941. *A nontechnical treatment of soil as a basic resource, its properties, and management.*

Marbut, C. F.: "Soils of the United States," *Atlas of American Agriculture,* part 3, U.S. Government Printing Office, Washington, D.C., 1935. *A summary of the principal soil characteristics of the United States, with excellent illustrations and descriptions of typical soil profiles.*

Marshall, C. E.: *Colloids in Agriculture,* Edward Arnold & Co., London, 1935. *An extremely useful small volume on colloids, with special emphasis on the inorganic and organic colloids contained within soils, their characteristics, functions, and role in soil management programs and soil properties. Written for the general student or lay reader.*

Mohr, E. C. J.: *The Soils of Equatorial Regions,* trans. by Robert L. Pendleton, J. W. Edwards, Publisher, Inc., Ann Arbor, Mich., 1944. *A treatise on the genesis, morphology, classification, and use of tropical soils with special reference to the soils of Indonesia.*

Robinson, Gilbert W.: *Soils: Their Origin, Constitution, and Classification,* 2d ed., Thomas Murby and Co., London, 1936. *An authoritative treatise on soil types and their development by an outstanding English soil scientist. Particularly valuable for its international examples of soil processes and characteristics.*

"Soil," *Yearbook of Agriculture, 1957,* U.S. Department of Agriculture. *This new agricultural yearbook presents the results of research on soil management since the publication of the 1938 volume. This one admirably supplements, but does not displace, the older volume.*

"Soils and Men," *Yearbook of Agriculture, 1938,* U.S. Department of Agriculture. *A valuable reference volume on nearly all aspects of soils —their genesis, characteristics, and use. Unfortunately this volume is out of print.*

Wolfanger, L. A.: *The Major Soil Divisions of the United States.* John Wiley & Sons, Inc., New York, 1930. *A small volume which presents a general summary of the great soil group within the United States. Useful for student reference.*

CHAPTER 13

Bateman, A. M.: *Economic Mineral Deposits,* 3d ed., John Wiley & Sons, Inc., New York, 1956. *A good general reference book on the origin, distribution, and extraction of mineral resources.*

DeMille, John B.: *Strategic Minerals,* McGraw-Hill Book Company, Inc., New York, 1947. *A summary of uses, world output, sources, stockpiling, and procurement programs for strategic minerals in United States industry. Special emphasis is given to wartime emergency requirements and the history of procurement programs during World War II.*

Fanning, Leonard M.: *Our Oil Resources,* 2d ed., McGraw-Hill Book Company, Inc., New York, 1950. *One of the best and most readable treatments of the petroleum industry, its technology, political implications, and resource appraisal.*

Industrial Minerals and Rocks, 2d ed., American Institute of Mining and Metallurgical Engineers, Committee on Industrial Minerals, New York, 1949. *A comprehensive reference volume on nonmetallic minerals other than fuels.*

Ladoo, R. B., and W. M. Myers: *Nonmetallic Minerals,* 2d ed., McGraw-Hill Book Company, Inc., New York, 1951. *A good reference volume on the nonmetallic minerals, their properties, uses, and distribution.*

Lovering, T. S.: *Minerals in World Affairs,* Prentice-Hall, Inc., Englewood Cliffs, N.J., 1943. *An excellent reference on the implications of mineral resources. Easy to read, yet penetrating in analysis.*

Mineral Facts and Problems, U.S. Bureau of Mines Bulletin 556, 1956. *A comprehensive reference volume on various aspects of the mineral industry, by separate minerals. Treats new techniques of processing and extraction and presents problems connected with the industry.*

Minerals Yearbook, U.S. Bureau of Mines. *This annual publication is a basic statistical source of information on mineral resource production and reserves, both domestic and foreign.*

Moore, Edwood S.: *Coal,* 2d ed., John Wiley & Sons, Inc., New York, 1940. *The standard reference book on coal, its origin, occurrence, extraction, and reserves. Suitable for student use.*

Nininger, Robert D.: *Minerals for Atomic Energy,* D. Van Nostrand Company, Inc., Princeton, N.J., 1954. *A comprehensive treatment of the location, characteristics, uses, and exploration methods of the main atomic energy minerals—uranium and thorium. Excellent student reference. Nontechnical.*

Pratt, Wallace E., and Dorothy Good: *World Geography of Petroleum,* American Geographic Society and Princeton University Press, New York, 1950. *An excellent treatise on the global geography of petroleum and on methods of prospecting and production.*

Ries, H.: *Economic Geology,* John Wiley & Sons, Inc., New York, 1930. *An introductory treatment of economic geology, more suitable for student reference than most such texts. Covers the entire mineral field.*

Spurr, Josiah E.: *The Ore Magmas,* McGraw-Hill Book Company, Inc., New York, 1923. *A classic analysis of mineral geography. Somewhat too technical for the average student, but a good reference for the teacher with an elementary background in mineralogy and economic geology.*

Van Royen, W., and Oliver Bowles: "The Mineral Resources of the World," *Atlas of the World's Resources,* vol. II, Prentice-Hall, Inc., Englewood Cliffs, N.J., 1952. *An atlas of major global minerals, complete with descriptive material, production and reserve statistics, and maps at various scales. An excellent reference volume.*

World Oil, Gulf Publishing Company, Houston, Tex. *This is an extremely valuable monthly publication, designed to keep abreast of new developments in the petroleum industry. The annual summaries of global production are especially useful.*

CHAPTER 14

Bennison, E. E.: *Ground Water: Its Development, Uses, and Conservation,* Edward E. Johnson, Inc., St. Paul, Minn., 1947. *A technical reference volume on ground water. Particularly useful for its treatment of new techniques for ground-water conservation. Prepared mainly as a service to the well-drilling industry.*

Dixey, Frank: *A Practical Handbook of Water Supply,* Thomas Murby and Company, Ltd., London, 1950. *A thorough treatment of the practical aspects of water supply, written for nonspecialists. Contains an interesting section on the water supply of southern, central, and eastern Africa and a chapter on water location.*

Ellis, Cecil B.: *Fresh Water from the Ocean,* The Ronald Press Company, New York, 1954. *A survey of the implications and methods used in obtaining fresh water from sea water. It is readily understandable by the lay reader.*

Frank, Bernard, and A. Netboy: *Water, Land and People,* Alfred A. Knopf, Inc., New York, 1950. *A semipopular and dramatic account of water problems in the United States. Excellent regional examples. Highly recommended for student reading.*

Graham, J. B., and M. F. Burrill (eds.): *Water for industry,* American Association for the Advancement of Science, Washington, D.C., 1951. *A most useful, modern summary of the general problems of industrial water supply.*

Hurst, H. E.: *The Nile,* Constable & Co., Ltd., London, 1952. *A detailed, extremely readable, and valuable reference book on the various hydrologic aspects of the Nile and their human implications, written by an English hydrologist.*

King, Thomas: *Water,* The Macmillan Company, New York, 1953. *A semipopular treatment of water with its various physical and human implications. Will hold reader interest. Particularly useful for the history of water use.*

Kuenen, P. H.: *Realms of Water,* John Wiley & Sons, Inc., New York, 1955. *An excellent new reference work on the physical aspects of water in nature by a world-renowned hydrologist. Prepared especially for nonspecialists. Originally written in Dutch, the English translation is unusually fluent.*

The Physical and Economic Foundation of Natural

Resources, U.S. Congress, House of Representative Committee on Interior and Insular Affairs, 1952–1953. *A comprehensive analysis of water-supply problems in the United States.*

Thomas, Hard E.: *The Conservation of Ground Water,* McGraw-Hill Book Company, Inc., New York, 1951. *The most authoritative reference work on ground water in the United States. It surveys the natural factors influencing ground-water occurrence and comprehensively analyzes the problems of its utilization. Recommended for both student and teacher reference. Contains an excellent bibliography of regional ground-water problems.*

"Water," *Yearbook of Agriculture, 1955,* U.S. Department of Agriculture. *This yearbook is devoted to a treatment of water resources in the United States in all its various aspects. An excellent reference volume compiled by governmental experts. Special emphasis on agricultural uses for water.*

White, Gilbert F. (ed.): *The Future of Arid Lands,* American Association for the Advancement of Science, Washington, D.C., 1956. *A collection of papers and recommendations of an international symposium on arid-land problems. Particularly valuable as a summary of the current status of research on methods of increasing the productivity of arid lands.*

CHAPTER 15

Carson, Rachel: *The Sea around Us,* Oxford University Press, New York, 1951. *One of the best sellers in the United States. A classic popularization of oceanography, skillfully and lucidly written by a competent student of the subject. Highly recommended for supplementary reading.*

Chapin, Henry, and F. G. Walton Smith: *The Ocean River,* Charles Scribner's Sons, New York, 1952. *A remarkably comprehensive and readable treatment of the North Atlantic, its history, regional differences, and mechanics. The geophysical and meteorological treatments are somewhat inadequate.*

Coker, R. E.: *The Great and Wide Sea,* The University of North Carolina Press, Chapel Hill, N.C., 1947. *An excellent and well-written reference book on the sea. The treatment of marine biology is particularly good.*

Kuenen, P. H.: *Realms of Water,* John Wiley & Sons, Inc., New York, 1955. *One particularly excellent chapter in this readable reference book on water is a condensed summary of some of the highlights of oceanography. Highly recommended for supplementary reading.*

———: *Marine Geology,* John Wiley & Sons, Inc., New York, 1950. *A technical but valuable reference book on the structure of ocean basins and various geologic processes in and around the margins of the oceans.*

Lane, Ferdinand C.: *The Mysterious Sea,* Doubleday & Company, Inc., New York, 1947. *A semi-popular book on the sea. Excellent especially for its historical anecdotes concerning human relationships to the sea.*

Morgan, Robert: *World Sea Fisheries,* Pitman Publishing Corporation, New York, 1955. *A splendid reference work on world fisheries. Includes material on environmental factors, techniques, and details on the industry throughout the world.*

Murray, Sir John: *The Ocean: A General Account of the Science of the Sea,* Henry Holt and Company, Inc., New York, 1910. *An old, but interesting small volume by one of the oceanographic pioneers. Excellent for comparing the status of the science of oceanography at the turn of the century with that of today.*

Ommanney, F. D.: *The Ocean,* Oxford University Press, New York, 1949. *A handy, small reference volume on the sea, with special emphasis on marine biology and sea fisheries. Recommended for student reference.*

Sverdrup, H. U., Martin W. Johnson, and Richard H. Fleming: *The Oceans: Their Physics, Chemistry, and General Biology,* Prentice-Hall, Inc., Englewood Cliffs, N.J., 1942. *The standard reference work on oceanography. It is exceptionally comprehensive and authoritative. Useful mainly to students and teachers who wish to penetrate more deeply into selected topics.*

APPENDIX C

Glossary of terms

ABERRATION The failure of the zenithal extension of the earth axis to maintain a fixed position with respect to the background of stars.

ABSOLUTE INSTABILITY A condition in the atmosphere when the lapse rate throughout a column of air is greater than the dry adiabatic rate (greater than 5.6°F per 1,000 feet).

ABSOLUTE STABILITY A condition of the atmosphere in which the lapse rate is less than 2.5°F per 1,000 feet.

ABSORPTION In meteorology, the transformation of radiant energy into some other type of energy.

ACACIA A thorny, deciduous tree of tropical woodlands.

ACIDIC ROCK Igneous rock containing a high percentage of silica (above 50 to 55 per cent) and a low percentage of metallic bases (iron, calcium, magnesium, etc.). See also *Sial.*

ACIDITY The concentration of hydrogen ions in an aqueous solution. A concentration greater than 10^{-7} is termed acidic, and a concentration less than 10^{-7} is termed alkaline.

ADIABATIC HEATING AND COOLING Changes in temperature that do not involve an addition or withdrawal of heat. In the atmosphere these are associated with the compression or expansion of air following an increase or decrease in atmospheric pressure. Also known as *dynamic heating and cooling.*

ADVECTION Horizontal transfer of heat by winds.

AGGRADATION The process of building up a land surface by deposition.

AGGREGATES (SOIL) Soil structural units, consisting of many soil particles held together.

A HORIZON See *Zone of eluviation.*

AIR CURRENTS Air movements that have upward or downward components.

AIR DRAINAGE The gravity flow of air into topographic depressions after radiational cooling.

AIR MASS An extensive body of air with more or less homogeneous characteristics in a horizontal plane.

ALBEDO The radiation that is lost to outer space by direct reflection or scattering.

ALGAE Single-celled plants, usually colonial.

ALKALI Sodium or potassium carbonates that accumulate in poorly drained desert soils.

ALKALINE EARTHS Several of the bivalent oxides, such as those of calcium, magnesium, barium, and strontium.

ALKALINE SOIL A soil that has a pH above 7, or one in which negative OH^- ions predominate over positive H^+ ions.

ALLUVIAL FAN A depositional slope composed of alluvial material at the mouth of a valley. It slopes outward with gradually decreasing gradients (convex).

ALLUVIAL FLOOD PLAIN A broad plain resulting from alluvial deposition along the course of a river.

ALLUVIAL TERRACE A terrace composed of alluvium, and marking a former higher level of stream deposition.

ALLUVIUM Unconsolidated fragmental material recently deposited by streams. Does not include the material deposited in ponded waters.

ALPINE Pertaining to high altitudes near and above the timberline of mountains.

AMORPHOUS Without a definite or distinctive form. When pertaining to rocks or minerals, the term implies the absence of a definite crystal structure.

ANAEROBIC pertaining to life forms that are active despite a deficiency of free oxygen.

ANGULAR MOMENTUM The tendency for a body moving in a curved path to maintain its angular velocity.

ANGULAR VELOCITY The velocity of movement

along a curved path, measured in angles of arc per unit of time.

ANOMALY, GRAVIMETRIC An abnormal gravity reading at the earth surface. A positive anomaly implies readings that are greater than normal; a negative anomaly indicates readings that are less than normal.

ANOMALY, TEMPERATURE A temperature that is different from the mean expected for the particular latitude.

ANTHOCYANIN A variety of plant sugar with a red coloration, produced in the leaves of some plants.

ANTHRACITE A lustrous, black, hard coal, containing a relatively high percentage (85 per cent) of fixed carbon. *Meta-anthracite* consists almost entirely of fixed carbon.

ANTICLINE A rock upfold, or a rock fold in which the strata dip downward away from the center, or axis, of the fold.

ANTICYCLONE (OR HIGH) An area of relatively high atmospheric pressure, characterized by subsiding, diverging, rotational wind motion. The rotation is clockwise in the northern hemisphere and counterclockwise in the southern hemisphere.

ANTIPODE A point on the globe that is directly opposite a given point.

APHANITIC A fine-grained igneous rock.

APPROPRIATED WATER RIGHTS A doctrine pertaining to the use of water and maintaining that whoever first puts a surface-water supply to beneficial use has priority on the use of that water.

AQUIFER A permeable rock strata from which flowing water may be obtained.

ARCTIC FRONT The line of discontinuity between very cold arctic air recently subsided within polar anticyclones and older, cool air in the upper mid-latitudes.

AREA A delimited section of the earth surface.

AREA SLOPE The generalization of slope conditions within a particular area.

ARÊTE A jagged, narrow mountain-ridge crest resulting from glacial erosion. Also known as a *comb ridge*.

ARROYOS See *Wadi*.

ARTESIAN SYSTEM A structure whereby water contained within a rock stratum will rise within the tube of a drilled well or along a natural fissure. Such water may or may not reach the surface.

ASH The nonvolatile remains resulting from the burning of organic material. Also, fine-textured material ejected from a volcano.

ASPHALT A dark-colored, solid or semisolid bituminous material chemically belonging to a group of hydrocarbons.

ASSOCIATION See *Plant association*.

ATMOSPHERIC PRESSURE The mass weight of a column of air above a given point.

ATOLL A more or less circular coral reef enclosing a lagoon and often surmounted by low sandy islands.

ATOMIC ENERGY Energy released as the result of fission in the nuclei of atoms.

AURORA A luminous phenomenon in the upper atmosphere caused by the ionization of gases. Termed *aurora borealis* in the northern hemisphere and *aurora australis* south of the equator.

AVALANCHE A large mass of snow or ice that moves rapidly down a mountain slope.

AZIMUTH The true direction of a meridian passing through a given point. Also, the horizontal direction of a line measured clockwise from the meridional plane. The azimuth of west, for example, is 270°.

AZIMUTHAL Pertaining to the property of map projections in which directions are true from a central point.

AZONAL SOILS Unconsolidated materials that have not yet developed distinct soil-profile characteristics.

BACK MARSH The poorly drained areas on an alluvial flood plain, which are generally located well away from the river and its natural levees.

BACTERIA Single-celled microorganisms, whose affinities to the plant or animal kingdom are debatable.

BADLANDS A highly dissected land surface, sculptured largely by rainwash and usually lacking an appreciable vegetation cover. It often is composed of fine-textured, unconsolidated sediments.

BAJADA A piedmont alluvial plain.

BARCHAN A crescentic sand dune that has its ends pointing in the direction of the wind.

BARRIER BEACH A ridge of sand paralleling the coast and thrown up by storm waves some distance off a gradually sloping coast line. Also known as an *offshore bar*.

BARRIER REEF A coral reef that lies some distance offshore and is separated from the coast line by a deep lagoon.

BASALT A dark-colored, fine-textured igneous

rock. It usually is volcanic, or formed at or near the earth surface.

BASE A substance that supplies various positive ions and negative OH− ions when dissolved in water. The positive ions associated with bases comprise many important plant foods.

BASE EXCHANGE The process of exchanging cations (positive ions) at the interfaces of colloidal systems.

BASEMENT COMPLEX The crystalline rock base that forms the outer portion of the earth crust.

BASIC ROCK Igneous rock that contains a relatively low percentage (below 50 to 55 per cent) of silica and a high percentage of metallic bases (iron, calcium, magnesium, etc.) See also *Sima.*

BASIN FLOODING A system of irrigation in which river floodwaters are guided into successive basins in order to saturate soils.

BATHOLITH A large, irregular instrusive mass of igneous rock that intersects the rock structure and has no apparent floor. It usually is greater than 40 square miles in area.

BAUXITE The principal ore of aluminum. It is composed of hydrated aluminum oxide containing various impurities.

BAY-MOUTH BAR A sand bar which extends across the mouth of a bay, from one coastal promontory to another.

BEARING The horizontal angular measurement of a line from a cardinal point—for example, N 30° E.

B HORIZON See *Zone of illuviation.*

BIOSPHERE The zone of life forms at the earth surface.

BITUMINOUS COAL An intermediate coal, as classified according to percentage of fixed carbon and volatile material. Sometimes known as *soft coal.*

BLOCK MOUNTAIN A mountain mass bordered by faults.

BOG A thick, spongy morass composed largely of water-saturated peat or muck; usually mossy.

BOLSON A desert basin rimmed by mountains.

BORE A sudden, steep wave caused by the convergence of ocean tidal flow into a rapidly narrowing estuary.

BTU British thermal unit, or the amount of heat energy required to raise one pound of water one degree Fahrenheit at sea-level atmospheric pressure.

BUTTE A prominent, isolated, cliffed erosional remnant in dry regions, usually bordered by talus slopes; often turret-shaped.

CAATINGA A scrub, thorny, open woodland in northeastern Brazil.

CACTI A group of desert plants having fleshy stems and branches with scales or spines instead of leaves.

CALCAREOUS Containing a large proportion of calcium carbonate.

CALCIFICATION The soil-forming process of dry regions, whereby lime accumulates in the *B* horizon and the surface soil colloidal material, which is stable, is kept saturated with exchangeable calcium ions.

CALDERA A large, basin-shaped depression associated with a volcano, the diameter of which is many times greater than the included volcanic vent.

CALICHE A more or less cemented depositional layer of alkaline earth carbonates found in tropical and subtropical dry-land soils.

CALORIE The amount of heat energy necessary to raise the temperature of one gram of water one degree centigrade at sea level when the air temperature is 15 degrees centigrade.

CAMPO The Brazilian savanna.

CAPILLARITY The action by which the surface of a liquid in an opening or tube is raised or lowered because of surface tension.

CARTOGRAPHY The art and science of map making.

CENTER POINT The central point from which a map projection is geometrically based.

CENTRIFUGAL An apparent force directed outward by a body moving in a curved path.

CENTRIPETAL A force directed inward by a body moving in a curved path.

CHALK A soft, amorphous rock composed of calcium carbonate.

CHAPARRAL A dense, mostly broadleaf, evergreen thicket. Known also as *maquis* or *mallée.*

CHERNOZEM A dark-colored–to–black zonal soil, having a lime-accumulation layer in the *B* horizon. Typically developed under a tall-grass vegetation in the mid-latitudes.

CHERT An amorphous rock composed mainly of hardened colloidal silica. Usually occurs as an impurity in limestones.

CHINOOK (OR FOEHN) A dry, warm wind that descends a mountain slope from high elevations and that has been warmed by compression.

CHLOROPHYLL A complex organic molecule that is a necessary catalyst in photosynthesis. Its bright-green color is distinctive.

C HORIZON The underlying parent material of a soil.

CHOROGRAPHIC Regional or subcontinental in scale. More specifically, the term refers to a scale of reduction of between 1:500,000 and 1:5,000,000.

CHRONOMETER An accurate timepiece, usually used to determine longitude.

CINDER CONE A cone-shaped mound of fragmental material accumulated at the vent or opening of an explosive volcano. Usually contains a crater at its summit.

CIRQUE An amphitheaterlike depression in mountainous terrain produced by the sapping effect of mountain glaciers.

CIRRUS High-elevation, wispy cloud forms that do not cast a shadow.

CLAY Soil fragmental material with a particle size below 0.002 millimeters in diameter. Also, a group of crystalline minerals, colloidal in size and composed largely of iron and aluminum silicates.

CLIMATE The over-all, or aggregate, weather conditions of an area.

CLIMATOLOGY The science of climatic areal differences and similarities.

CLIMAX VEGETATION A plant community that represents a relatively long-term equilibrium with respect to its constituent plant forms and their environment.

COAL A simple mixture of carbon in a solid, noncrystalline form, containing various organic impurities.

COASTAL PLAIN Any plain which has its margin on the shore of a large body of water, especially the sea. Generally represents a strip of recently emerged sea bottom.

COCCOLITHOPHORES Microscopic marine animals that have calcareous body casings.

COL A pass or saddle along a mountain ridge. Usually formed by the intersection of cirques.

COLD FRONT A steep frontal surface between cold and warm air masses in which the cold air is displacing warm air in its path.

COLLOID A finely divided system of particles with unique physical and chemical properties and interfacial relationships.

COLLUVIUM A heterogeneous mass of soil and rock debris accumulated at the base of a slope as the result of mass wastage.

COMPENSATED DRY PERIOD A dry period which results in no major adaptation on the part of dominant vegetation, because of an abundance of rain during the remainder of the year.

COMPOST Partially decayed organic wastes used as fertilizers.

COMPROMISE A property of map projections in which all distortion is kept as low as possible at the expense of having no characteristic of the surface truly represented.

CONDENSATION A change in phase from a gas to a liquid.

CONDITIONAL INSTABILITY A condition in which air that contains sufficient water vapor and that is located where the lapse rate is steep enough can sustain lifting once the condensational level is reached. A condition where the lapse rate lies between the values of the wet and dry adiabatic rates.

CONDUCTION The transmission of heat from a warmer to a cooler body by direct contact.

CONFORMALITY A property of map projections in which shapes are true for limited areas.

CONGLOMERATE A sedimentary rock composed of cemented gravel or water-worn pebbles. Also known as *pudding stone.*

CONIFEROUS A plant (usually a needleleaf tree) belonging to the order Coniferae. Such plants utilize cones in their reproductive structure.

CONTINENTAL AIR MASSES An air mass whose source area lies within a continental interior.

CONTINENTAL SHELF A gradually sloping submarine plain or terrace that borders the continents. Its steep outer edge generally lies at a depth of about 350 feet, but may extend to about 600 feet.

CONTINENTAL SLOPE The steep outer slope of the continental shelf.

CONTOUR INTERVAL The vertical distance represented by the spacing between contours on a contour map.

CONTOUR LINE A line connecting points of equal elevation.

CONTOUR PRESSURE RIDGE A low ridge paralleling the contours along a hillside and resulting from soil slumping.

CONVECTION A localized upward or downward movement of material involving a transfer of heat away from a heating source.

CONVECTIONAL PRECIPITATION Precipitation in which the initial updraft of air is caused by convection.

CONVERGENCE The condition that exists when there is a net horizontal inflow of air or water toward a common center or line.

COPEPODA A variety of shrimplike zooplankton.

CORDILLERA A mountain chain comprising several separate ridges or ranges that may or may not be parallel. The entire chain, however, has one general direction.

CORIOLIS EFFECT The apparent deflective force of the earth's rotation. See *Ferrel's law*.

CRATER A steep-sided pit or depression at the summit or the flanks of a volcano.

CREVASSE A fissure or cleft in glacial ice resulting from stresses and strains during movement.

CROSS CHANNEL A lateral drainage way cut by glacial drainage across interstream areas.

CROSS GRADING The process of developing a dendritic pattern by rills and gullies as they dissect a slope.

CRUST (OF THE EARTH) The outer portion of the solid earth.

CRYSTALLINE ROCK A rock whose constituent minerals have developed crystal forms as the result of cooling from a molten state, or as the result of excessive heating and compression.

CUESTA An unsymmetrical ridge with a steep slope or cliff on one side and a gentle slope on the other. The latter generally conforms to the slope, or dip, of the underlying rock strata.

CUMULUS Cloud types that typically have domed summits and flat bases.

CYCLONE (OR LOW) An area of relatively low atmospheric pressure, characterized by converging, ascending, rotating winds. The rotation is counterclockwise in the northern hemisphere and clockwise in the southern hemisphere.

CYCLONIC PRECIPITATION Precipitation in which the initial updraft of air is caused by convergence within a cyclone.

DECIDUOUS Pertaining to plants that shed their leaves during a particular period or season.

DECOMPOSITION Chemical breakdown of compounds. The term sometimes pertains specifically to chemical rock weathering.

DEGRADATION The general process of lowering the land surface by erosion.

DEGRADED CHERNOZEM A chernozem soil in which the lime has been removed from the *B* horizon. Usually develops where a forest vegetation has encroached upon a prairie.

DEGREE CURVE A measurement of the amplitude of a curve. It is equal to the angle at the center of a circle subtended by 100 feet of the curve.

DEGREE-DAY The number of degrees difference between the mean daily temperatures and an arbitrary base point of 65°F. The degrees below 65° are termed *heating degree-days*, and those above 65° are termed *cooling degree-days*.

DEGREE SLOPE The angular measurement of slope from a horizontal plane; expressed in degrees.

DELTA An accumulation of sediment in ponded water at the mouth of a stream.

DENDRITIC Pertaining to an aborescent, or tree-like, pattern. The term usually refers to a drainage pattern with tributaries joining the main valley at acute angles.

DENSITY The ratio of mass, or weight, to volume.

DEPRESSION CONTOUR A hachured contour that indicates a depression below the general land surface.

DESERT PAVEMENT A thin mantle of wind-polished pebbles that covers a desert land surface.

DESERT VARNISH A glaze which forms on the surface of rock fragments in a desert.

DEUTERIUM A hydrogen isotope with an atomic weight of 2.

DEW Water that condenses on a surface that is cooler than the adjacent air.

DIATOMACEOUS OOZE A fine, siliceous, deep-sea mud comprised largely of diatom remains.

DIATOMS A variety of microscopic aquatic plants that usually have a siliceous body casing.

DIBBLE STICK A pointed stick used by many non-literate forest dwellers for planting purposes.

DIFFERENTIAL EROSION Irregular erosion resulting from differences in resistance of surface materials.

DIKE A tabular body of igneous rock that cross-cuts the grain, or structure, of the surrounding rock.

DINOFLAGELLATES One-celled, microscopic, marine organisms that move by waving a whiplike appendage, or flagellum.

DIP The angle made by a rock strata or any other plane surface, measured from the horizontal.

DISCONTINUITY The meteorological condition characterized by a relatively rapid change in air-mass characteristics within a narrow zone.

DISINTEGRATION Physical or mechanical rock weathering.

DISSECTION The erosional process of sculpturing the land surface.

DISTRIBUTARIES The various discharge channels of a river on its delta.

DIURNAL Of or pertaining to a 24-hour period.

DIVERGENCE A condition in which there is a net outflow of air or water from an area.

DOLDRUMS A zone of calms or light variable winds located between the trade-wind zones.

DOLINE See *Sinkhole.*

DOLOMITE A calcium-magnesium carbonate.

DOME A roughly symmetrical rock upfold, in which the included rock strata dip outward in all directions from the center.

DOMINANT PLANTS The largest common members of a plant community.

DRIFT (GLACIAL) A collective term for all detrital material derived from a glacier. Includes both till and stratified fluvioglacial material.

DRIFTLESS AREA A section in southwestern Wisconsin and adjacent parts of Illinois, Iowa, and Minnesota that was surrounded, but not covered, by the Pleistocene continental ice sheets.

DRUMLIN An oval-shaped mound of compact glacial till that has its long axis oriented in the direction of ice motion.

DRY ADIABATIC RATE The rate at which an ascending body of unsaturated air cools because of adiabatic expansion: approximately 5.6° per 1,000 feet.

DRY FARMING A system of farming designed primarily to conserve and retain moisture in the soil for crop use.

DUST DEVIL A small whirling vortex produced by mechanical instability of air over a highly heated surface. Usually found in dry regions.

EARTHQUAKE Earth tremors, or elastic waves caused by rock rupturing or displacing along a fault.

EASTERLY WAVE A wavelike undulation that moves from east to west in the isobars of a pressure gradient. Usually found on the equatorial flanks of subtropical anticyclones.

ECLIPTIC The plane of the earth orbit around the sun.

ECOLOGY The science of interrelationship between organisms and their environment.

EDAPHIC Pertaining to soil influences.

EELGRASS A marine plant (*Zostera*) with long, narrow leaves that abounds in shallow, cool sea water. It is a favorite food of fish.

EFFLUENT STREAM A stream whose flow is supplied almost entirely by ground water.

EKMAN'S LAW The law that surface water tends to move at an angle of 45° to the right of the direction of prevailing winds in the northern hemisphere and to the left in the southern hemisphere.

ELEVATION A linear measurement of the vertical distance above some reference point or plane.

EL NIÑO A warm ocean current that sometimes flows southward along the Peruvian coast and replaces the normal northward-flowing cold Peruvian Current.

ELUVIATION The movement of soil material within the profile. Usually the direction is downward.

ENCLAVE An area of dissimilarity enclosed within a region.

EPHEMERAL PLANTS Short-lived annual plants.

EPIPHYTES Plants that use other plants for support (e.g., some mosses and orchids).

EQUATOR A great circle of the earth that is equidistant from the two poles, or the ends of the earth axis.

EQUINOX The date on which the vertical rays of the sun are on the equator and the days and nights are of equal length at all latitudes. Usually on or about March 22 (*vernal equinox*) and September 22 (*autumnal equinox*).

EQUIVALENCE A property of map projections in which the ratio between areas on the map is the same as that of the corresponding areas on earth.

ERG A sandy desert.

EROSION Any or all of the processes that tend to loosen and remove earth or rock material.

ERRATIC A boulder that has been transported by glacial ice and is not native to the area in which it is found.

ESKER A long, narrow ridge composed of stratified sand and gravel, formed by a stream in association with glacial ice.

EVAPOTRANSPIRATION The return of water to the atmosphere via evaporation and plant transpiration from a plant-covered land surface.

EXCLAVE An area of similarity located apart from, or outside, a region.

EXOTIC RIVER A river in a dry region which has its source in a distant humid area.

EXTRATROPICAL CYCLONE A cyclone low-pressure center originating outside the tropics.

EXTRUSIVE ROCK An igneous rock that has cooled and solidified rapidly at or near the surface.

FAULT A fracture in the crust of the earth along which there has been displacement of the two sides relative to one another.

FAULT LINE ESCARPMENT A steep slope or cliff that conforms closely to a line of faulting and that has resulted from differential movement along the fault.

FAULT, NORMAL A dipping fault where displacement has shifted the overhanging side downward with reference to the footwall, or basal, side.

Fault line scarp A steep slope or escarpment that has resulted from differential erosion along a fault rather than from displacement, as in a fault escarpment.

Fault, thrust or reverse A fault where displacement has moved the overhanging wall upward with reference to the footwall side.

Feldspar A group or family of aluminum silicates, carrying varying proportions of various bases (sodium, calcium, magnesium, etc.).

Felsenmeer An area of irregular, broken rock fragments resulting from the splitting action of freezing water in cracks and crevices. Found mainly in polar regions and at high elevations.

Felsite A light-colored, fine-textured volcanic or extrusive rock containing much quartz and feldspar. Usually has different-sized crystals.

Ferrallite A humid tropical soil which has developed under ideal conditions of ferrallization.

Ferrallitic Pertaining to soils that have characteristic features of ferrallization. Sometimes defined as soils that have a silica-sesquioxide ratio of less than 2.

Ferrallization The soil-forming process of warm, humid regions, which is characterized by leaching of silica and bases by mildly acidic-to-neutral soil solutions.

Ferrel's law The law that all moving bodies of air or water tend to be deflected toward the right in the direction of motion in the northern hemisphere and to the left in the southern hemisphere. Also known as the *Coriolis effect*.

Ferric Pertaining to iron compounds that are saturated with oxygen.

Ferroalloy A combination of iron and some other metal, producing distinctive physical properties. The common alloy elements, along with iron, are manganese, chromium, nickel, molybdenum, tungsten, and vanadium.

Ferrous Pertaining to iron compounds that are unsaturated with oxygen and that usually result from the deoxidation (reduction) of ferric compounds.

Ferruginous Containing a relatively high content of iron oxide.

Fetch The horizontal distance over water in which wind is developing waves.

Field-fallow agriculture A form of sedentary agriculture in which fertility is replenished by a cyclical period of rest.

Fire succession A plant succession that follows a fire.

Fissure-flow volcano An outpouring of highly fluid lava from a fissure or crack in the earth crust.

Fjord A glaciated U-shaped mountain valley that opens onto the sea.

Flocculation The union, or coagulation, of colloidal particles into masses, or structural aggregates.

Fluvioglacial Pertaining to streams resulting from glacial melt water.

Fog A cloud of tiny water droplets at the earth surface.

Foraminifera Small, marine, one-celled animals that have a lime body casing.

Fossil fuels The mineral fuels resulting from organic carbon: petroleum, coal, and natural gas.

Fringing reef A coral reef that is attached to a shore line.

Front The surface boundary between two air masses.

Frost Ice crystals formed from the freezing of vapor on terrestrial objects.

Fungi A group of spore-bearing plants without chlorophyll (molds, mushrooms, etc.).

Galeria A forest growth along streams in grasslands, in which the treetops interlace over the stream.

Generic Pertaining to things of the same kind or class.

Genetic Pertaining to the genesis, or natural origin, of things.

Geographic grid The system of parallels and meridians used to locate points on the earth surface.

Geography The science of earth space; the descriptive and analytical study of areal differences and similarities on the earth surface.

Geology The science of earth history.

Geomorphology The branch of geology that deals with the form of the earth, the general surface configuration, and the evolution of landforms.

Geostrophic wind A wind that parallels the isobars.

Geosyncline A large sedimentary trough formed as the result of progressive downward warping and deposition.

Glacial pavement A polished rock surface caused by glacial erosion and abrasion.

Glacial spillway A valley or drainage way that

was eroded by melt water flowing from the margins of a continental ice sheet.

GLACIER A flowing mass of ice.

GLAUCONITE A greenish mineral composed of a hydrous potassium iron silicate. Usually associated with marine deposits.

GLAZE An icy coating formed by the sudden freezing of rain after it strikes terrestrial objects.

GLEI (GLEY) A soil horizon characterized by a sticky, compact clay that is generally bluish-gray or olive-gray in color. It develops as the result of water saturation.

GLEIIZATION The process of deoxidation of ferric iron compounds in a soil resulting from water saturation. The general process of forming *glei* characteristics in poorly drained soils.

GLOBAL SCALE A scale of areal generalization involving all or a major part of the earth surface. Maps at this level of generalization have scales smaller than 1:5,000,000.

GLOBAL THERMAL BALANCE The general balance between the total amount of incoming and outgoing radiation with respect to the entire earth.

GNEISS A banded, crystalline, coarse-grained metamorphic rock.

GORE A triangular or lune-shaped piece forming part of the surface of a globe.

GRABEN An elongated trough, or depression, resulting from subsidence between parallel normal faults.

GRANITE A light-colored, coarsely crystalline igneous rock, composed largely of quartz and feldspar.

GRANITIC A coarse-textured igneous rock.

GRAPHITE A form of soft, pure, amorphous carbon.

GRAVITY WINDS Density air currents that flow down a topographic slope under the influence of gravity.

GREAT CIRCLE All or part of an outer circumference of the earth. The shortest surface distance between any two points on the earth.

GREAT SOIL GROUP A major classification of soils according to form and structure.

GREENHOUSE EFFECT The selective screening of longer wavelengths of radiation by the atmosphere. The transmission of short-wavelength insolation and the absorption of longer terrestrial radiation.

GREEN MANURE Green plants that are plowed into the soil to increase the humus content.

GRID Any orderly, systematized series of lines.

GRID REFERENCE SYSTEM A world-wide system of separate military grids, each 6° of longitude wide and 8° of latitude long.

GROUND WATER The portion of the subsurface water that is below the water table.

GROUND-WATER PODZOL A hardpan in a soil resulting from mineral precipitation at the top of a ground-water table.

GULLYING The erosion of soil resulting from the excavation of trenches greater than 2 to 3 feet in depth.

GUYOT See *Sea mount.*

GYPSUM A crystalline mineral of hydrous calcium sulfate. Sometimes precipitated from ground water in the soils of dry regions.

GYRE A balanced, circular movement in a fluid medium.

HABITAT The effective areal range of action of an organism.

HACHURE Short lines on a map trending in the direction of slope.

HAIL Round or irregular lumps of ice formed by the concentric layering of ice or snow derived from collisions with supercooled drops of water during thunderstorms.

HALF-BOG SOILS A shallow (3-foot) layer of organic soil overlying a gray mineral soil. Usually associated with a swamp-forest type of vegetation.

HALOPHYTES Plants tolerant of high salinity in the soil.

HAMADA A dry, rocky plain.

HANGING VALLEY A tributary valley that enters the main valley at a level well above the floor of the latter.

HARDPAN A compact, indurated, or cemented horizon in soils that impedes the downward movement of water.

HAYSTACK TOPOGRAPHY A land surface consisting of knobby, cone-shaped limestone hills with rounded summits. Such landforms are the result of solution and are found in the tropics or subtropics.

HEAT The kinetic energy of molecular motion.

HEAT LOW (THERMAL LOW) A low-atmospheric-pressure area caused by abnormal land-surface heating.

HEAT SINK An area in which terrestrial radiation exceeds insolation, that is, an area that loses more energy through radiation than it receives through absorption of insolation.

HEMATITE The principal ore of iron; usually brick-red in color. Has the chemical formula Fe_2O_3.

HERBACEOUS Pertaining to plants whose stems do not develop woody tissue.

HIGH See *Anticyclone*.

HIGH PLAINS Plains that lie at elevations above 2,000 feet. The term is also used specifically for a relatively undissected section of the American Great Plains.

HIGH-SUN SEASON The summer season. The term is used primarily in referring to the tropics, where temperature seasons are not pronounced.

HILL STATION A high-elevation climatic refuge in the tropics.

HILLY Describing an area characterized by a predominance of slopes greater than 5 per cent and a local relief of between 200 and 2,000 feet.

HORIZON The intersection of a horizontal plane with the sky. For the use of the term in connection with soils, see *Soil horizon*.

HORN A steep-sided pyramidal mountain peak resulting from the intersection of three or more cirques.

HORNBLENDE A dark mineral found in basic rocks. A complex iron and calcium aluminum silicate belonging to the amphibole group of minerals.

HORSE LATITUDE The belt of calms, light variable winds, and subsident air that is found near the center of the subtropical anticyclones.

HUMIDITY Water vapor in the air.

HUMIDITY, ABSOLUTE The weight of water vapor per unit of air volume.

HUMIDITY, RELATIVE The ratio of the amount of water vapor contained in the air to the amount held at saturation, or the vapor pressure divided by vapor-pressure saturation.

HUMIDITY, SPECIFIC A measurement of the mass of water vapor contained in the air, expressed in proportional weight.

HUMUS The well-decomposed organic material in a soil. Frequently colloidal in nature and relatively stable.

HURRICANE A severe tropical cyclone with winds exceeding 75 miles per hour.

HYDROCARBON A chain compound of carbon and hydrogen links.

HYDROGRAPHY A description of distributional patterns of drainage.

HYDROLOGIC Pertaining to drainage characteristics.

HYDROLOGIC CYCLE The course taken by water in moving from the oceans to the land via evaporation and precipitation and returning via stream flow.

HYDROPHYTE A plant that thrives in an abundance of water.

HYDROSPHERE The zone of liquid water at or near the earth surface.

HYDROXYL ION A union of oxygen with a hydrogen atom that contains an extra electron; hence the molecule has a net negative charge. Usually expressed as OH^-.

ICECAP An ice mass that moves outward fairly evenly from a single center.

ICE SHEET An icecap that mantles all of the land surface in its path, except the highest mountains, and whose general direction of flow is not influenced by terrain features.

ICE SHELF (OR SHELF ICE) A glacial ice mass that extends beyond the land and is supported by the buoyancy of water at the outer edge of the glacier.

IGNEOUS ROCK Rock that has solidified from a molten state.

IMMATURE SOIL A young soil lacking a well-developed profile.

INFLUENT STREAM A stream whose flow consists of surface runoff and whose channel lies above the water table.

INFRARED Invisible radiation whose wavelengths are just beyond the long, or red, end of the visible light spectrum.

INSOLATION Radiant energy from the sun that is received at the earth surface.

INSTABILITY, GENERAL A state of the atmosphere in which the lapse rate is such that a particle of air, if moved either upward or downward, tends to accelerate away from its source position.

INTERFACES The boundaries between solids and gases, solids and liquids, solids and solids, liquids and gases, etc., in a colloidal system.

INTERGLACIAL PERIODS Intervals separating glacial advances.

INTERTROPICAL CONVERGENCE (ITC) The general zone of convergence between the trade-wind zones.

INTERTROPICAL FRONT A front that may develop within the zone of intertropical convergence.

INTRAZONAL SOILS Soils whose dominant characteristics are derived largely from local topographic conditions of slope, drainage, and parent material.

INTRUSIVE ROCKS Igneous rocks that have cooled slowly beneath the earth surface.

ION An atom that has either an excess or a deficency of electrons, thus bearing a net electrical charge. A positive ion is termed a *cation;* a negative ion is an *anion.*

IONIZATION The process of creating ions from atoms through the addition or removal of electrons.

IONOSPHERE A thick zone in the outer atmosphere in which the atmospheric gases become ionized by incoming solar energy. Variations in the intensity of ionization separate this zone into distinct layers, labeled the *D, E, F,* and F_1 layers.

IRREVERSIBLE COLLOID A colloidal system which is not reversible once it has undergone a change in physical state. Curdled milk is an irreversible colloidal system.

ISARITH A line connecting points of equal numerical quantity.

ISOBAR A line connecting points of equal atmospheric pressure.

ISOBATH A line connecting points of equal depth below sea level.

ISOHYET A line connecting points of equal rainfall.

ISOLINE A line connecting points of equal value.

ISOPLETH A line connecting points of equal ratios.

ISOTHERM A line connecting points of equal temperature.

ISOTOPE A form of an element that has the identical chemical properties (similar atomic number) of another form of the element but that differs in atomic weight.

JET STREAM A swift, narrow westerly stream of air usually located near the top of the troposphere in mid-latitudes.

KAME A mound, variously shaped, composed of stratified glacial drift. A *kame terrace* is a terrace of stratified glacial drift formed between an ice mass and the side walls of a valley.

KANAT (QANAT, OR FOGGARA) A partially lined tunnel used to collect ground water in arid regions.

KAOLINITE A group of clays, found mainly in the humid tropics, which have a relatively low absorptive rate and a low base-exchange capacity.

KARST TOPOGRAPHY An irregular land surface produced mainly by solution in a limestone upland.

KELP A variety of brown algae, or seaweed.

KETTLE A depression in stratified glacial drift, resulting principally from the melting of included ice blocks.

KOEPPEN-GEIGER SYSTEM A code system for classifying climates (see Appendix A).

KUNAI A coarse savanna grass (*Imperata*). Also known as *cogon* or *alang-alang.*

LACCOLITH An intrusive rock mass which is injected between rock layers and which has domed up the overlying rocks.

LACUSTRINE Pertaining to lakes.

LAGOON A former portion of the sea which has been sheltered from direct wave attack by some depositional feature, such as a coral reef or a barrier beach.

LAMINAR FLOW A flow in which layers of the liquid move smoothly, without appreciable variation in direction or speed.

LAND-AND-SEA BREEZE A nightly seaward wind and a daily landward wind frequently encountered along ocean coast lines.

LANDFORM A recognizable feature of the earth surface, with characteristic form and composition.

LANDSCAPE The sum total of the features that give a topographic area or region its distinctiveness.

LANDSLIDE The sudden, rapid movement of a large mass of soil and rock debris down a steep slope.

LAPSE RATE The decrease in air temperature encountered as one passes from a lower to a higher altitude. It averages about 3.56°F per 1,000 feet.

LATENT HEAT The amount of heat energy necessary to produce a change in phase—for example, from a solid to a liquid or from a liquid to a gas. The former is termed the *latent heat of fusion;* the latter, the *latent heat of vaporization.*

LATERITE An iron hardpan that develops in poorly drained tropical soils.

LATITUDE The angular distance measured north and south of the equator.

LEACHING The removal of soluble material from a soil through the action of aqueous solutions.

LEGUME A pea or beanlike plant whose roots contain nodular colonies of nitrogen-fixing bacteria.

LICHEN A mutually supporting plant combination of a fungus and an alga.

LIGHTNING A flash of light produced in the air by the flow of electrons across a gap between two oppositely charged positions.

LIGNITE Brown coal, or a form of low-grade soft coal.

LIMESTONE An amorphous sedimentary rock composed mainly of calicum carbonate.

LIMONITE A hydrous iron oxide; usually yellowish brown in color; has the formula $Fe_2O_3 \cdot 2H_2O$.

LINE SQUALL A sudden and violent windstorm of short duration that frequently precedes large thunderstorms.

LITHOSPHERE The solid portion of the earth, as contrasted with the atmosphere and hydrosphere.

LLANOS A savanna grassland located in the Orinoco drainage basin of Venezuela.

LOAM An open soil texture resulting from an admixture of sand, clay, and silt.

LOCAL RELIEF The general difference in elevation within an area between the summits of hills or mountains and the adjacent valleys of lowlands.

LOESS A nonstratified deposit of yellowish-brown silt, having a uniform texture and frequently exhibiting a vertical, columnar structure. Most of it is believed deposited by the wind.

LONGITUDE The angular distance measured east and west of the prime meridian.

LONGITUDINAL WAVES Parallel sinuosities, or waves, occurring in the upper-air isobars and having exceptionally long axes.

LORAN A directional device utilizing long-range radar beams.

LOW See *Cyclone.*

LOW-SUN SEASON The winter season. The term is used mainly in referring to the tropics, where seasonal temperature differences are not pronounced.

LOXODROME A line connecting points that have similar bearing. Such lines are chords of great circles. Short sections of loxodromes are termed *rhumb lines.*

MAGMA A mass of mobile molten rock beneath the earth surface.

MAGMATIC SEGREGATION The tendency for different minerals to segregate themselves into distinct zones in the process of crystallizing from a magma.

MAGNETIC DECLINATION The deviation of the magnetic compass from true north.

MANGROVE A tropical tree or shrub, belonging to the genus *Rhizophora,* that is adapted for growth in the saline waters of muddy coast lines.

MAP PROJECTION The orderly or systematic arrangement of the earth grid on a plane surface.

MAP SCALE The ratio between the total size of a map and the area on the earth it represents.

MARBLE Metamorphosed limestone, in which the calcium carbonate has crystallized, owing to heat and pressure.

MARITIME AIR MASS An air mass whose source area lies over an ocean area.

MARL A white-to-gray calcareous clay.

MARSH An essentially treeless area of grass, sedges, reeds, or low shrubs, where water stands slightly above or below the surface.

MASS WASTAGE The mass movement of material down a slope by the direct action of gravity.

MATURE SOIL A well-drained soil which has clearly marked characteristics produced by soil-forming processes and which is in relative equilibrium with its environment.

MEAN SEA LEVEL The datum plane about which the tide oscillates.

MEANDER A loop in a river as it winds back and forth across its flood plain.

MECHANICAL INSTABILITY The condition of an air mass in which the lapse rate is greater than 19°F per 1,000 feet. In such cases, air will rise without any external lifting mechanism.

MERIDIAN An imaginary line connecting points of equal longitude; half of any great circle that passes through the poles.

MERIDIONAL Pertaining to a north-south or a south-north orientation.

MESA A broad, flat-topped, erosional remnant flanked on at least one side by a steep cliff and associated talus.

MESOPHYTE A plant with moderate water preferences.

METABOLIC Pertaining to the synthesis or the destruction of protoplasm in living cells.

METALLOGENIC REGION A large area that contains noteworthy concentrations of metallic ores, usually comprising a variety of metals.

METAMORPHIC ROCK A rock that has been altered in form when in a solid state, mainly as the result of pressure, heating, or a change in chemical environment.

METEOROLOGY The science of weather.

METES AND BOUNDS A system of describing property location by using local, topographic reference points.

MICA A group or family of silicate minerals having a tendency to split into thin sheets.

MIGRATORY AGRICULTURE A type of agriculture which involves progressive land abandonment following a decline in fertility.

MILITARY GRID A system of rectangular coordinates used for spot location.

MILLIBAR A unit of force equal to one-thousandth of a *bar,* or 1,000 *dynes.* One inch of barometric mercury equals 34 millibars. A millibar also is equivalent to 0.014 pound per square inch.

Mineral A naturally occurring aggregate of inorganic substances that has a definite chemical composition and more or less characteristic physical properties.

Mirage An optical image at or near the horizon resulting from the refraction of light. In a *superior mirage,* refraction caused by rapidly decreasing air density with altitude causes an object below the horizon to be seen above the horizon and to appear inverted. In an *inferior mirage,* the density pattern is reversed; the object again appears to be inverted, but it is seen below its true position.

Mistral A cold, northern wind that descends into the western Mediterranean basin from higher elevations to the north. A similar wind in the Adriatic Sea is known as a *bora.*

Mogote A limestone knob.

Monadnock A residual hill or mountain rising above a plain that has been beveled by erosion.

Monsoon A seasonal wind reversal; usually a land-and-sea wind in which the change in direction is sudden.

Monte A region of low xerophytic shrubs bordering the Argentine pampas.

Montmorillonite A group of clays that has a high absorptive rate and a high base-exchange capacity. Found mainly in the mid-latitudes.

Moraine An accumulation of glacial drift deposited directly from glacial ice.

Moraine, end An irregular ridge of morainic material deposited at the outer end of a glacier.

Moraine, ground A fairly even layer of morainic material deposited during the gradual recession of an ice sheet.

Moraine, interlobate A moraine deposited between the protuberances, or lobes, of a glacier.

Moraine, lateral A morainic ridge deposited along the sides of a mountain glacier.

Moraine, medial A morainic ridge deposited in the mid-portion of a mountain valley. Results from the joining of lateral moraines.

Moraine, recessional An end moraine marking a temporary halt in the recession of an ice mass.

Moraine, terminal An end moraine marking the farthest extent of glacial movement.

Morphology Pertaining to the form and structure of things.

Mountain-and-valley breezes Nightly downvalley and daily upvalley winds frequently encountered in mountain valleys.

Mountainous Describing an area characterized by narrow summits and a local relief of over 2,000 feet.

Muck The granular or finely divided black mass of partially decayed organic material found in bogs. Usually slightly acidic or weakly alkaline in reaction.

Muskeg A type of acid bog found in northern regions. Represents an intermediate stage in a hydrarch succession.

Mutation A sudden alteration in chromosome structure (the "blueprint" of organic development), which is heriditary.

Natural gas A natural mixture of gaseous hydrocarbons. Includes methane, ethane, propane, and butane.

Natural gasoline Liquid hydrocarbons within the gasoline range that are diffused as tiny droplets in natural gas.

Natural levee A ridge of alluvium that adjoins the river channel on a flood plain.

Naval stores A group of products, such as turpentine and resin, derived from coniferous trees.

Neutral air mass An air mass which does not have well-developed characteristics of stability or instability.

Neutron A subatomic particle with a neutral charge.

Norther A severe winter windstorm or blizzard.

Notched cliff An undercut cliff resulting from wave erosion along a rocky coast line.

Nuclear fission The process of splitting the nuclei of atoms.

Nuclear fuels Fissionable or potentially fissionable elements that are a source of atomic energy.

Nuclear fusion A form of thermonuclear reaction in which energy is liberated by the fusion of neutrons or nuclei of hydrogen isotopes.

Nuclear reactor A system in which a chain reaction of atomic fission can be controlled. A type of atomic "furnace."

Nunatak An isolated rocky peak that protrudes from a glacier.

Nutrients, plant The elements essential to the growth and reproduction of plants.

Obsidian Pertaining to a dark volcanic glass.

Occluded front The front formed when a cold front overtakes a warm front or another cold front. The process is known as an *occlusion.* If the intruding mass is colder than the older mass, a *cold-front occlusion* develops. If the newer mass is warmer, a *warm-front occlusion* is formed.

OCEAN SWELL Long, low waves that are derived from distant sources.

OCEANOGRAPHY The science of the ocean; the descriptive and analytic study of regional patterns in the sea.

OEKOMENE An ancient Greek term for the habitable world.

OIL SHALE A shale that contains a high proportion of diffused liquid hydrocarbons.

OLIVENE A light-green magnesium and iron silicate commonly found in basic rocks.

ORBIT The path of a body in circular or elliptical revolution about a focal point.

ORBITAL ECCENTRICITY The degree of flatness of an elliptical orbit.

ORE A mineral deposit of commercial significance.

OROGRAPHIC PRECIPITATION Precipitation in which the initial updraft of air is caused by air moving against a topographic obstacle.

ORTHOCLASE A mineral of the feldspar group that has a high content of potassium. A common constituent of granite.

OSCILLATORY WAVE A wave in which each particle oscillates about a point with little or no permanent change in position.

OUTWASH Stratified sand and gravel resulting from fluvioglacial deposition in front of a glacial margin.

OUTWASH PLAIN A plain resulting from the deposition of fluvioglacial sands and gravels. A *pitted outwash plain* is one that contains many irregular depressions.

OVERPOPULATION A condition wherein the standard of living in any area is lowered by the addition of population.

OXBOW LAKE A crescentic lake or slough found on a flood plain; marks the former channel of a meandering river.

OZONE A temporary molecule of oxygen, consisting of three atoms of oxygen.

OZONOSPHERE A zone in the upper atmosphere with an unusually high concentration of ozone. It is generally between 15 and 35 miles above the earth surface and is sometimes referred to as the *G layer*.

PALEOZOIC An era of geologic time, from late Pre-Cambrian time through the Permian period.

PAMPAS A prairie grassland of Argentina.

PARALLEL An imaginary line connecting points of equal latitude.

PARENT MATERIAL The horizon of unconsolidated and weathered rock material from which soil is made. See also *C horizon*.

PEAT A fibrous, brown, acidic mass of partially decayed plant remains found in bogs.

PEDALFERS Humid soils which contain higher percentages of iron and aluminum oxides in the subsoil than are found in the parent material. Such soils are without accumulated lime.

PEDIMENT A gently sloping erosion rock plain found bordering mountains in dry regions. Usually veneered with sand and gravel.

PEDOCALS Soils that contain precipitated masses of calcium carbonate in the *B* horizon.

PEDOLOGY The science of soils.

PEGMATITE A relatively coarse-grained igneous rock usually found in granite dikes and associated with large masses of finer-textured igneous rocks.

PELAGIC Pertaining to marine organisms that dwell above or off the bottom of the sea.

PENEPLAIN A beveled, flat-to-undulating surface of considerable extent, resulting from erosion.

PEPTIZATION The process of dispersing a flocculated colloidal system.

PER CENT SLOPE The direct ratio between the vertical distance and the horizontal distance for a particular slope; for example, a 1-foot rise in 10 feet horizontal distance would be a 10 per cent slope.

PERMAFROST The zone of permanently frozen ground below the surface.

PERMEABILITY The property of rock, sediments, or soils that permits liquids to pass through them.

PETROLEUM A natural mixture of various liquid hydrocarbons. It may also contain diffused gases or solids.

pH A measurement of acidity, or the concentration of hydrogen ions. A pH of 7 indicates a neutral solution. Lower numbers indicate increasing acidity.

PHASE A uniform physical state of matter within a variable system (e.g., the three phases of water).

PHASE EQUILIBRIUM The tendency for a solid, gas, or liquid to remain in the same phase within a given temperature range and at a given pressure.

PHOSPHATE ROCK A sedimentary rock that has a high content of calcium phosphate. The major ore of phosphate fertilizers.

PHOTOSYNTHESIS The manufacture of starches and sugars by plants, utilizing air, water, sunlight, and chlorophyll.

PHOTOTROPISM The tendency of plants to adjust themselves to changing light conditions.

PHREATOPHYTE A low, xerophytic shrub with an unusually deep, well-developed root system.

PHYTOPLANKTON Microscopic plant life in the sea.

PIEDMONT ALLUVIAL PLAIN A sloping plain at the foot of a mountain range, produced by the joining of alluvial fans.

PITCHBLENDE An amorphous (noncrystalline) mineral of uranium oxide.

PLACER A deposit of heavy, usually valuable minerals concentrated as the result of erosion and sedimentation.

PLAIN An extensive area characterized by a local relief of less than 200 feet and having slopes generally less than 5 per cent.

PLANOSOL A clay hardpan soil resulting from the poor drainage associated with shallow soils in areas without appreciable relief.

PLANT ASSOCIATIONS Localized plant communities characterized by one or more dominant species of plant forms.

PLANT COMMUNITY Any ecological (interrelated as to site) grouping of plant forms.

PLANT FORMATIONS The major global plant communities, generally considered to be the forests, grasslands, desert shrubs, and tundra.

PLANT INDICATORS Plants that can be used as evidence for a specific associated environmental characteristic.

PLANT SUCCESSION The sequence of plant communities that evolves on a bare surface and proceeds toward the climax stage.

PLAYA A shallow enclosed desert basin which collects water following a rain. In northern Africa, known also as a *shott.*

PLEISTOCENE The last geological epoch, characterized by continental glaciation. Approximately 1 million years in duration.

PLUTONIUM A synthetic, fissionable isotope of uranium.

PODZOL A zonal soil characterized by an ash-gray *A* horizon and a well-developed zone of accumulation, or *B* horizon.

PODZOLIC A soil which exhibits characteristic properties resulting from podzolization. Sometimes defined as soils that have a silica-sesquioxide ratio greater than 2.

PODZOLIZATION A soil-forming process resulting from leaching by highly acid soil solutions. Found mainly in cool, humid regions.

POLAR FRONT A line of discontinuity at the surface between air from polar sources and air from tropical sources.

POLAR HIGHS High-atmospheric-pressure centers in high latitudes, believed to be thermally induced, at least in part.

POROSITY The degree to which the total volume of a rock, sediment, or soil is made up of empty space.

PORPHYRY An igneous rock with large crystals set in a finely textured groundmass.

POTENTIAL EVAPOTRANSPIRATION The total mean estimated quantity of evapotranspiration from a specific vegetation-covered area. It is a calculated figure based on mean precipitation by months, temperature by months, and length of daylight.

PRAIRIE A humid-climate grassy vegetation containing a large proportion of herbaceous plants.

PRAIRIE EARTH A black soil of humid grasslands that has no included lime precipitates in the *B* horizon.

PRE-CAMBRIAN Pertaining to earth history prior to the Cambrian period or Paleozoic era.

PRESSURE GRADIENT The slope of pressure change. In the atmosphere, it is at right angles to the isobars.

PRIME MERIDIAN An arbitrary meridian selected as the base line from which to measure longitude. The meridian conventionally used for this purpose is the one that passes through Greenwich, England.

PROFILE The shape of a surface along a line and in vertical section. A *longitudinal profile* of a stream valley is its profile along its length. A *transverse profile* of a valley is its profile along a line at right angles to the valley. As applied to soils, see *Soil profile.*

PROVED RESERVES Mineral resources that are economically obtainable in amounts that have been definitely determined.

PSEUDOPODZOLIZATION The formation of podzol-like soils by the leaching of exposed laterite by rain water.

PUBLIC-LAND-SURVEY SYSTEM The system used to divide much of the United States in 1785 into a rectangular grid system, using townships, sections, and fractions of sections.

PYROXENE A dark magnesium, iron, and calcium silicate mineral often found in basic rocks.

QUARTZ The crystalline mineral of silicon dioxide

(SiO_2). Also, a general term for a variety of noncrystalline minerals having the same chemical composition as quartz.

QUARTZITE A metamorphic rock composed largely of quartz. Usually metamorphosed sandstone.

QUEBRACHO A South American tree whose bark is used in the tanning industry.

RADAR Directional short-wave radio impulses.

RADIANT ENERGY Energy that is transmitted in waves and that requires no medium for its transmission.

RADIATION A general term for radiant energy.

RADIOACTIVITY The gradual natural disintegration of some atomic nuclei.

RADIOLARIA A form of single-celled marine animals (protozoa) that have glassy, perforated body casings.

RAIN Drops of liquid water falling from the atmosphere.

RAINFALL EFFECTIVENESS The degree to which precipitation is made available for plant growth.

RAIN SHADOW A dry zone on the lee side of a topographic obstacle, usually a mountain range.

RARE EARTHS A large group of earthy and metallic elements with somewhat related physical and chemical properties.

REFRACTION The bending of light in passing from one medium into another having a different density.

REFRACTORIES Materials that have a high melting point, or that tend to keep their shape and form under high temperatures.

REG A rocky desert plain covered with a mantle of wind-polished gravel.

REGION An area that exhibits a certain degree of likeness or homogeneity in contrast to the surrounding territory.

RELATIVE HUMIDITY See *Humidity*.

RELATIVE RELIEF The general collective unevenness of the land surface.

RELIC PLANTS Plants which have survived an environmental change and which were members of earlier climax communities.

RENDZINA A black intrazonal soil developed over soft limestones, chalks, or marls.

REPRESENTATIVE FRACTION The fraction that presents the linear ratio between a map and the area that it represents.

RESIDUAL MINERALS Minerals that have been concentrated in place through rock weathering and leaching.

RESIDUAL SOILS Soils that have developed in place from the underlying rock, without having been transported.

RESPIRATION The inhalation of oxygen for metabolic purposes and the exhalation of waste products.

REVOLUTION AND ROTATION The motions of the earth spheroid. *Revolution* is the movement of the earth around the sun; *rotation* is the turning of the earth around its axis.

RHUMB LINE See *Loxodrome*.

RHYOLITE An extrusive equivalent of a granite.

RIDGE-AND-VALLEY TOPOGRAPHY A succession of parallel ridges and valleys resulting from the differential erosion of highly folded rock layers of varying resistances.

RILLING The erosion of soil through the development of shallow trenches.

RIPARIAN RIGHTS The right to use water from a surface source, provided that such use does not deny others a similar right.

ROCHES MOUTONNÉES A series of small, elongated, rocky knobs that are smoothed and striated by glacial erosion.

ROCK A solid, natural aggregate of a mineral or minerals.

ROCK STRUCTURE Features produced by movement following rock consolidation.

ROCKWEED A form of brown algae that thrives in shallow sea water.

RUNOFF The discharge of water from surface streams.

SALINA A salt-encrusted flat, resulting from the evaporation of a playa lake.

SALINE SOILS Soils that contain an excess of water-soluble salts but that are not excessively alkaline. The pH range is roughly from 7.3 to 8.5.

SALINIZATION The process of salt accumulation resulting from poor drainage in dry regions.

SALT The product, other than water, of the reaction of a base with an acid. Also, often refers specifically to sodium chloride.

SAND Fragmental material whose constituent particles lie roughly between 0.05 and 2 millimeters in diameter.

SANTA ANA A dry, local gravity wind that descends from the Basin Range region of the southwestern United States into the coastal lowlands of Southern California.

SAVANNA A tropical grassland, usually with scattered trees and shrubs.

SCHIST A foliated (having fine, leaflike layers)

metamorphic rock, containing, micalike minerals.

SCLEROPHYLL A woody, evergreen, hardleaf plant.

SEA MOUNT A steep, isolated pinnacle or peak that rises from the ocean floor. Also termed a *guyot*.

SECONDARY FOREST An immature stage of forest regrowth.

SECTION A square-mile areal unit used as a subdivision of townships in the public-land-survey system.

SEDGES Marsh grasses characterized by leaf blades that are triangular in cross section.

SEDIMENTARY ROCK A rock resulting from the compaction, cementation, or induration of depositional sediments.

SEICHE A periodic, oscillatory wave observed in large but confined bodies of water.

SELECTIVE LOGGING A lumbering procedure whereby only trees of a selected size are removed from a forest.

SELVA The tropical rain forest, composed of broadleaf evergreen trees.

SENSIBLE TEMPERATURE The temperature that our bodies feel.

SERE A complete series of successional stages leading to the establishment of a climax vegetation.

SERE, HYDRARCH A sere that develops to occupy a body of open water with plant growth.

SERE, XERARCH A succession of plant communities that follow one another in occupying a bare, waterless surface.

SEROZEM A gray soil found along the margins of deserts.

SESQUIOXIDES Metallic oxides in which the ratio of the metal to oxygen is 1:1½. Iron and aluminum oxides are the most common soil sesquioxides.

SEXTANT An instrument used to measure the angle of elevation of heavenly bodies, such as the sun or the stars.

SHADOUF A well sweep; used for lifting water.

SHALE A layered sedimentary rock in which the constituent particles are largely of clay size. Sometimes termed *mudstone*.

SHEET EROSION The mass removal of the topmost layer of soil from a broad area.

SHELTER BELT Linear plantings of trees in a dry region.

SHIELD A large, stable continental upland block of crystalline rocks; usually composed of crystalline Pre-Cambrian rocks.

SHIELD VOLCANO A broad shieldlike or domelike volcano resulting from successive outpourings of highly viscous, basaltic lavas; usually several tens or hundreds of square miles in extent.

SHINGLE BEACH A beach composed of flattened, rounded stones.

SHORAN An accurate device to determine position by short-range radar.

SHOTT The local term for playa lake in North Africa.

SIAL Acidic continental igneous rocks; light in color and high in silica.

SIDEREAL TIME (OR STAR TIME) Time that is based on the apparent motions of the stars in their courses across the heavens.

SILICA A general term for silicon dioxide (SiO_2). Material containing silica is termed *siliceous*.

SILICON One of the chemical elements; intermediate between the metals and the nonmetals.

SILICONES A family of chain molecules containing silicon and oxygen atoms.

SILL An intrusive rock mass of more or less uniform thickness that is injected parallel to the enclosing rock strata. It is relatively thin in comparison to its lateral extent.

SILT A soil textural class having particle sizes between 0.002 and 0.05 millimeter in diameter.

SIMA Dark, basic igneous rocks.

SINKHOLES A funnel-shaped depression in the land surface caused by solution of limestone by underground water. Also known as a *doline*.

SIROCCO A dry, hot wind entering the Mediterranean basin from the Sahara. Known also as *khamsin, laveche,* and *samiel*.

SLATE A fine-grained metamorphic rock that tends to split in one direction.

SLEET Frozen or partly frozen raindrops that lack the concentric layering of hail.

SLOPE LENGTH The linear measurement of distance between the top and bottom of a slope. Measured along the slope.

SLUMPING The mass movement of soil and rock fragments downslope when saturated with water.

SMOG A dense mixture of fog, smoke, and gases resulting from combustion.

SNOW Crystalline water that has sublimated in free air around a nucleus directly from a vapor phase.

SNOWLINE The limit, or height, beyond which snow is present throughout the year.

SOIL A naturally occurring body—a mixture of fragmental rock material and varying proportions of gases, water solutions, and organic material—that exhibits changes in chemical and physical properties with depth.

SOIL FAMILY A group of soils having closely similar profiles and composed of one or more soil series. Intermediate in classification between the series and the great soil group.

SOIL HORIZONS Clearly distinguishable horizontal zones in a soil profile.

SOIL PHASES Subdivisions of soil types based largely on features related to agricultural use.

SOIL PROFILE The genetically related vertical differences in a soil body, taken as a unit.

SOIL SERIES A soil grouping, or classification, which distinguishes major differences in profile characteristics. Differences within the series are related mainly to surface texture.

SOIL STRUCTURE The arrangement and grouping of soil particles.

SOIL TEXTURE The gradation of soils according to size of constituent particles.

SOIL TYPES Subdivisions of soil series that are based mainly on the texture of the topsoil.

SOLAR CONSTANT The number of calories received per square centimeter per minute on a standard flat surface held perpendicular to the sun.

SOLIFLUCTION Soil flowage downslope; usually the result of water saturation.

SOLODI Soils in which the desalinization of saline soils has been complete. They exhibit many features common to podzols.

SOLONCHAK Soils that contain observable accumulations of water-soluble salt crystals.

SOLONETZ Black alkali soils, resulting from the recent desalinization of solonchak soils. The black color is the result of small amounts of humus combined with sodium and potassium carbonates.

SOLSTICE The longest or shortest day of the year. The two solstices occur, respectively, on or about June 21 and December 21.

SPECIFIC HEAT The number of calories needed to raise one cubic centimeter of a substance one degree centigrade at sea-level atmospheric pressure.

SPHAGNUM A coarse, fibrous, highly acid moss found in northern bogs.

SPIT A tongue of sand or gravel extending out from a promontory along a coast line.

STABILITY As applied to air, a tendency to resist upward motion. More specifically, the condition of an air layer that has a lapse rate less than the dry adiabatic rate. See also *Absolute stability*.

STACK A column of rock found as an erosional remnant along rocky coast lines.

STALACTITE Stone icicles of calcium carbonate that hang from the roofs of limestone caverns.

STALAGMITE A column of dropstone extending upward from the floor of a limestone cavern.

STANDARD PARALLEL Any parallel of latitude that is selected as a standard on which to base a grid system.

STEPPE A mid-latitude, short-grass vegetation cover that mantles the ground with a fairly continuous sod.

STOMATA Breathing pores on leaves and stems of plants.

STONE RIVERS Linear belts of boulders following shallow drainage ways in arctic regions.

STONE STRIPES Alternate strips of coarse rock fragments and finer material found along hillsides and aligned at right angles to the contour.

STRAND FLAT A flat rock bench which borders a coast line and which may be partially submerged. Most commonly found in arctic and subarctic regions.

STRATA Distinct rock layers, or beds.

STRATOSPHERE An isothermal zone of the atmosphere lying above the tropopause. It is probably about 10 to 15 miles in thickness and is characterized by the absence of a distinct lapse rate.

STRATUS Pertaining to sheet- or layerlike cloud forms.

STREAM FREQUENCY The areal spacing of streams.

STRIATIONS Fine parallel scratches, or grooves, found on the surfaces of rocks.

STRUCTURAL DEPRESSION A depression in the land surface caused by structural deformation of the crust.

SUBAERIAL In the open air, as contrasted with *submarine*.

SUBARCTIC A general term for the tundra and *Dfc climates*.

SUBCLIMAX COMMUNITY A plant community that represents a stage in a sere or plant succession near the climax.

SUBHUMID Humid, but transitional to the semiarid climates. Occasionally has pronounced droughts.

SUBLIMATION The passage of a substance directly from a gaseous to a solid phase or vice versa (e.g., water vapor turning into snow or ice crystals or snow evaporating without melting).

SUBPOLAR LOWS Centers of low atmospheric pressure located over the ocean areas of high latitudes. These occur only during the winter season in the northern hemisphere.

SUBSOIL Normally, that portion of the soil below plow depth.

SUBTROPICAL Pertaining to the subtropics, a zone straddling the outer margin of the tropics; generally lat 25 to 35°.

SUBTROPICAL HIGHS, OR ANTICYCLONES Permanent or semipermanent anticyclonic centers of air subsidence and divergence, located roughly between lat 25 and 35°.

SUCCULENCE The tendency of some plants to have an unusually high water content in their cells.

SUN COMPASS A compass used to determine direction, utilizing solar observation.

SUNSPOTS Cyclonic vortexes in the incandescent atmosphere of the sun.

SUNTIME Time based on the position of the sun in its apparent course across the heavens.

SUPERCOOLING The cooling of drops of liquid water below the freezing point without a change in phase.

SUPERIOR AIR Air that is subsiding from a high elevation.

SUPERSATURATION The crowding of water-vapor molecules into a given mass of air beyond its normal capacity.

SURFACE CONFIGURATION Qualitative properties of the general lay of the land, such as slope, relief, and elevation.

SWAMP An area of tree or bush vegetation, where water stands slightly above or below the surface.

SYENITE An igneous intrusive rock composed largely of feldspar.

SYMBIOSIS A state of mutual support between two unlike organisms that are juxtaposed.

SYNCLINE A rock downfold, or a rock fold in which the strata dip downward toward the center, or axis, of the fold.

TABLELAND A broad, flat upland area.

TAIGA The northern coniferous forest.

TALUS The loose mass of rock rubble that lies at the foot of rock cliffs.

TARN A small mountain lake located in a cirque.

TECTONIC Pertaining to crustal movements of the earth.

TEMPERATURE A measurement of the amount of heat present in a substance.

TEMPERATURE GRADIENT The slope or rate of temperature change.

TEMPERATURE INVERSION A sudden change from a decrease in temperature with elevation to an increase in temperature with elevation. Warmer air overlying colder air.

TERRA ROXA Red soils developed mainly on limestones in the areas bordering the Mediterranean Sea.

THERMODYNAMIC Pertaiinng to the mechanical movements associated with heating and cooling.

THERMOPERIODISM Rhythmic patterns of plant growth and development that conform to variations in temperature.

THORIUM An element with an atomic weight of 232 which can be transformed into fissionable U^{233}.

THUNDERSTORM Any thermodynamic storm accompanied by thunder and lightning.

TIDAL INLET A passageway for incoming and outgoing tidal currents through a coastal obstruction, such as a coral reef or barrier beach.

TIDAL MARSH A marsh that borders a low coast and is subject to tidal inundation.

TIDE The alternate rising and falling of sea level caused by the gravitational attraction of the moon and the sun.

TIDE, NEAP A low tidal range that occurs fortnightly when the moon is in its first or third quarter-phase.

TIDE, SPRING A high tidal range that occurs fortnightly when the moon is in its new or full phase.

TIERRA FRIA The mountain zone between the upper timber line and the zone of perpetual frost.

TILL Unassorted glacial debris deposited directly from glacial ice.

TILL PLAIN A flat-to-undulating plain composed of glacial till.

TOPOGRAPHIC MAP A map that portrays the surface features of an area at a scale greater than 1:500,000.

TOPOGRAPHIC SCALE A scale of reduction greater than 1:500,000.

TOPOGRAPHY The surface content and characterization of an area.

TOPSOIL A general term for the surface portion of the soil, either the *A* horizon or the zone above plow depth.

TORNADO A violent, localized cyclonic vortex, containing a visible, pendulous, funnel-shaped cloud.

TOWNSHIP A square, basic areal unit, comprising 36 square miles, in the public-land-survey system. Also, a township unit measured north of the *base line*.

TOXIC Pertaining to a condition that hinders the maintenance of good health in an organism.

TRACE ELEMENTS Chemical elements utilized in minute quantities in the development of organic cell structures.

TRADE WINDS The winds with an easterly component that are located on the equatorward sides of subtropical anticyclones.

TRANSPIRATION Exhalation of water vapor by plants.

TRELLIS DRAINAGE A drainage pattern characterized by parallel main streams intersected at or near right angles by their tributaries.

TRENCH A deep, steep-sided cleft in the ocean floor.

TRITUM An isotope of hydrogen with an atomic weight of 3.

TROPIC OF CANCER The parallel of lat 23½° N. Indicates the northern limit of the sun's vertical rays.

TROPIC OF CAPRICORN The parallel of lat 23½° S. Indicates the southern limit of the sun's vertical rays.

TROPICAL RED LOAMS Reddish soils which show ferrallitic tendencies.

TROPOPAUSE The level in the atmosphere at which the decline in temperature associated with increasing elevation (lapse rate) suddenly stops.

TROPOPHYTES Plants that undergo seasonal changes in form in adjusting to seasonal differences in moisture availability.

TROPOSPHERE The lower portion of the atmosphere, from the earth surface to the tropopause. That portion of the atmosphere in which temperature decreases fairly regularly with elevation.

TSUNAMI A large ocean wave caused by a sudden dislocation of the ocean floor.

TUNDRA A treeless expanse of low vegetation in arctic and subarctic areas.

TURBULENT FLOW The type of flow of gases or liquids in which the stream lines are thoroughly confused because of irregular mixing.

TYPHOON See *Hurricane.*

ULTRAVIOLET Invisible radiation whose wavelengths are just beyond the violet, or short, end of the visible light spectrum.

U-SHAPED VALLEY Typically, a valley that has been widened and deepened as the result of glacial erosion and that thus had the general form of the letter U.

UVALA A broad depression in limestone country, produced as the result of coalesced sinkholes.

VALLEY TRAIN A narrow outwash plain occupying the floor of a valley.

VAPOR PRESSURE That part of the total atmospheric pressure that is due to the included water vapor.

VARVE CLAYS Lake clays that show a distinct layering resulting from seasonal differences in deposition.

VELDT A grassland region in South Africa.

VOLCANO A vent at the surface of the earth for the extrusion of molten lava.

WADI A dry stream channel in arid regions.

WARM FRONT A gently sloping frontal surface between two air masses, in which there is an active movement of warm air over cold air.

WATERSPOUT A tornadolike vortex occurring over water.

WATER SPREADING Spreading of water outside a stream channel in order to replenish subsurface supplies of ground water.

WATER TABLE The upper surface of the zone of water saturation in the soil, except where that surface is formed by an impermeable body.

WAVE-BUILT TERRACE A sloping surface below water level formed as the result of deposition by waves or currents.

WAVE-CUT TERRACE A sloping plain below water level resulting from erosion by waves and currents.

WAVE DEPTH The depth below which particle motion is not influenced by wave motion. In water waves, this depth is normally about one-half the wave length.

WAVE LENGTH The distance from crest to crest of a waveform.

WEATHER The general condition of the atmosphere at a given time and place.

WEATHERING The breakdown of rocks caused by the action of atmospheric agents.

WESTERLIES The winds with a westerly component that are located on the poleward sides of the subtropical anticyclones.

WET ADIABATIC RATE The rate of cooling in ascending air which has already reached the condensation point, and in which the lapse rate is being increased as the result of the release of latent heat of condensation.

WIND Horizontal or nearly horizontal air movement.

WOODLAND An open stand of trees without a continuous canopy of leaves overhead.

XANTHOPHYLL A yellow pigment present in the leaf cells of plants.

XEROPHYTE A drought-resistant plant.

YERBA MATÉ A South American shrub whose leaf is used as a type of tea.

ZENITH A point directly overhead, or a point at right angles to the horizontal and opposite the direction of earth's gravity.

ZONAL FLOW The general flow of air from west to east or from east to west.

ZONAL SOILS Soils whose dominant characteristics are derived mainly from climatic or biological conditions.

ZONE OF ELUVIATION The soil horizon that is characterized by the removal of material by percolation. Also known as the *A horizon.*

ZONE OF ILLUVIATION, OR ACCUMULATION The soil horizon that is characterized by an addition of material resulting from percolation. Also known as the *B horizon.*

ZOOPLANKTON A collective term for small marine animal life ranging in size from microscopic forms to varieties ¼ to ½ inch in length.

INDEX